Math Connects
Concepts, Skills, and Problem Solving
Course 2

Contents in Brief

D0617045

Volume 1

Volume 2

About the Cover

Nothing beats the thrill of a giant water slide! Next time you are at a water park, think about math. The water slide is exciting because there is a big vertical drop in a small horizontal distance. In math, that is expressed as a ratio $\frac{rise}{run}$, which is called slope. You'll learn more about slope in Chapter 6.

Cover image photographed on location courtesy Busch Gardens/Adventure Island, Tampa, Florida. Credit Richard Hutchings.

About the Graphics

Twisted torus. Created with *Mathematica.*
A torus with rose-shaped cross section is constructed. Then the cross section is rotated around its center as it moves along a circle to form a twisted torus. For more information, and for programs to construct such graphics, see: www.wolfram.com/r/textbook.

Three Horizontally Aligned Programs

Grade 7
NSF-funded, integrated performance assessment aligned with investigative instruction

Grade 7
Intensive Intervention for students two or more years below grade level (Tier 3 RtI)

The McGraw-Hill Companies

 Glencoe

Send all inquiries to:
Glencoe/McGraw-Hill
8787 Orion Place
Columbus, OH 43240-4027

ISBN: 978-0-07-874046-6 *(Student Edition)*
MHID: 0-07-874046-0 *(Student Edition)*
ISBN: 978-0-07-874048-0 *(Teacher Edition, Vol. 1)*   ISBN: 978-0-07-888292-0 *(Teacher Edition, Vol. 2)*
MHID: 0-07-874048-7 *(Teacher Edition, Vol. 1)*   MHID: 0-07-888292-3 *(Teacher Edition, Vol. 2)*

Printed in the United States of America.

3 4 5 6 7 8 9 10 006/055 16 15 14 13 12 11 10 09

Benefits of Student Edition Organization

Math Connects, Course 2 Student Edition, has a 4-part organization.

1. **Start Smart** gets students ready for grade 7 with a review of key math standards from grade 6 that are prerequisites for grade 7.

2. **Chapters 1–12** Each chapter has coherent groups of lessons focused on related grade 7 math standards and the NCTM Focal Points.

3. **Preparing for Standardized Tests** provides test success tips, step-by-step solutions for standards-based multiple-choice questions, and an extensive practice section to review before your state test.

4. **Looking Ahead** prepares students for success with lessons on several key math standards.

The organization and pacing of *Math Connects* helps ensure in-depth coverage of all grade 7 standards, success on your state test, and a good start for grade 8.

The School Year

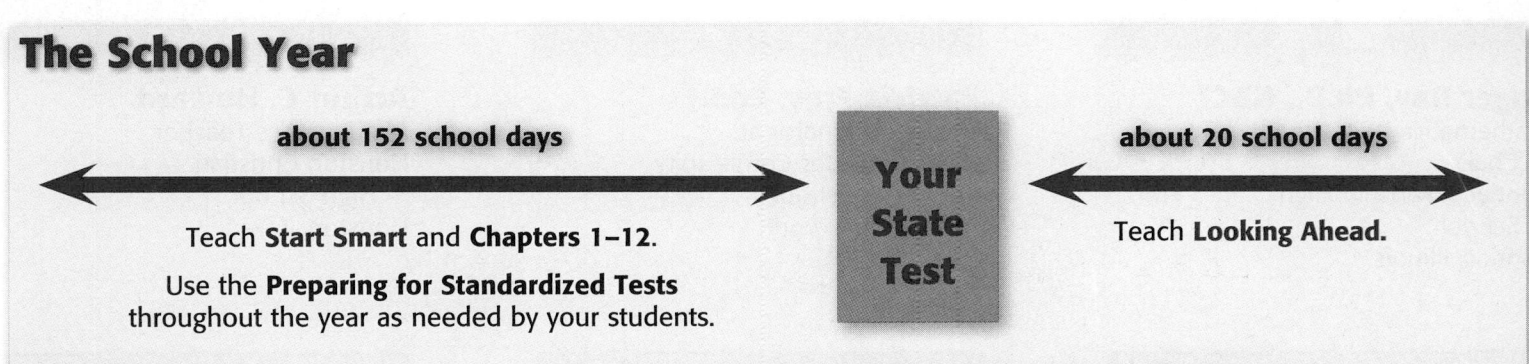

about 152 school days

Teach **Start Smart** and **Chapters 1–12**.

Use the **Preparing for Standardized Tests** throughout the year as needed by your students.

Your State Test

about 20 school days

Teach **Looking Ahead**.

Pacing Guide
Each chapter includes days for review and assessment.

Start Smart	Optional
Chapter 1	13 days
Chapter 2	11 days
Chapter 3	12 days
Chapter 4	15 days
Chapter 5	10 days
Chapter 6	14 days
Chapter 7	11 days
Chapter 8	12 days
Chapter 9	11 days
Chapter 10	15 days
Chapter 11	16 days
Chapter 12	12 days
Total	152 days
State Test	
Looking Ahead	20 days

Authors

Roger Day, Ph.D., NBCT
Mathematics Department
   Chair
Pontiac Township High
   School
Pontiac, Illinois

Patricia Frey, Ed.D.
Math Coordinator at
   Westminster Community
   Charter School
Buffalo, New York

Arthur C. Howard
Mathematics Teacher
Houston Christian
   High School
Houston, Texas

**Deborah A. Hutchens,
   Ed.D.**
Principal
Chesapeake, Virginia

Beatrice Luchin
Mathematics Consultant
League City, Texas

Kay McClain, Ed.D.
Assistant Professor
Vanderbilt University
Nashville, Tennessee

Math Online Meet the Authors at glencoe.com

Rhonda J. Molix-Bailey
Mathematics Consultant
Mathematics by Design
DeSoto, Texas

Jack M. Ott, Ph.D.
Distinguished Professor
    of Secondary Education
    Emeritus
University of South Carolina
Columbia, South Carolina

Ronald Pelfrey, Ed.D.
Mathematics Specialist
Appalachian Rural
    Systemic Initiative and
    Mathematics Consultant
Lexington, Kentucky

Jack Price, Ed.D.
Professor Emeritus
California State
    Polytechnic University
Pomona, California

Kathleen Vielhaber
Mathematics Consultant
St. Louis, Missouri

Teri Willard, Ed.D.
Assistant Professor
Department of Mathematics
Central Washington
    University
Ellensburg, Washington

Contributing Author

FOLDABLES Dinah Zike
Educational Consultant
Dinah-Might Activities, Inc.
San Antonio, Texas

Consultants

Glencoe/McGraw-Hill wishes to thank the following professionals for their feedback. They were instrumental in providing valuable input toward the development of this program in these specific areas.

Mathematical Content

Viken Hovsepian
Professor of Mathematics
Rio Hondo College
Whittier, California

Grant A. Fraser, Ph.D.
Professor of Mathematics
California State University, Los Angeles
Los Angeles, California

Arthur K. Wayman, Ph.D.
Professor of Mathematics Emeritus
California State University, Long Beach
Long Beach, California

English Language Learners

Josefina V. Tinajero, Ph.D.
Dean, College of Education
The University of Texas at El Paso
El Paso, Texas

Gifted and Talented

Ed Zaccaro
Author and Consultant
Bellevue, Iowa

Graphing Calculator

Ruth M. Casey
National Mathematics
  Consultant
National Instructor,
  Teachers Teaching with
  Technology
Frankfort, Kentucky

Learning Disabilities

Kate Garnett, Ph.D.
Chairperson, Coordinator
  Learning Disabilities
School of Education
Department of Special Education
Hunter College, CUNY
New York, New York

Mathematical Fluency

Jason Mutford
Mathematics Instructor
Coxsackie-Athens Central School District
Coxsackie, New York

Pre-AP

Dixie Ross
Mathematics Teacher
Pflugerville High School
Pflugerville, Texas

Reading and Vocabulary

Douglas Fisher, Ph.D.
Professor of Language and Literacy Education
San Diego State University
San Diego, California

Lynn T. Havens
Director of Project CRISS
Kalispell, Montana

Reviewers

Each reviewer reviewed at least two chapters of the Student Edition, giving feedback and suggestions for improving the effectiveness of the mathematics instruction.

Sheila J. Allen
Mathematics Teacher
A.I. Root Middle School
Medina, Ohio

Paula Barnes
Mathematics Teacher
Minisink Valley CSD
Slate Hill, New York

Deborah Barnett
Mathematics Consultant
Lake Shore Public Schools
St. Clair Shores, Michigan

Laurel W. Blackburn
Teacher/Mathematics
   Department Chair
Hillcrest Middle School
Simpsonville, South Carolina

Drista Bowser
Mathematics Teacher
New Windsor Middle School
New Windsor, Maryland

Matthew Bowser
Teacher
Oil City Middle School
Oil City, Pennsylvania

Susan M. Brewer
Mathematics Teacher
Brunswick Middle School
Brunswick, Maryland

Patricia A. Bruzek
Mathematics Teacher
Glenn Westlake Middle School
Lombard, Illinois

Luanne Budd
Supervisor of Mathematics
Randolph Township
Randolph, New Jersey

Ella Violet Burch
Mathematics Teacher
Penns Grove High School
Carneys Point, New Jersey

Hailey Caldwell
7th Grade Mathematics Teacher
Greenville Middle Academy of
   Traditional Studies
Greenville, South Carolina

Linda K. Chandler
7th Grade Mathematics Teacher
Willard Middle School
Willard, Ohio

Debra M. Cline
7th Grade Mathematics Teacher
Thomas Jefferson Middle School
Winston-Salem, North Carolina

Randall G. Crites
Principal
Bunker R-3
Bunker, Missouri

Rose Dickinson
Science and Mathematics
   Teacher
Seneca Middle School
Clinton Township, Michigan

Joyce Wolfe Dodd
6th Grade Mathematics Teacher
Bryson Middle School
Simpsonville, South Carolina

John G. Doyle
Middle School Chairperson/
   Mathematics Teacher
Wyoming Valley West School
   District
Kingston, Pennsylvania

Katie England
Secondary Mathematics Resource
   Teacher
Carroll County Public Schools
Westminster, Maryland

Carol A. Fincannon
6th Grade Mathematics Teacher
Southwood Middle School
Anderson, South Carolina

Sally J. Fulmer
7th Grade Mathematics Teacher/
   Department Chair
C.E. Williams Middle School
Charleston, South Carolina

Marian K. Geist
Mathematics Teacher/Leadership
   Team
Baker Prairie Middle School
Canby, Oregon

Becky Gorniack
Middle School Mathematics
   Teacher
Fremont Middle School
Mundelein, Illinois

Donna Tutterow Hamilton
Curriculum Facilitator
Corriher Lipe Middle School
Landis, North Carolina

Danny Liebertz
8th Grade Mathematics
   Instructor
Fowler Middle School
Tigard, Oregon

Marie Merkel
Learning Support
North Pocono School District
Scranton, Pennsylvania

Tonda North
Algebra 1/8th Grade Mathematics
   Teacher
Indian Valley Middle School
Enon, Ohio

Natasha L.M. Nuttbrock
7th Grade Mathematics Teacher
Ferguson Middle School
Beavercreek, Ohio

Paul Penn
Curriculum Team Leader,
   Mathematics
Lima City Schools
Lima, Ohio

Casey Condran Plackett
7th Grade Mathematics Teacher
Kennedy Junior High School
Lisle, Illinois

E. Elaine Rafferty
Mathematics Consultant
Summerville, South Carolina

Edward M. Repko
Mathematics Teacher
Kilbourne Middle School
Worthington, Ohio

Alfreda Reynolds
Teacher
Charlotte-Mecklenburg School
   System
Charlotte, North Carolina

Alice Roberts
Mathematics Teacher
Oakdale Middle School
Ijamsville, Maryland

Jennifer L. Rodriguez
Mathematics Teacher
Glen Crest Middle School
Glen Ellyn, Illinois

Natalie Rohaley
6th Grade Mathematics
Riverside Middle School
Greer, South Carolina

Annika Lee Schilling
Mathematics and Science
   Teacher
Duniway Middle School
McMinnville, Oregon

Sherry Scott
Mathematics Teacher
E.A. Tighe School
Margate, New Jersey

Eli Shaheen
Mathematics Teacher/
   Department Chair
Plum Senior High School
Pittsburgh, Pennsylvania

Kelly Eady Shaw
7th Grade Mathematics Teacher
Rawlinson Road Middle School
Rock Hill, South Carolina

Evan J. Silver
Mathematics Teacher
Walkersville Middle School
Frederick, Maryland

Charlotte A. Thore
6th/7th Grade Mathematics
   Teacher
Northwest School of the Arts
Charlotte, North Carolina

Gene A. Tournoux
Mathematics Department Head
Shaker Heights High School
Shaker Heights, Ohio

Pamela J. Trainer
Mathematics Teacher
Roland-Grise Middle School
Wilmington, North Carolina

David A. Trez
Mathematics Teacher
Bloomfield Middle School
Bloomfield, New Jersey

Pauline D. Von Hoffer
Mathematics Teacher
Wentzville School District
Wentzville, Missouri

Kentucky Consultants

Jenn Crase
8th Grade Mathematics Teacher/
   Department Chair
South Oldham Middle School
Crestwood, Kentucky

Max DeBoer Lux
8th Grade Mathematics
Summit View Middle School
Independence, Kentucky

Jennifer Wells Phipps
Middle School Mathematics
   Teacher
Corbin Middle School
Corbin, Kentucky

Bea Torrence
Teacher/Mathematics Content
   Leader
Camp Ernst Middle School
Burlington, Kentucky

J. Ron Vanover
Advanced Placement Calculus
Boone County High School
Florence, Kentucky

Mathematics Teacher Handbook

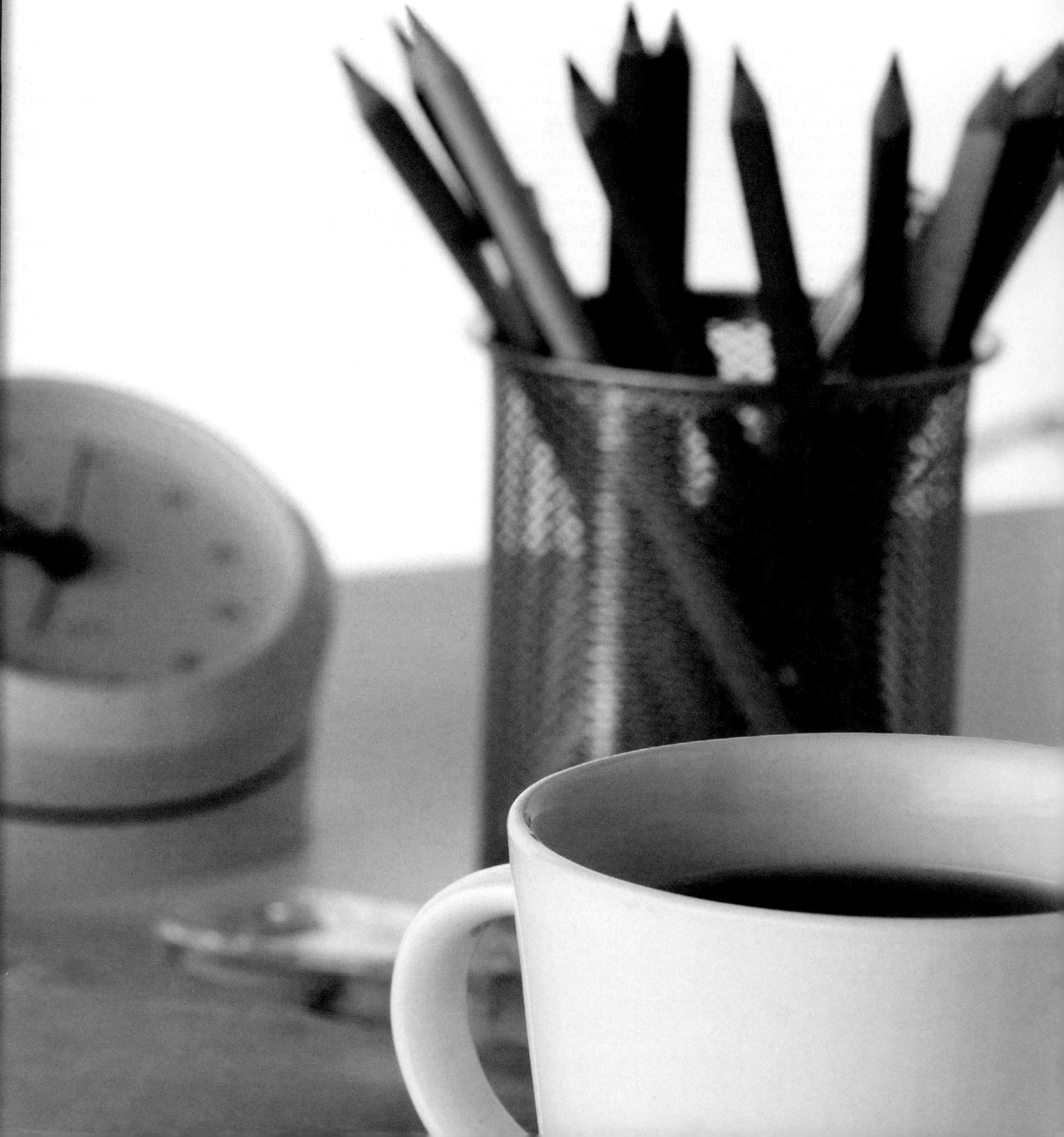

Table of Contents
PreK–12 Mathematics: Focus on Grade 7

Welcome to
Math Connects

Concepts • Skills • Problem Solving

The only true vertically aligned PreK–12 Mathematics Curriculum

Math Connects offers three dimensions of vertical alignment.

❶ Content Design

Vertical content alignment is a process that ensures you and your students experience an articulated, coherent sequence of content from grade level to grade level. This provides you with the assurance that content is introduced, reinforced, and assessed at appropriate times in the series, eliminating gaps and unnecessary duplication. You are able to target your instruction to student needs because you are not teaching content intended to be covered later or that students have previously mastered.

❷ Instructional Design

Our strong vertical alignment in instructional approach from PreKindergarten through Algebra 2 provides a smooth transition for students from elementary to middle school to high school. Our common vocabulary, technology, manipulatives, lesson planning, and Data-Driven Decision Making reduces the confusion students often encounter when transitioning between grade levels without this built-in articulation.

❸ Visual Design

The student pages of *Math Connects* have a consistent visual design from grade to grade. This aids students' transition from elementary school to middle school and from middle school to Algebra 1. Students are more likely to succeed when they are already familiar with how to navigate student pages.

PreK–2

3–5

5 Keys to Success

❶ Backmapping

According to College Board research, about 80% of students who successfully complete Algebra 1 and Geometry by 10th grade attend and succeed in college. (Changing the Odds: Factors Increasing Access to College, 1990) *Math Connects* was conceived and developed by backmapping with the final result in mind—student success in Algebra 1 and beyond.

❷ Balanced, In-Depth Content

Math Connects was developed to specifically target the skills and topics that give students the most difficulty, such as Problem Solving, in each grade span.

Grades K–2	Grades 3–5
1. Problem Solving	1. Problem Solving
2. Money	2. Fractions
3. Time	3. Measurement
4. Measurement	4. Decimals
5. Fractions	5. Time
6. Computation	6. Algebra
Grades 6–8	**Grades 9–12**
1. Fractions	1. Problem Solving
2. Problem Solving	2. Fractions
3. Measurement	3. Algebra
4. Algebra	4. Geometry
5. Computation	5. Computation
	6. Probability

– *K–12 Math Market Analysis Survey*, Open Book Publishing, 2006

❸ Ongoing Assessment

Math Connects includes diagnostic, formative, and summative assessment; data-driven instruction; intervention options; and performance tracking, as well as remediation, acceleration, and enrichment tools throughout the program.

❹ Intervention and Differentiated Instruction

A three-tiered Response To Intervention (RTI) is provided.

TIER 1 **Daily Intervention** Options for Differentiated Instruction in the Teacher Edition address concepts for different modalities or learning styles.

TIER 2 **Strategic Intervention** Teachers can use the myriad of intervention tips and ancillary materials, such as the Strategic Intervention Guide (1–5) and Study Guide and Intervention (6–8).

TIER 3 **Intensive Intervention** For students who are two or more years below grade level, *Math Triumphs* provides step-by-step instruction, vocabulary support, and data-driven decision making to help students succeed.

❺ Professional Development

Math Connects includes many opportunities for teacher professional development. Additional learning opportunities in various formats—video, online, and on-site instruction—are fully aligned and articulated from Kindergarten through Algebra 2.

| 6-8 | Pre-Algebra and Algebra 1 | Geometry and Algebra 2 |

The Research Base

Continuous research with teachers, students, academician, and leading experts helps to build a solid foundation for *Math Connects.*

1 Program Development Research

- Evaluating state and local standards
- Qualitative market research
- Academic content research

For more detailed information about our classroom research results, please consult the *Math Connects* Program Efficacy Research Report.

The Research Base for

Math Connects

Program Efficacy Research

Mc Graw Hill **Glencoe**   Mc Graw Hill **Macmillan McGraw-Hill**

The McGraw-Hill Companies

for *Math Connects*

② Formative Research

- Pedagogical research base
- Classroom field tests
- Teacher advisory boards
- Academic consultants and reviewers

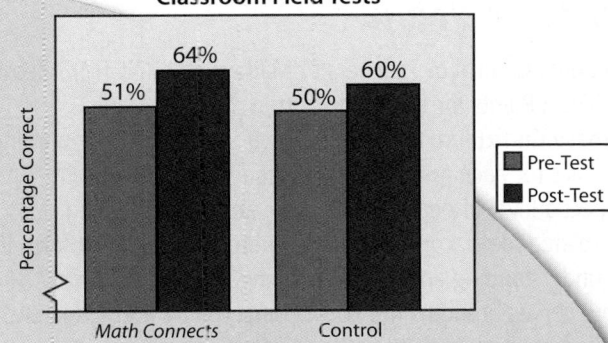

Student Data from 2006–2007 Classroom Field Tests

Percentage Correct

Math Connects	Control
51%	50%
64%	60%

Pre-Test
Post-Test

Classroom Type

Students using a field test of the *Math Connects* program **(experimental group)** had *higher* pre-test to post-test gains than students using other textbook programs **(control group)**.

③ Summative Research

- Evidence of increased test scores
- Quasi-experimental program efficacy research
- Longitudinal studies
- Qualitative program evaluations

Access all *Math Connects* research at glencoe.com.

NCTM Focal Points

The NCTM Focal Points

In 2006, the National Council of Teachers of Mathematics (NCTM) released the Curriculum Focal Points for Pre-Kindergarten through Grade 8 Mathematics. These Curriculum Focal Points focus on the most important mathematical topics for each grade level. The concepts are vertically aligned and expect a level of depth, complexity, and rigor at each level. They comprise related ideas, concepts, skills, and procedures that form the foundation for understanding and lasting learning. The Focal Points emphasize depth versus breadth. The Focal Points will be addressed and highlighted throughout our PreK-8 and Pre-Algebra series.

What is the benefit to you in your classroom?

These Focal Points identify content for each grade level that should be mastered in order for your students to have true mathematical understanding—being able to not only calculate the answer, but to explain the answer and how to apply the calculation. The NCTM Focal Points were used as the basis in the development of *Math Connects*. The authors have incorporated the Focal Points into the content to assist you in building depth of understanding.

NCTM Focal Points for Grade 7	Supporting Chapters in *Math Connects*
Number and Operations and *Algebra* and *Geometry*	Chapters 6, 7, 12
Measurement and *Geometry* and *Algebra*	Chapters 10, 11
Number and Operations and *Algebra*	Chapters 1, 2, 3, 4, 5
Connections to the Focal Points	
Measurement and *Geometry*	Chapter 11
Number and Operations	Chapter 4
Data Analysis	Chapter 8
Probability	Chapter 9

KEY

G7-FP1	G7-FP5C
Grade 7 Focal Point 1	Grade 7 Focal Point 5 Connection
G7-FP2	
Grade 7 Focal Point 2	**G7-FP6C**
G7-FP3	Grade 7 Focal Point 6 Connection
Grade 7 Focal Point 3	
G7-FP4C	**G7-FP7C**
Grade 7 Focal Point 4 Connection	Grade 7 Focal Point 7 Connection

The Curriculum Focal Points identify key mathematical ideas for this grade. They are not discrete topics or a checklist to be mastered; rather, they provide a framework for the majority of instruction at a particular grade level and the foundation for future mathematics study. The complete document may be viewed at www.nctm.org/focalpoints.

G7-FP1 *Number and Operations* and *Algebra* and *Geometry:* **Developing an understanding of and applying proportionality, including similarity**

Students extend their work with ratios to develop an understanding of proportionality that they apply to solve single and multistep problems in numerous contexts. They use ratio and proportionality to solve a wide variety of percent problems, including problems involving discounts, interest, taxes, tips, and percent increase or decrease. They also solve problems about similar objects (including figures) by using scale factors that relate corresponding lengths of the objects or by using the fact that relationships of lengths within an object are preserved in similar objects. Students graph proportional relationships and identify the unit rate as the slope of the related line. They distinguish proportional relationships ($\frac{y}{x} = k$, or $y = kx$) from other relationships, including inverse proportionality ($xy = k$, or $y = \frac{k}{x}$).

G7-FP2 *Measurement* and *Geometry* and *Algebra:* **Developing an understanding of and using formulas to determine surface areas and volumes of three-dimensional shapes**

By decomposing two- and three-dimensional shapes into smaller, component shapes, students find surface areas and develop and justify formulas for the surface areas and volumes of prisms and cylinders. As students decompose prisms and cylinders by slicing them, they develop and understand formulas for their volumes (*Volume = Area of base $\times$ Height*). They apply these formulas in problem solving to determine volumes of prisms and cylinders. Students see that the formula for the area of a circle is plausible by decomposing a circle into a number of wedges and rearranging them into a shape that approximates a parallelogram. They select appropriate two- and three dimensional shapes to model real-world situations and solve a variety of problems (including multistep problems) involving surface areas, areas and circumferences of circles, and volumes of prisms and cylinders.

G7-FP3 *Number and Operations* and *Algebra:* **Developing an understanding of operations on all rational numbers and solving linear equations**

Students extend understandings of addition, subtraction, multiplication, and division, together with their properties, to all rational numbers, including negative integers. By applying properties of arithmetic and considering negative numbers in everyday contexts (e.g., situations of owing money or measuring elevations above and below sea level), students explain why the rules for adding, subtracting, multiplying, and dividing with negative numbers make sense. They use the arithmetic of rational numbers as they formulate and solve linear equations in one variable and use these equations to solve problems. Students make strategic choices of procedures to solve linear equations in one variable and implement them efficiently, understanding that when they use the properties of equality to express an equation in a new way, solutions that they obtain for the new equation also solve the original equation.

Connections to the Focal Points

G7-FP4C *Measurement* and *Geometry:* Students connect their work on proportionality with their work on area and volume by investigating similar objects. They understand that if a scale factor describes how corresponding lengths in two similar objects are related, then the square of the scale factor describes how corresponding areas are related, and the cube of the scale factor describes how corresponding volumes are related. Students apply their work on proportionality to measurement in different contexts, including converting among different units of measurement to solve problems involving rates such as motion at a constant speed. They also apply proportionality when they work with the circumference, radius, and diameter of a circle; when they find the area of a sector of a circle; and when they make scale drawings.

G7-FP5C *Number and Operations:* In grade 4, students used equivalent fractions to determine the decimal representations of fractions that they could represent with terminating decimals. Students now use division to express any fraction as a decimal, including fractions that they must represent with infinite decimals. They find this method useful when working with proportions, especially those involving percents. Students connect their work with dividing fractions to solving equations of the form $ax = b$, where a and b are fractions. Students continue to develop their understanding of multiplication and division and the structure of numbers by determining if a counting number greater than 1 is a prime, and if it is not, by factoring it into a product of primes.

G7-FP6C *Data Analysis:* Students use proportions to make estimates relating to a population on the basis of a sample. They apply percentages to make and interpret histograms and circle graphs.

G7-FP7C *Probability:* Students understand that when all outcomes of an experiment are equally likely, the theoretical probability of an event is the fraction of outcomes in which the event occurs. Students use theoretical probability and proportions to make approximate predictions.

Program Philosophy

Balanced Instruction, Vertically-Aligned from Grades PreK through Algebra 1

The vertical alignment of *Math Connects* PreK-8 and *Algebra 1* incorporates a balance of instruction throughout. These programs provide students a balanced approach to mathematics by:

- investigating concepts and building conceptual understanding.
- developing, reinforcing, and mastering computational and procedural skills.
- applying mathematics to problem-solving situations.

This sequence of Student Edition pages illustrates the vertically-aligned development of the conceptual understanding and corresponding computational and procedural skills for an important algebra topic.

Primary Students use two-color counters to model addition sentences. This activity forms a basis for future understanding of and success in solving algebraic equations.

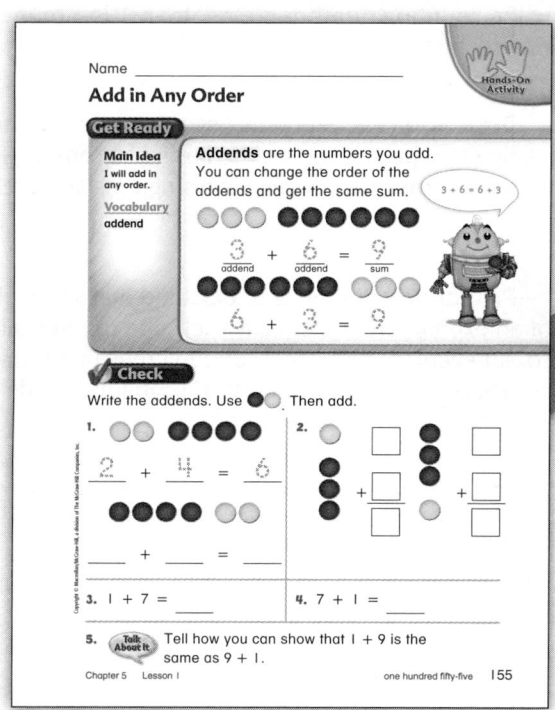

Math Connects, Grade 1,
Student Edition, page 155

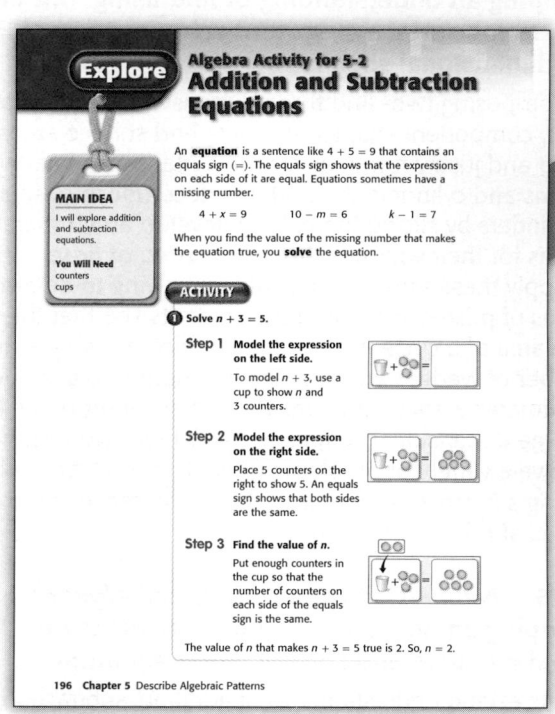

Math Connects, Grade 4,
Student Edition, page 196

Intermediate Students build on their experience with counters to using cups and counters to model and solve addition and subtraction equations. The exercises are designed to help students bridge the gap from using cups and counters to solving equations symbolically.

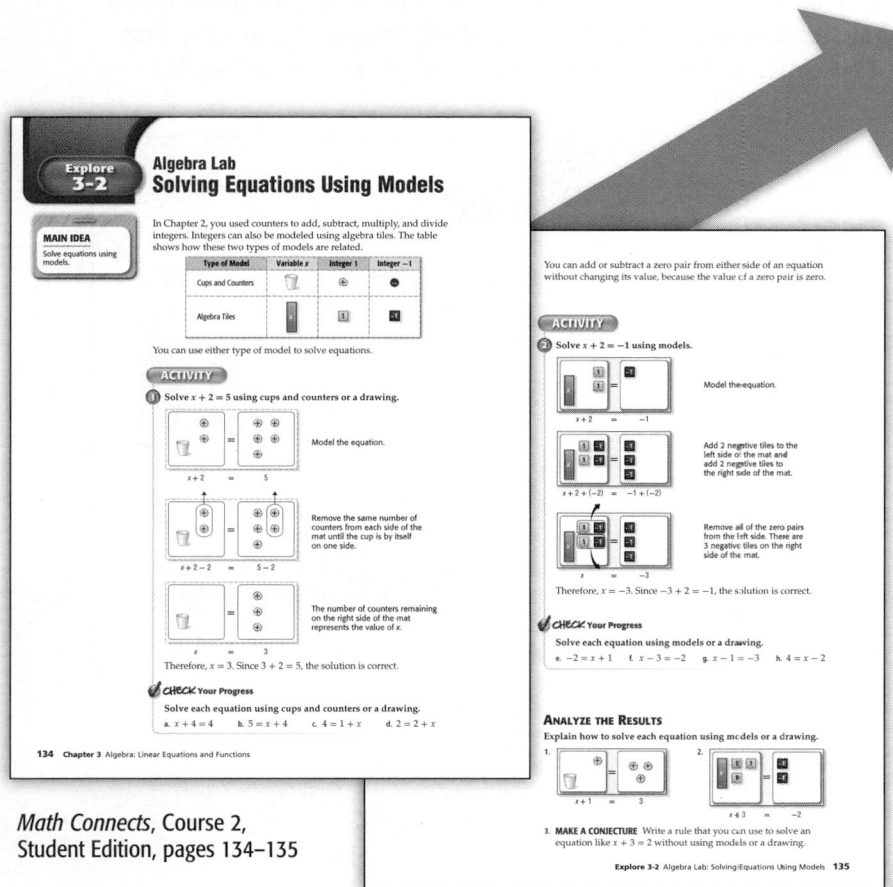

Math Connects, Course 2,
Student Edition, pages 134–135

Glencoe Algebra 1,
Student Edition, page 91

Algebra 1 Students continue the use of
algebra tiles to investigate solving multi-
step equations. In the next lesson, students
apply the procedure developed in the
Algebra Lab to a symbolic approach.

Middle School Students represent the variable x as
a cup, as a counter, or as a written x. In this Algebra
Lab, students make the transition from cups and
counters to the more abstract algebra tiles. In the
next lesson, students solve simple equations
symbolically.

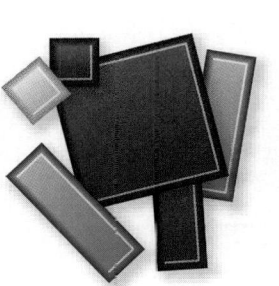

Continuity of Instruction The instructional sequence described demonstrates
the power of backward mapping from the desired result, success in Algebra 1.
This process of development avoids gaps and overlaps between grade levels and
ensures that at each grade level the concepts and skills are built on the strong
foundation developed in previous grades. The same approach was used across
all strands throughout the entire PreK-12 series.

Program Philosophy
Balance of Instruction

Relevant Problem Solving

Math Connects provides students with the appropriate development of problem-solving strategies, skills, and applications from PreK through grade 5. In grades 6–8, students continue to learn and apply problem-solving skills and strategies. Students are provided with ongoing opportunities to apply their math skills and solve problems using visual thinking, logical reasoning, number sense, and algebra.

Problem-Solving Investigations

Problem-Solving Investigations help students learn different problem-solving strategies for attacking word problems.

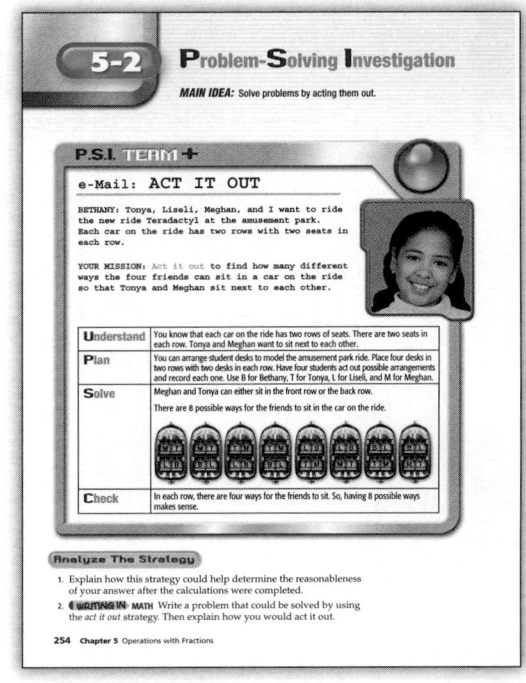

Math Connects, Course 1
Student Edition, page 254

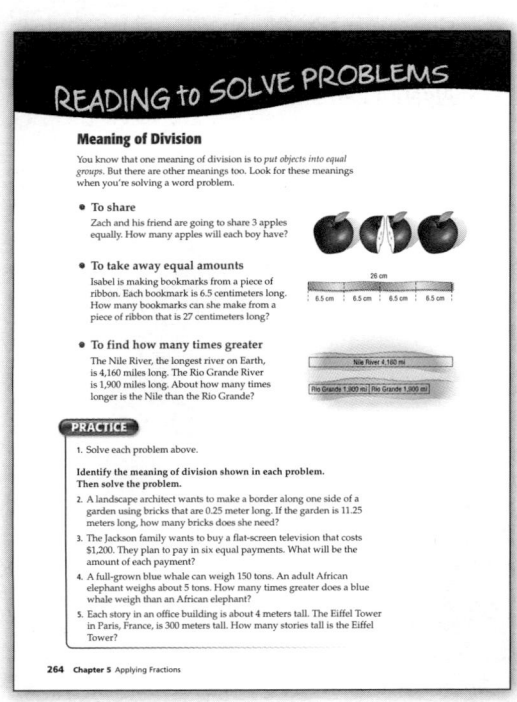

Math Connects, Course 2
Student Edition, page 264

Reading to Solve Problems

Help students understand and interpret mathematical language.

Real-World Problem-Solving Graphic Novels

Motivating, teen-relevant problem solving in graphic novel format provides practice with Number Sense, Algebraic Thinking, Geometry, Measurement, Statistics and Probability, and Mathematical Reasoning.

Hands-On Labs

Some labs act as an introduction to a mathematical topic, while others extend the topic just presented. **Algebra, Geometry, Measurement, Statistics,** and **Probability** labs use models to bridge the gap between concrete understanding and mathematical symbolism.

Concepts in Motion

Concepts in Motion are online illustrations of key concepts through animations, Interactive Labs, and BrainPOPs®.

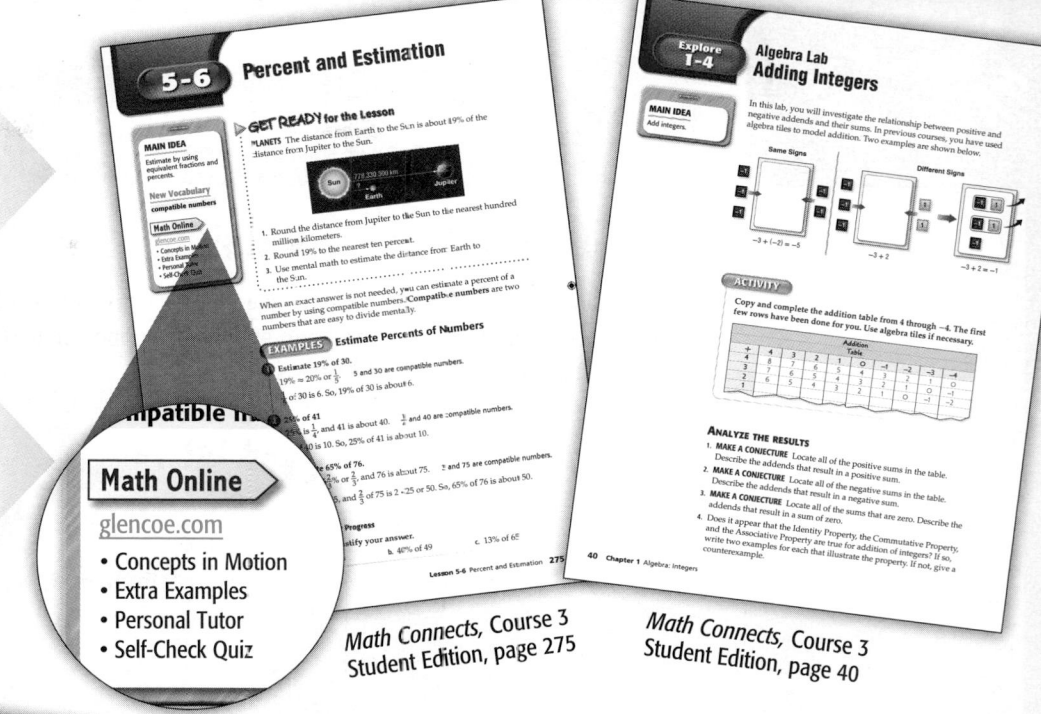

Math Online

glencoe.com

- Concepts in Motion
- Extra Examples
- Personal Tutor
- Self-Check Quiz

Math Connects, Course 3
Student Edition, page 275

Math Connects, Course 3
Student Edition, page 40

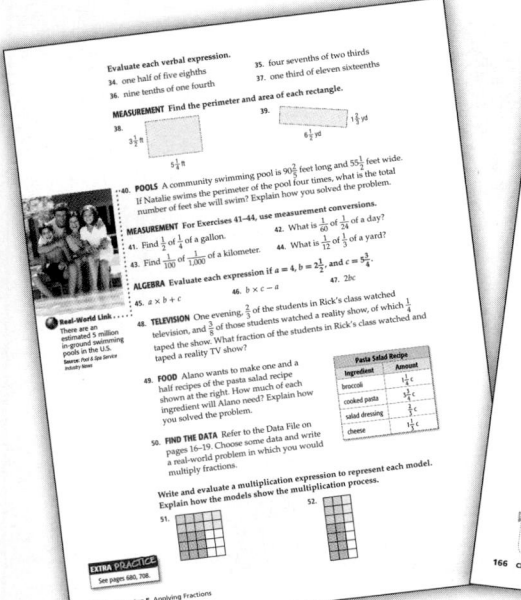

Math Connects, Course 2
Student Edition, page 256

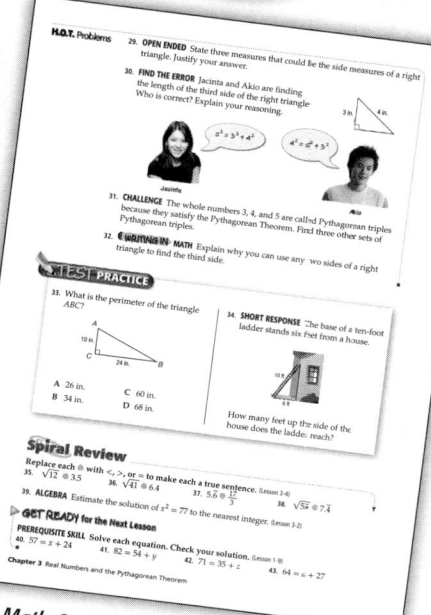

Math Connects, Course 3
Student Edition, page 166

Multi-Step Word Problems

Multi-step word problems are not simple computation problems using the numbers given. Students must analyze exactly what the problem is asking and how to use the information given. These problems are starred in the Teacher Edition.

H.O.T. Problems

H.O.T. Problems require students to use **Higher Order Thinking** skills to solve problems.

Looking Ahead

Looking Ahead lessons introduce important concepts and skills that students can use to prepare for the coming year.

Math Connects, Course 2
Student Edition, page LA0–LA1

Comprehensive Assessment System

Data-Driven Decision Making

Math Connects offers frequent and meaningful assessment of student progress within the curriculum structure and printed teacher support materials. See pages T22 and T23 for digital assessment solutions.

Assessment and Intervention System

1 Diagnostic

2 Formative

3 Summative

1 Diagnostic

Initial Assessment Assess students' knowledge **at the beginning of the year** with the *Diagnostic and Placement Tests*. This booklet will help you determine whether your students need additional materials and resources to meet grade-level standards.

Entry-Level Assessment Assess students' prior knowledge **at the beginning of a chapter or lesson** with one of the following options.

Student Edition
- Get Ready

Teacher Edition
- Options for Differentiated Instruction
- 5-Minute Check

Additional Resources
- Chapter Resource Masters, Anticipation Guide

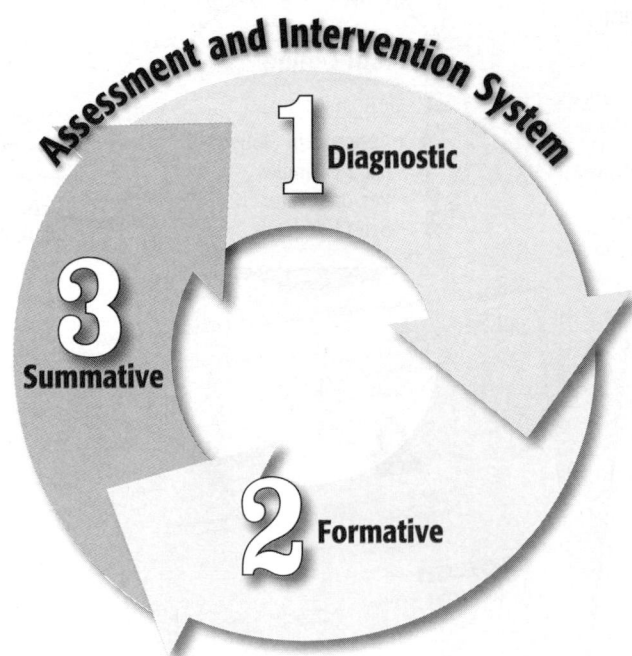

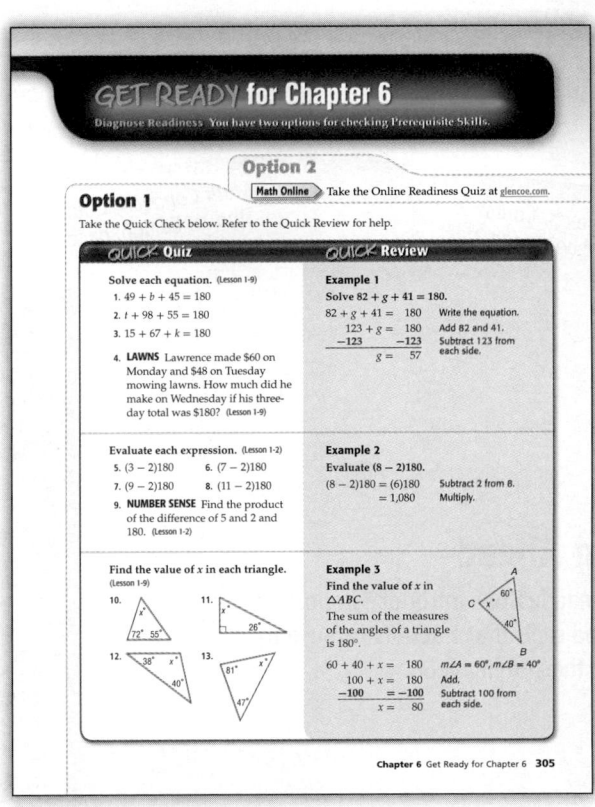

Math Connects, Course 3
Student Edition, page 305

2 Formative

Progress Monitoring Determine if students are progressing adequately as you teach each lesson. Use the assessments to differentiate lesson instruction and practice.

Student Edition
- Mid-Chapter Quiz
- Find the Error
- Check Your Understanding
- Writing in Math
- Study Guide and Review
- Foldables™

Teacher Edition
- Options for Differentiated Instruction
- Step 4 (Assess) of the Teaching Plan
- Data-Driven Decision Making

Additional Resources
Chapter Resource Masters
- Mid-Chapter Test
- 4 Quizzes
- Standardized Test Practice

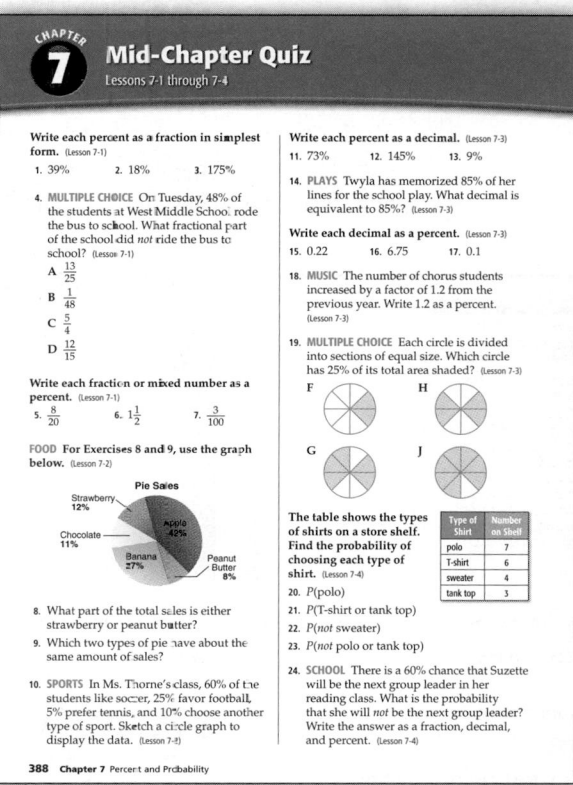

Math Connects, Course 1
Student Edition, page 388

3 Summative

Summative Evaluation Assess student success in learning the concepts in each chapter.

Student Edition
- Chapter Test
- Test Practice
- Foldables™

Teacher Edition
- Data-Driven Decision Making

Additional Resources
Chapter Resource Masters
- Vocabulary Test
- 6 Leveled Chapter Tests
- Extended Response Test

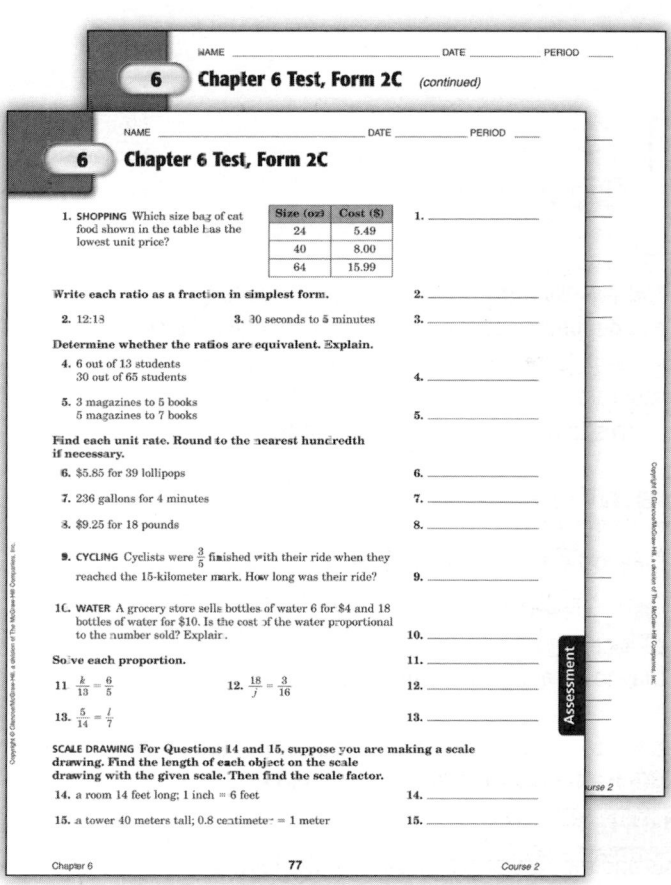

Math Connects, Course 2
Chapter 6 Resource Masters, pages 77–78

 # Comprehensive Assessment System

Data-Driven Decision Making

Math Connects provides digital assessment options to create, customize, administer, and instantly score a variety of assessments. These digital solutions offer the same quality assessments and reporting as the print resources in easy-to-use technology tools.

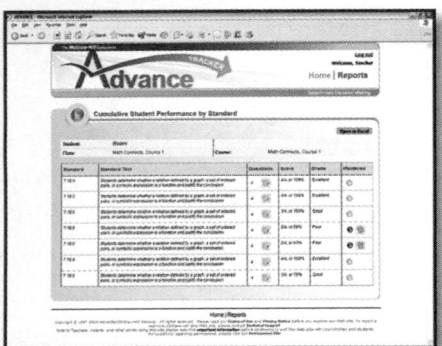

Math Connects, Course 1

Advance Tracker helps teachers administer online tests, diagnose student achievement, and create prescriptive reports for a student or class.

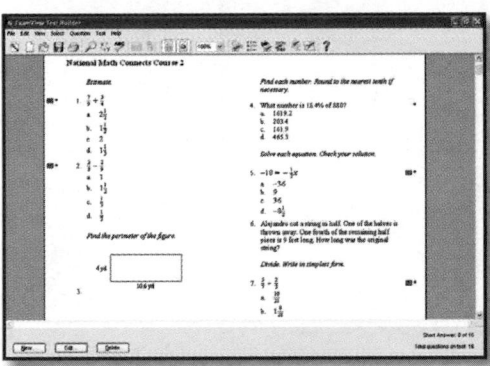

Math Connects, Course 2

ExamView® Assessment Suite allows teachers to create and customize their own assessment and assignments. Print in one or two columns to match state test.

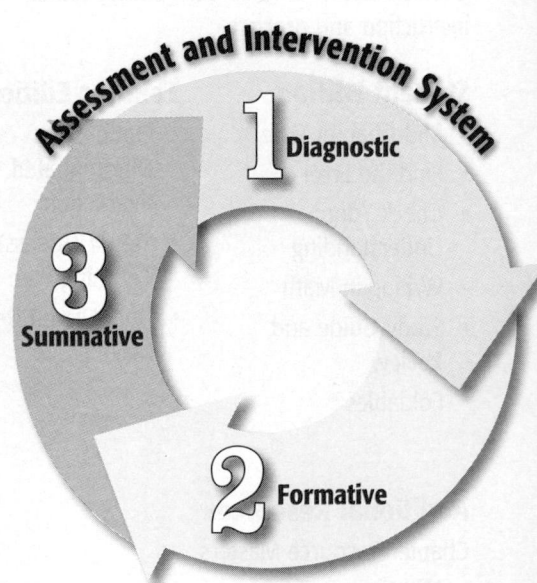

Assessment and Intervention System

1 Diagnostic

2 Formative

3 Summative

1 Diagnostic

Initial Assessment Assess students' knowledge **at the beginning of the year** with the *Diagnostic and Placement Tests.* These assessments will help you determine whether your students need additional materials and resources to meet grade-level standards.

- Diagnostic and Placement Tests

- Diagnostic and Placement Tests

Entry–Level Assessment Assess students' prior knowledge **at the beginning of a chapter or lesson.**

Math Online glencoe.com Students can complete online tests and the results are emailed to the teacher.

- Chapter Readiness

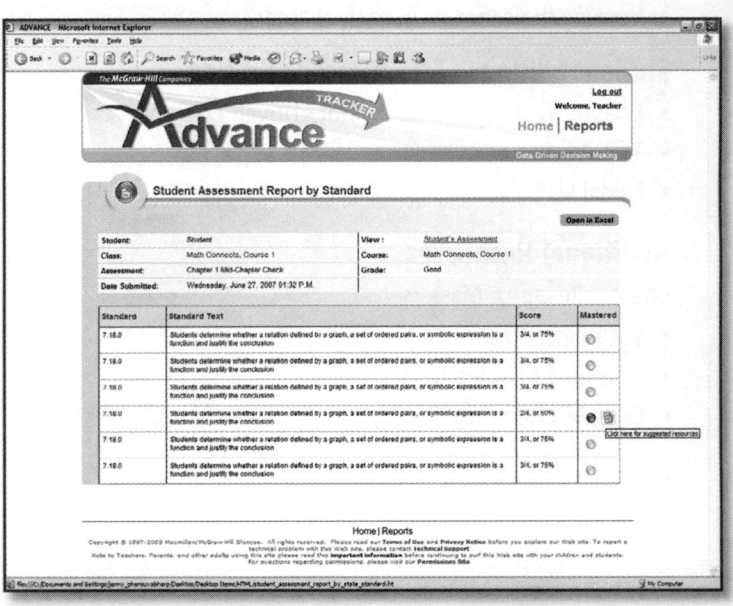

Math Connects, Course 1 Advance Tracker

Formative

Progress Monitoring Determine if students are progressing adequately as you teach each lesson. Use the assessments to differentiate lesson instruction and practice.

- Mid-Chapter Test
- Study Guide and Review

MindJogger, Super DVD

 glencoe.com

- Self-Check Quizzes

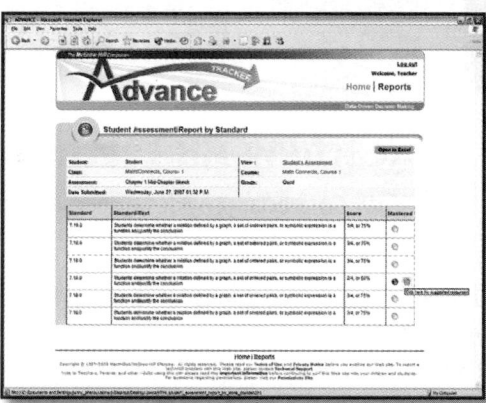

Math Connects, Course 1, Advance Tracker

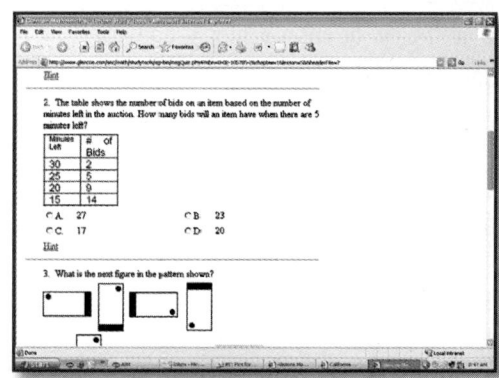

Math Connects, Course 3, Self-Check Quiz

Summative

Summative Evaluation Assess students' success in learning the concepts in each chapter.

ExamView Assessment Suite

- Chapter Tests
- Cumulative Standardized Test Practice

- Chapter Tests
- Cumulative Standardized Test Practice

 glencoe.com

- Chapter Tests

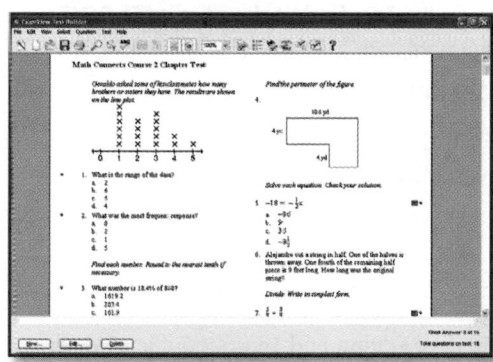

Math Connects, Course 2, ExamView® Assessment Suite

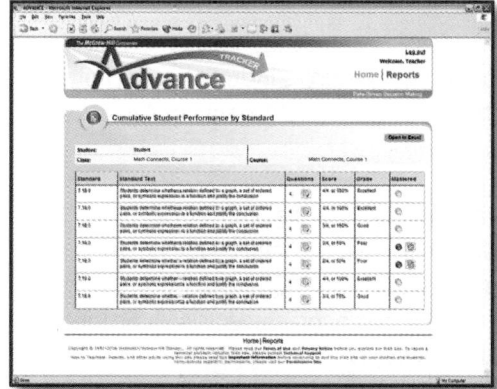

Math Connects, Course 1, Advance Tracker

Differentiated Instruction

Reaching All Learners

Math Connects, provides extensive support for reaching all learners.

Every chapter and lesson includes suggestions for identifying and meeting your students' needs. Strategies include differentiation in pacing and student grouping, alternate approaches, ways to enhance instruction with manipulatives, questions to promote higher-order thinking, and language hints.

Personalize instruction for:

BL Students who are below or approaching grade level

ELL English language learners

AL Students who are above or beyond grade level

Leveled Exercise Sets

The assignments for each lesson are leveled for students.

BL Below or Approaching Grade Level

OL on Grade Level

AL Above or Beyond Grade Level

Leveled Resources

All of the blackline masters and transparencies that accompany the program, as well as all of the Teacher Edition pages, are available on the **TeacherWorks Plus™ CD-ROM.** Resources and assignments are leveled for students who are:

BL Below or Approaching Grade Level

OL On Grade Level

AL Above or Beyond Grade Level

ELL English Language Learners

Technology

In addition to the Student Edition and Teacher Edition, *Math Connects* includes extensive resources online, on CD-ROM, and on DVD.

Online Resources for teachers, students, and parents can be found at glencoe.com. These resources include a variety of activities to teach, reinforce, review, and assess mathematical concepts.

CD-ROM/DVD In addition to all of the Student Edition pages, all of the student workbooks that accompany the program are available on the StudentWorks Plus™ CD-ROM. This resource offers full audio of the text to support students with hearing challenges or language difficulty.

Additional tools for class presentations and assessment are available on a variety of CD-ROMs and DVDs.

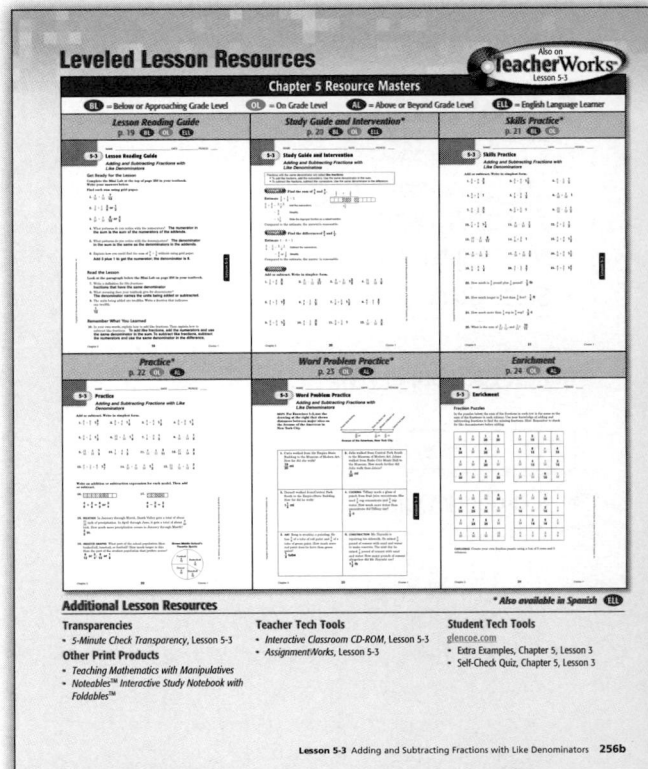

Math Connects, Course 1
Teacher Edition, page 256b

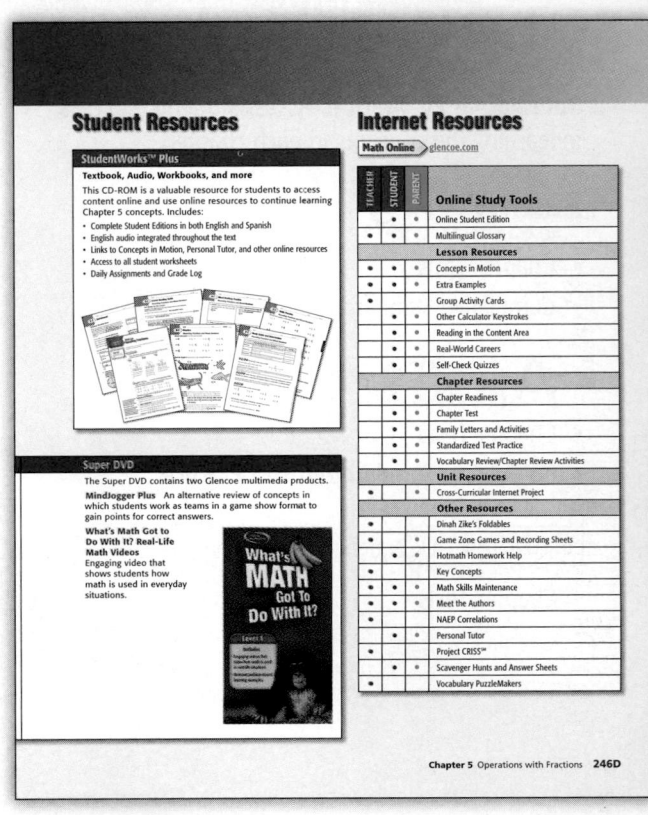

Math Connects, Course 1
Teacher Edition, page 246D

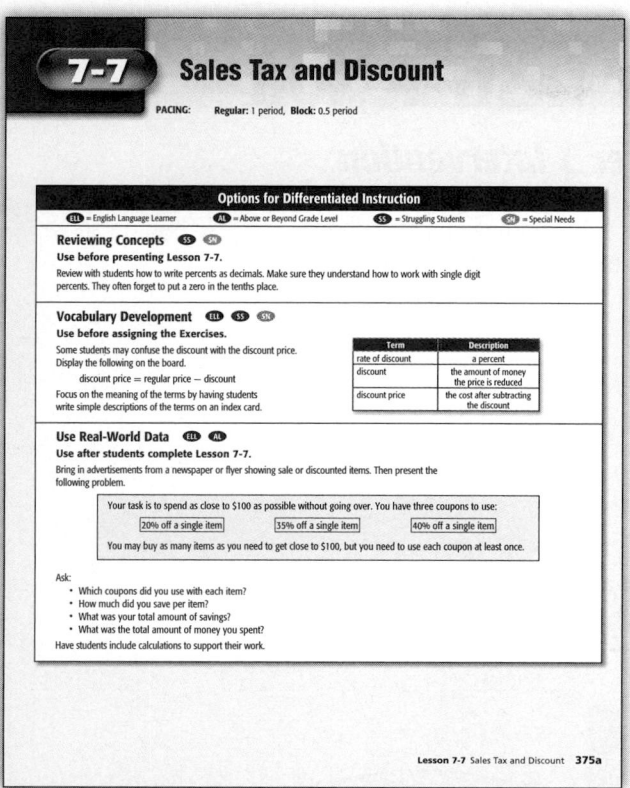

Math Connects, Course 2,
Teacher Edition, page 375a

Meeting Students' Needs

Diagnostic Teaching Every chapter and lesson includes suggestions for identifying and meeting your students' needs. Strategies include differentiation in pacing and student grouping, alternate approaches, ways to enhance instruction with manipulatives, questions to promote higher order thinking, and language hints.

Personalize instruction for:

- Struggling students
- English language learners
- Students with special needs
- Students who are above or beyond grade level in their comprehension of mathematics

Advanced Learners

Acceleration and Enrichment Resources and assignments that are coded for students who are above or beyond level may be used with advanced learners. In particular, the **Enrichment Masters** may provide students with valuable opportunities for extending your lessons. **Pre-AP Activities** in the Teacher Edition provide additional opportunities for extension.

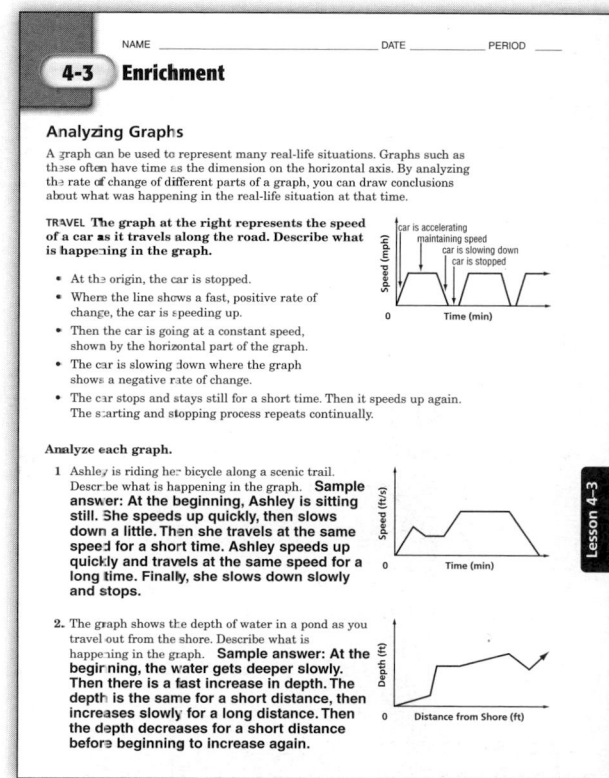

Math Connects, Course 3,
Chapter 4 Resource Masters, page 27

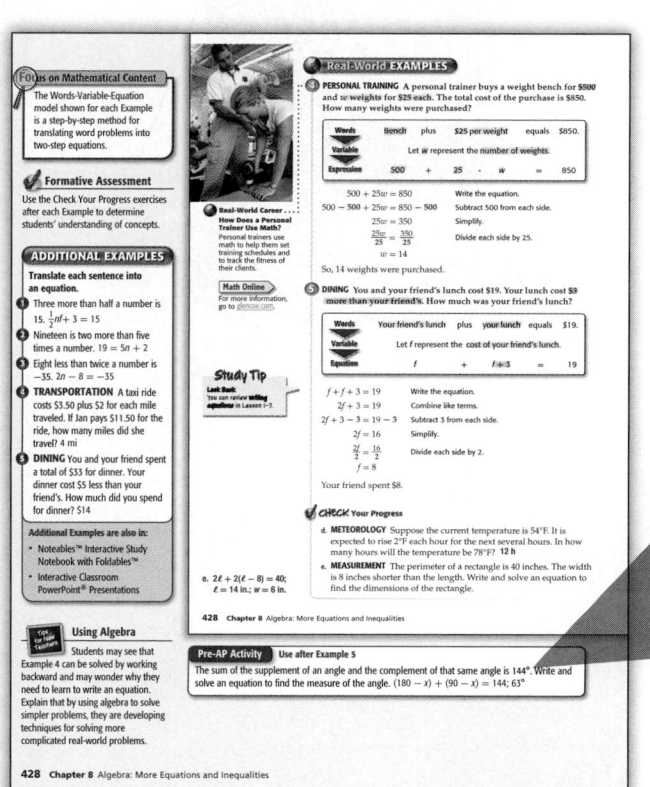

Pre-AP Activity Use after Example 5

The sum of the supplement of an angle and the complement of that same angle is 144°. Write and solve an equation to find the measure of the angle. $(180 - x) + (90 - x) = 144$; 63°

Math Connects, Course 3,
Teacher Edition, page 428

Blending Your Instruction
Basal – NSF-Funded – Tier 3 Intervention

Math Connects, MathScape, and *Math Triumphs* provide a three-pronged approach to mathematics instruction. This unique combination provides built-in strategies to easily tip the balance of instruction to a more conceptual approach or to a more skills-based approach, depending on the needs of your students.

Basal Program–Focused on Comprehensive Instruction

NSF Program–Focused on Investigations

Intensive Intervention (Tier 3 RtI)–Focused on Skills

Investigative Approach

This project was supported, in part, by the
National Science Foundation

MathScape is a mathematics curriculum for grades 6–8 developed by the Seeing and Thinking Mathematically Project at the Education Development Center.

Graphs and Averages
What Does the Data Say?

How to Use *MathScape* with Chapter 2
The unit *What Does the Data Say?* can be used to enhance Lessons 2-3 and 2-8.

- **Enrich** After you complete **Lesson 2-3**, you can use the activities on pages 22–25 to provide students with the opportunity to collect their own data, graph the data, and make predictions.
- **Introduce** Before you begin **Lesson 2-8**, you can introduce the idea that different scales can change the appearance of the data by using the activities on page 15.

Investigative Approach

The Chapter Planner, in the Teacher Edition of *Math Connects,* references alternative lessons found in *MathScape.* These lessons provide opportunities for investigative instruction with hands-on explorations.

RtI (Response to Intervention)

In the *Math Connects* Teacher Editions, the Data-Driven Decision Making chart provides a comprehensive RtI (Response to Intervention) beginning with diagnostic review and continuing with prescriptions at all three RtI tiers.

- **Tier 1** – Leveled exercise sets and leveled resources
- **Tier 2** – Strategic Intervention Guide (1–5), Study Guide and Intervention (6–8)
- **Tier 3** – Intensive Intervention, *Math Triumphs*

Differentiated Instruction

Investigative Approach

This project was supported, in part, by the
National Science Foundation

MathScape is a mathematics curriculum for grades 6–8 developed by the Seeing and Thinking Mathematically Project at the Education Development Center.

Graphs and Averages
What Does the Data Say?

How to Use *MathScape* with Chapter 2
The unit *What Does the Data Say?* can be used to enhance Lessons 2-3 and 2-8.

- **Enrich** After you complete **Lesson 2-3**, you can use the activities on pages 22–25 to provide students with the opportunity to collect their own data, graph the data, and make predictions.
- **Introduce** Before you begin **Lesson 2-8**, you can introduce the idea that different scales can change the appearance of the data by using the activities on page 15.

RTI (Response to Intervention)

① On-Level Instruction Use the *Math Connects* program as instruction for your on-level students.

② Strategic Intervention For options to instruct struggling students, refer to the Diagnostic Assessment table on page 77.

③ Intensive Intervention *Math Triumphs* can provide intensive intervention for students who are at risk of not meeting the objectives addressed in Chapter 2.

Diagnose student readiness with the Quick Check and Quick Review on page 77.

Practice and Review

Quick Review Math Handbook* is Glencoe's mathematical handbook for students and parents.

Hot Words includes a glossary of terms.

Hot Topics consists of two parts:
- explanations of key mathematical concepts
- exercises to check students' understanding.

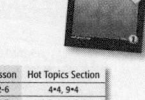

Lesson	Hot Topics Section	Lesson	Hot Topics Section
2-2	4•2	2-6	4•4, 9•4
2-3	4•3	2-7	4•2, 4•4, 9•1
2-4	4•2	2-8	4•3

*Also available in Spanish

Chapter 2 Statistics and Graphs **76F**

Math Connects, Course 1
Teacher Edition, page 76F

RTI (Response to Intervention)

① On-Level Instruction Use the *Math Connects* program as instruction for your on-level students.

② Strategic Intervention For options to instruct struggling students, refer to the Diagnostic Assessment table on page 77.

③ Intensive Intervention *Math Triumphs* can provide intensive intervention for students who are at risk of not meeting the objectives addressed in Chapter 2.

Diagnose student readiness with the Quick Check and Quick Review on page 77.

Planning for Success

Ease of Use

Math Connects has a strong instructional model that includes differentiated instructional options, reteaching, reinforcement, and extension options, Teacher Tips to help address various learners, Pre-AP/Advanced items, and assessment linked with instruction.

Convenient Lesson Planning at Your Fingertips

The **Chapter Overview** helps you plan your instruction by showing the objectives to be covered, suggested pacing, and coverage of Focal Points.

TeacherWorks™ Plus

This electronic lesson planner contains multi-purpose management software including the Teacher Edition pages, program blackline masters, and daily calendars that make planning a snap.

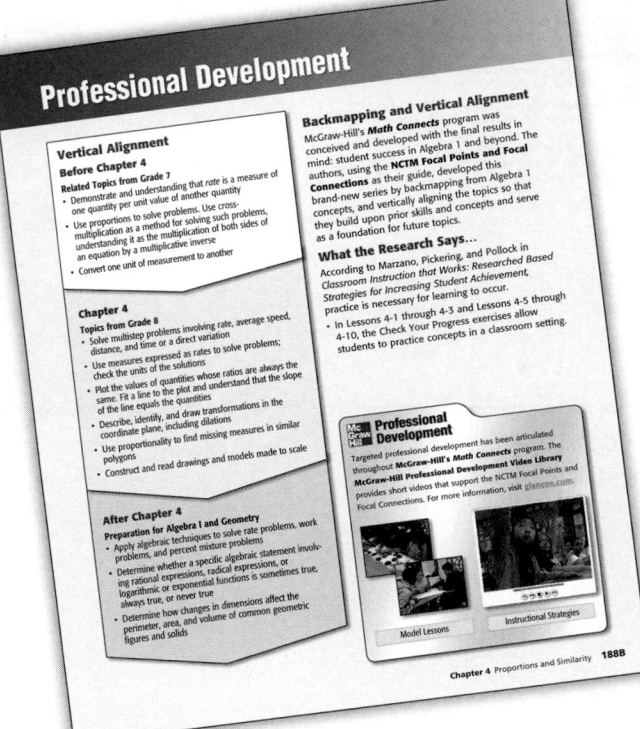

Math Connects, Course 3
Teacher Edition, page 188A

Vertical Alignment

Topics are presented to build upon prior grade level skills and concepts and to serve as a foundation for future topics.

What the Research Says

Citations from research help to validate *Math Connects* program. An additional Research Bibliography can be found in the **Teacher Reference Handbook.**

Professional Development

Targeted professional development has been articulated throughout the program. Actual classroom video clips are especially helpful when planning lessons and differentiating instruction. See page T32 for more information.

Math Connects, Course 3
Teacher Edition, page 188B

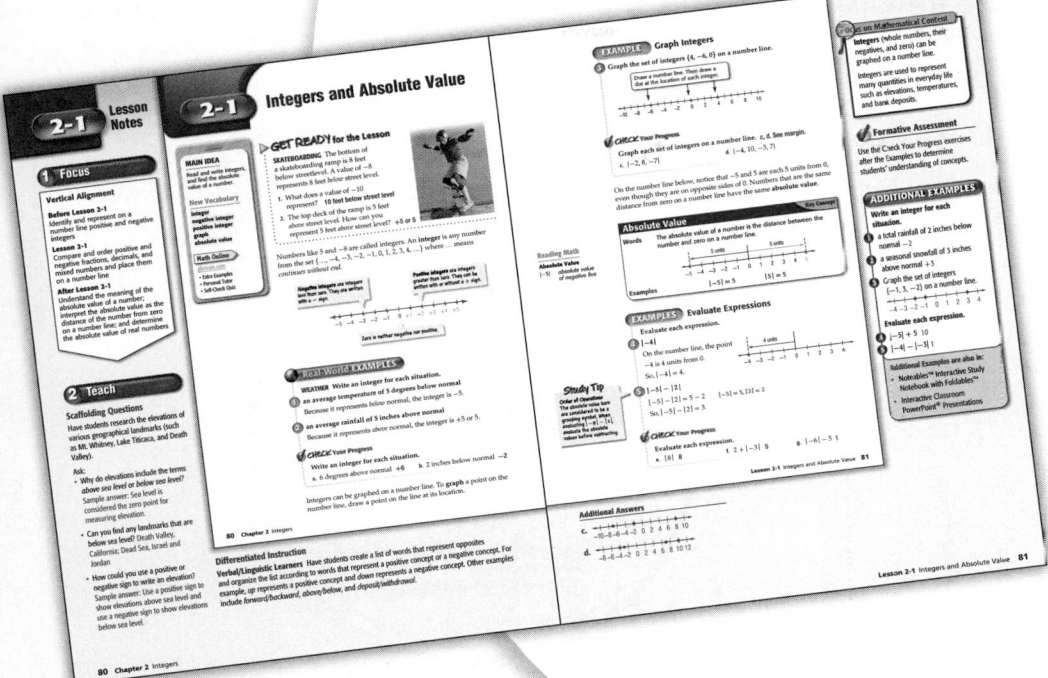

Math Connects, Course 2
Teacher Edition, pages 80–81

Four-Step Teaching Plan

Organizes your instruction as you **Focus** and **Teach** and help your students **Practice** and **Assess** what they've learned.

Vertical Alignment

Vertical Alignment at the beginning of each lesson shows the objectives that lead into and follow the current lesson's content for a coherent PreK–12 scope and sequence.

Scaffolding Questions

Each lesson contains **Scaffolding Questions** for you to use to help students investigate and understand the main ideas of the lesson.

Additional Examples

Each **Additional Example** mirrors the example in the Student Edition. The Additional Examples are also available as a PowerPoint® presentation on the **Interactive Classroom** CD-ROM.

Differentiated Homework Options

Because most classrooms include students at a wide range of ability levels, **Differentiated Homework Options** allow you to customize your assignments.

Assessment Activities

Formative Assessment activities provide alternate ways to determine student comprehension at the end of each lesson.

- **Ticket Out the Door** Students must answer the given question and hand to the teacher as they leave the classroom.
- **Yesterday's News** Students connect what they learned today to yesterday's lesson.
- **Crystal Ball** Students predict how today's lesson will relate to the next lesson.
- **Name the Math** Students tell what mathematics is used in a problem.

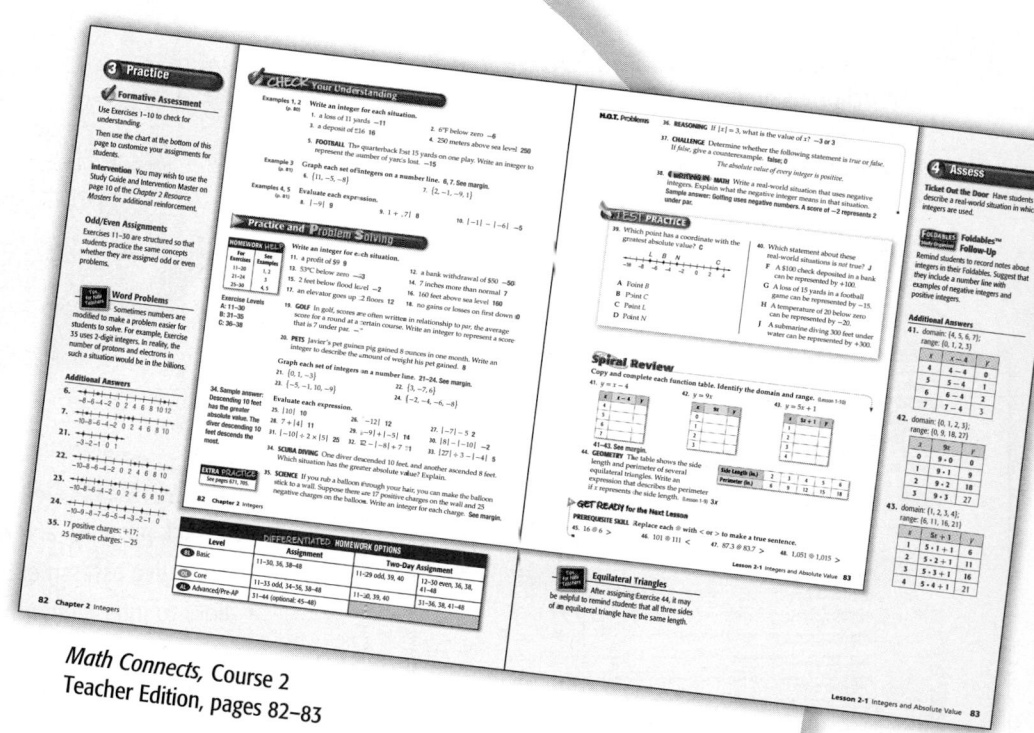

Math Connects, Course 2
Teacher Edition, pages 82–83

Planning for Success
State-of-the-Art Technology

Math Connects provides fully integrated technology resources for teachers, students, and parents.

For Teachers

 TeacherWorks™ Plus is your all-in-one planner and resource center.
- entire Teacher Edition
- all print ancillaries
- electronic lesson planner

 Exam*View*® Assessment Suite allows teachers to create and customize their own assessment and assignments.

New features:
- correlated to state standards
- online content update
- one- or two-column formatting

 Use **Interactive Classroom** to guide instruction using PowerPoint ™
- In-Class Examples
- 5-Minute Check Transparencies
- Concepts in Motion
- links to Math Online

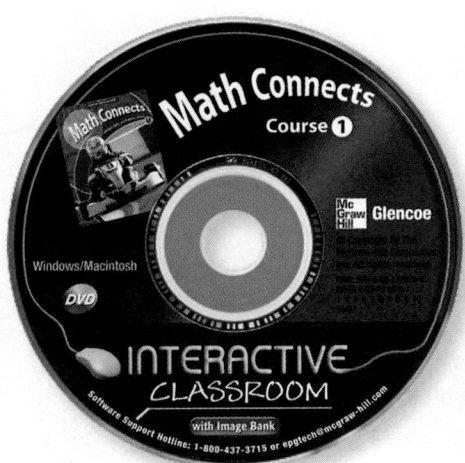

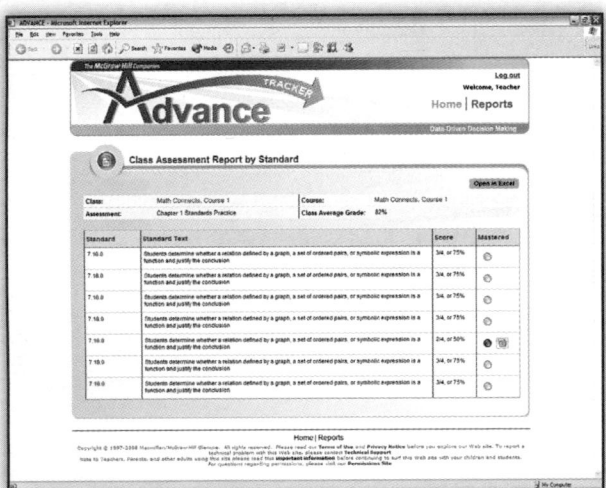

Advance ᵀᴿᴬᶜᴷᴱᴿ Learner Management System helps you track progress and differentiate your instruction.
- formative assessments aligned to standards
- links to intervention help

Math Connects, Course 1

For Students

 StudentWorks™ Plus is your students' backpack solution.
- entire Student Edition
- all student worksheets
- links to | Math Online >

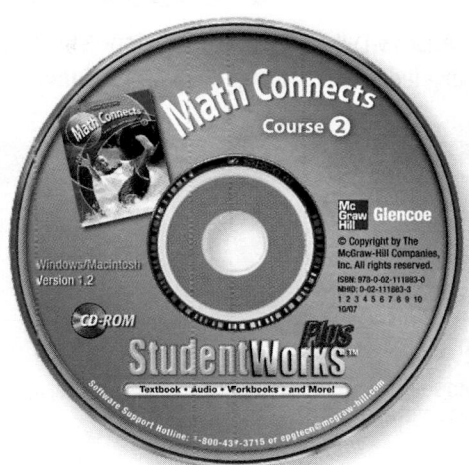

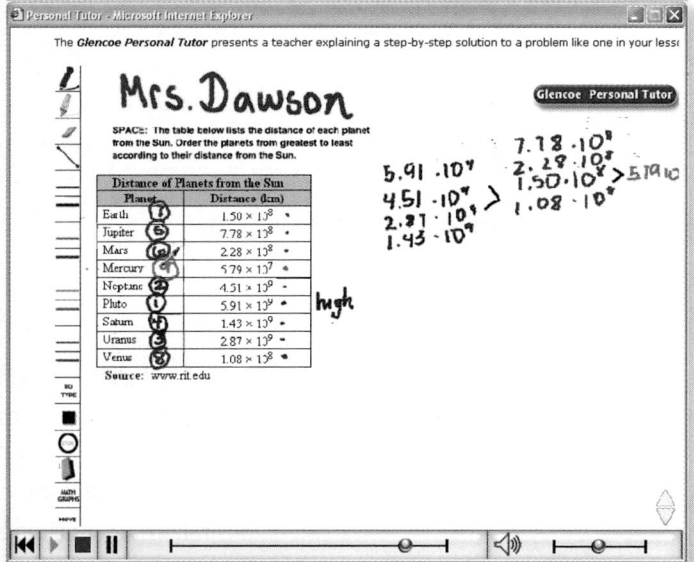

Math Connects, Course 1
Web site, Personal Tutor

| Math Online > provides a wealth of resources — convenient for students and parents!

- Self-Check Quizzes
- Personal Tutor
- Concepts in Motion
- eGlossary (14 languages)
- And much, much more!

| Math Online > *Math Connect's* **eBook** is easy to use, easy to read, and packed with features.

- links to online study tools and resources right from the page
- includes audio

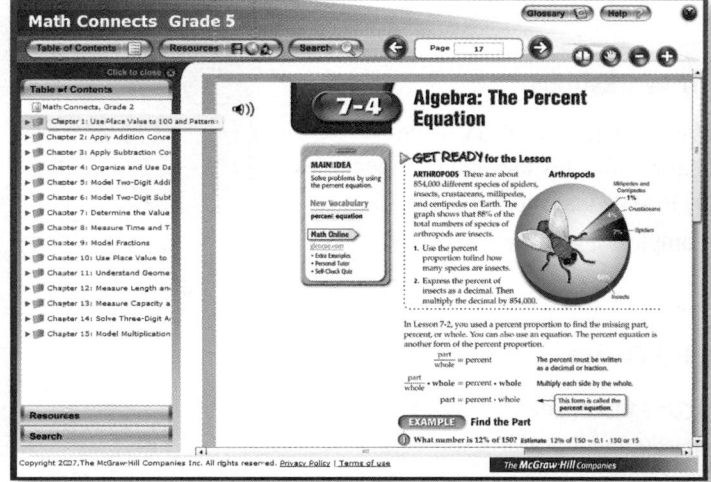

Math Connects, Course 2
eBook, page 361

PreK-12 Data-Driven Professional Development

McGraw-Hill Professional Development (MHPD) provides a comprehensive plan for mathematics that is fully aligned and articulated with **Math Connects K–8** and the **Glencoe Mathematics** high school series.

Professional Development Needs	Online Courses	DVD Workshops	Video Library	Teach-Use-Succeed	Ready-Access Math
Has immediate classroom application	✓	✓	✓	✓	✓
Builds content knowledge	✓	✓			✓
Promotes best teaching practices		✓	✓		
Supports new and experienced teachers	✓	✓	✓	✓	✓
Allows customization of courses	✓				✓
Can be self-paced	✓	✓		✓	✓
Adaptable for various timeframes	✓	✓	✓	✓	✓
Is grade-level specific		✓		✓	✓
Promotes a learning community	✓	✓			✓
Provides vertically-aligned content	✓	✓	✓		✓
Helps with RtI (Response to Intervention), Tiers 1–3	✓	✓	✓		✓

Use students' mathematics achievement data to help develop a targeted Professional Development Plan.

Accredited Online Courses

(available for purchase)
- Watch video clips of math classrooms
  Complete interactive exercises
  Develop electronic portfolios.
- Complete each 3- to 5-hour online module one segment at a time.
- University credit (additional tuition charge)

DVD Workshops

- Watch video clips of classroom mathematics lessons and commentaries by leading educators.
- Complete lessons and activities.

MHPD Online

- Access this online Professional Development resource for K–12 educators.
- Link to relevant Web sites.
- Download grade-level student resources.

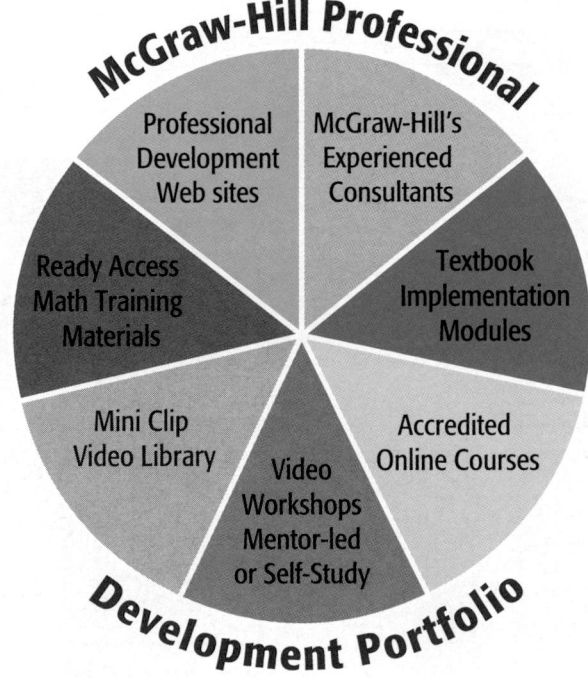

McGraw-Hill Professional
Development Portfolio

- Professional Development Web sites
- McGraw-Hill's Experienced Consultants
- Textbook Implementation Modules
- Accredited Online Courses
- Video Workshops Mentor-led or Self-Study
- Mini Clip Video Library
- Ready Access Math Training Materials

Video Library | Math Online

- Access hundreds of K–12 video clips.
- See clips that illustrate mathematics content and instructional strategies.
- Watch demonstrations or commentaries by math specialists

Teach-Use-Succeed Textbook Implementation Modules

- Watch an experienced teacher demonstrate the *Math Connects* K–8 Student Editions, Teacher Editions, and program ancillaries
- Online or DVD

Ready-Access Math, Personalized Professional Development

- Access training materials for nearly 300 mathematics professional development lessons.
- Create a customized sequence of professional development sessions.
- Deliver 45–60 minute after-school professional development sessions.

Teacher Edition

Glencoe McGraw-Hill

Math Connects

Concepts, Skills, and Problem Solving

Course 2

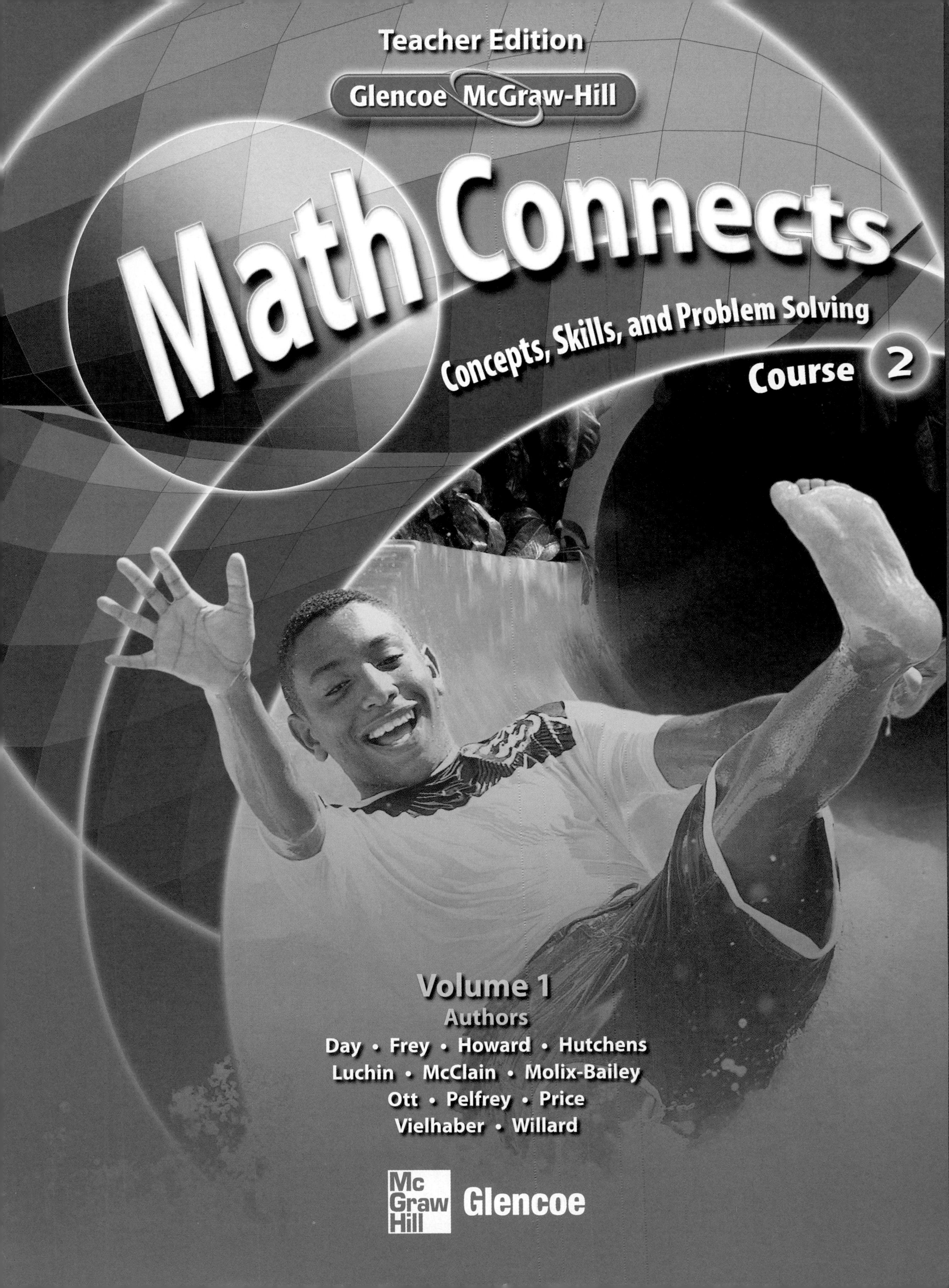

Volume 1

Authors

Day • Frey • Howard • Hutchens
Luchin • McClain • Molix-Bailey
Ott • Pelfrey • Price
Vielhaber • Willard

McGraw Hill Glencoe

Contents

Start Smart

Unit 1
Algebra and Functions

CHAPTER 1 Introduction to Algebra and Functions

Focal Points and Connections
See page iv for key.

G7-FP3 Number and Operations and Algebra

TEST PRACTICE
- Extended Response 77
- Multiple Choice   29, 33, 37, 41, 47, 51, 52, 56, 61, 67
- Short Response/Grid In 52, 77
- Worked Out Example 50

H.O.T. Problems
Higher Order Thinking
- Challenge   29, 33, 37, 41, 47, 52, 56, 61, 67
- Find the Error 41, 52
- Number Sense 56
- Open Ended 29, 33, 37, 47, 56, 61, 67
- Select a Tool 61
- Which One Doesn't Belong? 33

CHAPTER 2 Integers

**Focal Points
and Connections**
See page iv for key.

G7-FP3 Number and Operations and Algebra

TEST PRACTICE

• Extended Response   125
• Multiple Choice   83, 85, 87, 92, 106, 113, 118
• Short Response/Grid In   99, 125
• Worked Out Example   85

H.O.T. Problems
Higher Order Thinking

• Challenge   83, 87, 92, 99, 106, 111, 118
• Find the Error   99, 106
• Number Sense   87, 111
• Open Ended   92, 106, 111, 118
• Patterns   118
• Reasoning   83
• Select a Technique   111
• Which One Doesn't Belong?   118

Algebra: Linear Equations and Functions

Table of Contents

Focal Points and Connections
See page iv for key.

G7-FP3 Number and Operations and Algebra

Unit 2
Number Sense: Fractions

CHAPTER 4
Fractions, Decimals, and Percents

Focal Points and Connections
See page iv for key.

G7-FP3 Number and Operations and Algebra
G7-FP5C Number and Operations

TEST PRACTICE

- Extended Response 227
- Multiple Choice 184, 189, 195, 200, 205, 210, 214, 220
- Short Response/Grid In 214, 227
- Worked Out Example 217

H.O.T. Problems
Higher Order Thinking

- Challenge 184, 189, 195, 200, 205, 210, 214, 220
- Find the Error 195, 210
- Geometry 205
- Number Sense 191
- Open Ended 184, 194, 200, 210, 214
- Research 184
- Reasoning 213
- Select a Technique 214
- Which One Doesn't Belong? 205, 220

Table of Contents

Focal Points
and Connections
See page iv for key.

G7-FP3 Number and Operations and Algebra

TEST PRACTICE

- Extended Response 277
- Multiple Choice 235, 241, 246, 257, 260, 262, 270
- Short Response/Grid In 235, 277
- Worked Out Example 260

H.O.T. Problems
Higher Order Thinking

- Challenge 234, 240, 246, 257, 262, 269
- Find the Error 240, 270
- Number Sense 234, 246
- Open Ended 234, 240, 257
- Reasoning 262
- Select a Technique 235
- Select a Tool 269
- Which One Doesn't Belong? 262

Unit 3

Algebra and Number Sense: Proportions and Percents

CHAPTER 6 Ratios and Proportions

Focal Points and Connections
See page iv for key.

G7-FP1 Number and Operations and Algebra and Geometry

TEST PRACTICE

H.O.T. Problems
Higher Order Thinking

CHAPTER 7 Applying Percents

Focal Points and Connections
See page iv for key.

G7-FP1 Number and Operations and Algebra and Geometry

TEST PRACTICE

H.O.T. Problems
Higher Order Thinking

Unit 4
Statistics, Data Analysis, and Probability

CHAPTER 8
Statistics: Analyzing Data

Focal Points and Connections
See page iv for key.

G7-FP6C Data Analysis

TEST PRACTICE

- Extended Response   457
- Multiple Choice   401, 405, 408, 414, 421, 431, 435, 443, 449
- Short Response/Grid In   421, 457
- Worked Out Example   404

H.O.T. Problems
Higher Order Thinking

- Challenge   400, 407, 413, 420, 430, 436, 443, 449
- Data Sense   420
- Find the Error   400, 413
- Open Ended   400, 407, 430, 436, 449
- Reasoning   400, 407
- Select a Technique   421
- Select a Tool   437
- Which One Doesn't Belong?   407, 437

x

CHAPTER

9 Probability

Focal Points and Connections
See page iv for key.

G7-FP7C Probability

TEST PRACTICE

- Extended Response   505
- Multiple Choice   464, 467, 470, 474, 478, 483, 490, 497
- Short Response/Grid In   474, 505
- Worked Out Example   466

H.O.T. Problems
Higher Order Thinking

- Challenge   464, 469, 474, 478, 483, 490, 497
- Find the Error   469, 483
- Reasoning   464, 490
- Select a Tool   469, 477
- Which One Doesn't Belong?   464, 474

Unit 5

Geometry and Measurement

CHAPTER 10 Geometry: Polygons

Focal Points and Connections
See page iv for key.

G7-FP2 Measurement and Geometry and Algebra

TEST PRACTICE

- Extended Response   569
- Multiple Choice   513, 517, 523, 529, 537, 545, 551, 557, 562
- Short Response/Grid In   551, 569
- Worked Out Example   527

H.O.T. Problems
Higher Order Thinking

- Challenge   513, 517, 523, 529, 537, 545, 550, 556, 562
- Collect the Data   523
- Find the Error   537
- Open Ended   529, 550, 562
- Reasoning   529, 537, 550, 556
- Which One Doesn't Belong?   552

Measurement: Two- and Three-Dimensional Figures

Focal Points and Connections
See page iv for key.

G7-FP2 Measurement and Geometry and Algebra
G7-FP4C Measurement and Geometry

TEST PRACTICE

H.O.T. Problems
Higher Order Thinking

CHAPTER

12

Geometry and Measurement

Focal Points and Connections
See page iv for key.

G7-FP1 Number and Operations and Algebra and Geometry

TEST PRACTICE

H.O.T. Problems
Higher Order Thinking

Looking Ahead

Student Handbook

Table of Contents

DO NOT GET ON/OFF RIDE WHILE RIDE IS IN MOTION

TO THE STUDENT
Lesson Notes

1 Focus

Give students a glance at what the year's focus will be for their mathematics experience.

Familiarize students with standard format of various resources and tools provided to them throughout the text.

2 Teach

Read the three focus areas and discuss what advantages there are to gaining this type of knowledge.

Ask:

- Which of these areas do you recognize from your past math classes?

- Which areas look new to you?

- Which areas do you think might help you in your future life experiences? Explain how.

Encourage students to become familiar with their textbook in order to take full advantage of the resources they are provided.

- Select a chapter and help students find each of the features listed on the page.

To the Student

As you gear up to study mathematics, you are probably wondering, "What will I learn this year?" You will focus on these three areas.

- **Number and Operations, Algebra, and Geometry:** Develop and apply an understanding of proportions, including similarity.

- **Measurement and Geometry:** Find surface areas and volumes of three-dimensional shapes.

- **Number and Operations and Algebra:** Solve linear equations and deepen an understanding of operations on all rational numbers.

Along the way, you'll learn more about problem solving, how to use the tools and language of mathematics, and how to THINK mathematically.

To the Student

How to Use Your Math Book

Have you ever been in class and not understood all of what was being presented? Or, you understood everything in class, but got stuck on how to solve some of the homework problems? Don't worry. You can find answers in your math book!

- **Read** the **MAIN IDEA** at the beginning of the lesson.

- **Find** the **New Vocabulary** words, **highlighted in yellow**, and read their definitions.

- **Review** the **EXAMPLE** problems, solved step-by-step, to remind you of the day's material.

- **Refer** to the **HOMEWORK HELP** boxes that show you which examples may help with your homework problems.

- **Go** to **Math Online** where you can find extra examples to coach you through difficult problems.

- **Review** the notes you've taken on your **FOLDABLES**.

- **Find** the answers to odd-numbered problems in the back of the book. Use them to see if you are solving the problems correctly.

How to Use Your Math Book 1

Remind students that the goal is to learn to THINK in a logical and mathematical way, not just to mimic a process.

Scavenger Hunt

Let's Get Started

CHAPTER 1

Use the Scavenger Hunt below to learn where things are located in each chapter.

1. What is the title of Chapter 1? **Introduction to Algebra and Functions**

2. How can you tell what you'll learn in Lesson 1-1? **the main idea**

3. Sometimes you may ask, "When am I ever going to use this?" Name a situation that uses the concepts from Lesson 1-2. **computing power in a computer chip**

4. In the margin of Lesson 1-2, there is a Vocabulary Link. What can you learn from that feature? **the everyday use of a word and its corresponding math use**

5. What is the key concept presented in Lesson 1-3? **squares and square roots**

6. How many examples are presented in Lesson 1-3? **5**

7. What is the title of the feature in Lesson 1-3 that tells you how to read square roots? **Reading Math**

8. What is the Web address where you could find extra examples? **www.glencoe.com**

9. Suppose you're doing your homework on page 40 and you get stuck on Exercise 18. Where could you find help? **Example 3**

10. What problem-solving strategy is presented in the Problem-Solving Investigation in Lesson 1-5? **guess and check**

11. List the new vocabulary words that are presented in Lesson 1-7. **equation, solution, solving an equation, defining the variable**

12. What is the web address that would allow you to take a self-check quiz to be sure you understand the lesson? **www.glencoe.com**

13. There is a Real-World Career mentioned in Lesson 1-10. What is it? **botanist**

14. On what pages will you find the Study Guide and Review for Chapter 1? **pages 70–74**

15. Suppose you can't figure out how to do Exercise 25 in the Study Guide and Review on page 72. Where could you find help? **pages 34–37**

MATH? SYMBOLS•

2 Scavenger Hunt

Start Smart

Let's Review!

The Statue of Liberty
on the Fourth of July

Start Smart

Begin the year with the lessons found in the **Start Smart** section. These lessons help students get ready for the coming year by reviewing and reinforcing skills and concepts they learned in the previous grade. The **Start Smart** lessons also prepare for skills and concepts students will need for success in the upcoming year.

Lesson Notes

Identify and use the steps in the four-step problem-solving plan.

2 Teach

Read and discuss the introduction.

- Lead a discussion about farms and complete a 4-column table. The first column should contain information that is known. Label this column "U" for "understand".

- **What do we know about this problem? What do we need to find?** List students' responses in the "U" column.

- The second column should contain a plan of how to go about solving the problem. Label this column "P" for "plan".

- **What will we do to solve the problem? What operation or strategy will we use?** List students' responses in the "P" column.

- The third column should contain the information used to solve the problem. Label this column "S" for "solve".

- **How do we execute the plan? What is the answer?** List students' responses in the "S" column.

- The fourth column should give an explanation of why the solution is reasonable. Label this column "C" for "check".

- **Does our answer make sense? Do we need to solve the problem in a different way?** List students' responses in the "C" column.

 **A Plan for Problem Solving**

Amber Waves of Grain

There are about 2.13 million farms in the United States. The average size of each farm is about 440 acres. One acre is about the size of a football field, without the end zones. The table shows the number of pounds of each crop that one acre will produce in a season.

How many more pounds of rice can one acre produce in a season than wheat?

Production from One Acre

Crop	Amount (lb)
Cotton	725
Lettuce	35,000
Potatoes	36,700
Rice	5,500
Strawberries	42,800
Sweet Corn	11,600
Wheat	2,880

Source: American Farm Bureau

You can use the four-step problem-solving plan to solve many kinds of problems. The four steps are Understand, Plan, Solve, and Check.

Understand

- **Read the problem carefully.**
- **What facts do you know?**
- **What do you need to find?**

You know the number of pounds of rice and wheat produced by each acre. You need to find how many more pounds of rice the average farm produces in a season than wheat.

Plan

- How do the facts relate to each other?
- Plan a strategy to solve the problem.

One acre produces 5,500 pounds of rice or 2,880 pounds of wheat. Subtract 2,880 from 5,500.

Solve

- Use your plan to solve the problem.

$$
\begin{array}{r}
{}^{4}\overset{14}{\cancel{5}}\overset{10}{\cancel{5}}\cancel{0}0 \\
-2,880 \\
\hline
2,620
\end{array}
$$

In one season, one acre can produce 2,620 more pounds of rice than wheat.

Check

- Look back at the problem.
- Does your answer make sense?
- If not, solve the problem another way.

Estimate. Round 5,500 to 6,000 and 2,880 to 3,000.
6,000 – 3,000 = 3,000

Since 3,000 is close to 2,620, the answer is reasonable.

✓ CHECK Your Understanding

1. One pound of wheat can make 0.98 pound of whole-wheat flour but only 0.74 pound of refined flour. How many more pounds of whole wheat flour could one acre of wheat make than refined flour? **691.2 lb flour**

2. **WRITING IN MATH** How many more pounds of rice can the average-size farm in the United States produce in one season than wheat? Explain. **1,152,800 pounds; You know that one acre can produce 2,620 more pounds than wheat. Multiply 2,620 by 440 to find the number of pounds the average-size farm can produce in one season.**

Using the Exercises

Exercise 1 Remind students that adding or subtracting decimals requires aligning the decimal.

Writing in Math Remind students that in a process, steps are done in order to complete a task. They should list and describe the four steps in the correct order.

4 Assess

Discuss the **More FUN Facts.** Have students work in groups and create their own word problems using the statistics given. Have groups trade problems and follow the four-step problem-solving plan to solve the problems.

More FUN Facts

- The number of farms in the United States peaked with 7 million farms in 1935.

- As of 2006, there were approximately 2.1 million farms in the United States.

- The largest number of farms raise cattle for beef. 27% of all American farms are cattle ranches.

- The most prevalent crop is hay. 7.9% of all farms are hay farms.

- Corn is grown by 5.3% of the farms in our country.

1 Focus

Compare, order, and find sums and differences of decimals.

2 Teach

Adding and Subtracting Decimals

- Computing and estimating with decimals is a very important life skill as they will deal with money on a daily basis.

Scaffolding Questions

Use the information in the table on page 7 regarding lap speeds to answer the following questions.

Ask:

- Which year had the fastest lap speed: 2006 or 2007? 2007

- Which is the fastest lap speed on record at the Indianapolis 500? 229.188 mph

- How much faster is the fastest lap speed than the slowest lap speed in the recorded data? 10.787 mph

Number and Operations

Start Your Engines

The Indianapolis 500 consists of 200 laps covering a total distance of 500 miles. Each lap covers 2.5 miles. The table shows the winners of the Indianapolis 500 and their average speeds in miles per hour from 2000 to 2007.

Winners of the Indianapolis 500 2000–2007		
Year	Winner	Average Speed (mph)
2000	Juan Montoya	167.607
2001	Helio Castroneves	153.601
2002	Helio Castroneves	166.499
2003	Gil de Ferran	156.291
2004	Buddy Rice	138.518
2005	Dan Wheldon	157.603
2006	Sam Hornish, Jr.	157.085
2007	Dario Franchitti	151.774

Source: ESPN

6   Start Smart

 **CHECK Your Understanding**   **Compare and Order Decimals** .....

When comparing and ordering decimals, first line up the decimal points. Then compare the digits in each place to order the amounts.

Use the information in the table on page 6 to answer each question.

1. Which of the Indianapolis 500 winners listed in the table had the greatest average speed? the least? **Juan Montoya; Buddy Rice**

2. Between Dan Wheldon and Gil de Ferran, who had the lower average speed? **Gil de Ferran**

3. List the Indianapolis 500 winners in order from least to greatest average speed. **Buddy Rice, Dario Franchitti, Helio Castroneves (2001), Gil de Ferran, Sam Hornish Jr., Dan Wheldon, Helio Castroneves (2002), Juan Montoya**

 **CHECK Your Understanding**   **Subtract Decimals** ....

When subtracting decimals, first line up the decimal points. Then subtract as with whole numbers and place the decimal point in the answer.

Use the table on page 6 to answer each question.

4. How much greater was the average speed in 2000 than in 2007? **15.833 mph**

5. How much greater was the average speed in 2007 than in 2004? **13.256 mph**

6. How much greater was the average speed in 2006 than in 2007? **5.311 mph**

7. **WRITING IN MATH** The table shows the fastest lap speeds on record for the Indianapolis 500 from 2002 to 2007. Use the information to write and solve a real-world problem about the fastest lap speeds. **Sample answer: How much greater was the fastest lap speed in 2003 than the fastest lap speed in 2007? 5.768 mph**

Year	Fastest Lap Speed (mph)
2002	226.499
2003	229.188
2004	218.401
2005	228.102
2006	221.251
2007	223.420

Using the Exercises
Exercises 1 through 3 Remind students that when comparing and ordering decimals, they may have to inspect numerous place values.
Exercises 4 through 6 Emphasize the importance of properly aligning the decimal before performing the operation.
Writing in Math Have students work in groups to time themselves walking a measured distance. Students should determine the fastest and slowest time. Have them order their group times from least to greatest.

4 Assess

- Ask several questions using the data from fastest lap speeds on page 7. Invite volunteers to show on the board how to answer each question.

- Using the average speed data on page 6, have students figure average times for the entire race for each driver.

- Have students work in pairs to make up several word problems using the information in the **More FUN Facts.**

More FUN Facts

- The Indianapolis 500 held its inaugural race in 1911. The total purse winnings went to Ray Harroun's team in the amount of $27,550. Dario Franchitti's team won a total purse amount of $10,668,815 in 2007.

- The youngest driver to ever win the Indy 500 was Troy Ruttman at age 22 in 1952.

- The oldest driver to ever win the Indy 500 was Al Unser at age 47 in 1987.

- Janet Guthrie was the first woman to qualify for the race in 1977. Danica Patrick was the first woman to ever lead the race (for 19 laps) and held the highest female finish of 4th place in 2005.

Lesson Notes

1 Focus

Write and evaluate algebraic expressions to represent data given in a table.

2 Teach

Writing Expressions

- Remind students that when writing an expression, a variable should be used to represent the unknown value.

- Encourage students to look for key words to indicate the operation to be represented in the expression. Common key words are "more than", "times", "less than", and "divided by".

Scaffolding Questions

Write the following on the board:

The wingspan of a Boeing F/A-18 Hornet is 16 feet less than its length.

Ask:

- What variable can be used to represent the length of the Boeing F/A-18 Hornet? ℓ

- Write an expression that could be used to represent the Boeing F/A-18 Hornet's wingspan. $\ell - 16$

- If the Boeing F/A-18 Hornet has a length of 56 feet, evaluate the expression to find its wingspan. 40 ft

Lcdr Anthony Walley

The Sky's the Limit

Since 1946, the Blue Angels have represented the United States Navy in flight demonstrations around the country. There are six jets in the formation during each demonstration. The pilots perform approximately 30 maneuvers during a demonstration that lasts for approximately 1 hour 15 minutes. The table shows several speeds of the Boeing F/A-18 Hornet jets used in the demonstration.

Boeing F/A-18 Hornet	Speed (mph)
Slowest Cruising Speed	120
Sneak Pass Maneuver	700
Top Speed	1,400

CHECK Your Understanding

Variables and Equations . . . .

Use the table on page 8 to answer the following questions.

1. The average speed of the Boeing F/A-18 Hornet Jet is 200 miles per hour less than its top speed. If *s* represents its top speed, write an expression that represents its average speed. **s − 200**

2. Evaluate the expression you wrote in Exercise 1. What is the average speed of the Boeing F/A-18 Hornet jet? **1,200 miles per hour**

3. The equation $d = rt$ represents the distance *d* in miles that the jet can travel at its average speed of *r* miles per hour in *h* hours. Use your answer from Exercise 2 to find the distance the jet can travel in 2 hours. **2,400 miles**

4. The jets are transported by the C-130 Hercules aircraft *Fat Albert* which has an average speed 230 more miles per hour than the jet's slowest cruising speed. Write an equation that could be used to represent *Fat Albert's* average speed *s*. **s = 230 + 120**

5. Evaluate the expression you wrote in Exercise 4. What is *Fat Albert's* average speed? **s = 350 miles per hour**

For Exercises 6 and 7, use the table and the information below.

The table shows the heights of two of the most famous maneuvers of the Blue Angels.

6. The maximum rate of climb for the Boeing F/A-18 Hornet jet is 30,000 feet per minute. How long would take the jet to climb 15,000 feet? **0.5 min**

Maneuver	Height (ft)
Sneak Pass	50
Vertical Roll	15,000

7. ⟨WRITING IN⟩ MATH Write a real-world problem to represent the relationship between the heights of a Sneak Pass and a Vertical Roll. Then solve the equation. **Sample answer: How many times greater is the height of Vertical Roll than Sneak Pass? 50x = 15,000; x = 300**

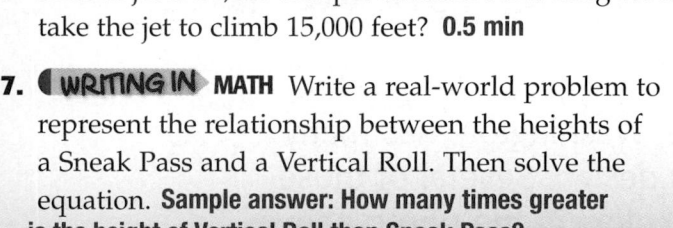

Using the Exercises
Exercises 1 through 5 Emphasize the importance of paying close attention to the order in which the variable and constants should occur in the expression.

Exercise 6 Suggest students set up a proportion to solve this problem.

Writing in Math Consolidate all of the classes problems onto a worksheet and have the students complete it as an assignment.

4 Assess

• Ask several questions using the data from the maneuver table on page 9. For example, what expression can be used to represent the difference in heights? Invite volunteers to come to the front of the room and formulate questions to ask the students regarding the table.

• Have students work in pairs to make up several word problems using the information in **More FUN Facts**.

More FUN Facts

• The Blue Angels have been flying since 1946. As of 2007, they have performed for 427 million spectators.

• There have been eight different types of aircraft flown throughout the history of the Blue Angels.

• The fleet currently consists of 10 single-seat F/A–18 A Hornets and 2 two-seat F/A–18 B Hornets.

• Each plane in the fleet cost approximately $21,000,000.00.

• An F/A–18 weighs approximately 24,500 pounds, which is over 12 tons.

Lesson Notes

1 Focus

Estimate angle measures and use a protractor to measure an angle precisely.

2 Teach

Scaffolding Questions

Have students observe the architecture of their classroom and objects around the room. Record the students' responses on the board.

Ask:

- Where might you observe a right angle in the classroom? See students' work.

- Do you see an angle that could be estimated at over 100°? Explain. See students' work.

- Can you think of some architectural buildings that would have a good display of common angles? See students' work.

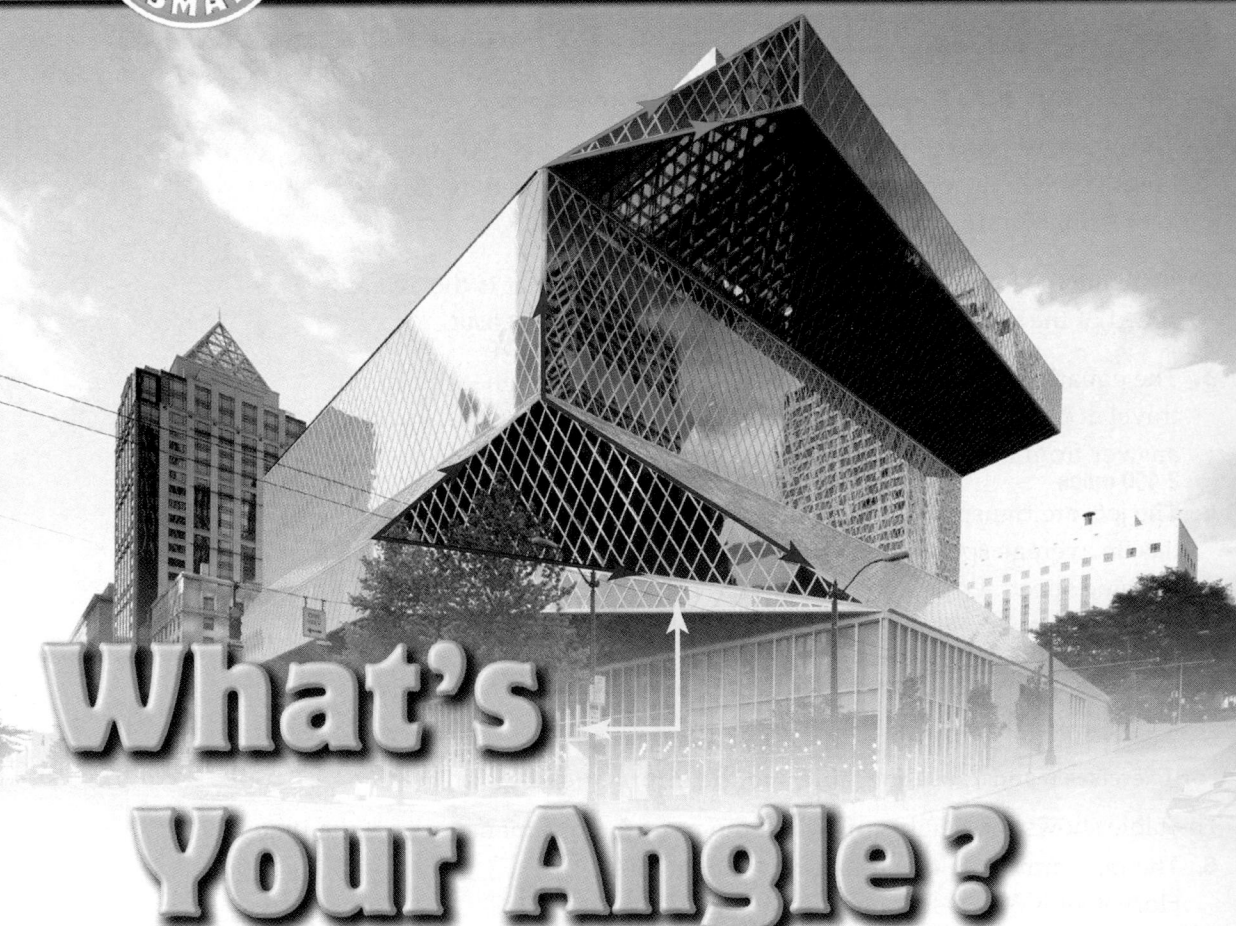

What's Your Angle?

Geometric angles are used in architectural design. The Seattle Central Library in Seattle, Washington, has many different geometric angles in its design. Several of those angles are outlined in different colors in the photo above.

 **CHECK Your Understanding** **Estimate Angle Measures** ....

Use the photo of the Seattle Central Library to estimate the measure of each of the following angles.

1. the angle outlined in red
   Sample answer: 120°

2. the angle outlined in green Sample answer: 30°

3. the angle outlined in yellow Sample answer: 90°

4. the angle outlined in purple Sample answer: 60°

10 Start Smart

 **CHECK** Your Understanding **Measure Angles** ·

The photo below is of the interior of the Denver Art Museum in Denver, Colorado. Use a protractor to measure each of the following angles.

5. the angle outlined in blue **Sample answer: 60°**

6. the measure of the angle outlined in yellow **Sample answer: 120°**

7. the angle outlined in green **Sample answer: 120°**

8. the angle outlined in red **Sample answer: 75°**

9. Use the Internet or another source to find a photo that uses geometric angles in art or architecture. Estimate the measure of several angles in the photo. Then use a protractor to measure the angles. Compare to your estimates. **See students' work.**

10. **WRITING IN MATH** Write a few sentences explaining how to use a protractor to find the measure of an angle.
   Sample answer: Place the center point of the protractor's base on the vertex of the angle. Align the straight side with the base of the angle so that the marker for 0° is on that side. Use the scale that begins with 0° on the angle's base. Read where the other side of the angle crosses this scale.

Start Smart 11

More FUN Facts

• Geometry has been in use in architectural buildings since the beginning of history. Pythagoras (560–480 B.C.) was especially interested in the Golden Ratio. (1.618… : 1).

• The Parthenon in Athens, Greece, is one of the best examples of a mathematical approach to building. The Golden Rectangle, which is a rectangle with a proportion of length to width equal to the Golden Ratio, is used throughout the Parthenon.

• Pythagoras proved that many human body parts are built upon the Golden Ratio. In general, a person's height compared to the height of their navel is very close to the Golden Ratio.

Using the Exercises

Exercises 1 through 4 Remind students that when they estimate the measure of an angle, they should use certain reference angles. Knowing what a 90° angle and a 180° straight angle look like will help to narrow down to a reasonable estimation.

Exercises 5 through 8 Review the rules for using a protractor. Students should be cautious to read the correct measurement line and line up the sides of the angle carefully.

Exercise 9 Have students print their examples and mark the angles with colored pencils or markers.

Writing in Math Have students pretend they are writing the instructions for using a protractor for a third-grade class. They should assume the students they are writing for have never seen a protractor.

4 Assess

• Ask several questions regarding the photo of the Denver Art Museum on p. 11. Allow students to play a game of "I Spy" and give clues to see if other students can see the same relationships.

• After discussing **More FUN Facts**, have students work with a partner to measure their height and the height of their navel. Students should divide their height by the height of their navel and compare to the Golden Ratio.

Lesson Notes

1 Focus

Convert and determine reasonableness of measurements of length within the customary system

2 Teach

Converting Units

• Emphasize that when changing from a smaller unit to a larger unit, students should use division. When changing from a larger unit to a smaller unit, the students should use multiplication.

• Remind students to make sure they check to see if their solution is reasonable.

Scaffolding Questions

Use the table on page 12 for students to answer the following questions.

Ask:

• What unit of length is used in the table? feet

• What is the height of the head? 60 ft

• How many inches are in one foot? 12 in.

• To find the height of the head in inches, would you multiply or divide by 12? Explain. Multiply; to convert from a larger unit to a smaller unit, you need to multiply.

• What is the height of the head in inches? 720 in.

Dynamite Dimensions!

Mount Rushmore, located in the Black Hills of South Dakota, is a tribute to four American presidents: George Washington, Thomas Jefferson, Theodore Roosevelt, and Abraham Lincoln. More than 90% of the monument was carved by dynamite! The table gives the measurements of several of the facial features for one of the presidents.

Feature	Measurement (ft)
head	60 (height)
nose	20 (height)
mouth	18 (length)
eye	11 (length)

Source: Mount Rushmore National Monument

Standard units of measurement are most commonly used in the United States. They include *inch, foot, yard,* and *mile.*

CHECK Your Understanding — Use Appropriate Units

1. How many inches are in one foot? How many feet are in one yard? **12 in.; 3 ft**

2. Which is a more reasonable estimate for the height in yards of each president's head on Mount Rushmore: 20 yards or 180 yards? Justify your response. **20 yd; Sample answer: Yards are a larger unit of measurement than feet. The number of yards in 60 feet will be smaller than 60.**

3. How tall or long is each presidential feature in yards? Round to the nearest tenth if necessary. **head: 20 yd; nose: 6.7 yd; mouth: 6 yd; eye: 3.7**

4. Which is a more reasonable estimate for the length in inches of each president's eye on Mount Rushmore: 1 inch or 120 inches? Justify your response. **120 in.; Sample answer: Inches are a smaller unit of measurement than feet. The number of inches in 11 feet will be larger than 11.**

5. How tall or long is each presidential feature in inches? Round to the nearest tenth if necessary. **head: 720 in.; nose: 240 in.; mouth: 216 in.; eye: 132 in.**

6. Mount Rushmore is about 6,000 feet above sea level. Which is a more reasonable estimate for this height: about 2,000 yards or about 18,000 yards? Justify your response. **about 2,000 yd; Sample answer: Yards are a larger unit of measurement than feet. The number of yards in 6,000 feet will be smaller than 6,000.**

7. **WRITING IN MATH** The photo below shows the Stone Mountain Confederate Memorial Carving in Atlanta, Georgia. The carving measures 90 feet by 190 feet. Explain how to find the carving's dimensions in yards. Then find the carving's dimensions in yards, rounding to the nearest tenth if necessary.
Sample answer: There are 3 feet in 1 yard. Divide 90 by 3 to get 30. Then divide 190 by 3 to get 63.3, rounded to the nearest tenth. The carving's dimensions in yards are 30 ft by 63.3 ft.

Start Smart 13

Using the Exercises
Exercise 1 You may want to have students investigate a yardstick to answer this question.

Exercises 2 through 6 Have students measure something large, such as the classroom door or a wall in inches to remind them to use reasonable units.

Writing in Math Have students create a table that has one column with dimensions in feet and the second column with dimensions in yards.

4 **Assess**

- Ask several questions regarding the photo of the carving on p. 13. Have students synthesize what type of carving they would like to create and what size it would be.

- Have students work in pairs to design a large carving of a common classroom object and give the new dimensions of the larger object.

More FUN Facts

- The Iwo Jima Memorial in Washington, D.C., is a bronze sculpture of a photograph taken after the Battle of Iwo Jima during World War II.

- Felix DeWeldon was so moved by the picture that within 72 hours he had a completed clay sculpture.

- Hundreds of artisans worked 8 years to create the Iwo Jima Memorial.

- Each figure is 32 feet high. The pole is 60 feet long.

- Standing on its pedestal, the monument stands 78 feet high, the tallest bronze statue in the world.

Lesson Notes

1 Focus

Analyze data in a table and arrange the data in a pictograph.

2 Teach

Pictographs

- Emphasize to students that reading pictographs is not an exact science. Estimating a partial picture cannot be exact.

Scaffolding Questions

Make a table with 4 rows and 3 columns. Label the rows as 1–3, 4–6, 7–9, and more than 9. Label the columns as "number of vowels", "frequency", and "pictograph". Poll the students by asking them how many vowels they have in their full names (first, middle, and last). In the frequency column, use tally marks to represent each student that falls in the interval. Now allow a star to equal two students.

Ask:

- How many stars would we need for the third column for each interval? See students' work.

- If we did not choose a reasonable number to equal the star, how could this type of graph be misleading? See students' work.

Data Analysis

Do You Hear What I Hear?

Bats have a much greater range of hearing than humans. They use this sense to locate food and prey. Many other animals also have a greater hearing range than humans. The frequency of a dog whistle is about 22,000 Hertz (Hz) which is greater than the maximum hearing frequency for humans. The table shows the minimum and maximum frequencies for hearing of ten animal species, including humans.

Hearing Ranges of Animal Species		
Species	Minimum Frequency (Hz)	Maximum Frequency (Hz)
bat	2,000	110,000
Beluga whale	1,000	123,000
cat	45	64,000
dog	67	45,000
elephant	16	12,000
goldfish	20	3,000
horse	55	33,500
human	64	20,000
mouse	1,000	91,000
owl	200	12,000

Source: Louisiana State University

1. Copy and complete the pictograph below using the data of the maximum hearing frequencies in the table on page 14.

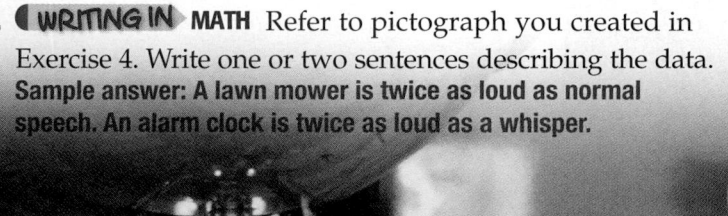

Maximum Hearing Frequencies (Hz) of Different Animal Species

bat	🦻🦻🦻🦻🦻🦻🦻🦻🦻🦻🦻
Beluga whale	🦻🦻🦻🦻🦻🦻🦻🦻🦻🦻🦻🦻🦻
cat	🦻🦻🦻🦻🦻🦻
dog	🦻🦻🦻🦻🦻
elephant	🦻
goldfish	
horse	🦻🦻🦻
human	🦻🦻
mouse	🦻🦻🦻🦻🦻🦻🦻🦻🦻🦻
owl	🦻🦻🦻🦻🦻🦻🦻

🦻 = 10,000 Hz

2. Name two animals whose maximum hearing frequencies are about the same. **Sample answer: cat and dog**

3. About how many times greater is a Beluga whale's maximum hearing frequency than a cat's?
about 2 times greater

4. The table gives the loudness of different sounds measured in decibels (dB). Construct a pictograph of the information. **See margin.**

5. **WRITING IN MATH** Refer to pictograph you created in Exercise 4. Write one or two sentences describing the data.
Sample answer: A lawn mower is twice as loud as normal speech. An alarm clock is twice as loud as a whisper.

Sound	Decibels (dB)
jet engine	140
chainsaw	120
lawn mower	100
alarm clock	80
normal speech	60
whisper	40

Start Smart **15**

More FUN Facts

• Mammals' sense of smell is the most acute and discriminating of the five senses. Humans are the only mammal where this is not true.

• Most birds cannot smell.

• Smell is the only sense that cannot be measured.

• Smell is responsible for 80% of humans' taste.

---

3 Practice

Using the Exercises
Exercise 1 Encourage students to copy and complete the table in an organized, neat manner. Being able to interpret the data is dependent upon the presentation of the data.

Exercises 2 and 3 Emphasize the importance of carefully reading and interpreting the data. Careful analysis of the data ensures proper conclusions.

Exercise 4 You may want to explain that 20 decibels is 10 times louder than 10 decibels. Therefore, 30 decibels (20 decibels higher than 10) is 10^2 or 100 times louder than 10 decibels.

Writing in Math Discuss how the table could be misleading and how to accurately describe the data.

4 Assess

• After discussing **More FUN Facts**, have students do research on the Internet regarding animals' ability to smell. Have them make a pictograph with categories listed as "no smell", "some smell", "acute smell". They may want to start with a frequency table and then transfer the data to a pictograph.

Additional Answer

4.

Loudness (dB) of Different Sounds

jet engine	🦻🦻🦻🦻🦻🦻🦻🦻🦻🦻🦻🦻🦻🦻
chainsaw	🦻🦻🦻🦻🦻🦻🦻🦻🦻🦻🦻🦻
lawn mower	🦻🦻🦻🦻🦻🦻🦻🦻🦻🦻
alarm clock	🦻🦻🦻🦻🦻🦻🦻🦻
normal speech	🦻🦻🦻🦻🦻🦻
whisper	🦻🦻🦻🦻

🦻 = 10 dB

Data File

Each chapter has a Find the Data exercise that asks students to write a real-world problem using the data on these pages.

Data File

The following pages contain data that you'll use throughout the book.

Vertical Velocity Roller Coaster

Amusement Park: Six Flags Great America, Illinois

Length: 2,700 feet

Height: 185 feet

Speed: 65 miles per hour

Duration: 1 minute

Vehicles: 1

Riders per vehicle: 28

Source: Coaster Buzz

Temperature

Record Temperatures in New York State					
Record	°F	°C	Date	Location	Elevation (feet)
High	108	42.2	July 22, 1976	Troy	35
Low	−52	−46.7	February 18, 1979	Old Forge	1,720

Source: National Climatic Data Center

Kentucky Stadiums

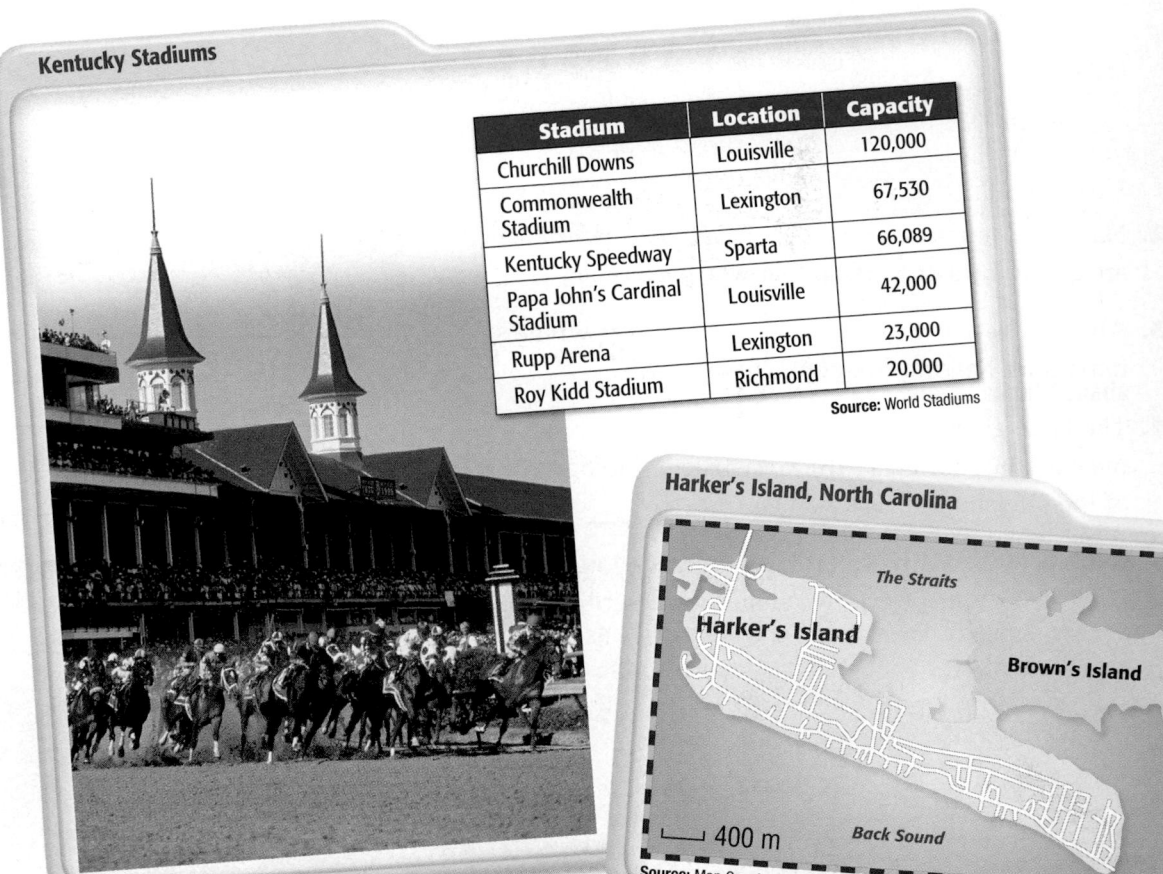

Stadium	Location	Capacity
Churchill Downs	Louisville	120,000
Commonwealth Stadium	Lexington	67,530
Kentucky Speedway	Sparta	66,089
Papa John's Cardinal Stadium	Louisville	42,000
Rupp Arena	Lexington	23,000
Roy Kidd Stadium	Richmond	20,000

Source: World Stadiums

Harker's Island, North Carolina

The Straits

Harker's Island

Brown's Island

400 m

Back Sound

Source: Map Quest

Museum of Glass, Tacoma

WASHINGTON

Regular Ticket Prices

- $10 Adults
- $8 Seniors (age 62+), Military, and Students (age 13+)
- $4 Children (age 6–12)
- $30 Families (two adults and up to four children under age 18)
- Free: Museum of Glass Members, Children under age 6, and Third Thursday of each month (5-8 P.M.)

...den Eagle

Source: National Geographic

Height: about 3 feet (91 cm)

Wingspan: 7 feet (213 cm)

Habitat: Usually found in high altitudes throughout the mountains of Arizona and along the Colorado River.

U.S. Bank Center, Milwaukee

WISCONSIN

Height: 183 meters

Floors: 42

Exterior: 66% glass

Windows: 5,000

Foundation: 500 steel H-piles capable of holding 640 tons each

Source: Emporis

Delicate Arch, Arches National Park

Source: Climb-Utah

UTAH   Delicate Arch, located in Arches National Park, is found along a hiking trail that is 1.5 miles each way. The average time to hike the trail is $1\frac{1}{4}$ hours each way. The elevation of the arch is 4,800 feet, and the arch towers 80 feet above the average hiker. It is recommended that each person carries 2 liters of water for the hike.

Riverbanks Zoo and Garden, Columbia

SOUTH CAROLINA

Number of Animals: more than 2,000

Number of Animal Species: 350

Number of Plant Species: 4,200

Annual Attendance: about 900,000

Hours: 9 A.M.–5 P.M.

Admission: $9.75 for adults
$7.25 ages 3–12

Sea Lion Feedings: 10:30 A.M. and 3 P.M.

Penguin Feedings: 11 A.M. and 3:30 P.M.

Elephant Training: 11:30 A.M.

Source: Riverbanks Zoo and Garden

George S. Mickelson Trail

SOUTH DAKOTA Bicyclists of all ages and abilities can enjoy the George S. Mickelson Trail, in the Black Hills of South Dakota, which runs for a total of 114 miles. It tops out at 6,100 feet but never exceeds a 4% grade.

Source: Travel South Dakota

Boston Baked Beans

Boston Baked Beans

Ingredients
2 cups navy beans
$\frac{1}{2}$ cup brown sugar
$\frac{1}{4}$ cup molasses
1 cup bean liquid
1 teaspoon salt

Rock City

KANSAS Rock City is a tiny park, located 3.5 miles from Minneapolis, Kansas. It contains about 200 huge sandstone concretions. The rocks are up to 27 feet in diameter. There is no other place in the world where there are so many rocks of such giant size.

Source: Kansas Travel and Tourism

Montana Rivers

The longest and shortest rivers in the United States can be found in Montana. The Roe River is exclusively located in Montana and is also the shortest river in the world.

Source: Montana Kids

River	Total Length	Length in Montana
Missouri	2,540 mi (13,411,200 ft)	1,029 mi (5,433,120 ft)
Roe	$\frac{5}{132}$ mi (200 ft)	$\frac{5}{132}$ mi (200 ft)

Mackinac Island

MICHIGAN Mackinac Island is an island covering 3.8 square miles. There are 61 miles of roads and trails within Mackinac Island State Park, most of which are wooded inland trails for hikers, bikers, and horseback riders in spring, summer, and fall. Fort Holmes is at the island's highest point, 320 feet above lake level.

Source: Mackinac State Historic Parks

Baltimore Oriole

Habitat: Usually found in Maryland during the summer months and in the southern states during winter months. Male orioles have a bright orange color on their shoulders and underbelly. Females are light orange.

Size: 7 to $8\frac{1}{4}$ inches

Weight: $1\frac{1}{5}$ ounces

Source: National Geographic

Philadelphia 76ers

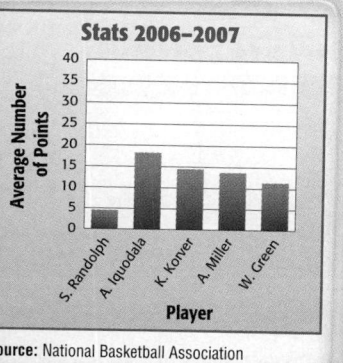

Source: National Basketball Association

Denver International Airport

COLORADO

Opening Date: February 28, 1995

Size: 34,000 acres, 53 square miles

Runways: 6 (five are 12,000 feet long, and the sixth is 16,000 feet long)

Concourses: 3

Gates: 89

Passenger Airlines: 23

Source: Denver International Airport

Flight and baggage information display monitors: 1,500

Accommodation: 50 million passengers per year

Introduction

In this unit, students will explore numbers and operations. They will learn how to solve problems using a four-step plan. They will examine powers, exponents, square roots, the order of operations, and sequences. In addition, they will use their knowledge of algebraic variables, expressions, and properties to solve equations and make function tables.

Students will find absolute values, compare and order integers, and add, subtract, multiply, and divide integers. Finally, they will apply their knowledge of operations to write and solve one- and two-step equations and graph linear equations.

Assessment Options

Unit 1 Test Pages 75–76 of the *Chapter 3 Resource Masters* may be used as a test or a review for Unit 1. This assessment contains both multiple-choice and short-response items.

Create additional customized Unit Tests and review worksheets for differentiated instruction.

Unit 1
Algebra and Functions

Focus
Use appropriate operations to solve problems and linear equations.

CHAPTER 1
Introduction to Algebra and Functions

BIG Idea Represent relationships in numerical, verbal, geometric and symbolic form.

CHAPTER 2
Integers

BIG Idea Know the properties of, and compute with, integers.

CHAPTER 3
Algebra: Linear Equations and Functions

BIG Idea Solve linear equations in one variable.

20

Real-Life Math Videos engage students, showing them how math is used in everyday situations. Use Video 1 with this unit to discuss how linear equations are used in soccer, baseball, and horseback riding. (also available on one Super DVD combined with MindJogger Videoquizzes)

Stand Up and Be Counted

This cross-curricular project is a project in which students do research on the Internet, gather data, and make presentations using word processing, graphing, page-making, or presentation software. In each chapter, students advance to the next step in their project. At the end of Chapter 3, the project culminates with a presentation of their findings.

Math Online

glencoe.com Log on for teaching suggestions and sample answers for this project.

Team Teaching You can use this cross-curricular project with your students' social studies teacher to make the connection from mathematics to the social studies your students are studying.

*The **Real-World Unit Projects** send students to the Web to work on ongoing interdisciplinary projects.*

Problem Solving in Social Studies

Real-World Unit Project

Stand Up and Be Counted! Every 10 years, the U.S. Census takes a count of the U.S. population. How does the U.S. Census affect the number of members in the House of Representatives from each state? You're on a mission to find out! Along the way, you will create a map of the United States, make a line plot, and write a paragraph about these changes. Don't forget to bring your math tool kit. This adventure will appeal to your "census."

Math Online Log on to glencoe.com to begin.

Unit 1 Algebra and Functions **21**

More Cross-Curricular Connections

You may wish to share these suggestions with your students' other teachers.

Math and Language Arts
Research the U.S. Census. Write an essay about an aspect of the U.S. Census. Why is the U.S. Census taken? How could the U.S. Census become more accurate? How are the results used?

Math and Science
Research the computer science behind polling and the U.S. Census. Have students come up with different ways the census could be taken, and investigate how the census works.

CHAPTER 1

Chapter Overview

Introduction to Algebra and Functions

Lesson Plan	Pacing Your Lessons		
LESSONS AND OBJECTIVES	State/Local Standards	40-50 Minute Periods	90-Minute Periods
1-1 A Plan for Problem Solving (pp. 25–29) • Solve problems using the four-step plan.		1	0.5
1-2 Powers and Exponents (pp. 30–33) • Use powers and exponents.		1	0.5
1-3 Squares and Square Roots (pp. 34–37) • Find squares of numbers and square roots of perfect squares.		1	0.5
1-4 Order of Operations (pp. 38–41) • Evaluate expressions using the order of operations.		1	0.5
1-5 Problem-Solving Investigation: Guess and Check (pp. 42–43) • Solve problems using the guess and check strategy.		1	0.5
1-6 Algebra: Variables and Expressions (pp. 44–47) • Evaluate simple algebraic expressions.		1	0.5
1-7 Algebra: Equations (pp. 49–52) • Solve equations using mental math.		1	0.5
1-8 Algebra: Properties (pp. 53–56) • Use Commutative, Associative, Identity, and Distributive properties to		1	0.5
1-9 Algebra: Arithmetic Sequences (pp. 57–61) • Describe the relationships and extend terms in arithmetic sequences. **Extend 1-9 Algebra Lab: Exploring Sequences** (p. 62) • Explore patterns in sequences of geometric figures.		1.5	0.5
1-10 Algebra: Equations and Functions (pp. 63–67) • Make function tables and write equations. **Extend 1-10 Graphing Calculator Lab: Functions and Tables** (p. 68–69) • Use technology to represent and compare functions.		1.5	1
REVIEW		1	0.5
ASSESSMENT		1	0.5*
TOTAL		13	6.5

*The complete **Assessment Planner** for Chapter 1 is provided on page 23.*

* Begin Chapter 2 in the second half of the chapter.

G7-FP3 Algebra
For the complete wording of the Focal Points for Grade 7, please see page iv.

Professional Development

Vertical Alignment

Before Chapter 1

Related Topics from Grade 6
- calculate with positive and negative integers
- use a letter to represent an unknown number; write and evaluate simple algebraic expressions in one variable by substitution
- solve problems involving linear functions with integer values and write the equation

Chapter 1

Topics from Grade 7
- analyze problems by identifying relationships, distinguishing relevant from irrelevant information, identifying missing information
- write and solve one-step linear equations in one variable
- solve problems manually by using the correct order of operations
- apply algebraic order of operations and properties and justify each step in the process
- use a variety of methods to explain mathematical reasoning

After Chapter 1

Preparation for Grade 8
- multiply and divide expressions involving exponents with a common base
- use variables and appropriate operations to write an expression, an equation, an inequality, or a system of equations or inequalities that represents a verbal
- use the correct order of operations to evaluate algebraic expressions
- multiply and divide monomials; extend the process of taking powers and extracting roots to monomials

Backmapping and Vertical Alignment

McGraw-Hill's **Math Connnects** program was conceived and developed with the final results in mind: student success in Algebra 1 and beyond. The authors, using the **NCTM Focal Points and Focal Connections** as their guide, developed this brand-new series by backmapping from Algebra 1 concepts and vertically aligning the topics so that they build upon prior skills and concepts and serve as a foundation for future topics.

What the Research Says...

According to Olson in "Up Close and Personal," which appeared in Education Week, classroom assessment that teachers use day in and day out provides one of the most powerful tools available for improving student achievement.

- Every lesson contains Standards-based questions, providing practice and ongoing assessment.
- The Study Guide and Review at the end of the chapter allows students to assess their understanding of each lesson's key concepts.

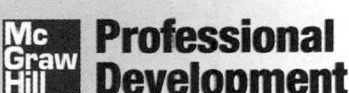

McGraw Hill Professional Development

Targeted professional development has been articulated throughout **McGraw-Hill's** *Math Connects* program. The **McGraw-Hill Professional Development Video Library** provides short videos that support the NCTM Focal Points and Focal Connections. For more information, visit glencoe.com.

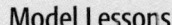

| Model Lessons | Instructional Strategies |

CHAPTER 1

Technology Solutions

Teacher Resources

TeacherWorks™ All-in-One Planner and Resource Center

All of the print materials from the Classroom Resource Masters are available on your TeacherWorks™ CD-ROM.

BL = Below or Approaching Grade Level   **OL** = On Grade Level   **AL** = Above or Beyond Grade Level   **ELL** = English Language Learner

Chapter Resource Masters					1-1	1-2	1-3	1-4	1-5	1-6	1-7	1-8	1-9	1-10
BL	**OL**		**ELL**	Lesson Reading Guide	9	15	22	29		40	47	53	60	67
BL	**OL**		**ELL**	Study Guide and Intervention*	10	16	23	30	36	41	48	54	61	68
BL	**OL**			Skills Practice*	11	17	24	31	37	42	49	55	62	69
	OL	**AL**		Practice*	12	18	25	32	38	43	50	56	63	70
	OL	**AL**		Word Problem Practice*	13	19	26	33	39	44	51	57	64	71
	OL	**AL**		Enrichment	14	20	27	34		45	52	58	65	72
	OL	**AL**		Calculator and Spreadsheet Activities		21	28	35		46		59	66	73
	OL	**AL**		Chapter Assessments*	75–96									
BL	**OL**	**AL**		5-Minute Check Transparencies	✓	✓	✓	✓	✓	✓	✓	✓	✓	✓
BL	**OL**			Teaching Mathematics with Manipulatives		✓				✓			✓	
BL	**OL**	**AL**		Real-World Investigations for Differentiated Instruction	21–26									

Also available in Spanish.

Graphing Calculator Easy Files

- Timesaving Tech Tools for the TI-Navigator
- Quick Checks to diagnose student progress
- Deliver Differentiated Instruction with Ready Files
- Vocabulary Review

AssignmentWorks

Differentiated Assignments, Answers, and Solutions

- Print a customized assignment worksheet using the Student Edition exercises along with an answer key or worked-out solutions.
- Use default lesson assignments as outlined in the Differentiated Homework Options in the Teacher Edition.

Interactive Classroom

This CD-ROM is a customizable Microsoft® PowerPoint® presentation that includes:

- In-Class Examples
- Your Turn Exercises*
- 5-Minute Check Transparencies*
- Links to Online Study Tools
- Concepts in Motion

compatible with response pad technology

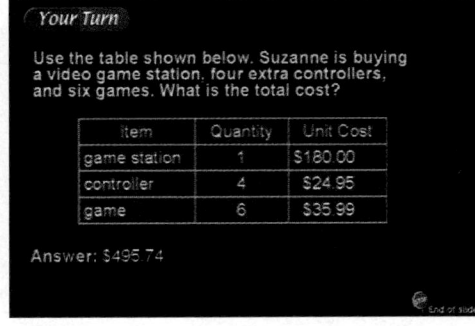

ExamView® Assessment Suite

- Create, edit, and customize tests and worksheets using QuickTest Wizard
- Create multiple versions of tests and modify them for a desired level of difficulty
- Translate from English to Spanish and vice versa
- Build tests aligned with your state standards
- Track students' progress using the Teacher Management System

*This program is supported by a wealth of **technology options** on CD-ROM, on DVD, and online.*

Student Tools

StudentWorks™ Plus

Textbook, Audio, Workbooks, and more

This CD-ROM is a valuable resource for students to access content online and use online resources to continue learning Chapter 1 concepts. Includes:

- Complete Student Editions in both English and Spanish
- English audio integrated throughout the text
- Links to Concepts in Motion, Personal Tutor, and other online resources
- Access to all student worksheets
- Daily Assignments and Grade Log

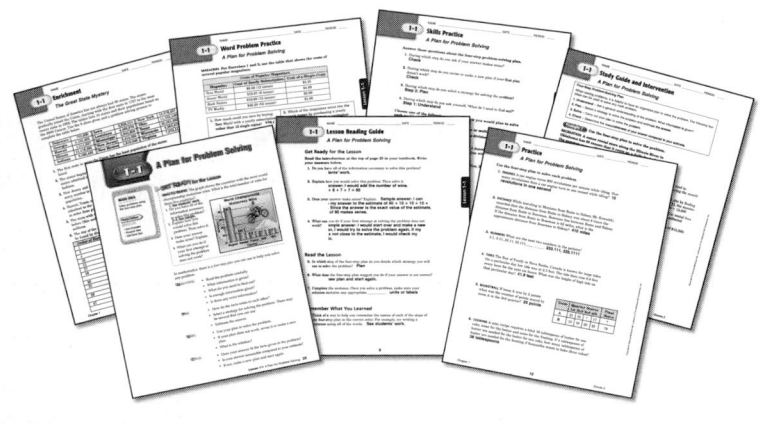

Super DVD

The Super DVD contains two Glencoe multimedia products.

MindJogger Plus An alternative review of concepts in which students work as teams in a game show format to gain points for correct answers.

What's Math Got to Do With It? Real-Life Math Videos
Engaging video that shows students how math is used in everyday situations.

Internet Resources

Math Online ⟩ glencoe.com

TEACHER	STUDENT	PARENT	Online Study Tools
	●	●	Online Student Edition
●	●	●	Multilingual Glossary
			Lesson Resources
	●	●	BrainPOP®
●	●	●	Concepts in Motion
●	●	●	Extra Examples
●			Group Activity Cards
	●	●	Other Calculator Keystrokes
	●	●	Reading in the Content Area
	●	●	Real-World Careers
	●	●	Self-Check Quizzes
			Chapter Resources
	●	●	Chapter Readiness
	●	●	Chapter Test
	●	●	Family Letters and Activities
	●	●	Standardized Test Practice
	●	●	Vocabulary Review/Chapter Review Activities
			Unit Resources
●	●		Cross-Curricular Internet Project
			Other Resources
●			Dinah Zike's Foldables
●	●		Game Zone Games and Recording Sheets
	●	●	Hotmath Homework Help
●			Key Concepts
●	●	●	Math Skills Maintenance
●	●	●	Meet the Authors
●			NAEP Correlations
	●	●	Personal Tutor
●			Project CRISS℠
	●	●	Scavenger Hunts and Answer Sheets
●			Vocabulary PuzzleMakers

Reading and Writing in Mathematics

Noteables™ Interactive Study Notebook with Foldables™

This workbook is a study organizer that provides helpful steps for students to follow to organize their notes for Chapter 1.

• Students use Noteables to record notes and to complete their Foldables as you present the material for each lesson.

• Noteables correspond to the Examples in the *Teacher Edition* and *Interactive Classroom CD-ROM*.

Real-World Problem Solving Graphic Novels

Mathematical problem solving is presented in a motivating, graphic novel format. The novels contain real-world problems for each of the following mathematical strands: Number Sense, Algebraic Thinking, Geometry, Measurement, Statistics and Probability, and Mathematical Reasoning.

READING in the Content Area

This online worksheet provides strategies for reading and analyzing Lesson 1-4, Order of Operations. Students are guided through questions about the main idea, subject matter, supporting details, conclusion, clarifying details, and vocabulary of the lesson.

glencoe.com

Recommended Outside Reading for Students

Mathematics and Travel Adventures

• *A Gebra Named Al: A Novel* by Wendy Isdell ©1993 [fiction]

The story of a girl who is having problems learning algebra. She travels to the Land of Mathematics and meets a "gebra named Al." She travels through the land encountering many algebraic concepts, finally finding the equation she needs to return home.

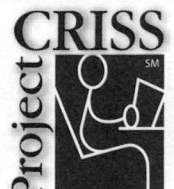

Project CRISS℠

STUDY SKILL

containing an exponent. Have students develop a similar structure to help them solve sequence problems and other types of problems they encounter in this chapter.

A problem-solution graphic structure can be used by students to develop a step-by-step plan for solving a problem. Students begin by writing details of the problem. Next, they write steps that are necessary to solve the problem. Finally, they solve the problem and write out their result. The graphic structure at the right applies the four-step plan presented in Chapter 1 to solving a problem

Problem	Evaluate the expression 4×6^3.	
	Step	**Result**
Steps to Solution	1. Explore	1. The exponent means the 6 is used as a factor 3 times.
	2. Plan	2. Write out all the factors and multiply.
	3. Solve	3. $4 \times 6^3 = 4 \times 6 \times 6 \times 6 = 864$
	4. Examine	4. $4 \times 6^3 = 864$ is a reasonable answer.
End Result	$4 \times 6^3 = 864$	

CReating **I**ndependence through **S**tudent-owned **S**trategies

Differentiated Instruction

Investigative Approach

MathScape™

This project was supported, in part, by the
National Science Foundation

MathScape is a mathematics curriculum for grades 6–8 developed by the Seeing and Thinking Mathematically Project at the Education Development Center.

Writing and Solving Equations
Exploring the Unknown

How to Use *MathScape* with Chapter 1

The unit *Exploring the Unknown* can be used to enhance Lessons 1-6 and 1-9.

- **Enrich** → Before you complete **Lesson 1-6**, you can introduce Lab Gear Blocks and play "What's in the Bag" on page 184.

- **Reinforce** → Before you begin **Lesson 1-9**, you can help students who are still having difficulty with patterns by using the activities on pages 198–199.

RTI (Response to Intervention)

① On-Level Instruction Use the *Math Connects* program as instruction for your on-level students.

② Strategic Intervention For options to instruct struggling students, refer to the Diagnostic Assessment table on page 23.

③ Intensive Intervention *Math Triumphs* can provide intensive intervention for students who are at risk of not meeting the objectives addressed in Chapter 1.

Diagnose student readiness with the Quick Check and Quick Review on page 23. Then use *Math Triumphs* to accelerate their achievment.

Introduction to Algebra and Functions

Prerequisite Skill	Math Triumphs
Variables and Expressions	Chapter 4
Order of Operations	Chapter 9

Practice and Review

Quick Review Math Handbook* is Glencoe's mathematical handbook for students and parents.

Hot Words includes a glossary of terms.

Hot Topics consists of two parts:

- explanations of key mathematical concepts

- exercises to check students' understanding.

Lesson	Hot Topics Section	Lesson	Hot Topics Section
1-1	1•5	1-6	6•1
1-2	3•1	1-7	6•1
1-3	3•2	1-8	1•2
1-4	1•3	1-10	6•7, 6•8

*Also available in Spanish

Notes

FOLDABLES™ Study Organizer
Dinah Zike's Foldables

Focus This Foldable is a study guide where students will write about algebra and functions.

Teach Students should use their Foldables to take notes, define terms, record key concepts, and write examples. Encourage students to record what they learn about the parts of each lesson that they find most difficult.

When to Use It At the end of each lesson, students should record their notes on the Foldable page with the appropriate tab.

A version of a completed Foldable is shown on p. 70.

Differentiated Instruction

CRM Student-Built Glossary, p. 1

Students complete the chart by providing a definition for each term and an example as they progress through Chapter 1.

This study tool can also be used to review for the chapter test.

Materials Needed for Chapter 1

- square tiles (Lesson 1-3)
- butcher block paper (Lesson 1-5)
- isometric dot paper (Lesson 1-6)
- index cards (Lessons 1-6, 1-7, 1-8)
- centimeter cubes and grid paper (Lesson 1-9)
- toothpicks (Extend 1-9)
- graphing calculator (Extend 1-10)

CHAPTER 1
Introduction to Algebra and Functions

BIG Idea
- Represent relationships in numerical, verbal, geometric, and symbolic form.

Key Vocabulary
algebra (p. 44)
defining the variable (p. 50)
evaluate (p. 31)
numerical expression (p. 38)

🌐 Real-World Link
PARKS Admission to the Kentucky Horse Park in Lexington, Kentucky, costs $15 for each adult and $8 for each child. You can use the four-step problem-solving plan to determine the cost of admission for a family of 2 adults and 3 children.

Introduction to Algebra and Functions Make this Foldable to help you organize your notes. Begin with eleven sheets of notebook paper.

1 **Staple** the eleven sheets together to form a booklet.

2 **Cut** tabs. Make each one 2 lines longer than the one before it.

3 **Write** the chapter title on the cover and label each tab with the lesson number.

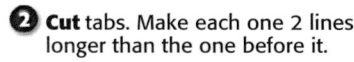
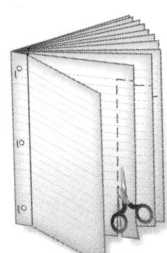
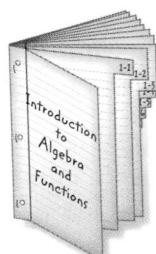

Foldables™ are a unique way to enhance students' study skills. Encourage students to add to their Foldable as they work through the chapter and to use it to review for their chapter test.

GET READY for Chapter 1

Diagnose Readiness You have two options for checking Prerequisite Skills.

Option 1

Take the Quick Quiz below. Refer to the Quick Review for help.

Option 2

Math Online Take the Online Readiness Quiz at glencoe.com.

QUICK Quiz

(Used in Lessons 1-1, 1-4 through 1-10)
Add. (Prior Grade)

1. $89.3 + 16.5$ **105.8**
2. $7.9 + 32.45$ **40.35**
3. $54.25 + 6.39$ **60.64**
4. $10.8 + 2.6$ **13.4**

5. **TECHNOLOGY** Patrick bought a personal electronic organizer for $59.99 and a carrying case for $12.95. What was his total cost, not including tax? (Prior Grade) **$72.94**

(Used in Lessons 1-1, 1-4 through 1-10)
Subtract. (Prior Grade)

6. $24.6 - 13.3$ **11.3**
7. $9.1 - 6.6$ **2.5**
8. $30.55 - 2.86$ **27.69**
9. $17.4 - 11.2$ **6.2**

(Used in Lessons 1-1 through 1-10)
Multiply. (Prior Grade)

10. 4×7.7 **30.8**
11. 9.8×3 **29.4**
12. 2.7×6.3 **17.01**
13. 8.5×1.2 **10.2**

(Used in Lessons 1-1, 1-4 through 1-10)
Divide. (Prior Grade)

14. $37.49 \div 4.6$ **8.15**
15. $14.31 \div 2.7$ **5.3**
16. $6.16 \div 5.6$ **1.1**
17. $11.15 \div 2.5$ **4.46**

18. **PIZZA** Four friends decided to split the cost of a pizza evenly. The total cost was $25.48. How much does each friend need to pay? (Prior Grade) **$6.37**

QUICK Review

Example 1 Find $17.89 + 43.2$.

$$
\begin{array}{r}
17.89 \\
+\ 43.20 \\
\hline
61.09
\end{array}
$$

Line up the decimal points.
Annex a zero.

Example 2 Find $37.45 - 8.52$.

$$
\begin{array}{r}
37.45 \\
-\ 8.52 \\
\hline
28.93
\end{array}
$$

Line up the decimal points.

Example 3 Find 1.7×3.5.

$$
\begin{array}{r}
1.7 \quad \leftarrow \quad \text{1 decimal place} \\
\times\ 3.5 \quad \leftarrow + \text{1 decimal place} \\
\hline
5.95 \quad \leftarrow \quad \text{2 decimal places}
\end{array}
$$

Example 4 Find $24.6 \div 2.5$.

$2.5\overline{)24.6} \rightarrow 25.\overline{)246.}$ Multiply both numbers by the same power of 10.

$$
\begin{array}{r}
9.84 \\
25\overline{)246.00} \\
-225 \\
\hline
210 \\
-200 \\
\hline
100 \\
-100 \\
\hline
0
\end{array}
$$

Annex zeros.

Divide as with whole numbers.

The one-stop **Assessment Planner** *organizes the resources available for diagnostic, formative, and summative assessment in this chapter.*

Chapter 1

Diagnostic Assessment

Exercises	State/Local Standards	Intervention
1–5		*Math Skills Maintenance Masters* 17, 19, pp. 34–35, 38–40
6–9		*Math Skills Maintenance Masters* 18–19, pp. 36–40
10–13		*Math Skills Maintenance Masters* 20, pp. 41–42
14–18		*Math Skills Maintenance Masters* 21, pp. 43–44

ASSESSMENT PLANNER

CHAPTER 1

✓ Formative Assessment

CRM Anticipation Guide, pp. 7–8
Spotting Preconceived Ideas
Students complete this survey to determine prior knowledge about ideas from Chapter 1. Revisit this worksheet after completing the chapter. Also see page 74.

TE Lesson Activities

- Ticket Out the Door, pp. 29, 52, 61
- Crystal Ball, pp. 33, 41
- Name the Math, pp. 37, 47, 56
- Yesterday's News, pp. 43, 67

Chapter Checkpoints

SE Mid-Chapter Quiz, p. 48
SE Study Guide and Review, pp. 70–74
SE Test Practice, pp. 76–77
CRM Quizzes, pp. 77–78
CRM Standardized Test Practice, pp. 94–96

Math Online glencoe.com

- Self-Check Quizzes
- Practice Test
- Test Practice

✓ Summative Assessment

SE Chapter Practice Test, p. 75
CRM Mid-Chapter Test, p. 79
CRM Vocabulary Test, p. 80
CRM Extended-Response Test, p. 93
CRM Leveled Chapter Tests, pp. 81–92
⊙ ExamView Pro® Assessment Suite

KEY

CRM *Chapter 1 Resource Masters*
SE Student Edition
TE Teacher Edition
⊙ CD-ROM

READING to SOLVE PROBLEMS

READING to SOLVE PROBLEMS

1 Focus

Sometimes students read word problems too quickly. As a result, they may plan an incorrect solution, performing the wrong operation(s). In this activity, students learn to check their work by asking whether their solutions make sense.

2 Teach

Make sure students realize that multiplication does not make sense because it would result in a greater distance, and the problem states that Miguel lives closer to school than Kelly does.

Encourage students to analyze the key terms of word problems, looking for clues about the operation(s) to use.

Before students begin the exercises, you might want to use a yardstick and a 1-foot ruler to model addition and subtraction. Point out that placing them end-to-end models an addition problem (3 ft + 1 ft), while placing them side-by-side models a subtraction problem (3 ft − 1 ft).

3 Assess

Tell students you made some cookies, which you want to distribute equally among 6 friends. Have students write which operation you should use to find the number of cookies to give each friend. **division**

Making Sense

When you solve a word problem, the first thing to do is to read the problem carefully. The last thing to do is to see whether your answer makes sense. Sometimes a picture or diagram can help.

> Kelly lives 5 miles from school. This is 4 times as far as Miguel lives from school. How far does Miguel live from school?

If you look just at the key words in the problem, it might seem that 4 *times* 5 would give the solution.

Kelly's House
5 miles

Miguel's House
5 × 4 or 20 miles

But the important question is, "Does this solution make sense?" In this case, the solution does *not* make sense because Kelly lives farther away. This problem is solved by dividing.

Miguel's House
5 ÷ 4 or 1.25 miles

Kelly's House
5 miles

So, Miguel lives 1.25 miles away from school.

> *Reading to Solve Problems features help students learn and use the language of mathematics.*

PRACTICE

For Exercises 1 and 2, choose the model that illustrates each problem. Explain your reasoning. Then solve.

1. Jennifer has saved $210 to purchase an MP3 player. She needs $299 to buy it. How much more money does she need? **See margin.**

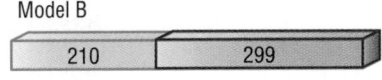
Model A
299
210

Model B
210
299

2. The school cafeteria sold 465 lunches on Thursday. They expect to sell 75 more lunches on Friday because they serve pizza that day. How many lunches do they expect to sell on Friday? **See margin.**

Model C
465
75

Model D
465
75

24 Chapter 1 Introduction to Algebra and Functions

Tips for New Teachers
Meaning of Multiplication

The correct use of the word *times* is to multiply 4 by the distance Miguel lives from school. This product is equal to the distance Kelly lives from school, which is five miles. So, Miguel's distance is 5 ÷ 4, or 1.25 miles.

Additional Answers

1. Model A; Even though the word *more* is in the problem, adding $210 to $299 does not make sense. The problem is solved by subtracting; $89.

2. Model D; In this case, *more* does mean to add, because number of lunches expected on Friday is in *addition* to the 465 lunches sold on Thursday; 540 lunches

1-1 A Plan for Problem Solving

PACING: **Regular:** 1 period, **Block:** 0.5 period

Options for Differentiated Instruction

 = English Language Learner   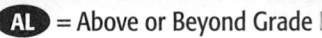 = Above or Beyond Grade Level   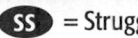 = Struggling Students   = Special Needs

Brainstorming

Use before presenting Example 1.

Before students look at the list of problem-solving strategies on page 25, have them brainstorm a list of strategies that they have used in past courses.

Ask:
- Which strategies have you used before?
- Which strategies do you think work best for you and why?
- What type of problem might lend itself to a given problem-solving strategy?

Organizing Student Work and Thinking

Use while presenting Example 1.

Create a template for the students to organize their work. A sample template can be found on page 33 of *Teaching Mathematics with Manipulatives*.

Understand	What is the
Read the problem carefully. What facts do you know? What do you need to find out? Is enough information given? Is there extra information?	question you need to answer?
Plan	What strategy will
How are the facts related to each other? Plan a strategy for solving the problem. Estimate the answer.	you use? Estimate:
Solve	Workspace
Use your plan to solve the problem. If your plan does not work, revise it or make a new plan. What is the solution?	Your answer:
Check	Does your
Reread the problem. Does the answer fit the facts given in the problem? Is the answer close to my estimate? Does the answer make sense? If not, solve the problem in another way.	answer make sense?

Working in Pairs

Use with Exercises 1 and 2.

Use the think-pair-share technique to help students choose problem-solving strategies. Have students read Exercises 1 and 2. Then pair them up and have them discuss with their partners which strategy would work the best to solve the problems. The pair then presents their results and the problem-solving strategy that they used to the class. If time allows, regroup students into different pairs and have them repeat the process with a different exercise.

Leveled Lesson Resources

Chapter 1 Resource Masters

BL = Below or Approaching Grade Level   **OL** = On Grade Level   **AL** = Above or Beyond Grade Level   **ELL** = English Language Learner

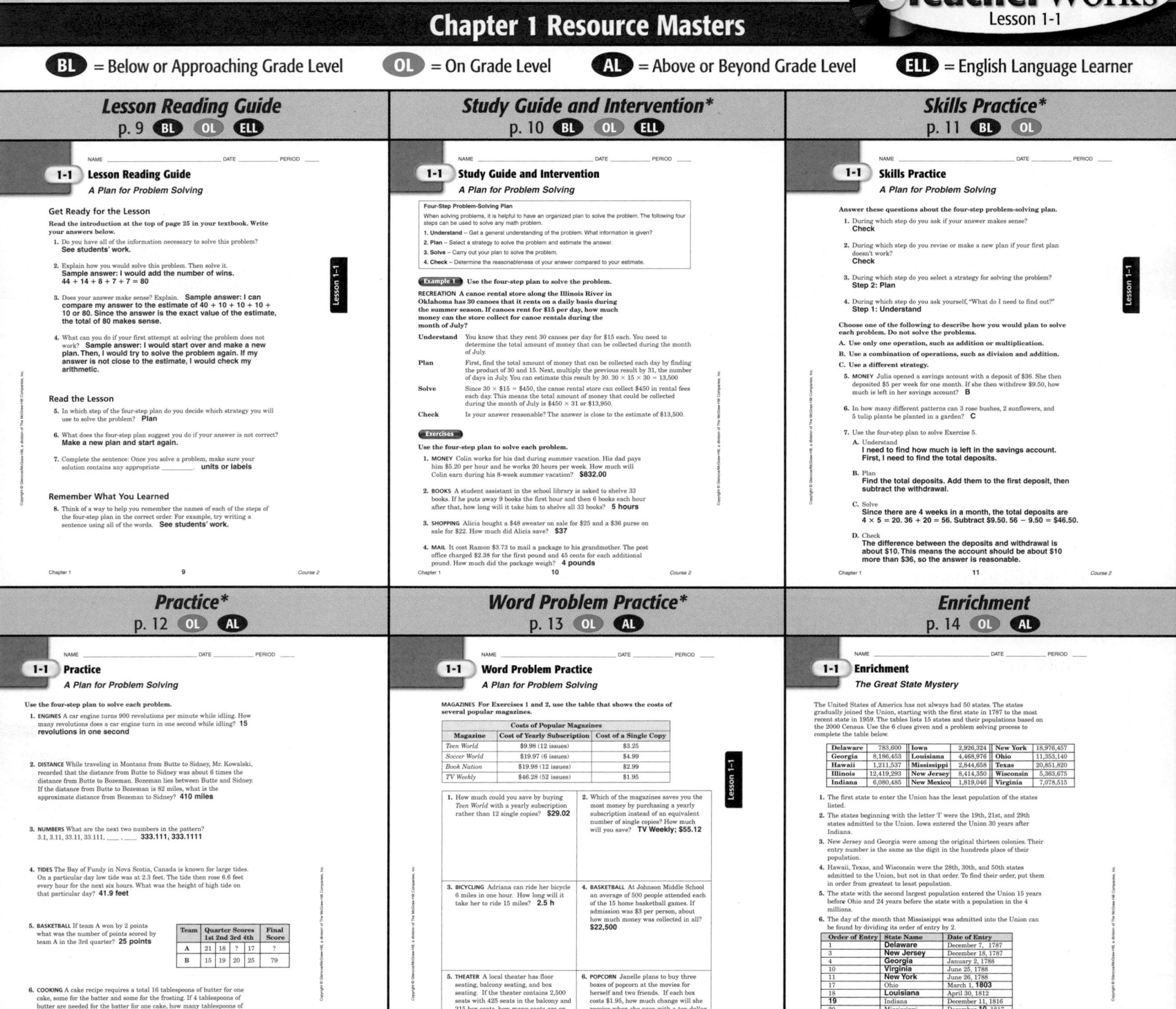

Additional Lesson Resources

Transparencies
- *5-Minute Check Transparency*, Lesson 1-1

Other Print Products
- *Noteables™ Interactive Study Notebook with Foldables™*

Teacher Tech Tools
- *Interactive Classroom CD-ROM*, Lesson 1-1
- *AssignmentWorks*, Lesson 1-1

Student Tech Tools
glencoe.com
- Extra Examples, Chapter 1, Lesson 1
- Self-Check Quiz, Chapter 1, Lesson 1

* Also available in Spanish **ELL**

A Plan for Problem Solving

MAIN IDEA

Solve problems using the four-step plan.

Math Online

glencoe.com

• Extra Examples
• Personal Tutor
• Self-Check Quiz

▷ **GET READY** for the Lesson

ANALYZE GRAPHS The graph shows the countries with the most world championship motocross wins. What is the total number of wins for these five countries?

1. See students' work.

1. Do you have all of the information necessary to solve this problem?

2–4. See margin.

2. Explain how you would solve this problem. Then solve it.

3. Does your answer make sense? Explain.

4. What can you do if your first attempt at solving the problem does not work?

World Championship Motocross Wins

Belgium 44, Sweden 14, France 8, Italy 7, USA 7

In mathematics, there is a *four-step plan* you can use to help you solve any problem.

Understand
• Read the problem carefully.
• What information is given?
• What do you need to find out?
• Is enough information given?
• Is there any extra information?

Plan
• How do the facts relate to each other?
• Select a strategy for solving the problem. There may be several that you can use.
• Estimate the answer.

Solve
• Use your plan to solve the problem.
• If your plan does not work, revise it or make a new plan.
• What is the solution?

Check
• Does your answer fit the facts given in the problem?
• Is your answer reasonable compared to your estimate?
• If not, make a new plan and start again.

Lesson 1-1 A Plan for Problem Solving **25**

Additional Answers

2. Sample answer: I would add the number of wins. $44 + 14 + 8 + 7 + 7 = 80$

3. Sample answer: I can compare my answer to the estimate of $40 + 10 + 10 + 10 + 10$ or 80. Since the answer is the exact value of the estimate, the total of 80 makes sense.

4. Sample answer: I would start over and make a new plan. Then, I would try to solve the problem again. If my answer is not close to the estimate, I would check my arithmetic.

---

1 Focus

Vertical Alignment

Before Lesson 1-1
Analyze problems by identifying relationships and distinguishing relevant from irrelevant information

Lesson 1-1
Analyze problems by identifying relationships, distinguishing relevant from irrelevant information, identifying missing information

After Lesson 1-1
Analyze problems by identifying relationships and distinguishing relevant from irrelevant information

2 Teach

Scaffolding Questions

Before you begin the opening activity, present the class with the following scenario. Tell students that you want to determine the two months in which the most members of the class were born.

Ask:
• What question(s) do you need to ask? What month were you born?

• How could you gather the data? class survey

• What would be a good way to record the data? tally chart; table

• How might you organize and display the data? table; bar graph; circle graph

Tips for New Teachers

Draw a Picture

For some learners, it may be beneficial to actually draw a picture of the problem during the *"plan"* stage of the *four-step* problem solving plan.

Real-World Link . . . . .
In a recent year, worldwide consumers purchased 8.8 million LCD (Liquid Crystal Display) TVs.
Source: DisplaySearch

EXAMPLE   Use the Four-Step Plan

1 **TELEVISION** There were about 268 million TVs in the U.S. in 2007. This amount increases by 4 million each year after 2007. In what year will there be at least 300 million TVs?

Understand   *What are you trying to find?*
In what year will there be at least 300 million TVs in the U.S.?

What information do you need to solve the problem?
You know how many TVs there were in 2007. Also, the number increases by 4 million each year.

Plan   Find the number of TVs needed to reach 300 million. Then divide this number by 4 to find the number of years that will pass before the total reaches 300 million TVs.

Solve   The change in the number of TVs from 268 million to 300 million is $300 - 268$ or 32 million TVs. Dividing the difference by 4, you get $32 \div 4$ or 8.

You can also use the *make a table* strategy.

Year	'07	'08	'09	'10	'11	'12	'13	'14	'15
Number (millions)	268	272	276	280	284	288	292	296	300

+4 +4 +4 +4 +4 +4 +4 +4

So, there will be at least 300 million TVs in the U.S. in the year 2015.

Check   8 years × 4 million = 32 million
268 million + 32 million = 300 million ✔

✔ CHECK Your Progress   a. about 8 pounds

a. **WHALES** A baby blue whale gains about 200 pounds each day. About how many pounds does a baby blue whale gain per hour?

Problems can be solved using different operations or strategies.

Problem-Solving Strategies	Concept Summary
guess and check	use a graph
look for a pattern	work backward
make an organized list	eliminate possibilities
draw a diagram	estimate reasonable answers
act it out	use logical reasoning
solve a simpler problem	make a model

Use a Strategy in the Four-Step Plan

2 GEOMETRY A *diagonal* connects two nonconsecutive vertices in a figure, as shown at the right. Find how many diagonals a figure with 7 sides would have.

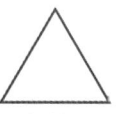 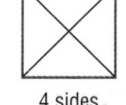 

3 sides
0 diagonals

4 sides
2 diagonals

5 sides
5 diagonals

Understand You know the number of diagonals for figures with three, four, and five sides.

Plan You can look for a pattern by organizing the information in a table. Then continue the pattern until you find the diagonals for an object with 7 sides.

Solve

Sides	3	4	5	6	7
Diagonals	0	2	5	9	14

+2 +3 +4 +5

So, a 7-sided figure would have 14 diagonals.

Check Check your answer by making a drawing.

 CHECK Your Progress

b. 1, 3, 6, 10, 15, 21, 28, 36; Add 2 to the first term, add 3 to the second term, add 4 to the third term, and so on.

b. **GEOMETRY** Numbers that can be represented by a triangular arrangement of dots are called *triangular numbers*. The first five triangular numbers are shown below. Write a sequence formed by the first eight triangular numbers. Write a rule for generating the sequence.

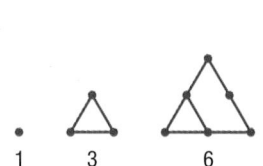 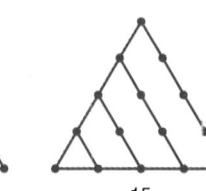

1   3   6   10   15

★ indicates multi-step problem

 **CHECK Your Understanding**

Use the four-step plan to solve each problem.

Example 1
(p. 26)

1. **ANALYZE TABLES** The table lists the sizes of six of the largest lakes in North Carolina. About how many times as large is High Rock Lake than Hyco Lake?

1. Sample answer: 4 times; 16,000 ÷ 4,000 = 4

Example 2
(p. 27)

2. **ALGEBRA** What are the next two numbers in the pattern below?

1, 1, 2, 6, 24, ■ , ■ 120, 720

Lake	Size (acres)
Lake Mattamuskeet	40,000
Falls Lake	12,000
Hyco Lake	3,750
Lake Gaston	20,000
Lake James	6,500
High Rock Lake	15,000

ADDITIONAL EXAMPLE

 2 POPULATION For every 100,000 people in the United States, there are 5,750 radios. For every 100,000 people in Canada, there are 323 radios. Suppose Sheamus lives in Des Moines, Iowa, and Alex lives in Windsor, Ontario. Both cities have about 200,000 residents. About how many more radios are there in Sheamus' city than in Alex's city? 10,854 radios

3 Practice

✓ **Formative Assessment**

Use Exercises 1–2 to check for understanding.

Then use the chart at the bottom of the next page to customize your assignments for students.

Intervention You may wish to use the Study Guide and Intervention Master on page 10 of the *Chapter 1 Resource Masters* for additional reinforcement.

Odd/Even Assignments

Exercises 3–10 are structured so that students practice the same concepts whether they are assigned odd or even problems.

Differentiated Instruction

Interpersonal Learners After assigning Exercise 13, have students write their problems on index cards with the solution on the back. Then have students exchange index cards with each other and solve each others' problems.

> The Differentiated Homework Options provide suggestions for the exercises that are appropriate for basic, core, or advanced students. Many of the homework exercises are paired, so that students could do the odds one day and the evens the next day.

> **Practice and** Problem Solving

HOMEWORK HELP

For Exercises	See Examples
3–6	1
7–10	2

Exercise Levels
A: 3–10
B: 11–15
C: 16–18

Use the four-step plan to solve each problem.

3. **BIRDS** Most hummingbirds flap their wings about 50 times a second. How many times can a hummingbird flap its wings in one minute? **3,000**

4. **PLANETS** Jupiter is about 3 times the size of Neptune. If the diameter of Jupiter is 88,736 miles, estimate the diameter of Neptune.
Sample answer: 30,000 miles; 90,000 ÷ 3 = 30,000

5. **FIELD TRIPS** To attend a field trip to a museum, each student will have to pay $6.00 for transportation and $5.75 for admission. If there are 65 students attending the field trip, how much money will their teacher need to collect? **$763.75**

6. **CANOE RENTALS** A state park took in $12,000 in canoe rentals during March. June rentals are expected to double that amount. If canoes rent for $40, how many canoe rentals are expected in June? **600 canoe rentals**

7. **GEOMETRY** What are the next two figures in the pattern?

8. **ALGEBRA** What are the next two numbers in the pattern below?
9, 27, 81, 243, 729, ▨ , ▨ **2,187 and 6,561**

ANALYZE TABLES For Exercises 9 and 10, use the commuter train schedule shown.

A commuter train departs from a train station and travels to the city each day. The schedule shows the first five departure and arrival times.

Commuter Train Schedule	
Departure	**Arrival**
6:30 A.M.	6:50 A.M.
7:15 A.M.	7:35 A.M.
8:00 A.M.	8:20 A.M.
8:45 A.M.	9:05 A.M.
9:30 A.M.	9:50 A.M.

9. How often does the commuter train arrive in the city? **every 45 minutes**

★ 10. What is the latest time that passengers can depart from the train station if they need to arrive in the city no later than noon? **11:00 A.M.**

11. **HOMEWORK** Angel has guitar practice at 7:00 P.M. He has homework in math, science, and history that will take him 30 minutes each to complete. He also has to allow 20 minutes for dinner. What is the latest time Angel can start his homework? **5:10 P.M.**

★ 12. **ESTIMATION** Terry opened a savings account in December with $132 and saved $27 each month beginning in January. Estimate the value of Terry's account in July. Then calculate the amount and evaluate the reasonableness of your estimate. **Sample answer: about $130 + $30 × 7 or $340;**
$132 + $27 × 7 = $321; The estimate is reasonable.

13. **FIND THE DATA** Refer to the Data File on pages 16–19 of your book. Choose some data and write a real-world problem in which you would use the four-step plan to solve the problem. **See students' work.**

DIFFERENTIATED HOMEWORK OPTIONS			
Level	**Assignment**	**Two-Day Option**	
BL Basic	3–10, 17–24	3–9 odd, 19–24	4–10 even, 17–18
OL Core	3–15, 17–24	3–10, 19–24	11–15, 17–18
AL Advanced/Pre-AP	11–20 (optional: 21–24)		

★ **14. ANALYZE TABLES** The sizes of Earth's oceans in millions of square kilometers are shown in the table. If the combined size of Earth's oceans is 367 million square kilometers, what is the size of the Pacific Ocean? **156 million km²**

Earth's Oceans	
Ocean	**Size (million km²)**
Arctic	45
Atlantic	77
Indian	69
Pacific	
Southern	20

Source: *The World Factbook*

15. MONEY Meli wants to buy a pair of rollerblades that cost $140.75. So far, she has saved $56.25. If she saves $6.50 every week, in how many weeks will she be able to purchase the rollerblades? **13 weeks**

EXTRA PRACTICE
See pages 668, 704.

H.O.T. Problems

18. Sample answer: It helps to organize your thoughts and focus on how to approach solving the problem.

16. CHALLENGE Use the digits 5, 6, 7, and 8 to form two 2-digit numbers so that their product is as great as possible. Use each digit only once.
$85 \times 76 = 6,460$

17. OPEN ENDED Create a real-world problem that can be solved by adding 79 and 42 and then multiplying the result by 3. **See margin.**

18. **WRITING IN MATH** Explain why it is important to plan before solving a problem.

TEST PRACTICE

19. Sheryl has $2 to spend at the school store. Based on the choices below, which three items from the table could Sheryl purchase? **C**

Item	Cost
Folder	$1.50
Pencil	$0.20
Pen	$0.50
Ruler	$1.75
Highlighter	$0.40

A folder, pencil, pen

B folder, highlighter, pencil

C pencil, pen, highlighter

D ruler, highlighter, pencil

20. Mr. Brooks went on a business trip. The trip was 380 miles, and the average price of gasoline was $3.15 per gallon. What information is needed to find the amount Mr. Brooks spent on gasoline for the trip? **G**

F Number of times Mr. Brooks stopped to fill his tank with gasoline

G Number of miles the car can travel using one gallon of gasoline

H Number of hours the trip took

J Average number of miles Mr. Brooks drove per day

GET READY for the Next Lesson

PREREQUISITE SKILL Multiply.

21. 10×10 **100**   **22.** $3 \times 3 \times 3$ **27**   **23.** $5 \times 5 \times 5 \times 5$ **625**   **24.** $2 \times 2 \times 2 \times 2 \times 2$ **32**

Lesson 1-1 A Plan for Problem Solving **29**

---

4 Assess

Tips for New Teachers

Writing

If students have difficulty with Exercise 17, have them first decide what objects or units the numbers represent. Encourage them to be creative. For example, if the numbers represent fish, what real-world situation might require finding the sum of 79 fish and 42 fish? And why would the sum be multiplied by 3?

Ticket Out the Door Read the following problem to students. Then tell them to write how they would follow the four-step plan to find the answer.

The seventh grade had a bake sale to raise money for a class trip. On Monday they made $30. On Tuesday they made $20. On Wednesday they made $50. School was closed on Thursday and Friday. How much money did they make that week?

FOLDABLES Study Organizer **Foldables™ Follow-Up**

Remind students to note key concepts in their Foldables. For example, they might want to write the steps of the four-step plan and the names of the problem-solving strategies that they find most useful.

Additional Answer

17. Sample answer: For the school bake sale, Samantha bakes 79 cookies and 42 brownies. If two other students baked the same amount of cookies and brownies, how many items did they bake altogether?

Options for Differentiated Instruction

ELL = English Language Learner   **AL** = Above or Beyond Grade Level   **SS** = Struggling Students   **SN** = Special Needs

Vocabulary Development **ELL** **SS** **SN**

Use after introducing the term *power*.

Have students compare multiplying integers and evaluating powers. Suggest that they write out a short series of products and a short series of powers having the same base. An example is shown below. Have them explain how the terms increase in each case. Sample answer: In the first case, the terms increase by 3. In the second case, the terms increase by powers of 3.

Products
$3 \times 1 = 3$
$3 \times 2 = 6$
$3 \times 3 = 9$
$3 \times 6 = 18$

Powers
$3^1 \qquad\qquad = 3$
$3^2 = 3 \times 3 \qquad = 9$
$3^3 = 3 \times 3 \times 3 \qquad = 27$
$3^6 = 3 \times 3 \times 3 \times 3 \times 3 \times 3 = 729$

Graphic Organizers **ELL** **SS** **SN**

Use before presenting Examples 1 and 2.

It is easier for students to remember related terms if the terms are clustered around a natural heading or category. Having students create *vocabulary charts* is one way to do this. Distribute copies of the following vocabulary chart for this lesson. As a class, have students find examples for each term in the chart. Students can use this chart to create vocabulary charts for other lessons. Sample examples are given.

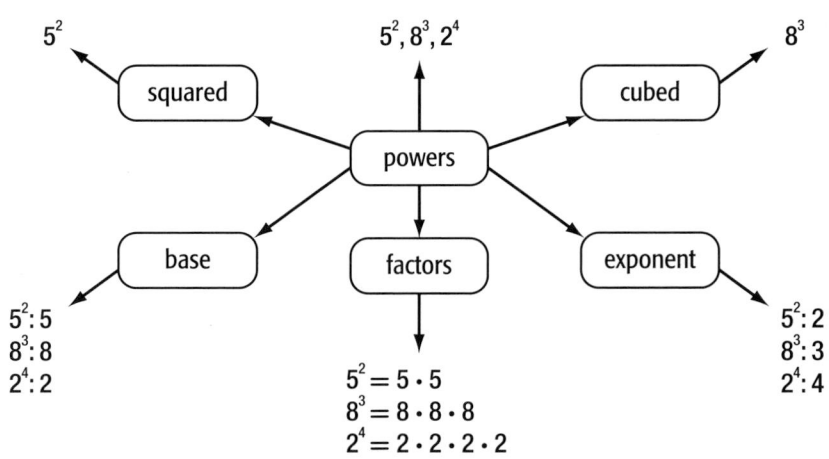

Each chapter includes ideas for **differentiating instruction** in your classroom. These hints are keyed for English learners, students above grade level, struggling students, and students with special needs.

Leveled Lesson Resources

Chapter 1 Resource Masters

BL = Below or Approaching Grade Level   **OL** = On Grade Level   **AL** = Above or Beyond Grade Level   **ELL** = English Language Learner

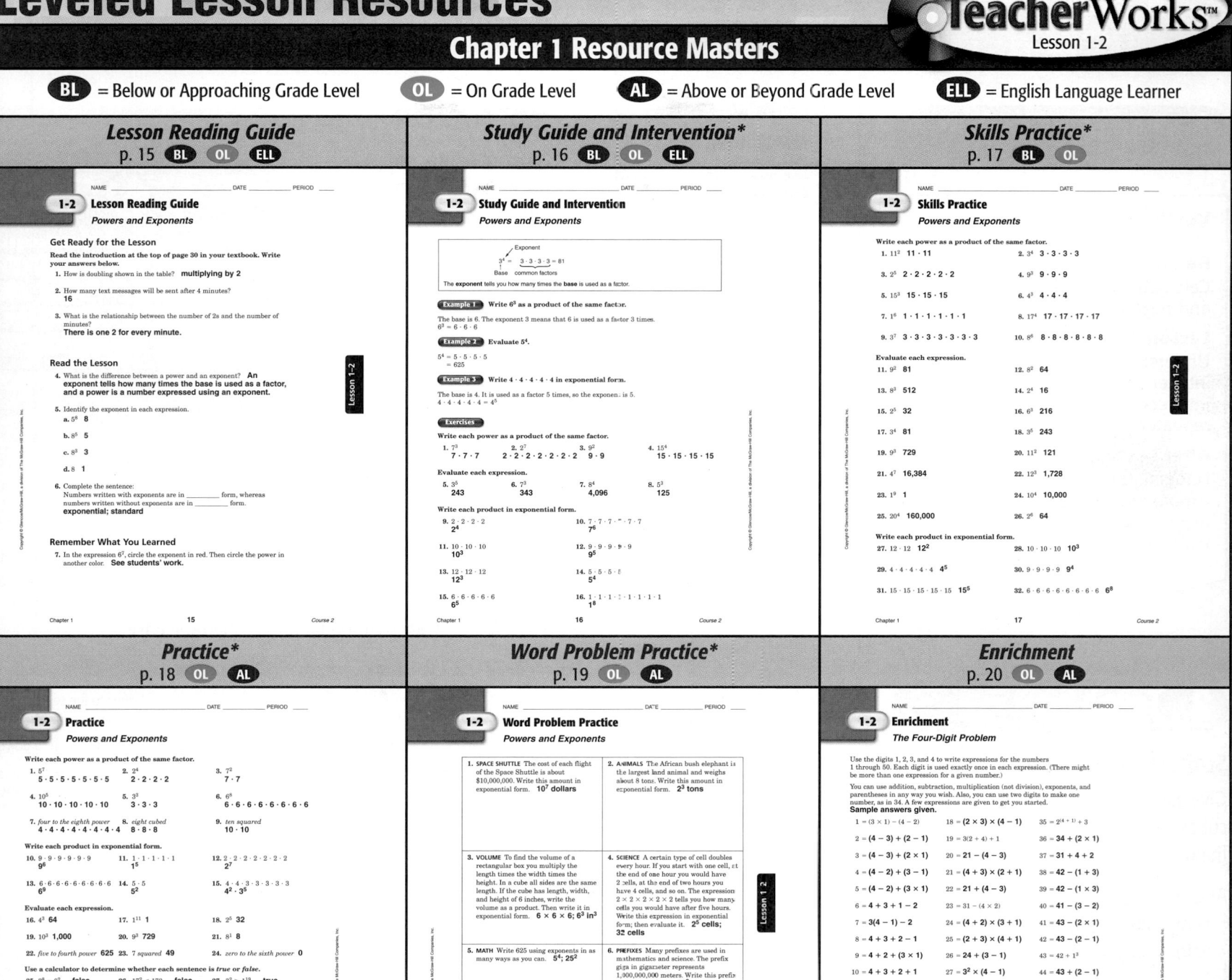

Lesson Reading Guide
p. 15 **BL** **OL** **ELL**

1-2 Lesson Reading Guide
Powers and Exponents

Get Ready for the Lesson
Read the introduction at the top of page 30 in your textbook. Write your answers below.
1. How is doubling shown in the table? **multiplying by 2**
2. How many text messages will be sent after 4 minutes? **16**
3. What is the relationship between the number of 2s and the number of minutes? **There is one 2 for every minute.**

Read the Lesson
4. What is the difference between a power and an exponent? **An exponent tells how many times the base is used as a factor, and a power is a number expressed using an exponent.**
5. Identify the exponent in each expression.
   a. 5^8 **8**
   b. 8^5 **5**
   c. 8^3 **3**
   d. 8 **1**
6. Complete the sentence:
   Numbers written with exponents are in _____ form, whereas numbers written without exponents are in _____ form. **exponential; standard**

Remember What You Learned
7. In the expression 6^7, circle the exponent in red. Then circle the power in another color. **See students' work.**

Study Guide and Intervention*
p. 16 **BL** **OL** **ELL**

1-2 Study Guide and Intervention
Powers and Exponents

$$3^4 = 3 \cdot 3 \cdot 3 \cdot 3 = 81$$
Base   common factors
The **exponent** tells you how many times the **base** is used as a factor.

Example 1 Write 6^3 as a product of the same factor.
The base is 6. The exponent 3 means that 6 is used as a factor 3 times.
$6^3 = 6 \cdot 6 \cdot 6$

Example 2 Evaluate 5^4.
$5^4 = 5 \cdot 5 \cdot 5 \cdot 5$
$= 625$

Example 3 Write $4 \cdot 4 \cdot 4 \cdot 4$ in exponential form.
The base is 4. It is used as a factor 5 times, so the exponent is 5.
$4 \cdot 4 \cdot 4 \cdot 4 \cdot 4 = 4^5$

Exercises
Write each power as a product of the same factor.
1. 7^3 **7 · 7 · 7**   2. 2^7 **2 · 2 · 2 · 2 · 2 · 2 · 2**   3. 9^2 **9 · 9**   4. 15^4 **15 · 15 · 15 · 15**

Evaluate each expression.
5. 3^5 **243**   6. 7^3 **343**   7. 8^4 **4,096**   8. 5^3 **125**

Write each product in exponential form.
9. $2 \cdot 2 \cdot 2 \cdot 2$ **2^4**   10. $7 \cdot 7 \cdot 7 \cdot 7 \cdot 7 \cdot 7$ **7^6**
11. $10 \cdot 10 \cdot 10$ **10^3**   12. $9 \cdot 9 \cdot 9 \cdot 9 \cdot 9$ **9^5**
13. $12 \cdot 12 \cdot 12$ **12^3**   14. $5 \cdot 5 \cdot 5 \cdot 5$ **5^4**
15. $6 \cdot 6 \cdot 6 \cdot 6 \cdot 6$ **6^5**   16. $1 \cdot 1 \cdot 1 \cdot 1 \cdot 1 \cdot 1 \cdot 1 \cdot 1$ **1^8**

Skills Practice*
p. 17 **BL** **OL**

1-2 Skills Practice
Powers and Exponents

Write each power as a product of the same factor.
1. 11^2 **11 · 11**   2. 3^4 **3 · 3 · 3 · 3**
3. 2^5 **2 · 2 · 2 · 2 · 2**   4. 9^3 **9 · 9 · 9**
5. 15^3 **15 · 15 · 15**   6. 4^3 **4 · 4 · 4**
7. 1^6 **1 · 1 · 1 · 1 · 1 · 1**   8. 17^4 **17 · 17 · 17 · 17**
9. 3^7 **3 · 3 · 3 · 3 · 3 · 3 · 3**   10. 8^6 **8 · 8 · 8 · 8 · 8 · 8**

Evaluate each expression.
11. 9^2 **81**   12. 8^2 **64**
13. 8^3 **512**   14. 2^4 **16**
15. 2^5 **32**   16. 6^3 **216**
17. 3^4 **81**   18. 3^5 **243**
19. 9^3 **729**   20. 11^2 **121**
21. 4^7 **16,384**   22. 12^3 **1,728**
23. 1^9 **1**   24. 10^4 **10,000**
25. 20^4 **160,000**   26. 2^6 **64**

Write each product in exponential form.
27. $12 \cdot 12$ **12^2**   28. $10 \cdot 10 \cdot 10$ **10^3**
29. $4 \cdot 4 \cdot 4 \cdot 4$ **4^5**   30. $9 \cdot 9 \cdot 9 \cdot 9$ **9^4**
31. $15 \cdot 15 \cdot 15 \cdot 15 \cdot 15$ **15^5**   32. $6 \cdot 6 \cdot 6 \cdot 6 \cdot 6 \cdot 6 \cdot 6 \cdot 6$ **6^8**

Practice*
p. 18 **OL** **AL**

1-2 Practice
Powers and Exponents

Write each power as a product of the same factor.
1. 5^7 **5 · 5 · 5 · 5 · 5 · 5 · 5**   2. 2^4 **2 · 2 · 2 · 2**   3. 7^2 **7 · 7**
4. 10^5 **10 · 10 · 10 · 10 · 10**   5. 3^3 **3 · 3 · 3**   6. 6^8 **6 · 6 · 6 · 6 · 6 · 6 · 6 · 6**
7. *four to the eighth power* **4 · 4 · 4 · 4 · 4 · 4 · 4 · 4**   8. *eight cubed* **8 · 8 · 8**   9. *ten squared* **10 · 10**

Write each product in exponential form.
10. $9 \cdot 9 \cdot 9 \cdot 9 \cdot 9$ **9^6**   11. $1 \cdot 1 \cdot 1 \cdot 1 \cdot 1$ **1^5**   12. $2 \cdot 2 \cdot 2 \cdot 2 \cdot 2 \cdot 2 \cdot 2$ **2^7**
13. $6 \cdot 6 \cdot 6 \cdot 6 \cdot 6 \cdot 6 \cdot 6$ **6^9**   14. $5 \cdot 5$ **5^2**   15. $4 \cdot 4 \cdot 3 \cdot 3 \cdot 3 \cdot 3 \cdot 3$ **$4^2 \cdot 3^5$**

Evaluate each expression.
16. 4^3 **64**   17. 1^{11} **1**   18. 2^5 **32**
19. 10^3 **1,000**   20. 9^3 **729**   21. 8^1 **8**
22. *five to fourth power* **625**   23. *7 squared* **49**   24. *zero to the sixth power* **0**

Use a calculator to determine whether each sentence is *true* or *false*.
25. $2^6 = 8^2$ **false**   26. $17^2 < 172$ **false**   27. $3^2 > 1^{19}$ **true**

Order the following powers from least to greatest.
28. $7^2, 5^3, 3^4, 2^5$ **$2^5, 5^3, 3^4, 7^2$**   29. $1^{13}, 4^3, 12^2, 8^3$ **$1^{13}, 4^3, 12^2, 8^3$**   30. $3^9, 5^7, 7^5, 9^3$ **$9^3, 7^5, 3^9, 5^7$**

31. **INTERACTIVE MAPS** Manai is using an interactive map on her computer that allows her to zoom in or zoom out. Each time she zooms out the scale of the map increases by a power of ten. If she zooms out four times the scale is 10^4 times greater. Write this number in standard form. **$10^4 = 10,000$**

32. **BACTERIA** A lab technician observed 5 bacteria growing in a lab dish. One hour later he observed 25 bacteria. Every hour he notices about 5 times as many as the hour before. After several hours of observation, he determined the lab dish had 5^9 bacteria. Use a calculator to find the number in standard form that represents the bacteria in the lab dish. **$5^9 = 1,953,125$**

Word Problem Practice*
p. 19 **OL** **AL**

1-2 Word Problem Practice
Powers and Exponents

1. **SPACE SHUTTLE** The cost of each flight of the Space Shuttle is about $10,000,000. Write this amount in exponential form. **10^7 dollars**

2. **ANIMALS** The African bush elephant is the largest land animal and weighs about 8 tons. Write this amount in exponential form. **2^3 tons**

3. **VOLUME** To find the volume of a rectangular box you multiply the length times the width times the height. In a cube all sides are the same length. If the cube has length, width, and height of 6 inches, write the volume as a product. Then write it in exponential form. **$6 \times 6 \times 6$; 6^3 in^3**

4. **SCIENCE** A certain type of cell doubles every hour. If you start with one cell, at the end of one hour you would have 2 cells, at the end of two hours you have 4 cells, and so on. The expression $2 \times 2 \times 2 \times 2 \times 2$ tells you how many cells you would have after five hours. Write this expression in exponential form; then evaluate it. **2^5 cells; 32 cells**

5. **MATH** Write 625 using exponents in as many ways as you can. **$5^4; 25^2$**

6. **PREFIXES** Many prefixes are used in mathematics and science. The prefix giga in gigameter represents 1,000,000,000 meters. Write this prefix as a power of ten. **10^9 meters**

7. **LIBRARY** The school library contains 9^4 books. How many library books are in the school library? **6,561 books**

8. **HOT DOGS** The concession stand at the county fair sold 6^3 hot dogs on the first day. How many hot dogs did they sell? **216 hot dogs**

Enrichment
p. 20 **OL** **AL**

1-2 Enrichment
The Four-Digit Problem

Use the digits 1, 2, 3, and 4 to write expressions for the numbers 1 through 50. Each digit is used exactly once in each expression. (There might be more than one expression for a given number.)
You can use addition, subtraction, multiplication (not division), exponents, and parentheses in any way you wish. Also, you can use two digits to make one number, as in 34. A few expressions are given to get you started.
Sample answers given.

$1 = (3 \times 1) - (4 - 2)$	$18 = (2 \times 3) \times (4 - 1)$	$35 = 2^{(4+1)} + 3$
$2 = (4 - 3) + (2 - 1)$	$19 = 3(2 + 4) + 1$	$36 = 34 + (2 \times 1)$
$3 = (4 - 3) + (2 \times 1)$	$20 = 21 - (4 - 3)$	$37 = 31 + 4 + 2$
$4 = (4 - 2) + (3 - 1)$	$21 = (4 \times 3) \times (2 + 1)$	$38 = 42 - (1 + 3)$
$5 = (4 - 2) + (3 \times 1)$	$22 = 21 + (4 - 3)$	$39 = 42 - (1 \times 3)$
$6 = 4 + 3 + 1 - 2$	$23 = 31 - (4 \times 2)$	$40 = 41 - (3 - 2)$
$7 = 3(4 - 1) - 2$	$24 = (4 + 2) \times (3 + 1)$	$41 = 43 - (2 \times 1)$
$8 = 4 + 3 + 2 - 1$	$25 = (4 \times 3) \times (4 + 1)$	$42 = 43 - (2 \times 1)$
$9 = 4 + 2 + (3 \times 1)$	$26 = 24 + (3 - 1)$	$43 = 42 + 1^3$
$10 = 4 + 3 + 2 + 1$	$27 = 3^2 \times (4 - 1)$	$44 = 43 + (2 - 1)$
$11 = (4 \times 3) - (2 - 1)$	$28 = 21 + 4 + 3$	$45 = 43 + (2 \times 1)$
$12 = (4 \times 3) \times (2 - 1)$	$29 = 2^{(4+1)} - 3$	$46 = 43 + (2 + 1)$
$13 = (4 \times 3) + (2 - 1)$	$30 = (2 \times 3) \times (4 + 1)$	$47 = 31 + 4^2$
$14 = (4 \times 3) + (2 \times 1)$	$31 = 34 - (2 + 1)$	$48 = 4^2 \times (3 \times 1)$
$15 = 2(3 + 4) + 1$	$32 = 34 - (2 \times 1)$	$49 = 41 + 2^3$
$16 = (4 \times 2) \times (3 - 1)$	$33 = 21 + (4 \times 3)$	$50 = 41 + 3^2$
$17 = 3(4 + 2) - 1$	$34 = 2 \times (14 + 3)$	

Additional Lesson Resources

* *Also available in Spanish* **ELL**

Transparencies
• *5-Minute Check Transparency,* Lesson 1-2

Other Print Products
• *Teaching Mathematics with Manipulatives*
• *Noteables™ Interactive Study Notebook with Foldables™*

Teacher Tech Tools
• *Interactive Classroom CD-ROM,* Lesson 1-2
• *AssignmentWorks,* Lesson 1-2

Student Tech Tools
glencoe.com
• Extra Examples, Chapter 1, Lesson 2
• Self-Check Quiz, Chapter 1, Lesson 2

1 Focus

Vertical Alignment

Before Lesson 1-2
Calculate with positive and negative integers

Lesson 1-2
Understand and compute positive integer powers of nonnegative integers; compute examples as repeated multiplication

After Lesson 1-2
Understand whole-number exponents. Multiply and divide expressions involving exponents with a common base

2 Teach

Scaffolding Questions

Give each pair of students ten unit cubes (1 × 1 × 1). Have students use the unit cubes to make squares.

Ask:

• How many unit cubes are in a square with sides of 1? **1**

• How many unit cubes are in a square with sides of 2? **4**

• How many unit cubes are in a square with sides of 3? **9**

• How many unit cubes do you predict will be in a square with sides of 4? with sides of 5? **16; 25**

• What is the relationship between the number of unit cubes needed to build a square and the number of units per side? **The number of cubes needed to build a square equals the number of squares per side multiplied by the same number.**

MAIN IDEA

Use powers and exponents.

New Vocabulary

factors
exponent
base
powers
squared
cubed
evaluate
standard form
exponential form

Math Online

glencoe.com
• Extra Examples
• Personal Tutor
• Self-Check Quiz

▶ **GET READY for the Lesson**

TEXT MESSAGING Suppose you text message one of your friends. That friend then text messages two friends after one minute. The pattern continues.

Minutes	Number of Text Messages	
0	1	= 1
1	1 × 2	= 2
2	2 × 2	= 4
3	2 × 2 × 2	= 8

1. How is doubling shown in the table? **multiplying by 2**

2. How many text messages **16** will be sent after 4 minutes?

3. What is the relationship between the number of 2s and the number of minutes? **There is one 2 for every minute.**

Two or more numbers that are multiplied together to form a product are called **factors**. When the same factor is used, you may use an exponent to simplify the notation. The **exponent** tells how many times the base is used as a factor. The common factor is called the **base**.

$$16 = 2 \cdot 2 \cdot 2 \cdot 2 = 2^4 \leftarrow \text{exponent}$$

 base

Numbers expressed using exponents are called **powers**.

Powers	Words
5^2	five to the second power or five **squared**
4^3	four to the third power or four **cubed**
2^4	two to the fourth power

EXAMPLES Write Powers as Products

Write each power as a product of the same factor.

1 7^5

Seven is used as a factor five times.

$7^5 = 7 \cdot 7 \cdot 7 \cdot 7 \cdot 7$

2 3^2

Three is used as a factor twice.

$3^2 = 3 \cdot 3$

✓ **CHECK Your Progress**

Write each power as a product of the same factor.

a. 6^4 **6 · 6 · 6 · 6**   b. 1^3 **1 · 1 · 1**   c. 9^5 **9 · 9 · 9 · 9 · 9**

Scaffolding Questions give direction and momentum to the lesson, clarify its purpose, and keep students on task.

You can **evaluate**, or find the value of, powers by multiplying the factors. Numbers written without exponents are in **standard form**.

EXAMPLES Write Powers in Standard Form

Evaluate each expression.

3 2^5

$2^5 = 2 \cdot 2 \cdot 2 \cdot 2 \cdot 2$ 2 is used as a factor 5 times.

   $= 32$ Multiply.

4 4^3

$4^3 = 4 \cdot 4 \cdot 4$ 4 is used as a factor 3 times.

   $= 64$ Multiply.

✓ **CHECK Your Progress**

Evaluate each expression.

d. 10^2 **100**   e. 7^3 **343**   f. 5^4 **625**

Numbers written with exponents are in **exponential form**.

EXAMPLE Write Numbers in Exponential Form

5 Write $3 \cdot 3 \cdot 3 \cdot 3$ in exponential form.

3 is the base. It is used as a factor 4 times. So, the exponent is 4.

$3 \cdot 3 \cdot 3 \cdot 3 = 3^4$

✓ **CHECK Your Progress**

Write each product in exponential form.

g. $5 \cdot 5 \cdot 5$ $\mathbf{5^3}$ h. $12 \cdot 12 \cdot 12 \cdot 12 \cdot 12 \cdot 12$ $\mathbf{12^6}$

★ indicates multi-step problem

✓ CHECK Your Understanding

Examples 1, 2
(p. 30)

Write each power as a product of the same factor.

1. 9^3 $\mathbf{9 \cdot 9 \cdot 9}$ 2. 3^4 $\mathbf{3 \cdot 3 \cdot 3 \cdot 3}$ 3. 8^5 $\mathbf{8 \cdot 8 \cdot 8 \cdot 8 \cdot 8}$

Examples 3, 4
(p. 31)

Evaluate each expression.

4. 2^4 **16**   5. 7^2 **49**   6. 10^3 **1,000**

7. **POPULATION** There are approximately 5^{10} people living in North Carolina. About how many people is this? **9,765,625 people**

Example 5
(p. 31)

Write each product in exponential form.

8. $5 \cdot 5 \cdot 5 \cdot 5 \cdot 5 \cdot 5$ $\mathbf{5^6}$ 9. $1 \cdot 1 \cdot 1 \cdot 1$ $\mathbf{1^4}$ 10. $4 \cdot 4 \cdot 4 \cdot 4 \cdot 4$ $\mathbf{4^5}$

Lesson 1-2 Powers and Exponents   **31**

▶ Practice and Problem Solving

HOMEWORK HELP

For Exercises	See Examples
11–16	1, 2
17–24	3, 4
25–28	5

Exercise Levels
A: 11–28
B: 29–39
C: 40–43

Write each power as a product of the same factor.

11. 1^5 **1 • 1 • 1 • 1 • 1**   12. 4^2 **4 • 4**   13. **3 • 3 • 3 • 3 • 3 • 3 • 3 • 3**

13. 3^8

14. 8^6 **8 • 8 • 8 • 8 • 8 • 8**   15. 9^3 **9 • 9 • 9**   16. 10^4 **10 • 10 • 10 • 10**

Evaluate each expression.

17. 2^6 **64**   18. 4^3 **64**   19. 7^4 **2,401**

20. 4^6 **4,096**   21. 1^{10} **1**   22. 10^1 **10**

23. **BIKING** In a recent year, the number of 12- to 17-year-olds that went off-road biking was 10^6. Write this number in standard form. **1,000,000**

24. **TRAINS** The Maglev train in China is the fastest passenger train in the world. Its average speed is 3^5 miles per hour. Write this speed in standard form.
243 mph

Write each product in exponential form.

25. $3 \cdot 3$ **3^2**   26. $7 \cdot 7 \cdot 7 \cdot 7$ **7^4**

27. $1 \cdot 1 \cdot 1 \cdot 1 \cdot 1 \cdot 1 \cdot 1 \cdot 1$ **1^8**   28. $6 \cdot 6 \cdot 6 \cdot 6 \cdot 6$ **6^5**

Write each power as a product of the same factor.

29. *four to the fifth power* **4 • 4 • 4 • 4 • 4**   30. *nine squared* **9 • 9**

Evaluate each expression.

31. *six to the fourth power* **1,296**   32. *6 cubed* **216**

GEOMETRY For Exercises 33 and 34, use the puzzle cube below.

34. Sample answer: A number taken to the third power is the same as the volume of a cube, or the amount of space inside a cube.

33. Suppose the puzzle cube is made entirely of unit cubes. Find the number of unit cubes in the puzzle. Write your answer using exponents. **3^3**

34. Why do you think the expression 3^3 is sometimes read as *3 cubed*?

35. **NUMBERS** Write $5 \cdot 5 \cdot 5 \cdot 5 \cdot 4 \cdot 4 \cdot 4$ in exponential form. **$5^4 \cdot 4^3$**

★36. **COMPUTERS** A gigabyte is a measure of computer data storage capacity. One gigabyte stores 2^{30} bytes of data. Use a calculator to find the number in standard form that represents two gigabytes. **2,147,483,648**

Order the following powers from least to greatest.

★37. $6^5, 1^{14}, 4^{10}, 17^3$ ★38. $2^8, 15^2, 6^3, 3^5$ ★39. $5^3, 4^6, 2^{11}, 7^2$
$1^{14}, 17^3, 6^5, 4^{10}$ **$6^3, 15^2, 3^5, 2^8$**   **$7^2, 5^3, 2^{11}, 4^6$**

EXTRA PRACTICE

See pages 668, 704.

40. **OPEN ENDED** Select a number between 1,000 and 2,000 that can be expressed as a power. **Sample answer: $4^5 = 1,024$**

32   Chapter 1 Introduction to Algebra and Functions

DIFFERENTIATED HOMEWORK OPTIONS

Level	Assignment	Two-Day Option	
BL Basic	11–28, 41–50	11–27 odd, 44	12–28 even, 41–43, 45–50
OL Core	11–21 odd, 23–24, 25–31 odd, 33–37, 39, 41–50	11–28, 44	29–39, 41–43, 45–50
AL Advanced/Pre-AP	29–46 (optional: 47–50)		

H.O.T. Problems

41. **CHALLENGE** Write two different powers that have the same value.
$8^2 = 64$ and $4^3 = 64$

42. **Which One Doesn't Belong?** Identify the number that does not belong with the other three. Explain your reasoning.

43. Sample answer: The pattern is that each successive term is $\frac{1}{2}$ of the previous one, so $2^0 = 1$ and $2^{-1} = \frac{1}{2}$.

| 121 | 361 | 576 | 1,000 |

1,000; 1,000 cannot be expressed as a square: $11^2 = 121$, $19^2 = 361$, $24^2 = 576$

43. **WRITING IN MATH** Analyze the number pattern shown at the right. Then write a convincing argument as to the value of 2^0. Based on your argument, what do you think will be the value of 2^{-1}?

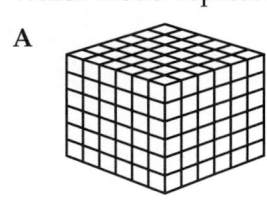

$2^4 = 16$
$2^3 = 8$
$2^2 = 4$
$2^1 = 2$
$2^0 = ?$

TEST PRACTICE

44. Which model represents 6^3? **A**

A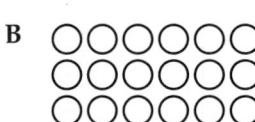

B (circles)

C (rectangle, 6 by 12)

D (grid)

Spiral Review

45. **FOOTBALL** The graph shows the number of wins the Pittsburgh Steelers had from 2003–2006. How many more wins did the Steelers have in 2004 than 2006? (Lesson 1-1)
7 wins

46. **COOKING** Ms. Jackson is serving fried turkey at 5:00 P.M. The 12-pound turkey has to cook 3 minutes for every pound, and then cool for at least 45 minutes. What is the latest time she can start frying? (Lesson 1-1) **3:39 P.M.**

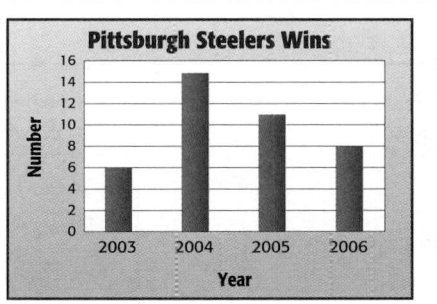

Source: National Football League

GET READY for the Next Lesson

PREREQUISITE SKILL Multiply.

47. $2 \cdot 2$ **4**   48. $3 \cdot 3$ **9**   49. $5 \cdot 5$ **25**   50. $7 \cdot 7$ **49**

Lesson 1-2 Powers and Exponents   **33**

4 Assess

Crystal Ball Tell students that tomorrow's lesson is about squaring numbers and finding the square roots of numbers. Have students write how they think what they learned today will connect with tomorrow's lesson.

Pre-AP Activities help you cultivate skills that students will need to have success in higher mathematics.

Pre-AP Activity   Use as an Extension

You might want to have students compare a standard multiplication series with an exponential series. Suggest that they write a series of products, such as $3 \times 1 = 3$, $3 \times 2 = 6$, $3 \times 3 = 9$, and so on. Then have them write a series of exponents using the same factor, such as $3^1 = 3$, $3^2 = 9$, $3^3 = 27$, and so on. Ask them to write a sentence that compares how the products of each series increase.

PACING: **Regular:** 1 period,   **Block:** 0.5 period

Options for Differentiated Instruction

ELL = English Language Learner   **AL** = Above or Beyond Grade Level   **SS** = Struggling Students   **SN** = Special Needs

Building Vocabulary   **ELL**   **SN**

Use while presenting the lesson.

Have students create visual vocabulary cards for the terms in Lesson 1-3. An example of a visual vocabulary card for *perfect square* is shown below.

Vocabulary word and definition	Picture or diagram
Example	A personal way to remember the term

Perfect Square A number that is the square of an integer.	 $3 \times 3 = 9$, so 9 is a perfect square.
25 is a perfect square because $25 = 5^2$.	A number to the second power means square. 4^2 is a 4×4 square, or 16.

Cooperative Groups   **ELL**   **SS**   **SN**

Use before presenting Example 3.

Have students create a resource sheet listing the first ten perfect squares and their square roots.

$$1^2 = 1 \longrightarrow \sqrt{1} = 1$$
$$2^2 = 4 \longrightarrow \sqrt{4} = 2$$
$$3^2 = 9 \longrightarrow \sqrt{9} = 3$$

$$10^2 = 100 \longrightarrow \sqrt{100} = 10$$

Challenge Beyond the Lesson Content   **AL**

Use after presenting the lesson.

Propose the following question to students.

If you double the sides of a square, will the area of the square *sometimes*, *always*, or *never* double? Explain your reasoning. Never; the area will be 2 • 2 or 4 times greater.

Leveled Lesson Resources

Chapter 1 Resource Masters

BL = Below or Approaching Grade Level   **OL** = On Grade Level   **AL** = Above or Beyond Grade Level   **ELL** = English Language Learner

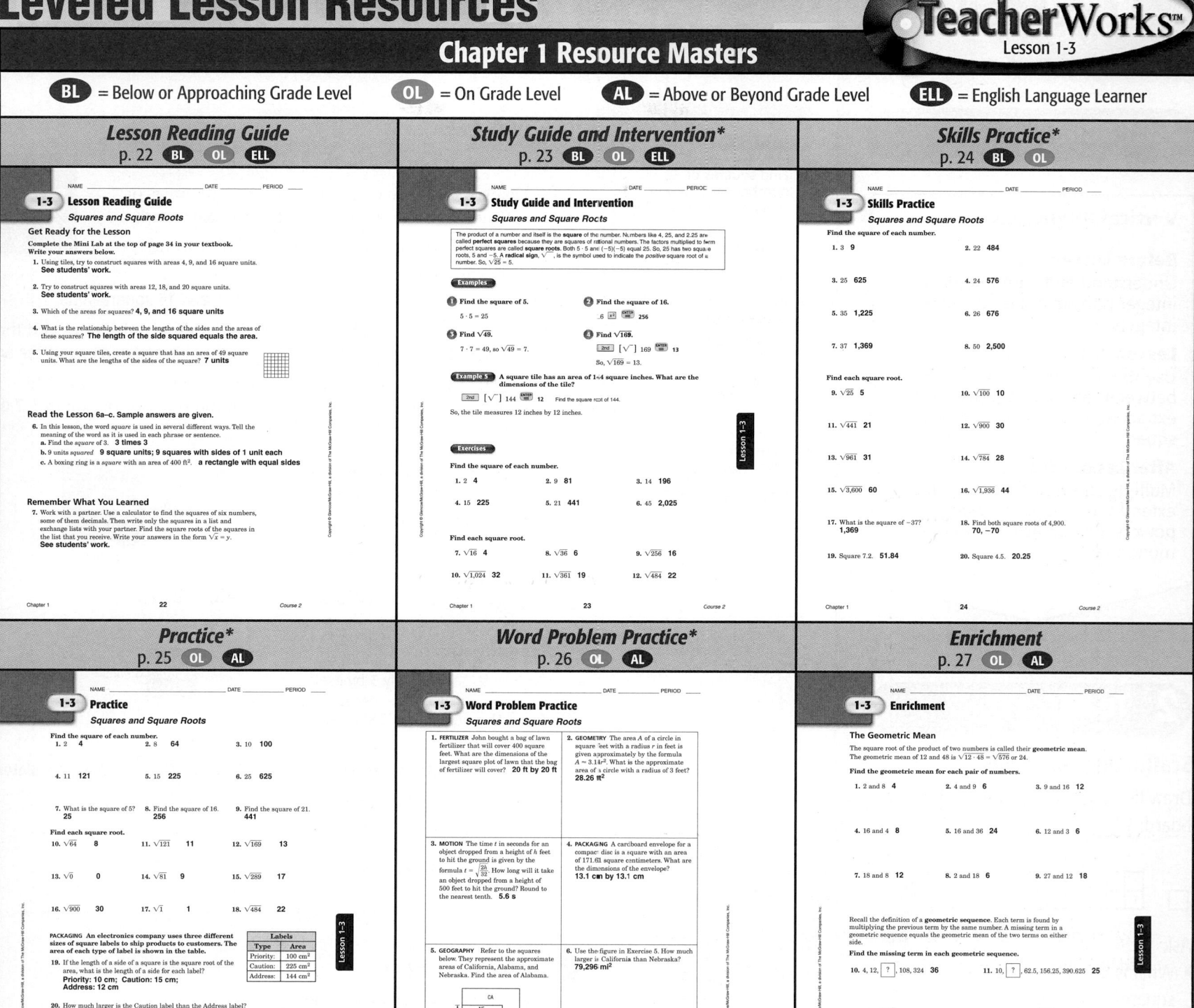

Lesson Reading Guide
p. 22 **BL** **OL** **ELL**

1-3 Lesson Reading Guide
Squares and Square Roots

Get Ready for the Lesson

Complete the Mini Lab at the top of page 34 in your textbook.
Write your answers below.

1. Using tiles, try to construct squares with areas 4, 9, and 16 square units.
See students' work.

2. Try to construct squares with areas 12, 18, and 20 square units.
See students' work.

3. Which of the areas for squares? **4, 9, and 16 square units**

4. What is the relationship between the lengths of the sides and the areas of these squares? **The length of the side squared equals the area.**

5. Using your square tiles, create a square that has an area of 49 square units. What are the lengths of the sides of the square? **7 units**

Read the Lesson 6a–c. Sample answers are given.

6. In this lesson, the word *square* is used in several different ways. Tell the meaning of the word as it is used in each phrase or sentence.
a. Find the *square* of 3. **3 times 3**
b. 9 units *squared* **9 square units; 9 squares with sides of 1 unit each**
c. A boxing ring is a *square* with an area of 400 ft². **a rectangle with equal sides**

Remember What You Learned

7. Work with a partner. Use a calculator to find the squares of six numbers, some of them decimals. Then write only the squares in a list and exchange lists with your partner. Find the square roots of the squares in the list that you receive. Write your answers in the form $\sqrt{x} = y$.
See students' work.

Chapter 1   22   *Course 2*

Study Guide and Intervention*
p. 23 **BL** **OL** **ELL**

1-3 Study Guide and Intervention
Squares and Square Roots

The product of a number and itself is the **square** of the number. Numbers like 4, 25, and 2.25 are called **perfect squares** because they are squares of rational numbers. The factors multiplied to form perfect squares are called **square roots**. Both $5 \cdot 5$ and $(-5)(-5)$ equal 25. So, 25 has two square roots, 5 and –5. A **radical sign**, $\sqrt{}$, is the symbol used to indicate the *positive* square root of a number. So, $\sqrt{25} = 5$.

Examples

① Find the square of 5.
$5 \cdot 5 = 25$

② Find the square of 16.
16 x² ENTER 256

③ Find $\sqrt{49}$.
$7 \cdot 7 = 49$, so $\sqrt{49} = 7$.

④ Find $\sqrt{169}$.
2nd [√] 169 ENTER 13
So, $\sqrt{169} = 13$.

Example 5 A square tile has an area of 144 square inches. What are the dimensions of the tile?
2nd [√] 144 ENTER 12   Find the square root of 144.
So, the tile measures 12 inches by 12 inches.

Exercises

Find the square of each number.

1. 2   **4**   2. 9   **81**   3. 14   **196**

4. 15   **225**   5. 21   **441**   6. 45   **2,025**

Find each square root.

7. $\sqrt{16}$ **4**   8. $\sqrt{36}$ **6**   9. $\sqrt{256}$ **16**

10. $\sqrt{1,024}$ **32**   11. $\sqrt{361}$ **19**   12. $\sqrt{484}$ **22**

Chapter 1   23   *Course 2*

Skills Practice*
p. 24 **BL** **OL**

1-3 Skills Practice
Squares and Square Roots

Find the square of each number.

1. 3   **9**   2. 22   **484**

3. 25   **625**   4. 24   **576**

5. 35   **1,225**   6. 26   **676**

7. 37   **1,369**   8. 50   **2,500**

Find each square root.

9. $\sqrt{25}$ **5**   10. $\sqrt{100}$ **10**

11. $\sqrt{441}$ **21**   12. $\sqrt{900}$ **30**

13. $\sqrt{961}$ **31**   14. $\sqrt{784}$ **28**

15. $\sqrt{3,600}$ **60** 16. $\sqrt{1,936}$ **44**

17. What is the square of –37?   **1,369**
18. Find both square roots of 4,900.   **70, –70**

19. Square 7.2.   **51.84**   20. Square 4.5.   **20.25**

Chapter 1   24   *Course 2*

Practice*
p. 25 **OL** **AL**

1-3 Practice
Squares and Square Roots

Find the square of each number.
1. 2   **4**   2. 8   **64**   3. 10   **100**

4. 11   **121**   5. 15   **225**   6. 25   **625**

7. What is the square of 5?   **25**
8. Find the square of 16.   **256**
9. Find the square of 21.   **441**

Find each square root.
10. $\sqrt{64}$ **8**   11. $\sqrt{121}$ **11**   12. $\sqrt{169}$ **13**

13. $\sqrt{0}$ 14. $\sqrt{81}$ **9**   15. $\sqrt{289}$ **17**

16. $\sqrt{900}$ **30**   17. $\sqrt{1}$ **1**   18. $\sqrt{484}$ **22**

PACKAGING An electronics company uses three different sizes of square labels to ship products to customers. The area of each type of label is shown in the table.

Labels	
Type	Area
Priority:	100 cm²
Caution:	225 cm²
Address:	144 cm²

19. If the length of a side of a square is the square root of the area, what is the length of a side for each label?
Priority: 10 cm; Caution: 15 cm; Address: 12 cm

20. How much larger is the Caution label than the Address label?
81 cm²

21. **RECREATION** A square hot tub is outlined by a 2-foot wide tile border. In an overhead view, the area of the hot tub and the border together is 144 square feet. What is the length of one side of the hot tub itself?
8 feet

Chapter 1   25   *Course 2*

Word Problem Practice*
p. 26 **OL** **AL**

1-3 Word Problem Practice
Squares and Square Roots

1. **FERTILIZER** John bought a bag of lawn fertilizer that will cover 400 square feet. What are the dimensions of the largest square plot of lawn that the bag of fertilizer will cover?   **20 ft by 20 ft**

2. **GEOMETRY** The area A of a circle in square feet with a radius r in feet is given approximately by the formula $A = 3.14r^2$. What is the approximate area of a circle with a radius of 3 feet?   **28.26 ft²**

3. **MOTION** The time t in seconds for an object dropped from a height of h feet to hit the ground is given by the formula $t = \sqrt{\frac{h}{32}}$. How long will it take an object dropped from a height of 500 feet to hit the ground? Round to the nearest tenth.   **5.6 s**

4. **PACKAGING** A cardboard envelope for a compact disc is a square with an area of 171.61 square centimeters. What are the dimensions of the envelope?   **13.1 cm by 13.1 cm**

5. **GEOGRAPHY** Refer to the squares below. They represent the approximate areas of California, Alabama, and Nebraska. Find the area of Alabama.

CA
NE   395 mi
277 mi   AL
         225 mi

50,625 mi²

6. Use the figure in Exercise 5. How much larger is California than Nebraska?
79,296 mi²

Chapter 1   26   *Course 2*

Enrichment
p. 27 **OL** **AL**

1-3 Enrichment

The Geometric Mean

The square root of the product of two numbers is called their **geometric mean**. The geometric mean of 12 and 48 is $\sqrt{12 \cdot 48} = \sqrt{576}$ or 24.

Find the geometric mean for each pair of numbers.

1. 2 and 8   **4**   2. 4 and 9   **6**   3. 9 and 16   **12**

4. 16 and 4   **8**   5. 16 and 36   **24**   6. 12 and 3   **6**

7. 18 and 8   **12**   8. 2 and 18   **6**   9. 27 and 12   **18**

Recall the definition of a **geometric sequence**. Each term is found by multiplying the previous term by the same number. A missing term in a geometric sequence equals the geometric mean of the two terms on either side.

Find the missing term in each geometric sequence.

10. 4, 12, [?], 108, 324   **36**   11. 10, [?], 62.5, 156.25, 390.625   **25**

12. 1, 0.4, [?], 0.064, 0.0256   **0.16**   13. 700, 70, 7, 0.7, [?], 0.007   **0.07**

14. 6, [?], 24   **12**   15. 18, [?], 32   **24**

Chapter 1   27   *Course 2*

Additional Lesson Resources

*** Also available in Spanish ELL**

Transparencies
• *5-Minute Check Transparency*, Lesson 1-3

Other Print Products
• *Noteables™ Interactive Study Notebook with Foldables™*

Teacher Tech Tools
• *Interactive Classroom CD-ROM*, Lesson 1-3
• *AssignmentWorks*, Lesson 1-3

Student Tech Tools
glencoe.com
• Extra Examples, Chapter 1, Lesson 3
• Self-Check Quiz, Chapter 1, Lesson 3

1 Focus

Vertical Alignment

Before Lesson 1-3
Understand and compute positive integer powers of nonnegative integers

Lesson 1-3
Use the inverse relationship between raising to a power and extracting the root of a perfect square

After Lesson 1-3
Multiply and divide monomials; extend the process of taking powers and extracting roots to monomials

2 Teach

Scaffolding Questions

Draw the following squares on the board: 1×1, 2×2, and 3×3.

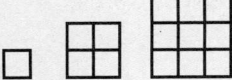

Ask:

• What is the area of the first square? 1 sq. unit

• What are two methods you could use to find the area of the second square? count the number of units or multiply length of the sides ($2 \times 2 = 4$)

• What is the area of the third square? 9 sq. units

• Could you make a square with an area of 6 square units? If not, what shape would you make that has an area of 6 square units? No; it is not possible to make a square, but you could make a rectangle.

MAIN IDEA

Find squares of numbers and square roots of perfect squares.

New Vocabulary

square
perfect squares
square root
radical sign

Math Online

glencoe.com

• Extra Examples
• Personal Tutor
• Self-Check Quiz

▷ **MINI Lab**

A square with an area of 36 square units is shown.

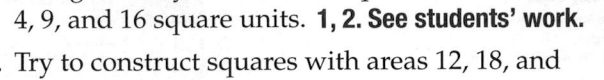

1. Using tiles, try to construct squares with areas of 4, 9, and 16 square units. **1, 2. See students' work.**

2. Try to construct squares with areas 12, 18, and 20 square units.

3. Which of the areas form squares? **4, 9, and 16 square units**

4. What is the relationship between the lengths of the sides and the areas of these squares? **The length of the side squared equals the area.**

5. Using your square tiles, create a square that has an area of 49 square units. What are the lengths of the sides of the square? **7 units**

The area of the square at the right is 5 · 5 or 25 square units. The product of a number and itself is the **square** of that number. So, the square of 5 is 25.

5 units   25 units²

5 units

EXAMPLES Find Squares of Numbers

① Find the square of 3.

$3 \cdot 3 = 9$ Multiply 3 by itself.

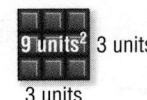

9 units² 3 units

3 units

② Find the square of 28.

METHOD 1	Use paper and pencil.
28	Multiply 28 by itself.
× 28	
224	
+ 560	Annex a zero.
784	

METHOD 2	Use a calculator.
28 $\boxed{x^2}$ $\boxed{\text{ENTER}}$ 784	

☑ **CHECK Your Progress**

Find the square of each number.

a. 8 **64**   b. 12 **144**   c. 23 **529**

Numbers like 9, 16, and 225 are called square numbers or **perfect squares** because they are squares of whole numbers.

New Vocabulary is listed at the beginning of every lesson. Review Vocabulary is listed where appropriate. Some lessons also have a Vocabulary Link, which shows how mathematical words are related to everyday words.

The factors multiplied to form perfect squares are called **square roots**. A **radical sign**, $\sqrt{}$, is the symbol used to indicate a square root of a number.

Reading Math

Square Roots Read $\sqrt{16} = 4$ as *the square root of 16 is 4.*

Square Root   Key Concept

Words   A square root of a number is one of its two equal factors.

Examples   **Numbers**   **Algebra**

$4 \cdot 4 = 16$, so $\sqrt{16} = 4$.   If $x \cdot x$ or $x^2 = y$, then $\sqrt{y} = x$.

EXAMPLES Find Square Roots

③ Find $\sqrt{81}$.

  $9 \cdot 9 = 81$, so $\sqrt{81} = 9$.   What number times itself is 81?

④ Find $\sqrt{225}$.

  [2nd] [$\sqrt{}$] 225 [ENTER] 15

  So, $\sqrt{225} = 15$.

✓ **CHECK Your Progress**

Find each square root.

d. $\sqrt{64}$ **8**

e. $\sqrt{289}$ **17**

🌐 **Real-World EXAMPLE**

⑤ **SPORTS** The infield of a baseball field is a square with an area of 8,100 square feet. What are the dimensions of the infield?

The infield is a square. By finding the square root of the area, 8,100, you find the length of one side of the infield.

$90 \cdot 90 = 8,100$, so $\sqrt{8,100} = 90$.

The length of one side of the infield is 90 feet. So, the dimensions of the infield are 90 feet by 90 feet.

Real-World Link · · · ·
The average lifespan of a major league baseball is 7 pitches.
Source: SuperKids

2nd base
Pitcher's Mound
3rd base   1st base
Home plate

✓ **CHECK Your Progress**

f. 20 ft by 20 ft

f. **SPORTS** The largest ring in amateur boxing is a square with an area of 400 square feet. What are the dimensions of the ring?

Focus on Mathematical Content

Square Roots In Example 3, both $9 \cdot 9$ and $(-9)(-9)$ equal 81. So, 81 has two square roots, 9 and -9. The radical sign, $\sqrt{}$, indicates the *positive* square root of a number. Thus, the expression $\sqrt{81}$ indicates the positive square root of 81, or 9. To indicate the *negative* square root of 81, or -9, use the expression $-\sqrt{81}$. For any positive number x, we indicate the positive square root of x by $\sqrt{x}$ and the negative square root by $-\sqrt{x}$.

✓ **Formative Assessment**

Use the Check Your Progress exercises after Examples to determine students' understanding of concepts.

ADDITIONAL EXAMPLES

① Find the square of 5. 25
② Find the square of 19. 361
③ Find $\sqrt{36}$. 6
④ Find $\sqrt{676}$. 26
⑤ **GAMES** A checkerboard is a square with an area of 1,225 square centimeters. What are the dimensions of the checkerboard? 35 cm × 35 cm

Additional Examples are also in:
• Noteables™ Interactive Study Notebook with Foldables™
• Interactive Classroom PowerPoint® Presentations

Additional Examples, which are included for every example in the Student Edition, exactly parallel the examples in the text. Step-by-step solutions for these examples are included in **Interactive Classroom** and **Noteables: Interactive Study Notebook with Foldables™.**

Tips for New Teachers

Square Roots

After presenting Example 3, you may wish to mention that every positive number has two square roots. The square roots of 81 are 9 and -9 since 9^2 is equal to 81 and $(-9)^2$ is equal to 81. The square roots of a positive number are always two numbers with the same absolute value and opposite signs, such as 9 and -9.

The square root of 0 is always 0. A negative number has no square roots, since the square of any number is at least 0.

Practice

3

Formative Assessment

Use Exercises 1–9 to check for understanding.

Then use the chart at the bottom of this page to customize your assignments for students.

Intervention You may wish to use the Study Guide and Intervention Master on page 23 of the *Chapter 1 Resource Masters* for additional reinforcement.

Odd/Even Assignments

Exercises 10–27 are structured so that students practice the same concepts whether they are assigned odd or even problems.

Differentiated Instruction

Visual/Spatial Learners If students are having difficulty visualizing the square root of a number in completing Exercises 5–8 and 18–25, have them draw square grids as geometric models. For example, in Exercise 18, have students draw a square grid containing 4 squares. Then ask them how many squares are on each side of the grid. This number represents the square root of 4.

Additional Answer

33.

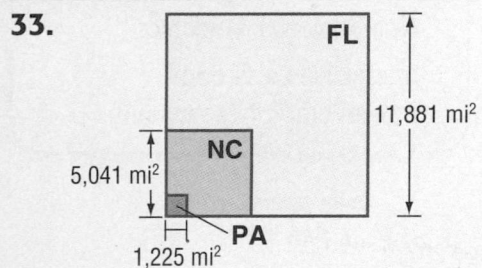

★ indicates multi-step problem

✓ CHECK Your Understanding

Examples 1, 2 (p. 34) — Find the square of each number.

1. 6 **36**   2. 10 **100**   3. 17 **289**   4. 30 **900**

Examples 3, 4 (p. 35) — Find each square root.

5. $\sqrt{9}$ **3**   6. $\sqrt{36}$ **6**   7. $\sqrt{121}$ **11**   8. $\sqrt{169}$ **13**

Example 5 (p. 35) — 9. **ROAD SIGNS** Historic Route 66 from Chicago to Los Angeles is known as the Main Street of America. If the area of a Route 66 sign measures 576 square inches and the sign is a square, what are the dimensions of the sign? **24 in. by 24 in.**

▶ Practice and Problem Solving

HOMEWORK HELP

For Exercises	See Examples
10–17	1, 2
18–25	3, 4
26–27	5

Exercise Levels
A: 10–27
B: 28–34
C: 35–39

Find the square of each number.

10. 4 **16**   11. 1 **1**   12. 7 **49**   13. 11 **121**

14. 16 **256**   15. 20 **400**   16. 18 **324**   17. 34 **1,156**

Find each square root.

18. $\sqrt{4}$ **2**   19. $\sqrt{16}$ **4**   20. $\sqrt{49}$ **7**   21. $\sqrt{100}$ **10**

22. $\sqrt{144}$ **12**   23. $\sqrt{256}$ **16**   24. $\sqrt{529}$ **23**   25. $\sqrt{625}$ **25**

26. **MEASUREMENT** Emma's bedroom is shaped like a square. What are the dimensions of the room if the area of the floor is 196 square feet? **14 ft by 14 ft**

27. **SPORTS** For the floor exercise, gymnasts perform their tumbling skills on a mat that has an area of 1,600 square feet. How much room does a gymnast have to run along one side of the mat? **40 ft**

28. What is the square of 12? **144**   29. Find the square of 19. **361**

★ 30. **GARDENING** A square garden has an area of 225 square feet. How much fencing will a gardener need to buy in order to place fencing around the garden? **60 ft**

GEOGRAPHY For Exercises 31–33, refer to the squares in the diagram. They represent the approximate areas of Florida, North Carolina, and Pennsylvania.

31. What is the area of North Carolina in square miles? **53,824 mi²**

32. How much larger is Florida than Pennsylvania? **19,311 mi²**

EXTRA PRACTICE
See pages 668, 704.

33. The water areas of Florida, North Carolina, and Pennsylvania are 11,881 square miles; 5,041 square miles; and 1,225 square miles, respectively. Make a similar diagram comparing the water areas of these states. **See margin.**

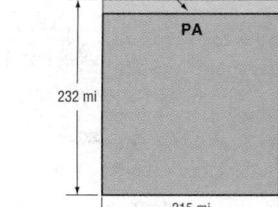

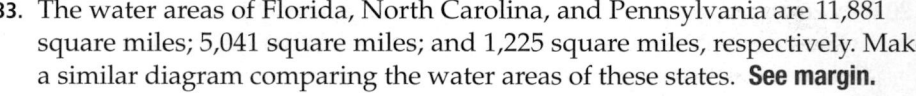

DIFFERENTIATED HOMEWORK OPTIONS

Level	Assignment	Two-Day Option	
BL Basic	10–27, 36, 39–50	11–27 odd, 40–41	10–26 even, 36, 39, 42–50
OL Core	11–25 odd, 26–34, 36, 39–50	10–27, 40–41	28–34, 36, 39, 42–50
AL Advanced/Pre-AP	28–46 (optional: 47–50)		

★ 34. **MEASUREMENT** A chessboard has an area of 324 square inches. There is a 1-inch border around the 64 squares on the board. What is the length of one side of the region containing the small squares? **16 in.**

35. **MEASUREMENT** The area of a square that is 7 meters by 7 meters is how much greater than the area of a square containing 8 square meters? Explain.
41 m² greater; The area of a 7 by 7 square has an area of 49 m².

H.O.T. Problems

37. Yes; For example, a pen that measures 10 feet by 10 feet has the same perimeter, but its area is 100 square feet, which is greater than 84 square feet.

38. See margin.

36. **OPEN ENDED** Write a number whose square is between 100 and 150.
Sample answer: 12

CHALLENGE For Exercises 37 and 38, use the diagram shown.

37. Could the area of the dog's pen be made larger using the same amount of fencing? Explain.

38. Describe the largest pen area possible using the same amount of fencing. How do the perimeter and area compare to the original pen?

6 ft

14 ft

39. **WRITING IN MATH** Explain why raising a number to the second power is called *squaring* the number. **Sample answer: It is called squaring the number because the area of a square is found by multiplying the two side lengths together.**

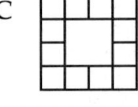

TEST PRACTICE

40. Which model represents the square of 4? **D**

A [figure]   C [figure]

B [figure]   D [figure]

41. Which measure can be the area of a square if the measure of the side length is a whole number? **J**

F   836 sq ft

G   949 sq ft

H   1,100 sq ft

J   1,225 sq ft

Spiral Review

Write each power as a product of the same factor. (Lesson 1-2)

42. 3^4 **3 • 3 • 3 • 3**   43. 8^5 **8 • 8 • 8 • 8 • 8**   44. 7^2 **7 • 7**   45. 2^6 **2 • 2 • 2 • 2 • 2 • 2**

46. **SHIPPING** Jocelyn spent a total of $24 to ship 4 packages. If the packages are equal in size and weight, how much did it cost to ship each package? (Lesson 1-1) **$6**

▷ **GET READY for the Next Lesson**

PREREQUISITE SKILL Add, subtract, multiply, or divide.

47. $13 + 8$ **21**   48. $10 - 6$ **4**   49. 5×6 **30**   50. $36 \div 4$ **9**

4 Assess

Name the Math Have students describe a real-world problem that involves finding either the square or square root of a number. Make sure students identify the operation as "finding the square" or "finding the square root."

Formative Assessment

Check for student understanding of concepts in Lessons 1-1 through 1-3.

CRM Quiz 1, p. 77

Additional Answer

38. A square that measures 10 feet on each side; the perimeter is the same, and the area is 100 square feet, or 16 square feet greater than that of the original pen.

Pre-AP Activity   Use after Exercise 39.

Ask students what they think the cube of a number is. Ask them what they think the cube root of a number is. Have them give examples and relate the concepts to squares and square roots.

1-4 Order of Operations

PACING: **Regular:** 1 period, **Block:** 0.5 period

Options for Differentiated Instruction

ELL = English Language Learner   **AL** = Above or Beyond Grade Level   **SS** = Struggling Students   **SN** = Special Needs

Assessing Students' Understanding **SS** **SN**

Use after presenting Examples 1 and 2.

A common misconception regarding the order of operations is that multiplication is always done before division instead of working left to right, and that addition is always done before subtraction instead of working left to right. To assess students' understanding of the order of operations, display the following expressions on the board or overhead and have students evaluate them.

$20 \div 2 \times 5$ 50 $7 - 3 + 4$ 8

Extensions and Challenges **AL**

Use after completing the lesson.

Insert the symbols $+$, $-$, $\times$, or $\div$ to make each sentence true. Sample answers are given.

$2\ 2\ 2\ 2 = 0$	$2 + 2 - 2 - 2 = 0$
$2\ 2\ 2\ 2 = 1$	$2 - 2 + 2 \div 2 = 1$
$2\ 2\ 2\ 2 = 2$	$2 \div 2 + 2 \div 2 = 2$
$2\ 2\ 2\ 2 = 3$	$2 \times 2 - 2 \div 2 = 3$
$2\ 2\ 2\ 2 = 4$	$2 \times 2 + 2 - 2 = 4$
$2\ 2\ 2\ 2 = 5$	$2 + 2 + 2 \div 2 = 5$

Creating Problems **ELL** **AL**

Use after completing the lesson.

Organize small groups of students with different learning abilities. Have them write problems that can be solved using the order of operations. Encourage them to include some real-life problems related to activities that interest them. Have groups trade problems and work through them.

After students complete each other's word problems, have the class share their work and discuss the different strategies they used to complete the problems.

Leveled Lesson Resources

Chapter 1 Resource Masters

BL = Below or Approaching Grade Level   **OL** = On Grade Level   **AL** = Above or Beyond Grade Level   **ELL** = English Language Learner

Lesson Reading Guide
p. 29 **BL OL ELL**

1-4 Lesson Reading Guide
Order of Operations

Get Ready for the Lesson
Read the introduction at the top of page 38 in your textbook. Write your answers below.

1. List the differences between their calculations. **Megan multiplied 4 by 3 and then added 6. Dexter added 6 and 4, and then multiplied the result by 3.**

2. Whose calculations are correct? **Megan**

3. Make a conjecture about what should be the first step in simplifying 6 + 4 · 3. **Multiply 4 by 3.**

Read the Lesson

4. Why did mathematicians agree on an order of operations? **so that numerical expressions would have only one value**

5. What are three ways to indicate multiplication in a mathematical expression? **×, ·, and parentheses**

Remember What You Learned

6. In your own words, describe the order of operations that is used in finding the value of a mathematical expression.
1. Do all operations within grouping symbols first.
2. Evaluate all powers before other operations.
3. Multiply and divide in order from left to right.
4. Add and subtract in order from left to right.

Chapter 1   29   Course 2

Study Guide and Intervention*
p. 30 **BL OL ELL**

1-4 Study Guide and Intervention
Order of Operations

Use the **order of operations** to evaluate numerical expressions.
1. Evaluate the expressions inside grouping symbols.
2. Evaluate all powers.
3. Multiply and divide in order from left to right.
4. Add and subtract in order from left to right.

Example 1 Evaluate $(10 - 2) - 4 \cdot 2$.

$(10 - 2) - 4 \cdot 2 = 8 - 4 \cdot 2$ Subtract first since 10 − 2 is in parentheses.
$= 8 - 8$ Multiply 4 and 2.
$= 0$ Subtract 8 from 8.

Example 2 Evaluate $8 + (1 + 5)^2 + 4$.

$8 + (1 + 5)^2 + 4 = 8 + 6^2 + 4$ First, add 1 and 5 inside the parentheses.
$= 8 + 36 + 4$ Find the value of 6^2.
$= 8 + 9$ Divide 36 by 4.
$= 17$ Add 8 and 9.

Exercises

Evaluate each expression.

1. $(1 + 7) \times 3$ **24**
2. $28 - 4 \cdot 7$ **0**
3. $5 + 4 \cdot 3$ **17**

4. $(40 \div 5) - 7 + 2$ **3**
5. $35 + 7(2)$ **10**
6. 3×10^3 **3,000**

7. $45 + 5 + 36 \div 4$ **18**
8. $42 \div 6 \times 2 - 9$ **5**
9. $2 \times 8 - 3^2 + 2$ **9**

10. $5 \times 2^2 + 32 \div 8$ **24**
11. $3 \times 6 - (9 - 8)^3$ **17**
12. 3.5×10^2 **350**

Chapter 1   30   Course 2

Skills Practice*
p. 31 **BL OL**

1-4 Skills Practice
Order of Operations

Evaluate each expression.

1. $9 - 3 + 4$ **10**
2. $8 + 6 - 5$ **9**
3. $12 + 4 + 5$ **8**

4. $25 \times 2 - 7$ **43**
5. $36 + 9(2)$ **8**
6. $6 + 3(7 - 2)$ **21**

7. $3 \times 6.2 + 5^2$ **43.6**
8. $(1 + 11)^2 + 3$ **48**
9. $12 - (2 + 8)$ **2**

10. $15 - 24 \div 4 \cdot 2$ **3**
11. $(4 + 2) \cdot (7 + 4)$ **66**
12. $(3 \cdot 18) + (2 \cdot 9)$ **2**

13. $24 + 6 + 4^2$ **20**
14. $3 \times 8 - (9 - 7)^3$ **16**
15. $9 + (9 - 8 + 3)^4$ **265**

16. $3 \times 2^2 + 24 + 8$ **15**
17. $(15 + 3)^2 + 9 + 3$ **28**
18. $(52 + 4) + 5^3$ **138**

19. 26×10^3 **26,000**
20. 7.2×10^2 **720**
21. $5 \times 4^2 - 3 \times 2$ **74**

22. $24 + 6 + 2$ **2**
23. $13 - (6 - 5)^3$ **12**
24. $(8 - 3 \times 2) \times 6$ **12**

25. $(11 \cdot 4 - 10) + 2$ **17**
26. $10 + 2 \times (4 - 3)$ **5**
27. 1.82×10^5 **182,000**

28. $35 + 7 \times 2 - 4$ **6**
29. $2^5 + 7(9 - 1)$ **88**
30. $12 + 16 \div (3 + 1)$ **16**

Chapter 1   31   Course 2

Practice*
p. 32 **OL AL**

1-4 Practice
Order of Operations

Evaluate each expression.

1. $(2 + 9) \times 4$ **44**
2. $8 - (5 + 2)$ **1**
3. $(15 + 3) + 7$ **12**

4. $(14 + 7) + 7$ **3**
5. $5 \cdot 6 - 12 + 4$ **27**
6. $8 + 2 + 8 - 2$ **10**

7. $16 - 8 + 2 + 5$ **17**
8. $15 - 3 \cdot 5 + 7$ **7**
9. 7×10^3 **7,000**

10. $2 \times 5^2 + 6$ **56**
11. $7 \cdot 2^3 - 9$ **47**
12. $27 + 3 \times 2 + 4^2$ **34**

13. $6^2 - 12 \times 4 \cdot 3$ **72**
14. $(15 - 3) + (8 + 4)$ **1**
15. $(9 - 4) \cdot (7 - 7)$ **0**

16. $8 + 3(5 + 2) - 7 \cdot 2$ **15**
17. $5(6 - 1) - 4 \cdot 6 + 3$ **17**
18. $(5 + 7)^2 + 12$ **12**

19. $12 + (8 - 6)^2$ **3**
20. $(7 + 2)^2 + 3^2$ **9**
21. $(11 - 9)^2 \cdot (8 - 5)^2$ **36**

22. $64 + 8 - 3(4 - 3) + 2$ **7**
23. $8 \times 5.1 - (4.1 + 1.4) + 7.1$ **42.4**

For Exercises 24 and 25, write an expression for each situation. Then evaluate the expression to find the solution.

24. **LAWN AREA** The Solomons need to find the area of their front and side yards since they want to reseed the lawn. Both side yards measure 3 meters by 10 meters, while the front yard is a square with side of 9 meters. They do not need to reseed a portion of the front yard covering 16 square meters where a flower bed is located. What is the area of the yard that the Solomons want to reseed?
$2(3 \times 10) + 9^2 - 16 = 125$; The area is 125 m².

25. **COMMUNITY SERVICE** Jariah volunteers at the hospital during the week. She volunteers 3 hours on Monday and Thursday, 4 hours on Saturday and Sunday, and 2 hours on Tuesday. How many hours does Jariah volunteer at the hospital during the week?
$2 \cdot 3 + 2 \cdot 4 + 2 = 16$; Jariah volunteers 16 hours a week.

Chapter 1   32   Course 2

Word Problem Practice*
p. 33 **OL AL**

1-4 Word Problem Practice
Order of Operations

1. **FOOTBALL** The middle school team scored three field goals worth three points each and two touchdowns with extra points worth seven points each. Write a numerical expression to find the team's score. Then evaluate the expression. **3(3) + 2(7); 23 points**

2. **BOOKS** Juan goes to the school book fair where paperback books are $1.50 and hardback books are $3.00. Juan buys 5 paperback and 2 hardback books. Write a numerical expression to find how much Juan paid for the books. Then evaluate the expression. **5(1.5) + 2(3); $13.50**

3. **GEOMETRY** The perimeter of a hexagon is found by adding the lengths of all six sides of the hexagon. For the hexagon below write a numerical expression to find the perimeter. Then evaluate the expression. **4(5) + 2(8); 36**

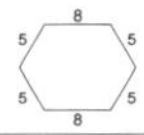

4. **MONEY** Aisha bought school supplies consisting of 5 spiral notebooks costing $0.39 each, 2 packages of pencils at $0.79 each, and a 3-ring binder for $1.99. Write an expression to find the total amount Aisha spent on school supplies. Then evaluate the expression. **6 × 0.39 + 2 × 0.79 + 1.99; $5.91**

5. **REASONING** Use the order of operations and the digits 2, 4, 6, and 8 to create an expression with a value of 2. **Sample answer: $4^2 - (8 + 6)$**

6. **NUMBER SENSE** Without parentheses, the expression $8 + 30 - 2 + 4$ equals 27. Place parentheses in the expression so that it equals 13; then 23.
$8 + 30 \div (2 + 4); (8 + 30) - 2 + 4$

7. **MONEY** Tyrone bought 5 postcards at $0.55 each and a set of postcards for $1.20. Write an expression to find the total amount Tyrone spent on postcards. Then evaluate the expression. **5(0.55) + 1.2; $3.95**

8. **DINING** Mr. Firewalks took his family out to eat. They ordered 3 meals costing $8.99 each, 2 sodas at $1.50 each, and 1 glass of tea for $1.25. Write an expression to find the total amount the Firewalks family spent on dinner before taxes and tip. Then evaluate the expression. **3(8.99) + 2(1.5) + 1.25; $31.22**

Chapter 1   33   Course 2

Enrichment
p. 34 **OL AL**

1-4 Enrichment
Nested Expressions

Sometimes more than one set of parentheses are used to group the quantities in an expression. These expressions are said to have "nested" parentheses. The expression below has "nested" parentheses.

$(4 + (3 \cdot (2 + 3)) + 8) + 9$

Expressions with several sets of grouping symbols are clearer if braces such as { } or brackets such as [ ] are used. Here is the same example written with brackets and braces.

$\{4 + [3 \cdot (2 + 3)] + 8\} + 9$

To evaluate expressions of this type, work from the inside out.

$\{4 + [3 \cdot (2 + 3)] + 8\} + 9 = \{4 + [3 \cdot 5] + 8\} + 9$
$= [4 + 15 + 8] + 9$
$= 27 + 9$
$= 3$

Evaluate each expression.

1. $3 + [(24 + 8) \cdot 7] - 20$ **4**
2. $[(16 - 7 + 5) + 2] - 7$ **0**

3. $[2 \cdot (23 - 6) + 14] + 6$ **8**
4. $50 - [3 \cdot (15 - 5)] + 25$ **45**

5. $12 + [28 - [2 \cdot (11 - 7)] + 3]$ **35**
6. $[75 + 3 \cdot](17 - 9) + 2)] \cdot 2$ **174**

7. $20 + [3 \cdot [6 + (56 + 8)]]$ **59**
8. $[4 + [5 \cdot (12 - 5)] + 15] \cdot 10$ **540**

9. $[15 \cdot [(38 - 26) + 4]] - 15$ **30**
10. $[[34 + (6 \cdot 5)] \div 8] + 40$ **48**

Chapter 1   34   Course 2

Additional Lesson Resources

Also available in Spanish **ELL**

Transparencies
- *5-Minute Check Transparency,* Lesson 1-4

Other Print Products
- *Noteables™ Interactive Study Notebook with Foldables™*

Teacher Tech Tools
- *Interactive Classroom CD-ROM,* Lesson 1-4
- *AssignmentWorks,* Lesson 1-4

Student Tech Tools
glencoe.com
- Extra Examples, Chapter 1, Lesson 4
- Self-Check Quiz, Chapter 1, Lesson 4

1-4 Order of Operations

1 Focus

Vertical Alignment

Before Lesson 1-4
Understand and compute positive integer powers of nonnegative integers

Lesson 1-4
Apply algebraic order of operations to evaluate expressions. Solve problems manually by using the correct order of operations

After Lesson 1-4
Use the correct order of operations to evaluate algebraic expressions

2 Teach

Scaffolding Questions

Write the following expression on the board: $5 + 3 \times 4$.

Ask:

• What is the value of the expression if you add first? 32

• What is the value of the expression if you multiply first? 17

• How do you know which operation to perform first? order of operations

Additional Answers

1. Megan multiplied 4 by 3 and then added 6. Dexter added 6 and 4 and then multiplied the result by 3.

a. Sample answer: Add first, since $9 + 4$ is in parentheses. Then divide 39 by 13.

b. Sample answer: Divide first, because division comes before addition or subtraction. Then add 10 and subtract 6 in order from left to right.

MAIN IDEA
Evaluate expressions using the order of operations.

New Vocabulary
numerical expression
order of operations

Math Online
glencoe.com
• Extra Examples
• Personal Tutor
• Self-Check Quiz
• Reading in the Content Area

▷ **GET READY** for the Lesson

SPORTS The Kent City football team made one 6-point touchdown and four 3-point field goals in its last game. Megan and Dexter each use an expression to find the total number of points the team scored.

Megan	Dexter
$6 + 4 \cdot 3 = 6 + 12$	$(6 + 4) \cdot 3 = 10 \cdot 3$
$= 18$	$= 30$
The team scored 18 points.	The team scored 30 points.

1. List the differences between their calculations. **See margin.**

2. Whose calculations are correct? **Megan**

3. Make a conjecture about what should be the first step in simplifying $6 + 4 \cdot 3$. **Multiply 4 by 3.**

The expression $6 + 4 \cdot 3$ is a **numerical expression**. To evaluate expressions, use the **order of operations**. These rules ensure that numerical expressions have only one value.

Order of Operations   Key Concept

1. Evaluate the expressions inside grouping symbols.
2. Evaluate all powers.
3. Multiply and divide in order from left to right.
4. Add and subtract in order from left to right.

EXAMPLES Use Order of Operations

① Evaluate $5 + (12 - 3)$. Justify each step.

$5 + (12 - 3) = 5 + 9$	Subtract first, since $12 - 3$ is in parentheses.
$= 14$	Add 5 and 9.

② Evaluate $8 - 3 \cdot 2 + 7$. Justify each step.

$8 - 3 \cdot 2 + 7 = 8 - 6 + 7$	Multiply 3 and 2.
$= 2 + 7$	Subtract 6 from 8.
$= 9$	Add 2 and 7.

✓ **CHECK Your Progress**   a–b. See margin for justification.

Evaluate each expression. Justify each step.

a. $39 \div (9 + 4)$ **3**   b. $10 + 8 \div 2 - 6$ **8**

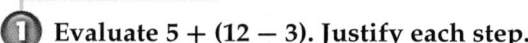
Web addresses, or URLs, are provided to point students to online assets such as **Personal Tutor, Extra Examples, Self-Check Quizzes** and **Concepts in Motion.**

Lesson 1-4 Order of Operations **39**

Study Tip

Scientific Calculators
If you have a scientific calculator, you can enter numbers and operations in order from left to right. The scientific calculator follows the order of operations.

 EXAMPLE **Use Order of Operations**

3 Evaluate $5 \cdot 3^2 - 7$. Justify each step.

$$5 \cdot 3^2 - 7 = 5 \cdot 9 - 7 \quad \text{Find the value of } 3^2.$$
$$= 45 - 7 \quad \text{Multiply 5 and 9.}$$
$$= 38 \quad \text{Subtract 7 from 45.}$$

✓ CHECK Your Progress c–d. See margin for justification.

c. 3×10^4 **30,000**   d. $(5 - 1)^3 \div 4$ **16**

In addition to using the symbols $\times$ and $\cdot$, multiplication can be indicated by using parentheses. For example, $2(3 + 5)$ means $2 \times (3 + 5)$.

 EXAMPLE **Use Order of Operations**

4 Evaluate $14 + 3(7 - 2)$. Justify each step.

$$14 + 3(7 - 2) = 14 + 3(5) \quad \text{Subtract 2 from 7.}$$
$$= 14 + 15 \quad \text{Multiply 3 and 5.}$$
$$= 29 \quad \text{Add 14 and 15.}$$

✓ CHECK Your Progress

e. $20 - 2(4 - 1) \cdot 3$ **2**   f. $6 + 8 \div 2 + 2(3 - 1)$ **14**

e–f. See justification at left.

e. Subtract first, since $4 - 1$ is in parentheses. Next, multiply by 2 and multiply by 3 in order from left to right. Finally, subtract the product from 20.

f. Subtract first, since $3 - 1$ is in parentheses. Next, divide 8 by 2 and multiply 2 by 2 in order from left to right. Finally, add 6, 4, and 4.

Real-World EXAMPLE

5 **MONEY** Julian orders crepe paper, balloons, and favors for the school dance. What is the total cost?

Item	Quantity	Unit Cost
crepe paper	3 rolls	$2
favors	2 boxes	$7
balloons	4 boxes	$5

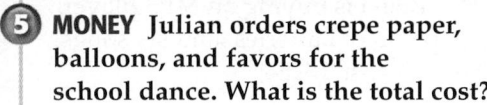

Words	cost of 3 rolls of crepe paper	+	cost of 4 boxes of balloons	+	cost of 2 boxes of favors
Expression	3×2	+	4×5	+	2×7

$$3 \times 2 + 4 \times 5 + 2 \times 7 = 6 + 20 + 14 \quad \text{Multiply from left to right.}$$
$$= 40 \quad \text{Add.}$$

The total cost is $40.

Real-World Link · · · ·
Crepe paper originated in the late 1700s. It was critical to the invention of masking tape! The texture allows the tape to partially adhere to the surface, making it easily removable.
Source: Wilsonart International

✓ CHECK Your Progress

g. What is the total cost of twelve rolls of crepe paper, three boxes of balloons, and three boxes of favors? **$60**

Lesson 1-4 Order of Operations **39**

 Focus on Mathematical Content

Order of Operations Sometimes it is necessary to evaluate powers before evaluating an expression inside grouping symbols. For example, when evaluating the expression $2(4^3 + 5)$, it is necessary to evaluate 4^3 before evaluating the expression inside the parentheses.

✓ Formative Assessment

Use the Check Your Progress exercises after each Example to determine students' understanding of concepts.

ADDITIONAL EXAMPLES

1 Evaluate $27 - (18 + 2)$. 7

2 Evaluate $15 + 5 \cdot 3 - 2$. 28

3 Evaluate $12 \times 3 - 2^2$. 32

4 Evaluate $28 \div (3 - 1)^2$. 7

5 **VIDEO GAMES** Use the table shown in Example 5 in the Student Edition. Julian is buying one box of favors, one box of balloons, and three rolls of crepe paper. What is the total cost? $18

Additional Examples are also in:

- Noteables™ Interactive Study Notebook with Foldables™
- Interactive Classroom PowerPoint® Presentations

Additional Answers

c. Evaluate 10^4 first because it is a power. Then multiply by 3.

d. Subtract first, since $5 - 1$ is in parentheses. Then evaluate the power. Finally, divide by 4.

Formative Assessment

Use Exercises 1–9 to check for understanding. Then use the chart at the bottom of this page to customize your assignments for students.

Intervention You may wish to use the Study Guide and Intervention Master on page 30 of the *Chapter 1 Resource Masters* for additional reinforcement.

Odd/Even Assignments

Exercises 10–29 are structured so that students practice the same concepts whether they are assigned odd or even problems.

Order of Operations

A common mnemonic for helping students remember the order of operations is, "*P*lease *e*xcuse *m*y *d*ear *A*unt *S*ally." The first letters of each word stand for *parentheses, exponents, multiply, divide, add,* and *subtract.* Stress to students that multiplication and division is *always* evaluated in the order that the expression is written. In the expression $15 \div 5 \times 2$, students *must* first divide before multiplying. The same is true for addition and subtraction. In the expression $10 - 7 + 3$, students must subtract before adding.

Scientific Calculators

Scientific calculators are useful for evaluating expressions. Encourage students to become familiar with using a scientific calculator in some of the exercises, especially in understanding how to enter entries correctly.

Check Your Understanding exercises are intended to be completed in class. **Example references** show students where to look back for review. In the Exercises, **Homework Help** boxes function in the same way.

★ indicates multi-step problem

 CHECK Your Understanding

Evaluate each expression. Justify each step. 1–8. See Ch. 1 Answer Appendix for justification.

Examples 1, 2 (p. 38)

1. $8 + (5 - 2)$ **11**
2. $25 \div (9 - 4)$ **5**
3. $14 - 2 \cdot 6 + 9$ **11**
4. $8 \cdot 5 - 4 \cdot 3$ **28**

Examples 3, 4 (p. 39)

5. 4×10^2 **400**
6. $45 \div (4 - 1)^2$ **5**
7. $17 + 2(6 - 3) - 3 \times 4$ **11**
8. $22 - 3(8 - 2) + 12 \div 4$ **7**

Example 5 (p. 39)

★ 9. **COINS** Isabelle has 3 nickels, 2 quarters, 2 dimes, and 7 pennies. Write an expression that can be used to find how much money Isabelle has altogether. How much money does Isabelle have?
$3(0.05) + 2(0.25) + 2(0.10) + 7(0.01)$; **$0.92**

Practice and Problem Solving

10–27. See Ch. 1 Answer Appendix for justification.

Evaluate each expression. Justify each step.

HOMEWORK HELP

For Exercises	See Examples
10–17	1, 2
18–23	3
24–27	4
28, 29	5

10. $(1 + 8) \times 3$ **27**
11. $10 - (3 + 4)$ **3**
12. $(25 \div 5) + 8$ **13**
13. $(11 - 2) \div 9$ **1**
14. $3 \cdot 2 + 14 \div 7$ **8**
15. $4 \div 2 - 1 + 7$ **8**
16. $12 + 6 \div 3 - 4$ **10**
17. $18 - 3 \cdot 6 + 5$ **5**
18. 6×10^2 **600**
19. 3×10^4 **30,000**
20. $5 \times 4^3 + 2$ **322**
21. $8 \times 7^2 - 6$ **386**
22. $8 \div 2 \times 6 + 6^2$ **60**
23. $9^2 - 14 \div 7 \cdot 3$ **75**
24. $(17 + 3) \div (4 + 1)$ **4**
25. $(6 + 5) \cdot (8 - 6)$ **22**
26. $6 + 2(4 - 1) + 4 \times 9$ **48**
27. $3(4 + 7) - 5 \cdot 4 \div 2$ **23**

Exercise Levels
A: 10–29
B: 30–34
C: 35–37

For Exercises 28 and 29, write an expression for each situation. Then evaluate to find the solution.

28. **MP3 PLAYERS** Reina is buying an MP3 player, a case, three packs of batteries, and six songs. What is the total cost? **$254**

Item	Quantity	Unit Cost
MP3 player	1	$200
case	1	$30
pack of batteries	3	$4
songs	6	$2

29. **BOOKS** Ian goes to the library's used book sale. Paperback books are $0.25, and hardback books are $0.50. If Ian buys 3 paperback books and 5 hardback books, how much does he spend? **$3.25**

Evaluate each expression. Justify each step.

30–33. See Ch. 1 Answer Appendix for justification.

30. $(2 + 10)^2 \div 4$ **36**
31. $(3^3 + 8) - (10 - 6)^2$ **19**
32. $3 \cdot 4(5.2 + 3.8) + 2.7$ **110.7**
33. $7 \times 9 - (4 - 3.2) + 1.8$ **64**

EXTRA PRACTICE

See pages 669, 704.

★ 34. **MONEY** Suppose that your family orders 2 pizzas, 2 orders of garlic bread, and 1 order of BBQ wings from Mario's Pizza Shop. Write an expression to find the amount of change you would receive from $30. Then evaluate the expression. $30 - (2 \times 8 + 2 \times 2 + 4)$; **$6**

Mario's Pizza Shop	
Item	**Cost**
14" pizza	$8
garlic bread	$2
BBQ wings	$4

40 Chapter 1 Introduction to Algebra and Functions

DIFFERENTIATED HOMEWORK OPTIONS

Level	Assignment	Two-Day Option	
BL Basic	10–29, 35, 36, 38–45	11–29 odd, 38–40	10–28 even, 35, 36, 38, 41–45
OL Core	11–27 odd, 28, 29, 31, 33, 34–36, 38–45	10–29, 38–40	30–36, 41–45
AL Advanced/Pre-AP	30–44 (optional: 45)		

H.O.T. Problems

35. Peggy; the first step is to do the division, 24 ÷ 6. Phoung incorrectly multiplied 6 and 2 first.

35. **FIND THE ERROR** Phoung and Peggy are evaluating $16 - 24 \div 6 \cdot 2$. Who is correct? Explain your reasoning.

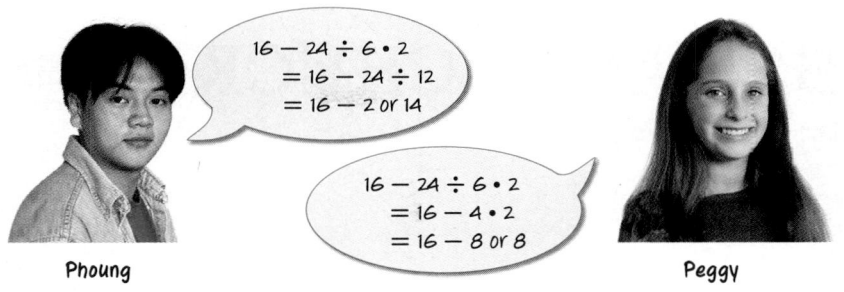

Phoung

$16 - 24 \div 6 \cdot 2$
$= 16 - 24 \div 12$
$= 16 - 2 \text{ or } 14$

$16 - 24 \div 6 \cdot 2$
$= 16 - 4 \cdot 2$
$= 16 - 8 \text{ or } 8$

Peggy

36. $72 \div (9 + 27) -$
$2 = 0$

36. **CHALLENGE** Insert parentheses to make $72 \div 9 + 27 - 2 = 0$ a true statement.

37. **WRITING IN MATH** Write a real-world problem in which you would need to use the order of operations or a scientific calculator to solve it.
See students' work.

TEST PRACTICE

38. Simplify $3^2 + 9 \div 3 + 3$. **C**

   A 3   C 15
   B 9   D 18

39. Grace has 2 boxes that contain 24 straws each and 3 boxes that contain 15 cups each. Which expression *cannot* be used to find the total number of items she has? **H**

   F $2(24) + 3(15)$
   G $3 \times 15 + 2 \times 24$
   H $5 \times (24 + 15)$
   J $15 + 15 + 15 + 24 + 24$

40. The steps Alana took to evaluate the expression $4y + 4 \div 4$ when $y = 7$ are shown below.

   $4y + 4 \div 4$ when $y = 7$
   $4 \times 7 = 28$
   $28 + 4 = 32$
   $32 \div 4 = 8$

   What should Alana have done differently in order to evaluate the expression correctly? **C**

   A divided $(28 + 4)$ by (28×4)
   B divided $(28 + 4)$ by $(28 + 4)$
   C added $(4 \div 4)$ to 28
   D added 4 to $(28 \div 4)$

Spiral Review

Find each square root. (Lesson 1-3)

41. $\sqrt{64}$ **8**   42. $\sqrt{2,025}$ **45**   43. $\sqrt{784}$ **28**

44. **INTERNET** Each day, Internet users perform 2^5 million searches using a popular search engine. How many searches is this? (Lesson 1-2) **32 million**

▷ **GET READY for the Next Lesson**

45. **PREREQUISITE SKILL** A Chinese checkerboard has 121 holes. How many holes can be found on eight Chinese checkerboards? (Lesson 1-1) **968**

Lesson 1-4 Order of Operations   **41**

⚠ **Exercise Alert!**

Find the Error Exercise 35 illustrates that by not following the order of operations, Phoung found the wrong answer. Remind students to multiply and divide in order from left to right. Multiplication does not automatically come before division.

4 Assess

Crystal Ball Tell students that tomorrow's lesson is about using the guess and check strategy to solve word problems. Have students write how they think what they learned today will connect with tomorrow's lesson.

FOLDABLES
Study Organizer

Foldables™ Follow-Up

Suggest to students that they summarize the order of operations in their Foldables for this chapter. They might include an example illustrating how to use the order of operations to evaluate expressions.

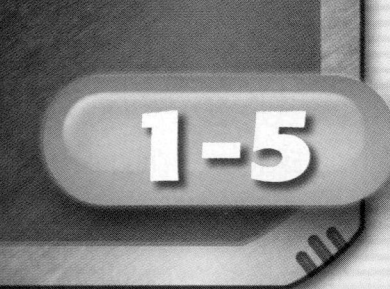

Problem-Solving Investigation
GUESS AND CHECK

PACING: **Regular:** 1 period, **Block:** 0.5 period

Options for Differentiated Instruction

ELL = English Language Learner   **AL** = Above or Beyond Grade Level   **SS** = Struggling Students   **SN** = Special Needs

Visual Learners   **ELL** **SS** **SN**

Use while presenting Lesson 1-5.

Have students hang butcher block paper or large packing paper on the wall. Use this paper to make a table to chart the *guess and check* strategy used on page 42.

Number of cars	Number of SUVs	Total Cost ($)	Too High or Too Low?
5	5	$5(5) + 7(5) = \$60$	too high
5	4	$5(5) + 7(4) = \$49$	too low
6	4	$5(6) + 7(4) = \$58$	correct

Have students check reasonable answers rather than guess randomly.

Making Study Tools   **ELL** **SS**

Use after presenting Lesson 1-5.

Have students create a personal problem-solving booklet. Have them include a description, examples, the best time to use, and advantages and disadvantages of the following problem-solving strategies.
- Use the four-step plan
- Guess and check

Have students add new strategies to the booklet as they are introduced.

Organizing Student Work and Thinking   **SS** **SN**

Use with Exercise 3.

Students with learning disabilities often have difficulty organizing information.
Provide a table like the one below for students to organize their work as they solve Exercise 3.

Number of Adults	Number of Students	Total Cost ($)	Too High or Too Low?

Leveled Lesson Resources

Chapter 1 Resource Masters

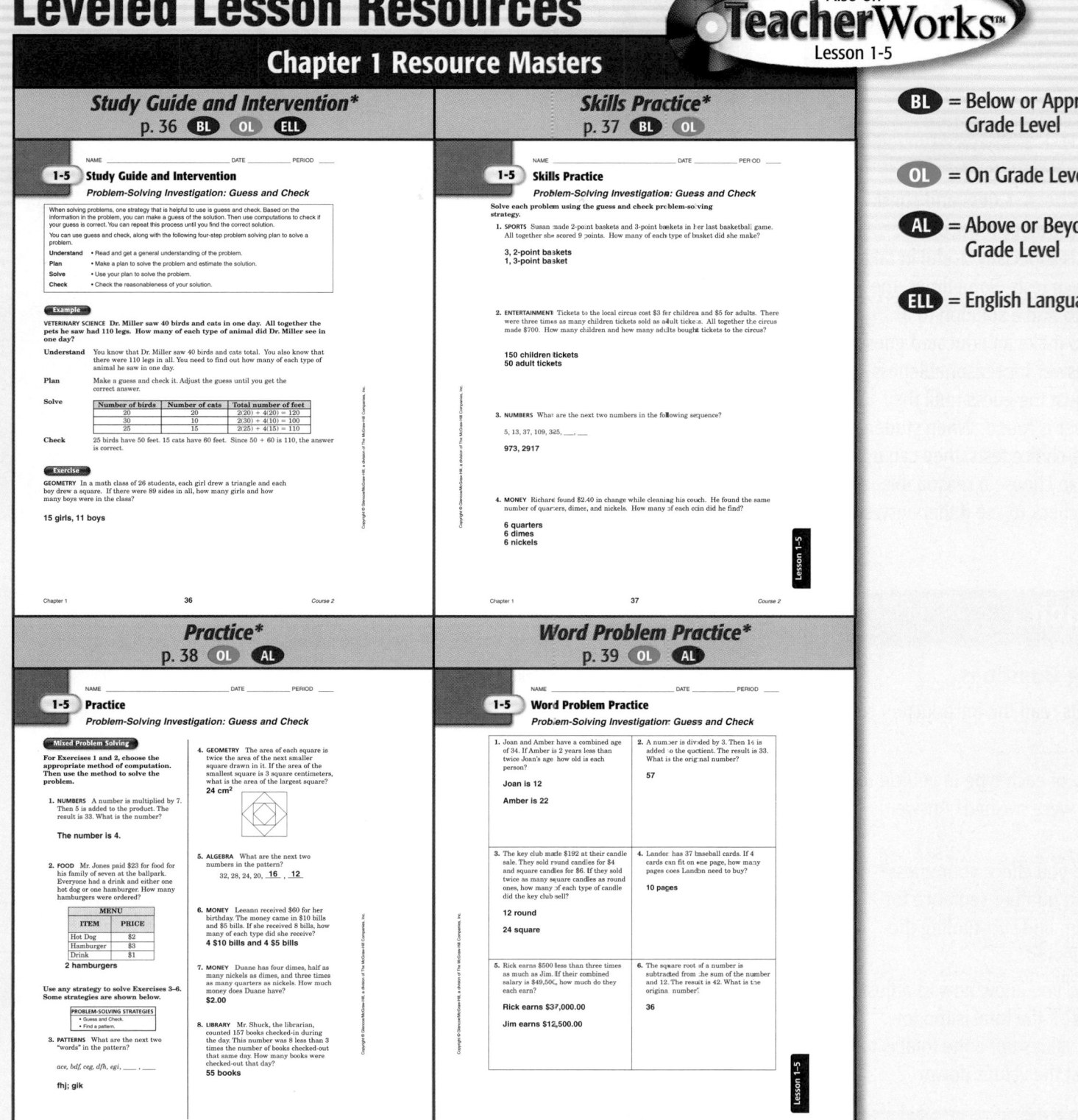

Study Guide and Intervention*
p. 36 BL OL ELL

Skills Practice*
p. 37 BL OL

Practice*
p. 38 OL AL

Word Problem Practice*
p. 39 OL AL

BL = Below or Approaching Grade Level

OL = On Grade Level

AL = Above or Beyond Grade Level

ELL = English Language Learner

* Also available in Spanish ELL

Additional Lesson Resources

Transparencies
• *5-Minute Check Transparency,* Lesson 1-5

Other Print Products
• *Noteables™ Interactive Study Notebook with Foldables™*

Teacher Tech Tools
• *Interactive Classroom CD-ROM,* Lesson 1-5
• *AssignmentWorks,* Lesson 1-5

Student Tech Tools
glencoe.com
• Extra Examples, Chapter 1, Lesson 5
• Self-Check Quiz, Chapter 1, Lesson 5

1-5 Lesson Notes

MAIN IDEA: Solve problems using the guess and check strategy.

1 Focus

Guess and Check Guess and check is an important strategy for problem solving, and is especially useful in taking multiple-choice tests. Sometimes, the easiest way to find a solution to a problem is to make an educated guess, check the answer for reasonableness, and then adjust the guess until the correct answer is found. When students take multiple-choice tests, they can use this strategy to choose a reasonable answer and check to see if that answer is correct.

2 Teach

Scaffolding Questions

Have students read the introduction to the lesson.

- How many of each type of vehicle do you guess were washed? **Answers will vary.**

- How could you check your guess? **by writing a number sentence for the problem and substituting the values I guessed**

- How would you know how to adjust your guess? **If the total is too low, adjust the values up; if the total is too high, adjust the values down.**

ADDITIONAL EXAMPLE

Solve. Use the *guess and check* strategy.

CONCESSIONS The concession stand at the school play sold lemonade for $0.50 and cookies for $0.25. They sold 7 more lemonades than cookies, and they made a total of $39.50. How many lemonades and cookies were sold?
55 lemonades; 48 cookies

P.S.I. TEAM +

e-Mail: GUESS AND CHECK

TREVOR: My soccer team held a car wash to help pay for a trip to a tournament. We charged $5 for a car and $7 for an SUV. During the first hour, we washed 10 vehicles and earned $58.

YOUR MISSION: Use guess and check to find how many of each type of vehicle were washed.

Understand	You know car washes are $5 for cars and $7 for SUVs. Ten vehicles were washed for $58.
Plan	Make a guess and check it. Adjust the guess until you get the correct answer.
Solve	Make a guess.
	5 cars and **5** SUVs $5(5) + 7(5) = \$60$ too high
	Adjust the number of SUVs downward.
	5 cars and **4** SUVs $5(5) + 7(4) = \$53$ too low
	Adjust the number of cars upward.
	6 cars and **4** SUVs $5(6) + 7(4) = \$58$ correct ✔
	So, 6 cars and 4 SUVs were washed.
Check	Six cars cost $30, and four SUVs cost $28. Since $30 + \$28 = \$58$, the guess is correct.

Analyze The Strategy

1. Explain why you should keep a careful record of each of your guesses. **See margin.**

2. **WRITING IN MATH** Write a problem that could be solved by guess and check. Then write the steps you would take to find the solution to your problem. **See Ch. 1 Answer Appendix.**

Additional Examples are also in:
- Noteables™ Interactive Study Notebook with Foldables™
- Interactive Classroom PowerPoint® Presentations

Additional Answer

1. Sample answer: You need to keep track of what numbers you have already guessed, so that you do not make the same guess twice. You also need to know what numbers produce answers that are too large or too small, so you can make better guesses.

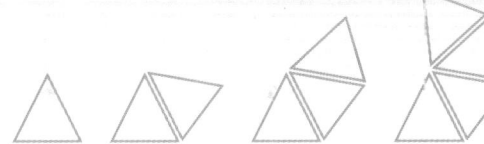

EXTRA PRACTICE
See pages 669, 704.

Use the *guess and check* strategy to solve Exercises 3–6.

3. **TICKET SALES** The total ticket sales for the
★ school basketball game were $1,625. Adult tickets were $7, and student tickets were $3. Twice as many students bought tickets as adults. How many adult and student tickets were sold?
125 adult tickets and 250 student tickets

4. **NUMBERS** A number is multiplied by 6. Then
★ 4 is added to the product. The result is 82. What is the number? **13**

5. **ANALYZE TABLES** Camila is transferring her
★ home videos onto a DVD. Suppose the DVD holds 60 minutes. Which videos should Camila select to have the maximum time on the DVD without going over?

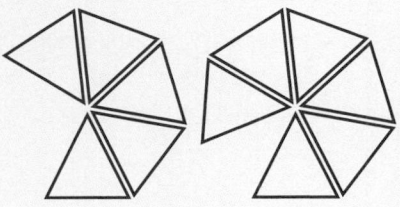

Video	Time
birthday	25 min 15 s
family picnic	18 min 10 s
holiday	15 min 20 s
vacation	19 min 20 s

birthday, holiday, and vacation

6. **MONEY** Susan has $1.60 in change in her
★ purse. If she has an equal number of nickels, dimes, and quarters, how many of each does she have?
Susan has 4 nickels, 4 dimes, and 4 quarters.

Use any strategy to solve Exercises 7–13. Some strategies are shown below.

PROBLEM-SOLVING STRATEGIES
· Guess and check.
· Find a pattern.

7. **BRIDGES** The total length of wire used in the
★ cables supporting the Golden Gate Bridge in San Francisco is about 80,000 miles. This is 5,300 miles longer than three times the distance around Earth at the Equator. What is the distance around Earth at the Equator?
See margin.

8. **GEOMETRY** What are the next two figures in the pattern? **See margin.**

9. **ALGEBRA** What are the next two numbers in the pattern? **512 and 1,024**

16, 32, 64, 128, 256, ■ , ■

10. **FRUIT** Mason places 4 apples and 3 oranges into each fruit basket he makes. If he has used 24 apples and 18 oranges, how many fruit baskets has he made? **6**

11. **ANALYZE TABLES** The table gives the average
★ snowfall, in inches, for Valdez, Alaska, for the months of October through April.

Month	Snowfall
October	11.6
November	40.3
December	73.0
January	65.8
February	59.4
March	52.0
April	22.7

Source: National Climatic Data Center

How many inches total of snowfall could a resident of Valdez expect to receive from October to April? **324.8 in. of snow**

12. **ROLLER COASTERS** The Jackrabbit roller
★ coaster can handle 1,056 passengers per hour. The coaster has 8 vehicles. If each vehicle carries 4 passengers, how many runs are made in one hour? **See margin.**

13. **NUMBERS** Della is thinking of 3 numbers from 1 through 9 with a product of 36. Find the numbers. **2, 3, 6**

---

3 Practice

Using the Exercises

Exercises 1 and 2 can be used to check for understanding.

Exercises 3–6 require students to determine first whether they can compute mentally or need to use a pencil and paper.

Exercises 7–13 are structured so that students have the opportunity to practice many different problem-solving strategies. You may wish to review some of the strategies they have studied.

• Use the four-step plan p. 25
• Guess and check p. 42

4 Assess

Yesterday's News Remind students that yesterday's lesson was about the order of operations. Ask students to write how the order of operations helped them to solve today's problems.

Formative Assessment

Check for student understanding of concepts in Lessons 1-4 and 1-5.

[CRM] Quiz 2, p. 77

Problem-Solving Investigations help students learn different problem-solving strategies for attacking word problems.

Additional Answers

7. The circumference of the Earth is 24,900 miles long at the Equator.

8.

12. Thirty-three runs are made in one hour.

1-6 Algebra: Variables and Expressions

PACING: **Regular:** 1 period,   **Block:** 0.5 period

Options for Differentiated Instruction

 = English Language Learner   = Above or Beyond Grade Level   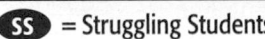 = Struggling Students   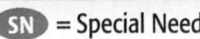 = Special Needs

Using Symbols 

Use after presenting Examples 1–4.

Make sure students understand that in word problems, there is nothing special about the letters that are used for variables. Point out that it is common to use letters signifying the object being replaced, such as using *a* for age. However, this is merely a convenience.

- Have students practice writing expressions with different variables to become accustomed to using a variety of letters.
- Have ELL students write the following words in their primary language and choose variables to represent the quantities: age, time, number.

Using Math Games

Use before assigning the Exercises.

Write each of the numbers 1-15 on a separate index card and place the cards in a bag. Write ten different rules, each on a separate index card and place those cards in a different bag. Three examples of rules are shown below.

Find a number plus 2.	**Double a number, and then subtract 1.**	**Multiply a number by itself, and then add 3.**

Pick one card from each bag and ask students to use the number on the card and the mathematical rule to calculate the answer. The first person to raise his or her hand and give the correct answer gets a point. For each round, choose a new number for the same rule, choose a new rule for the same number, or choose both a new number and a new rule. The student with the most points after the predetermined time is the winner.

Make the connection that playing this game is the same as evaluating expressions. The rules above represent $n + 2$, $2n - 1$, and $n^2 + 3$, respectively.

Leveled Lesson Resources

Chapter 1 Resource Masters

BL = Below or Approaching Grade Level   **OL** = On Grade Level   **AL** = Above or Beyond Grade Level   **ELL** = English Language Learner

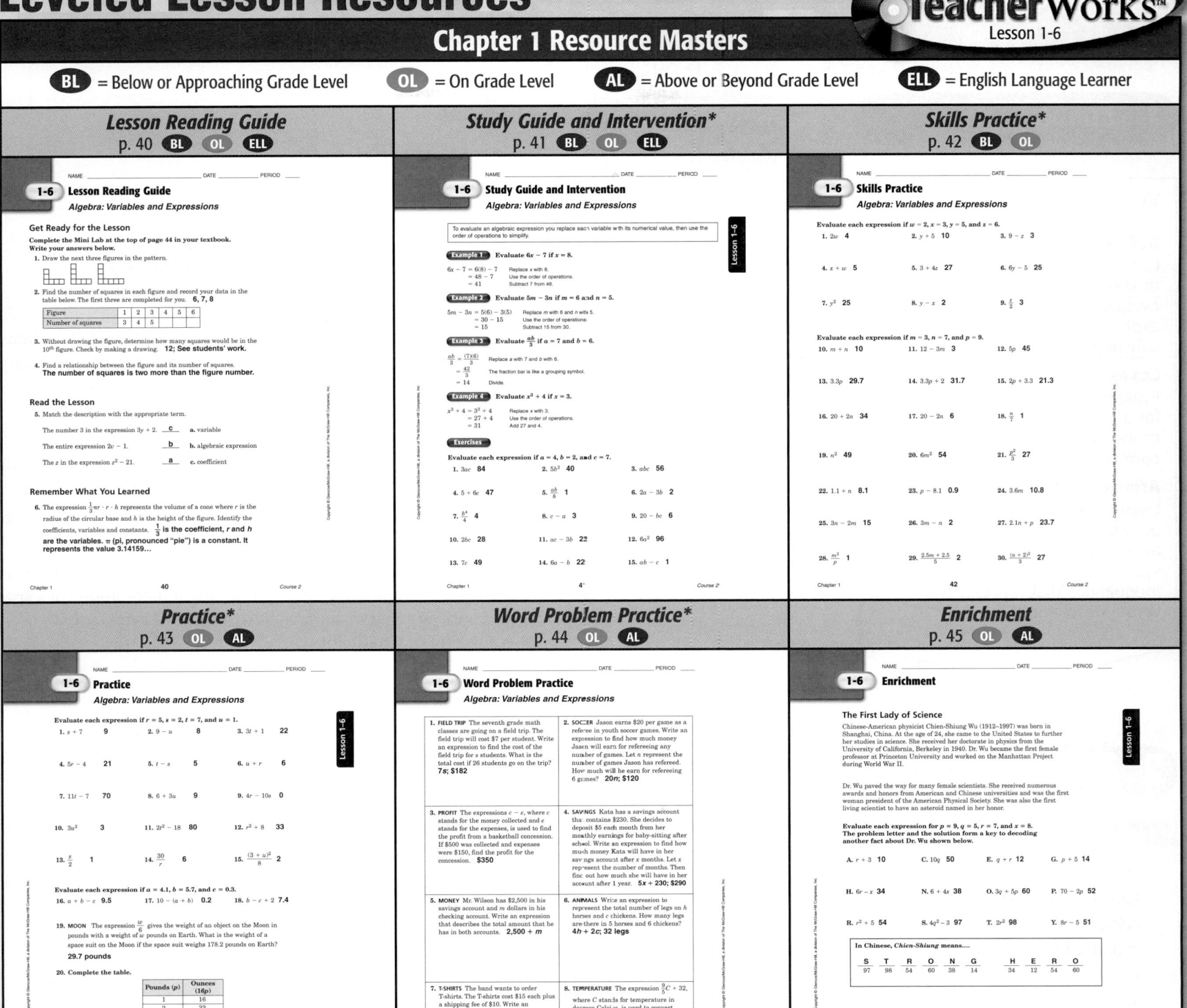

Lesson Reading Guide
p. 40 **BL** **OL** **ELL**

Study Guide and Intervention*
p. 41 **BL** **OL** **ELL**

Skills Practice*
p. 42 **BL** **OL**

Practice*
p. 43 **OL** **AL**

Word Problem Practice*
p. 44 **OL** **AL**

Enrichment
p. 45 **OL** **AL**

* Also available in Spanish **ELL**

Additional Lesson Resources

Transparencies
- *5-Minute Check Transparency,* Lesson 1-6

Other Print Products
- *Teaching Mathematics with Manipulatives*
- *Noteables™ Interactive Study Notebook with Foldables™*

Teacher Tech Tools
- *Interactive Classroom CD-ROM,* Lesson 1-6
- *AssignmentWorks,* Lesson 1-6

Student Tech Tools
glencoe.com
- Extra Examples, Chapter 1, Lesson 6
- Self-Check Quiz, Chapter 1, Lesson 6

Lesson Notes 1-6

1 Focus

Vertical Alignment

Before Lesson 1-6
Use a letter to represent an unknown number; write and evaluate simple algebraic expressions in one variable by substitution

Lesson 1-6
Evaluate an algebraic expression for a given situation. Solve problems manually by using the correct order of operations

After Lesson 1-6
Use variables and appropriate operations to write an expression, an equation, an inequality, or a system of equations or inequalities that represents a verbal description

2 Teach

▷ MINI Lab

• The purpose of the lab is to find a relationship between two series of numbers and to express that relationship algebraically.

• Provide isometric dot paper for students to complete the drawing activity in the Mini Lab.

Scaffolding Questions

Ask:

• What does the word *variable* mean in an everyday context? subject to change

• What do you think *variable* means in math? a letter or symbol with no fixed quantitative value

---

MAIN IDEA

Evaluate simple algebraic expressions.

New Vocabulary

variable
algebra
algebraic expression
coefficient

Math Online ▷

glencoe.com

• Concepts In Motion
• Extra Examples
• Personal Tutor
• Self-Check Quiz

▷ MINI Lab

A pattern of squares is shown.

1. Draw the next three figures in the pattern.

2. Find the number of squares in each figure and record your data in a table like the one shown below. The first three are completed for you.

Figure	1	2	3	4	5	6
Number of Squares	3	4	5	6	■ 7	■ 8

3. Without drawing the figure, determine how many squares would be in the 10th figure. Check by making a drawing.

4. Find a relationship between the figure and its number of squares.

1, 3, and 4. See Ch. 1 Answer Appendix.

In the Mini Lab, you found that the number of squares in the figure is two more than the figure number. You can use a placeholder, or variable, to represent the number of squares. A **variable** is a symbol that represents an unknown quantity.

$$\text{figure number} \longrightarrow \underline{n + 2}$$
$$\longrightarrow \text{number of squares}$$

The branch of mathematics that involves expressions with variables is called **algebra**. The expression $n + 2$ is called an **algebraic expression** because it contains variables, numbers, and at least one operation.

EXAMPLE **Evaluate an Algebraic Expression**

① Evaluate $n + 3$ if $n = 4$.

$n + 3 = 4 + 3$ Replace n with 4.

     $= 7$ Add 4 and 3.

✓ CHECK Your Progress

Evaluate each expression if $c = 8$ and $d = 5$.

a. $c - 3$ **5**   b. $15 - c$ **7**   c. $c + d$ **13**

• Why are *variables* important in math? They can be used whenever you do not know a number or when the number could change based on the situation.

Tips for New Teachers **Algebraic Expressions**

Students may require additional practice reading and writing algebraic expressions. For example, the phrase *two less than m* can be written as $m - 2$. The expression $\frac{a}{2}$ can be read *a divided by 2, the quotient of a and 2,* or *half of a.*

In algebra, the multiplication sign is often omitted.

$$6d \qquad 9st \qquad mn$$

6 times d 9 times s times t m times n

The numerical factor of a multiplication expression that contains a variable is called a **coefficient**. So, 6 is the coefficient of $6d$.

EXAMPLES   Evaluate Expressions

2   **Evaluate $8w - 2v$ if $w = 5$ and $v = 3$.**

$8w - 2v = 8(5) - 2(3)$ Replace w with 5 and v with 3.

$\quad\quad\quad = 40 - 6$ Do all multiplications first.

$\quad\quad\quad = 34$ Subtract 6 from 40.

3   **Evaluate $4y^2 + 2$ if $y = 3$.**

$4y^2 + 2 = 4(3)^2 + 2$ Replace y with 3.

$\quad\quad\quad = 4(9) + 2$ Evaluate the power.

$\quad\quad\quad = 38$ Multiply, then add.

✓ CHECK Your Progress

Evaluate each expression if $a = 4$ and $b = 3$.

d. $9a - 6b$ **18**   e. $\dfrac{ab}{2}$ **6**   f. $2a^2 + 5$ **37**

The fraction bar is a grouping symbol. Evaluate the expressions in the numerator and denominator separately before dividing.

🌐 Real-World EXAMPLE

4   **HEALTH**   **Use the formula at the left to find Latrina's minimum training heart rate if she is 15 years old.**

$\dfrac{3(220 - a)}{5} = \dfrac{3(220 - 15)}{5}$ Replace a with 15.

$\quad\quad\quad = \dfrac{3(205)}{5}$ Subtract 15 from 220.

$\quad\quad\quad = \dfrac{615}{5}$ Multiply 3 and 205.

$\quad\quad\quad = 123$ Divide 615 by 5.

Latrina's minimum training heart rate is 123 beats per minute.

✓ CHECK Your Progress

g.   **MEASUREMENT**   To find the area of a triangle, you can use the formula $\dfrac{bh}{2}$, where h is the height and b is the base. What is the area in square inches of a triangle with a height of 6 inches and base of 8 inches? **24 in²**

Real-World Link . . . .
Athletic trainers use the formula $\dfrac{3(220 - a)}{5}$, where a is a person's age, to find their minimum training heart rate.
Source: CMPMedica Ltd.

Focus on Mathematical Content

In an algebraic expression, a **variable** represents an unknown number or numbers. Make sure students understand there is nothing special about which letters are used for variables. It is common to use letters signifying the object being replaced, such as *a* for *age*. However, this is merely a convenience. Have students practice using expressions with different variables to become accustomed to using a variety of letters.

To evaluate an algebraic expression, replace the variables with their given values and follow the **order of operations**.

✓ Formative Assessment

Use the Check Your Progress exercises after the Examples to determine students' understanding of concepts.

ADDITIONAL EXAMPLES

1   Evaluate $t - 4$ if $t = 6$. **2**

2   Evaluate $5x + 3y$ if $x = 7$ and $y = 9$. **62**

3   Evaluate $5 + a^2$ if $a = 5$. **30**

4   **TEMPERATURE**   The formula for rewriting a Fahrenheit temperature as a Celsius temperature is $\dfrac{5(F - 32)}{9}$, where F equals the temperature in degrees Fahrenheit. Find the Celsius equivalent of 99°F. about 37.2°C

Additional Examples are also in:

- Noteables™ Interactive Study Notebook with Foldables™

- Interactive Classroom PowerPoint® Presentations

3 Practice

Formative Assessment

Use Exercises 1–13 to check for understanding.

Then use the chart at the bottom of this page to customize your assignments for students.

Intervention You may wish to use the Study Guide and Intervention Master on page 41 of the *Chapter 1 Resource Masters* for additional reinforcement.

Odd/Even Assignments

Exercises 14–31 are structured so that students practice the same concepts whether they are assigned odd or even problems.

★ indicates multi-step problem

✓ CHECK Your Understanding

Example 1
(p. 44)

Evaluate each expression if $a = 3$ and $b = 5$.

1. $a + 7$ **10**
2. $8 - b$ **3**
3. $b - a$ **2**

4. **HEALTH** The standard formula for finding your maximum heart rate is $220 - a$, where a represents a person's age in years. What is your maximum heart rate? **See students' work.**

Examples 2–4
(p. 45)

Evaluate each expression if $m = 2$, $n = 6$, and $p = 4$.

5. $6n - p$ **32**
6. $7m - 2n$ **2**
7. $3m + 4p$ **22**
8. $n^2 + 5$ **41**
9. $15 - m^3$ **7**
10. $3p^2 - n$ **42**
11. $\frac{mn}{4}$ **3**
12. $\frac{3n}{9}$ **2**
13. $\frac{5n + m}{8}$ **4**

▶ Practice and Problem Solving

HOMEWORK HELP	
For Exercises	**See Examples**
14–29	1–3
30–31	4

Exercise Levels
A: 14–31
B: 32–38
C: 39–41

Evaluate each expression if $d = 8$, $e = 3$, $f = 4$, and $g = 1$.

14. $d + 9$ **17**
15. $10 - e$ **7**
16. $4f + 1$ **17**
17. $8g - 3$ **5**
18. $f - e$ **1**
19. $d + f$ **12**
20. $10g - 6$ **4**
21. $8 + 5d$ **48**
22. $\frac{d}{5}$ **1.6**
23. $\frac{16}{f}$ **4**
24. $\frac{5d - 25}{5}$ **3**
25. $\frac{(5 + g)^2}{2}$ **18**
26. $6f^2$ **96**
27. $4e^2$ **36**
28. $d^2 + 7$ **71**
29. $e^2 - 4$ **5**

★ 30. **BOWLING** The expression $5n + 2$ can be used to find the total cost in dollars of bowling where n is the number of games bowled. How much will it cost Vincent to bowl 3 games? **$17**

31. **HEALTH** The expression $\frac{w}{30}$, where w is a person's weight in pounds, is used to find the approximate number of quarts of blood in the person's body. How many quarts of blood does a 120-pound person have? **4 quarts**

Evaluate each expression if $x = 3.2$, $y = 6.1$, and $z = 0.2$.

32. $x + y - z$ **9.1**
33. $14.6 - (x + y + z)$ **5.1**
34. $xz + y^2$ **37.85**

35. **CAR RENTAL** A car rental company charges $19.99 per day and $0.17 per mile to rent a car. Write an expression that gives the total cost in dollars to rent a car for d days and m miles. **$19.99d + 0.17m$**

36. **MUSIC** A Web site charges $0.99 to download a song onto an MP3 player and $12.49 to download an entire album. Write an expression that gives the total cost in dollars to download a albums and s songs. **$12.49a + 0.99s$**

46 Chapter 1 Introduction to Algebra and Functions

DIFFERENTIATED HOMEWORK OPTIONS

Level	Assignment	Two-Day Option	
BL Basic	14–31, 39, 41–52	15–31 odd, 42, 43	14–30 even, 39, 41, 44–52
OL Core	15–29 odd, 30, 31, 33, 35, 37–39, 41–52	14–31, 42, 43	32–39, 41, 44–52
AL Advanced/Pre-AP	32–49 (optional: 50–52)		

★ 37. **SCIENCE** The expression $\frac{32t^2}{2}$ gives the falling distance of an object in feet after t seconds. How far would a bungee jumper fall 2 seconds after jumping? **64 ft**

★ 38. **GEOMETRY** To find the total number of diagonals for any given polygon, you can use the expression $\frac{n(n-3)}{2}$, where n is the number of sides of the polygon. What is the total number of diagonals for a 10-sided polygon? **35**

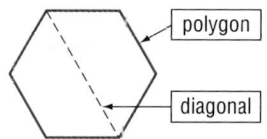

EXTRA PRACTICE
See pages 669, 704.

H.O.T. Problems

39. **OPEN ENDED** Write an algebraic expression with the variable x that has a value of 3 when evaluated. **Sample answer: $5x - 37$ if $x = 8$**

40. **CHALLENGE** Name values of x and y so that the value of $5x + 3$ is greater than the value of $2y + 14$. **Sample answer: $x = 15$, $y = 30$**

41. **WRITING IN MATH** Tell whether the statement below is *sometimes*, *always*, or *never* true. Justify your reasoning.

The expressions $x - 3$ and $y - 3$ represent the same value.
Sometimes; Sample answer: $x - 3$ and $y - 3$ represent the same value only when $x = y$.

TEST PRACTICE

42. Which expression could be used to find the cost of buying b books at $7.95 each and m magazines at $4.95 each? **A**

   A $7.95b + 4.95m$

   B $7.95b - 4.95m$

   C $12.9(b + m)$

   D $12.9(bm)$

43. Tonya has x quarters, y dimes, and z nickels in her pocket. Which of the following expressions gives the total amount of change she has in her pocket? **G**

   F $\$0.25x + \$0.05y + \$0.10z$

   G $\$0.25x + \$0.10y + \$0.05z$

   H $\$0.05x + \$0.25y + \$0.10z$

   J $\$0.10x + \$0.05y + \$0.25z$

Spiral Review

44. **SHOPPING** A grocery store sells hot dog buns in packages of 8 and 12. How many 8-packs and 12-packs could you buy if you needed 44 hot dog buns? Use the *guess and check* strategy. (Lesson 1-5) **three 12-packs and one 8-pack, or four 8-packs and one 12-pack**

Evaluate each expression. (Lesson 1-4)

45. $6(5) - 2$ **28**   46. $9 + 9 \div 3$ **12**   47. $4 \cdot 2(8 - 1)$ **56**   48. $(17 + 3) \div 5$ **4**

49. Find $\sqrt{361}$. (Lesson 1-3) **19**

▷ **GET READY** for the Next Lesson

PREREQUISITE SKILL Determine whether each sentence is *true* or *false*. (Lesson 1-4)

50. $15 - 2(3) = 9$ **true**   51. $20 \div 5 \times 4 = 1$ **false**   52. $4^2 + 6 \cdot 7 = 154$ **false**

Name the Math Have students describe a word problem with a variable (or variables). Make sure they identify the variable.

The Four-step Teaching Plan shows you how to Focus, Teach, Practice, and Assess each lesson. Each lesson ends with a creative strategy for closing the lesson.

CHAPTER
1 **Mid-Chapter Quiz**
Lessons 1-1 through 1-6

 Formative Assessment

Use the Mid-Chapter Quiz to assess students' progress in the first half of the chapter.

Have students review the lesson indicated for the problems they answered incorrectly.

 Summative Assessment

[CRM] Mid-Chapter Test, p. 79

ExamView
Assessment Suite
Customize and create multiple versions of your Mid-Chapter Test and their answer keys.

FOLDABLES
Study Organizer
Dinah Zike's Foldables

Before students complete the Mid-Chapter Quiz, encourage them to review the information on the first three pages of their Foldables.

The Mid-Chapter Quiz reviews skills and concepts presented in previous lessons. Students' results on the quiz can be used for Data-Driven Decision Making.

---

1. **MULTIPLE CHOICE** A cycling club is planning an 1,800-mile trip. The cyclers average 15 miles per hour. What additional information is needed to determine the number of days it will take them to complete the trip? (Lesson 1-1) **C**

   A The number of cyclists in the club

   B The number of miles of rough terrain

   C The number of hours they plan to cycle each day

   D Their average speed per minute

Write each power as a product of the same factor. (Lesson 1-2)

2. 4^5 **4 · 4 · 4 · 4 · 4**   3. 9^6 **9 · 9 · 9 · 9 · 9 · 9**

4. **OCEANS** The world's largest ocean, the Pacific Ocean, covers approximately 4^3 million square miles. Write this area in standard form. (Lesson 1-2) **64 million mi²**

5. **ZOOS** The Lincoln Park Zoo in Illinois is 2 · 2 · 2 · 2 · 2 · 2 · 2 years old. Write this age in exponential form. (Lesson 1-2) **2^7 yr**

6. **MULTIPLE CHOICE** The model below represents $\sqrt{49} = 7$.

   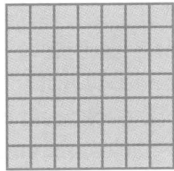

   Which arrangement of small squares can be used to model a large square that represents $\sqrt{324}$? (Lesson 1-3) **G**

   F 9 rows of 36 squares

   G 18 rows of 18 squares

   H 12 rows of 27 squares

   J 6 rows of 54 squares

Find the square of each number. (Lesson 1-3)

7. 4 **16**   8. 12 **144**

Find each square root. (Lesson 1-3)

9. $\sqrt{64}$ **8**   10. $\sqrt{289}$ **17**

11. **LANDSCAPING** A bag of lawn fertilizer covers 2,500 square feet. Describe the largest square that one bag of fertilizer could cover. (Lesson 1-3) **50 ft by 50 ft**

Evaluate each expression. (Lesson 1-4)

12. $25 - (3^2 + 2 \times 5)$ **6**   13. $\dfrac{2(7-3)}{2^2}$ **2**

14. **MEASUREMENT** The perimeter of a rectangle
★ is 42 inches, and its area is 104 square inches. Find the dimensions of the rectangle. Use the *guess and check* strategy. (Lesson 1-5) **8 in. by 13 in.**

15. **MULTIPLE CHOICE** Ana buys some baseball bats at \$35 each and some baseball gloves at \$48 each. Which expression could be used to find the total cost of the sports items? (Lesson 1-6) **C**

   A $35b \cdot 48g$

   B $\dfrac{35b}{48g}$

   C $35b + 48g$

   D $48g - 35b$

Evaluate each expression if $x = 12$, $y = 4$, and $z = 8$. (Lesson 1-6)

16. $x - 5$ **7**   17. $3y + 10z$ **92**

18. $\dfrac{yz}{2}$ **16**   19. $\dfrac{(y+8)^2}{x}$ **12**

20. **HEALTH** A nurse can use the expression
★ $110 + \dfrac{A}{2}$, where A is a person's age, to estimate a person's normal systolic blood pressure. Estimate the normal systolic blood pressure for a 16-year-old. (Lesson 1-6) **118**

Data-Driven Decision Making	**Exercises**	**Lesson**	**State/Local Standards**	**Resources for Review**
	1	1-1		[CRM] Study Guide and Intervention pp. 10, 16, 23, 30, 36, and 41
Diagnostic Teaching Based on the results of the Chapter 1 Mid-Chapter Quiz, use the following to review concepts that students continue to find challenging.	2–5	1-2		**Math Online** glencoe.com
	6–11	1-3		• Extra Examples
	12, 13	1-4		• Personal Tutor
	14	1-5		• Concepts in Motion
	15–20	1-6		

1-7 Algebra: Equations

PACING: **Regular:** 1 period, **Block:** 0.5 period

Options for Differentiated Instruction

ELL = English Language Learner **AL** = Above or Beyond Grade Level **SS** = Struggling Students **SN** = Special Needs

---

Connections to Prior Knowledge **SN** **SS**

Use before presenting the lesson.

It is helpful if students are able to make connections between concepts with which they are familiar and algebra. Being able to do so can make new algebraic concepts seem less intimidating. Write the following equations on the board.

■ + 3 = 7

■ − 2 = 6

■ ÷ 2 = 5

3 × ■ = 18

Ask:
* What number can be written in each box to make the equation true? 4; 8; 10; 6
* Have you seen problems like this before? If so, when?

Building Vocabulary **ELL** **SS** **SN**

Use while presenting the lesson.

Have students use one index card for each new vocabulary term and create a *vocabulary index*. On each card, have students define or describe the term in their own words and give an example of the term. They should file all the cards alphabetically in their index. Have students keep their index on their desks so they have easy access to definitions.

Kinesthetic Learner **ELL** **AL**

Use before assigning the Exercises.

Have students work in groups of three. Have them write a simple equation such as $n + \$0.05 = \$0.10$. Then have them use actual coins to model the equation and solve for n.

$n + $  $=$

Have students take turns writing an equation, modeling it, and solving for n. Encourage them to challenge each other with difficult equations.

Leveled Lesson Resources

Chapter 1 Resource Masters

BL = Below or Approaching Grade Level   **OL** = On Grade Level   **AL** = Above or Beyond Grade Level   **ELL** = English Language Learner

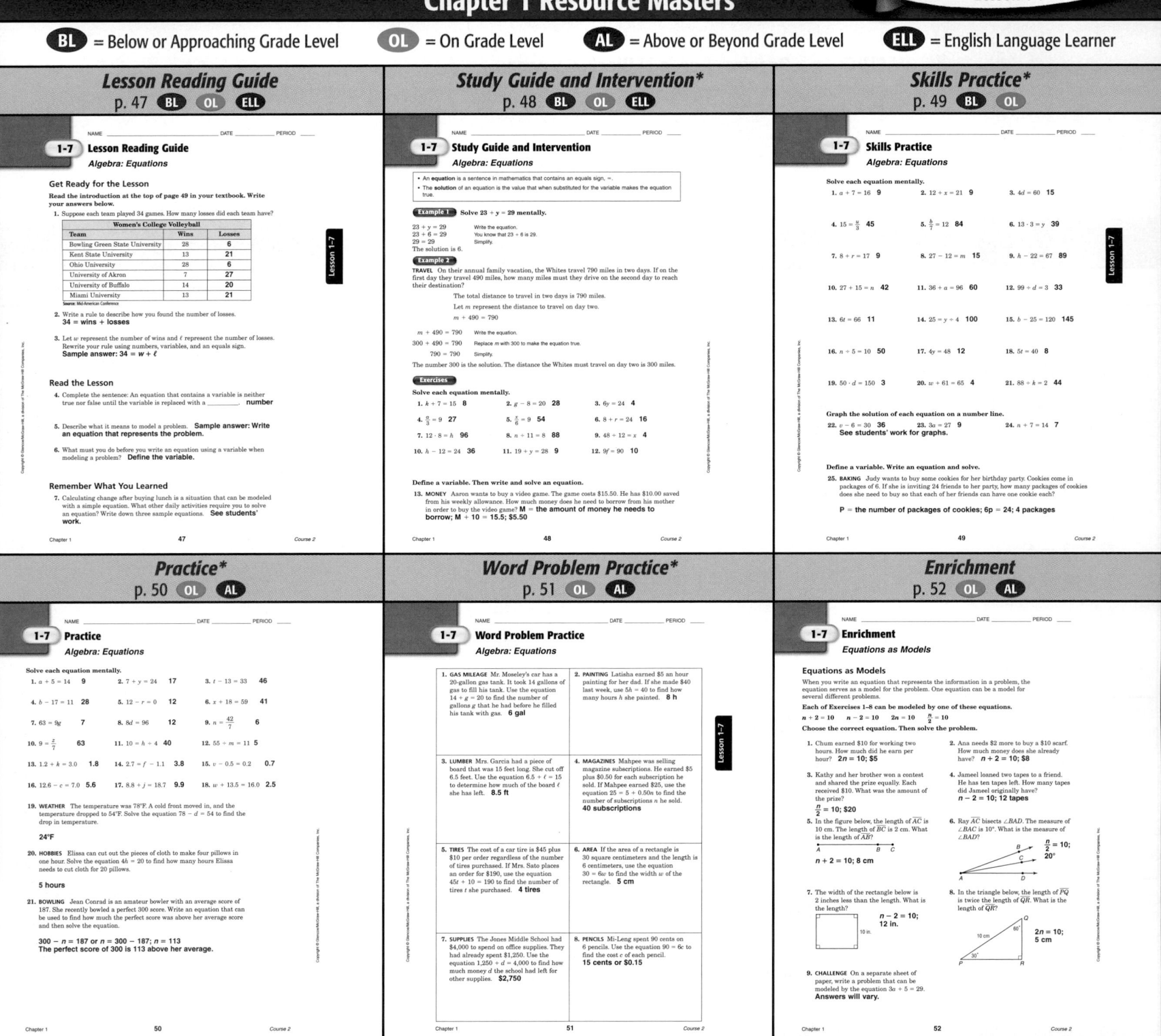

Lesson Reading Guide
p. 47 **BL OL ELL**

1-7 Lesson Reading Guide
Algebra: Equations

Get Ready for the Lesson
Read the introduction at the top of page 49 in your textbook. Write your answers below.

1. Suppose each team played 34 games. How many losses did each team have?

Women's College Volleyball		
Team	**Wins**	**Losses**
Bowling Green State University	28	6
Kent State University	13	21
Ohio University	28	6
University of Akron	7	27
University of Buffalo	14	20
Miami University	13	21

Source: Mid-American Conference

2. Write a rule to describe how you found the number of losses.
34 = wins + losses

3. Let w represent the number of wins and ℓ represent the number of losses. Rewrite your rule using numbers, variables, and an equals sign. **Sample answer: 34 = w + ℓ**

Read the Lesson

4. Complete the sentence: An equation that contains a variable is neither true nor false until the variable is replaced with a _____. **number**

5. Describe what it means to model a problem. **Sample answer: Write an equation that represents the problem.**

6. What must you do before you write an equation using a variable when modeling a problem? **Define the variable.**

Remember What You Learned

7. Calculating change after buying lunch is a situation that can be modeled with a simple equation. What other daily activities require you to solve an equation using a variable? Write down three sample equations. **See students' work.**

Chapter 1   47   Course 2

Study Guide and Intervention*
p. 48 **BL OL ELL**

1-7 Study Guide and Intervention
Algebra: Equations

• An **equation** is a sentence in mathematics that contains an equals sign, =.
• The **solution** of an equation is the value that when substituted for the variable makes the equation true.

Example 1 Solve $23 + y = 29$ mentally.

$23 + y = 29$	Write the equation.
$23 + 6 = 29$	You know that 23 + 6 is 29.
$29 = 29$	Simplify.

The solution is 6.

Example 2

TRAVEL On their annual family vacation, the Whites travel 790 miles in two days. If on the first day they travel 490 miles, how many miles must they drive on the second day to reach their destination?

The total distance to travel in two days is 790 miles.
Let m represent the distance to travel on day two.

$m + 490 = 790$	
$m + 490 = 790$	Write the equation.
$300 + 490 = 790$	Replace m with 300 to make the equation true.
$790 = 790$	Simplify.

The number 300 is the solution. The distance the Whites must travel on day two is 300 miles.

Exercises

Solve each equation mentally.

1. $k + 7 = 15$ **8**   2. $g - 8 = 20$ **28**   3. $6y = 24$ **4**

4. $\frac{n}{3} = 9$ **27**   5. $\frac{a}{6} = 9$ **54**   6. $8 + r = 24$ **16**

7. $12 \cdot 8 = h$ **96**   8. $n + 11 = 8$ **88**   9. $48 \div 12 = x$ **4**

10. $h - 12 = 24$ **36**   11. $19 + y = 28$ **9**   12. $9f = 90$ **10**

Define a variable. Then write and solve an equation.

13. **MONEY** Aaron wants to buy a video game. The game costs $15.50. He has $10.00 saved from his weekly allowance. How much money does he need to borrow from his mother in order to buy the video game? **M = the amount of money he needs to borrow; M + 10 = 15.5; $5.50**

Chapter 1   48   Course 2

Skills Practice*
p. 49 **BL OL**

1-7 Skills Practice
Algebra: Equations

Solve each equation mentally.

1. $a + 7 = 16$ **9**   2. $12 + x = 21$ **9**   3. $4d = 60$ **15**

4. $15 = \frac{n}{3}$ **45**   5. $\frac{h}{7} = 12$ **84**   6. $13 \cdot 3 = y$ **39**

7. $8 + r = 17$ **9**   8. $27 - 12 = m$ **15**   9. $h - 22 = 67$ **89**

10. $27 + 15 = n$ **42**   11. $36 + a = 96$ **60**   12. $99 \div d = 3$ **33**

13. $6t = 66$ **11**   14. $25 = y + 4$ **100**   15. $b - 25 = 120$ **145**

16. $n \div 5 = 10$ **50**   17. $4y = 48$ **12**   18. $5t = 40$ **8**

19. $50 \cdot d = 150$ **3**   20. $w + 61 = 65$ **4**   21. $88 - k = 2$ **44**

Graph the solution of each equation on a number line.

22. $v - 6 = 30$ **36**   23. $3a = 27$ **9**   24. $n + 7 = 14$ **7**
See students' work for graphs.

Define a variable. Write an equation and solve.

25. **BAKING** Judy wants to buy some cookies for her birthday party. Cookies come in packages of 6. If she is inviting 24 friends to her party, how many packages of cookies does she need to buy so that each of her friends can have one cookie each?
P = the number of packages of cookies; 6p = 24; 4 packages

Chapter 1   49   Course 2

Practice*
p. 50 **OL AL**

1-7 Practice
Algebra: Equations

Solve each equation mentally.

1. $a + 5 = 14$ **9**   2. $7 + y = 24$ **17**   3. $t - 13 = 33$ **46**

4. $b - 17 = 11$ **28**   5. $12 - r = 0$ **12**   6. $x + 18 = 59$ **41**

7. $63 = 9g$ **7**   8. $8d = 96$ **12**   9. $n = \frac{42}{7}$ **6**

10. $9 = \frac{z}{7}$ **63**   11. $10 = h + 4$ **40**   12. $55 = m = 11$ **5**

13. $1.2 + k = 3.0$ **1.8**   14. $2.7 = f - 1.1$ **3.8**   15. $v - 0.5 = 0.2$ **0.7**

16. $12.6 - c = 7.0$ **5.6**   17. $8.8 + j = 18.7$ **9.9**   18. $w + 13.5 = 16.0$ **2.5**

19. **WEATHER** The temperature was 78°F. A cold front moved in, and the temperature dropped to 54°F. Solve the equation $78 - d = 54$ to find the drop in temperature.

24°F

20. **HOBBIES** Elissa can cut out the pieces of cloth to make four pillows in one hour. Solve the equation $4h = 20$ to find how many hours Elissa needs to cut out cloth for 20 pillows.

5 hours

21. **BOWLING** Jean Conrad is an amateur bowler with an average score of 187. She recently bowled a perfect 300 score. Write an equation that can be used to find how much the perfect score was above her average score and then solve the equation.

$300 - n = 187$ or $n = 300 - 187$; $n = 113$
The perfect score of 300 is 113 above her average.

Chapter 1   50   Course 2

Word Problem Practice*
p. 51 **OL AL**

1-7 Word Problem Practice
Algebra: Equations

1. **GAS MILEAGE** Mr. Moseley's car has a 20-gallon gas tank. It took 14 gallons of gas to fill his tank. Use the equation $14 + g = 20$ to find the number of gallons g that he had before he filled his tank with gas. **6 gal**

2. **PAINTING** Latisha earned $5 an hour painting for her dad. If she made $40 last week, use $5h = 40$ to find how many hours h she painted. **8 h**

3. **LUMBER** Mrs. Garcia had a piece of board that was 15 feet long. She cut off 6.5 feet. Use the equation $6.5 + \ell = 15$ to determine how much of the board ℓ she has left. **8.5 ft**

4. **MAGAZINES** Mahpee was selling magazine subscriptions. He earned $5 plus $0.50 for each subscription he sold. If Mahpee earned $25, use the equation $25 = 5 + 0.50n$ to find the number of subscriptions n he sold. **40 subscriptions**

5. **TIRES** The cost of a car tire is $45 plus $10 per order regardless of the number of tires purchased. If Mrs. Sato places an order for $190, use the equation $45t + 10 = 190$ to find the number of tires t she purchased. **4 tires**

6. **AREA** If the area of a rectangle is 30 square centimeters and the length is 6 centimeters, use the equation $30 = 6w$ to find the width w of the rectangle. **5 cm**

7. **SUPPLIES** The Jones Middle School had $4,000 to spend on office supplies. They had already spent $1,250. Use the equation $1,250 + d = 4,000$ to find how much money d the school had left for other supplies. **$2,750**

8. **PENCILS** Mi-Leng spent 90 cents on 6 pencils. Use the equation $90 = 6c$ to find the cost c of each pencil. **15 cents or $0.15**

Chapter 1   51   Course 2

Enrichment
p. 52 **OL AL**

1-7 Enrichment
Equations as Models

Equations as Models

When you write an equation that represents the information in a problem, the equation serves as a model for the problem. One equation can be a model for several different problems.

Each of Exercises 1–8 can be modeled by one of these equations.

$n + 2 = 10$ $n - 2 = 10$ $2n = 10$ $\frac{n}{2} = 10$

Choose the correct equation. Then solve the problem.

1. Chum earned $10 for working two hours. How much did he earn per hour? **2n = 10; $5**

2. Ana needs $2 more to buy a $10 scarf. How much does she already have? **n + 2 = 10; $8**

3. Kathy and her brother won a contest and shared the prize equally. Each received $10. What was the amount of the prize? **$\frac{n}{2}$ = 10; $20**

4. Jameel loaned two tapes to a friend. He has ten tapes left. How many tapes did Jameel originally have? **n − 2 = 10; 12 tapes**

5. In the figure below, the length of $\overline{AC}$ is 10 cm. The length of $\overline{BC}$ is 2 cm. What is the length of $\overline{AB}$?

A——————B——C

n + 2 = 10; 8 cm

6. Ray $\overrightarrow{AC}$ bisects $\angle BAD$. The measure of $\angle BAC$ is 10°. What is the measure of $\angle BAD$?

$\frac{n}{2}$ = 10; 20°

7. The width of the rectangle below is 2 inches less than the length. What is the length?

10 in.

n − 2 = 10; 12 in.

8. In the triangle below, the length of $\overline{PQ}$ is twice the length of $\overline{QR}$. What is the length of $\overline{QR}$?

10 cm

2n = 10; 5 cm

9. **CHALLENGE** On a separate sheet of paper, write a problem that can be modeled by the equation $3x + 5 = 29$. **Answers will vary.**

Chapter 1   52   Course 2

*** Also available in Spanish** **ELL**

Additional Lesson Resources

Transparencies
• *5-Minute Check Transparency*, Lesson 1-7

Other Print Products
• *Noteables™ Interactive Study Notebook with Foldables™*

Teacher Tech Tools
• *Interactive Classroom CD-ROM*, Lesson 1-7
• *AssignmentWorks*, Lesson 1-7

Student Tech Tools
glencoe.com
• Extra Examples, Chapter 1, Lesson 7
• Self-Check Quiz, Chapter 1, Lesson 7

MAIN IDEA

Write and solve equations using mental math.

New Vocabulary

equation
solution
solving an equation
defining the variable

Math Online

glencoe.com

• Extra Examples
• Personal Tutor
• Self-Check Quiz

▷ **GET READY** for the Lesson

VOLLEYBALL The table shows the number of wins for six women's college volleyball teams.

1. Suppose each team played 34 games. How many losses did each team have? **See table.**

2. Write a rule to describe how you found the number of losses. **34 = wins + losses**

3. Let w represent the number of wins and ℓ represent the number of losses. Rewrite your rule using numbers, variables, and an equals sign.

Women's College Volleyball		
Team	Wins	Losses
Bowling Green State University	28	■ 6
Kent State University	13	■ 21
Ohio University	28	■ 6
University of Akron	7	■ 27
University at Buffalo	14	■ 20
Miami University	13	■ 21

Source: Mid-American Conference

3. $34 = w + \ell$

An **equation** is a sentence that contains two expressions separated by an equals sign, =. The equals sign tells you that the expression on the left is equivalent to the expression on the right.

$$7 = 8 - 1 \qquad 3(4) = 12 \qquad 17 = 13 + 2 + 2$$

An equation that contains a variable is neither true nor false until the variable is replaced with a number. A **solution** of an equation is a numerical value for the variable that makes the sentence true.

The process of finding a solution is called **solving an equation**. Some equations can be solved using mental math.

EXAMPLE Solve an Equation Mentally

① Solve $18 = 14 + t$ mentally.

$18 = 14 + t$	Write the equation.
$18 = 14 + 4$	You know that $14 + 4$ is 18.
$18 = 18$	Simplify.

So, $t = 4$. The solution is 4.

✓ **CHECK** Your Progress

Solve each equation mentally.

a. $p - 5 = 20$ **25**   b. $8 = y \div 3$ **24**   c. $7h = 56$ **8**

Lesson 1-7 Algebra: Equations   **49**

Examples illustrate all of the concepts taught in the lesson and closely mirror the exercises in the exercise sets. Check Your Progress exercises give students an opportunity to try a similar problem on their own.

Vertical Alignment

Before Lesson 1-7
Solve problems involving linear functions with integer values; write the equation; and graph the resulting ordered pairs of integers on a grid

Lesson 1-7
Write and solve one-step linear equations in one variable

After Lesson 1-7
Solve two-step linear equations and inequalities in one variable over the rational numbers and verify the reasonableness of the results

② **Teach**

Scaffolding Questions

Tell the class that Emily received her $4 allowance and went to the ice cream store to buy a treat.

Ask:

• How much money would Emily have left if she bought a banana split for $3.25? **$0.75**

• How much money would she have left if she bought an ice cream cone for $1.50? **$2.50**

• What is the rule for finding how much money Emily will have left? **allowance − cost of treat = amount left**

ADDITIONAL EXAMPLE

① Solve $p - 14 = 5$ mentally. **19**

An algebraic **equation** includes an equals sign, while an algebraic **expression** does not.

Students should use **mental math** to solve the problems in this lesson.

✓ Formative Assessment

Use the Check Your Progress exercises after each Example to determine students' understanding of concepts.

ADDITIONAL EXAMPLES

2 **TEST EXAMPLE** A store sells pumpkins for $2 per pound. Paul has $18. Use the equation $2x = 18$ to find how large a pumpkin Paul can buy with $18. D

A 6 lb
B 7 lb
C 8 lb
D 9 lb

3 **ENTERTAINMENT** An adult paid $18.50 for herself and two students to see a movie. If the student tickets cost $11 altogether, what is the cost of an adult ticket? $7.50

Additional Examples are also in:

• Noteables™ Interactive Study Notebook with Foldables™

• Interactive Classroom PowerPoint® Presentations

Test-Taking Tip

Backsolving To find which answer choice is the solution, you can also substitute each value for *x* to see which answer choice makes the left side of the equation equal to the right side.

TEST EXAMPLE

2 Each day, Sierra cycles 3 miles on a bicycle trail. The equation $3d = 36$ represents how many days it will take her to cycle 36 miles. How many days *d* will it take her to cycle 36 miles?

A 10   **B** 12   **C** 15   **D** 20

Read the Item

Solve $3d = 36$ to find how many days it will take to cycle 36 miles.

Solve the Item

$3d = 36$ Write the equation.

$3 \cdot \mathbf{12} = 36$ You know that 3 · 12 is 36.

Therefore, $d = 12$. The answer is B.

✓ CHECK Your Progress

d. Jordan has 16 video games. This is 3 less than the number Casey has. To find how many video games Casey has, the equation $v - 3 = 16$ can be used. How many video games *v* does Casey have?

F 13   **G** 15   **H** 18   **J** 19   J

Choosing a variable to represent an unknown quantity is called **defining the variable**.

Study Tip

Defining the Variable
Although any symbol can be used, it is a good idea to use the first letter of the word you are defining as a variable. For example, *m* stands for the number of miles.

Real-World EXAMPLE

3 **WHALES** Each winter, Humpback whales migrate 1,500 miles to the Indian Ocean. However, one whale migrated 5,000 miles in one season. How many miles farther than normal did this whale travel?

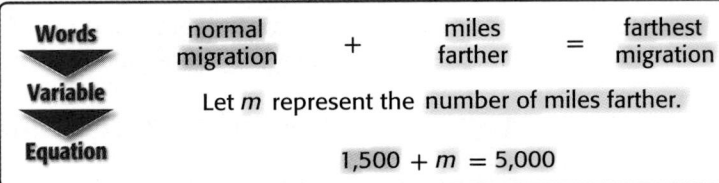

| Words | normal migration | + | miles farther | = | farthest migration |

Variable   Let *m* represent the number of miles farther.

Equation $1{,}500 + m = 5{,}000$

$1{,}500 + m = 5{,}000$ Write the equation.

$1{,}500 + \mathbf{3{,}500} = 5{,}000$ Replace *m* with 3,500 to make the equation true.

So, $m = 3{,}500$. The whale went 3,500 miles farther than normal.

✓ CHECK Your Progress

e. Aaron buys a movie rental, popcorn, and a soft drink for a total cost of $6.25. What is the cost of the popcorn if the movie rental and soft drink cost $4.70 together? **$1.55**

Differentiated Instruction

Kinesthetic Learners Separate students into groups of three. Have the students in each group take turns writing simple money equations such as $n + \$0.10 = \$0.25$, modeling the equation with coins, and then solving the equation. Encourage students to challenge each other with increasingly difficult equations.

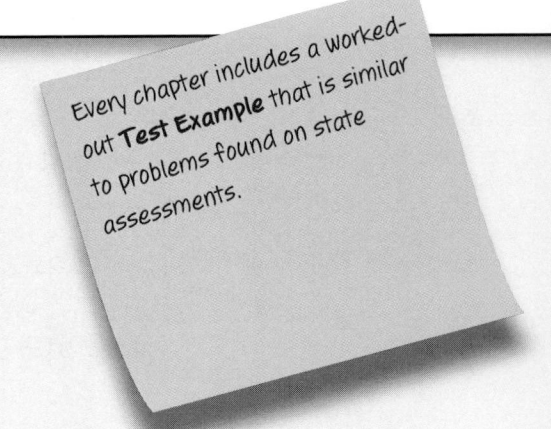

Every chapter includes a worked-out **Test Example** that is similar to problems found on state assessments.

★ indicates multi-step problem

✔ CHECK Your Understanding

Example 1
(p. 49)

Solve each equation mentally.

1. $75 = w + 72$ **3**   2. $y - 18 = 20$ **38**   3. $\frac{r}{9} = 6$ **54**

Example 2
(p. 50)

4. **MULTIPLE CHOICE** Daniel scored 7 points in a football game. Together, he and Judah scored 28 points. Solve the equation $7 + p = 28$ to find how many points p Judah scored. **B**

    A 14   **B** 21   **C** 23   **D** 35

Example 3
(p. 50)

5. **MONEY** Jessica buys a notebook and a pack of pencils for a total of $3.50. What is the cost of the notebook if the pack of pencils costs $1.25? **$2.25**

▶ Practice and Problem Solving

For Exercises	See Examples
6–17	1
18–19 33–34	2
20–21	3

Exercise Levels
A: 6–21
B: 22–29
C: 30–32

Solve each equation mentally.

6. $b + 7 = 13$ **6**   7. $8 + x = 15$ **7**   8. $y - 14 = 20$ **34**

9. $a - 18 = 10$ **28**   10. $25 - n = 19$ **6**   11. $x + 17 = 63$ **46**

12. $77 = 7t$ **11**   13. $3d = 99$ **33**   14. $n = \frac{30}{6}$ **5**

15. $16 = \frac{u}{4}$ **64**   16. $20 = y \div 5$ **100**   17. $84 \div z = 12$ **7**

18. **MONEY** Rosa charges $9 per hour of baby-sitting. Solve the equation $9h = 63$ to find how many hours h Rosa needs to baby-sit to earn $63.
7 hours

19. **SNACKS** A box initially contained 25 snack bars. There are 14 snack bars remaining. Solve the equation $25 - x = 14$ to find how many snack bars x were eaten. **11**

For Exercises 20 and 21, define a variable. Then write and solve an equation.

★ 20. **BASKETBALL** During one game of his rookie year, LeBron James scored 41 of the Cleveland Cavaliers' 107 points. How many points did the rest of the team score? **Let $p =$ the rest of the team's points; $41 + p = 107$; 66 points**

★ 21. **EXERCISE** On Monday and Tuesday, Derrick walked a total of 6.3 miles. If he walked 2.5 miles on Tuesday, how many miles did he walk on Monday? **Let $m =$ the number of miles Derrick walked on Monday; $m + 2.5 = 6.3$; 3.8 miles**

Solve each equation mentally.

22. $1.5 + j = 10.0$ **8.5**   23. $1.2 = m - 4.2$ **5.4**   24. $n - 1.4 = 3.5$ **4.9**

25. $13.4 - h = 9.0$ **4.4**   26. $9.9 + r = 24.2$ **14.3**   27. $w + 15.8 = 17.0$ **1.2**

28. $275 + l = 372$; $l = 97$

28. **CATS** The table shows the average weight of lions. Write and solve an addition equation to find how much more male lions weigh than female lions.

Lions	Weight (lb)
Female	275
Male	372

EXTRA PRACTICE
See pages 670, 704.

---

3 Practice

✔ Formative Assessment

Use Exercises 1–5 to check for understanding.

Then use the chart at the bottom of this page to customize your assignments for students.

Intervention You may wish to use the Study Guide and Intervention Master on page 48 of the *Chapter 1 Resource Masters* for additional reinforcement.

Odd/Even Assignments

Exercises 6–21 are structured so that students practice the same concepts whether they are assigned odd or even problems.

DIFFERENTIATED HOMEWORK OPTIONS			
Level	**Assignment**	**Two-Day Option**	
BL Basic	6–21, 31–44	7–21 odd, 33, 34	6–20 even, 31, 32, 36–44
OL Core	7–17 odd, 18–21, 23–27 odd, 28, 29, 31–44	6–21, 33, 34	22–29, 31, 32, 36–44
AL Advanced/Pre-AP	22–39 (optional: 41–44)		

Find the Error In Exercise 31, Justin made an error by using the wrong operation (addition). Remind students to ask themselves which operation they need to perform to solve the equation.

4 Assess

Ticket Out the Door Write a simple algebraic equation (such as $35 = 2 + x$) on the board. Have each student write the solution to the equation on a small piece of paper.

29. **FOOD** The total cost of a chicken sandwich and a drink is $6.25. The drink costs $1.75. Write and solve an equation that can be used to find how much the chicken sandwich is alone. **$1.75 + c = $6.25; c = $4.50**

H.O.T. Problems

30. **CHALLENGE** Find the values of a and b if $0 \cdot a = b$. Explain your reasoning. **Sample answer: $b = 0$; a is any number.**

31. **FIND THE ERROR** Justin and Antonio each solved $w - 35 = 70$. Whose solution is correct? Explain your reasoning.

31. Antonio;
$105 - 35 = 70$ is
a true statement.
$35 - 35 \neq 70$

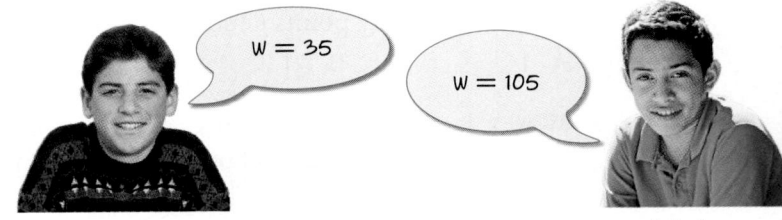

w = 35

w = 105

Justin

Antonio

32. **WRITING IN MATH** Explain what it means to solve an equation. **Sample answer: Find the value of the variable that makes the equation true.**

TEST PRACTICE

33. The diagram shows the distance from Madison to Hudson and from Lawrence to Hudson. Which equation can be used to find how many more miles x Lawrence is from Madison? **A**

```
Lawrence   Madison            Hudson
   •──────────•──────────────────•
              |──── 36 mi ────|
   |──────────── 58 mi ────────|
```

A $58 = x + 36$ **C** $36 \cdot 58 = x$

B $58 = \frac{x}{36}$ **D** $x - 36 = 58$

34. **SHORT RESPONSE** What value of h makes the following equation true? **128**
$$h \div 4 = 32$$

35. Solve $u + 8 = 15$. **J**

  F 23   **H** 8

  G 22   **J** 7

Spiral Review

36. **ALGEBRA** Evaluate $3a + b^2$ if $a = 2$ and $b = 3$. (Lesson 1-6) **15**

Evaluate each expression. (Lesson 1-4)

37. $11 \cdot 6 \div 3 + 9$ **31**   38. $5 \cdot 13 - 6^2$ **29**   39. $1 + 2(8 - 5)^2$ **19**

40. **FARMING** A farmer planted 389 acres of land with 78,967 corn plants. How many plants were planted per acre? (Lesson 1-1) **203 plants**

▷ **GET READY for the Next Lesson**

PREREQUISITE SKILL Multiply. (Lesson 1-4)

41. $2 \cdot (4 + 10)$ **28**   42. $(9 \cdot 1) \cdot 8$ **72**   43. $(5 \cdot 3)(5 \cdot 2)$ **150**   44. $(6 + 8) \cdot 12$ **168**

Algebra: Properties

PACING: **Regular:** 1 period, **Block:** 0.5 period

Options for Differentiated Instruction

ELL = English Language Learner   **AL** = Above or Beyond Grade Level   **SS** = Struggling Students   **SN** = Special Needs

Conceptual Understanding

Use with Example 1.

Remind students of the relationship between multiplication and addition.

Multiplication	Meaning in Words	Addition
4×3	4 groups of 3	$3 + 3 + 3 + 3$
$5(3 + 2)$	5 groups of $(3 + 2)$	$(3 + 2) + (3 + 2) + (3 + 2) + (3 + 2) + (3 + 2)$

The second addition expression above shows 5 groups of 3 and 5 groups of 2, so it can be written as $5(3) + 5(2)$.
Explain that in the same way, $3(x + 2)$ can be written as $(x + 2) + (x + 2) + (x + 2)$, which is $3x + 3(2)$, or $3x + 6$.

Study Helps   **ELL**   **SS**

Use after presenting the lesson.

Have students use an index card to explain each of the properties presented in Lesson 1-8.

- Distributive
- Commutative
- Associative
- Identity

Each card should include a definition, examples, and an indication of which of the four operations that it applies.

Commutative Property

The order in which numbers are added or multiplied does not matter.

Examples	
Addition	**Multiplication**
$2 + 3 = 3 + 2$	$2 \cdot 3 = 3 \cdot 2$

- The Commutative Property does not hold true for subtraction or division.

Peer Teaching

Use after presenting the lesson.

Students who lack confidence tend to not participate in whole-class discussions. Working in small groups reduces the isolation of these students and allows them to share their ideas and knowledge in a more relaxed environment.

- Organize students into groups of four, grouping them heterogeneously according to ability, skills, background, and so on.
- Assign each student one of the properties in the lesson. Have them meet with the other students assigned the same property to coach/tutor each other on that property.

Have the students rejoin their original groups and teach the other students about the property they studied.

Leveled Lesson Resources

Also on TeacherWorks™ Lesson 1-8

Chapter 1 Resource Masters

BL = Below or Approaching Grade Level OL = On Grade Level AL = Above or Beyond Grade Level ELL = English Language Learner

Lesson Reading Guide*
p. 53 BL OL ELL

NAME ______________ DATE ________ PERIOD ____

1-8 Lesson Reading Guide
Algebra: Properties

Get Ready for the Lesson

Read the introduction at the top of page 53 in your textbook. Write your answers below.

1. Find the total cost of admission and a movie ticket for a 4-person family.
   $80
2. Describe the method you used to find the total cost.
   See students' work.

Read the Lesson

3. Describe what is meant by *equivalent expressions*. **Equivalent expressions are expressions that have the same value.**
4. The Identity Property says that adding ________ to a number results in the number and multiplying ________ by a number is the number.
   zero; one

Lesson 1–8

Remember What You Learned

5. Why are the Distributive Property, Commutative Property, Associative Property, and Identity Property called properties?
   because they are true for any number

   Use a dictionary to find the meanings of *distribute* and *commute* that apply to mathematics. Then write an explanation of why the Distributive Property and Commutative Property are named that way.
   Sample answer:
   Distribute means to divide among several. The Distributive Property shows that when a sum is multiplied by a number, when the number is distributed and multiplied by each addend the result is the same. Commute means to move. The Commutative Property shows that when two numbers are added or multiplied the numbers can move around the operation symbol and the result is the same.

Chapter 1 53 Course 2

Study Guide and Intervention*
p. 54 BL OL ELL

NAME ______________ DATE ________ PERIOD ____

1-8 Study Guide and Intervention
Algebra: Properties

Property	Arithmetic	Algebra
Distributive Property	$5(3 + 4) = 5(3) + 5(4)$	$a(b + c) = a(b) + a(c)$
Commutative Property of Addition	$5 + 3 = 3 + 5$	$a + b = b + a$
Commutative Property of Multiplication	$5 \times 3 = 3 \times 5$	$a \times b = b \times a$
Associative Property of Addition	$(2 + 3) + 4 = 2 + (3 + 4)$	$(a + b) + c = a + (b + c)$
Associative Property of Multiplication	$(4 \times 5) \times 6 = 4 \times (5 \times 6)$	$(a \times b) \times c = a \times (b \times c)$
Identity Property of Addition	$5 + 0 = 5$	$a + 0 = a$
Identity Property of Multiplication	$5 \times 1 = 5$	$a \times 1 = a$

Example 1 **Use the Distributive Property to write 6(4 + 3) as an equivalent expression. Then evaluate the expression.**

$6(4 + 3) = 6 \cdot 4 + 6 \cdot 3$ Apply the Distributive Property.
$= 24 + 18$ Multiply.
$= 42$ Add.

Example 2 **Name the property shown by each statement.**

$5 \times 4 = 4 \times 5$ Commutative Property of Multiplication
$12 + 0 = 12$ Identity Property of Addition
$7 + (6 + 3) = (7 + 6) + 3$ Associative Property of Addition

Exercises

Use the Distributive Property to write each expression as an equivalent expression. Then evaluate the expression.

1. $5(7 + 2)$ **5(7) + 5(2); 45** 2. $4(9 + 1)$ **4(9) + 4(1); 40** 3. $2(6 + 7)$ **2(6) + 2(7); 26**

Name the property shown by each statement.

4. $9 \times 1 = 9$ **Identity Property (×)**
5. $7 \times 3 = 3 \times 7$ **Commutative Property (×)**
6. $(7 + 8) + 2 = 7 + (8 + 2)$ **Associative Property (+)**
7. $6(3 + 2) = 6(3) + 6(2)$ **Distributive Property**
8. $15 + 12 = 12 + 15$ **Commutative Property (+)**
9. $1 \times 20 = 20$ **Identity Property (×)**
10. $(9 \times 5) \times 2 = 9 \times (5 \times 2)$ **Associative Property (×)**
11. $3 = 0 + 3$ **Identity Property (+)**

Chapter 1 54 Course 2

Skills Practice*
p. 55 BL OL

NAME ______________ DATE ________ PERIOD ____

1-8 Skills Practice
Algebra: Properties

Use the Distributive Property to write each expression as an equivalent expression. Then evaluate the expression.

1. $3(5 + 1)$ **3(5) + 3(1); 18**
2. $(2 + 7)5$ **2(5) + 7(5); 45**
3. $(10 + 2)7$ **10(7) + 2(7); 84**
4. $2(9 - 8)$ **2(9) − 2(8); 2**
5. $4(10 - 2)$ **4(10) − 4(2); 32**
6. $6(13 + 4)$ **6(13) + 6(4); 102**

Name the property shown by each statement.

7. $2 \times (3 \times 7) = (2 \times 3) \times 7$ **Associative Property (×)**
8. $6 + 3 = 3 + 6$ **Commutative Property (+)**
9. $3(9 - 7) = 3(9) - 3(7)$ **Distributive Property**
10. $18 \times 1 = 18$ **Identity Property (×)**
11. $7 \times 2 = 2 \times 7$ **Commutative Property (×)**
12. $6 + (1 + 4) = (6 + 1) + 4$ **Associative Property (+)**
13. $7 + 0 = 7$ **Identity Property (+)**
14. $0 + 12 = 12$ **Identity Property (+)**
15. $625 + 281 = 281 + 625$ **Commutative Property (+)**
16. $(12 \times 18) \times 5 = 12 \times (18 \times 5)$ **Associative Property (×)**
17. $2(8 + 2) = 2(8) + 2(2)$ **Distributive Property**
18. $(15 + 11) + 9 = 15 + (11 + 9)$ **Associative Property (+)**
19. $(6 + r) + s = 6 + (r + s)$ **Associative Property (+)**
20. $(4 \times 8) \times a = 4 \times (8 \times a)$ **Associative Property (×)**
21. $p \times 1 = p$ **Identity Property (×)**
22. $a + 5 = 5 + a$ **Commutative Property (+)**
23. $y \times 3 = 3 \times y$ **Commutative Property (×)**
24. $b + 0 = b$ **Identity Property (+)**
25. $(x + y) + z = x + (y + z)$ **Associative Property (+)**
26. $6(200 + 50) = 6(200) + 6(50)$ **Distributive Property**

Lesson 1–8

Chapter 1 55 Course 2

Practice*
p. 56 OL AL

NAME ______________ DATE ________ PERIOD ____

1-8 Practice
Algebra: Properties

Use the Distributive Property to evaluate each expression.

1. $4(5 + 7)$ **4(5) + 4(7) = 48**
2. $6(3 + 1)$ **6(3) + 6(1) = 24**
3. $(10 + 8)2$ **(10)2 + (8)2 = 36**
4. $5(8 - 3)$ **5(8) − 5(3) = 25**
5. $7(4 - 1)$ **7(4) − 7(1) = 21**
6. $(9 - 2)3$ **(9)3 − (2)3 = 21**

Name the property shown by each statement.

7. $7 + (6 + t) = (7 + 6) + t$ **Associative Property (+)**
8. $23 \cdot 15 = 15 \cdot 23$ **Commutative Property (×)**
9. $0 + x = x$ **Identity Property (+)**
10. $3(g + 7) = 3 \cdot g + 3 \cdot 7$ **Distributive Property**
11. $8 \times 1 = 8$ **Identity Property (×)**
12. $y + 11 = 11 + y$ **Commutative Property (+)**
13. $5(w + 1) = (w + 1)5$ **Commutative Property (×)**
14. $(4 \cdot d) \cdot 1 = 4 \cdot (d \cdot 1)$ **Associative Property (×)**
15. $(6 + 2)7 = (6)7 + (2)7$ **Distributive Property**

Use one or more properties to rewrite each expression as an equivalent expression that does not use parentheses.

16. $(b + 3) + 6$ **$b + 9$**
17. $7(5x)$ **$35x$**
18. $4(a + 4)$ **$4a + 16$**
19. $7 + (3 + t)$ **$10 + t$**
20. $(2z)0$ **0**
21. $(9 + k)5$ **$45 + 5k$**
22. $8(y - 5) + y$ **$9y - 40$**
23. $(h + 2)3 - 2h$ **$h + 6$**
24. GROCERY A grocery store sells an imported specialty cheesecake for $11 and its own store-baked cheesecake for $5. Use the Distributive Property to mentally find the total cost for 6 of each type of cheesecake.
    6($5 + $11) = 6 · $5 + 6 · $11 = $30 + $66 = $96
25. CHECKING ACCOUNT Mr. Kenrick balances his checking account statement each month two different ways as shown by the equation, $(b + d) - c = b + (d - c)$, where b is the previous balance, d is the amount of deposits made, and c is the amount of checks written. Name the property that Mr. Kenrick uses to double check his arithmetic.
    Associative Property
26. SPEED A train is traveling at a speed of 65 miles per hour. The train travels for one hour. What property is used to solve this problem as shown by the statement $65 \cdot 1 = 65$?
    Identity Property

Chapter 1 56 Course 2

Word Problem Practice*
p. 57 OL AL

NAME ______________ DATE ________ PERIOD ____

1-8 Word Problem Practice
Algebra: Properties

1. MUSIC Mr. Escalante and Mrs. Turner plan to take their music classes to a musical revue. Tickets cost $6 each. Mr. Escalante's class needs 22 tickets, and Mrs. Turner's class needs 26 tickets. Use the Distributive Property to write a sentence to express how to find the total cost of tickets in two ways.
   6(22) + 6(26) = 6(22 + 26)
2. SAVINGS Mrs. Perez was looking at her bank account statement. She noticed that her beginning balance was $500, and she had added nothing to her account. What was the ending balance on her statement? What property did you apply? **$500; Identity Property of Addition**
3. ADDITION Mr. Brooks was working on addition using dominos with a group of 1st graders. When picking the domino with 3 dots on one end and 5 dots on the other, some students read. "3 plus 5 equal 8" while others read it as "5 plus 3 equals 8." What property were these children using? Explain.
   Commutative Property of Addition; the order was different.
4. AREA Aleta noticed that for the rectangle below she could either multiply 2 times 3 or 3 times 2 to get its area of 6 square inches. What property allows her to do this?

   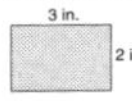

   Commutative Property of Multiplication
5. NUMBER CUBES Students in Mr. Rivas' class were practicing their multiplication skills by rolling three 6-sided number cubes. Wapi rolled a 2, a 3, and a 5 on his roll. He multiplied the three numbers as follows using the order of operations: $(2 \times 3) \times 5 = 30$. Write another way Wapi could have performed the multiplication without changing the order of the numbers. State the property you used.
   2 × (3 × 5) = 30; Associative Property of Multiplication
6. FACTS Bik was working on memorizing her multiplication facts. She noticed that anytime she multiplied a number by 1, she got the same number she started with. What property allows this to be true? **Identity Property of Multiplication**
7. MONEY Mei was trying to figure out the cost of 4 boxes of cereal for $2.25 each. Write a sentence to show Mei an easy way to do her calculations. What property did you apply to help her?
   4(2.25) = 4(2.00 + 0.25); Distributive Property
8. WALKING Jacob walked 3 blocks to Ping's house, then 5 blocks to Jamal's house. Write a sentence to show that the distance from Ping's to Jamal's is the same as the return walk home. Name the property illustrated in your sentence.
   3 + 5 = 5 + 3; Commutative Property of Addition

Lesson 1–8

Chapter 1 57 Course 2

Enrichment
p. 58 OL AL

NAME ______________ DATE ________ PERIOD ____

1-8 Enrichment
Name That Property

Name That Property

You know that the Commutative Property applies to the operations of addition and multiplication. You also know that the Associative Property applies to operations of addition and multiplication. What about the other operations? Does the Commutative Property apply to division? Does the Associative Property apply to subtraction? Does the Distributive Property apply to subtraction or division?

Look at these examples to determine if the properties also apply to subtraction or division.

Commutative Property

Subtraction *Try this:* $5 - 4 \stackrel{?}{=} 4 - 5$

Division *Try this:* $8 \div 2 \stackrel{?}{=} 2 \div 8$

1. Does the Commutative Property apply to division and subtraction? Explain.
   Sample answer: The Commutative Property does not apply to subtraction because 1 ≠ −1. It does not apply to division since 4 ≠ 0.25.

Associative Property

Subtraction *Try this:* $7 - (3 - 2) \stackrel{?}{=} (7 - 3) - 2$

Division *Try this:* $8 \div (4 \div 2) \stackrel{?}{=} (8 \div 4) \div 2$

2. Does the Associative Property apply to subtraction and division? Explain.
   Sample answer: The Associative Property does not apply to subtraction because 7 − 1 ≠ 4 − 2. It does not apply to division since 8 ÷ 2 ≠ 2 ÷ 2.

Distributive Property

Subtraction *Try this:*
$3(8 - 2) \stackrel{?}{=} 3 \times 8 - 3 \times 2$
$3(6) \stackrel{?}{=} 24 - 6$
$18 = 18$ ✓

Division *Try this:*
$3(8 \div 2) \stackrel{?}{=} 3 \times 8 \div 3 \times 2$
$3(4) \stackrel{?}{=} 24 \div 6$
$12 \neq 4$

3. Does the Distributive Property apply to multiplication over subtraction? Does it apply to multiplication over division? Explain.
   The Distributive Property applies to multiplication over subtraction, but does not apply to multiplication over division.

Chapter 1 58 Course 2

*** Also available in Spanish ELL**

Additional Lesson Resources

Transparencies

- *5-Minute Check Transparency,* Lesson 1-8

Other Print Products

- *Noteables™ Interactive Study Notebook with Foldables™*

A Study Guide and Intervention, Skills Practice, Practice, Word Problem Practice, Lesson Reading Guide, and Enrichment Master is shown for every lesson in the Student Edition. These masters can be found in the Chapter Resource Masters.

Teacher Tech Tools

- *Interactive Classroom CD-ROM,* Lesson 1-8
- *AssignmentWorks,* Lesson 1-8

Student Tech Tools

glencoe.com

- Extra Examples, Chapter 1, Lesson 8
- Self-Check Quiz, Chapter 1, Lesson 8

MAIN IDEA

Use Commutative, Associative, Identity, and Distributive properties to solve problems.

New Vocabulary

equivalent expressions
properties

Math Online

glencoe.com

• Extra Examples
• Personal Tutor
• Self-Check Quiz

▷ **GET READY** for the Lesson

MUSEUMS The admission costs for the Louisville Science Center are shown.

Louisville Science Center Admission	
Admission	$12
IMAX Movie	$8

Source: Louisville Science Center

1. Find the total cost of admission and a movie ticket for a 4-person family. **$80**

2. Describe the method you used to find the total cost.

2. See students' work.

Here are two ways to find the total cost.

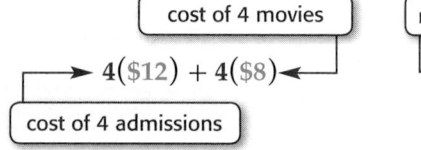

The expressions 4($12) + 4($8) and 4($12 + $8) are **equivalent expressions** because they have the same value, $80. This shows how the **Distributive Property** combines addition and multiplication.

Distributive Property		**Key Concept**
Words	To multiply a sum by a number, multiply each addend of the sum by the number outside the parentheses.	
Examples	**Numbers**	**Algebra**
	$3(4 + 6) = 3(4) + 3(6)$	$a(b + c) = a(b) + a(c)$
	$5(7) + 5(3) = 5(7 + 3)$	$a(b) + a(c) = a(b + c)$

EXAMPLES Write Sentences as Equations

Use the Distributive Property to rewrite each expression. Then evaluate it.

1 $5(3 + 2)$

$5(3 + 2) = 5(3) + 5(2)$
$\quad\quad\quad = 15 + 10$ Multiply.
$\quad\quad\quad = 25$ Add.

2 $3(7) + 3(4)$

$3(7) + 3(4) = 3(7 + 4)$
$\quad\quad\quad\quad\quad = 3(11)$ Add.
$\quad\quad\quad\quad\quad = 33$ Multiply.

✓ **CHECK** Your Progress

a. $6(1 + 4)$ **6 • 1 + 6 • 4; 30**

b. $6(9) + 6(3)$ **6(9 + 3); 72**

Lesson 1-8 Algebra: Properties   **53**

Key Concept boxes highlight definitions, formulas, and other important ideas. Multiple representations—words, symbols, examples, models—help students understand the concepts.

Tips for New Teachers

Distributive Property

You may want to show students that the Distributive Property can also be illustrated as:
$(a + b)c = (a)c + (b)c$ and
$(a)c + (b)c = (a + b)c$

1 Focus

Vertical Alignment

Before Lesson 1-8
Know and use the distributive property in equations and expressions

Lesson 1-8
Apply algebraic order of operations and properties and justify each step in the process

After Lesson 1-8
Use the correct order of operations to evaluate algebraic expressions

2 Teach

Scaffolding Questions

Ask:

• What is the product of 9 × 8? 72

• What is the product of 8 × 9? 72

• Does changing the order of the factors change the product? no

• What is the sum of 3 + 2 + 5? 10

• What is the sum of 5 + 3 + 2? 10

• Does changing the order of the addends change the sum? no

• What is the product of $a × 1$? a

• What is the sum of $b + 0$? b

ADDITIONAL EXAMPLES

Use the Distributive Property to rewrite each expression. Then evaluate it.

1 $8(5 + 7)$ 96

2 $6(9) + 6(2)$ 66

Focus on Mathematical Content

The **Distributive Property** allows you to find the product of a sum and a number by multiplying each addend by the number and then adding the products.

The **Commutative Property** allows you to change the order in which two numbers are multiplied or added without changing the product or sum. For all numbers a and b, $a + b = b + a$ and $ab = ba$.

The **Associative Property** allows you to change the grouping of numbers being multiplied or added without changing the product or sum. For all numbers a, b, and c, $a + (b + c) = (a + b) + c$ and $a(bc) = (ab)c$.

The **Identity Property** allows you to add 0 to an addend without changing the addend and to multiply a factor by 1 without changing the factor. For all numbers a, $a + 0 = a$ and $a \cdot 1 = a$.

✔ Formative Assessment

Use the Check Your Progress exercises after each Example to determine students' understanding of concepts.

ADDITIONAL EXAMPLES

3 **VACATIONS** Mr. Harmon has budgeted $150 per day for his hotel and meals during his vacation. If he plans to spend six days on vacation, how much money will he spend? **$900**

4 Find $5 \cdot 13 \cdot 20$ mentally. Justify each step. $5 \cdot 13 \cdot 20 = 5 \cdot 20 \cdot 13$ Comm. Prop. ($\times$) $= (5 \cdot 20) \cdot 13$ Assoc. Prop. ($\times$) $= 100 \cdot 13$ or 1,300 Multiply 100 and 13 mentally.

 Real-World Link . . . . .
American Lance Armstrong won the Tour de France seven times in a row from 1999 through 2005.
Source: Capital Sports Entertainment

c. 5($100 + $20) = $600; The expression $100 + $20 represents the amount of money Jennifer saved each month. The expression 5($100 + $20) represents the amount of money she saved for five months. Since 5 × $100 = $500 and 5 × $20 = $100, find $500 + $100, or $600, to find the amount of money Jennifer saved for five months.

Study Tip

Mental Math Look for sums or products that end in zero. They are easy to compute mentally.

🌐 Real-World EXAMPLE

3 **TOUR DE FRANCE** The Tour de France is a cycling race through France that lasts 22 days. If a cyclist averages 90 miles per day, about how far does he travel?

Use the Distributive Property to multiply 90×22 mentally.

$$90(22) = 90(20 + 2) \qquad \text{Rewrite 22 as } 20 + 2.$$
$$= 90(20) + 90(2) \qquad \text{Distributive Property}$$
$$= 1,800 + 180 \qquad \text{Multiply.}$$
$$= 1,980 \qquad \text{Add.}$$

The cyclist travels about 1,980 miles.

✔ CHECK Your Progress

c. Jennifer saved $120 each month for five months. How much did she save in all? Explain your reasoning.

Properties are statements that are true for all numbers.

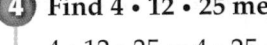

Real Number Properties   Concept Summary

Commutative Properties	The order in which two numbers are added or multiplied does not change their sum or product. $a + b = b + a \qquad a \cdot b = b \cdot a$
Associative Properties	The way in which three numbers are grouped when they are added or multiplied does not change their sum or product. $a + (b + c) = (a + b) + c \qquad a \cdot (b \cdot c) = (a \cdot b) \cdot c$
Identity Properties	The sum of an addend and 0 is the addend. The product of a factor and 1 is the factor. $a + 0 = a \qquad a \cdot 1 = a$

EXAMPLE   Use Properties to Evaluate Expressions

4 Find $4 \cdot 12 \cdot 25$ mentally. Justify each step.

$$4 \cdot 12 \cdot 25 = 4 \cdot 25 \cdot 12 \qquad \text{Commutative Property of Multiplication}$$
$$= (4 \cdot 25) \cdot 12 \qquad \text{Associative Property of Multiplication}$$
$$= 100 \cdot 12 \text{ or } 1,200 \qquad \text{Multiply 100 and 12 mentally.}$$

✔ CHECK Your Progress   d–e. See Ch. 1 Answer Appendix for justification.

Find each of the following. Justify each step.

d. $40 \cdot (7 \cdot 5)$ **1,400**   e. $(89 + 15) + 1$ **105**

Pre-AP Activity   Use after Example 4

Ask students whether there are Commutative and Associative Properties of Subtraction. Have them explain their reasoning and give examples. Repeat the question for division, again having students explain their reasoning and give examples.

Algebra: Arithmetic Sequences

PACING: **Regular:** 1.5 periods, **Block:** 0.5 period

Options for Differentiated Instruction

ELL = English Language Learner   **AL** = Above or Beyond Grade Level   **SS** = Struggling Students   **SN** = Special Needs

Visual Learners   **SS**   **SN**

Use after presenting the Mini Lab.

Have students build the following patterns with cubes.

Ask:

Figure 1   Figure 2   Figure 3

- What pattern do you see? Describe it in words. Each figure increases by 2 blocks.
- Suppose this pattern continues. How many blocks would be in Figure 5? 11 blocks

Have students create two different visual patterns that represent the same arithmetic sequence. For example, they could create two different patterns that increase by 3 each term.

Visual Cues   **SS**   **SN**

Use with Example 1.

Have students use number lines drawn on grid paper to plot the sequence 8, 11, 14, 17, 20, … and the sequence given in Example 1.

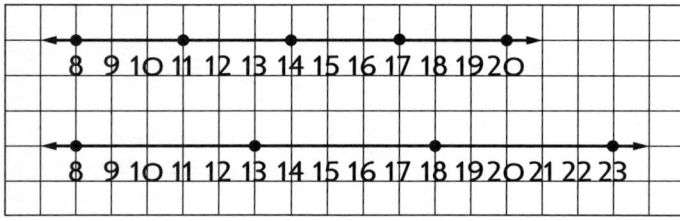

Then have them graph a non-arithmetic sequence such as 2, 4, 8, 16, … This will help students visualize the distinction between sequences that are arithmetic and those that are not.

Leveled Lesson Resources

Chapter 1 Resource Masters

BL = Below or Approaching Grade Level   **OL** = On Grade Level   **AL** = Above or Beyond Grade Level   **ELL** = English Language Learner

---

Lesson Reading Guide*
p. 60 **BL** **OL** **ELL**

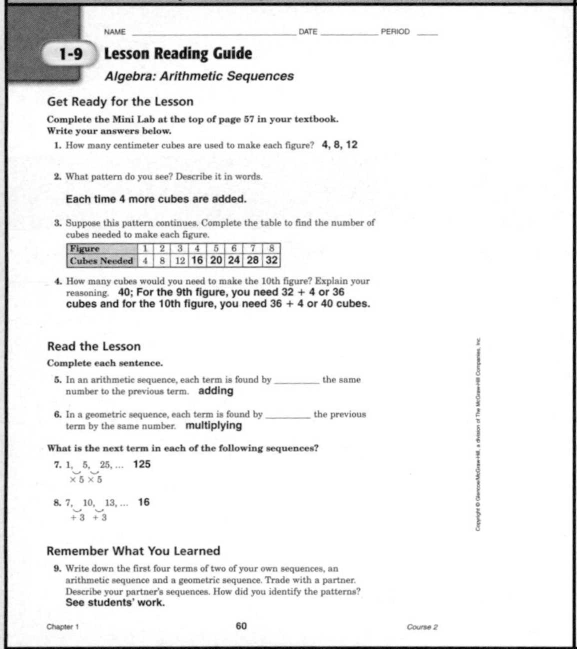

NAME _____ DATE _____ PERIOD _____

1-9 Lesson Reading Guide
Algebra: Arithmetic Sequences

Get Ready for the Lesson

Complete the Mini Lab at the top of page 57 in your textbook.
Write your answers below.

1. How many centimeter cubes are used to make each figure? **4, 8, 12**

2. What pattern do you see? Describe it in words.
Each time 4 more cubes are added.

3. Suppose this pattern continues. Complete the table to find the number of cubes needed to make each figure.

Figure	1	2	3	4	5	6	7	8
Cubes Needed	4	8	12	**16**	**20**	**24**	**28**	**32**

4. How many cubes would you need to make the 10th figure? Explain your reasoning. **40; For the 9th figure, you need 32 + 4 or 36 cubes and for the 10th figure, you need 36 + 4 or 40 cubes.**

Read the Lesson

Complete each sentence.

5. In an arithmetic sequence, each term is found by _____ the same number to the previous term. **adding**

6. In a geometric sequence, each term is found by _____ the previous term by the same number. **multiplying**

What is the next term in each of the following sequences?

7. 1, 5, 25, ... **125**

8. 7, 10, 13, ... **16**

Remember What You Learned

9. Write down the first four terms of two of your own sequences, an arithmetic sequence and a geometric sequence. Trade with a partner. Describe your partner's sequences. How did you identify the patterns? **See students' work.**

Chapter 1   60   Course 2

Study Guide and Intervention*
p. 61 **BL** **OL** **ELL**

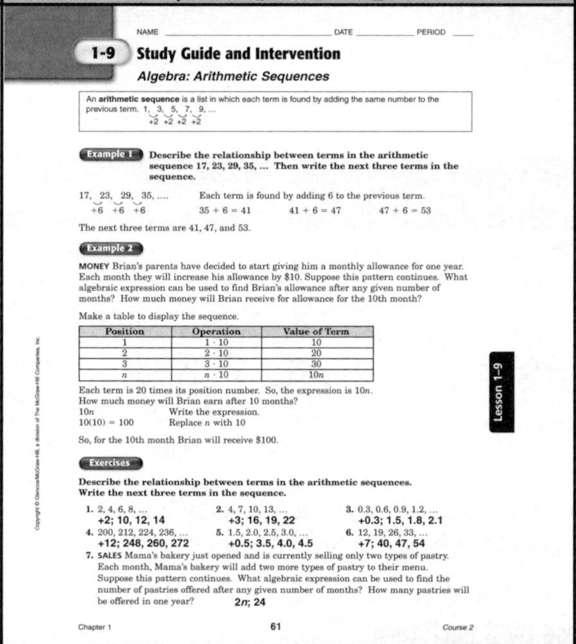

NAME _____ DATE _____ PERIOD _____

1-9 Study Guide and Intervention
Algebra: Arithmetic Sequences

An *arithmetic sequence* is a list in which each term is found by adding the same number to the previous term. 1, 3, 5, 7, 9, ...
+2 +2 +2 +2

Example 1 Describe the relationship between terms in the arithmetic sequence 17, 23, 29, 35, ... Then write the next three terms in the sequence.

17, 23, 29, 35, ...   Each term is found by adding 6 to the previous term.
+6 +6 +6   35 + 6 = 41   41 + 6 = 47   47 + 6 = 53

The next three terms are 41, 47, and 53.

Example 2
MONEY Brian's parents have decided to start giving him a monthly allowance for one year. Each month they will increase his allowance by $10. Suppose this pattern continues. What algebraic expression can be used to find Brian's allowance after any given number of months? How much money will Brian receive for allowance for the 10th month?

Make a table to display the sequence.

Position	Operation	Value of Term
1	1 · 10	10
2	2 · 10	20
3	3 · 10	30
n	n · 10	10n

Each term is 10 times its position number. So, the expression is 10n. How much money will Brian earn after 10 months?
10n   Write the expression.
10(10) = 100   Replace n with 10
So, for the 10th month Brian will receive $100.

Exercises

Describe the relationship between terms in the arithmetic sequences. Write the next three terms in the sequence.

1. 2, 4, 6, 8, ...   2. 4, 7, 10, 13, ...   3. 0.3, 0.6, 0.9, 1.2, ...
+2; 10, 12, 14   **+3; 16, 19, 22**   **+0.3; 1.5, 1.8, 2.1**

4. 200, 212, 224, 236, ...   5. 1.5, 2.0, 2.5, 3.0, ...
+12; 248, 260, 272   **+0.5; 3.5, 4.0, 4.5**   **+7; 40, 47, 54**

7. SALES Mama's bakery just opened and is currently selling only two types of pastry. Each month, Mama's bakery will add two more types of pastry to their menu. Suppose this pattern continues. What algebraic expression can be used to find the number of pastries offered after any given number of months? How many pastries will be offered in one year? **2n; 24**

Chapter 1   61   Course 2

Skills Practice*
p. 62 **BL** **OL**

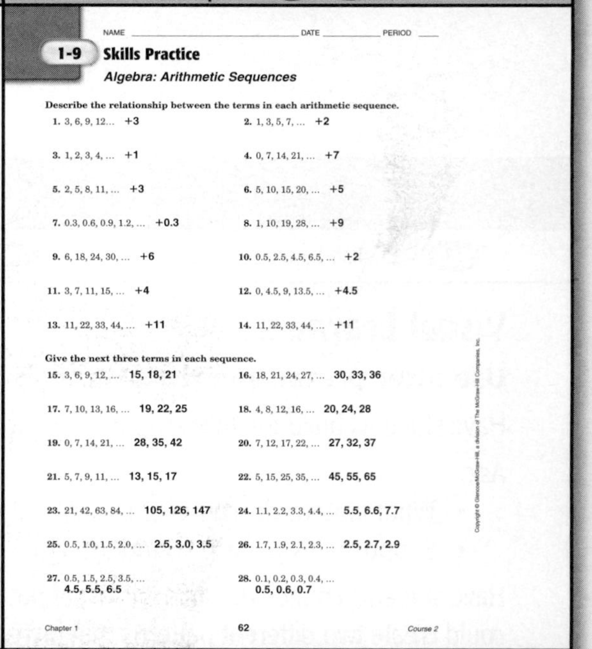

NAME _____ DATE _____ PERIOD _____

1-9 Skills Practice
Algebra: Arithmetic Sequences

Describe the relationship between the terms in each arithmetic sequence.

1. 3, 6, 9, 12... **+3**   2. 1, 3, 5, 7, ... **+2**

3. 1, 2, 3, 4, ... **+1**   4. 0, 7, 14, 21, ... **+7**

5. 2, 5, 8, 11, ... **+3**   6. 5, 10, 15, 20, ... **+5**

7. 0.3, 0.6, 0.9, 1.2, ... **+0.3**   8. 1, 10, 19, 28, ... **+9**

9. 6, 18, 24, 30, ... **+6**   10. 0.5, 2.5, 4.5, 6.5, ... **+2**

11. 3, 7, 11, 15, ... **+4**   12. 0, 4.5, 9, 13.5, ... **+4.5**

13. 11, 22, 33, 44, ... **+11**   14. 11, 22, 33, 44, ... **+11**

Give the next three terms in each sequence.

15. 3, 6, 9, 12, ... **15, 18, 21**   16. 18, 21, 24, 27, ... **30, 33, 36**

17. 7, 10, 13, 16, ... **19, 22, 25**   18. 4, 8, 12, 16, ... **20, 24, 28**

19. 0, 7, 14, 21, ... **28, 35, 42**   20. 7, 12, 17, 22, ... **27, 32, 37**

21. 5, 7, 9, 11, ... **13, 15, 17**   22. 5, 15, 25, 35, ... **45, 55, 65**

23. 21, 42, 63, 84, ... **105, 126, 147**   24. 1.1, 2.2, 3.3, 4.4, ... **5.5, 6.6, 7.7**

25. 0.5, 1.0, 1.5, 2.0, ... **2.5, 3.0, 3.5**   26. 1.7, 1.9, 2.1, 2.3, ... **2.5, 2.7, 2.9**

27. 0.5, 1.5, 2.5, 3.5, ... **4.5, 5.5, 6.5**   28. 0.1, 0.2, 0.3, 0.4, ... **0.5, 0.6, 0.7**

Chapter 1   62   Course 2

Practice*
p. 63 **OL** **AL**

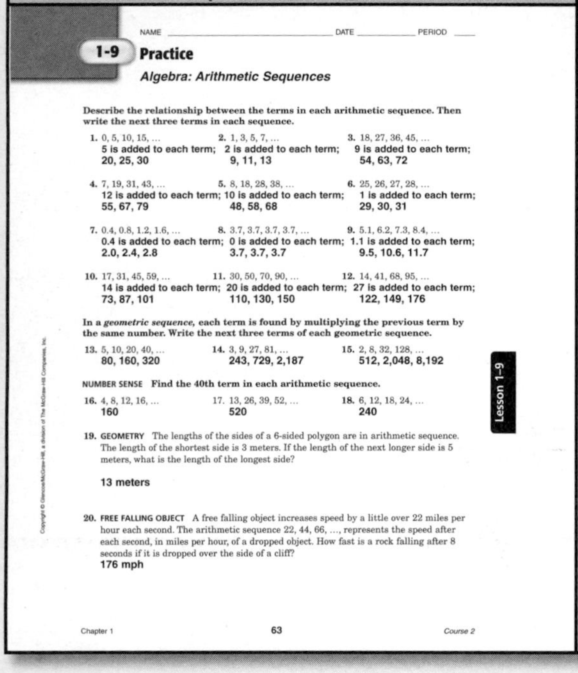

NAME _____ DATE _____ PERIOD _____

1-9 Practice
Algebra: Arithmetic Sequences

Describe the relationship between the terms in each arithmetic sequence. Then write the next three terms in each sequence.

1. 0, 5, 10, 15, ...   2. 1, 3, 5, 7, ...   3. 18, 27, 36, 45, ...
5 is added to each term; 2 is added to each term; 9 is added to each term;
20, 25, 30   **9, 11, 13**   **54, 63, 72**

4. 7, 19, 31, 43, ...   5. 8, 18, 28, 38, ...   6. 25, 26, 27, 28, ...
12 is added to each term; 10 is added to each term; 1 is added to each term;
55, 67, 79   **48, 58, 68**   **29, 30, 31**

7. 0.4, 0.8, 1.2, 1.6, ...   8. 3.7, 3.7, 3.7, 3.7, ...   9. 5.1, 6.2, 7.3, 8.4, ...
0.4 is added to each term; 0 is added to each term; 1.1 is added to each term;
2.0, 2.4, 2.8   **3.7, 3.7, 3.7**   **9.5, 10.6, 11.7**

10. 17, 31, 45, 59, ...   11. 30, 50, 70, 90, ...   12. 14, 41, 68, 95, ...
14 is added to each term; 20 is added to each term; 27 is added to each term;
73, 87, 101   **110, 130, 150**   **122, 149, 176**

In a *geometric sequence*, each term is found by multiplying the previous term by the same number. Write the next three terms of each geometric sequence.

13. 5, 10, 20, 40, ...   14. 3, 9, 27, 81, ...   15. 2, 8, 32, 128, ...
80, 160, 320   **243, 729, 2,187**   **512, 2,048, 8,192**

NUMBER SENSE Find the 40th term in each arithmetic sequence.

16. 4, 8, 12, 16, ...   17. 13, 26, 39, 52, ...   18. 6, 12, 18, 24, ...
160   **520**   **240**

19. **GEOMETRY** The lengths of the sides of a 6-sided polygon are in arithmetic sequence. The length of the shortest side is 3 meters. If the length of the next longer side is 5 meters, what is the length of the longest side?
13 meters

20. **FREE FALLING OBJECT** A free falling object increases speed by a little over 22 miles per hour each second. The arithmetic sequence 22, 44, 66, ..., represents the speed after each second, in miles per hour, of a dropped object. How fast is a rock falling after 8 seconds if it is dropped over the side of a cliff?
176 mph

Chapter 1   63   Course 2

Word Problem Practice*
p. 64 **OL** **AL**

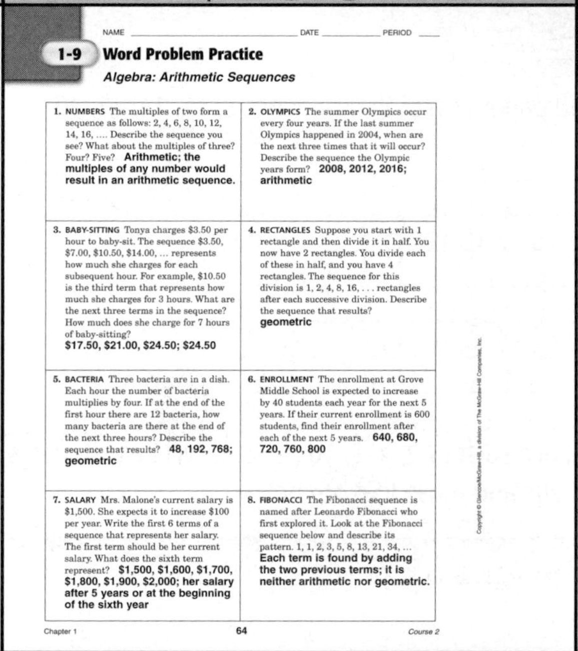

NAME _____ DATE _____ PERIOD _____

1-9 Word Problem Practice
Algebra: Arithmetic Sequences

1. **NUMBERS** The multiples of two form a sequence as follows: 2, 4, 6, 8, 10, 12, 14, 16, ... Describe the sequence you see? What about the multiples of three? Four? Five? **Arithmetic; the multiples of any number would result in an arithmetic sequence.**

2. **OLYMPICS** The summer Olympics occur every four years. If the last summer Olympics happened in 2004, when are the next three times that it will occur? Describe the sequence the Olympic years form? **2008, 2012, 2016; arithmetic**

3. **BABY-SITTING** Tonya charges $3.50 per hour to baby-sit. The sequence $3.50, $7.00, $10.50, $14.00, ... represents how much she charges for each subsequent hour. For example, $10.50 is the third term that represents how much she charges for 3 hours. What are the next three terms in the sequence? How much does she charge for 7 hours of baby-sitting?
$17.50, $21.00, $24.50; $24.50

4. **RECTANGLES** Suppose you start with 1 rectangle and then divide it in half. You now have 2 rectangles. You divide each of these in half, and you have 4 rectangles. The sequence for this division is 1, 2, 8, 16, ... rectangles after each successive division. Describe the sequence that results?
geometric

5. **BACTERIA** Three bacteria are in a dish. Each hour the number of bacteria multiplies by four. If at the end of the first hour there are 12 bacteria, how many bacteria are there at the end of the next three hours? Describe the sequence that results?
48, 192, 768; geometric

6. **ENROLLMENT** The enrollment at Grove Middle School is expected to increase by 40 students each year for the next 5 years. If their current enrollment is 600 students, find their enrollment after each of the next 5 years.
640, 680, 720, 760, 800

7. **SALARY** Mrs. Malone's current salary is $1,500. She expects it to increase $100 per year. Write the first 6 terms of a sequence that represents her salary. The first term should be her current salary. What does the sixth term represent? **$1,500, $1,600, $1,700, $1,800, $1,900, $2,000; her salary after 5 years or at the beginning of the sixth year**

8. **FIBONACCI** The Fibonacci sequence is named after Leonardo Fibonacci who first explored it. Look at the Fibonacci sequence below and describe its pattern. 1, 1, 2, 3, 5, 8, 13, 21, 34, ... **Each term is found by adding the two previous terms; it is neither arithmetic nor geometric.**

Chapter 1   64   Course 2

Enrichment
p. 65 **OL** **AL**

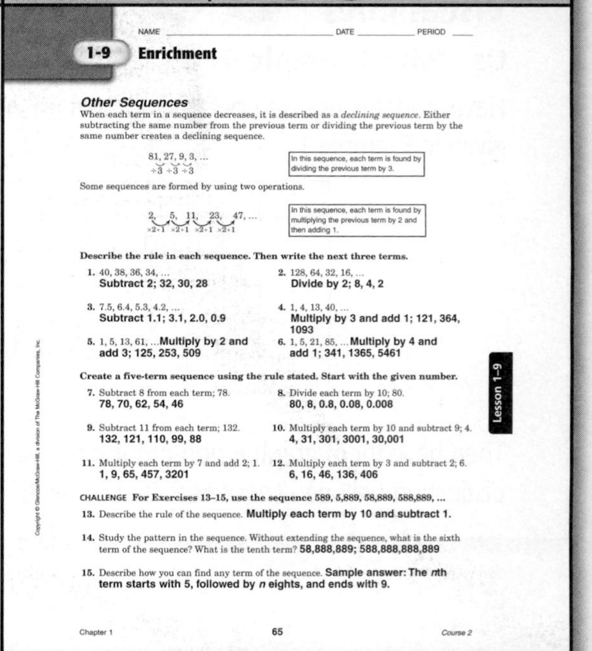

NAME _____ DATE _____ PERIOD _____

1-9 Enrichment

Other Sequences
When each term in a sequence decreases, it is described as a *declining sequence*. Either subtracting the same number from the previous term or dividing the previous term by the same number creates a declining sequence.

81, 27, 9, 3, ...   In this sequence, each term is found by
÷3 ÷3 ÷3   dividing the previous term by 3.

Some sequences are formed by using two operations.

1, 2, 11, 23, 47, ...   In this sequence, each term is found by
×2+1 ×2+1 ×2+1 ×2+1   multiplying the previous term by 2 and then adding 1.

Describe the rule in each sequence. Then write the next three terms.

1. 40, 38, 36, 34, ...   2. 128, 64, 32, 16, ...
Subtract 2; 32, 30, 28   **Divide by 2; 8, 4, 2**

3. 7.5, 6.4, 5.3, 4.2, ...   4. 1, 4, 13, 40, ...
Subtract 1.1; 3.1, 2.0, 0.9   **Multiply by 3 and add 1; 121, 364, 1093**

5. 1, 5, 21, 85, ...   6. 5, 21, 85, ...
Multiply by 2 and add 3; 125, 253, 509   **Multiply by 4 and add 1; 341, 1365, 5461**

Create a five-term sequence using the rule stated. Start with the given number.

7. Multiply by 8 from each term; 78.   8. Divide by 10; 80.
78, 70, 62, 54, 46   **80, 8, 0.8, 0.08, 0.008**

9. Subtract 11 from each term; 132.   10. Multiply each term by 10 and subtract 9; 4.
132, 121, 110, 99, 88   **4, 31, 301, 3001, 30,001**

11. Multiply each term by 7 and add 2; 1.   12. Multiply each term by 3 and subtract 2; 6.
1, 9, 65, 457, 3201   **6, 16, 46, 136, 406**

CHALLENGE For Exercises 13–15, use the sequence 589, 5,889, 58,889, 588,889, ...

13. Describe the rule of the sequence. **Multiply each term by 10 and subtract 1.**

14. Study the pattern in the sequence. Without extending the sequence, what is the sixth term of the sequence? What is the tenth term? **58,888,889; 588,888,888,889**

15. Describe how you can find any term of the sequence. **Sample answer: The nth term starts with 5, followed by n eights, and ends with 9.**

Chapter 1   65   Course 2

Additional Lesson Resources

Transparencies
- *5-Minute Check Transparency*, Lesson 1-9

Other Print Products
- *Teaching Mathematics with Manipulatives*
- *Noteables™ Interactive Study Notebook with Foldables™*

Teacher Tech Tools
- *Interactive Classroom CD-ROM*, Lesson 1-9
- *AssignmentWorks*, Lesson 1-9

Student Tech Tools
glencoe.com
- Extra Examples, Chapter 1, Lesson 9
- Self-Check Quiz, Chapter 1, Lesson 9

Algebra: Arithmetic Sequences

MAIN IDEA

Describe the relationships and extend terms in arithmetic sequences.

New Vocabulary

sequence
term
arithmetic sequence

Math Online

glencoe.com

• Concepts In Motion
• Extra Examples
• Personal Tutor
• Self-Check Quiz

▶ MINI Lab

Use centimeter cubes to make the three figures shown.

Figure 1   Figure 2   Figure 3

1. How many centimeter cubes are used to make each figure?

2. What pattern do you see? Describe it in words.

3. Suppose this pattern continues. Copy and complete the table to find the number of cubes needed to make each figure.

Figure	1	2	3	4	5	6	7	8
Cubes Needed	4	8	12	16	20	24	28	32

4. How many cubes would you need to make the 10th figure? Explain your reasoning. **1, 2, 4. See margin.**

A **sequence** is an ordered list of numbers. Each number in a sequence is called a **term**. In an **arithmetic sequence**, each term is found by adding the same number to the previous term. An example of an arithmetic sequence is shown.

$$8, \ 11, \ 14, \ 17, \ 20, \ \ldots$$
$$+3 \ +3 \ +3 \ +3$$

Each term is found by adding 3 to the previous term.

EXAMPLE   Describe and Extend Sequences

① Describe the relationship between the terms in the arithmetic sequence 8, 13, 18, 23, … Then write the next three terms in the sequence.

$$8, \ 13, \ 18, \ 23, \ \ldots$$
$$+5 \ +5 \ +5$$

Each term is found by adding 5 to the previous term. Continue the pattern to find the next three terms.

$$23 + 5 = 28 \qquad 28 + 5 = 33 \qquad 33 + 5 = 38$$

The next three terms are 28, 33, and 38.

✓ **CHECK Your Progress**

a. 13 is added to each term; 52, 65, 78
b. 3 is added to each term; 16, 19, 22

Describe the relationship between the terms in each arithmetic sequence. Then write the next three terms in the sequence.

a. 0, 13, 26, 39, …   b. 4, 7, 10, 13 …

Vertical Alignment

Before Lesson 1-9
Use a letter to represent an unknown number; write and evaluate simple algebraic expressions in one variable by substitution

Lesson 1-9
Write and evaluate an algebraic expression for a given situation

After Lesson 1-9
Use variables and appropriate operations to write an expression, an equation, an inequality, or a system of equations or inequalities that represents a verbal description

2 Teach

▶ MINI Lab

You might want to point out that each figure's number is the same as its height, so students can also multiply to find the total number of cubes in later figures.

Scaffolding Questions

Ask:

• What is the next number in the sequence 10, 12, 14, 16, . . . ? 18

• What is the next number in the sequence 25, 30, 35, 40, . . . ? 45

• What is the next number in the sequence 0, 3, 6, 9, . . . ? 12

• How did you find the next number in each sequence? by adding the difference between consecutive numbers to the last number in the sequence

Additional Answers

1. 4, 8, 12

2. Each time, 4 more cubes are added.

4. 40; For the 9th figure, you need 32 + 4 or 36 cubes, and for the 10th figure, you need 36 + 4 or 40 cubes.

ADDITIONAL EXAMPLES

1 Describe the relationship between the terms in the arithmetic sequence 7, 11, 15, 19 . . . Then write the next three terms in the sequence. 4 is added to each term; 23, 27, 31

2 Describe the relationship between the terms in the arithmetic sequence 0.1, 0.5, 0.9, 1.3, . . . Then write the next three terms in the sequence. Each term is 0.4 greater than the previous term; 1.7, 2.1, 2.5

Additional Examples are also in:

• Noteables™ Interactive Study Notebook with Foldables™

• Interactive Classroom PowerPoint® Presentations

Focus on Mathematical Content

A **sequence** is a list of numbers in a certain order.

Each **term** in a sequence has a position (first, second, third, and so on).

In an **arithmetic sequence**, the same number is added to each term to get the following term. This is the relationship between consecutive terms.

The **Focus on Mathematical Content** provides background information for each lesson. This information would be especially valuable to new teachers or those new to teaching mathematics.

---

c. 0.3 is added to each term; 2.2, 2.5, 2.8
d. 0.5 is added to each term; 4.5, 5.0, 5.5

Arithmetic sequences can also involve decimals.

EXAMPLE **Describe and Extend Sequences**

2 Describe the relationship between the terms in the arithmetic sequence 0.4, 0.6, 0.8, 1.0, ... Then write the next three terms in the sequence.

$$0.4, \ 0.6, \ 0.8, \ 1.0, \ \ldots$$
$$+0.2 \ +0.2 \ +0.2$$

Each term is found by adding 0.2 to the previous term. Continue the pattern to find the next three terms.

$$1.0 + 0.2 = 1.2 \qquad 1.2 + 0.2 = 1.4 \qquad 1.4 + 0.2 = 1.6$$

The next three terms are 1.2, 1.4, and 1.6.

CHECK Your Progress

Describe the relationship between the terms in each arithmetic sequence. Then write the next three terms in the sequence.

c. 1.0, 1.3, 1.6, 1.9, …   d. 2.5, 3.0, 3.5, 4.0, …

In a sequence, each term has a specific position within the sequence. Consider the sequence 2, 4, 6, 8, 10, …

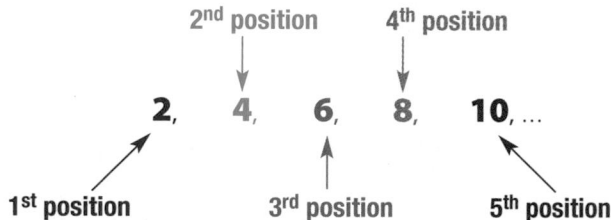

The table below shows the position of each term in this sequence. Notice that as the position number increases by 1, the value of the term increases by 2.

Position	Operation	Value of Term
1	$1 \cdot 2 = 2$	2
2	$2 \cdot 2 = 4$	4
3	$3 \cdot 2 = 6$	6
4	$4 \cdot 2 = 8$	8
5	$5 \cdot 2 = 10$	10

You can also write an algebraic expression to represent the relationship between any term in a sequence and its position in the sequence. In this case, if n represents the position in the sequence, the value of the term is $2n$.

③ GREETING CARDS The homemade greeting cards that Meredith makes are sold in boxes at a local gift store. Each week, the store sells five more boxes.

Week 1

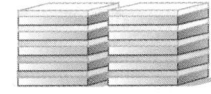
Week 2

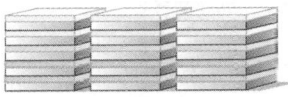
Week 3

If this pattern continues, what algebraic expression can be used to help her find the total number of boxes sold at the end of the 100th week? Use the expression to find the total.

Study Tip

Arithmetic Sequences
When looking for a pattern between the position number and each term in the sequence, it is often helpful to make a table.

Make a table to display the sequence.

Position	Operation	Value of Term
1	1 • 5	5
2	2 • 5	10
3	3 • 5	15
n	n • 5	$5n$

Each term is 5 times its position number. So, the expression is $5n$.

$5n$ Write the expression.

$5(100) = 500$ Replace n with 100.

So, at the end of 100 weeks, 500 boxes will have been sold.

✓ CHECK Your Progress   e. $3n$, 150

e. **GEOMETRY** If the pattern continues, what algebraic expression can be used to find the number of circles used in the 50th figure? How many circles will be in the 50th figure?

Figure 1   Figure 2   Figure 3

★ indicates multi-step problem

✓ CHECK Your Understanding

Examples 1, 2
(pp. 57–58)

Describe the relationship between the terms in each arithmetic sequence. Then write the next three terms in each sequence. **1–4. See margin.**

1. 0, 9, 18, 27, …

2. 4, 9, 14, 19, …

3. 1, 1.1, 1.2, 1.3, …

4. 5, 5.4, 5.8, 6.2, …

Example 3
(p. 59)

5. **PLANTS** The table shows the height of a certain plant each month after being planted. If this pattern continues, what algebraic expression can be used to find the height of the plant at the end of twelve months? Find the plant's height after 12 months. **$3n$, 36 in.**

Month	Height (in.)
1	3
2	6
3	9
4	12

ADDITIONAL EXAMPLE

③ **EXERCISE** Mehmet started a new exercise routine. The first day, he did 2 sit-ups. Each day after that, he did 2 more sit-ups than the previous day. If he continues this pattern, what algebraic expression can be used to help find the total number of sit-ups on the tenth day? Use the expression to find the number. $2d$; 20

③ Practice

✓ Formative Assessment

Use Exercises 1–5 to check for understanding.

Then use the chart at the bottom of the next page to customize your assignments for students.

Intervention You may wish to use the Study Guide and Intervention Master on page 61 of the *Chapter 1 Resource Masters* for additional reinforcement.

Additional Answers

1. 9 is added to each term; 36, 45, 54

2. 5 is added to each term; 24, 29, 34

3. 0.1 is added to each term; 1.4, 1.5, 1.6

4. 0.4 is added to each term; 6.6, 7.0, 7.4

Odd/Even Assignments

Exercises 6–19 are structured so that students practice the same concepts whether they are assigned odd or even problems.

 Exercise Alert!

Use the Internet Exercise 31 requires students to use the Internet or another source to research the Fibonacci sequence.

Additional Answers

6. 7 is added to each term; 28, 35, 42

7. 6 is added to each term; 25, 31, 37

8. 8 is added to each term; 58, 66, 74

9. 12 is added to each term; 67, 79, 91

10. 10 is added to each term; 46, 56, 66

11. 5 is added to each term; 53, 58, 63

12. 0.3 is added to each term; 1.3, 1.6, 1.9

13. 0.8 is added to each term; 5.6, 6.4, 7.2

14. 1.1 is added to each term; 6.4, 7.5, 8.6

15. 1.5 is added to each term; 10.5, 12.0, 13.5

16. 2 is added to each term; 9.2, 11.2, 13.2

17. 4 is added to each term; 20.6, 24.6, 28.6

31. The Fibonacci sequence is 1, 1, 2, 3, 5, 8, 13, ... In this sequence, each term after the second term is the sum of the two terms before it. Fibonacci numbers occur in many areas of nature, including pine cones, shell spirals, and branching plants.

▶ Practice and Problem Solving

HOMEWORK HELP

For Exercises	See Examples
6–11	1
12–17	2
18, 19	3

Exercise Levels
A: 6–19
B: 20–31
C: 32–36

Describe the relationship between the terms in each arithmetic sequence. Then write the next three terms in each sequence. 6–17. See margin.

6. 0, 7, 14, 21, …   **7.** 1, 7, 13, 19, …   **8.** 26, 34, 42, 50, …

9. 19, 31, 43, 55, …   **10.** 6, 16, 26, 36, …   **11.** 33, 38, 43, 48, …

12. 0.1, 0.4, 0.7, 1.0, …   **13.** 2.4, 3.2, 4.0, 4.8, …   **14.** 2.0, 3.1, 4.2, 5.3, …

15. 4.5, 6.0, 7.5, 9.0, …   **16.** 1.2, 3.2, 5.2, 7.2, …   **17.** 4.6, 8.6, 12.6, 16.6, …

18. COLLECTIONS Hannah is starting a doll collection. Each year, she buys 6 dolls. Suppose she continues this pattern. What algebraic expression can be used to find the number of dolls in her collection after any number of years? How many dolls will Hannah have after 25 years? **$6n$; 150 dolls**

19. EXERCISE The table shows the number of laps that Jorge swims each week. Jorge's goal is to continue this pace. What algebraic expression can be used to find the total number of laps he will swim after any given number of weeks? How many laps will Jorge swim after 6 weeks? **$7n$; 42 laps**

Week	Number of Laps
1	7
2	14
3	21
4	28

20. 15 is added to each term; 78, 93, 108
21. 25 is added to each term; 120, 145, 170
22. 23 is added to each term; 130, 153, 176

Describe the relationship between the terms in each arithmetic sequence. Then write the next three terms in each sequence.

20. 18, 33, 48, 63, …   **21.** 20, 45, 70, 95, …   **22.** 38, 61, 84, 107, …

In a *geometric sequence*, each term is found by multiplying the previous term by the same number. Write the next three terms of each geometric sequence.

23. 1, 4, 16, 64, … **256, 1,024, 4,096**   **24.** 2, 6, 18, 54, … **162, 486, 1,458**   **25.** 4, 12, 36, 108, … **324, 972, 2,916**

★ **26. GEOMETRY** Kendra is stacking boxes of tissues for a store display. Each minute, she stacks another layer of boxes. If the pattern continues, how many boxes will be displayed after 45 minutes? **135 boxes**

1 Minute   2 Minutes   3 Minutes

NUMBER SENSE Find the 100th number in each sequence.

27. 12, 24, 36, 48, … **1,200**   **28.** 14, 28, 42, 56, … **1,400**

29. 0, 50, 100, 150, … **4,950**   **30.** 0, 75, 150, 225, … **7,425**

EXTRA PRACTICE
See pages 670, 704.

31. RESEARCH The Fibonacci sequence is one of the most well-known sequences in mathematics. Use the Internet or another source to write a paragraph about the Fibonacci sequence. **See margin.**

60 Chapter 1 Introduction to Algebra and Functions

DIFFERENTIATED HOMEWORK OPTIONS

Level	Assignment	Two-Day Option	
BL Basic	6–19, 34–47	7–19 odd, 37, 38	6–18 even, 34–36, 39–47
OL Core	7–17 odd, 18, 19, 21–25 odd, 26, 27, 29, 31, 34–47	6–19, 37, 38	20–31, 34–36, 39–47
AL Advanced/Pre-AP	20–44 (optional: 45–47)		

CHALLENGE Not all sequences are arithmetic. But, there is still a pattern. Describe the relationship between the terms in each sequence. Then write the next three terms in the sequence.

32. 1, 2, 4, 7, 11, …
$+ 1, + 2, + 3, + 4, \dots; 16, 22, 29$

33. 0, 2, 6, 12, 20, …
$+ 2, + 4, + 6, + 8, \dots; 30, 42, 56$

34. OPEN ENDED Write five terms of an arithmetic sequence and describe the rule for finding the terms. **Sample answer: 5, 6, 7, 8, …; $n + 4$**

35. SELECT A TOOL Suppose you want to begin saving $15 each month. Which of the following tools would you use to determine the amount you will have saved after 2 years? Justify your selection(s). Then use the tool(s) to solve the problem. **See margin.**

| paper/pencil | real object | technology |

36. **WRITING IN MATH** Janice earns $6.50 per hour running errands for her neighbor. Explain how the hourly earnings form an arithmetic sequence. **See margin.**

TEST PRACTICE

37. Which sequence follows the rule $3n - 2$, where n represents the position of a term in the sequence? **D**

- **A** 21, 18, 15, 12, 9, …
- **B** 3, 6, 9, 12, 15, …
- **C** 1, 7, 10, 13, 16, …
- **D** 1, 4, 7, 10, 13, …

38. Which expression can be used to find the nth term in this sequence? **F**

Position	1	2	3	4	5	nth
Value of Term	2	5	10	17	26	

- **F** $n^2 + 1$
- **G** $2n + 1$
- **H** $n + 1$
- **J** $2n^2 + 2$

Spiral Review

Find each expression mentally. Justify each step. (Lesson 1-8)

39. $(23 + 18) + 7$ **48**

40. $5 \cdot (12 \cdot 20)$ **1,200**

39–40. See margin for justification.

Solve each equation mentally. (Lesson 1-7)

41. $f - 26 = 3$ **29**

42. $\frac{a}{4} = 8$ **32**

43. $30 + y = 50$ **20**

44. SCIENCE At normal temperatures, sound travels through water at a rate of $5 \cdot 10^3$ feet per second. Write this rate in standard form. (Lesson 1-2) **5,000 ft/s**

GET READY for the Next Lesson

PREREQUISITE SKILL Find the value of each expression. (Lesson 1-6)

45. $2x$ if $x = 4$ **8**

46. $d - 5$ if $d = 8$ **3**

47. $3m - 3$ if $m = 2$ **3**

Lesson 1-9 Algebra: Arithmetic Sequences **61**

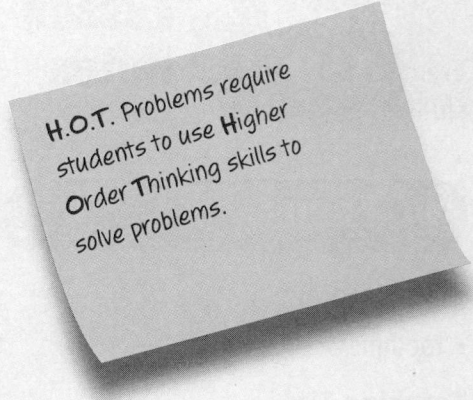

H.O.T. Problems require students to use Higher Order Thinking skills to solve problems.

4 Assess

Ticket Out the Door Write an arithmetic sequence such as 8, 16, 24, 32, … on the board. Have students write a term of the sequence (for example, the 9th term) on a small piece of paper.

Additional Answers

35. Sample answer: paper/pencil; Write the equation that represents this situation, 15n. Since 2 years = 24 months, evaluate the expression when n is 24. 15(24) = 360. So, after 2 years, $360 will be saved.

36. Sample answer: The total amount earned forms the sequence 6.5, 13, 19.5 , 26, …. Since each term is 6.5 more than the previous term, the sequence is arithmetic.

39. Sample answer: Rewrite $(23 + 18) + 7$ as $(18 + 23) + 7$ using the Commutative Property of Addition. Rewrite $(18 + 23) + 7$ as $18 + (23 + 7)$ using the Associative Property of Addition. Find $23 + 7$, or 30, mentally. Then find $18 + 30$, or 48, mentally.

40. Sample answer: Rewrite $5 \cdot (12 \cdot 20)$ as $5 \cdot (20 \cdot 12)$ using the Commutative Property of multiplication. Rewrite $5 \cdot (20 \cdot 12)$ as $(5 \cdot 20) \cdot 12$ using the Associative Property of Multiplication. Find $5 \cdot 20$, or 100, mentally. Then find $100 \cdot 12$, or 1,200, mentally.

Pre-AP Activity   Use after Exercise 38.

Explain that the first term of some arithmetic sequences isn't the number that is added to each term to get the following term. Write a sequence such as 3, 5, 7, 9, … on the board. Have students make a table showing the positions and terms of the sequence. Have them find the 5th and 6th terms and then write an expression to find the nth term. $2n + 1$

Position	1	2	3	4	5	6
Value of Term	3	5	7	9	11	13

Extend 1-9 — Lesson Notes

1 Focus

Materials
• toothpicks

Teaching Tip

You may wish to have students work in pairs for this lab.

2 Teach

Working in Cooperative Groups
You may wish for students to work in groups of two or three. Student 1 can build the figures, Student 2 can count the toothpicks, and Student 3 can record the results in the table.

Activity Some students will be able to perform the activity and analyze the results without toothpicks, either by visualizing the pattern or by drawing the figures.

3 Assess

 Formative Assessment

Use Exercises 3 and 4 to determine whether students comprehend how to use toothpicks to create and analyze arithmetic sequences.

From Concrete to Abstract Use Exercise 5 to bridge the gap between using toothpicks to create arithmetic sequences and writing an expression to describe such a sequence.

Algebra Labs use manipulatives and models to help students learn key concepts. There are teacher notes for every Algebra Lab in the Student Edition. Other labs include Measurement, Geometry, Statistics, and Probability.

Extend 1-9 — Algebra Lab: Exploring Sequences

MAIN IDEA

Explore patterns in sequences of geometric figures.

ACTIVITY

STEP 1 Use toothpicks to build the figures below.

Figure 1   Figure 2   Figure 3

STEP 2 Make a table like the one shown and record the figure number and number of toothpicks used in each figure.

Figure Number	Number of Toothpicks
1	4
2	7
3	10

STEP 3 Construct the next figure in this pattern. Record your results.

STEP 4 Repeat Step 3 until you have found the next four figures in the pattern.

ANALYZE THE RESULTS 1, 3, 4, 6, and 7. See Ch. 1 Answer Appendix.

1. How many additional toothpicks were used each time to form the next figure in the pattern? Where is this pattern found in the table?

2. Based on your answer to Exercise 1, how many toothpicks would be in Figure 0 of this pattern? **1**

3. Remove one toothpick from your pattern so that Figure 1 is made up of just three toothpicks as shown. Then create a table showing the number of toothpicks that would be in the first 7 figures by continuing the same pattern as above.

   Figure 1

4. How many toothpicks would there be in Figure n of this new pattern?

5. How could you adapt the expression you wrote in Exercise 4 to find the number of toothpicks in Figure n of the original pattern? **$3n + 1$**

6. **MAKE A PREDICTION** How many toothpicks would there be in Figure 10 of the original pattern? Explain your reasoning. Then check your answer by constructing the figure.

7. Find the number of toothpicks in Figure n of the pattern below, and predict the number of toothpicks in Figure 12. Justify your answer.

Figure 1   Figure 2   Figure 3

Extending the Concept Ask students to write an expression for the number of toothpicks in figure n of a sequence in which each figure is composed of equilateral triangles and an expression for the number of toothpicks in figure n of a sequence in which each figure is composed of regular pentagons. **$2n + 1$; $4n + 1$**

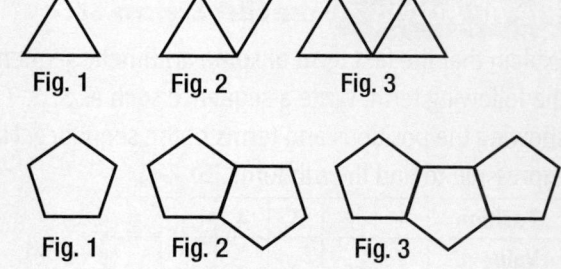

Fig. 1   Fig. 2   Fig. 3

Fig. 1   Fig. 2   Fig. 3

1-10

Algebra: Equations and Functions

PACING: **Regular:** 1.5 periods, **Block:** 1 period

Options for Differentiated Instruction

ELL = English Language Learner   **AL** = Above or Beyond Grade Level   **SS** = Struggling Students   **SN** = Special Needs

Auditory Learning   **ELL** **SS**
Use while presenting Examples 1–3.

Some students take in information more easily through listening than through reading. Think aloud as you demonstrate the steps for completing a function table and writing and using an equation. Verbalize what you would normally perform automatically.

Organizing Student Work and Thinking   **SS** **SN**
Use with the Exercises.

For students with organizational difficulties, it may be helpful to provide enlarged photocopies of the function tables in Exercises 1, 2, 6–8, and 15–18 so that they do not have to copy them. It may also be helpful to provide a template like the one shown below for the exercises that require students to make a function table.

Input	Function Rule	Output

Use for both homework and class work, making sure that they identify both the page number and the problem number as a reference.

Extensions and Challenges   **AL**
Use with the H.O.T. Problems.

Remind students that a function rule can often have more then one operation.
Have them examine the following function tables and determine the function rule for each.

Input x	Output y
1	5
2	8
3	11
4	14

$$y = 3x + 2$$

Input x	Output y
1	0
2	2
3	4
4	6

$$y = 2x - 2$$

Input x	Output y
1	2
2	5
3	10
4	17

$$y = x^2 + 1$$

Leveled Lesson Resources

Also on **TeacherWorks™** Lesson 1-10

Chapter 1 Resource Masters

BL = Below or Approaching Grade Level **OL** = On Grade Level **AL** = Above or Beyond Grade Level **ELL** = English Language Learner

*Lesson Reading Guide** p. 67 BL OL ELL

NAME ______________ DATE ________ PERIOD ____

1-10 Lesson Reading Guide

Algebra: Equations and Functions

Get Ready for the Lesson

Read the introduction at the top of page 63 in your textbook. Write your answers below.

1. Complete the table to find the cost of 2, 3, and 4 magazines.

Magazines		
Number	Multiply by 4	Cost($)
1	4 × 1	4
2	4 × 2	8
3	4 × 3	12
4	4 × 4	16

2. Describe the pattern in the table between the cost and the number of magazines. **The cost increases by 4 each time the number of magazines increases by 1.**

Read the Lesson

3. Complete each function table. Then identify the domain and range.

a.

x	$2x - 1$	y
−1	2(−1) − 1	−3
0	2(0) − 1	−1
1	2(1) − 1	1

domain: {−1, 0, 1}
range: {−3, −1, 1}

b.

x	$4x$	y
−1	4(−1)	−4
0	4(0)	0
1	4(1)	4

domain: {−1, 0, 1}
range: {−4, 0, 4}

4. MONEY John earns $15 per lawn that he mows.
   a. Write an equation in two variables showing the relationship between lawns mowed and the money John earns. **m = lawns mowed, d = dollars earned, $15m = d$**
   b. How much money does John earn after mowing 3, 5, and 10 lawns? **3, $45 5, $75 10, $150**

Remember What You Learned

5. Draw a picture of a "machine" that shows how a function works. Your picture should illustrate input, a function rule, and output. **See students' work.**

Lesson 1-10

Chapter 1 67 Course 2

*Study Guide and Intervention** p. 68 BL OL ELL

NAME ______________ DATE ________ PERIOD ____

1-10 Study Guide and Intervention

Algebra: Equations and Functions

The solution of an equation with two variables consists of two numbers, one for each variable that makes the equation true. When a relationship assigns exactly one output value for each input value, it is called a function. Function tables help to organize input numbers, output numbers, and function rules.

Example 1 **Complete a function table for $y = 5x$. Then state the domain and range.**

Choose four values for x. Substitute the values for x into the expression. Then evaluate to find the y value.

x	$5x$	y
0	5(0)	0
1	5(1)	5
2	5(2)	10
3	5(3)	15

The domain is {0, 1, 2, 3}. The range is {0, 5, 10, 15}.

Exercises

Complete the following function tables. Then state the domain and range.

1. $y = x + 4$

x	$x + 4$	y
0	0+4	4
1	1+4	5
2	2+4	6
3	3+4	7

domain: {0, 1, 2, 3}
range: {4, 5, 6, 7}

2. $y = 10x$

x	$10x$	y
1	10(1)	10
2	10(2)	20
3	10(3)	30
4	10(4)	40

domain: {1, 2, 3, 4}
range: {10, 20, 30, 40}

3. $y = x - 1$

x	$x - 1$	y
2	2−1	1
3	3−1	2
4	4−1	3
5	5−1	4

domain: {2, 3, 4, 5}
range: {1, 2, 3, 4}

4. $y = 3x$

x	$3x$	y
10	3(10)	30
11	3(11)	33
12	3(12)	36
13	3(13)	39

domain: {10, 11, 12, 13}
range: {30, 33, 36, 39}

Chapter 1 68 Course 2

*Skills Practice** p. 69 BL OL

NAME ______________ DATE ________ PERIOD ____

1-10 Skills Practice

Algebra: Equations and Functions

Copy and complete each function table. Identify the domain and range.

1. $y = x - 1$

x	$x - 1$	y
1	1 − 1	0
2	2 − 1	1
3	3 − 1	2
4	4 − 1	3

domain: {1, 2, 3, 4}
range: {0, 1, 2, 3}

2. $y = x + 7$

x	$x + 7$	y
1	1 + 7	8
2	2 + 7	9
3	3 + 7	10
4	4 + 7	11

domain: {1, 2, 3, 4}
range: {8, 9, 10, 11}

3. $y = 3x$

x	$3x$	y
1	3(1)	3
2	3(2)	6
3	3(3)	9
4	3(4)	12

domain: {1, 2, 3, 4}
range: {3, 6, 9, 12}

4. $y = 4x$

x	$4x$	y
2	4(2)	8
3	4(3)	12
4	4(4)	16
5	4(5)	20

domain: {2, 3, 4, 5}
range: {8, 12, 16, 20}

5. $y = x - 0.5$

x	$x - 0.5$	y
1	1 − 0.5	0.5
2	2 − 0.5	1.5
3	3 − 0.5	2.5
4	4 − 0.5	3.5

domain: {1, 2, 3, 4}
range: {0.5, 1.5, 2.5, 3.5}

6. $y = 10x$

x	$10x$	y
0	10(0)	0
1	10(1)	10
2	10(2)	20
3	10(3)	30

domain: {0, 1, 2, 3}
range: {0, 10, 20, 30}

Solve each word problem.

For Exercises 7 and 8, use the following information.

TRAVEL **For every gallon of gas, a car can travel 30 miles.**

7. Write an equation using two variables to show the relationship between the distance the car travels and the gallons of gas it uses. **d = distance, g = gallons of gas, $30g = d$**

8. If a car had 8 gallons of gas left in its tank, how many miles can it travel before the tank runs out? **240 miles**

For Exercises 9 and 10, use the following information.

FARMING **Every row of corn in Mr. Jones' garden has 5 cornstalks.**

9. Write an equation using two variables to show the relationship between the number of rows and the number of cornstalks. **r = rows, s = stalks, $5r = s$**

10. If Mr. Jones has 7 rows of corn, how many cornstalks will he need to harvest? **35 cornstalks**

Lesson 1-10

Chapter 1 69 Course 2

*Practice** p. 70 OL AL

NAME ______________ DATE ________ PERIOD ____

1-10 Practice

Algebra: Equations and Functions

Complete each function table. Then identify the domain and range.

1. $y = 5x$

x	$5x$	y
1	5 · 1	5
2	5 · 2	10
3	5 · 3	15
4	5 · 4	20

Domain: {1, 2, 3, 4}
Range: {5, 10, 15, 20}

2. $y = 8x$

x	$8x$	y
1	8 · 1	1
2	8 · 2	16
3	8 · 3	24
4	8 · 4	32

Domain: {1, 2, 3, 4}
Range: {1, 16, 24, 32}

3. $y = 7x$

x	$7x$	y
3	7 · 3	21
4	7 · 4	28
5	7 · 5	35
6	7 · 6	42

Domain: {3, 4, 5, 6}
Range: {21, 28, 35, 42}

4. $y = x - 2$

x	$x - 2$	y
2	2 − 2	0
3	3 − 2	1
4	4 − 2	2
5	5 − 2	3

Domain: {2, 3, 4, 5}
Range: {0, 1, 2, 3}

5. $y = x + 3$

x	$x + 3$	y
2	2 + 3	5
3	3 + 3	6
4	4 + 3	7
5	5 + 3	8

Domain: {2, 3, 4, 5}
Range: {5, 6, 7, 8}

6. $y = x + 0.75$

x	$x + 0.75$	y
0	0 + 0.75	0.75
1	1 + 0.75	1.75
2	2 + 0.75	2.75
3	3 + 0.75	3.75

Domain: {0, 1, 2, 3}
Range: {0.75, 1.75, 2.75, 3.75}

7. PRODUCTION A car manufacturer makes 15,000 hybrid cars a month. Using the function table, find the number of hybrid cars produced after 3, 6, 9, and 12 months.

m	$15{,}000m$	P
3	15,000 · 3	45,000
6	15,000 · 6	90,000
9	15,000 · 9	135,000
12	15,000 · 12	180,000

8. SUNSPOTS The changing activity of sunspots, which are cooler and darker areas of the sun, occur in 11-year cycles. Use the function $y = 11c$ to find the numbers of years necessary to complete 1, 2, 3, and 4 sunspot cycles.

11 years, 22 years, 33 years, and 44 years

Chapter 1 70 Course 2

*Word Problem Practice** p. 71 OL AL

NAME ______________ DATE ________ PERIOD ____

1-10 Word Problem Practice

Algebra: Equations and Functions

1. TECHNOLOGY The fee for your pager service is $22 per month. Make a function table that shows your total charge for 1, 2, 3, and 4 months of service.

x, Months	y, Total Charge
1	22
2	44
3	66
4	88

2. MEASUREMENT Joe takes 2 steps for every one step that Kim takes. Write an equation in two variables showing the relationship between Joe's steps and Kim's steps. If Kim takes 15 steps, how many steps will Joe have to take to cover the same distance?
j = the number of steps Joe takes
k = the number of steps Kim takes, $2k = j$
30 steps

3. TRAINS Between Hiroshima and Kokura, Japan, the bullet train averages a speed of 164 miles per hour, which is the fastest scheduled train service in the world. Make a function table that shows the distance traveled at that speed in 1, 2, 3, and 4 hours.

x, Hours	y, Distance
1	164
2	328
3	492
4	656

4. BUSINESS Grant earns $5 for each magazine that he sells. Write an equation in two variables showing the relationship between the number of magazines sold and the amount of money made. If Grant sells 12 magazines, how much money will he make?
m = the number of magazines sold, d = Grant's earnings in dollars, $5m = d$
$60

5. GEOMETRY The formula for the volume of a rectangular prism whose base has an area of 8 square units is $V = 8h$, where V is the volume and h is the height. Make a function table that shows the volume of a rectangular prism with a height of 3, 4, 5, and 6 units.

h	$8h$	V
3	8(3)	24
4	8(4)	32
5	8(5)	40
6	8(6)	48

6. GEOMETRY The fastest insect in the world is the dragonfly with a top speed of 36 miles per hour. Write an equation in two variables describing the relationship between the length of the dragonfly's flight and the distance traveled. If a dragonfly flies for 3 hours, how far can he travel?
y = time, d = distance, $36t = d$
108 miles

Lesson 1-10

Chapter 1 71 Course 2

Enrichment p. 72 OL AL

NAME ______________ DATE ________ PERIOD ____

1-10 Enrichment

To solve equations containing two variables, find ordered pair solutions for the equation by selecting values for x and completing a table. Although any value can be selected for x, values usually selected include −2, −1, 0, 1, and 2.

For example, to solve the equation $y = 2x$ given below in Exercise 1, first select values for x, then complete a table.

Ordered pair solutions for the equation $y = 2x$ include (−2, −4), (−1, −2), (0, 0), (1, 2), and (2, 4).

Match each equation with the point whose coordinates are a solution of the equation. Then, at the bottom of the page, write the letter of the point on the line directly above the number of the equation *each time it appears*. (The first one has been done as an example.) If you have matched the equations and solutions correctly, the letters below will reveal a message.

1. $y = 2x$	$A(-3, 8)$	$N(-1, 0)$
2. $y = x - 3$	$B(0, 2)$	$O(3, 0)$
3. $y = -x + 1$	$C(-2, 1)$	$P(1, 5)$
4. $y = 3x - 2$	$D(0, -5)$	$Q(0, 6)$
5. $y = -2x - 4$	$E(-1, -5)$	$R(1, 6)$
6. $y = x + (-2)$	$F(1, 3)$	$S(2, 1)$
7. $y = -4x - 1$	$G(0, -4)$	$T(-2, 3)$
8. $y = \frac{1}{2}x$	$H(-1, 3)$	$U(1, 2)$
9. $y = x + 3$	$I(2, 0)$	$V(-3, 5)$
10. $y = 7x + 7$	$J(0, 4)$	$W(0, -7)$
11. $y = -2x - 6$	$K(-3, 1)$	$X(-3, -3)$
12. $y = -x + 5$	$L(-4, 2)$	$Y(1, 8)$
13. $y = -5x + 8$	$M(-2, 2)$	$Z(0, -8)$
14. $y = -x$		

M A T H E M A T I C S   I S   T H E
14 12 3 7 4 14 12 3 6 9 8   6 8   3 7 4

L A N G U A G E   O F   S C I E N C E
11 12 10 5 1 12 5 4   2 13   8 9 6 4 10 9 4

Chapter 1 72 Course 2

*** Also available in Spanish** ELL

Additional Lesson Resources

Transparencies

- *5-Minute Check Transparency,* Lesson 1-10

Other Print Products

- *Noteables™ Interactive Study Notebook with Foldables™*

Teacher Tech Tools

- *Interactive Classroom CD-ROM,* Lesson 1-10
- *AssignmentWorks,* Lesson 1-10

Student Tech Tools

glencoe.com

- Extra Examples, Chapter 1, Lesson 10
- Self-Check Quiz, Chapter 1, Lesson 10

MAIN IDEA

Make function tables and write equations.

New Vocabulary

function
function rule
function table
domain
range

Math Online

glencoe.com

• Concepts In Motion
• Extra Examples
• Personal Tutor
• Self-Check Quiz

▷ GET READY for the Lesson

MAGAZINES Suppose you can buy magazines for $4 each.

1. Copy and complete the table to find the cost of 2, 3, and 4 magazines.

2. Describe the pattern in the table between the cost and the number of magazines.

Atomic Math MAGAZINE **MATH WIZARD MAGAZINE**

Number	Multiply by 4	Cost ($)
1	4 × 1	4
2	4 × 2	8
3	4 × 3	12
4	4 × 4	16

2. The cost increases by 4 each time the number of magazines increases by 1. A relationship that assigns exactly one *output* value for each *input* value is called a **function**. In a function, you start with an input number, perform one or more operations on it, and get an output number. The operation performed on the input is given by the **function rule**.

Input ⟹ Function Rule ⟹ Output

You can organize the input numbers, output numbers, and the function rule in a **function table**. The set of input values is called the **domain**, and the set of output values is called the **range**.

EXAMPLE Make a Function Table

1 **MONEY** Javier saves $20 each month. Make a function table to show his savings after 1, 2, 3, and 4 months. Then identify the domain and range.

The domain is {1, 2, 3, 4}, and the range is {20, 40, 60, 80}.

Input	Function Rule	Output
Number of Months	Multiply by 20	Total Savings ($)
1	20 × 1	20
2	20 × 2	40
3	20 × 3	60
4	20 × 4	80

✓ CHECK Your Progress

a. See Ch. 1 Answer Appendix for table.

a. Suppose a student movie ticket costs $3. Make a function table that shows the total cost for 1, 2, 3, and 4 tickets. Then identify the domain and range. **domain: {1, 2, 3, 4}; range: {$3, $6, $9, $12}**

Lesson 1-10 Algebra: Equations and Functions **63**

Tips for New Teachers

Braces

The symbols { and }, which are called braces, are used to list the elements in a set.

Additional Answer

1.

Number of Hours	Multiply by 6	Total Earnings ($)
1	6 × 1	6
2	6 × 2	12
3	6 × 3	18
4	6 × 4	24

Vertical Alignment

Before Lesson 1-10
Solve problems involving linear functions with integer values and write the equation

Lesson 1-10
Write and evaluate an algebraic expression for a given situation, using up to three variables. Use a variety of methods to explain mathematical reasoning

After Lesson 1-10
Graph linear functions, noting that the vertical change per unit of horizontal change is always the same and know that the ratio is called the slope of a graph

2 Teach

Scaffolding Questions

Ask:

• If an insect has 6 legs, how many legs do 2 insects have altogether? 3 insects? 4 insects? 12, 18, 24

• If a zebra has 4 legs, how many legs do 2 zebras have altogether? 3 zebras? 4 zebras? 8, 12, 16

• If a camp stool has 3 legs, how many legs do 2 camp stools have altogether? 3 camp stools? 4 camp stools? 6, 9, 12

ADDITIONAL EXAMPLE

1 Asha earns $6.00 an hour working at a grocery store. Make a function table that shows Asha's total earnings for working 1, 2, 3, and 4 hours.

A good way to explore functional relationships is to create a **function table**.

You can write a function as an **equation** with one variable representing the input number and a different variable representing the output number.

✓ Formative Assessment

Use the Check Your Progress exercises after the Examples to determine students' understanding of concepts.

ADDITIONAL EXAMPLES

2 **READING** Melanie read 14 pages of a detective novel each hour. Write an equation using two variables to show how many pages p she read in h hours.
$p = 14h$

3 Use your equation to find how many pages Melanie read in 7 hours. **98 pages**

Additional Examples are also in:
- Noteables™ Interactive Study Notebook with Foldables™
- Interactive Classroom PowerPoint® Presentations

Additional Answer

c. Sample answer: Replace h with 6 in the equation $g = 4h$ to find the growth in inches for this species of bamboo after 6 months.

Study Tip

Input and Output
When x and y are used in an equation, x usually represents the input, and y usually represents the output.

Study Tips offer students helpful information about the topics they are studying.

Functions are often written as equations with two variables—one to represent the input and one to represent the output. Here's an equation for the situation in Example 1.

Function rule: multiply by 20

$$20x = y$$

Input: number of months ——— ——— Output: total savings

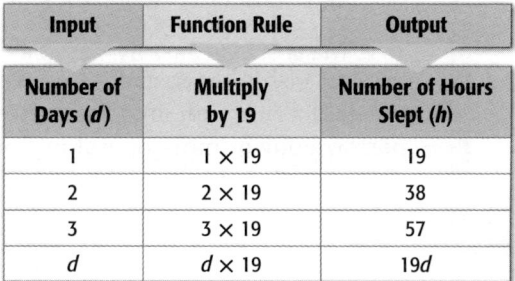

Real-World EXAMPLES

2 **ANIMALS** An armadillo sleeps 19 hours each day. Write an equation using two variables to show the relationship between the number of hours h an armadillo sleeps in d days.

Input	Function Rule	Output
Number of Days (d)	Multiply by 19	Number of Hours Slept (h)
1	1×19	19
2	2×19	38
3	3×19	57
d	$d \times 19$	$19d$

Words	Number of hours slept	equals	number of days	times	19 hours each day.
Variable	Let d represent the number of days. Let h represent the number of hours.				
Equation	$h = 19d$				

3 How many hours does an armadillo sleep in 4 days?

$h = 19d$ — Write the equation.

$h = 19(4)$ — Replace d with 4.

$h = 76$ — Multiply.

An armadillo sleeps 76 hours in 4 days.

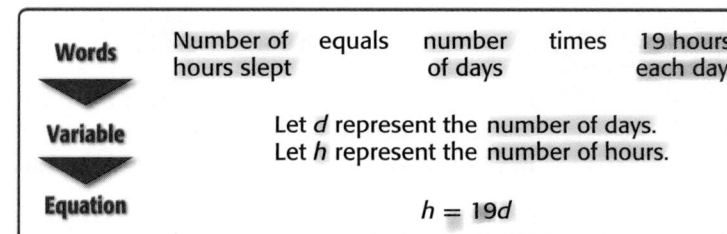
Real-World Career · · · ·
How Does a Botanist Use Math? A botanist gathers and studies plant statistics to solve problems and draw conclusions about various plants.

✓ CHECK Your Progress

· · · **BOTANIST** A botanist discovers that a certain species of bamboo grows 4 inches each hour. **b.** $g = 4h$

b. Write an equation using two variables to show the relationship between the growth g in inches of this bamboo plant in h hours.

c. Use your equation to explain how to find the growth in inches of this species of bamboo after 6 hours. **24 in.; See margin for explanation.**

64 Chapter 1 Introduction to Algebra and Functions

★ indicates multi-step problem

CHECK Your Understanding

Example 1
(p. 63)

Copy and complete each function table. Then identify the domain and range.

1. $y = 3x$

x	3x	y
1	3 • 1	3
2	3 • 2	6
3	3 • 3	9
4	**3 • 1**	**12**

domain: {1, 2, 3, 4}; range: {3, 6, 9, 12}

2. $y = 4x$

x	4x	y
0	4 • 0	0
1	4 • 1	4
2	4 • 2	8
3	4 • 3	12

domain: {0, 1, 2, 3}; range: {0, 4, 8, 12}

★ 3. **MUSIC** Jonas downloads 8 songs each month onto his digital music player. Make a function table that shows the total number of songs downloaded after 1, 2, 3, and 4 months. Then identify the domain and range.
domain: {1, 2, 3, 4}; range: {8, 16, 24, 32}; See margin for table.

Examples 2, 3
(p. 64)

SPORTS For Exercises 4 and 5, use the following information.

The top speed reached by a race car is 231 miles per hour.

4. Write an equation using two variables to show the relationship between the number of miles m that a race car can travel in h hours. **$m = 231h$**

5. Use your equation to explain how to find the distance in miles the race car will travel in 3 hours. **693 mi; See margin for explanation.**

Practice and Problem Solving

HOMEWORK HELP

For Exercises	See Examples
6–10	1
11–14	2, 3

Exercise Levels
A: 6–14
B: 15–23
C: 24–28

6. domain: {0, 1, 2, 3}; range: {0, 2, 4, 6}
7. domain: {1, 2, 3, 4}; range: {6, 12, 18, 24}
8. domain: {1, 2, 3, 4}; range: {9, 18, 27, 36}

Copy and complete each function table. Then identify the domain and range.

6. $y = 2x$

x	2x	y
0	2 • 0	0
1	2 • 1	2
2	**2 • 2**	**4**
3	**2 • 3**	**6**

7. $y = 6x$

x	6x	y
1	**6 • 1**	**6**
2	**6 • 2**	**12**
3	**6 • 3**	**18**
4	**6 • 4**	**24**

8. $y = 9x$

x	9x	y
1	**9 • 1**	**9**
2	**9 • 2**	**18**
3	**9 • 3**	**27**
4	**9 • 4**	**36**

Make a function table for each situation. Then identify the domain and range. 9–10. See margin for tables.

9. **PIZZA** A pizza shops sells 25 pizzas each hour. Find the number of pizzas sold after 1, 2, 3, and 4 hours. **domain: {1, 2, 3, 4}; range: {25, 50, 75, 100}**
★

10. **TYPING** Suppose you can type 60 words per minute. What is the total number of words typed after 5, 10, 15, and 20 minutes?
★ **domain: {5, 10, 15, 20}; range: {300, 600, 900, 1,200}**

CELL PHONES For Exercises 11 and 12, use the following information.

A cell phone provider charges a customer $40 for each month of service.

11. Write an equation using two variables to show the relationship between the total amount charged c, after m months of cell phone service. **$c = 40m$**

12. Use your equation to explain how to find the total cost for 6 months of cell phone service. **$120; See margin for explanation.**

Lesson 1-10 Algebra: Equations and Functions **65**

DIFFERENTIATED HOMEWORK OPTIONS

Level	Assignment	Two-Day Option	
BL Basic	6–14, 27–36	7–13 odd, 29, 30	6–10 even, 27, 28, 31–36
OL Core	7, 9–15, 17, 19–23, 27–36	6–14, 29, 30	15–23, 27, 28, 31–36
AL Advanced/Pre-AP	15–36		

3 Practice

Formative Assessment

Use Exercises 1–5 to check for understanding.

Then use the chart at the bottom of this page to customize your assignments for students.

Intervention You may wish to use the Study Guide and Intervention Master on page 68 of the *Chapter 1 Resource Masters* for additional reinforcement.

Odd/Even Assignments

Exercises 6–14 are structured so that students practice the same concepts whether they are assigned odd or even problems.

Additional Answers

3.

x	8x	y
1	8 • 1	8
2	8 • 2	16
3	8 • 3	24
4	8 • 4	32

5. Sample answer: Replace h with 3 in the equation $m = 231h$ to find the distance in miles the race car travels in 3 hours.

9.

x	25x	y
1	25 • 1	25
2	25 • 2	50
3	25 • 3	75
4	25 • 4	100

10.

x	60x	y
5	60 • 5	300
10	60 • 10	600
15	60 • 15	900
20	60 • 20	1,200

12. Sample answer: Replace m with 6 in the equation $c = 40m$ to find the total cost for 6 months of cell phone service.

Variables

You may wish to point out that mathematicians and scientists call y the *dependent variable* of a function because it depends on the input, or *independent variable*, x.

New teachers, or teachers new to teaching mathematics, may especially appreciate the **Tips for New Teachers**.

Additional Answers

14. Sample answer: Replace m with 15 in the equation $t = 35m$ to find the number of times a cricket will have chirped after 15 minutes at this temperature.

23. Sample answer: Replace s with 60 in the equation $m = 8s$ and in the equation $m = 19s$ to find the number of miles Jupiter travels in 1 minute and the number of miles Earth travels in 1 minute, respectively.

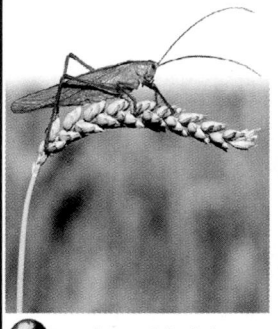

Real-World Link · · · ·
Crickets are among the 800,000 different types of insects in the world.

15. domain: {1, 2, 3, 4}; range: {0, 1, 2, 3}
16. domain: {1, 2, 3, 4}; range: {6, 7, 8, 9}
17. domain: {0, 1, 2, 3}; range: {0.25, 1.25, 2.25, 3.25}
18. domain: {2, 3, 4, 5}; range: {0.5, 1.5, 2.5, 3.5}

19.

w	6w	A
2	6 · 2	12
3	6 · 3	18
4	6 · 4	24
5	6 · 5	30

INSECTS For Exercises 13 and 14, use the following information.

A cricket will chirp approximately 35 times per minute when the outside temperature is 72°F.

13. Write an equation using two variables to show the relationship between the total number of times a cricket will chirp t, after m minutes at this temperature. **$t = 35m$**

14. Use your equation to explain how to find the number of times a cricket will have chirped after 15 minutes at this temperature. **525 times; See margin for explanation.**

Copy and complete each function table. Then identify the domain and range.

15. $y = x - 1$

x	x − 1	y
1	1 − 1	0
2	2 − 1	1
3	3 − 1	2
4	4 − 1	3

16. $y = x + 5$

x	x + 5	y
1	1 + 5	6
2	2 + 5	7
3	3 + 5	8
4	4 + 5	9

17. $y = x + 0.25$

x	x + 0.25	y
0	0 + 0.25	0.25
1	1 + 0.25	1.25
2	2 + 0.25	2.25
3	3 + 0.25	3.25

18. $y = x - 1.5$

x	x − 1.5	y
2	2 − 1.5	0.5
3	3 − 1.5	1.5
4	4 − 1.5	2.5
5	5 − 1.5	3.5

MEASUREMENT For Exercises 19 and 20, use the following information.

The formula for the area of a rectangle with length 6 units is $A = 6w$.

19. Make a function table that shows the area in square units of a rectangle with a width of 2, 3, 4, and 5 units.

20. Study the pattern in your table. Explain how the area of a rectangle with a length of 6 units changes when the width is increased by 1 unit. **The area increases by 6 square units.**

ANALYZE TABLES For Exercises 21–23, use the table that shows the approximate velocity of certain planets as they orbit the Sun.

21. Write an equation to show the relationship between the total number of miles m Jupiter travels in s seconds as it orbits the Sun. **$m = 8s$**

22. What equation can be used to show the total number of miles Earth travels? **$m = 19s$**

23. Use your equation to explain how to find the number of miles Jupiter and Earth each travel in 1 minute. **480 mi; 1,140 mi; See margin for explanation.**

Orbital Velocity Around Sun	
Planet	**Velocity (mi/s)**
Mercury	30
Earth	19
Jupiter	8
Saturn	6
Neptune	5

H.O.T. Problems

CHALLENGE Write an equation for the function shown in each table.

24.

x	y
1	3
2	4
3	5
4	6

$y = x + 2$

25.

x	y
2	6
4	12
6	18
8	24

$y = 3x$

26.

x	y
1	3
2	5
3	7
4	9

$y = 2x + 1$

27. **OPEN ENDED** Write about a real-world situation that can be represented by the equation $y = 3x$. **See margin.**

28. **WRITING IN MATH** Explain the relationship among an *input*, an *output*, and a *function rule*. **You start with an input number, perform the operations in the function rule, and the result is the output number.**

TEST PRACTICE

29. The table shows the number of hand-painted T-shirts Mi-Ling can make after a given number of days.

Number of Days (x)	Total Number of T-Shirts (y)
1	6
2	12
3	18
4	24

Which function rule represents the data? **C**

A $y = 4x$ C $y = 6x$

B $y = 5x$ D $y = 12x$

30. Cristina needs to have 50 posters printed to advertise a community book fair. The printing company charges $3 to print each poster. Which table represents this situation? **G**

F

Posters	Cost ($)
3	3
6	6
9	9
p	p

H

Posters	Cost ($)
1	3
2	6
3	9
p	3 + p

G

Posters	Cost ($)
1	3
2	6
3	9
p	3p

J

Posters	Cost ($)
3	1
6	2
9	3
p	p ÷ 3

Spiral Review

31. **ALGEBRA** Write the next three terms of the sequence 27, 36, 45, 54, … (Lesson 1-9) **63, 72, 81**

Use the Distributive Property to rewrite each expression. Then evaluate it. (Lesson 1-8)

32. $5(9 + 7)$
5(9) + 5(7); 80

33. $(12 + 4)4$
(12)4 + (4)4; 64

34. $8(7) - 8(2)$
8(7 - 2); 40

35. $10(6) - 10(5)$
10(6 - 5); 10

36. **ALLOWANCE** If Karen receives a weekly allowance of $8, about how much money in all will she receive in two years? (Lesson 1-1) **Sample answer: $8 × 50 × 2 or $800**

Lesson 1-10 Algebra: Equations and Functions **67**

4 Assess

Yesterday's News Remind students that yesterday's lesson was about arithmetic sequences. Have students write how yesterday's concepts helped them with today's material.

 Formative Assessment

Check for student understanding of concepts in Lessons 1-9 and 1-10.

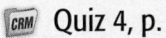 Quiz 4, p. 78

 **Foldables™ Follow-Up**

Suggest to students that they create a function table in their Foldables and label the domain, range, and rule.

Additional Answer

27. Sample answer: Sam charges $3 for each dog that he walks. In the equation $y = 3x$, x represents the number of dogs and y represents the total amount of money earned.

Extend 1-10
Lesson Notes

1 Focus

Materials

• graphing calculators

Teaching Tip

If your class does not have enough graphing calculators for every student, have students work in pairs or groups of three, sharing calculators.

2 Teach

Activity 1 If students have difficulty, have volunteers create a function table (such as in Lesson 1-10) on the chalkboard. Make sure everyone sees how the calculator performs the same work.

Additional Answer

1. 6 bottles; The table shows that 6 bottles will cost $9.80 and 7 bottles will cost $11.60. Since $11.60 > $10, you can only buy 6 bottles for $10.

Extend 1-10
Graphing Calculator Lab
Functions and Tables

You can use a graphing calculator to represent functions.

MAIN IDEA

Use technology to represent and compare functions.

Math Online

glencoe.com

• Other Calculator Keystrokes

ACTIVITY

① **GROCERIES** A grocery store has 12-ounce bottles of sports drink on sale for $1.80 each, with no limit on how many you can buy. In addition, you can use a coupon for $1 off one bottle. Make a table showing the cost for 3, 4, 5, 6, and 7 bottles of this drink.

STEP 1 Write an equation to show the relationship between the number of bottles purchased x and their cost y.

Cost is $1.80 per bottle less $1.

$$y = 1.80x - 1$$

STEP 2

Press $\boxed{Y=}$ on your calculator. Then enter the function into Y_1 by pressing 1.80 $\boxed{X,T,\theta,n}$ $\boxed{-}$ 1 $\boxed{ENTER}$.

STEP 3

Next, set up a table of x- and y-values. Press $\boxed{2nd}$ [TBLSET] to display the table setup screen. Then press $\boxed{\Downarrow}$ $\boxed{\Downarrow}$ $\boxed{\Rightarrow}$ $\boxed{ENTER}$ to highlight Indpnt: Ask.

STEP 4 Access the table by pressing $\boxed{2nd}$ [TABLE]. Then key in each number of bottles, pressing $\boxed{ENTER}$ after each entry.

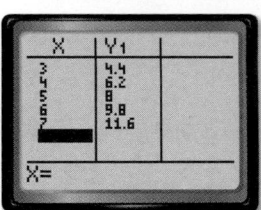

ANALYZE THE RESULTS

1. Analyze the table to determine how many bottles you can buy for $10. Explain your reasoning. **See margin.**

2. **MAKE A CONJECTURE** Notice that you can purchase 5 bottles for the whole dollar amount of $8. How many bottles will you be able to purchase for $9, the next whole dollar amount? Use the calculator to test your conjecture. **5 bottles**

---

② **CAMPING** Out-There Campground charges each group a camping fee of $20 plus $4.25 per person per night. Roughing-It Campground charges $6.25 per person per night. Make a table showing the one-night fee for 2, 3, 4, 5, and 6 people to camp at each campground.

STEP 1 Write an equation to show the relationship between the number of people x and the one-night fee y for them to camp at each campground.

Reading Math

The phrase *$4.25 per person* means *$4.25 for each person.*

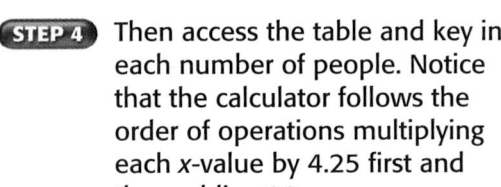

Out-There Campground

Fee   is $20   plus $4.25 per person.

$$y = 20 + 4.25x$$

Roughing-It Campground

Fee   is $6.25 per person.

$$y = 6.25x$$

STEP 2 Enter the function for the Out-There Campground into Y_1 and the function for the Roughing-It Campground into Y_2.

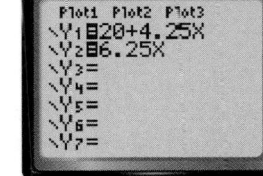

STEP 3 Next, set up a table of x- and y-values as in Activity 1.

STEP 4 Then access the table and key in each number of people. Notice that the calculator follows the order of operations multiplying each x-value by 4.25 first and then adding 20.

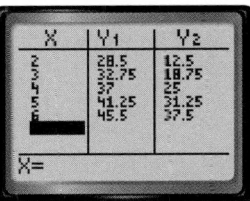

ANALYZE THE RESULTS

3. For 2, 3, 4, 5, and 6 people, which campground charges the greater total nightly cost to camp? **Out-There Campground**

4. yes; 10 people

4. **MAKE A CONJECTURE** Will the total nightly cost to camp at each campground ever be the same? If so, for what number of people?

5. Use the graphing calculator to test your conjecture from Exercise 4. Were you correct? If not, use the graphing calculator to guess and check until you find the correct number of people. **See students' work.**

6. If all other aspects of these two campgrounds are equal, write a recommendation as to which campground a group of n people should choose based on your cost analysis. **See margin.**

Extend 1-10 Graphing Calculator Lab: Functions and Tables **69**

Activity 2 Make sure students realize that the differences between each pair of fees (y-values) decrease as the number of people (x-values) increases.

③ Assess

✓ Formative Assessment

Use Exercise 3 to determine whether students comprehend how to use a graphing calculator to write and compare functions.

From Concrete to Abstract
Use Exercise 4 to bridge the gap between using a graphing calculator to write functions and making conjectures about functions.

Extending the Concept Have students write their own word problems involving functions. Then have students exchange problems and use their graphing calculators to solve the problems.

Additional Answer

6. Sample answer: If n is less than 10, the Roughing-It Campground is cheaper. If n is greater than 10, the Out-There Campground is cheaper. If n equals 10, then both campgrounds charge the same fee, so it doesn't matter which campground the group chooses.

 **CHAPTER 1** Study Guide and Review

 **FOLDABLES™**
Study Organizer

Dinah Zike's Foldables

Have students look through the chapter to make sure they have included notes in their Foldables for each lesson.

Encourage students to refer to their Foldables while completing the Study Guide and Review and while preparing for the Chapter Test.

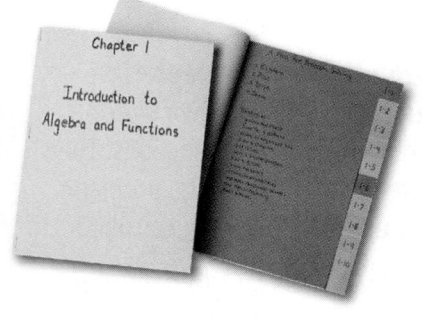

Formative Assessment

Key Vocabulary The page references after each word denote where that term was first introduced. If students have difficulty answering Exercises 1–7, remind them that they can use these page references to refresh their memories about the vocabulary terms.

Math Online glencoe.com

Vocabulary PuzzleMaker improves students' mathematics vocabulary using four puzzle formats—crossword, scramble, word search using a word list, and word search using clues. Students can work online or from a printed worksheet.

Summative Assessment

CRM Vocabulary Test, p. 80

FOLDABLES®
Study Organizer ▶ **GET READY to Study**

Be sure the following Big Ideas are noted in your Foldable.

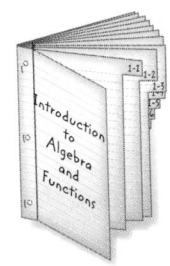

BIG Ideas

Squares and Square Roots (Lesson 1-3)
• The square of a number is the product of a number and itself.
• A square root of a number is one of its two equal factors.

Order of Operations (Lesson 1-4)
• Do all operations within grouping symbols first. Evaluate all powers before other operations. Multiply and divide in order from left to right. Add and subtract in order from left to right.

Properties (Lesson 1-8)
• Distributive Property
  $5(2 + 4) = 5 \cdot 2 + 5 \cdot 4$
  $(3 + 2)4 = 3 \cdot 4 + 2 \cdot 4$
• Commutative Property
  $3 + 2 = 2 + 3$
  $7 \cdot 4 = 4 \cdot 7$
• Associative Property
  $6 + (3 + 8) = (6 + 3) + 8$
  $5 \cdot (2 \cdot 3) = (5 \cdot 2) \cdot 3$
• Identity Property
  $4 + 0 = 4$
  $4 \cdot 1 = 4$

Functions (Lesson 1-10)
• A function is a relationship that assigns exactly one *output* value for each *input* value.
• In a function, the function rule gives the operation to perform on the input.

Key Vocabulary

algebra (p. 44)	function rule (p. 63)
algebraic expression (p. 44)	numerical expression (p. 38)
arithmetic sequence (p. 57)	order of operations (p. 38)
base (p. 30)	perfect square (p. 34)
coefficient (p. 45)	powers (p. 30)
defining the variable (p. 50)	radical sign (p. 35)
domain (p. 63)	range (p. 63)
equation (p. 49)	sequence (p. 57)
equivalent expressions (p. 53)	solution (p. 49)
	square (p. 34)
evaluate (p. 31)	square root (p. 35)
exponent (p. 30)	term (p. 57)
factors (p. 30)	variable (p. 44)
function (p. 63)	

Vocabulary Check

State whether each sentence is *true* or *false*. If *false*, replace the underlined word or number to make a true sentence.

1. <u>Numerical expressions</u> have the same value. **false; equivalent expressions**

2. Two or more numbers that are multiplied together are called <u>powers</u>. **false; factors**

3. The <u>range</u> of a function is the set of input values. **false; domain**

4. A function assigns exactly <u>two</u> *output* values for each *input* value. **false; one**

5. An <u>equation</u> is a sentence that contains an equals sign. **true**

6. A <u>sequence</u> is an ordered list of numbers. **true**

7. The product of a number and itself is the <u>square root</u> of the number. **false; square**

 Students can use the **Vocabulary Check** in the Study Guide and Review and the **Vocabulary PuzzleMaker** to review the vocabulary of the chapter.

Lesson-by-Lesson Review

1-1 **A Plan for Problem Solving** (pp. 25–29)

Use the four-step plan to solve each problem.

8. **PHONE CALLS** When Tamik calls home from college, she talks ten minutes per call for 3 calls each week. How many minutes does she use in a 15-week semester? **450 min**

9. **RUNNING** Darren runs at a rate of 6 feet per second, and Kim runs at a rate of 7 feet per second. If they both start a race at the same time, how far apart are they after one minute? **60 ft**

10. **WORK** Alan was paid $9 per hour and earned $128.25. How many hours did he work? **14.25 h**

Example 1 One quart of paint covers 40 square feet of wall space. Brock uses 5 quarts of paint to cover his walls. How many square feet did Brock paint?

Understand	Brock uses 5 quarts of paint, each covering 40 square feet.
Plan	Multiply 40 by 5.
Solve	$40 \cdot 5 = 200$ Brock painted 200 square feet.
Check	$200 \div 5 = 40$, so the answer is reasonable.

1-2 **Powers and Exponents** (pp. 30–33)

Write each power as a product of the same factor.

11. 3^4 **$3 \cdot 3 \cdot 3 \cdot 3$**   12. 9^6 **$9 \cdot 9 \cdot 9 \cdot 9 \cdot 9 \cdot 9$**

13. 5^1 **5**   14. 7^5 **$7 \cdot 7 \cdot 7 \cdot 7 \cdot 7$**

15. Write *5 to the fourth power* as a product of the same factor. **$5 \cdot 5 \cdot 5 \cdot 5$**

Evaluate each expression.

16. 3^5 **243**   17. 7^9 **40,353,607**

18. 2^8 **256**   19. 18^2 **324**

20. 10^4 **10,000**   21. 100^1 **100**

22. Write $15 \cdot 15 \cdot 15$ in exponential form. **15^3**

23. **PATHS** At the edge of a forest, there are two paths. At the end of each path, there are two additional paths. If at the end of each of those paths there are two more paths, how many paths are there at the end? **8**

Example 2 Write 2^3 as a product of the same factor.

The base is 2. The exponent 3 means that 2 is used as a factor 3 times.

$2^3 = 2 \cdot 2 \cdot 2$

Example 3 Evaluate 4^5.

The base is 4. The exponent 5 means that 4 is used as a factor 5 times.

$4^5 = 4 \cdot 4 \cdot 4 \cdot 4 \cdot 4$

$\quad\; = 1,024$

Lesson-by-Lesson Review

Intervention If the given examples are not sufficient to review the topics covered by the questions, remind students that the page references tell them where to review that topic in their textbooks.

Two-Day Option Have students complete the Lesson-by-Lesson Review on pages 71–74. Then you can use ExamView® Assessment Suite to customize another review worksheet that practices all the objectives of this chapter or only the objectives on which your students need more help.

For more information on ExamView® Assessment Suite, see page 22C.

Differentiated Instruction

Super DVD: MindJogger Plus
Use this DVD as an alternative format of review for the test. For more information on this game show format, see page 22D.

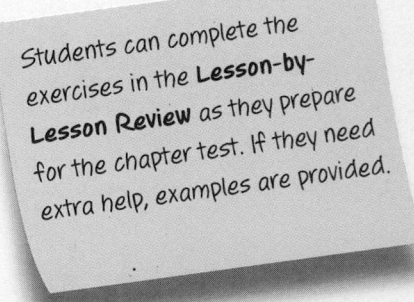
Students can complete the exercises in the **Lesson-by-Lesson Review** as they prepare for the chapter test. If they need extra help, examples are provided.

1-3 **Squares and Square Roots** (pp. 34–37)

Find the square of each number.

24. 4 **16**

25. 13 **169**

Find each square root.

26. $\sqrt{81}$ **9**

27. $\sqrt{324}$ **18**

28. **MEASUREMENT** The area of a certain kind of ceramic tile is 25 square inches. What is the length of one side? **5 in.**

Example 4 Find the square of 15.

$15 \cdot 15 = 225$ Multiply 15 by itself.

Example 5 Find the square root of **441.**

$21 \cdot 21 = 441$, so $\sqrt{441} = 21$.

1-4 **Order of Operations** (pp. 38–41)

Evaluate each expression.

29. $24 - 8 + 3^2$ **25**

30. $48 \div 6 + 2 \cdot 5$ **18**

31. $9 + 3(7 - 5)^3$ **33**

32. $15 + 9 \div 3 - 7$ **11**

33. **SEATING** In planning for a ceremony, 36 guests need to be seated with 4 guests per table. An additional 12 guests need to be seated with 3 guests per table. Write an expression to determine how many tables are needed. Then evaluate the expression. **$36 \div 4 + 12 \div 3$; 13**

Example 6 Evaluate $24 - (8 \div 4)^4$.

$24 - (8 \div 4)^4 = 24 - 2^4$ Divide 8 by 4.

$\qquad\qquad = 24 - 16$ Find the value of 2^4.

$\qquad\qquad = 8$ Subtract.

1-5 **PSI: Guess and Check** (pp. 42–43)

Solve. Use the *guess and check* strategy.

34. **TRAVEL** Lucinda is driving away from Redding at 50 miles per hour. When she is 100 miles away, Tom leaves Redding, driving at 60 miles per hour in the same direction. After how many hours will Tom pass Lucinda? **10 h**

35. **FARMING** A farmer sells a bushel of soybeans for $5 and a bushel of corn for $3. If he hopes to earn $164 and plans to sell 40 bushels in all, how many bushels of soybeans does he need to sell? **22**

Example 7 Find two numbers with a product of 30 and a difference of 13.

Make a guess, and check to see if it is correct. Then adjust the guess until it is correct.

5 and 6 $5 \cdot 6 = 30$ and $6 - 5 = 1$ incorrect

3 and 10 $3 \cdot 10 = 30$ and $10 - 3 = 7$ incorrect

2 and 15 $2 \cdot 15 = 30$ and $15 - 2 = 13$ correct

The two numbers are 2 and 15.

Mixed Problem Solving
For mixed problem-solving practice,
see page 704.

1-6 Algebra: Variables and Expressions (pp. 44–47)

Evaluate each expression if $a = 10$, $b = 4$, and $c = 8$.

36. $(a - b)^2$ **36**

37. $ab \div c$ **5**

38. $3b^2 + c$ **56**

39. $\dfrac{(b + c)^2}{3}$ **48**

40. CLOTHING The cost of buying h hats and s shirts is given by the expression $\$5.75h + \$8.95s$. Find the cost of purchasing 3 hats and 5 shirts. **$62**

Example 8 Evaluate $2m^2 - 5n$ if $m = 4$ and $n = 3$.

$$2m^2 - 5n = 2(4)^2 - 5(3) \quad \text{Replace } m \text{ with 4 and } n \text{ with 3.}$$
$$= 2(16) - 5(3) \quad \text{Find the value of } 4^2.$$
$$= 32 - 15 \quad \text{Multiply.}$$
$$= 17 \quad \text{Subtract.}$$

1-7 Algebra: Equations (pp. 49–52)

Solve each equation mentally.

41. $h + 9 = 17$ **8**

42. $31 - y = 8$ **23**

43. $\dfrac{t}{9} = 12$ **108**

44. $100 = 20g$ **5**

45. COUNTY FAIRS Five friends wish to ride the Ferris wheel, which requires 3 tickets per person. The group has a total of 9 tickets. Write and solve an equation to find the number of additional tickets needed for everyone to ride the Ferris wheel. **$9 + x = 15$; 6 tickets**

Example 9 Solve $14 = 5 + x$ mentally.

$14 = 5 + x$ Write the equation.

$14 = 5 + 9$ You know that $5 + 9 = 14$.

$14 = 14$ Simplify.

The solution is 9.

1-8 Algebra: Properties (pp. 53–56)

Find each expression mentally. Justify each step. **46–48. See margin for justification.**

46. $(25 \cdot 15) \cdot 4$ **1,500**

47. $14 + (38 + 16)$ **68**

48. $8 \cdot (11 \cdot 5)$ **440**

49. ROSES Wesley sold roses in his neighborhood for $2 a rose. He sold 15 roses on Monday and 12 roses on Tuesday. Use the Distributive Property to mentally find the total amount Wesley earned. Explain your reasoning. **$2(15 + 12)$; $54 See margin for explanation.**

Example 10 Find $8 + (17 + 22)$ mentally. Justify each step.

$8 + (17 + 22)$

$= 8 + (22 + 17)$ Commutative Property of Addition

$= (8 + 22) + 17$ Associative Property of Addition

$= 30 + 17$ or 47 Add 30 and 17 mentally.

Chapter 1 Study Guide and Review **73**

Additional Answers

46. Sample answer: Rewrite $(25 \cdot 15) \cdot 4$ as $(15 \cdot 25) \cdot 4$ using the Commutative Property of Multiplication. Rewrite $(15 \cdot 25) \cdot 4$ as $15 \cdot (25 \cdot 4)$ using the Associative Property of Multiplication. Find $25 \cdot 4$, or 100, mentally. Then find $15 \cdot 100$, or 1,500, mentally.

47. Sample answer: Rewrite $14 + (38 + 16)$ as $14 + (16 + 38)$ using the Commuative Property of Addition. Rewrite $14 + (16 + 38)$ as $(14 + 16) + 38$ using the Associative Property of Addition. Find $14 + 16$, or 30, mentally. Then find $30 + 38$, or 68, mentally.

48. Sample answer: Rewrite $8 \cdot (11 \cdot 5)$ as $8 \cdot (5 \cdot 11)$ using the Commutative Property of Multiplication. Rewrite $8 \cdot (5 \cdot 11)$ as $(8 \cdot 5) \cdot 11$ using the Associative Property of Multiplication. Find $8 \cdot 5$, or 40, mentally. Then find $40 \cdot 11$, or 440, mentally.

49. Sample answer: The expression $15 + 12$ represents the total number of roses Wesley sold. The expression $\$2(15 + 12)$ represents the total amount of money Wesley earned. Since $\$2 \times 15 = \$30$ and $\$2 \times 12 = \$24$, find $\$30 + \$24$, or $\$54$, to find the total amount Wesley earned.

Problem Solving Review

For additional practice in problem solving for Chapter 1, see the Mixed Problem Solving Appendix, page 704 in the Student Handbook section.

Anticipation Guide

Have students complete the Chapter 1 Anticipation Guide and discuss how their responses have changed now that they have completed Chapter 1.

CRM Anticipation Guide, p. 7

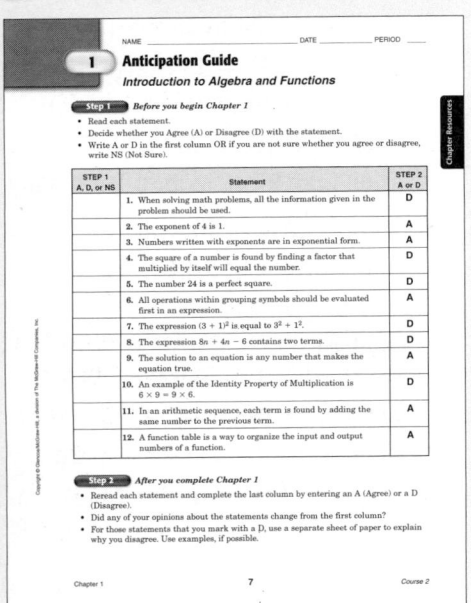

Additional Answers

50. Each term is found by adding 6 to the previous term; 33, 39, 45

51. Each term is found by adding 0.8 to the previous term; 6.6, 7.4, 8.2

52. Each term is found by adding 7 to the previous term; 35, 42, 49

56.

x	32x	y
3	32(3)	96
4	32(4)	128
5	32(5)	160
6	32(6)	192

1-9 **Algebra: Arithmetic Sequences** (pp. 57–61)

Describe the relationship between the terms in each arithmetic sequence. Then find the next three terms in each sequence. **50–52. See margin.**

50. 3, 9, 15, 21, 27, …

51. 2.6, 3.4, 4.2, 5, 5.8, …

52. 0, 7, 14, 21, 28, …

MONEY For Exercises 53 and 54, use the following information.

Tanya collected $4.50 for the first car washed at a band fund-raiser. After the second and third cars were washed, the donations totaled $9 and $13.50, respectively.

53. If this donation pattern continues, what algebraic expression can be used to find the amount of money earned for any number of cars washed? **$4.50n**

54. How much money will be collected after a total of 8 cars have been washed? **$36**

Example 11 At the end of day 1, Sierra read 25 pages of a novel. By the end of days 2 and 3, she read a total of 50 and 75 pages, respectively. If the pattern continues, what expression will give the total number of pages read after any number of days?

Make a table to display the sequence.

Position	Operation	Value of Term
1	1 · 25	25
2	2 · 25	50
3	3 · 25	75
n	n · 25	25n

Each term is 25 times its position number. So, the expression is $25n$.

1-10 **Algebra: Equations and Functions** (pp. 63–67)

Copy and complete the function table. Then identify the domain and range.

55. $y = 4x$

x	4x	y
5	4(5)	20
6	4(6)	24
7	4(7)	28
8	4(8)	32

The domain is {5, 6, 7, 8}. The range is {20, 24, 28, 32}.

56. **NAME TAGS** Charmaine can make 32 name tags per hour. Make a function table that shows the number of name tags she can make in 3, 4, 5, and 6 hours. **See margin.**

Example 12 Create and complete a function table for $y = 3x$. Then identify the domain and range.

Select any four values for the input x.

x	3x	y
3	3(3)	9
4	3(4)	12
5	3(5)	15
6	3(6)	18

The domain is {3, 4, 5, 6}. The range is {9, 12, 15, 18}.

74 Chapter 1 Introduction to Algebra and Functions

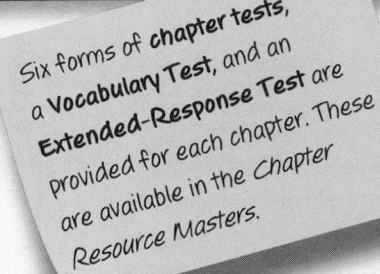
Six forms of chapter tests, a Vocabulary Test, and an Extended-Response Test are provided for each chapter. These are available in the Chapter Resource Masters.

1. **PIZZA** Ms. Carter manages a pizza parlor. The average daily cost is $40, plus $52 to pay each employee. It also costs $2 to make each pizza. If 42 pizzas were made one day, requiring the work of 7 employees, what was her total cost that day? **$488**

Write each power as a product of the same factor. Then evaluate the expression.

2. 3^5
$3 \cdot 3 \cdot 3 \cdot 3 \cdot 3$; **243**

3. 15^4
$15 \cdot 15 \cdot 15 \cdot 15$; **50,625**

4. **MEASUREMENT** Gregory wants to stain the 15-foot-by-15-foot deck in his backyard. One can of stain covers 200 square feet of surface. Is one can of stain enough to cover his entire deck? Explain your reasoning.
No; $15 \times 15 = 225$. Since $225 > 200$, one can is not enough.

Find each square root.

5. $\sqrt{121}$ **11**

6. $\sqrt{900}$ **30**

7. **MULTIPLE CHOICE** What is the value of $8 + (12 \div 3)^3 - 5 \times 9$? **C**

A 603
B 135
C 27
D 19

8. **ANIMALS** Sally has 6 pets, some dogs and some birds. Her animals have a total of 16 legs. How many of each pet does Sally have?
4 birds and 2 dogs

Evaluate each expression if $x = 12$, $y = 5$, and $z = 3$.

9. $x - 9$ **3**

10. $8y$ **40**

11. $(y - z)^3$ **8**

12. $\dfrac{xz}{y + 13}$ **2**

Solve each equation mentally.

13. $9 + m = 16$ **7**

14. $d - 14 = 37$ **51**

15. $32 = \dfrac{96}{t}$ **3**

16. $6x = 126$ **21**

17. **SAVINGS** Deb is saving $54 per month to buy a new camera. Use the Distributive Property to mentally find how much she has saved after 7 months. Explain. **See margin.**

Find each expression mentally. Justify each step.

18. $13 + (34 + 17)$ **64**

19. $50 \cdot (17 \cdot 2)$ **1,700**

18–19. See Ch. 1 Answer Appendix for justification.

20. **MULTIPLE CHOICE** The table shows the number of hours Teodoro spent studying for his biology test over four days. If the pattern continues, how many hours will Teodoro study on Sunday? **H**

Day	Study Time (hours)
Monday	0.5
Tuesday	0.75
Wednesday	1.0
Thursday	1.25

F 1.5 hours   H 2.0 hours
G 1.75 hours   J 2.5 hours

Describe the relationship between the terms in each arithmetic sequence. Then write the next three terms in the sequence.

21. 7, 16, 25, 34, …
See margin.

22. 59, 72, 85, 98, …
See margin.

23. **TRAVEL** Beth drove at the rate of 65 miles per hour for several hours. Make a function table that shows her distance traveled after 2, 3, 4, and 5 hours. Then identify the domain and range. **domain: {2, 3, 4, 5}; range: {130, 195, 260, 325}; See margin for table.**

MONEY For Exercises 24 and 25, use the following information.

Anthony earns extra money after school doing yard work for his neighbors. He charges $12 for each lawn he mows.

24. Write an equation using two variables to show the relationship between the number of lawns mowed m and number of dollars earned d. **$d = 12m$**

25. Then find the number of dollars earned if he mows 14 lawns. **$168**

CHAPTER 1 Practice Test

✓ Summative Assessment

CRM Chapter 1 Resource Masters

Leveled Chapter 1 Tests			
Form	Type	Level	Pages
1	MC	BL	81–82
2A	MC	OL	83–84
2B	MC	OL	85–86
2C	FR	OL	87–88
2D	FR	OL	89–90
3	FR	AL	91–92

MC = multiple-choice questions
FR = free-response questions
BL = below or approaching grade level
OL = on grade level
AL = above or beyond grade level

• Vocabulary Test, p. 80
• Extended-Response Test, p. 93

 **ExamView** Assessment Suite

Customize and create multiple versions of your chapter test and their answer keys. All of the questions from the leveled chapter tests in the *Chapter 1 Resource Masters* are also available on ExamView Assessment Suite.

Additional Answers

17. The number 54 can be written as $50 + 4$. You know that $7 \cdot 50 = 350$ and $7 \cdot 4 = 28$. Mentally adding 350 and 28 you get $378.

21. Add 9 to each term; 43, 52, 61

22. Add 13 to each term; 111, 124, 137

23.

x	65x	y
2	65 · 2	130
3	65 · 3	195
4	65 · 4	260
5	65 · 5	325

Data-Driven Decision Making	Exercises	Lesson	State/Local Standards	Resources for Review
Diagnostic Teaching Based on the results of the Chapter 1 Practice Test, use the following to review concepts that students continue to find challenging.	1–6	1-1, 1-2, 1-3		**CRM** Study Guide and Intervention pp. 48, 54, 61, and 68
	7–12	1-4, 1-5, 1-6		
	13–19	1-7, 1-8		**Math Online** glencoe.com • Extra Examples • Personal Tutor • Concepts in Motion
	20–25	1-9, 1-10		

CHAPTER 1 Test Practice

CHAPTER 1

Test Practice
Cumulative, Chapter 1

Math Online › glencoe.com
• Test Practice

Formative Assessment

You can use these two pages to benchmark student progress.

 *Chapter 1 Resource Masters*

• Standardized Test Practice, pp. 94–96

ExamView®
Assessment Suite

Create practice worksheets or tests that align to your state's standards, as well as TIMSS and NAEP tests.

The items in the Test Practice give students an opportunity to practice the kinds of questions found on state assessments. The Need Extra Help? box allows students to diagnose and address weaknesses.

PART 1   Multiple Choice

Read each question. Then fill in the correct answer on the answer document provided by your teacher or on a sheet of paper.

1. A store owner bought some paperback books and then sold them for $4.50 each. He sold 35 books on Monday and 52 books on Tuesday. What piece of information is needed to find the amount of profit made from sales on Monday and Tuesday? **D**

    A Number of books sold on Wednesday

    B Number of hardback books sold on Monday and Tuesday

    C Total number of paperback books sold

    D How much the owner paid for each of the paperback books

2. The table shows the number of milkshakes sold at an ice cream shop each day last week.

Day of Week	Number of Milkshakes
Sunday	31
Monday	9
Tuesday	11
Wednesday	15
Thursday	18
Friday	24
Saturday	28

Which statement does *not* support the data? **H**

    F There were almost three times as many milkshakes sold on Sunday as on Tuesday.

    G There were half as many milkshakes sold on Monday as on Thursday.

    H There were 11 more milkshakes sold on Tuesday than on Saturday.

    J The total number of milkshakes sold during the week was 136.

---

3. Which description shows the relationship between the value of a term and n, its position in the sequence? **C**

Position	1	2	3	4	5	n
Value of Term	3	6	9	12	15	

    A Add 2 to n.

    B Divide n by 3.

    C Multiply n by 3.

    D Subtract n from 2.

TEST-TAKING TIP

Question 3 Have students eliminate unlikely answer choices. Since the value of each term is greater than its position, eliminate answer choices B and D.

4. Andrew spent $\frac{1}{2}$ of his Saturday earnings on a pair of jeans and $\frac{1}{2}$ of the remaining amount on a DVD. After he spent $7.40 on lunch, he had $6.10 left. How much did Andrew earn on Saturday? **H**

    F $13.50

    G $27

    H $54

    J $108

5. Lemisha drove an average of 50 miles per hour on Sunday, 55 miles per hour on Monday, and 53 miles per hour on Tuesday. If s represents the number of hours she drove on Sunday, m represents the number of hours she drove on Monday, and t represents the number of hours she drove on Tuesday, which of the following expressions gives the total distance Lemisha traveled? **C**

    A $50s + 53m + 55t$

    B $55s + 50m + 53t$

    C $50s + 55m + 53t$

    D $53s + 55m + 50t$

CHAPTER
1
Test Practice

6. Mrs. Albert drove 850 miles and the average price of gasoline was $2.50 per gallon. What information is needed to find the amount Mrs. Albert spent on gasoline for the trip? **H**

   F Number of hours the trip took

   G Number of miles per hour traveled

   H Average number of miles the car traveled per gallon of gasoline

   J Average number of miles Mrs. Albert drove per day

7. Mr. Thompson wants to estimate the total amount he spends on insurance and fuel for his car each month. Insurance costs about $300 per month, and he expects to drive an average of 150 miles per week. What else does he need to estimate his monthly expenses? **B**

   A The cost of fuel and the one-way distance to work

   B The cost of fuel and the number of miles per gallon his car gets

   C The cost of fuel and his weekly pay

   D The gallons of fuel needed per week

8. Jeremy bought 3 hamburgers at $1.99 each, 2 orders of onion rings at $0.89 each, and 4 soft drinks at $1.25 each. He paid 6.75% tax on the whole order. What other information is necessary to find Jeremy's correct change? **J**

   F Total cost of the order

   G Amount he paid in tax

   H Reason for buying the food

   J Amount he gave the cashier

PART 2   Short Response/Grid In

Record your answers on the answer sheet provided by your teacher or on a sheet of paper.

9. Emily bought 2.5 pounds of salami for $1.99 per pound. About how much did she pay?
   between $4.50 and $5.50

10. How do you correctly evaluate the expression $4 \times (5 + 4) - 27$?
    Add first, since 5 + 4 is in parentheses.

11. What value of t makes the following equation true? **288**

    $$t \div 6 = 48$$

12. Use the Distributive Property to rewrite $4(3 + 5)$. **12 + 20**

PART 3   Extended Response

Record your answers on the answer sheet provided by your teacher or on a sheet of paper. Show your work.

13. **GEOMETRY** The first and fifth terms of a toothpick sequence are shown below.

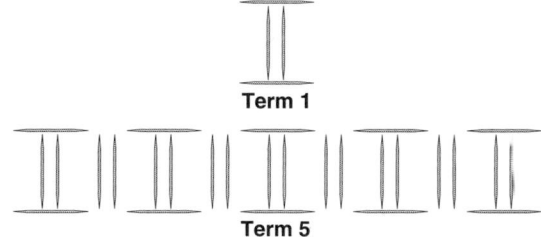

Term 1

Term 5

   a. What might the third term look like?
      See margin.

   b. Write a rule that connects the term number and the number of toothpicks in your sequence. **6x − 2**

NEED EXTRA HELP?													
If You Missed Question...	1	2	3	4	5	6	7	8	9	10	11	12	13
Go to Lesson...	1-1	1-1	1-9	1-1	1-6	1-1	1-1	1-1	1-1	1-4	1-6	1-8	1-9

Answer Sheet Practice

Have students simulate taking a standardized test by recording their answers on a practice recording sheet.

CRM **Student Recording Sheet, p. 75**

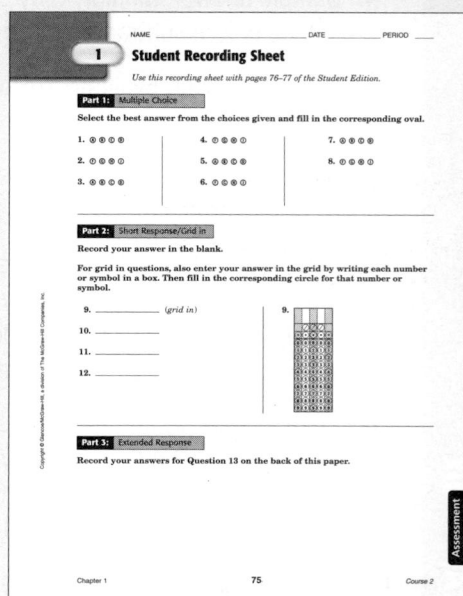

A **Student Recording Sheet** is provided for each chapter in the Chapter Resource Masters.

13a.

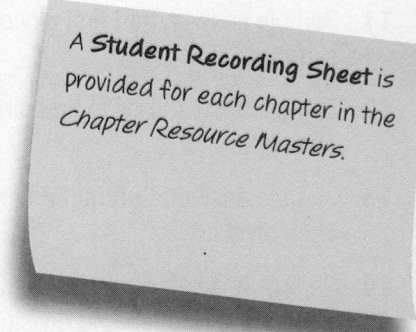

1. Sample answer: Subtract first since $5 - 2$ is in parentheses. Then add 8.

2. Sample answer: Subtract first since $9 - 4$ is in parentheses. Then divide 25 by 5.

3. Sample answer: Multiply 2 by 6 first since multiplication comes before addition or subtraction. Then subtract and add in order from left to right.

4. Sample answer: Multiply 8 by 5 and 4 by 3 since multiplication comes before subtraction. Then subtract.

5. Sample answer: Evaluate 10^2 first since it is a power. Then multiply by 4.

6. Sample answer: Subtract first since $4 - 1$ is in parentheses. Next, square the difference since 2 is a power. Finally, divide.

7. Sample answer: Subtract first since $6 - 3$ is in parentheses. Then multiply the difference by 2 and multiply 3 by 4 since multiplication comes before addition or subtraction. Finally, add $17 + 6$ and subtract 12 in order from left to right.

8. Sample answer: Subtract first since $8 - 2$ is in parentheses. Then multiply the difference by 3 and divide 12 by 4 since multiplication and division come before addition or subtraction. Finally, subtract 22 and 18 and add 3.

10. Sample answer: Add first since $1 + 8$ is in parentheses. Then multiply by 3.

11. Sample answer: Add first since $3 + 4$ is in parentheses. Then subtract.

12. Sample answer: Divide first since $25 \div 5$ is in parentheses. Then add.

13. Sample answer: Subtract first since $11 - 2$ is in parentheses. Then divide.

14. Sample answer: Multiply 3 by 2 first and then divide 14 by 7 since multiplication and division come before addition. Then add.

15. Sample answer: Divide first since division comes before addition or subtraction. Then subtract 1 and add 7 in order from left to right.

16. Sample answer: Divide first since division comes before addition or subtraction. Then add 12 and subtract 4.

17. Sample answer: Multiply first since multiplication comes before addition or subtraction. Then subtract the product from 118 and add 5.

18. Sample answer: Evaluate 10^2 first since it is a power. Then multiply by 6.

19. Sample answer: Evaluate 10^4 first since it is a power. Then multiply by 3.

20. Sample answer: Evaluate 4^3 first since it is a power. Then multiply by 5 since multiplication comes before addition. Finally, add.

21. Sample answer: Evaluate 7^2 first since it is a power. Then multiply by 8 since multiplication comes before subtraction. Finally, subtract.

22. Sample answer: Evaluate 6^2 first since it is a power. Then divide 8 by 2 and multiply the quotient by 6 since multiplication and division occur from left to right. Finally, add.

23. Sample answer: Evaluate 9^2 since it is a power. Then divide 14 by 7 and multiply the quotient by 3 since multiplication and division occur from left to right. Finally, subtract.

24. Sample answer: Add first since $17 + 3$ and $4 + 1$ are in parentheses. Then divide.

25. Sample answer: Add first since $6 + 5$ is in parentheses. Then subtract 6 from 8 since $8 - 6$ is in parentheses. Finally, multiply.

26. Sample answer: Subtract first since $4 - 1$ is in parentheses. Then multiply the difference by 2 and multiply 4 by 9 since multiplication comes before addition. Finally, add.

27. Sample answer: Add first since $4 + 7$ is in parentheses. Then multiply the sum by 3. Next, multiply 5 by 4 and divide the product by 2 since multiplication and division occur in order from left to right. Finally, subtract.

30. Sample answer: Add first since $2 + 10$ is in parentheses. Next, square the sum since 2 is a power. Then divide by 4.

31. Sample answer: Evaluate 3^3 first since it is a power. Then add 8. Next subtract 6 from 10 since $10 - 6$ is in parentheses. Then square the difference since the power is 2. Finally subtract 16 from 35.

32. Sample answer: Add first since $5.2 + 3.8$ is in parentheses. Since multiplication and division occur from left to right, multiply 3 by 4 and then multiply the product, 12, by 9. Finally, add 2.7 since addition and subtraction occur from left to right.

33. Sample answer: Subtract first since $4 - 3.2$ is in parentheses. Multiply 7 by 9 next since multiplication occurs from left to right. Then subtract 0.8 from the product, 63, and add 1.8 since addition and subtraction occur from left to right.

Page 42, Lesson 1-5

2. Sample answer: Julia scored 16 points in a basketball game. She missed 18 of her 28 attempts. All of her shots were either one- or two-point shots. How many one-and two point shots did Julia make?

Understand: We know how many points Julia scored and can find how many shots she made.

Plan: Let's make a guess until we get the correct answer.

Solve: Julia had $28 - 18 = 10$ successful shots. Make a guess.
5 one-point and 5 two-point $5(1) + 5(2) = 15$ *too low*
4 one-point and 6 two-point $4(1) + 6(2) = 16$ *correct*
Julia had 4 one-point and 6 two-point shots.

Check: 4 one-point shots are 4 points, and 6 two-point shots are 12 points. Since $4 + 12 = 16$ points and $4 + 6 + 18 = 28$ attempts, the guess is correct.

Page 44, Lesson 1-6 (Mini Lab)

1.

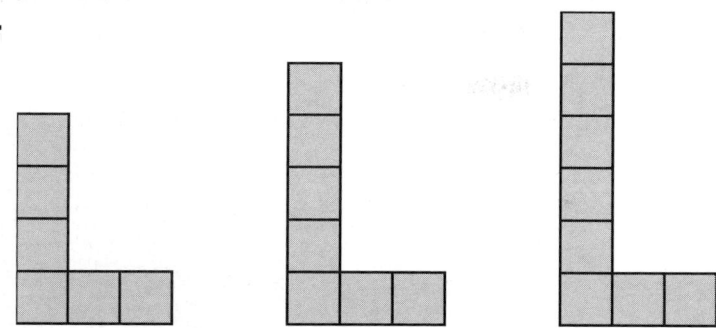

3. 12; See students' work.

4. The number of squares is two more than the figure number.

Page 54, Lesson 1-8

d. Sample answer: Rewrite 40 • (7 • 5) as 40 • (5 • 7) using the Commutative Property of Multiplication. Then rewrite 40 • (5 • 7) as (40 • 5) • 7 using the Associative Property of Multiplication. Find 40 • 5, or 200, mentally. Then find 200 • 7, or 1,400, mentally.

e. Sample answer: Rewrite (89 + 15) + 1 as (15 + 89) + 1 using the Commutative Property of Addition. Then rewrite (15 + 89) + 1 as 15 + (89 + 1) using the Associative Property of Addition. Find 89 + 1, or 90, mentally. Then find 15 + 90, or 105, mentally.

Page 55, Lesson 1-8

5. The expression 12 + 5 represents the cost of one ticket and one hot dog. The expression 4(12 + 5) represents the cost of four tickets and four hot dogs. Since 4 × 12 = 48 and 4 × 5 = 20, find 48 + 20, or 68, to find the total cost of four tickets and four hot dogs.

6. The expression 60 + 5 represents the cheetah's maximum speed. The expression 2(60 + 5) represents how far the cheetah could run in 2 hours at maximum speed. Since 2 × 60 = 120 and 2 × 5 = 10, find 120 + 10, or 130, to find the distance the cheetah could run in 2 hours.

13. Sample answer: Rewrite (8 + 27) + 52 as (27 + 8) + 52 using the Commutative Property of Addition. Rewrite (27 + 8) + 52 as 27 + (8 + 52) using the Associative Property of Addition. Find 8 + 52, or 60, mentally. Then find 60 + 27, or 87, mentally.

14. Sample answer: Rewrite (13 + 31) + 17 as (31 + 13) + 17 using the Commutative Property of Addition. Rewrite (31 + 13) + 17 as 31 + (13 + 17) using the Associative Property of Addition. Find 13 + 17, or 30, mentally. Then find 30 + 31, or 61, mentally.

15. Sample answer: Rewrite 91 + (15 + 9) as 91 + (9 + 15) using the Commutative Property of Addition. Rewrite 91 + (9 + 15) as (91 + 9) + 15 using the Associative Property of Addition. Find 91 + 9, or 100, mentally. Then find 100 + 15, or 115, mentally.

16. Sample answer: Rewrite 85 + (46 + 15) as 85 + (15 + 46) using the Commutative Property of Addition. Rewrite 85 + (15 + 46) as (85 + 15) + 46 using the Associative Property of Addition. Find 85 + 15, or 100, mentally. Then find 100 + 46, or 146, mentally.

17. Sample answer: Rewrite (4 • 18) • 25 as (18 • 4) • 25 using the Commutative Property of Multiplication. Rewrite (18 • 4) • 25 as 18 • (4 • 25) using the Associative Property of Multiplication. Find 4 • 25, or 100, mentally. Then find 100 • 18, or 1,800, mentally.

18. Sample answer: Rewrite (5 • 3) • 8 as (3 • 5) • 8 using the Commutative Property of Multiplication. Rewrite (3 • 5) • 8 as 3 • (5 • 8) using the Associative Property of Multiplication. Find 5 • 8, or 40, mentally. Then find 40 • 3, or 120, mentally.

19. Sample answer: Rewrite 15 • (8 • 2) as 15 • (2 • 8) using the Commutative Property of Multiplication. Rewrite 15 • (2 • 8) as (15 • 2) • 8 using the Associative Property of Multiplication. Find 15 • 2, or 30, mentally. Then find 30 • 8, or 240, mentally.

20. Sample answer: Rewrite 2 • (16 • 50) as 2 • (50 • 16) using the Commutative Property of Multiplication. Rewrite 2 • (50 • 16) as (2 • 50) • 16 using the Associative Property of Multiplication. Find 2 • 50, or 100, mentally. Then find 100 • 16, or 1,600, mentally.

21. Sample answer: Rewrite 5 • (30 • 12) as 5 • (12 • 30) using the Commutative Property of Multiplication. Rewrite 5 • (12 • 30) as (5 • 12) • 30 using the Associative Property of Multiplication. Find 5 • 12, or 60, mentally. Then find 60 • 30, or 1,800, mentally.

22. Sample answer: Rewrite 20 • (48 • 5) as 20 • (5 • 48) using the Commutative Property of Multiplication. Rewrite 20 • (5 • 48) as (20 • 5) • 48 using the Associative Property of Multiplication. Find 20 • 5, or 100, mentally. Then find 100 • 48, or 4,800, mentally.

23. Sample answer: The expression 20 + 7 represents the number of millions of people who visit Paris each year. The expression 5(20 + 7) represents the number of millions of people who visit Paris over a five-year period. Since 5 × 20 = 100 and 5 × 7 = 35, find 100 + 35, or 135, to find the number of millions of people who visit Paris over a five-year period.

24. Sample answer: The expression 100 + 8 represents the time, in seconds, to ride the roller coaster. The expression 3(100 + 8) represents the time, in seconds, to ride the roller coaster three times. Since 3 × 100 = 300 and 3 × 8 = 24, find 300 + 24, or 324 to find the time in seconds to ride the roller coaster three times.

Page 62, Extend 1-9

1. 3; add 3 to the previous row's number of toothpicks

3.

Figure Number	Number of Toothpicks
1	3
2	6
3	9
4	12
5	15
6	18
7	21

4. $3n$

6. 31; Evaluate the expression $3n + 1$ for $n = 10$. $3(10) + 1 = 31$.

```
——————— 10 toothpicks ———————
```
⬜⬜⬜⬜⬜⬜⬜⬜⬜⬜ ← 11 toothpicks
```
——————— 10 toothpicks ———————
```

7. $2n + 2$; 26; Sample answer: The number of toothpicks on the top and bottom of each figure is always twice the figure number ($2n$), but there are always two toothpicks added on either side of the figure ($+2$), so Figure n will have $2n + 2$ toothpicks. Evaluating $2n + 2$ for $n = 12$ gives $2(12) + 2$ or 26.

Page 63, Lesson 1-10

a.

Number of Tickets	Multiply by 3	Total Cost ($)
1	1×3	3
2	2×3	6
3	3×3	9
4	4×3	12

Page 75, Chapter 1 Practice Test

18. Sample answer: Rewrite $13 + (34 + 17)$ as $13 + (17 + 34)$ using the Commutative Property of Addition. Rewrite $13 + (17 + 34)$ as $(13 + 17) + 34$ using the Associative Property of Addition. Find $13 + 17$, or 30, mentally. Then find $30 + 34$, or 68, mentally.

19. Sample answer: Rewrite $(50 \bullet 17) \bullet 2$ as $(17 \bullet 50) \bullet 2$ using the Commutative Property of Multiplication. Rewrite $(17 \bullet 50) \bullet 2$ as $17 \bullet (50 \bullet 2)$ using the Associative Property of Multiplication. Find $50 \bullet 2$, or 100, mentally. Then find $17 \bullet 100$, or 1,700, mentally.

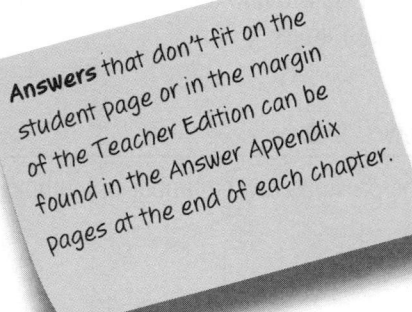

Answers that don't fit on the student page or in the margin of the Teacher Edition can be found in the Answer Appendix pages at the end of each chapter.

NOTES

Chapter Overview

Integers

Lesson Plan		Pacing Your Lessons		
LESSONS AND OBJECTIVES	State/Local Standards	40–50 Minute Periods	90-Minute Periods
2-1 Integers and Absolute Value (pp. 80–83) • Read and write integers, and find the absolute value of a number.		1	0.5
2-2 Comparing and Ordering Integers (pp. 84–87) • Compare and order integers.		1	0.5
2-3 The Coordinate Plane (pp. 88–92) • Graph points on a coordinate plane.		1	0.5
Explore 2-4 Algebra Lab: Adding Integers (pp. 93–94) • Use counters to model the addition of integers. **2-4 Adding Integers** (pp. 95–99) • Add integers.		1.5	0.5
Explore 2-5 Algebra Lab: Subtracting Integers (pp. 101–102) • Use counters to model the subtraction of integers. **2-5 Subtracting Integers** (pp. 103–106) • Subtract integers.		1.5	0.5
2-6 Multiplying Integers (pp. 107–111) • Multiply Integers.		1	0.5
2-7 Problem-Solving Investigation: Look for a Pattern (pp. 112–113) • Solve problems by looking for a pattern.		1	0.5
2-8 Dividing Integers (pp. 114–118) • Divide integers.		1	0.5
REVIEW		1	0.5
ASSESSMENT		1	0.5*

The complete **Assessment Planner** for Chapter 2 is provided on page 79.

TOTAL	11	5

* Begin Chapter 3 in the second half of the period.

G7-FP3 Number and Operations
For the complete wording of the Focal Points for Grade 7, please see page iv.

Professional Development

Vertical Alignment

Before Chapter 2

Related Topics from Grade 6

- identify and represent on a number line positive and negative integers
- add with negative integers; subtract positive integers from negative integers

Chapter 2

Topics from Grade 7

- compare and order positive and negative fractions, decimals, and mixed numbers and place them on a number line
- use graphs to explain mathematical reasoning
- solve addition, subtraction, multiplication, and division problems, including those arising in concrete situations, that use positive and negative integers and combinations of these operations

After Chapter 2

Preparation for Grade 8

- understand the meaning of the absolute value of a number; interpret the absolute value as the distance of the number from zero on a number line; and determine the absolute value of real numbers
- read, write and compare rational numbers in scientific notation with approximate numbers using scientific notation
- graph linear functions, noting that the vertical change per unit of horizontal change is always the same and know that the ratio is called the slope of a graph
- add, subtract, multiply, and divide rational numbers and take positive rational numbers to whole-number powers

Backmapping and Vertical Alignment

McGraw-Hill's **Math Connects** was conceived and developed with the final results in mind: student success in Algebra 1 and beyond. The authors, using the **NCTM Focal Points and Focal Connections** as their guide, developed this brand-new series by backmapping from Algebra 1 concepts, and vertically aligning the topics so that they build upon prior skills and concepts and serve as a foundation for future topics.

What the Research Says...

According to Kalathil and Sherin in *Role of Students' Representations in the Mathematics Classroom*, student-created representations can help teachers understand individual student thinking and be instructional tools to illustrate various solution methods.

- In Lessons 2-1, 2-2, 2-4, and 2-5, students make number lines to represent integers and to add and subtract integers.

 **Professional Development**

Targeted professional development has been articulated throughout **McGraw-Hill's Math Connects** program. The **McGraw-Hill Professional Development Video Library** provides short videos that support the NCTM Focal Points and Focal Connections. For more information, visit glencoe.com.

| Model Lessons | Instructional Strategies |

Technology Solutions

Teacher Resources

TeacherWorks™ All-in-One Planner and Resource Center

All of the print materials from the Classroom Resource Masters are available on your TeacherWorks™ CD-ROM.

BL = Below or Approaching Grade Level **OL** = On Grade Level **AL** = Above or Beyond Grade Level **ELL** = English Language Learner

	Chapter Resource Masters	2-1	2-2	2-3	2-4	2-5	2-6	2-7	2-8
BL **OL** **ELL**	Lesson Reading Guide	9	16	22	29	36	42		52
BL **OL** **ELL**	Study Guide and Intervention*	10	17	23	30	37	43	48	53
BL **OL**	Skills Practice*	11	18	24	31	38	44	49	54
OL **AL**	Practice*	12	19	25	32	39	45	50	55
OL **AL**	Word Problem Practice*	13	20	26	33	40	46	51	56
OL **AL**	Enrichment	14	21	27	34	41	47		57
OL **AL**	Calculator and Spreadsheet Activities	15		28	35				
OL **AL**	Chapter Assessments*	59–80							
BL **OL** **AL**	5-Minute Check Transparencies	✓	✓	✓	✓	✓	✓	✓	✓
BL **OL**	Teaching Mathematics with Manipulatives				✓	✓	✓	✓	
BL **OL** **AL**	Real-World Investigations for Differentiated Instruction	27–29							

Also available in Spanish.

Graphing Calculator Easy Files

- Timesaving Tech Tools for the TI-Navigator:
- **Quick Checks** to diagnose student progress
- Motivate students with **Concept Launchers**
- Deliver differentiated instruction with **Ready Files**
- **Vocabulary Review**

AssignmentWorks

Differentiated Assignments, Answers, and Solutions
- Print a customized assignment worksheet using the Student Edition exercises along with an answer key or worked-out solutions.
- Use default lesson assignments as outlined in the Differentiated Homework Options in the Teacher Edition.

Interactive Classroom

This CD-ROM is a customizable Microsoft® PowerPoint® presentation that includes:

- In-Class Examples
- Your Turn Exercises*
- 5-Minute Check Transparencies*
- Links to Online Study Tools
- Concepts in Motion

compatible with response pad technology

Example 3
GEOGRAPHY Use the map of Utah shown below. In which quadrant is Vernal located?

Vernal is located in the upper right quadrant, quadrant I.

Answer: Quadrant I

ExamView® Assessment Suite

ExamView®
Assessment Suite

- Create, edit, and customize tests and worksheets using QuickTest Wizard
- Create multiple versions of tests and modify them for a desired level of difficulty
- Translate from English to Spanish and vice versa
- Build tests aligned with your state standards
- Track students' progress using the Teacher Management System

Student Tools

StudentWorks™ Plus

Textbook, Audio, Workbooks, and more

This CD-ROM is a valuable resource for students to access content online and use online resources to continue learning Chapter 2 concepts. Includes:

- Complete Student Editions in both English and Spanish
- English audio integrated throughout the text
- Links to Concepts in Motion, Personal Tutor, and other online resources
- Access to all student worksheets
- Daily Assignments and Grade Log

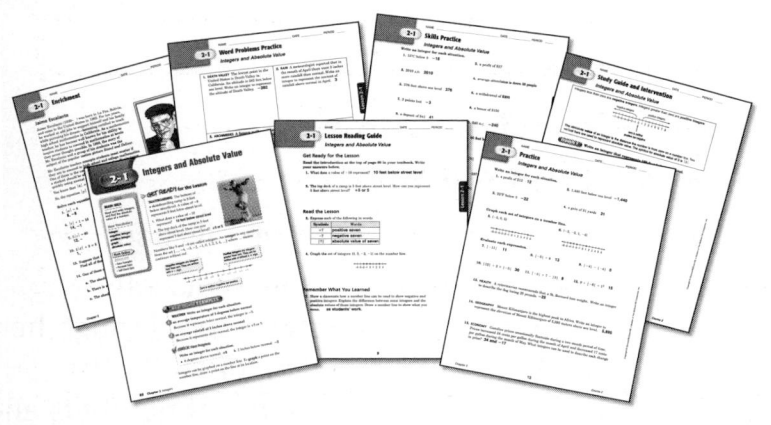

Super DVD

The Super DVD contains two Glencoe multimedia products.

MindJogger Plus   An alternative review of concepts in which students work as teams in a game show format to gain points for correct answers.

What's Math Got to Do With It?
Real-Life Math Videos
Engaging video that shows students how math is used in everyday situations.

Internet Resources

Math Online ▷ glencoe.com

TEACHER	STUDENT	PARENT	Online Study Tools
	●	●	Online Student Edition
●	●	●	Multilingual Glossary
			Lesson Resources
	●	●	Extra Examples
	●	●	BrainPOPS
	●	●	Self-Check Quizzes
●	●	●	Concepts in Motion
	●	●	Other Calculator Keystrokes
	●	●	Real-World Careers
	●	●	Reading in the Content Area
●			Group Activity Cards
			Chapter Resources
	●	●	Family Letters and Activities
	●		Chapter Readiness Quiz
	●	●	Vocabulary Review
	●	●	Chapter Test
	●	●	Standardized Test Practice
			Unit Resources
●	●		WebQuest Project
			Other Resources
	●		Personal Tutor
●			NAEP Correlations
●			Key Concepts
●	●	●	Meet the Authors
●	●		Game Zone
●	●	●	Math Skills Maintenance
●			National Resources (Professional Organizations)
●			State Resources
●			Vocabulary PuzzleMakers

CHAPTER 2
Reading and Writing in Mathematics

Noteables™ Interactive Study Notebook with Foldables™

This workbook is a study organizer that provides helpful steps for students to follow to organize their notes for Chapter 2.

- Students use Noteables to record notes and to complete their Foldables as you present the material for each lesson.

- Noteables correspond to the Examples in the *Teacher Edition* and *Interactive Classroom CD-ROM.*

Real-World Problem Solving Graphic Novels

Mathematical problem solving is presented in a motivating, graphic novel format. The novels contain real-world problems for each of the following mathematical strands: Number Sense, Algebraic Thinking, Geometry, Measurement, Statistics and Probability, and Mathematical Reasoning.

READING in the Content Area

This online worksheet provides strategies for reading and analyzing Lesson 2-2, Comparing and Ordering Integers. Students are guided through questions about the main idea, subject matter, supporting details, conclusion, clarifying details, and vocabulary of the lesson.

glencoe.com

Recommended Outside Reading for Students

Mathematics and Folklore

- *One Grain of Rice* by Demi ©1997 [fiction]

This book is about a young girl from India who saved the people of India from starvation through her cunningness and her understanding of math. The math is similar to the study of powers of numbers and patterns found in Chapter 1.

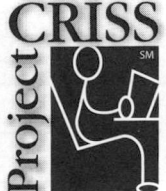

Project CRISS℠

STUDY SKILL

A pre-reading organizer can help students examine their background knowledge before they begin to study a new topic. The pre-reading organizer at the right shows the background a student might have for the lesson on integers and absolute value. Have students skim through a lesson and note any familiar concepts. Then have them complete a pre-reading organizer based on their individual experiences. Students can use their organizers as the basis for a discussion of the topics presented in the lesson.

Topic	What I Already Know
integers	• positive and negative numbers and zero • graphing points on number lines
absolute value	• always a nonnegative number • distances on number lines

CReating **I**ndependence through **S**tudent-owned **S**trategies

Differentiated Instruction

Investigative Approach

This project was supported, in part, by the
National Science Foundation

MathScape is a mathematics curriculum for grades 6–8 developed by the Seeing and Thinking Mathematically Project at the Education Development Center.

> Writing and Solving Equations
> Exploring the Unknown

How to Use *MathScape* with Chapter 2

The unit *Exploring the Unknown* can be used to enhance Lessons 2-4 and 2-5.

- **Enrich** ⟶ After you complete **Lessons 2-4 and 2-5**, you can use the activity on page 192 and 193 to reinforce operations with integers.

RTI (Response to Intervention)

1 On-Level Instruction Use the *Math Connects* program as instruction for your on-level students.

2 Strategic Intervention For options to instruct struggling students, refer to the Diagnostic Assessment table on page 79.

3 Intensive Intervention *Math Triumphs* can provide intensive intervention for students who are at risk of not meeting the objectives addressed in Chapter 1.

Diagnose student readiness with the Quick Check and Quick Review on page 79. Then use *Math Triumphs* to accelerate their achievement.

Integers

Prerequisite Skill	*Math Triumphs*
Whole Numbers and Integers	Chapter 8
Integer Operations	Chapter 9

Practice and Review

Quick Review Math Handbook* is Glencoe's mathematical handbook for students and parents.

Hot Words includes a glossary of terms.

Hot Topics consists of two parts:

- explanations of key mathematical concepts
- exercises to check students' understanding.

Lesson	Hot Topics Section	Lesson	Hot Topics Section
2-1	1•5	2-5	1•5
2-2	1•1, 1•5	2-7	1•5
2-3	6•7	2-8	1•5
2-4	1•5		

*Also available in Spanish

 **Dinah Zike's Foldables**

Focus This Foldable is designed to help students organize the information they learn about integers.

Teach After students make their Foldables, have them label pages with the titles of the lessons of the chapter. Students should use their Foldables to take notes, define terms, record key concepts, write examples, and describe how the subject matter relates to everyday life. Encourage students to record what they learn about difficult parts of each lesson.

When to Use It As students study each lesson in the chapter, they should record their notes on the appropriate page of their Foldables.

A version of a completed Foldable is shown on p. 119.

Differentiated Instruction

CRM Student-Built Glossary, p. 1

Students complete the chart by providing a definition for each term and an example as they progress through Chapter 2.

This study tool can be used to review for the chapter test.

Materials Needed for Chapter 2

- graph paper (Lesson 2-3)
- integer counters (Explore 2-4 and 2-5 and Lessons 2-7 and 2-8)
- integer mat (Explore 2-4 and 2-5 and Lessons 2-7 and 2-8)

CHAPTER 2 **Integers**

BIG Idea

- Add, subtract, multiply, or divide integers to solve problems and justify solutions.

Key Vocabulary

graph (p. 80)

integer (p. 80)

negative integer (p. 80)

positive integer (p. 80)

🌐 **Real-World Link**

Sports In miniature golf, a score above par can be written as a positive integer and a score below par can be written as a negative integer.

FOLDABLES **Study Organizer**

Integers Make this Foldable to help you organize your notes. Begin with two sheets of $8\frac{1}{2}$" by 11" paper.

❶ Fold one sheet in half from top to bottom. Cut along fold from edges to margin.

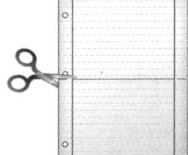

❷ Fold the other sheet in half from top to bottom. Cut along fold between margins.

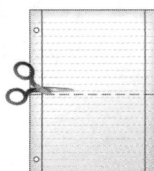

❸ Insert first sheet through second sheet and align folds.

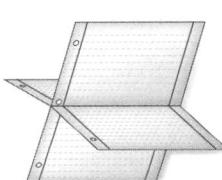

❹ Label each inside page with a lesson number and title.

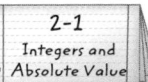

2-1
Integers and
Absolute Value

GET READY for Chapter 2

Diagnose Readiness You have two options for checking Prerequisite Skills.

Option 1

Take the Quick Check below. Refer to the Quick Review for help.

Option 2

Math Online > Take the Online Readiness Quiz at glencoe.com.

QUICK Quiz

(Used in Lesson 2-2)
Replace each ● with < or > to make a true sentence. (Prior Grade)

1. $1,458 ● 1,548$ **<**   2. $36 ● 34$ **>**

3. $1.02 ● 1.20$ **<**   4. $76.7 ● 77.6$ **<**

5. **COINS** Philippe has $5.17 in coins and Garrett has $5.71 in coins. Who has the greater amount? (Prior Grade) **Garrett**

(Used in Lessons 2-4 and 2-5)
Evaluate each expression if $a = 7$, $b = 2$, and $c = 11$. (Prior Grade)

6. $a + 8$ **15**   7. $a + b + c$ **20**

8. $c - b$ **9**   9. $a - b + 4$ **9**

10. **TEMPERATURE** At 8 a.m., it was 63°F. By noon, the temperature had risen 9 degrees Fahrenheit. What was the temperature at noon? (Prior Grade) **72°F**

(Used in Lessons 2-6 and 2-8)
Evaluate each expression if $m = 9$ and $n = 4$. (Prior Grade)

11. $6mn$ **216**   12. $n \div 2 - 1$ **1**

13. $m + 5 \times n$ **29**   14. $m^2 \div (n + 5)$ **9**

15. **PLANES** The distance in miles that an airplane travels is given by rt where r is the rate of travel and t is the time. Find the distance an airplane traveled if $t = 4$ hours and $r = 475$ miles per hour. (Prior Grade) **1,900 mi**

QUICK Review

Example 1

Replace the ● with < or > to make a true sentence.

$3.14 ● 3.41$

| 3.14 | Line up the decimal points. |
| 3.41 | Starting at the left, compare the digits in each place-value position. |

The digits in the tenths place are not the same. Since 1 tenth < 4 tenths, $3.14 < 3.41$.

Example 2

Evaluate the expression $11 - a + b$ if $a = 2$ and $b = 8$.

$11 - a + b = 11 - 2 + 8$ Replace a with 2 and b with 8.

$= 9 + 8$ Subtract 2 from 11.

$= 17$ Add 9 and 8.

Example 3

Evaluate the expression $n^2 \div 16 + m$ if $m = 3$ and $n = 8$.

$n^2 \div 16 + m = 8^2 \div 16 + 3$ Replace m with 3 and n with 8.

$= 64 \div 16 + 3$ Evaluate 8^2.

$= 4 + 3$ Divide 64 by 16.

$= 7$ Add 4 and 3.

Chapter 2 Get Ready for Chapter 2   **79**

Diagnostic Assessment

Exercises	State/Local Standards	Strategic Intervention
1–5		*Math Skills Maintenance Masters* pp. 2, 32–33
6–10		SE Review Lesson 1-6, pp. 44–47
11–15		SE Review Lesson 1-4, pp. 38–41

ASSESSMENT PLANNER

✓ Formative Assessment

CRM Anticipation Guide, pp. 7–8

Spotting Preconceived Ideas
Students complete this survey to determine prior knowledge about ideas from Chapter 2. Revisit the worksheet after completing the chapter. Also see page 122.

TE Lesson Activities

- Ticket Out the Door, p. 83
- Crystal Ball, pp. 87, 92, 111
- Name the Math, pp. 99, 113, 118
- Yesterday's News, p. 106

Chapter Checkpoints

SE Mid-Chapter Quiz, p. 100

SE Study Guide and Review, pp. 119–122

SE Test Practice, pp. 124–125

CRM Quizzes, pp. 61 and 62

CRM Standardized Test Practice, pp. 78–80

Math Online > glencoe.com

- Self-Check Quizzes
- Practice Test
- Test Practice

✓ Summative Assessment

SE Chapter Practice Test, p. 123

CRM Mid-Chapter Test, p. 63

CRM Vocabulary Test, p. 64

CRM Extended-Response Test, p. 77

CRM Leveled Chapter Tests, pp. 65–76

ExamView® Assessment Suite

KEY

CRM *Chapter 2 Resource Masters*

SE Student Edition

TE Teacher Edition

CD-ROM

2-1 Integers and Absolute Value

PACING: **Regular:** 1 period, **Block:** 0.5 period

Options for Differentiated Instruction

ELL = English Language Learner   **AL** = Above or Beyond Grade Level   **SS** = Struggling Students   **SN** = Special Needs

Making Real-World Connections **ELL** **SS** **SN**

Use after presenting Examples 1 and 2 on page 80.

Students do not learn as effectively if they are not interested in the topic being presented. Use as many different contexts for positive and negative numbers as possible to help students make connections between their own experiences and the study of integers. Some examples are shown below.

- temperature
- football yardage, gains and losses
- savings accounts, deposits and withdrawals
- elevators
- profit and losses in business

Kinesthetic Learning **ELL** **SS**

Use after presenting Absolute Value on page 81.

Many students think that the absolute value of a number is the opposite of that number. Make a number line on the floor using masking tape. Make sure the units for the number line are a comfortable stride length. Use index cards to label the number line. Then have students take turns finding the absolute value of various positive and negative integers by finding how many steps or units the number is from zero.

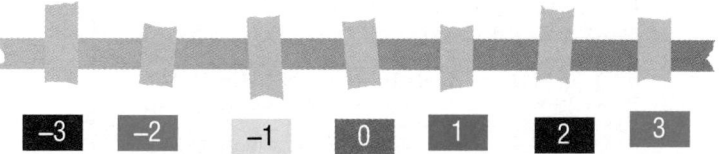

Simplifying Tasks **ELL** **SS** **SN**

Use before assigning the Exercises.

Create homework help sheets that have repeated entries like the one shown below.

Problem Number _____

Have students use these to help them tackle the exercises in which they are asked to graph integers on a number line.

Leveled Lesson Resources

Chapter 2 Resource Masters

BL = Below or Approaching Grade Level   **OL** = On Grade Level   **AL** = Above or Beyond Grade Level   **ELL** = English Language Learner

---

Lesson Reading Guide
p. 9 **BL** **OL** **ELL**

NAME _____ DATE _____ PERIOD _____

2-1 Lesson Reading Guide
Integers and Absolute Value

Get Ready for the Lesson

Read the introduction at the top of page 80 in your textbook. Write your answers below.

1. What does a value of −10 represent? **10 feet below street level**

2. The top deck of a ramp is 5 feet above street level. How can you represent 5 feet above street level? **+5 or 5**

Read the Lesson

3. Express each of the following in words.

Symbols	Words
+7	**positive seven**
−7	**negative seven**
|7|	**absolute value of seven**

4. Graph the set of integers {0, 3, −2, −1} on the number line.

−4 −3 −2 −1 0 1 2 3 4

Remember What You Learned

5. Show a classmate how a number line can be used to show negative and positive integers. Explain the difference between some integers and the absolute values of those integers. Draw a number line to show what you mean. **See students' work.**

Chapter 2   9   Course 2

Study Guide and Intervention*
p. 10 **BL** **OL** **ELL**

NAME _____ DATE _____ PERIOD _____

2-1 Study Guide and Intervention
Integers and Absolute Value

Integers less than zero are **negative integers**. Integers greater than zero are **positive integers**.

negative integers   positive integers

−7−6−5−4−3−2−1 0 1 2 3 4 5 6 7 8

zero is neither
positive nor negative

The **absolute value** of an integer is the distance the number is from zero on a number line. Two vertical bars are used to represent absolute value. The symbol for absolute value of 3 is \|3\|.

Example 1   Write an integer that represents 160 feet below sea level.

Because it represents *below* sea level, the integer is −160.

Example 2   Evaluate \|−2\|.

On the number line, the graph of −2 is 2 units away from 0. So, \|−2\| = 2.

−4 −3 −2 −1 0 1 2 3 4

Exercises

Write an integer for each situation.

1. 12°C above 0   **12**
2. a loss of $2~   **−24**
3. a gain of 20 pounds   **20**
4. falling 6 feet   **−6**

Evaluate each expression.

5. \|12\| **12**
6. \|−150\| **150**
7. \|−8\| **8**
8. \|75\| **75**
9. \|−19\| **19**
10. \|84\| **84**

Chapter 2   10   Course 2

Skills Practice*
p. 11 **BL** **OL**

NAME _____ DATE _____ PERIOD _____

2-1 Skills Practice
Integers and Absolute Value

Write an integer for each situation.

1. 15°C below 0   **−15**
2. a profit of $27   **27**
3. 2010 A.D.   **2010**
4. average attendance is down 38 people   **−38**
5. 376 feet above sea level   **376**
6. a withdrawal of $200   **−200**
7. 3 points lost   **−3**
8. a bonus of $150   **150**
9. a deposit of $41   **41**
10. 240 B.C.   **−240**
11. a wage increase of $120   **120**
12. 60 feet below sea level   **−60**

Evaluate each expression.

13. \|−1\| **1**
14. \|9\| **9**
15. \|23\| **23**
16. \|−107\| **107**
17. \|−45\| **45**
18. \|19\| **19**
19. \|0\| **0**
20. \|6\| − \|−2\| **4**
21. \|−8\| + \|4\| **12**
22. \|−12\| − \|12\| **0**

Graph each set of integers on a number line.

23. {0, 2, −3}

−4 −3 −2 −1 0 1 2 3 4

24. {−4, −1, 3}

−4 −3 −2 −1 0 1 2 3 4

Chapter 2   11   Course 2

Practice*
p. 12 **OL** **AL**

NAME _____ DATE _____ PERIOD _____

2-1 Practice
Integers and Absolute Value

Write an integer for each situation.

1. a profit of $12   **12**
2. 1,440 feet below sea level   **−1,440**
3. 22°F below 0   **−22**
4. a gain of 31 yards   **31**

Graph each set of integers on a number line.

5. {−5, 0, 5}

−6 −5 −4 −3 −2 −1 0 1 2 3 4 5 6

6. {−3, −2, 1, −4}

−6 −5 −4 −3 −2 −1 0 1 2 3 4 5 6

Evaluate each expression.

7. \|−11\| **11**
8. \|−5\| + \|8\| **13**
9. \|−4\| − \|−4\| **0**
10. \|12\| ÷ 2 × \|−5\| **30**
11. \|−4\| + 7 − \|3\| **8**
12. 9 + \|−6\| − 1²   **15**

13. **HEALTH** A veterinarian recommends that a St. Bernard lose weight. Write an integer to describe the dog losing 25 pounds. **−25**

14. **GEOGRAPHY** Mount Kilimanjaro is the highest peak in Africa. Write an integer to represent the elevation of Mount Kilimanjaro of 5,895 meters above sea level. **5,895**

15. **ECONOMY** Gasoline prices occasionally fluctuate during a two month period of time. Prices increased 34 cents per gallon during the month of April and decreased 17 cents per gallon during the month of May. What integers can be used to describe each change in price? **34 and −17**

Chapter 2   12   Course 2

Word Problem Practice*
p. 13 **OL** **AL**

NAME _____ DATE _____ PERIOD _____

2-1 Word Problems Practice
Integers and Absolute Value

1. **DEATH VALLEY** The lowest point in the United States is Death Valley in California. Its altitude is 282 feet below sea level. Write an integer to represent the altitude of Death Valley. **−282**

2. **RAIN** A meteorologist reported that in the month of April there was 3 inches more rainfall than normal. Write an integer to represent the amount of rainfall above normal in April. **3**

3. **ARCHIMEDES** A famous mathematician and physicist named Archimedes was born in 287 B.C. Write an integer to express the year of his birth. **−287**

4. **TEMPERATURE** In our world's tropical rain forests, the average temperature of every month is 64 degrees above zero or higher. Write an integer to express this temperature. **64**

5. **STOCK MARKET** A certain stock gained 5 points in one day and lost 4 points the next day. Write integers to represent the stock's gains and losses for the two days. **5; −4**

6. **ALTITUDE** An airplane pilot changed his altitude by 100 meters. Describe what this could mean. **either 100 or −100 meaning the plane is either 100 feet higher or 100 feet lower than its original position.**

Chapter 2   13   Course 2

Enrichment
p. 14 **OL** **AL**

NAME _____ DATE _____ PERIOD _____

2-1 Enrichment

Jaime Escalante

Jaime Escalante (1930–) was born in La Paz, Bolivia, and came to the United States in 1963. For ten years, he worked at odd jobs to support himself and his family while pursuing his dream—becoming certified to teach high school mathematics in California. As a mathematics teacher, he has become well known for his ability to inspire students to succeed in mathematics at levels they never thought possible. In 1988, the story of Mr. Escalante and a group of his students was the subject of the popular motion picture *Stand and Deliver*.

Mr. Escalante teaches concepts students must master if they are to succeed in high school and college mathematics. One of these is the concept of absolute value. For instance, a student should be able to solve an equation like \|y\| = 6 quickly using mental math. Here's how.

You know that \|6\| = 6 and \|−6\| = 6.

So, the equation \|y\| = 6 has *two* solutions: 6 and −6.

Solve each equation. (*Hint:* One equation has no solution.)

1. \|a\| = 8   **8, −8**
2. \|r\| = 0   **0**
3. \|j\| = −3   **no solution**
4. \|z\| + 1 = 15   **14, −14**
5. 10 − \|m\| = 3   **7, −7**
6. \|c\| − 4 = 16   **20, −20**
7. 5\|z\| = 60   **12, −12**
8. 12 ÷ \|g\| = 4   **3, −3**
9. 48 = 8\|x\| **6, −6**
10. 2\|d\| + 3 = 5   **1, −1**
11. 4\|p\| − 9 = 59   **17, −17**
12. 7\|z\| + 12 = 12   **0**

13. Suppose that the value of *x* can be selected from the set {−2, −1, 0, 1, 2}. Find all the solutions of the equation \|x\| = *x*. **0, 1, 2**

14. One of these statements is false. Which one is it? Explain.

a. The absolute value of every integer is positive.

b. There is at least one integer whose absolute value is zero.

c. The absolute value of an integer is never negative. **Statement a is false; the absolute value of 0 is 0, which is not positive.**

Chapter 2   14   Course 2

*** Also available in Spanish ELL**

Additional Lesson Resources

Transparencies
• *5-Minute Check Transparency*, Lesson 2-1

Other Print Products
• *Noteables™ Interactive Study Notebook with Foldables™*

Teacher Tech Tools
• *Interactive Classroom CD-ROM*, Lesson 2-1
• *AssignmentWorks*, Lesson 2-1

Student Tech Tools
glencoe.com
• Extra Examples, Chapter 2, Lesson 1
• Self-Check Quiz, Chapter 2, Lesson 1

2-1 Integers and Absolute Value

1 Focus

Vertical Alignment

Before Lesson 2-1
Identify and represent on a number line positive and negative integers

Lesson 2-1
Compare and order positive and negative fractions, decimals, and mixed numbers and place them on a number line

After Lesson 2-1
Understand the meaning of the absolute value of a number; interpret the absolute value as the distance of the number from zero on a number line; and determine the absolute value of real numbers

2 Teach

Scaffolding Questions

Have students research the elevations of various geographical landmarks (such as Mt. Whitney, Lake Titicaca, and Death Valley).

Ask:

- Why do elevations include the terms *above sea level* or *below sea level*?
  Sample answer: Sea level is considered the zero point for measuring elevation.

- Can you find any landmarks that are below sea level? Death Valley, California; Dead Sea, Israel and Jordan

- How could you use a positive or negative sign to write an elevation?
  Sample answer: Use a positive sign to show elevations above sea level and use a negative sign to show elevations below sea level.

MAIN IDEA

Read and write integers, and find the absolute value of a number.

New Vocabulary

integer
negative integer
positive integer
graph
absolute value

Math Online

glencoe.com

- Extra Examples
- Personal Tutor
- Self-Check Quiz

▷ GET READY for the Lesson

SKATEBOARDING The bottom of a skateboarding ramp is 8 feet below streetlevel. A value of −8 represents 8 feet *below* street level.

1. What does a value of −10 represent?   **10 feet below street level**

2. The top deck of the ramp is 5 feet *above* street level. How can you represent 5 feet *above* street level?   **+5 or 5**

Numbers like 5 and −8 are called integers. An **integer** is any number from the set $\{..., -4, -3, -2, -1, 0, 1, 2, 3, 4, ...\}$ where ... means *continues without end.*

Negative integers are integers less than zero. They are written with a − sign.

Positive integers are integers greater than zero. They can be written with or without a + sign.

$$-5 \quad -4 \quad -3 \quad -2 \quad -1 \quad 0 \quad +1 \quad +2 \quad +3 \quad +4 \quad +5$$

Zero is neither negative nor positive.

🌐 Real-World EXAMPLES

WEATHER Write an integer for each situation.

1. **an average temperature of 5 degrees below normal**
   Because it represents *below* normal, the integer is −5.

2. **an average rainfall of 5 inches above normal**
   Because it represents *above* normal, the integer is +5 or 5.

✓ CHECK Your Progress

Write an integer for each situation.

a. 6 degrees above normal   **+6**   b. 2 inches below normal   **−2**

Integers can be graphed on a number line. To **graph** a point on the number line, draw a point on the line at its location.

Differentiated Instruction

Verbal/Linguistic Learners Have students create a list of words that represent opposites and organize the list according to words that represent a positive concept or a negative concept. For example, *up* represents a positive concept and *down* represents a negative concept. Other examples include *forward/backward*, *above/below*, and *deposit/withdrawal*.

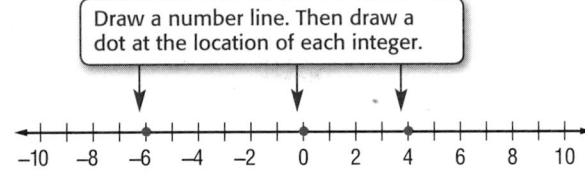

EXAMPLE Graph Integers

3 Graph the set of integers {4, −6, 0} on a number line.

Draw a number line. Then draw a dot at the location of each integer.

-10 -8 -6 -4 -2 0 2 4 6 8 10

✔ CHECK Your Progress

Graph each set of integers on a number line. **c, d. See margin.**

c. {−2, 8, −7}   **d.** {−4, 10, −3, 7}

On the number line below, notice that −5 and 5 are each 5 units from 0, even though they are on opposite sides of 0. Numbers that are the same distance from zero on a number line have the same **absolute value**.

Reading Math

Absolute Value

|−5| *absolute value of negative five*

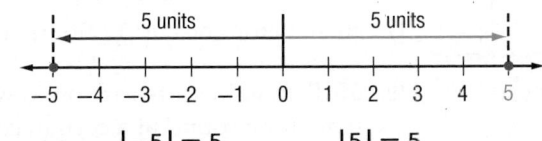

Absolute Value	Key Concept

Words   The absolute value of a number is the distance between the number and zero on a number line.

5 units   5 units

-5 -4 -3 -2 -1 0 1 2 3 4 5

Examples $|−5| = 5$ $|5| = 5$

EXAMPLES Evaluate Expressions

Evaluate each expression.

4 $|−4|$

On the number line, the point −4 is 4 units from 0.

So, $|−4| = 4$.

4 units

-4 -3 -2 -1 0 1 2 3 4

5 $|−5| − |2|$

$|−5| − |2| = 5 − 2$ $|−5| = 5, |2| = 2$

So, $|−5| − |2| = 3$.

Study Tip

Order of Operations
The absolute value bars are considered to be a grouping symbol. When evaluating $|−5| − |2|$, evaluate the absolute values before subtracting.

✔ CHECK Your Progress

Evaluate each expression.

e. $|8|$ **8**   **f.** $2 + |−3|$ **5**   **g.** $|−6| − 5$ **1**

Lesson 2-1 Integers and Absolute Value   **81**

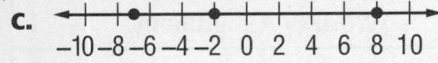

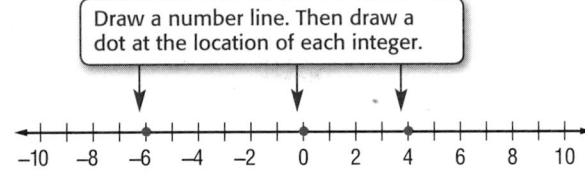

Focus on Mathematical Content

Integers (whole numbers, their negatives, and zero) can be graphed on a number line.

Integers are used to represent many quantities in everyday life such as elevations, temperatures, and bank deposits.

✔ Formative Assessment

Use the Check Your Progress exercises after the Examples to determine students' understanding of concepts.

ADDITIONAL EXAMPLES

Write an integer for each situation.

1 a total rainfall of 2 inches below normal −2

2 a seasonal snowfall of 3 inches above normal +3

3 Graph the set of integers {−1, 3, −2} on a number line.

-4 -3 -2 -1 0 1 2 3 4

Evaluate each expression.

4 $|−5| + 5$ **10**

5 $|−4| − |−3|$ **1**

Additional Examples are also in:

- Noteables™ Interactive Study Notebook with Foldables™
- Interactive Classroom PowerPoint® Presentations

Additional Answers

c.
-10 -8 -6 -4 -2 0 2 4 6 8 10

d.
-8 -6 -4 -2 0 2 4 6 8 10 12

Practice

Use Exercises 1–10 to check for understanding.

Then use the chart at the bottom of this page to customize your assignments for students.

Intervention You may wish to use the Study Guide and Intervention Master on page 10 of the *Chapter 2 Resource Masters* for additional reinforcement.

Odd/Even Assignments

Exercises 11–30 are structured so that students practice the same concepts whether they are assigned odd or even problems.

Tips for New Teachers **Word Problems**

Sometimes numbers are modified to make a problem easier for students to solve. For example, Exercise 35 uses 2-digit integers. In reality, the number of protons and electrons in such a situation would be in the billions.

Additional Answers

6.
   -8 -6 -4 -2 0 2 4 6 8 10 12

7.
   -10 -8 -6 -4 -2 0 2 4 6 8 10

21.
   -3 -2 -1 0 1

22.
   -10 -8 -6 -4 -2 0 2 4 6 8 10

23.
   -10 -8 -6 -4 -2 0 2 4 6 8 10

24.
   -10 -9 -8 -7 -6 -5 -4 -3 -2 -1 0

35. 17 positive charges: +17; 25 negative charges: −25

✓ CHECK Your Understanding

Examples 1, 2 (p. 80) **Write an integer for each situation.**

1. a loss of 11 yards **−11**
2. 6°F below zero **−6**
3. a deposit of $16 **16**
4. 250 meters above sea level **250**

5. **FOOTBALL** The quarterback lost 15 yards on one play. Write an integer to represent the number of yards lost. **−15**

Example 3 (p. 81) **Graph each set of integers on a number line. 6, 7. See margin.**

6. $\{11, -5, -8\}$
7. $\{2, -1, -9, 1\}$

Examples 4, 5 (p. 81) **Evaluate each expression.**

8. $|-9|$ **9**
9. $1 + |7|$ **8**
10. $|-1| - |-6|$ **−5**

▶ Practice and Problem Solving

HOMEWORK HELP	
For Exercises	See Examples
11–20	1, 2
21–24	3
25–30	4, 5

Exercise Levels
A: 11–30
B: 31–35
C: 36–38

Write an integer for each situation.

11. a profit of $9 **9**
12. a bank withdrawal of $50 **−50**
13. 53°C below zero **−53**
14. 7 inches more than normal **7**
15. 2 feet below flood level **−2**
16. 160 feet above sea level **160**
17. an elevator goes up 12 floors **12**
18. no gains or losses on first down **0**

19. **GOLF** In golf, scores are often written in relationship to *par*, the average score for a round at a certain course. Write an integer to represent a score that is 7 under par. **−7**

20. **PETS** Javier's pet guinea pig gained 8 ounces in one month. Write an integer to describe the amount of weight his pet gained. **8**

Graph each set of integers on a number line. 21–24. See margin.

21. $\{0, 1, -3\}$
22. $\{3, -7, 6\}$
23. $\{-5, -1, 10, -9\}$
24. $\{-2, -4, -6, -8\}$

34. Sample answer: Descending 10 feet has the greater absolute value. The diver descending 10 feet descends the most.

Evaluate each expression.

25. $|10|$ **10**
26. $|-12|$ **12**
27. $|-7| - 5$ **2**
28. $7 + |4|$ **11**
29. $|-9| + |-5|$ **14**
30. $|8| - |-10|$ **−2**
31. $|-10| \div 2 \times |5|$ **25**
32. $12 - |-8| + 7$ **11**
33. $|27| \div 3 - |-4|$ **5**

34. **SCUBA DIVING** One diver descended 10 feet, and another ascended 8 feet. Which situation has the greater absolute value? Explain.

EXTRA PRACTICE
See pages 671, 705.

35. **SCIENCE** If you rub a balloon through your hair, you can make the balloon stick to a wall. Suppose there are 17 positive charges on the wall and 25 negative charges on the balloon. Write an integer for each charge. **See margin.**

DIFFERENTIATED HOMEWORK OPTIONS

Level	Assignment	Two-Day Assignment	
BL Basic	11–30, 36, 38–48	11–29 odd, 39, 40	12–30 even, 36, 38, 41–48
OL Core	11–33 odd, 34–36, 38–48	11–30, 39, 40	31–36, 38, 41–48
AL Advanced/Pre-AP	31–44 (optional: 45–48)		

H.O.T. Problems

36. **REASONING** If $|x| = 3$, what is the value of x? **−3 or 3**

37. **CHALLENGE** Determine whether the following statement is *true* or *false*. If *false*, give a counterexample. **false; 0**

   The absolute value of every integer is positive.

38. 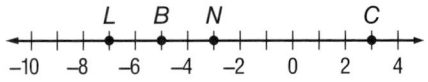 **MATH** Write a real-world situation that uses negative integers. Explain what the negative integer means in that situation. **Sample answer: Golfing uses negative numbers. A score of −2 represents 2 under par.**

TEST PRACTICE

39. Which point has a coordinate with the greatest absolute value? **C**

   ```
        L   B   N           C
   +--+--+--+--+--+--+--+--+--+--+--+
   −10 −8  −6  −4  −2   0   2   4
   ```

   A Point B

   B Point C

   C Point L

   D Point N

40. Which statement about these real-world situations is *not* true? **J**

   F A $100 check deposited in a bank can be represented by +100.

   G A loss of 15 yards in a football game can be represented by −15.

   H A temperature of 20 below zero can be represented by −20.

   J A submarine diving 300 feet under water can be represented by +300.

Spiral Review

Copy and complete each function table. Identify the domain and range. (Lesson 1-1C)

41. $y = x - 4$

x	x − 4	y
4		
5		
6		
7		

42. $y = 9x$

x	9x	y
0		
1		
2		
3		

43. $y = 5x + 1$

x	5x + 1	y
1		
2		
3		
4		

41–43. See margin.

44. **GEOMETRY** The table shows the side length and perimeter of several equilateral triangles. Write an expression that describes the perimeter if x represents the side length. (Lesson 1-9) **3x**

Side Length (in.)	2	3	4	5	6
Perimeter (in.)	6	9	12	15	18

▷ **GET READY** for the Next Lesson

PREREQUISITE SKILL Replace each ● with < or > to make a true sentence.

45. 16 ● 6 **>**

46. 101 ● 111 **<**

47. 87.3 ● 83.7 **>**

48. 1,051 ● 1,015 **>**

Lesson 2-1 Integers and Absolute Value **83**

Tips for New Teachers

Equilateral Triangles

After assigning Exercise 44, it may be helpful to remind students that all three sides of an equilateral triangle have the same length.

Comparing and Ordering Integers

PACING: **Regular:** 1 period, **Block:** 0.5 period

Options for Differentiated Instruction

ELL = English Language Learner   **AL** = Above or Beyond Grade Level   **SS** = Struggling Students   **SN** = Special Needs

Visual Cues SS

Use before presenting Example 1.

On an index card, have students create a number line that includes both positive and negative integers. Have them include reminders for comparing and ordering integers like the ones in arrows shown below.

Have students provide examples of statements using the signs < and >.

Numbers to the right are **GREATER THAN** numbers to the left.

Have students provide examples of statements using the signs < and >.

−10 −9 −8 −7 −6 −5 −4 −3 −2 −1 0 1 2 3 4 5 6 7 8 9 10

Numbers to the left are **LESS THAN** numbers to the right.

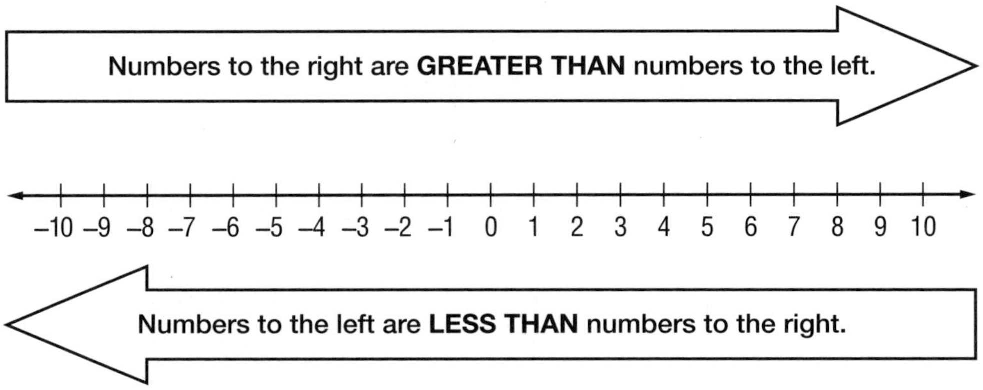

Kinesthetic Learning ELL AL SS SN

Use before assigning the Exercises.

Choose any integers between −50 and 50 and write one number per student on a piece of card stock.

- Pass out a number to each student.
- Have students stand up. Ask them to line up as quickly as possible from least to greatest *without* talking to each other.
- After students have correctly lined up, have a class discussion about strategies that might make the process go faster next time.
- Shuffle the cards, pass out the numbers, and have students line up again.

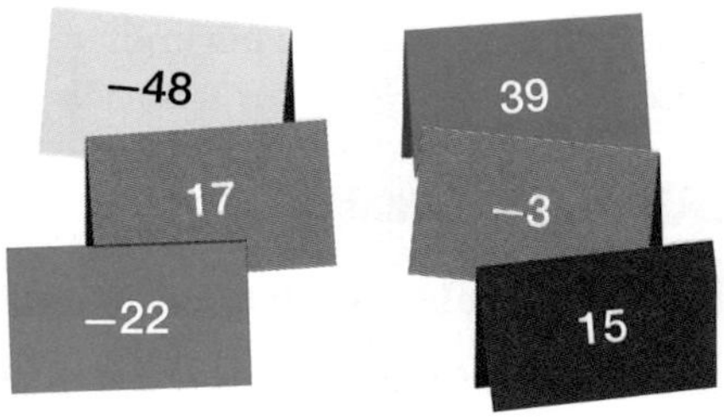

−48   39

17   −3

−22   15

Leveled Lesson Resources

Chapter 2 Resource Masters

BL = Below or Approaching Grade Level   **OL** = On Grade Level   **AL** = Above or Beyond Grade Level   **ELL** = English Language Learner

Lesson Reading Guide
p. 16 **BL** **OL** **ELL**

2-2 Lesson Reading Guide
Comparing and Ordering Integers

Get Ready for the Lesson
Read the introduction at the top of page 84 in your textbook. Write your answers below.

1. The yo-yo was invented around 500 B.C. Was it invented before or after the kite? **after**

2. Modern Chess was invented around 600 A.D. Between which two toys was this invented? **skates and videogames**

Read the Lesson
For Exercises 3 and 4, express each of the following in words. Then graph the numbers on a number line.

3. $-1 < 0$ **negative 1 is less than 0**

4. $3 > -2$ **3 is greater than negative 2**

5. When two numbers are graphed on a number line, what can you tell about the number to the left? the number to the right?
Sample answer: The number to the left is always less than the number to the right. The number to the right is always greater than the number to the left.

Remember What You Learned
6. Write a set of six numbers, some positive and some negative. Explain how you can use a number line to order the numbers from least to greatest.
See students' work.

Chapter 2   16   *Course 2*

Study Guide and Intervention*
p. 17 **BL** **OL** **ELL**

2-2 Study Guide and Intervention
Comparing and Ordering Integers

When two numbers are graphed on a number line, the number to the left is always less than (<) the number to the right. The number to the right is always greater than (>) the number to the left.

Model
$-4\ -3\ -2\ -1\ 0\ 1\ 2\ 3\ 4$

Words -3 is less than -1. -1 is greater than -3.
Symbols $-3 < -1$ $-1 > -3$

The symbol points to the lesser number.

Example 1 Replace the ● with < or > to make -1 ● -6 a true sentence.

Graph each integer on a number line.
$-7\ -6\ -5\ -4\ -3\ -2\ -1\ 0$

Since -1 is to the right of -6, $-1 > -6$.

Example 2 Order the integers 2, -3, 0, -5 from least to greatest.

To order the integers, graph them on a number line.
$-6\ -5\ -4\ -3\ -2\ -1\ 0\ 1\ 2\ 3$

Order the integers by reading from left to right: -5, -3, 0, 2.

Exercises

1. Replace the ● with < or > to make -5 ● -10 a true sentence.   **>**

2. Order -1, 5, -3, and 2 from least to greatest.   **-3, -1, 2, 5**

3. Order 0, -4, -2, and 7 from greatest to least.   **7, 0, -2, -4**

4. Order -3, $|-2|$, 4, 0, and -5 from greatest to least.
4, $|-2|$, 0, -3, -5

Chapter 2   17   *Course 2*

Skills Practice*
p. 18 **BL** **OL**

2-2 Skills Practice
Comparing and Ordering Integers

Replace each ● with < or > to make a true sentence.

1. -15 ● -16 **>**   2. -8 ● -7 **<**

3. 0 ● -2 **>**   4. -2 ● -5 **>**

5. -25 ● 3   **<**   6. -14 ● $|-20|$ **<**

7. -4 ● 3   **>**   8. $|-6|$ ● $-7|$ **<**

9. $|-7|$ ● $|2|$ **>**   10. -8 ● $|-9|$ **<**

Determine whether each sentence is *true* or *false*. If false, change one number to make the sentence true.

11. $-7 < 3$ **true**

12. $2 > 0$ **true**

13. $-20 < -22$ **false; Sample answer: $-20 < 22$**

14. $12 < 15$ **true**

15. $3 > |-5|$ **false; Sample answer: $3 > |-1|$**

16. $|-2| < -3$ **false; Sample answer: $|-2| < 3$**

17. $|8| < |-10|$ **true**

18. $|-11| = 11$ **true**

19. $-4 < 4$ **true**

20. $-9| < |-10|$ **true**

Order the integers from least to greatest.

21. 12, -6, 20, -47, -11
-47, -11, -6, 12, 20

22. 9, -6, 0, -4, 17, -11
-11, -6, -4, 0, 9, 17

Order the integers from greatest to least.

23. -40, 65, -7, 24, -6, 15
65, 24, 15, -6, -7, -40

24. -13, 0, 7, -8, -5, $|2|$
$|-13|$, 7, $|2|$, 0, -5, -8

Chapter 2   18   *Course 2*

Practice*
p. 19 **OL** **AL**

2-2 Practice
Comparing and Ordering Integers

Replace each ● with < or > to make a true sentence.

1. -5 ● 1   **<**   2. -27 ● -31 **>**   3. 7 ● 0   **>**

4. 4 ● -11 **>**   5. 7 ● -7 **>**   6. 12 ● -14 **>**

7. -54 ● -31 **<**   8. -49 ● 3   **<**   9. -1 ● 2   **<**

Order the integers in each set from least to greatest.

10. $\{-4, 4, -1, 7, 2\}$
$\{-4, -1, 2, 4, 7\}$

11. $\{8, -5, 0, 1, -2\}$
$\{-5, -2, 0, 1, 8\}$

12. $\{11, -17, 12, -9, 3, -1\}$
$\{-17, -9, -1, 3, 11, 12\}$

Replace each ● with <, >, or = to make a true sentence.

13. 4 ● $|-4|$ **=**   14. -27 ● $-31|$ **<**   15. 12 ● $|-18|$ **<**

16. **ANALYZE TABLES** Elements melt at different temperatures. Five elements and their melting points in °C, are listed in the table. Order the elements from the lowest melting point to the highest melting point.

Element	Melting Point °C
Carbon	3,500
Helium	-272
Mercury	-39
Oxygen	-218
Sodium	98

Source: science.co.il

helium, oxygen, mercury, sodium, carbon

BUSINESS For Exercises 17 and 18, use the information in the table. It shows the net profit or loss of a used-car dealership during the spring and summer months of a recent year.

Month	March	April	May	June	July	August	September
Net Profit Or Loss	$8,500	$1,800	$-2,300	$300	$-1,000	$9,400	$2,500

17. Order the months from the lowest net value to the highest.
May, July, June, April, September, March, August

18. Which net value is the middle, or **median**, value? **$1,800**

Chapter 2   19   *Course 2*

Word Problem Practice*
p. 20 **OL** **AL**

2-2 Word Problem Practice
Comparing and Ordering Integers

HISTORY OF WRITING For Exercises 1 and 2, use the table below. It shows important events in the history of writing.

Event	Approx. Year
The *Iliad* and the *Odyssey* are composed by Homer.	700 BC
T'sai Lun invents paper.	105 AD
Date of oldest existing papyrus	2200 BC
Ovid wrote *Metamorphosis*.	5 AD
Torah is compiled.	450 BC
Metal type developed in Korea	1241 AD

EXTREME TEMPERATURES For Exercises 3–5, use the table below. It shows the extreme temperatures for four states. Temperatures are in degrees Fahrenheit.

Extreme Temperatures (°F)

State	Highest	Lowest
Alabama	104	3
Nebraska	118	-47
Maine	101	-30
Florida	109	-2

1. Write each year as an integer. **-700, 105, -2200, 5, -450, 1241**

2. Order the integers from Exercise 1 least to greatest. Write a sentence describing the earliest and most recent events in the table. **-2200, -700, -450, 5, 135, 1241; See students' work.**

3. Arrange the highest temperatures from greatest to least. **118, 109, 104, 101**

4. What is the median low temperature for these four states? **-16**

5. Nebraska's lowest temperature was -47°F, and Maine's lowest temperature was -30°F. Write a true statement using the two temperatures with the symbol > or <. **Sample answer: $-47 < -30$**

6. **MONEY** Mr. Firewalks pays close attention to how much money is in his checking account. One week he deposited $220, spent $15 on a lunch, and loaned $35 to a friend. Write each transaction as an integer, and list them from least to greatest. **-25, -15, 230**

Chapter 2   20   *Course 2*

Enrichment
p. 21 **OL** **AL**

2-2 Enrichment

Quantitative Comparisons

An unusual type of problem is found on some standardized multiple-choice tests. This problem type is called the *quantitative comparison*.

In each quantitative comparison question, you are given two quantities, one in Column A and one in Column B. You are to compare the two quantities and shade one of four circles on an answer sheet.

Shade circle A   if the quantity in Column A is greater;
Shade circle B   if the quantity in Column B is greater;
Shade circle C   if the two quantities are equal;
Shade circle D   if the relationship cannot be determined from the information given.

Shade the correct oval to the left of each problem number.

	Column A	Column B
B 1.	$0.006 + 2$	$0.002 + 6$
A 2.	ten billion dollars	1,000 million dollars
C 3.	20 inches	the perimeter of a square with an area of 25 square inches
B 4.	half of one third	one fifth
A 5.	the greatest possible product of two odd positive numbers less than 20	the greatest possible product of two even positive numbers less than 20
A 6.	0.000000001	$-x$ if x is greater than 0
D 7.	$|x|$	$|x + 1|$
C 8.	$|y|$	$|-y|$
A 9.	$2|x|$ if $x \neq 0$	$|x|$ if $x \neq 0$
C 10.	$-x$ if x is less than 0	$|x|$ if x is less than 0

Chapter 2   21   *Course 2*

---

* Also available in Spanish **ELL**

Additional Lesson Resources

Transparencies
- *5-Minute Check Transparency*, Lesson 2-2

Other Print Products
- *Noteables™ Interactive Study Notebook with Foldables™*

Teacher Tech Tools
- *Interactive Classroom CD-ROM*, Lesson 2-2
- *AssignmentWorks*, Lesson 2-2

Student Tech Tools
glencoe.com
- Extra Examples, Chapter 2, Lesson 2
- Self-Check Quiz, Chapter 2, Lesson 2

2-2 Comparing and Ordering Integers

1 Focus

Vertical Alignment

Before Lesson 2-2
Identify and represent on a number line positive and negative integers

Lesson 2-2
Compare and order positive and negative fractions, decimals, and mixed numbers and place them on a number line

After Lesson 2-2
Read, write and compare rational numbers in scientific notation with approximate numbers using scientific notation

2 Teach

Scaffolding Questions

Have students look at the Toys Timeline on the first page of the lesson.

Ask:

• According to the timeline, which toy was invented earliest: checkers or video games? checkers

• How many years were between the invention of checkers and the invention of the kite? 400 years

• Which is the correct way to read the timeline to determine earliest to most recent toy inventions? left to right

---

MAIN IDEA

Compare and order integers.

Math Online

glencoe.com

• Concepts In Motion
• Extra Examples
• Personal Tutor
• Self-Check Quiz
• Reading in the Content Area

Comparing and Ordering Integers

▷ **GET READY** for the Lesson

TOYS The timeline shows when some toys were invented.

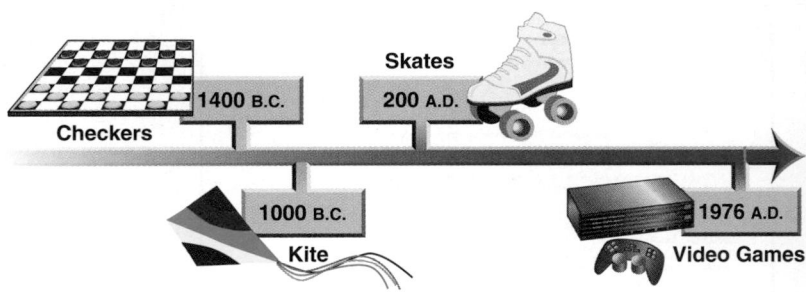

1. The yo-yo was invented around 500 B.C. Was it invented before or after the kite? **after**

2. Modern chess was invented around 600 A.D. Between which two toys was this invented? **skates and video games**

When two numbers are graphed on a number line, the number to the left is always less than the number to the right. The number to the right is always greater than the number to the left.

Compare Integers   Key Concept

Model	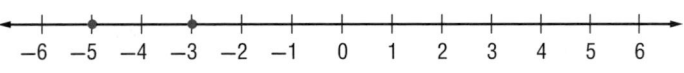
Words	−4 is less than −2. −2 is greater than −4.
Examples	−4 < −2 −2 > −4

EXAMPLE   Compare Two Integers

① **Replace the ● with < or > to make −5 ● −3 a true sentence.**

Graph each integer on a number line.

$$-6 \quad -5 \quad -4 \quad -3 \quad -2 \quad -1 \quad 0 \quad 1 \quad 2 \quad 3 \quad 4 \quad 5 \quad 6$$

Since −5 is to the left of −3, −5 < −3.

✓ **CHECK Your Progress**

Replace each ● with < or > to make a true sentence.

a. −8 ● −4   **<**   b. 5 ● −1   **>**   c. −10 ● −13   **>**

ADDITIONAL EXAMPLE

① Replace the ● with < or > to make −9 ● −5 a true sentence. **<**

Tips for New Teachers

Inequality Symbols

If students are having trouble identifying the inequality symbols < and >, point out that the symbol itself points to the lesser number. In the statement −5 < 3, the inequality symbol is pointing towards −5 which is less than 3.

② The elevations, in feet, for the lowest points in California, Oklahoma, Louisiana, and Kentucky are listed. Which list shows the elevation in order from highest to lowest?

State	Elevation (ft)
California	−282
Oklahoma	289
Louisiana	−8
Kentucky	257

A 289, −282, 257, −8

B −8, 257, −282, 289

C −282, −8, 257, 289

D 289, 257, −8, −282

Test-Taking Tip

Eliminating Answer Choices
If you are unsure of the correct answer, eliminate the choices you know are incorrect. Then consider the remaining choices. You can eliminate choices B and C since those lists begin with a negative number.

Read the Item

To order the integers, graph them on a number line.

Solve the Item

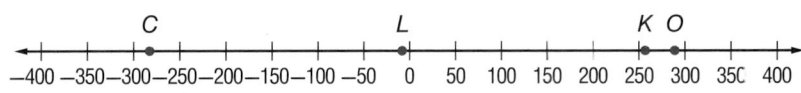

Order the integers by reading from right to left:
289, 257, −8, −282. So, the answer is D.

✓ CHECK Your Progress

d. A newspaper reporter lists the third round scores of the top five finishers in a golf tournament. Which list shows these scores from least to greatest? **H**

F 5, 2, 0, −1, −3   H −3, −1, 0, 2, 5

G −1, −3, 0, 2, 5   J 0, −1, 2, −3, 5

✓ CHECK Your Understanding

Example 1
(p. 84)

Replace each ● with < or > to make a true sentence.

1. −4 ● −6 **>**   2. −2 ● 8 **<**   3. 0 ● −10 **>**

Example 2
(p. 85)

Order the integers in each set from least to greatest.

4. {−13, 9, −2, 0, 4} **{−13, −2, 0, 4, 9}**   5. {12, −16, −10, 19, −18}
                                                   {−18, −16, −10, 12, 19}

6. **MULTIPLE CHOICE** The lowest temperatures in Hawaii, Illinois, Minnesota, and South Carolina are listed. Which list shows these temperatures in order from coldest to warmest? **C**

A −19, −36, −60, 12   C −60, −36, −19, 12

B 12, −19, −36, −60   D −60, −19, 12, −36

✓ Formative Assessment

Use the Check Your Progress exercises after each Example to determine students' understanding of concepts.

ADDITIONAL EXAMPLE

② **TEST EXAMPLE** The lowest temperatures in Europe, Greenland, Oceania, and Antarctica are listed in the table.

Place	Record Low Temperature (°F)
Europe	−67
Greenland	−87
Oceania	14
Antarctica	−129

Which list shows the temperatures in order from coldest to warmest? C

A −67, −87, 14, −129
B 14, −67, −87, −129
C −129, −87, −67, 14
D −67, −87, −129, 14

Additional Examples are also in:

• Noteables™ Interactive Study Notebook with Foldables™

• Interactive Classroom PowerPoint® Presentations

③ Practice

✓ Formative Assessment

Use Exercises 1–6 to check for understanding.

Then use the chart at the bottom of the next page to customize your assignments for students.

Intervention You may wish to use the Study Guide and Intervention Master on page 17 of the *Chapter 2 Resource Masters* for additional reinforcement.

Odd/Even Assignments

Exercises 7–20 are structured so that students practice the same concepts whether they are assigned odd or even problems.

Practice and Problem Solving

HOMEWORK HELP

For Exercises	See Examples
7–14	1
15–20	2
35–36	2

Exercise Levels
A: 7–20
B: 21–31
C: 32–34

Replace each ● with < or > to make a true sentence.

7. −7 ● −3 **<**
8. −21 ● −12 **<**
9. −6 ● −11 **>**
10. −15 ● −33 **>**
11. 17 ● −20 **>**
12. 4 ● −4 **>**
13. −5 ● 17 **<**
14. −12 ● 8 **<**

Order the integers in each set from least to greatest.

15. {−8, 11, 6, −5, −3} **15. {−8, −5, −3, 6, 11}**

16. {7, −2, 14, −9, 2} **{−9, −2, 2, 7, 14}**

17. {5, −6, −7, −4, 1, 3}
   {−7, −6, −4, 1, 3, 5}

18. {−12, 15, 8, −15, −23, 10}
   {−23, −15, −12, 8, 10, 15}

19. **ANALYZE TABLES** The ocean floor is divided into five zones according to how deep sunlight penetrates. Order the zones from closest to the surface to nearest to the ocean floor.
   Sunlight, Twilight, Midnight, Abyssal, Hadal

Zone	Beginning Ocean Depth
Abyssal	−4,000 m
Hadal	−6,000 m
Midnight	−1,000 m
Sunlight	0 m
Twilight	−200 m

20. **STOCK MARKET** Kevin's dad owns stock in five companies. The change in the stock value for each company was as follows: Company A, +12; Company B, −5; Company C, −25; Company D, +18; Company E, −10. Order the companies from the worst performing to best performing.
   Company C, Company E, Company B, Company A, Company D

Replace each ● with <, >, or = to make a true sentence.

21. −13 ● |−14| **<**
22. |36| ● −37 **>**
23. −12 ● |12| **<**
24. |−29| ● |92| **<**

FOOTBALL For Exercises 25 and 26, use the information at the right. It shows the yardage gained each play for five plays.

Play	1	2	3	4	5
Yardage	10	−2	5	−5	20

25. Order the yardage from least to greatest. **−5, −2, 5, 10, 20**

26. Which run is the middle, or *median*, yardage? **5**

27. **WEATHER** The wind chill index was invented in 1939 by Paul Siple, a polar explorer and authority on Antarctica. Wind chill causes the air to feel colder on human skin. Which feels colder: a temperature of 10° with a 15-mile-per-hour wind or a temperature of 5° with a 10 mile per hour wind?
   5° with a 10-mile-per-hour wind

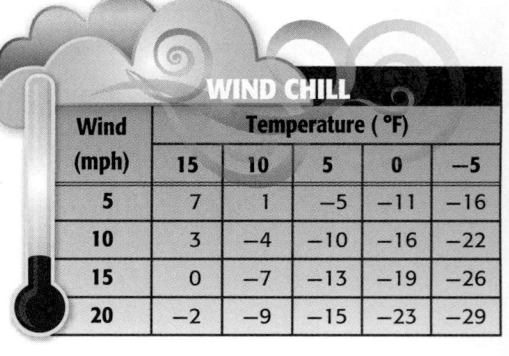

Wind (mph)	*WIND CHILL* Temperature (°F)				
	15	10	5	0	−5
5	7	1	−5	−11	−16
10	3	−4	−10	−16	−22
15	0	−7	−13	−19	−26
20	−2	−9	−15	−23	−29

EXTRA PRACTICE
See pages 671, 705.

Determine whether each sentence is *true* or *false*. If *false*, change one number to make the sentence true. 28, 30. Sample answers given.

28. −8 > 5
   false; 8 > 5

29. −7 < 0
   true

30. |5| < −6
   false; |5| < 6

31. 10 > |−8|
   true

DIFFERENTIATED HOMEWORK OPTIONS

Level	Assignment	Two-Day Assignment	
BL Basic	7–20, 32, 34–44	7–19 odd, 35, 36	8–20 even, 32, 34, 37–44
OL Core	7–25 odd, 26, 27, 29, 31, 32, 34–44	7–20, 35, 36	21–32, 34, 37–44
AL Advanced/Pre-AP	21–40 (optional: 41–44)		

H.O.T. Problems

32. **NUMBER SENSE** If 0 is the greatest integer in a set of five integers, what can you conclude about the other four integers? **They are negative integers.**

33. **CHALLENGE** What is the greatest integer value of n such that $n < 0$? **−1**

34. **WRITING IN MATH** Develop a method for ordering a set of negative integers from least to greatest without the aid of a number line. Explain your method and use it to order the set $\{-5, -8, -1, -3\}$. **See margin.**

TEST PRACTICE

35. On a certain game show, contestants receive positive numbers of points for correct responses and negative numbers of points for incorrect responses. Which list gives the points a contestant received during one round of the game in order from highest to lowest? **C**

   A −200, −400, −1000, 200, 600

   B 600, −1000, −400, −200, 200

   C 600, 200, −200, −400, −1000

   D −1000, −400, −200, 600, 200

36. Which statement about the values shown is *not* true? **J**

State	Low Temperature (°F)
AR	−29
GA	−17
MS	−19
VA	−30
TX	−23

Source: *The World Almanac*

   F Virginia's record low is less than the record low for Arkansas.

   G Arkansas' record low is less than the record low for Georgia.

   H Mississippi's record low is greater than the record low for Texas.

   J Texas' record low is less than the record low for Arkansas.

Spiral Review

Write an integer for each situation. (Lesson 2-1)

37. 9°C below zero **−9**

38. a gain of 20 feet **20**

HOBBIES For Exercises 39 and 40, use the following information. (Lesson 1-10)

Sophia estimates that she knits 6 rows of an afghan each hour.

39. Write an equation using two variables to represent the total number of rows r completed by Sophia after time t. **$r = 6t$**

40. How many rows will Sophia have completed after 4 hours? **24**

▷ **GET READY for the Next Lesson**

PREREQUISITE SKILL Graph each point on a vertical number line that goes from −10 on the bottom to 10 at the top. (Lesson 2-1) **41–44. See margin.**

41. −3   42. 0   43. 4   44. −7

Lesson 2-2 Comparing and Ordering Integers **87**

Crystal Ball Tell students that tomorrow's lesson is about graphing points on a coordinate plane. Ask them to write how they think what they learned today will connect with tomorrow's lesson.

 Formative Assessment

Check for student understanding of concepts in Lessons 2-1 and 2-2.

[CRM] Quiz 1, p. 61

Additional Answers

34. Sample answer: To order a set of negative integers from least to greatest, order the integers from greatest to least according to their absolute values. For example, to order the set $\{-5, -8, -1, -3\}$, first determine the absolute value of each integer. The set of absolute values is $\{5, 8, 1, 3\}$. Then, order these absolute values from greatest to least, $\{8, 5, 3, 1\}$. Replacing these absolute values with their original integers orders the original set integers from least to greatest, $\{-8, -5, -3, -1\}$.

41–44.
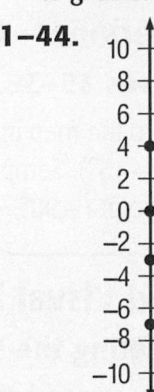

Differentiated Instruction

Logical Learners Have students work in groups to research how integers are used in journalism. Assign each group a different section of a print or online newspaper, including the following sections: Sports, Weather, News, and Business. Ask a volunteer from each group to describe how integers are used in their section of the newspaper and give examples.

Options for Differentiated Instruction

ELL = English Language Learner   **AL** = Above or Beyond Grade Level   **SS** = Struggling Students   **SN** = Special Needs

Scaffolding the Lesson **SS** **SN**

Use before presenting Example 1.

To scaffold this lesson, begin by having students name points and graph ordered pairs in the first quadrant only. Examples of possible exercises are shown below.

Write the ordered pair for each point graphed below.

1. *A* (1, 5)
2. *B* (3, 2)
3. *C* (0, 1)
4. *D* (6, 7)

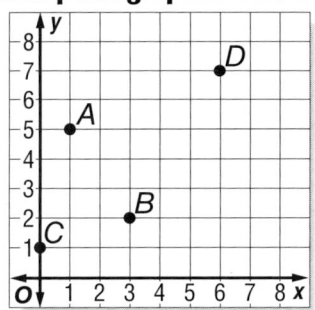

Graph and label each point below on the coordinate plane.

5. *L* (6, 5)
6. *M* (4, 0)
7. *N* (2, 4)
8. *P* (7, 2)

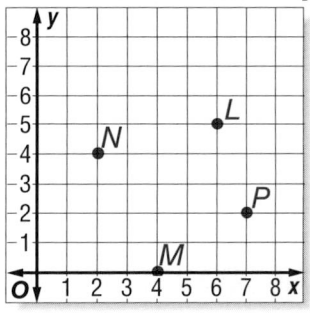

Once students are successful identifying the *x*- and *y*-coordinates of points and are able to plot points on a graph, expand to the four quadrants.

Verbal Explanations **ELL** **AL** **SS**

Use with Exercises 35–38.

Have students refer to the map in Exercises 35–38. Ask them to explain how they would determine what continent is located at (−90°, −15°). Sample answer: From the origin, move left to −90° and then down to −15° to find that the coordinate point (−90°, −15°) is located in South America.

Kinesthetic and Visual Learning **ELL** **AL** **SS** **SN**

Use after completing the lesson.

If possible, photocopy an aerial photo or schematic of the school grounds. Have students draw a grid on the photo and label where different features are located. Then take students outside and have them walk between landmarks to get a sense of the distance shown on the map. Have them plot their paths on their grids.

Leveled Lesson Resources

Also on
TeacherWorks™
Lesson 2-3

Chapter 2 Resource Masters

BL = Below or Approaching Grade Level   **OL** = On Grade Level   **AL** = Above or Beyond Grade Level   **ELL** = English Language Learner

---

Lesson Reading Guide
p. 22 BL OL ELL

NAME _____ DATE _____ PERIOD _____

2-3 Lesson Reading Guide
The Coordinate Plane

Get Ready for the Lesson

Read the introduction at the top of page 88 in your textbook. Write your answers below.

1. Suppose Mr. Diaz starts at Shaw University and drives 2 blocks north. Name the street he will cross. **E Cabarrus St**

2. Using the words *north*, *south*, *west*, and *east*, write directions to go from Chavis Park to Moore Square. **Sample answer: Drive west 3 blocks on E Lenoir St. Drive 5 blocks north on S Person St.**

Read the Lesson

3. The word *coordinate* comes from two Latin words that mean "to arrange together." How are coordinates used together to locate a point in a coordinate plane? **Sample answer: The location of a point in a coordinate plane depends on position along an x-axis and position along a y-axis. Both positions, called the x-coordinate and the y-coordinate, are needed in order to locate a point in a coordinate plane. The pair of coordinates is called an ordered pair. The pair of coordinates is ordered such that the x-coordinate is always the first number of the pair and the y-coordinate is always the second number of the pair.**

4. Look at the coordinate plane at the right. Name the ordered pair for each point graphed. **A(−3, 3); B(3, 2); C(3, −2)**

5. In the coordinate plane in Exercise 4, tell which quadrant each of the points is in. **Point A is in quadrant II, point B is in quadrant I, and point C is in quadrant IV.**

Remember What You Learned

6. Write a way to remember the names of the four quadrants of the coordinate plane. **Sample answer: Begin in the quadrant where both coordinates are positive (the upper-right quadrant). This is quadrant I. Name the rest of the quadrants by going counterclockwise around the quadrants: II (upper-left quadrant), III (lower-left quadrant), IV (lower-right quadrant).**

Chapter 2   22   Course 2

Study Guide and Intervention*
p. 23 BL OL ELL

NAME _____ DATE _____ PERIOD _____

2-3 Study Guide and Intervention
The Coordinate Plane

The **coordinate plane** is used to locate points. The horizontal number line is the **x-axis**. The vertical number line is the **y-axis**. Their intersection is the **origin**.

Points are located using **ordered pairs**. The first number in an ordered pair is the **x-coordinate**; the second number is the **y-coordinate**.

The coordinate plane is separated into four sections called **quadrants**.

Example 1 Name the ordered pair for point P. Then identify the quadrant in which P lies.

- Start at the origin.
- Move 4 units left along the x-axis.
- Move 3 units up on the y-axis.
  The ordered pair for point P is (−4, 3).
  P is in the upper left quadrant or quadrant II.

Example 2 Graph and label the point M(0, −4).

- Start at the origin.
- Move 0 units along the x-axis.
- Move 4 units down on the y-axis.
- Draw a dot and label it M(0, −4).

Exercises

Name the ordered pair for each point graphed at the right. Then identify the quadrant in which each point lies.

1. P (2, −3), IV   2. Q (−3, −2), III
3. R (1, 3), I   4. S (−2, 2), II

Graph and label each point on the coordinate plane.

5. A(−1, 1)   6. B(0, −3)
7. C(3, 2)   8. D(−3, −1)
9. E(1, −2)   10. F(1, 3)

Chapter 2   23   Course 2

Skills Practice*
p. 24 BL OL

NAME _____ DATE _____ PERIOD _____

2-3 Skills Practice
The Coordinate Plane

Name the ordered pair for each point graphed at the right. Then identify the quadrant in which each point lies.

1. A (−1, 1), II   2. B (5, 5), I
3. C (−5, −5), III   4. D (4, −3), IV
5. E (3, 0), x-axis   6. F (−5, 4), II
7. G (0, −5), y-axis   8. H (−2, −2), III
9. I (−3, 6), II   10. J (3, −5), IV

Graph and label each point on the coordinate plane.

11. N(−1, 3)   12. V(2, −1)
13. C(4, 0)   14. P(−6, 2)
15. M(−5, 0)   16. K(−1, 5)
17. I(−3, −3)   18. A(5, −3)
19. D(0, −5)

Name the ordered pair for each point on the city map at the right.

20. City Hall (0, 0)
21. Theater (−7, −5)
22. Gas Station (7, 2)
23. Grocery (−5, 5)

Chapter 2   24   Course 2

Practice*
p. 25 OL AL

NAME _____ DATE _____ PERIOD _____

2-3 Practice
The Coordinate Plane

Write the ordered pair for each point graphed at the right. Then name the quadrant or axis on which each point is located.

1. A (2, 5), I   2. B (−3, 4), II   3. C (−3, 0), x-axis
4. D (6, −1), IV   5. E (−1, −4), III   6. F (0, 3), y-axis
7. G (5, 2), I   8. H (1, −5), IV   9. I (−6, −3), III

Graph and label each point on the coordinate plane at the right.

10. J(2, 2)   11. K(−1, 4)   12. L(−4, 1)
13. M(−3, −3)   14. N(1, −4)   15. O(0, 0)
16. P(4, 5)   17. Q(4, −3)   18. R(−6, −5)

Determine whether each statement is *sometimes*, *always*, or *never* true. Explain or give a counterexample to support your answer.

19. The y-coordinate of a point in quadrant II is negative. **Never; quadrant II is above the x-axis, therefore the y-coordinate is positive.**

20. The x-coordinate of a point on the y-axis is zero. **Always; a point on the y-axis is neither to the right nor left of the y-axis.**

21. In quadrants I and III, the x-coordinate of a point is positive. **Sometimes; for example: (3, 2) is in quadrant I and the x-coordinate is positive while (−3, −2) is in quadrant III and the x-coordinate is negative.**

22. GEOMETRY Graph the points A(−3, −1), B(0, 4), C(4, 3), and D(1, −2) on the coordinate plane at the right. Connect the points from A to B, B to C, C to D, and D to A. Name the figure. **parallelogram**

Chapter 2   25   Course 2

Word Problem Practice*
p. 26 OL AL

NAME _____ DATE _____ PERIOD _____

2-3 Word Problem Practice
The Coordinate Plane

SCHOOL For Exercises 1–4, use the coordinate plane at the right. It shows a map of the rooms in a middle high school.

1. Thalia is in the room located at (−2, 1). What room is she in? Describe in words how to get from the origin to this point. **Computer Lab; move 2 units to the left and one unit up.**

2. Thalia's next class is 8 units to the right and 5 units down on the map from where she is now. In what room is Thalia's next class? Find the ordered pair that represents the location of that room. **Music room; (6, −4)**

3. Tyrone is in the Art room, but his next class is in the History room. Give Tyrone directions on how to get to the History room. **Sample answer: Walk 9 units to the right, and then 5 units down.**

4. On the map, which classrooms are located in the third quadrant? Describe the coordinates of all points in the third quadrant. **Science and Math rooms; the x- and y-coordinates are all negative.**

5. NEIGHBORHOOD Delsin made a map of his neighborhood in such a way that each intersection is a point on a coordinate plane. Right now, Delsin stands at point (−4, −3). Give the ordered pair of where he will be if moves 5 units to the right and 7 units up on the map. **(1, 4)**

6. NEIGHBORHOOD Refer to Exercise 5. In which quadrant is Delsin when he is done walking? Describe this quadrant. **Quadrant I; Sample answer: Quadrant I is the upper-right quadrant.**

Chapter 2   26   Course 2

Enrichment
p. 27 OL AL

NAME _____ DATE _____ PERIOD _____

2-3 Enrichment

Relic Hunter

The game of Relic Hunter is based on methods used to record the precise locations of artifacts discovered at archaeological digs. Archaeologists use string to position a grid over a dig site. An artifact's location is named by the row and column in the grid.

Relic Hunter is played with two players who each secretly place six artifacts on one of the coordinate grids below. Artifacts may not overlap. Each player should not be able to see where the other player's artifacts are hidden. A player must look for the artifacts by guessing an ordered pair. The other player then finds that location on the secret grid and tells the first player whether part of the artifact is located in that section and what the artifact is. Each player's empty coordinate grid should be used to mark the locations of guesses and of found artifacts. The winner is the player who first uncovers all of the opponent's artifacts.

For Exercises 1–6, list each ordered pair that could contain the rest of the artifact. Then play the game with a partner. Use one coordinate grid to keep track of the points where you hide your artifacts and another coordinate grid to keep track of the points you have guessed.

1. You uncover parts of the spear at points (−2, 3) and (−2, 4).
   (−2, 0), (−2, 1), (−2, 2) and (−2, 5)

2. You uncover part of the animal bone at points (2, 1) and (2, 3).
   (1, 1), (1, 2), (3, 1), and (3, 2)

3. You uncover part of the amulet at point (−4, −2).
   (−4, −3), (−4, −1), (−5, −2), and (−3, −2)

4. You uncover a part of the clay pot at point (0, −1).
   (−1, −2), (0, −2), (1, −2), (−1, −1), (1, −1), (−1, 0), (0, 0), and (1, 0)

5. You uncover a part of the bow at point (5, −5).
   (5, −3), (5, −4), (4, −4), (4, −5), and (3, −5)

6. Part of the amulet is located at point (−5, −2), and there is nothing at point (−2, −4). You uncover a part of the mosaic panel at point (−4, −4). What other points could contain the mosaic panel?
   (−5, −5), (−5, −4), (−5, −3), (−4, −5), (−4, −3), (−3, −5), (−3, −4), and (−3, −3)

Chapter 2   27   Course 2

Additional Lesson Resources

Transparencies
- *5-Minute Check Transparency*, Lesson 2-3

Other Print Products
- *Teaching Mathematics with Manipulatives*
- *Noteables™ Interactive Study Notebook with Foldables™*

Teacher Tech Tools
- *Interactive Classroom CD-ROM*, Lesson 2-3
- *AssignmentWorks*, Lesson 2-3

Student Tech Tools
glencoe.com
- Extra Examples, Chapter 2, Lesson 3
- Self-Check Quiz, Chapter 2, Lesson 3

2-3 The Coordinate Plane

1 Focus

Vertical Alignment

Before Lesson 2-3
Identify and graph ordered pairs in the four quadrants of the coordinate plane

Lesson 2-3
Use graphs to explain mathematical reasoning

After Lesson 2-3
Graph linear functions, noting that the vertical change per unit of horizontal change is always the same and know that the ratio is called the slope of a graph

2 Teach

Scaffolding Questions

Point to the classroom world map.

Ask:

• Is Mexico north or south of the United States? **south**

• Is Senegal west or east of Mexico? **east**

• What direction from Senegal is Spain? **north**

• How would you give directions to go from Spain to Peru? **go west and south**

• How would you give directions to go from Peru to Spain? **go east and north**

Additional Answer

2. Sample answer: Drive west 3 blocks on E Lenoir St. Drive 3 blocks north on S Person St.

MAIN IDEA

Graph points on a coordinate plane.

New Vocabulary

coordinate plane
quadrant
x-axis
y-axis
origin
ordered pair
x-coordinate
y-coordinate

Math Online

glencoe.com

• Extra Examples
• Personal Tutor
• Self-Check Quiz

▶ **GET READY** for the Lesson

GPS A GPS, or global positioning system, is a satellite based navigation system. A GPS map of Raleigh, North Carolina, is shown.

1. Suppose Mr. Diaz starts at Shaw University and drives 2 blocks north. Name the street he will cross. **E. Lenoir**

2. Using the words *north, south, east,* and *west,* write directions to go from Chavis Park to Moore Square. **See margin.**

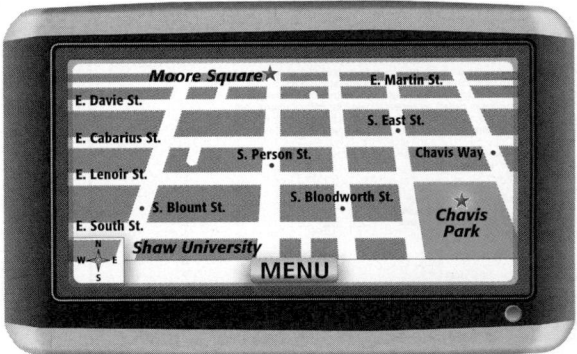

On a GPS, towns and streets are often located on a grid. In mathematics, we use a grid called a coordinate plane, to locate points. A **coordinate plane** is formed when two number lines intersect. The number lines separate the coordinate plane into four regions called **quadrants**.

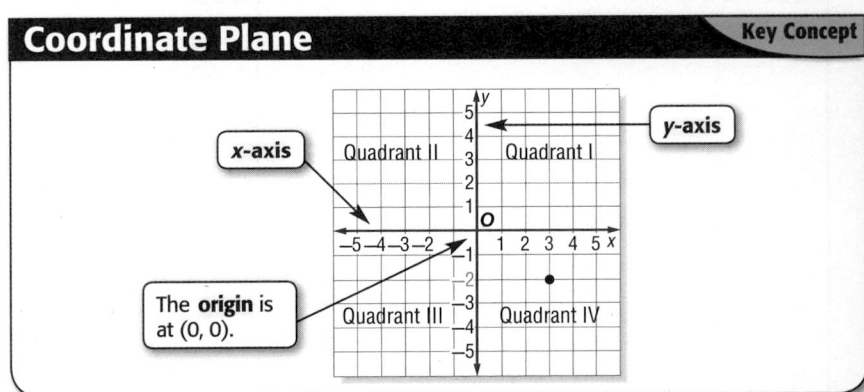

An **ordered pair** is a pair of numbers, such as $(3, -2)$, used to locate a point in the coordinate plane.

x-coordinate corresponds to a number on the *x*-axis. $(3, -2)$ *y*-coordinate corresponds to a number on the *y*-axis.

When locating an ordered pair, moving *right* or *up* on a coordinate plane is in the *positive* direction. Moving *left* or *down* is in the *negative* direction.

EXAMPLE **Naming Points Using Ordered Pairs**

1) Write the ordered pair that corresponds to point *D*. Then state the quadrant in which the point is located.

- Start at the origin.
- Move left on the *x*-axis to find the *x*-coordinate of point *D*, which is −4.
- Move up to find the *y*-coordinate, which is 2.

So, point *D* corresponds to the ordered pair (−4, 2). Point *D* is located in Quadrant II.

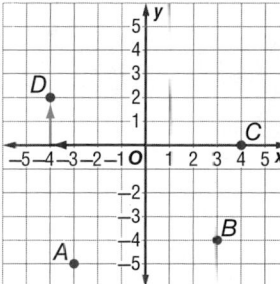

CHECK Your Progress

Write the ordered pair that corresponds to each point. Then state the quadrant or axis on which the point is located.

a. *A* (−3, −5); III
b. *B* (3, −4); IV
c. *C* (4, 0); *x*-axis

EXAMPLE **Graph an Ordered Pair**

2) Graph and label point *K* at (2, −5).

Reading Math

Scale When no numbers are shown on the *x*- or *y*-axis, you can assume that each square is 1 unit long on each side.

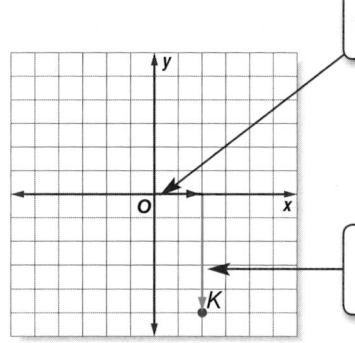

Start at the origin. The *x*-coordinate is 2. So, move 2 units to the right.

Next, since the *y*-coordinate is −5, move 5 units down. Draw a dot and label *K*.

CHECK Your Progress

On graph paper, draw a coordinate plane. Then graph and label each point. **d–f. See margin.**

d. *L*(−4, 2)
e. *M*(−5, −3)
f. *N*(0, 1)

Lesson 2-3 The Coordinate Plane **89**

Additional Answers

d–f.

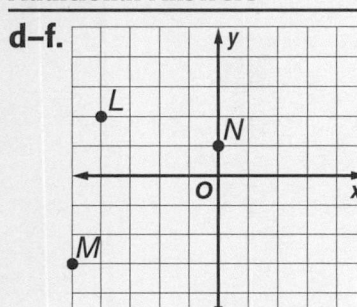

Focus on Mathematical Content

The first number of an ordered pair tells how far to move right or left along the **x-axis**. The second number of an ordered pair tells how far to move up or down along the **y-axis**.

Maps are a kind of coordinate plane.

Formative Assessment

Use the Check Your Progress exercises after each Example to determine students' understanding of concepts.

ADDITIONAL EXAMPLES

1) Write the ordered pair that corresponds to point *R*. Then state the quadrant in which the point is located.
(−2, 4); quadrant II

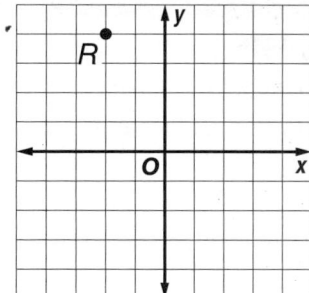

2) Graph and label point *M* at (3, 5).

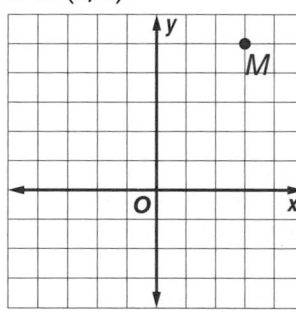

Additional Examples are also in:

- Noteables™ Interactive Study Notebook with Foldables™
- Interactive Classroom PowerPoint® Presentations

Formative Assessment

Use Exercises 1–10 to check for understanding.

Then use the chart at the bottom of the next page to customize your assignments for students.

Intervention You may wish to use the Study Guide and Intervention Master on page 23 of the *Chapter 2 Resource Masters* for additional reinforcement.

Coordinate Planes

Tips for New Teachers You may wish to point out that the quadrants of a coordinate plane are numbered in order, from I to IV, in a *counterclockwise* direction.

ADDITIONAL EXAMPLES

3 **GEOGRAPHY** Use the map of Utah shown below. In which quadrant is Vernal located?
Quadrant 1

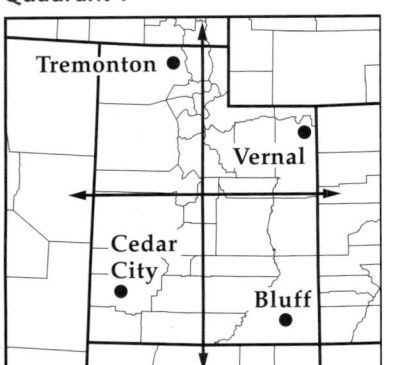

4 Which of the cities labeled on the map is located in Quadrant IV?
Bluff

Additional Answers

5–8.

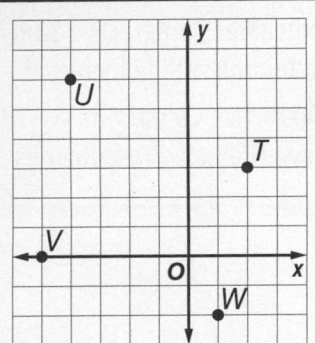

Real-World EXAMPLES

3 **AQUARIUMS** A map can be divided into a coordinate plane where the *x*-coordinate represents how far to move right or left and the *y*-coordinate represents how far to move up or down. What exhibit is located at (6, 5)?

New York Aquarium, Bronx, NY

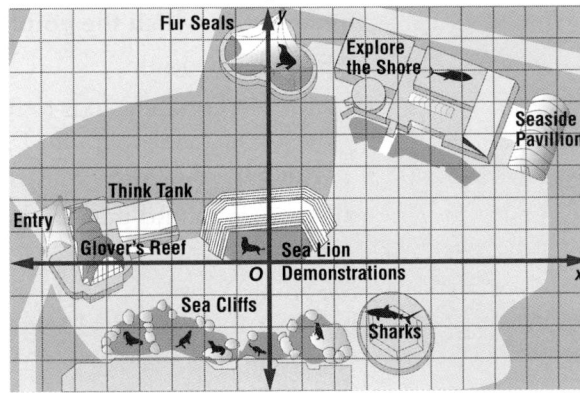

Start at the origin. Move 6 units to the right and then 5 units up. Explore the Shore is located at (6, 5).

4 In which quadrant is the Shark Exhibit located?

The Shark Exhibit is located in Quadrant IV.

CHECK Your Progress

For Exercises g and h, use the map above. **g. (−4, 2)**

g. Find the ordered pair that represents the location of the Think Tank.

h. What is located at the origin? **Sea Lion Demonstrations**

Real-World Link
New York Aquarium has a marine mammal exhibit that includes sea otters. Large male sea otters can grow to be over 4 feet in length.

CHECK Your Understanding

Example 1 (p. 89)

Write the ordered pair corresponding to each point graphed at the right. Then state the quadrant or axis on which each point is located.

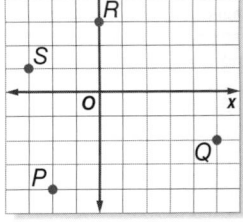

1. P **(−2, −4); III**
2. Q **(5, −2); IV**
3. R **(0, 3); y-axis**
4. S **(−3, 1); II**

Example 2 (p. 89)

On graph paper, draw a coordinate plane. Then graph and label each point. **5–8. See margin.**

5. $T(2, 3)$
6. $U(−4, 6)$
7. $V(−5, 0)$
8. $W(1, −2)$

Examples 3, 4 (p. 90)

GEOGRAPHY For Exercises 9 and 10, use the map in Example 3 above.

9. What exhibit is located at (0, −3)? **Sea Cliffs**

10. In which quadrant is the Seaside Pavilion located? **I**

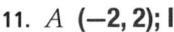

Practice and Problem Solving

HOMEWORK HELP

For Exercises	See Examples
11–22, 37	1
23–34, 38	2
35–36	3

Exercise Levels
A: 11–38
B: 39–46
C: 47–49

13. (−5, 0); *x*-axis
16. (−3, 5); II
19. (2, 2); I
22. (1, 0); *x*-axis

Write the ordered pair corresponding to each point graphed at the right. Then state the quadrant or axis on which each point is located.

11. *A* (−2, 2); II   12. *B* (5, 4); I   13. *C*
14. *D* (4, −3); IV   15. *E* (2, −2); IV   16. *F*
17. *G* (−4, −1); III   18. *H* (0, −4); *y*-axis   19. *I*
20. *J* (−4, −5); III   21. *K* (0, 4); *y*-axis   22. *L*

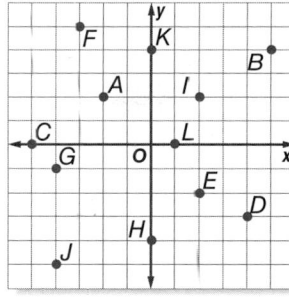

On graph paper, draw a coordinate plane.
Then graph and label each point. 23–34. See Ch. 2 Answer Appendix.

23. *M*(5, 6)   24. *N*(−2, 10)   25. *P*(7, −8)   26. *Q*(3, 0)
27. *R*(−1, −7)   28. *S*(8, 1)   29. *T*(−3, 7)   30. *U*(5, −2)
31. *V*(0, 6)   32. *W*(−5, −7)   33. *X*(−4, 0)   34. *Y*(0, −5)

GEOGRAPHY For Exercises 35–38, use the world map.

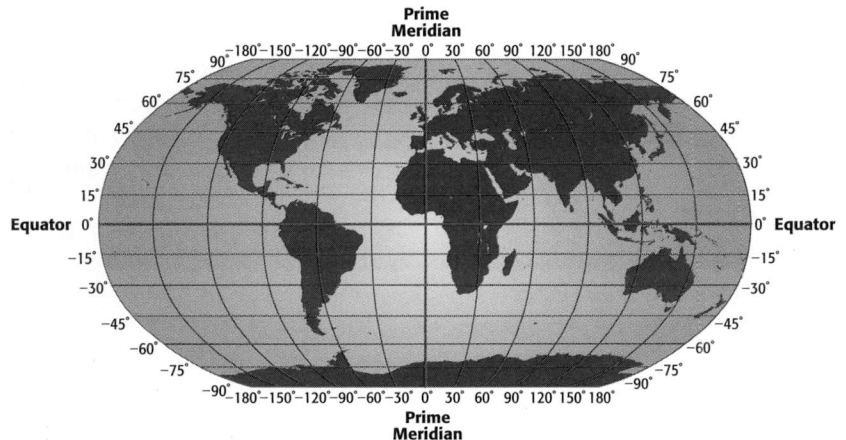

35. The world map can be divided into a coordinate plane where (*x*, *y*) represents (degrees longitude, degrees latitude). In what continent is the point (30° longitude, −15° latitude) located? **Africa**

36. Which of the continents is located entirely in Quadrant II? **North America**

37. South America   37. In what continent is the point (−90° longitude, 0° latitude) located?

38. Name a continent on the map that is located entirely in Quadrant I. **Asia**

On graph paper, draw a coordinate plane. Then graph and label each point.

39–41. See margin.   39. *X*(1.5, 3.5)   40. $Y\left(3\frac{1}{4}, 2\frac{1}{2}\right)$ 41. $Z\left(2, 1\frac{2}{3}\right)$

42. **GEOMETRY** Graph four points on a coordinate plane so that they form a square when connected. Identify the ordered pairs. **See margin for graph.**

43. **RESEARCH** Use the Internet or other resources to explain why the coordinate plane is sometimes called the Cartesian plane. **See margin.**

Lesson 2-3 The Coordinate Plane   **91**

Odd/Even Assignments

Exercises 11–38 are structured so that students practice the same concepts whether they are assigned odd or even problems.

Additional Answers

39–41.

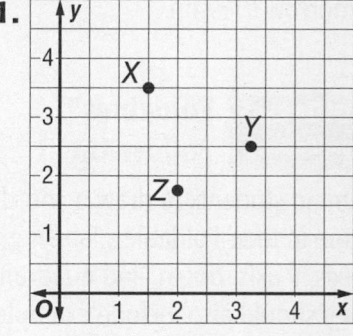

42.

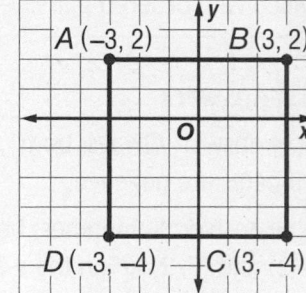

43. Sample answer: Rene Descartes is often credited with inventing the coordinate plane and so the coordinate plane is sometimes called the Cartesian plane, in his honor.

DIFFERENTIATED HOMEWORK OPTIONS

Level	Assignment	Two-Day Assignment	
BL Basic	11–38, 47, 49–61	11–37 odd, 50, 51	12–38 even, 47, 49, 52–61
OL Core	11–41 odd, 42–47, 49–61	11–38, 50, 51	39–47, 49, 52–61
AL Advanced /Pre-AP	39–57 (optional: 58–61)		

Crystal Ball Tell students that tomorrow's lesson is about finding the sums of integers, such $-4 + 5$. Ask students to write how they think what they learned today will connect with tomorrow's lesson.

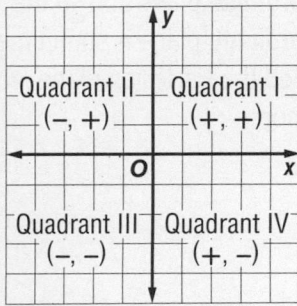

Foldables™ Follow-Up

Remind students to draw a coordinate plane in their Foldables, labeling the x-axis, y-axis, origin, and quadrants. They should also include examples of points labeled with ordered pairs.

Additional Answers

44. Sample answer: Always; both coordinates are negative.

45. Sample answer: Sometimes; both $(0, -2)$ and $(0, 2)$ lie on the y-axis.

47. Sample answer: Using the graphic, you can see that an ordered pair such as $(-5, -4)$ is in Quadrant III.

Quadrant II	Quadrant I
$(-, +)$	$(+, +)$
Quadrant III	Quadrant IV
$(-, -)$	$(+, -)$

48. Quadrant I when both x- and y-coordinates are positive; Quadrant III when both x- and y-coordinates are negative; the origin when both x- and y-coordinates are 0.

49. Sample answer: Point A is 1 unit to the right and 2 units down from the origin, in quadrant IV. Point B is 2 units to the left and 1 unit up from the origin, in quadrant II.

Determine whether each statement is *sometimes*, *always*, or *never* true. Explain or give a counterexample to support your answer.

EXTRA PRACTICE
See pages 672, 705.

44. Both x- and y-coordinates of a point in Quadrant III are negative. **See margin.**

45. The y-coordinate of a point that lies on the y-axis is negative. **See margin.**

46. The y-coordinate of a point in Quadrant II is negative. **Sample answer: never; the y-coordinate is always positive in Quadrant II.**

H.O.T. Problems

47. OPEN ENDED Create a display that shows how to determine in what quadrant a point is located without graphing. Then provide an example that demonstrates how your graphic is used. **See margin.**

48. CHALLENGE Find the possible locations for any ordered pair with x- and y-coordinates always having the same sign. Explain. **See margin.**

49. WRITING IN MATH Explain why the location of point $A(1, -2)$ is different than the location of point $B(-2, 1)$. **See margin.**

TEST PRACTICE

50. Which of the following points lie within the triangle graphed at the right? **C**

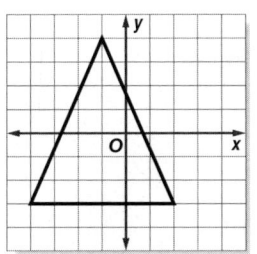

A $A(-4, -1)$

B $B(1, 3)$

C $C(-1, 2)$

D $D(2, -2)$

51. What are the coordinates of the point that shows the location of the lunch room on the map? **G**

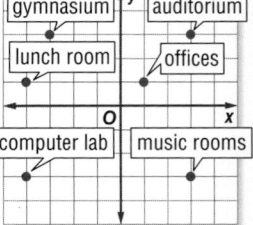

F $(4, -1)$

G $(-4, 1)$

H $(1, 4)$

J $(1, -4)$

Spiral Review

Replace each ● with $<$, $>$, or $=$ to make a true sentence. (Lesson 2-2)

52. -8 ● -3 **<**   **53.** 26 ● -30 **>**   **54.** 14 ● $|-15|$ **<**   **55.** -40 ● $|40|$ **<**

56. Find the absolute value of -101. (Lesson 2-1) **101**

57. RUNNING Salvador is training for a marathon. He runs 5 miles each day on weekdays and 8 miles each day on the weekends. How many miles does Salvador run in one week? (Lesson 1-1) **41 miles**

▷ **GET READY for the Next Lesson**

PREREQUISITE SKILL Add.

58. $138 + 246$ **384**   **59.** $814 + 512$ **1,326**   **60.** $2,653 + 4,817$ **7,470**   **61.** $6,003 + 5,734$ **11,737**

Algebra Lab
Adding Integers

MAIN IDEA

Use counters to model the addition of integers.

Math Online

glencoe.com

• Concepts In Motion

You can use positive and negative counters to model the addition of integers. The counter ⊕ represents 1, and the counter ⊖ represents −1. Remember that addition means *combining* two sets.

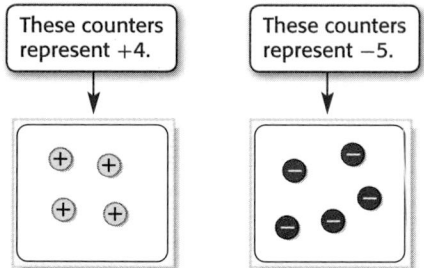

These counters represent +4.

These counters represent −5.

ACTIVITY

1 Use counters to find −3 + (−6).

Combine a set of 3 negative counters and a set of 6 negative counters.

Find the total number of counters.

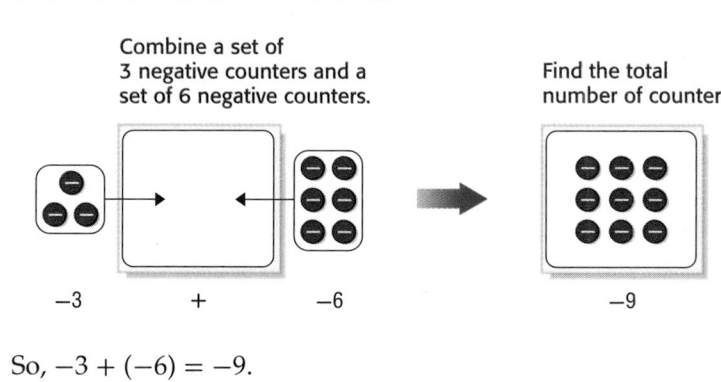

−3   +   −6   −9

So, −3 + (−6) = −9.

✓ CHECK Your Progress

Use counters or a drawing to find each sum. **a–f. See margin.**

a. 5 + 6   **b.** −3 + (−5)   **c.** −5 + (−4)

d. 7 + 3   **e.** −2 + (−5)   **f.** −8 + (−6)

The following two properties are important when modeling operations with integers.

• When one positive counter is paired with one negative counter, the result is called a **zero pair**. The value of a zero pair is 0.

• You can add or remove zero pairs from a mat because adding or removing zero does not change the value of the counters on the mat.

Explore 2-4 Algebra Lab: Adding Integers   **93**

1 Focus

Materials

• positive and negative counters

Easy-to-Make Manipulatives

Teaching Mathematics with Manipulatives, templates for:

• integer counters, p. 7

2 Teach

Activity 1 Point out that when the second addend of an expression is a negative integer, it is enclosed by parentheses so that the negative symbol (−) is separated from the addition symbol (+).

Make sure students realize that Exercises a–f involve adding like integers—positive and positive, or negative and negative.

Additional Answers

a.

(grid of positive counters)

5 + 6 = 11

b.

(grid of negative counters)

−3 + (−5) = −8

c.

(grid of negative counters)

−5 + (−4) = −9

d.

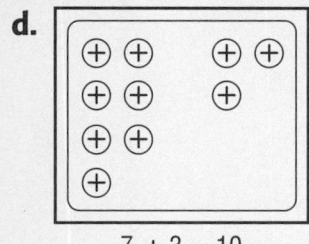

7 + 3 = 10

e.

(grid of negative counters)

−2 + (−5) = −7

f.

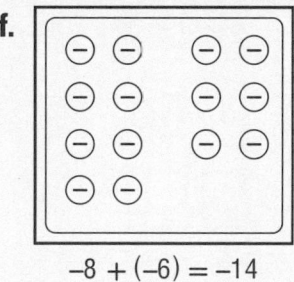

−8 + (−6) = −14

Activities 2 and 3 Make sure students realize that these problems involve adding unlike integers–positive and negative. Some students may realize that adding a negative integer is the same as subtracting the same number of positive counters.

3 Assess

✓ Formative Assessment

Use Exercises g–l to determine whether students comprehend how to use counters to model the addition of integers.

From Concrete to Abstract Use Exercises 1 and 2 to bridge the gap between using counters to add integers and writing addition problems with given (positive or negative) results.

Extending the Concept You might want to have students use counters to model repeated addition problems, such as $-2 + (-2) + (-2) + (-2)$. Point out that such a problem can be written as a multiplication problem: $4 \times (-2)$. Have students use what they know about adding integers to write a rule for multiplying integers with different signs.

Tips for New Teachers — Addends and Sums

Remind students the numbers you add are called *addends*. The result is called the *sum*.

3. **Sample answer:** If two integers have the same sign, add and keep the sign. If two integers have different signs, subtract and keep the sign of the integer with the greater absolute value.

Use counters to find each sum.

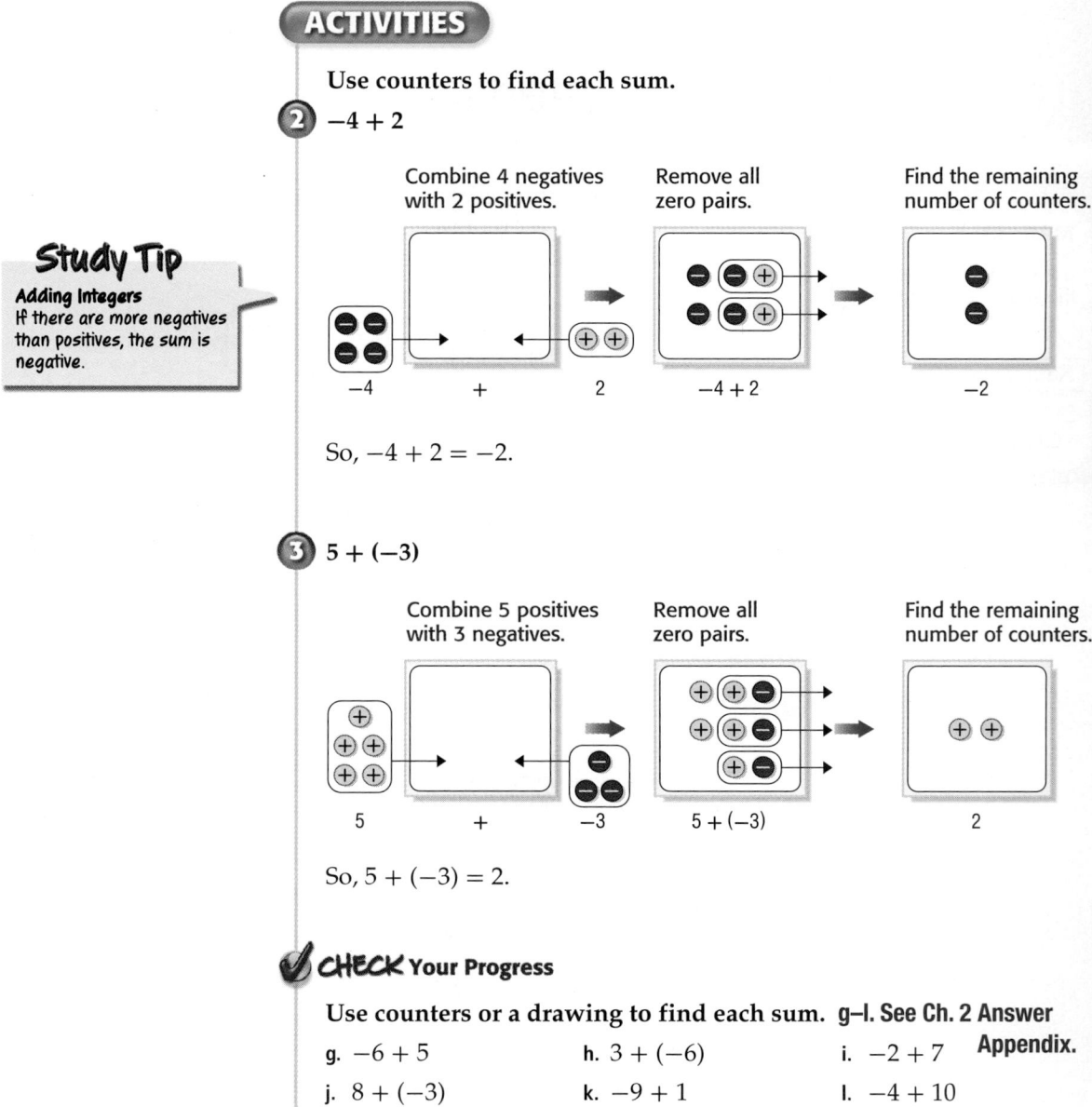

2 $-4 + 2$

Combine 4 negatives with 2 positives.

Remove all zero pairs.

Find the remaining number of counters.

-4 $+$ 2 $-4 + 2$ -2

So, $-4 + 2 = -2$.

Study Tip

Adding Integers If there are more negatives than positives, the sum is negative.

3 $5 + (-3)$

Combine 5 positives with 3 negatives.

Remove all zero pairs.

Find the remaining number of counters.

5 $+$ -3 $5 + (-3)$ 2

So, $5 + (-3) = 2$.

✓ CHECK Your Progress

Use counters or a drawing to find each sum.   **g–l.** See Ch. 2 Answer Appendix.

g. $-6 + 5$ h. $3 + (-6)$ i. $-2 + 7$

j. $8 + (-3)$ k. $-9 + 1$ l. $-4 + 10$

ANALYZE THE RESULTS

1. Write two addition sentences where the sum is positive. In each sentence, one addend should be positive and the other negative.
   Sample answer: $-1 + 2 = 1$; $5 + (-4) = 1$

2. Write two addition sentences where the sum is negative. In each sentence, one addend should be positive and the other negative.
   Sample answer: $2 + (-7) = -5$; $-10 + 5 = -5$

3. **MAKE A CONJECTURE** What is a rule you can use to determine how to find the sum of two integers with the same sign? two integers with different signs?

Adding Integers

PACING: **Regular:** 1.5 periods, **Block:** 0.5 period

Options for Differentiated Instruction

ELL = English Language Learner   **AL** = Above or Beyond Grade Level   **SS** = Struggling Students   **SN** = Special Needs

Using Manipulatives **ELL** **SS** **SN**

Use while presenting Examples 3 and 4.

Use positive and negative counters to model the addition of integers with different signs. Example 3 is shown at the right.

Remind students to remove all zero pairs. The remaining counters represent the solution. In this case, there are two positive counters remaining, so the answer is 2.

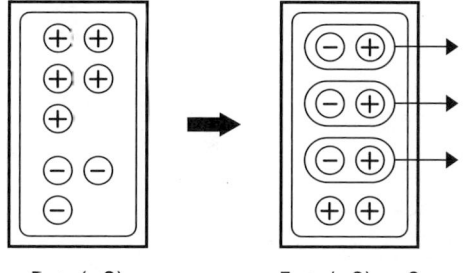

$5 + (-3)$ $5 + (-3) = 2$

Connections to Familiar Experiences **ELL** **AL** **SS** **SN**

Use after presenting Examples 1–8.

Engage students by providing the following application problem involving a video game.

The scoring system for a video game is shown in the table. Assume Dylan starts with zero points. What will be his score after he finds two treasure chests, captures a monster, and is knocked off three cliffs? +8

Action	Points
find treasure chest	+10
knocked off cliff	−5
capture monster	+3

Using Manipulatives **SS**

Use before assigning the Exercises.

Many students would benefit from having number lines to use as they do independent work. Provide number lines such as the ones shown below.

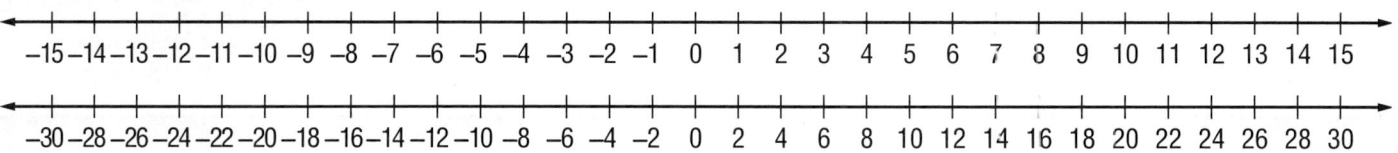

Give each student a copy of a number line sheet in a clear sheet protector so they can reuse the number lines with dry erase markers. Have students place the sheet in their three-ring binders so they can use it as a resource.

Leveled Lesson Resources

Also on **TeacherWorks**™
Lesson 2-4

Chapter 2 Resource Masters

BL = Below or Approaching Grade Level **OL** = On Grade Level **AL** = Above or Beyond Grade Level **ELL** = English Language Learner

Lesson Reading Guide
p. 29 **BL OL ELL**

NAME _____ DATE _____ PERIOD _____

2-4 Lesson Reading Guide
Adding Integers

Get Ready for the Lesson
Read the introduction at the top of page 95 in your textbook. Write your answers below.

1. Represent the number of electrons in an atom of helium with an integer.
−2

2. Represent the number of protons in an atom of helium with an integer.
2

3. Each proton-electron pair has a value of 0. What is the total charge of an atom of helium? 0

Read the Lesson
For Exercises 4 and 5, tell how you would find each sum on a number line. Then add.

4. −7 + (−9) **Starting at 0, move left 7 units, then move left another 9 units; −16.**

5. −7 + 9 **Starting at 0, move left 7 units, then move right 9 units; 2.**

6. What property are you applying when you add a number and its opposite only to find that its result is zero? **Additive Inverse Property**

7. How many units away from 0 is the number 17? How many units away from 0 is the number −17? What are 17 and −17 called? **17; 17; opposites or additive inverses**

Remember What You Learned

8. Work with a partner. Tell your partner how to use absolute values to add integers with different signs when the positive integer has the greater absolute value. Then have your partner explain to you how to use absolute values to add integers with different signs when the negative integer has the greater absolute value. **See students' work.**

Chapter 2   29   Course 2

Study Guide and Intervention*
p. 30 **BL OL ELL**

NAME _____ DATE _____ PERIOD _____

2-4 Study Guide and Intervention
Adding Integers

For integers with the same sign:
• the sum of two positive integers is positive.
• the sum of two negative integers is negative.
For integers with different signs, subtract their absolute values. The sum is:
• positive if the positive integer has the greater absolute value.
• negative if the negative integer has the greater absolute value.
To add integers, it is helpful to use counters or a number line.

Example Find 4 + (−6).

Method 1 Use counters.
Combine a set of 4 positive counters and a set of 6 negative counters on a mat.

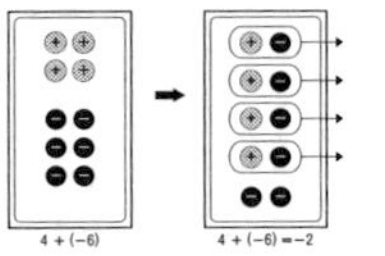

4 + (−6)
4 + (−6) = −2

Method 2 Use a number line.
• Start at 0.
• Move 4 units right.
• Then move 6 units left.

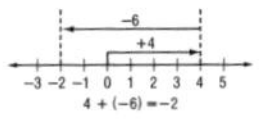

4 + (−6) = −2

Exercises
Add.

1. −5 + (−2) **−7**   2. 8 + 1 **9**   3. −7 + 10 **3**

4. 16 + (−11) **5**   5. −22 + (−7) **−29**   6. −50 + 50 **0**

7. −10 + (−10) **−20**   8. 100 + (−25) **75**   9. −35 + −20 **−55**

Evaluate each expression if a = 8, b = −8, and c = 4.

10. a + 15 **23**   11. b + (−9) **−17**   12. a + b **0**

13. b + c **−4**   14. −10 + c **−6**   15. 12 + b **4**

Chapter 2   30   Course 2

Skills Practice*
p. 31 **BL OL**

NAME _____ DATE _____ PERIOD _____

2-4 Skills Practice
Adding Integers

Add.

1. 5 + (−8) **−3**   2. −3 + 3 **0**

3. −3 + (−8) **−11**   4. −7 + (−7) **−14**

5. −8 + 10 **2**   6. −7 + 13 **6**

7. 15 + (−10) **5**   8. −11 + (−12) **−23**

9. 25 + (−12) **13**   10. −14 + (−13) **−27**

11. 14 + (−27) **−13**   12. −28 + 16 **−12**

Evaluate each expression if a = −8, b = 12, and c = −4.

13. 5 + a **−3**   14. b + (−9) **3**

15. c + (−5) **−9**   16. a + b **4**

17. a + 0 **−8**   18. b + c **8**

19. −12 + b **0**   20. a + (−7) **−15**

21. 21 + c **17**   22. a + c **−12**

Chapter 2   31   Course 2

Practice*
p. 32 **OL AL**

NAME _____ DATE _____ PERIOD _____

2-4 Practice
Adding Integers

Add.

1. 34 + 22 **56**   2. −29 + 30 **1**   3. 9 + (−32) **−23**

4. −16 + (−28) **−44**   5. 4 + (−50) **−46**   6. −12 + (−63) **−75**

7. −42 + 42 **0**   8. −28 + 14 **−14**   9. 13 + 63 **76**

10. 18 + (−12) + 5 **11**   11. −22 + (−10) + 15 **−17**   12. −14 + 0 + 13 **−1**

Write an addition expression to describe each situation. Then find each sum and explain its meaning.

13. WEIGHT An actor gains 20 pounds for a part and then loses 15 pounds during the filming of a movie to go along with the story.
20 + (−15) or 5 pounds; the actor is 5 pounds above his/her original weight.

14. TEMPERATURE At 4:00 A.M., the outside temperature was −28°F. By 4:00 P.M. that same day, it rose 38 degrees. **−28 + 38 or 10 degrees; the temperature at 4:00 P.M. was 10°F.**

ALGEBRA Evaluate each expression if a = 12, b = −15, and c = −10.

15. a + (−12) **0**   16. −20 + b **−35**   17. c + 23 **13**

18. b + c **−25**   19. a + c **2**   20. a + b **−3**

21. ROLLER COASTERS The latest thrill ride at a popular theme park takes roller coaster fans on an exciting ride. In the first 20 seconds, it carries its passengers up a 100-meter hill, plunges them down 72 meters, and quickly takes them back up a 48-meter rise. How much higher or lower from the start of the ride are they after these 20 seconds? **76 meters higher**

Chapter 2   32   Course 2

Word Problem Practice*
p. 33 **OL AL**

NAME _____ DATE _____ PERIOD _____

2-4 Word Problem Practice
Adding Integers

Write an addition expression to describe each situation. Then find each sum.

1. FOOTBALL A team gains 20 yards. Then they lose 7 yards. **20 + (−7); 13**

2. MONEY Roger owes his mom $5. He borrows another $6 from her. **(−5) + (−6); −11**

3. GOLF Juanita's score was 5 over par on the first 9 holes. Her score was 4 under par on the second 9 holes. **5 + (−4); 1**

4. HOT AIR BALLOON A balloon rises 340 feet into the air. Then it descends 130 feet. **340 + (−130); 210**

5. CYCLING A cyclist travels downhill for 125 feet. Then she travels up a hill 50 feet. **−125 + 50; −75**

6. AIRPLANE A plane descends 1,200 feet. Then it descends another 500 feet. **−1,200 + (−500); −1,700**

Chapter 2   33   Course 2

Enrichment
p. 34 **OL AL**

NAME _____ DATE _____ PERIOD _____

2-4 Enrichment

Adding a List of Integers
When you need to add a list of integers, sometimes it can be helpful to reorder the list of integers so you first add all the positive integers, and then all the negative integers.

Example
Marcy is studying weather conditions for her science fair project. During one 24-hour period, she recorded the changes in air temperature in the table at right. If the air temperature was 76°F at the start of her observations, what was the air temperature 24 hours later?

Time	Change in Temp. (°F)	Time	Change in Temp. (°F)
02:00	−1	14:00	−16
04:00	−2	16:00	+2
06:00	+2	18:00	+1
08:00	+4	20:00	+3
10:00	+4	22:00	−1
12:00	+3	00:00	−2

First add all the positive changes in air temperature and then all the negative changes in air temperature.
(+2) + (+4) + (+4) + (+3) + (+2) + (+1) + (+3) = +19
(−1) + (−2) + (−16) + (−1) + (−2) = −22
Next add the results to find the overall change and the new temperature.
+19 + (−22) = −3   76° + (−3°) = 73°F

Exercises

1. The passenger elevator in the Empire State Building registered the following journey log between 9:00 A.M. and 9:15 A.M. on a Monday morning. At which floor was the elevator at 9:15 A.M. if it started in the Lobby, which is Floor 1? **On the 8th floor**

Number of floors	↑ 17	↑ 21	↓ 16	↓ 3	↓ 4	↑ 11	↓ 19

2. A deep-sea diver attached to a safety cable was lowered into the water to a depth of 600 feet. During the next hour, the diver let out 250 feet, pulled in 36 feet, pulled in 69 feet, let out 23 feet, pulled in 51 feet, let out 68 feet, and pulled in 24 feet to allow the diver to explore. At the end of the hour, what was the depth of the diver? **761 ft below the surface or −761 ft**

3. The Franklin Wildcats football team was competing in the regional championship game. The offense had the ball at the 50-yard line as they tried to score to win the game. Their progress during each play was as follows.
gain 7, gain 2, loss 4, gain 5, gain 27, gain 4, gain 5, gain 0, gain 3, loss 2, loss 1, gain 1, gain 2
On what yard line did the Wildcats end? **On the 4-yard line**

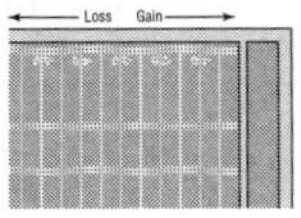

Chapter 2   34   Course 2

*** Also available in Spanish ELL**

Additional Lesson Resources

Transparencies
• *5-Minute Check Transparency*, Lesson 2-4

Other Print Products
• *Teaching Mathematics with Manipulatives*
• *Noteables™ Interactive Study Notebook with Foldables™*

Teacher Tech Tools
• *Interactive Classroom CD-ROM*, Lesson 2-4
• *AssignmentWorks*, Lesson 2-4

Student Tech Tools
glencoe.com
• Extra Examples, Chapter 2, Lesson 4
• Self-Check Quiz, Chapter 2, Lesson 4

MAIN IDEA

Add integers.

New Vocabulary

opposites
additive inverse

Math Online

glencoe.com

• Extra Examples
• Personal Tutor
• Self-Check Quiz

▷ **GET READY** for the Lesson

SCIENCE Atoms are made of negative charges (electrons) and positive charges (protons). The helium atom shown has a total of 2 electrons and 2 protons.

1. Represent the electrons in an atom of helium with an integer. **—2**

2. Represent the protons in an atom of helium with an integer. **2**

3. Each proton-electron pair has a value of 0. What is the total charge of an atom of helium? **0**

Combining protons and electrons in an atom is similar to adding integers.

EXAMPLE Add Integers with the Same Sign

1 Find −3 + (−2).

Use a number line.

• Start at 0.
• Move 3 units left to show −3.
• From there, move 2 units left to show −2.

So, −3 + (−2) = −5.

✓ **CHECK** Your Progress

a. −5 + (−7) **−12**

b. −10 + (−4) **−14**

These and other examples suggest the following rule.

Add Integers with the Same Sign	Key Concept
Words	To add integers with the same sign, add their absolute values. The sum is: • positive if both integers are positive. • negative if both integers are negative.
Examples	7 + 4 = 11 −7 + (−4) = −11

Lesson 2-4 Adding Integers **95**

---

1 Focus

Vertical Alignment

Before Lesson 2-4
Add with negative integers and subtract positive integers from negative integers

Lesson 2-4
Solve addition problems, including those arising in concrete situations, that use positive and negative integers

After Lesson 2-4
Add rational numbers and take positive rational numbers to whole-number powers

2 Teach

Scaffolding Questions

As you ask the following questions, take the appropriate numbers of steps in the appropriate directions.

Ask:

• If I walk 4 steps north and then 4 steps south, where am I relative to my starting point? at the starting point

• If I walk 5 steps west and then 5 steps east, where am I relative to my starting point? at the starting point

• If I walk 3 steps south and then 2 steps north, where am I relative to my starting point? 1 step south of the starting point

• If I walk 2 steps east and then 4 steps west, where am I relative to my starting point? 2 steps west of the starting point

ADDITIONAL EXAMPLE

1 Find −6 + (−3). −9

Focus on Mathematical Content

The **Commutative Property of Addition** states that the order in which you add does not change the sum. $a + b = b + a$.

The **Identity Property of Addition** states that the sum of any number and zero is that number. $a + 0 = a$

✓ Formative Assessment

Use the Check Your Progress exercises after the Examples to determine students' understanding of concepts.

ADDITIONAL EXAMPLES

2 Find $-34 + (-21)$. -55

3 Find $8 + (-7)$. 1

4 Find $-5 + 4$. -1

Additional Examples are also in:

- Noteables™ Interactive Study Notebook with Foldables™
- Interactive Classroom PowerPoint® Presentations

 **Add Integers with the Same Sign**

2 Find $-26 + (-17)$.

$-26 + (-17) = -43$ Both integers are negative, so the sum is negative.

✓ CHECK Your Progress

c. $-14 + (-16)$ **-30**   d. $23 + 38$ **61**

⊕ **Vocabulary Link** · · · ·
Opposite

Everyday Use something that is across from or is facing the other way, as in running the opposite way

Math Use two numbers that are the same distance from 0, but on opposite sides of 0 on the number line

The integers 5 and -5 are called **opposites** because they are the same distance from 0, but on opposite sides of 0. Two integers that are opposites are also called **additive inverses**.

Additive Inverse Property   **Key Concept**

Words	The sum of any number and its additive inverse is 0.
Examples	$5 + (-5) = 0$

Number lines can also help you add integers with different signs.

EXAMPLES   **Add Integers with Different Signs**

3 Find $5 + (-3)$.

Use a number line.

- Start at zero.
- Move 5 units right.
- Then move 3 units left.

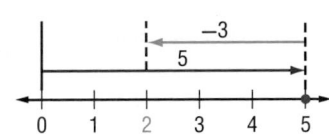

So, $5 + (-3) = 2$.

4 Find $-3 + 2$.

Use a number line.

- Start at zero.
- Move 3 units left.
- Then move 2 units right.

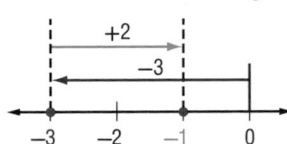

So, $-3 + 2 = -1$.

✓ CHECK Your Progress

e. $6 + (-7)$ **-1**   f. $-15 + 19$ **4**

Study Tip

Look Back You can review **absolute value** in Lesson 2-1.

Add Integers with Different Signs   **Key Concept**

Words	To add integers with different signs, subtract their absolute values. The sum is:
	• positive if the positive integer's absolute value is greater.
	• negative if the negative integer's absolute value is greater.
Examples	$9 + (-4) = 5$ $-9 + 4 = -5$

EXAMPLES Add Integers with Different Signs

5 Find $7 + (-1)$.

$7 + (-1) = 6$ Subtract absolute values; $7 - 1 = 6$. Since 7 has the greater absolute value, the sum is positive.

6 Find $-8 + 3$.

$-8 + 3 = -5$ Subtract absolute values; $8 - 3 = 5$. Since -8 has the greater absolute value, the sum is negative.

7 Find $2 + (-15) + (-2)$.

$$
\begin{aligned}
2 + (-15) + (-2) &= 2 + (-2) + (-15) & \text{Commutative Property (+)} \\
&= [2 + (-2)] + (-15) & \text{Associative Property (+)} \\
&= 0 + (-15) & \text{Additive Inverse Property} \\
&= -15 & \text{Additive Identity Property}
\end{aligned}
$$

> **Study Tip**
>
> **Properties** Using the Commutative, Associative, and Additive Inverse Properties allows the calculation to be as simple as possible.

✓ CHECK Your Progress

g. $10 + (-12)$ **−2**   h. $-13 + 18$ **5**   i. $(-14) + (-6) + 6$ **−14**

Real-World EXAMPLE

8 **ROLLER COASTERS** The graphic shows the change in height at several points on a roller coaster. Write an addition sentence to find the height at point *D* in relation to point *A*.

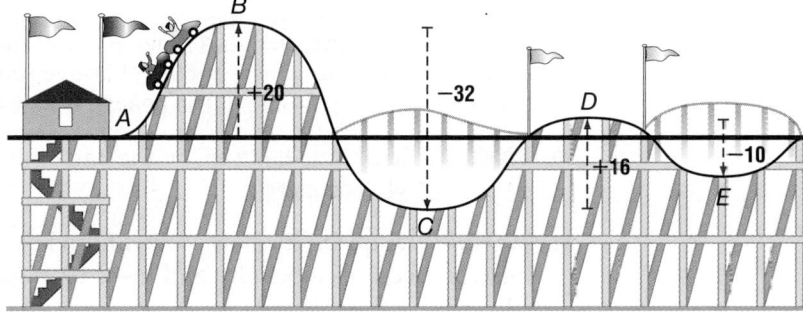

$$
\begin{aligned}
20 + (-32) + 16 &= 20 + 16 + (-32) & \text{Commutative Property (+)} \\
&= 36 + (-32) & 20 + 16 = 36 \\
&= 4 & \text{Subtract absolute values. Since 36 has the greater absolute value, the sum is positive.}
\end{aligned}
$$

The result is a positive integer. So, point *D* is 4 feet higher than point *A*.

CHECK Your Progress

j. **WEATHER** The temperature is $-3°$F. An hour later, it drops $6°$ and 2 hours later, it rises $4°$. Write an addition sentence to describe this situation. Then find the sum and explain its meaning.

j. $-3 + (-6) + 4$; -5; The new temperature is $-5°$F.

ADDITIONAL EXAMPLES

5 Find $2 + (-7)$. **−5**

6 Find $-9 + 6$. **−3**

7 Find $11 + (-4) + (-11)$. **−4**

8 **OCEANOGRAPHY**
Oceanographers divide the ocean into three light zones. The deeper the water, the less light shines through. The middle zone is called the Twilight Zone. The lowest part of this zone is 1,000 meters below the surface of the water. The top of the zone lies 800 meters above the lowest zone. What is the depth of the top of the zone? Write an addition sentence to describe this situation. Then find the sum and explain its meaning.
$-1,000 + 800$; -200; The depth of the top of the middle zone is 200 meters below the surface of the water.

 **Tips for New Teachers**

Adding Integers with Different Signs

Remind students that in adding integers with different signs, the larger absolute value does not always come first. For example, in adding $6 + (-11)$, the larger absolute value is 11, not 6.

Formative Assessment

Use Exercises 1–9 to check for understanding.

Then use the chart at the bottom of this page to customize your assignments for students.

Intervention You may wish to use the Study Guide and Intervention Master on page 30 of the *Chapter 2 Resource Masters* for additional reinforcement.

Odd/Even Assignments

Exercises 10–31 are structured so that students practice the same concepts whether they are assigned odd or even problems.

Differentiated Instruction

Kinesthetic Learners Separate students into pairs and give each pair 10 pennies (or 10 coin models). Determine which side (heads or tails) will represent –1 and which will represent 1. Have one student in each pair toss the 10 coins. The other student adds the negative and positive coins, removes the zero pairs, and writes the sum for that turn. Players take turns tossing and keeping score. The first player to reach an absolute value of 5 wins.

Additional Answers

30. $152 + (-20) + 84$; Stephanie now has $216 in the bank.

31. $-5 + (-15) + 12$; The team has lost a total of 8 yards.

 **Your Understanding**

Examples 1–6
(pp. 95–97)

Add.

1. $-6 + (-8)$ **–14**
2. $4 + 5$ **9**
3. $-3 + 10$ **7**
4. $-15 + 8$ **–7**
5. $7 + (-11)$ **–4**
6. $14 + (-6)$ **8**

Example 7
(p. 97)

7. $-17 + 20 + (-3)$ **0**
8. $15 + 9 + (-9)$ **15**

Example 8
(p. 97)

9. **MONEY** Camilia owes her brother $25, so she gives her brother the $18 she earned dog-sitting for the neighbors. Write an addition sentence to describe this situation. Then find the sum and explain its meaning.
–$25 + $18; –$7; Camilia still owes her brother $7.

Practice and Problem Solving

HOMEWORK HELP

For Exercises	See Examples
10–13	1, 2
14–21	3–6
22–27	7
28–31	8

Exercise Levels
A: 10–31
B: 32–37
C: 38–43

Add.

10. $-22 + (-16)$ **–38**
11. $-10 + (-15)$ **–25**
12. $6 + 10$ **16**
13. $17 + 11$ **28**
14. $18 + (-5)$ **13**
15. $13 + (-19)$ **–6**
16. $13 + (-7)$ **6**
17. $7 + (-20)$ **–13**
18. $-19 + 24$ **5**
19. $-12 + 10$ **–2**
20. $-30 + 16$ **–14**
21. $-9 + 11$ **2**
22. $21 + (-21) + (-4)$ **–4**
23. $-8 + (-4) + 12$ **0**
24. $-34 + 25 + (-25)$ **–34**
25. $-16 + 16 + 22$ **22**
26. $25 + 3 + (-25)$ **3**
27. $7 + (-19) + (-7)$ **–19**

Write an addition expression to describe each situation. Then find each sum and explain its meaning.

28. **SCUBA DIVING** Lena was scuba diving 14 meters below the surface of the water. She saw a nurse shark 3 meters above her.
–14 + 3;(–11); The shark is 11 feet below sea level.

29. **PELICANS** A pelican starts at 60 feet above sea level. It descends 60 feet to catch a fish. **60 + (–60); 0; The pelican is now at sea level.**

30. **BANKING** Stephanie has $152 in the bank. She withdraws $20. Then she deposits $84. **See margin.**

31. **FOOTBALL** A quarterback is sacked for a loss of 5 yards. On the next play, his team receives a penalty and loses 15 more yards. Then the team gains 12 yards on the third play.
See margin.

32. **MONEY** Josephine is saving money for a new bike and has already saved $17. Write the integers she should use to represent each entry.
+32, +19, +29, +25, +38

Deposit	Withdrawal	Balance
$15		◼
	$13	◼
$10		◼
	$4	◼
$13		◼

ALGEBRA Evaluate each expression if $x = -10$, $y = 7$, and $z = -8$.

33. $x + 14$ **4**
34. $z + (-5)$ **–13**
35. $x + y$ **–3**
36. $x + z$ **–18**

DIFFERENTIATED HOMEWORK OPTIONS

Level	Assignment	Two-Day Assignment	
BL Basic	10–31, 38, 43–55	11–31 odd, 44–46	10–30 even, 38, 43, 47–55
OL Core	11–35 odd, 36, 37, 38, 43–55	10–31, 44–46	32–38, 43, 47–55
AL Advanced/Pre-AP	32–50 (optional: 51–55)		

37. **FIND THE DATA** Refer to the Data File on pages 16–19 of your book. Choose some data and write a real-world problem in which you would add a positive and a negative integer. Then find the sum and explain its meaning. **See students' work.**

H.O.T. Problems

38. **FIND THE ERROR** Beth and Jordan are finding $-12 + 15$. Who is correct? Explain your reasoning.

38. Beth; Jordan added correctly but did not give the sum the sign of the integer with the greater absolute value.

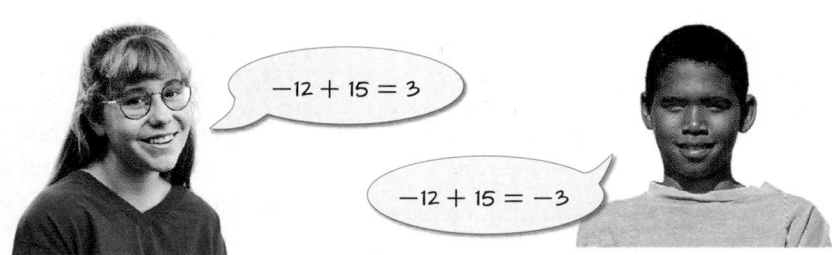

$-12 + 15 = 3$

Beth

$-12 + 15 = -3$

Jordan

CHALLENGE Simplify.

39. $8 + (-8) + a$
a

40. $x + (-5) + 1$
$x + (-4)$

41. $-9 + m + (-6)$
$m + (-15)$

42. $-1 + n + 7$
$n + 6$

43. **WRITING IN MATH** Explain how you know whether a sum is positive, negative, or zero without actually adding. **See margin.**

TEST PRACTICE

44. **SHORT RESPONSE** Find $-8 + (-11)$. **—19**

45. Find $-8 + 7 + (-3)$. **B**

A -18 C 2

B -4 D 18

46. At 8 A.M., the temperature was 3°F below zero. By 1 P.M., the temperature rose 14°F and by 10 P.M. dropped 12°F. What was the temperature at 10 P.M.? **J**

F 5°F above zero

G 5°F below zero

H 1°F above zero

J 1°F below zero

Spiral Review

Write the ordered pair for each point graphed at the right. Then name the quadrant or axis on which each point is located. (Lesson 2-3)

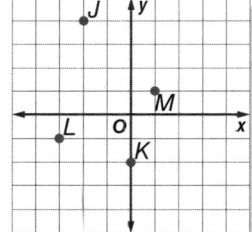

47. J
$(-2, 4)$; **II**

48. K
$(0, -2)$; **y-axis**

49. L
$(-3, -1)$; **III**

50. M
$(1, 1)$; **I**

51. Order $6, -3, 0, 4, -8, 1$, and -4 from least to greatest. (Lesson 2-2) **$-8, -4, -3, 0, 1, 4, 6$**

▷ **GET READY for the Next Lesson**

PREREQUISITE SKILL Subtract.

52. $287 - 125$ **162**   53. $420 - 317$ **103**   54. $5,684 - 2,419$ **3,265**   55. $7,000 - 3,891$ **3,109**

Lesson 2-4 Adding Integers   **99**

Additional Answer

43. Sample answer: Look at the signs. If the numbers being added are both positive, the sum is positive. If the numbers being added are both negative, the sum is negative. If the numbers being added have different signs, subtract their absolute values and give the sum the sign of the number with the greatest absolute value. If the numbers being added are opposites, the sum is zero.

 Formative Assessment

Use the Mid-Chapter Quiz to assess students' progress in the first half of the chapter.

Have students review the lesson indicated for the problems they answered incorrectly.

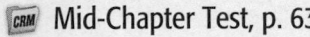 **Summative Assessment**

CRM Mid-Chapter Test, p. 63

 Customize and create multiple versions of your Mid-Chapter Test and their answer keys.

FOLDABLES Dinah Zike's
Study Organizer Foldables

Before students complete the Mid-Chapter Quiz, encourage them to review the information on the first three pages of their Foldables.

Additional Answers

16–19.

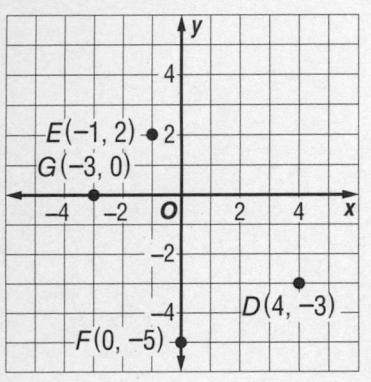

Write an integer for each situation. (Lesson 2-1)

1. dropped 45 feet **−45**

2. a bank deposit of $100 **100 or + 100**

3. gained 8 pounds **8 or + 8**

4. lost a $5 bill **−5**

5. **OCEANS** The deepest point in the world is the Mariana Trench in the Western Pacific Ocean at a depth of 35,840 feet below sea level. Write this depth as an integer. (Lesson 2-1) **−35,840**

Evaluate each expression. (Lesson 2-1)

6. $|-16|$ **16**   7. $|24|$ **24**

8. $|-9| - |3|$ **6**   9. $|-13| + |-1|$ **14**

10. **ANALYZE TABLES** The table shows the record low temperatures for January and February in Lincoln, Nebraska.

Month	Temperature (°F)
January	−33
February	−27

Source: University of Nebraska, Lincoln

Which month had the coldest temperature? (Lesson 2-2) **January**

11. **MULTIPLE CHOICE** The local news records the following changes in average daily temperature for the past week: 4°, −7°, −3°, 2°, 9°, −8°, 1°. Which list shows the temperatures from least to greatest? (Lesson 2-2) **C**

   A 9°, 4°, 2°, 1°, −3°, −7°, −8°

   B −7°, −8°, 1°, −3°, 2°, 4°, 9°

   C −8°, −7°, −3°, 1°, 2°, 4°, 9°

   D −8°, −7°, 1°, 2°, 3°, 4°, 9°

100   **Chapter 2** Integers

Replace each ● with <, >, or = to make a true sentence. (Lesson 2-2)

12. -4 ● 4 **<**   13. -8 ● -11 **>**

14. $|-14|$ ● $|3|$ **>**   15. $|-12|$ ● $|12|$ **=**

On graph paper, draw a coordinate plane. Then graph and label each point. (Lesson 2-3)

16. $D(4, -3)$ 17. $E(-1, 2)$

18. $F(0, -5)$ 19. $G(-3, 0)$

16–19. See margin.

20. **MULTIPLE CHOICE** Which line contains the ordered pair $(-1, 4)$? (Lesson 2-3) **F**

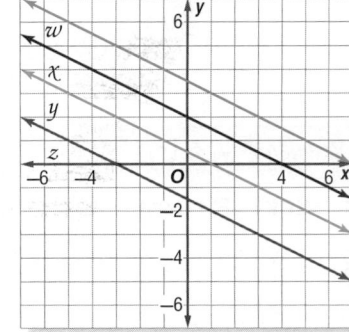

   F line w **H** line y

   G line x **J** line z

Add. (Lesson 2-4)

21. $3 + 4 + (-3)$ **4**   22. $7 + (-11)$ **−4**

23. $-5 + (-6)$ **−11**   24. $8 + (-1) + 1$ **8**

25. **MULTIPLE CHOICE** Kendra deposited $78 into her savings account. Two weeks later, she deposited a check for $50 into her account and withdrew $27. Which of the following expressions represents the amount of money left in her account? (Lesson 2-4) **C**

   A $78 + (−$50) + (−$27)

   B $78 + (−$50) + $27

   C $78 + $50 + (−$27)

   D $78 + $50 + $27

Data-Driven Decision Making	Exercises	Lesson	State/Local Standards	Resources for Review
Diagnostic Teaching Based on the results of the Chapter 2 Mid-Chapter Quiz, use the following to review concepts that students continue to find challenging.	1–10	2–1		**CRM** Study Guide and Intervention pp. 10, 17, 23, and 30
	11–15	2–2		**Math Online** glencoe.com
	16–20	2–3		• Extra Examples • Personal Tutor
	21–25	2–4		• Concepts in Motion

Algebra Lab
Subtracting Integers

You can also use counters to model subtraction of integers. Remember one meaning of subtraction is to *take away*.

MAIN IDEA

Use counters to model the subtraction of integers.

ACTIVITY

Use counters to find each difference.

① $5 - 2$

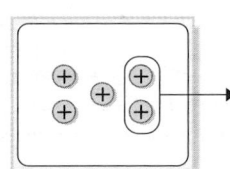

Place 5 positive counters on the mat. Remove 2 positive counters.

So, $5 - 2 = 3$.

② $4 - (-3)$

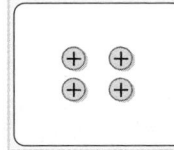

Place 4 positive counters on the mat. Remove 3 negative counters. However, there are 0 negative counters.

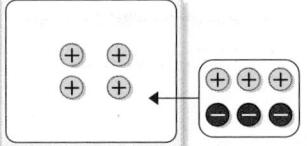

Add 3 zero pairs to the set.

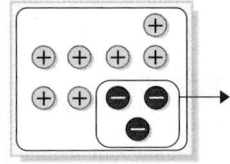

Now you can remove 3 negative counters. Find the remaining number of counters.

So, $4 - (-3) = 7$.

✔ CHECK Your Progress

Use counters or a drawing to find each difference. **a. See margin.**

b–d. See Ch. 2 Answer Appendix.

a. $7 - 6$ b. $5 - (-3)$ c. $6 - (-3)$ d. $5 - 8$

Explore 2-5 Algebra Lab: Subtracting Integers **101**

① Focus

Materials

• positive and negative counters

Easy-to-Make Manipulatives

Teaching Mathematics with Manipulatives templates for:

• integer counters, p. 7

② Teach

Activity 2 You may need to remind students that a zero pair—one positive counter and one negative counter—has a value of 0 and thus can be added to or subtracted from a set without changing the set's total value.

You may wish to point out that Exercises a–d involve positive minuends.

Additional Answer

a.

$7 - 6 = 1$

Activities 3 and 4 Point out that these problems have negative minuends. Some students may realize that subtracting a negative integer is the same as adding positive counters, and subtracting a positive integer is the same as adding negative counters.

3 Assess

✓ Formative Assessment

Use Exercises e–g to determine whether students comprehend how to use counters to model the subtraction of integers.

From Concrete to Abstract Use Exercises 1 and 2 to bridge the gap between using counters to subtract integers and writing subtraction problems with given (positive or negative) results.

Additional Answers

e.

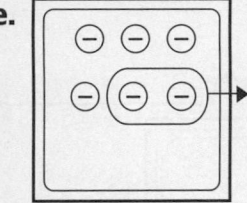

$-6 - (-2) = -4$

3. Sample answer: The difference of two integers is positive when the minuend is greater than the subtrahend. The difference of two integers is negative when the minuend is less than the subtrahend.

ACTIVITY

Use counters to find each difference.

3 $-6 - (-3)$

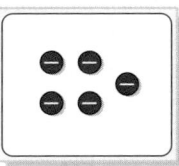

Place 6 negative counters on the mat. Remove 3 negative counters.

So, $-6 - (-3) = -3$.

4 $-5 - 1$

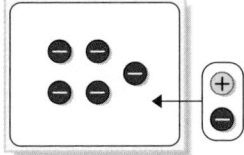

Place 5 negative counters on the mat. Remove 1 positive counter. However, there are 0 positive counters.

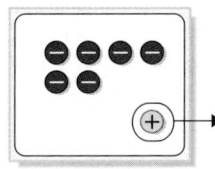

Add 1 zero pair to the set.

Now you can remove 1 positive counter. Find the remaining number of counters.

So, $-5 - 1 = -6$.

Reading Math

Minuends, Subtrahends, and Differences In the subtraction sentence $-5 - 1 = -6$, -5 is the *minuend*, 1 is the *subtrahend*, and -6 is the *difference*.

✓ CHECK Your Progress

Use counters or a drawing to find each difference. **e. See margin.**

e. $-6 - (-2)$ **f.** $-7 - 3$ **g.** $-5 - (-7)$

f, g. See Ch. 2 Answer Appendix.

1. Sample answers:
$8 - 2 = 6$;
$7 - (-6) = 13$;
$-3 - (-6) = 3$
2. Sample answers:
$-5 - (-2) = -3$;
$-1 - 4 = -5$;
$2 - 3 = -1$

ANALYZE THE RESULTS

1. Write two subtraction sentences where the difference is positive. Use a combination of positive and negative integers.

2. Write two subtraction sentences where the difference is negative. Use a combination of positive and negative integers.

3. **MAKE A CONJECTURE** Write a rule that will help you determine the sign of the difference of two integers. **See margin.**

102   **Chapter 2** Integers

Subtracting Integers

PACING: **Regular:** 1.5 periods, **Block:** 0.5 period

Options for Differentiated Instruction

ELL = English Language Learner   **AL** = Above or Beyond Grade Level   **SS** = Struggling Students   **SN** = Special Needs

Visualizing the Concept **SS** **SN**

Use before presenting Examples 1 and 2.

To further show that subtracting integers is the same as adding the opposite, use counters to compare the subtraction $6 - 3$ to the addition $6 + (-3)$.

The models show that $6 - 3 = 6 + (-3)$.

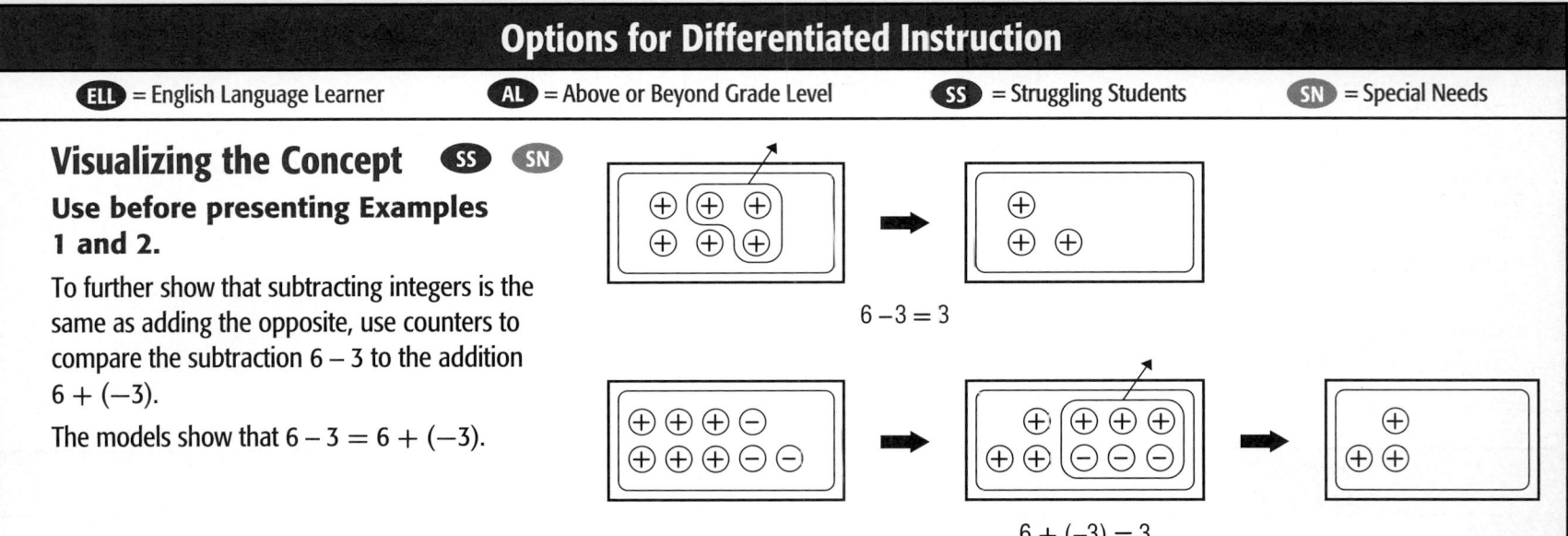

$6 - 3 = 3$

$6 + (-3) = 3$

Real-World Applications **ELL** **AL**

Use after presenting Examples 1–6.

The diagram below is a timeline showing the lives of three rulers of Rome. Present the diagram on the overhead or make a sketch of it on the board.

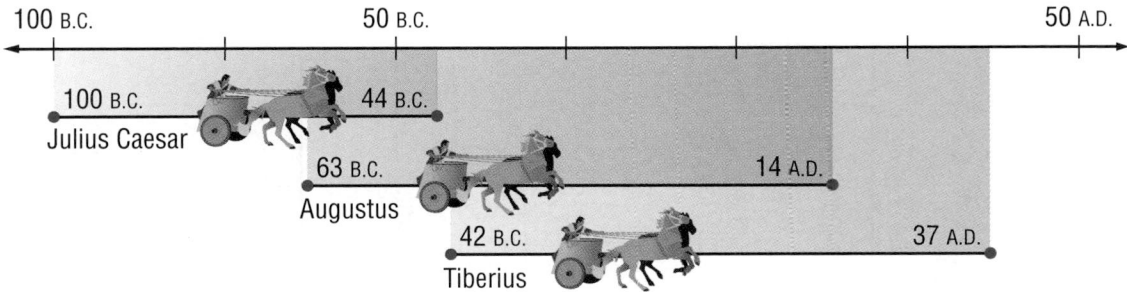

Ask:
- How old was Augustus when he died? 77 yr
- Which ruler lived the longest? How old was he when he died? Tiberius; 79 yr
- Find the number of years between Julius Caesar's birth and Augustus' birth. 37 yr
- How could you determine how long ago each of the three rulers were born?
  Explain. Add their birth year to the current year. This works because all three rulers were born in years B.C.

Leveled Lesson Resources

Chapter 2 Resource Masters

BL = Below or Approaching Grade Level   **OL** = On Grade Level   **AL** = Above or Beyond Grade Level   **ELL** = English Language Learner

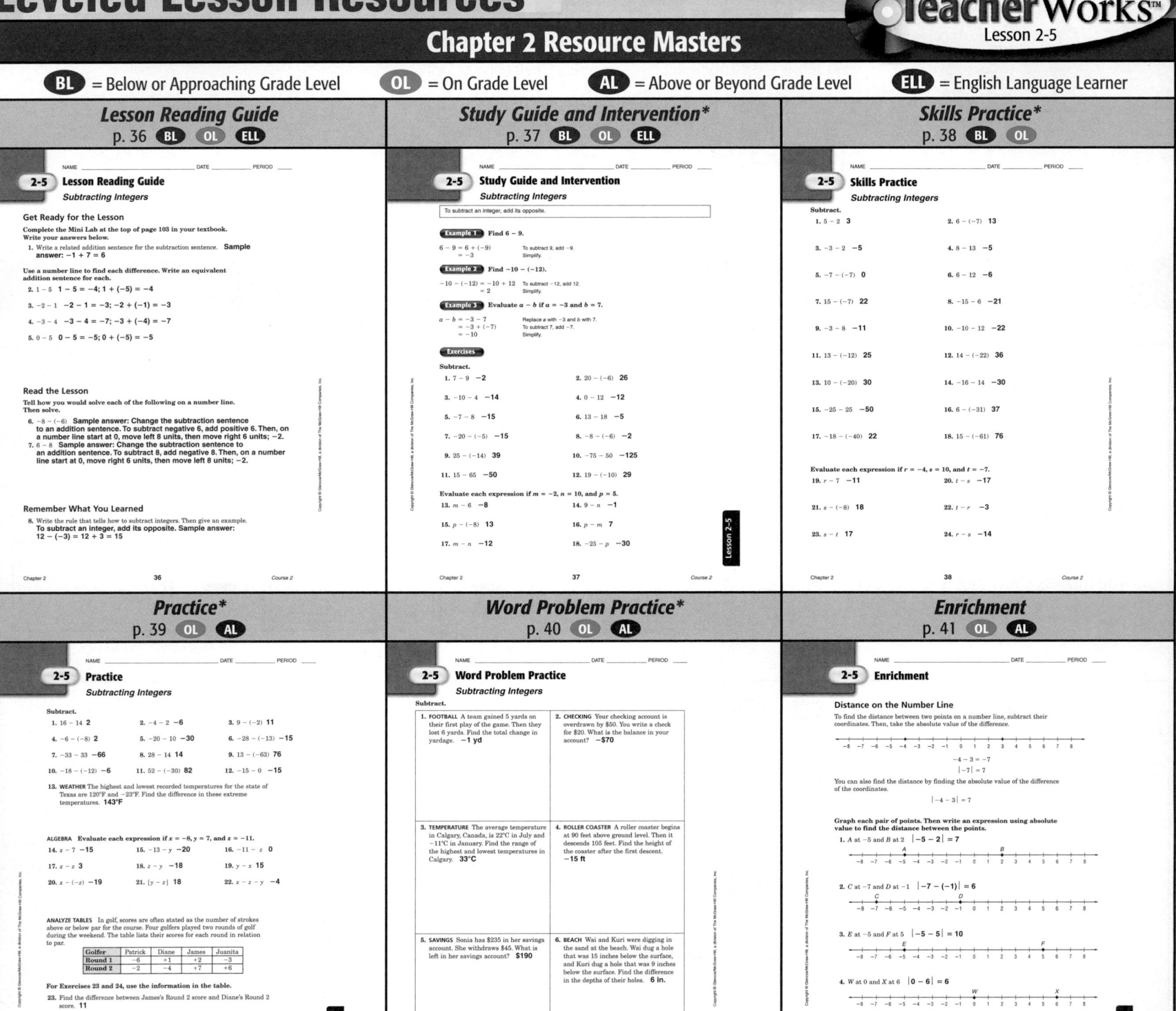

Lesson Reading Guide
p. 36 **BL** **OL** **ELL**

Study Guide and Intervention*
p. 37 **BL** **OL** **ELL**

Skills Practice*
p. 38 **BL** **OL**

Practice*
p. 39 **OL** **AL**

Word Problem Practice*
p. 40 **OL** **AL**

Enrichment
p. 41 **OL** **AL**

*** Also available in Spanish** **ELL**

Additional Lesson Resources

Transparencies
- *5-Minute Check Transparency,* Lesson 2-5

Other Print Products
- *Teaching Mathematics with Manipulatives*
- *Noteables™ Interactive Study Notebook with Foldables™*

Teacher Tech Tools
- *Interactive Classroom CD-ROM,* Lesson 2-5
- *AssignmentWorks,* Lesson 2-5

Student Tech Tools
glencoe.com
- Extra Examples, Chapter 2, Lesson 5
- Self-Check Quiz, Chapter 2, Lesson 5

MAIN IDEA

Subtract integers.

Math Online

glencoe.com

• Concepts In Motion
• Extra Examples
• Personal Tutor
• Self-Check Quiz

▷ **MINI Lab**

You can use a number line to model a subtraction problem.

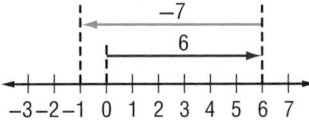

1. $6 + (-7) = -1$

1. Write a related addition sentence for the subtraction sentence.

Use a number line to find each difference. Write an equivalent addition sentence for each. 2–5. See Ch 2. Answer Appendix.

2. $1 - 5$ 3. $-2 - 1$ 4. $-3 - 4$ 5. $0 - 5$

When you subtract 7, the result is the same as adding its opposite, -7.

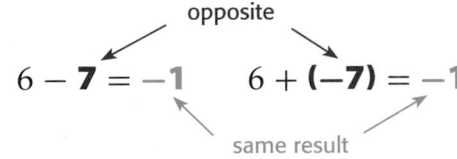

opposite

$6 - \mathbf{7} = \mathbf{-1}$ $6 + \mathbf{(-7)} = \mathbf{-1}$

same result

This and other examples suggest the following rule.

Subtract Integers		Key Concept
Words	To subtract an integer, add its opposite.	
Examples	$4 - 9 = 4 + (-9) = -5$	$7 - (-10) = 7 + (10) = 17$

EXAMPLES **Subtract Positive Integers**

1 Find $8 - 13$.

$8 - 13 = 8 + (-13)$ To subtract 13, add -13.

$\qquad = -5$ Simplify.

2 Find $-10 - 7$.

$-10 - 7 = -10 + (-7)$ To subtract 7, add -7.

$\qquad = -17$ Simplify.

 CHECK Your Progress

a. $6 - 12$ **−6**   b. $-20 - 15$ **−35**   c. $-22 - 26$ **−48**

Lesson 2-5 Subtracting Integers **103**

1 **Focus**

Vertical Alignment

Before Lesson 2-5
Subtract positive integers from negative integers

Lesson 2-5
Solve subtraction problems, including those arising in concrete situations, that use positive and negative integers

After Lesson 2-5
Subtract rational numbers and take positive rational numbers to whole-number powers

2 **Teach**

▷ **MINI Lab**

You might want to have students also model the related addition sentences on their number lines, thus "undoing" the original subtractions. For example, for the number done on the right, students could model $-1 - 4 = -5$ and then $-5 + 4 = -1$.

Scaffolding Questions

Draw a number line from -10 to 10 on the board. As you ask the following questions, move a pointer along the number line.

Ask:

• What direction do I move if I subtract 2 from 6? left

• What direction do I move if I subtract 1 from -6? left

• What direction do I move if I add -3 to 1? left

• What direction do I move if I add -9 to 0? left

Use the Check Your Progress exercises after the Examples to determine students' understanding of concepts.

ADDITIONAL EXAMPLES

1 Find $2 - 15$. -13

2 Find $-13 - 8$. -21

3 Find $12 - (-6)$. 18

4 Find $-21 - (-8)$. -13

5 **ALGEBRA** Evaluate $g - h$ if $g = -2$ and $h = -7$. 5

6 **GEOGRAPHY** In Mongolia, the temperature can fall to $-45°C$ in January. The temperature in July may reach $40°C$. What is the difference between these two temperatures in Mongolia? $85 °C$

Additional Examples are also in:

- Noteables™ Interactive Study Notebook with Foldables™

- Interactive Classroom PowerPoint® Presentations

Tips for New Teachers

Subtracting Integers

Students can use a number line to check their results. First, have them change the subtraction sentence to an addition sentence. Then, they can draw a number line.

EXAMPLES Subtract Negative Integers

3 Find $1 - (-2)$.

$$1 - (-2) = 1 + 2 \qquad \text{To subtract } -2, \text{ add } 2.$$
$$= 3 \qquad \text{Simplify.}$$

4 Find $-10 - (-7)$.

$$-10 - (-7) = -10 + 7 \qquad \text{To subtract } -7, \text{ add } 7.$$
$$= -3 \qquad \text{Simplify.}$$

CHECK Your Progress

d. $4 - (-12)$ **16**   e. $-15 - (-5)$ **−10**   f. $18 - (-6)$ **24**

EXAMPLE Evaluate an Expression

5 **ALGEBRA** Evaluate $x - y$ if $x = -6$ and $y = -5$.

$$x - y = -6 - (-5) \qquad \text{Replace } x \text{ with } -6 \text{ and } y \text{ with } -5.$$
$$= -6 + (5) \qquad \text{To subtract } -5, \text{ add } 5.$$
$$= -1 \qquad \text{Simplify.}$$

CHECK Your Progress

Evaluate each expression if $a = 5$, $b = -8$, and $c = -9$.

g. $b - 10$ **−18**   h. $a - b$ **13**   i. $c - a$ **−14**

Real-World EXAMPLE

Real-World Link . . . .
The mean surface temperature on the Moon during the day is 107°C.
Source: Views of the Solar System

6 **SPACE** The temperatures on the Moon vary from $-173°C$ to $127°C$. Find the difference between the maximum and minimum temperatures.

To find the difference in temperatures, subtract the lower temperature from the higher temperature.

Estimate $100 + 200 = 300$

$$127 - (-173) = 127 + 173 \qquad \text{To subtract } -173, \text{ add } 173.$$
$$= 300 \qquad \text{Simplify.}$$

So, the difference between the temperatures is 300°C.

CHECK Your Progress

j. **GEOGRAPHY** The Dead Sea's deepest part is 799 meters below sea level. A plateau to the east of the Dead Sea rises to about 1,340 meters above sea level. What is the difference between the top of the plateau and the deepest part of the Dead Sea? **2,139 m**

CHECK Your Understanding

Examples 1, 2
(p. 103)

Subtract.

1. $14 - 17$ **−3**
2. $10 - 30$ **−20**
3. $-4 - 8$ **−12**
4. $-2 - 23$ **−25**

Examples 3, 4
(p. 104)

5. $14 - (-10)$ **24**
6. $5 - (-16)$ **−21**
7. $-3 - (-1)$ **−2**
8. $-11 - (-9)$ **−2**

Example 5
(p. 104)

ALGEBRA Evaluate each expression if $p = 8$, $q = -14$, and $r = -6$.

9. $r - 15$ **−21**
10. $q - r$ **−8**
11. $p - q$ **22**

Example 6
(p. 104)

12. **EARTH SCIENCE** The sea-surface temperatures range from $-2°C$ to $31°C$.
    Find the difference between the maximum and minimum temperatures.
    33°C

Practice and Problem Solving

HOMEWORK HELP

For Exercises	See Examples
13–16, 21–24	1, 2
17–20, 25–28	3, 4
29–36	5
37–40	6

Exercise Levels
A: 13–40
B: 41–43
C: 44–47

Subtract.

13. $0 - 10$ **−10**
14. $13 - 17$ **−4**
15. $-9 - 5$ **−14**
16. $-8 - 9$ **−17**
17. $4 - (-19)$ **23**
18. $27 - (-8)$ **35**
19. $-11 - (-42)$ **31**
20. $-27 - (-19)$ **−8**
21. $12 - 26$ **−14**
22. $31 - 48$ **−17**
23. $-25 - 5$ **−30**
24. $-44 - 41$ **−85**
25. $52 - (-52)$ **104**
26. $15 - (-14)$ **29**
27. $-27 - (-33)$ **6**
28. $-18 - (-20)$ **2**

ALGEBRA Evaluate each expression if $f = -6$, $g = 7$, and $h = 9$.

29. $g - 7$ **0**
30. $f - 6$ **−12**
31. $-h - (-9)$ **0**
32. $f - g$ **−13**
33. $h - f$ **15**
34. $g - h$ **−2**
35. $5 - f$ **11**
36. $4 - (-g)$ **11**

ANALYZE TABLES For Exercises 37–40, use the information below.

State	California	Georgia	Louisiana	New Mexico	Texas
Lowest Elevation (ft)	−282	0	−8	2,842	0
Highest Elevation (ft)	14,494	4,784	535	13,161	8,749

37. What is the difference between the highest elevation in Texas and the lowest elevation in Louisiana? **8,757 ft**

38. Find the difference between the lowest elevation in New Mexico and the lowest elevation in California. **3,124 ft**

39. Find the difference between the highest elevation in Georgia and the lowest elevation in California. **5,066 ft**

40. What is the difference between the lowest elevations in Texas and Louisiana? **8 ft**

EXTRA PRACTICE
See pages 672, 705.

ALGEBRA Evaluate each expression if $h = -12$, $j = 4$, and $k = 15$.

41. $-j + h - k$ **−31**
42. $|h - j|$ **16**
43. $k - j - h$ **23**

---

3 Practice

Formative Assessment

Use Exercises 1–12 to check for understanding.

Then use the chart at the bottom of this page to customize your assignments for students.

Intervention You may wish to use the Study Guide and Intervention Master on page 37 of the *Chapter 2 Resource Masters* for additional reinforcement.

Odd/Even Assignments

Exercises 13–40 are structured so that students practice the same concepts whether they are assigned odd or even problems.

DIFFERENTIATED HOMEWORK OPTIONS

Level	Assignment	Two-Day Assignment	
BL Basic	13–40, 44, 45, 47–59	13–43 odd, 48, 49	14–42 even, 44, 45, 47, 50–56
OL Core	13–43 odd, 44, 45, 47–59	13–40, 48, 49	41–45, 47, 50–59
AL Advanced/Pre-AP	41–55 (optional: 56–59)		

Exercise Alert!

Find the Error For Exercise 45, Alicia knew that she could subtract the integer by adding its opposite, but she forgot to rewrite the integer as its opposite. Remind students to check the signs of the integers before they subtract or add.

4 Assess

Yesterday's News Remind students that yesterday's lesson was about adding integers. Have them write how yesterday's concepts helped them with today's material.

H.O.T. Problems

44. Sample answer:
$-5 - 11 = -5 + (-11) = -16$; Add 5 and 11 and keep the negative sign.

44. OPEN ENDED Write a subtraction sentence using integers. Then, write the equivalent addition sentence, and explain how to find the sum.

45. FIND THE ERROR Alicia and Mei are finding $-15 - (-18)$. Who is correct? Explain your reasoning. **Mei; Alicia did not add the additive inverse of -18.**

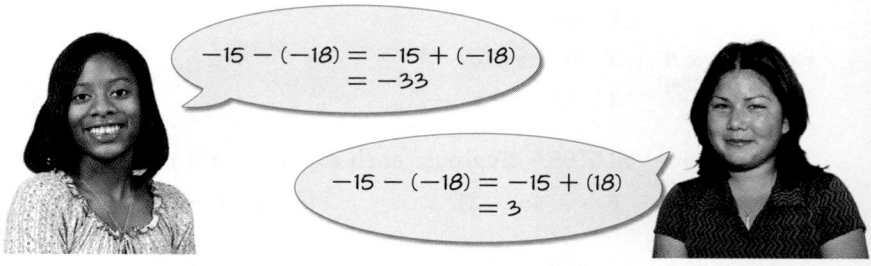

$$-15 - (-18) = -15 + (-18)$$
$$= -33$$

$$-15 - (-18) = -15 + (18)$$
$$= 3$$

Alicia   Mei

46. CHALLENGE *True or False?* When n is a negative integer, $n - n = 0$. **true**

47. WRITING IN MATH Explain how additive inverses are used in subtraction. **Sample answer: To subtract an integer, add its additive inverse.**

TEST PRACTICE

48. Which sentence about integers is *not* always true? **A**

A positive − positive = positive

B positive + positive = positive

C negative + negative = negative

D positive − negative = positive

49. Morgan drove from Los Angeles (elevation 330 feet) to Death Valley (elevation −282 feet). What is the difference in elevation between Los Angeles and Death Valley? **J**

F 48 feet   H 582 feet

G 148 feet   J 612 feet

Spiral Review

Add. (Lesson 2-4)

50. $10 + (-3)$ **7**   **51.** $-2 + (-9)$ **−11**   **52.** $-7 + (-6)$ **−13**   **53.** $-18 + 4$ **−14**

54. In which quadrant does the ordered pair $(5, -6)$ lie? (Lesson 2-3) **quadrant IV**

55. NUMBERS A number times 2 is added to 7. The result is 23. What is the number? Use the *guess and check* strategy. (Lesson 1-5) **8**

▷ GET READY for the Next Lesson

Add. (Lesson 2-4)

56. $-6 + (-6) + (-6) + (-6)$ **−24**   **57.** $-11 + (-11) + (-11)$ **−33**

58. $-2 + (-2) + (-2) + (-2)$ **−8**   **59.** $-8 + (-8) + (-8)$ **−24**

Pre-AP Activity   Use after Exercise 45.

Remind students that to subtract an integer they can add its opposite. Ask them whether when adding an integer they can subtract its opposite. Have them explain their reasoning and give examples.

PACING: **Regular:** 1 period, **Block:** 0.5 period

Options for Differentiated Instruction

ELL = English Language Learner   **AL** = Above or Beyond Grade Level   **SS** = Struggling Students   **SN** = Special Needs

---

Find the Error **AL**

Use after presenting Examples 1–7.

Display the following two expressions on the board: $(-3)^{15}$ $(-5)^{10}$

Share with the class each of the statements shown below and have students determine whether John's or Sarah's statement is correct. Have them explain their reasoning.

John	Sarah
$(-3)^{15}$ is greater than $(-5)^{10}$ because the exponent is greater.	$(-5)^{10}$ is greater because it is positive and $(-3)^{15}$ is negative.

Sarah; a negative number raised to an even power is positive and a negative number raised to an odd power is negative. So, $(-5)^{10}$ is greater than $(-3)^{15}$.

Alternative Methods **ELL** **SS** **SN**

Use before assigning the Exercises.

Some students may mistakenly assign the wrong sign to a product that involves one or more negative integers. Suggest that students multiply first, disregarding the signs, and then use the rules provided to affix the correct sign to the product.

Visualizing Substitutions **SS** **SN**

Use with Exercises 30–37 and 40–43.

To help students identify which values should be substituted for variables in an expression, suggest that they use different color highlighters to organize the information. It may be helpful to provide an enlarged photocopy of these exercises so that students can use the highlighters directly on the homework problems.

> **ALGEBRA** Evaluate each expression if $a = -6$, $b = -4$, $c = 3$, and $d = 9$.
>
> **40.** $-3a^2$ **41.** $-cd^2$ **42.** $-2a + b$ **43.** $b^2 - 4ac$

Leveled Lesson Resources

Chapter 2 Resource Masters

BL = Below or Approaching Grade Level   **OL** = On Grade Level   **AL** = Above or Beyond Grade Level   **ELL** = English Language Learner

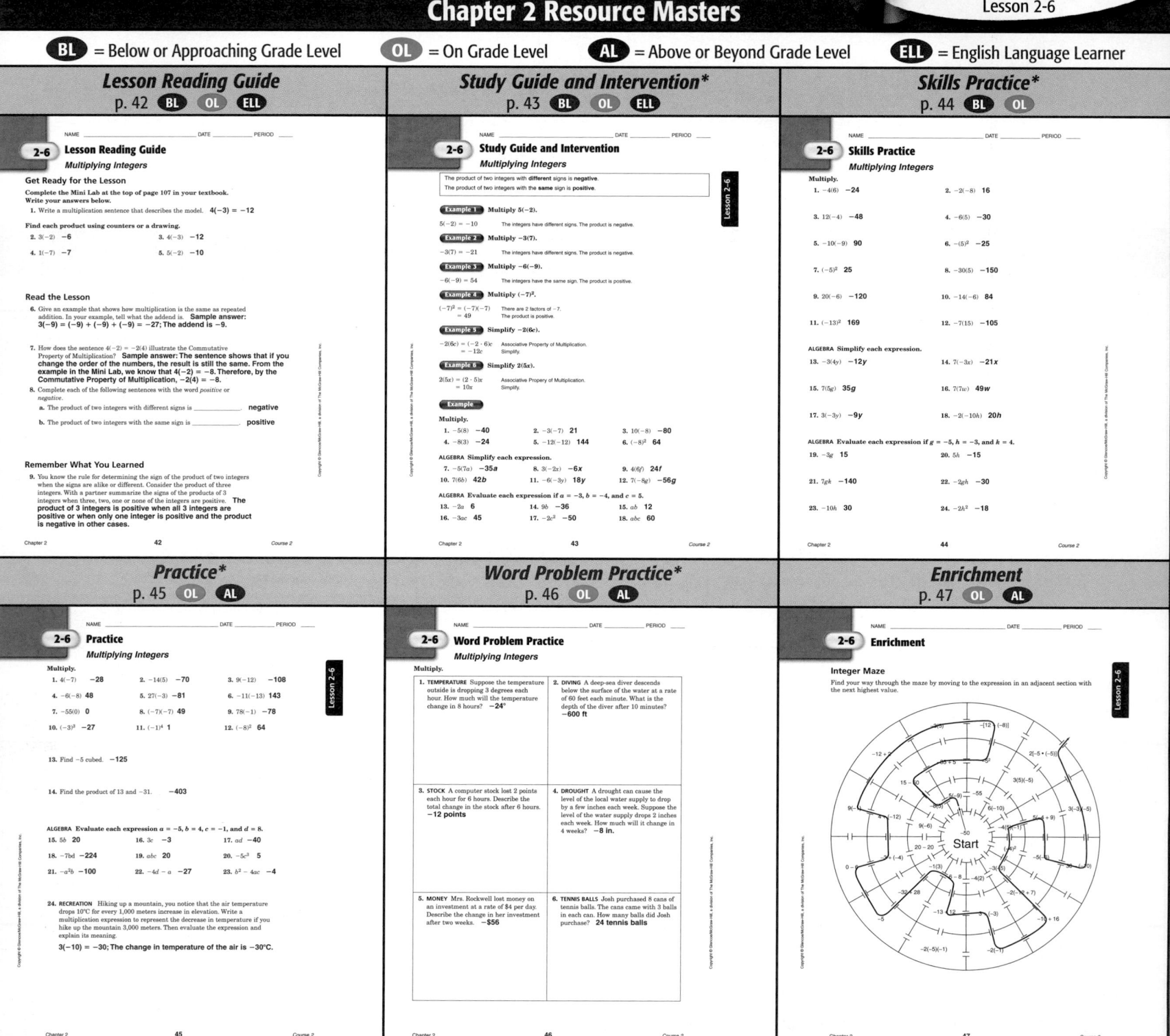

Lesson Reading Guide
p. 42 **BL** **OL** **ELL**

Study Guide and Intervention*
p. 43 **BL** **OL** **ELL**

Skills Practice*
p. 44 **BL** **OL**

Practice*
p. 45 **OL** **AL**

Word Problem Practice*
p. 46 **OL** **AL**

Enrichment
p. 47 **OL** **AL**

Additional Lesson Resources

* Also available in Spanish **ELL**

Transparencies
- *5-Minute Check Transparency,* Lesson 2-6

Other Print Products
- *Teaching Mathematics with Manipulatives*
- *Noteables™ Interactive Study Notebook with Foldables™*

Teacher Tech Tools
- *Interactive Classroom CD-ROM,* Lesson 2-6
- *AssignmentWorks,* Lesson 2-6

Student Tech Tools
glencoe.com
- Extra Examples, Chapter 2, Lesson 6
- Self-Check Quiz, Chapter 2, Lesson 6

Multiplying Integers

▷ MINI Lab

Counters can be used to multiply integers.

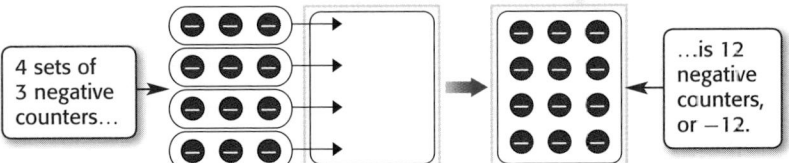

4 sets of 3 negative counters...   ...is 12 negative counters, or −12.

1. Write a multiplication sentence that describes the model above.
   4(−3) = −12

Find each product using counters or a drawing.

2. 3(−2) **−6**   3. 4(−3) **−12**   4. 1(−7) **−7**   5. 5(−2) **−10**

Remember that multiplication is the same as repeated addition.

$4(-3) = (-3) + (-3) + (-3) + (-3)$ −3 is used as an addend four times.

$= -12$

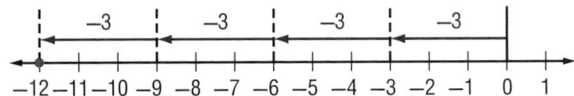

By the Commutative Property of Multiplication, $4(-3) = -3(4)$.

Multiply Integers with Different Signs   **Key Concept**

Words   The product of two integers with different signs is negative.

Examples $6(-4) = -24$ $-5(7) = -35$

EXAMPLES   Multiply Integers with Different Signs

1 Find $3(-5)$.

$3(-5) = -15$ The integers have different signs. The product is negative.

2 Find $-6(8)$.

$-6(8) = -48$ The integers have different signs. The product is negative.

✓ CHECK Your Progress

a. $9(-2)$ **−18**   b. $-7(4)$ **−28**

Tips for New Teachers   Multiplying Integers

Remind students that repeated addition can be used to check their work. For example, $3(-5) = (-5) + (-5) + (-5)$ or -15.

---

1 Focus

Vertical Alignment

Before Lesson 2-6
Add with negative integers; subtract positive integers from negative integers

Lesson 2-6
Solve multiplication problems, including those arising in concrete situations, that use positive and negative integers

After Lesson 2-6
Multiply rational numbers and take positive rational numbers to whole-number powers

2 Teach

▷ MINI Lab

Remind students that two numbers separated only by a parenthesis (such as in Exercises 2–5) are to be multiplied.

Scaffolding Questions

As students answer the following questions, write the expressions on the board.

Ask:

• How can I write $3 + 3 + 3 + 3$ as a multiplication problem? $4 \cdot 3$

• How can I write $7 + 7 + 7$ as a multiplication problem? $3 \cdot 7$

• How can I write $1 + 1 + 1 + 1 + 1 + 1$ as a multiplication problem? $6 \cdot 1$

• How can I write $(-2) + (-2) + (-2) + (-2)$ as a multiplication problem? $4 \cdot (-2)$

Focus on Mathematical Content

Number lines are a good way to model multiplying integers.

Multiplication can be shown as **repeated addition**.

The **Commutative Property of Multiplication** is related to the Commutative Property of Addition. The order in which you multiply (or add) does not change the product (or sum).

✓ Formative Assessment

Use the Check Your Progress exercises after the Examples to determine students' understanding of concepts.

ADDITIONAL EXAMPLES

1 Find $5(-4)$. -20

2 Find $-3(9)$. -27

3 Find $-6(-8)$. 48

4 Find $(-8)^2$. 64

5 Find $-2(-5)(-6)$. -60

Additional Examples are also in:

• Noteables™ Interactive Study Notebook with Foldables™

• Interactive Classroom PowerPoint® Presentations

The product of two positive integers is positive. You can use a pattern to find the sign of the product of two negative integers.

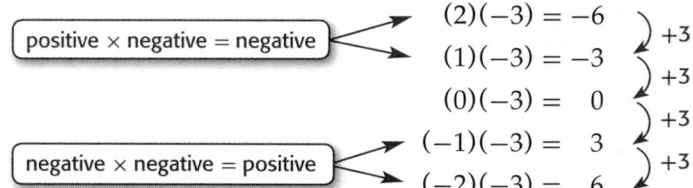

Each product is 3 more than the previous product. This pattern can also be shown on a number line.

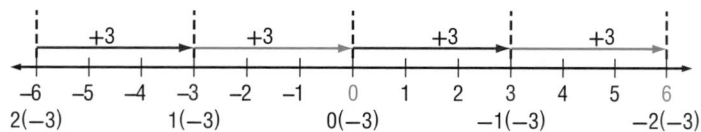

These and other examples suggest the following rule.

Study Tip

Multiplying by Zero
The Multiplicative Property of Zero states that when any number is multiplied by zero, the product is zero.

Multiply Integers with Same Sign   Key Concept

Words   The product of two integers with the same sign is positive.

Examples $2(6) = 12$ $-10(-6) = 60$

EXAMPLES   Multiply Integers with the Same Sign

3 Find $-11(-9)$.

   $-11(-9) = 99$ The integers have the same sign. The product is positive.

Study Tip

Look Back
You can review **exponents** in Lesson 1-2.

4 Find $(-4)^2$.

   $(-4)^2 = (-4)(-4)$ There are two factors of -4.

   $ = 16$ The product is positive.

5 Find $-3(-4)(-2)$.

   $-3(-4)(-2) = [-3(-4)](-2)$ Associative Property

   $ = 12(-2)$ $-3(-4) = 12$

   $ = -24$ $12(-2) = -24$

✓ CHECK Your Progress

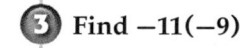

   c. $-12(-4)$ **48**   **d.** $(-5)^2$ **25**   **e.** $-7(-5)(-3)$ **−105**

Real-World EXAMPLE

6 **SUBMERSIBLES** A submersible is diving from the surface of the water at a rate of 90 feet per minute. What is the depth of the submersible after 7 minutes?

If the submersible descends 90 feet per minute, then after 7 minutes, the vessel will be at $7(-90)$ or -630 feet. Thus, the submersible will descend to 630 feet below the surface.

CHECK Your Progress

f. **MONEY** Mr. Simon's bank automatically deducts a $4 monthly maintenance fee from his savings account. What integer represents a change in his savings account from one year of fees? **−48**

Negative numbers are often used when evaluating algebraic expressions.

EXAMPLE Evaluate Expressions

7 **ALGEBRA** Evaluate pqr if $p = -3$, $q = 4$, and $r = -1$.

$$pqr = -3(4)(-1) \quad \text{Replace } p \text{ with } -3, q \text{ with } 4, \text{ and } r \text{ with } -1.$$
$$= (-12)(-1) \quad \text{Multiply } -3 \text{ and } 4.$$
$$= 12 \quad \text{Multiply } -12 \text{ and } -1.$$

CHECK Your Progress

g. Evaluate xyz if $x = -7$, $y = -4$, and $z = 2$. **56**

CHECK Your Understanding

Examples 1, 2 (p. 107)   Multiply.

1. $6(-10)$ **−60**   2. $11(-4)$ **−44**   3. $-2(14)$ **−28**   4. $-8(5)$ **−40**

Examples 3–5 (p. 108)   Multiply.

5. $-15(-3)$ **45**   6. $-7(-9)$ **63**   7. $(-8)^2$ **64**
8. $(-3)^3$ **−27**   9. $-1(-3)(-4)$ **−12**   10. $2(4)(5)$ **40**

Example 6 (p. 109)   11. **MONEY** Tamera owns 100 shares of a certain stock. Suppose the price of the stock drops by $3 per share. Write a multiplication expression to find the change in Tamera's investment. Explain the answer. **See margin.**

Example 7 (p. 109)   **ALGEBRA** Evaluate each expression if $f = -1$, $g = 7$, and $h = -10$.

12. $5f$ **−5**   13. fgh **70**

Lesson 2-6 Multiplying Integers   **109**

ADDITIONAL EXAMPLES

6 **MINES** A mine elevator descends at a rate of 300 feet per minute. How far below the earth's surface will the elevator be after 5 minutes? −1,500 ft

7 **ALGEBRA** Evaluate abc if $a = -3$, $b = 5$, and $c = -8$. 120

3 Practice

Formative Assessment

Use Exercises 1–13 to check for understanding.

Then use the chart at the bottom of the next page to customize your assignments for students.

Intervention You may wish to use the Study Guide and Intervention Master on page 43 of the *Chapter 2 Resource Masters* for additional reinforcement.

Additional Answer

11. $100(-3) = -300$; Tamera's investment is now worth $300 less than it was before the price of the stock dropped.

Differentiated Instruction

Visual/Spatial Learners If students are having difficulty completing the Exercises, have them use counters, drawings, or number lines to represent the multiplication of integers. For example, in Exercise 1, students could display 6 sets of 10 negative counters and count the total number of negative counters, or −60. Remind students to connect this representation with the rule that the product of two integers with different signs is negative.

Odd/Even Assignments

Exercises 14–39 are structured so that students practice the same concepts whether they are assigned odd or even problems.

Multiplication

When multiplying more than two integers, some students may find it easier to multiply first, ignoring the signs. Then they can apply the rules to find the product's sign. You may wish to point out that if the number of negative integers being multiplied is odd (1, 3, 5, and so on), the product will be negative.

Differentiated Instruction

Kinesthetic Learners If students are having difficulty, have them use algebra tiles or a drawing to model and find the product of a negative and a positive integer and the product of two negative integers.

Additional Answer

47.

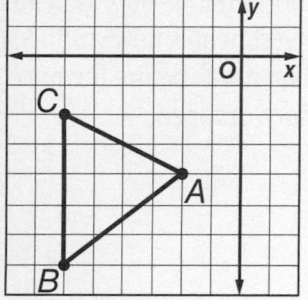

Sample answer: new triangle $A'B'C'$ is on the other side of the origin (in quadrant III) from original triangle ABC (which is in quadrant I).

EXTRA PRACTICE
See pages 673, 705.

38. $8(-3) = -24$;
The coastline's new position is 24 centimeters farther inland than it was 8 years ago.

44. $12(-150) + 2$ $(-300) = -2,400$;
A total of $2,400 is subtracted from her checking account each year for these expenses.

46. $A(2, 4)$ is now $(-2, -4)$; $B(6, 7)$ is now $(-6, -7)$; $C(6, 2)$ is now $(-6, -2)$.

Practice and Problem Solving

HOMEWORK HELP

For Exercises	See Examples
14–19, 28	1, 2
20–27, 29	3–5
30–37	7
38–39	6

Exercise Levels
A: 14–39
B: 40–48
C: 49–53

Multiply.

14. $8(-12)$ **−96**   **15.** $11(-20)$ **−220**   **16.** $-15(4)$ **−60**   **17.** $-7(10)$ **−70**

18. $-7(11)$ **−77**   **19.** $25(-2)$ **−50**   **20.** $-20(-8)$ **160**   **21.** $-16(-5)$ **80**

22. $(-6)^2$ **36**   **23.** $(-5)^3$ **−125**   **24.** $(-4)^3$ **−64**   **25.** $(-9)^2$ **81**

26. $-4(-2)(-8)$ **−64**   **27.** $-9(-1)(-5)$ **−45**

28. Find the product of 10 and −10. **−100**   **29.** Find −7 squared. **49**

ALGEBRA Evaluate each expression if $w = 4$, $x = -8$, $y = 5$, and $z = -3$.

30. $-4w$ **−16**   **31.** $3x$ **−24**   **32.** xy **−40**   **33.** xz **24**

34. $7wz$ **−84**   **35.** $-2wx$ **64**   **36.** xyz **120**   **37.** wyx **−160**

Write a multiplication expression to represent each situation. Then find each product and explain its meaning.

38. ECOLOGY Wave erosion causes a certain coastline to recede at a rate of 3 centimeters each year. This occurs uninterrupted for a period of 8 years.

39. EXERCISE Ethan burns 650 Calories when he runs for 1 hour. Suppose he runs 5 hours in one week.
$5(-650) = -3,250$; Ethan burns 3,250 Calories each week.

ALGEBRA Evaluate each expression if $a = -6$, $b = -4$, $c = 3$, and $d = 9$.

40. $-3a^2$ **−108**   **41.** $-cd^2$ **−243**   **42.** $-2a + b$ **8**   **43.** $b^2 - 4ac$ **88**

44. BANKING Tamika's aunt writes a check for $150 each month for her car loan. She writes another check for $300 twice a year to pay for car insurance. Write an expression involving multiplication and addition to describe how these expenses affect her checking account balance on a yearly basis. Then evaluate the expression and explain its meaning.

45. FIND THE DATA Refer to the Data File on pages 16–19 of your book. Choose some data and write a real-world problem in which you would multiply integers. **See students' work.**

GEOMETRY For Exercises 46–48, use the graph at the right.

46. Name the ordered pairs for A, B, and C. Multiply each x- and y-coordinate by −1 to get three new ordered pairs.

47. Graph the ordered pairs and connect them to form a new triangle. Describe its position with respect to the original triangle. **See margin.**

48. In which quadrant would a new triangle lie if only the y-coordinates of the original triangle are multiplied by −1? **quadrant IV**

DIFFERENTIATED HOMEWORK OPTIONS

Level	Assignment	Two-Day Assignment	
BL Basic	14–39, 49, 50, 52–66	15–39 odd, 54, 55	14–38 even, 49, 50, 52, 53, 56–66
OL Core	13–43 odd, 44–50, 52–66	14–39, 54, 55	40–50, 52, 53, 56–66
AL Advanced/Pre-AP	40–65 (optional: 66)		

49. **OPEN ENDED** Write a multiplication sentence with a product of −18.
   Sample answer: $-6 \times 3 = -18$

50. **NUMBER SENSE** Explain how to evaluate each expression as simply as possible. **See margin.**
   a. $(-9)(-6)(15)(-7 + 7)$ b. $(-15)(-26) + (-15)(25)$

51. **CHALLENGE** Evaluate $(-1)^{50}$. Explain your reasoning. **See margin.**

52. **SELECT A TECHNIQUE** Luis is trying to determine whether the product of three negative integers is negative or positive. Which of the following techniques might he use to determine the answer? Justify your selections. Then provide an example that illustrates the answer. **See margin.**

   | mental math | number sense | estimation |

53. **WRITING IN MATH** Explain when the product of three integers is positive. **See margin.**

TEST PRACTICE

54. The temperature drops 2 degrees per hour for 3 hours. Which expression does *not* describe the change in temperature? **D**

   A $-2(3)$ C $-2 - 2 - 2$
   B $-2 + (-2) + (-2)$ D $2(3)$

55. Which of the following numbers is the 7th number in the sequence shown?
   $$1, -2, 4, -8, 16, \ldots \text{ J}$$
   F −64   H 32
   G −32   J 64

Spiral Review

56. **TEMPERATURE** The highest and lowest recorded temperatures in Europe are 122°F and −57°F. Find the difference in these temperatures. (Lesson 2-5) **189°F**

Subtract. (Lesson 2-5)

57. $-25 - (-33)$ **8**   58. $-6 - 14$ **−20**   59. $9 - 30$ **−21**   60. $13 - (-12)$ **25**

ALGEBRA Evaluate each expression if $x = -4$, $y = 6$, and $z = 1$. (Lesson 2-4)

61. $x + (-2)$ **−6**   62. $-1 + z$ **0**   63. $-15 + y$ **−9**   64. $x + y$ **2**

65. **PENGUINS** The Emperor penguin's average height is 51 inches, and the Adelie's average height is 18 inches. Write and solve an addition equation to find how much taller Emperor penguins are than Adelie penguins. (Lesson 1-7) **$18 + x = 51; x = 33$**

▷ **GET READY for the Next Lesson**

66. **NUMBERS** A number is multiplied by −4. Then 15 is added to the product, and the result is 3. What is the number? Use the *guess and check* strategy. (Lesson 1-5) **3**

Lesson 2-6 Multiplying Integers   **111**

 Assess

Crystal Ball Tell students that tomorrow's lesson is about dividing integers. Ask them to write how they think what they learned today will connect with tomorrow's material.

✓ **Formative Assessment**

Check for student understanding of concepts in Lessons 2-5 and 2-6.

[CRM] Quiz 3, p. 62

FOLDABLES Foldables™
Study Organizer Follow-Up

Remind students to write what they learn about multiplying integers in their Foldables. Make sure they include examples of each case (negative × positive, positive × negative, negative × negative, and positive × positive).

Additional Answers

50a. Sample answer: Evaluate $-7 + 7$ first. Since $-7 + 7 = 0$, and any number times 0 is 0, the value of the expression is 0;

50b. Sample answer: First use the Distributive Property to rewrite the expression as $-15(-26 + 25)$. Then evaluate $-26 + 25$. Since $-26 + 25 = -1$ and $-15 \times -1 = 15$, the value of the expression is 15.

51. Sample answer: 1; $(-1)(-1) = 1$. Since there are $50 \div 2 = 25$ pairs of (-1) factors, $(-1)^{50} = 1^{25}$. One raised to any power is still 1.

52. Sample answer: number sense; A negative integer times a negative integer is positive. The resulting positive integer times the third negative number is negative. So, the product of three negative numbers is negative. For example, $-2 \times -5 \times -3 = 10 \times -3$ or -30.

53. Sample answer: The product of three integers is positive when exactly two of the integers are negative or all three integers are positive.

2-7

Problem-Solving Investigation
LOOK FOR A PATTERN

PACING: **Regular:** 1 period, **Block:** 0.5 period

Options for Differentiated Instruction

 = English Language Learner   = Above or Beyond Grade Level   **SS** = Struggling Students   **SN** = Special Needs

Using Pairs

Use before assigning Exercises 4–6.

Use the think-pair-share technique of cooperative learning. Assign Exercise 4, 5, or 6. Let students read over it individually. Then pair them up and have them look for the pattern to solve the problem. Repeat with pairs rearranged.

Breaking Down the Problem

Use with Exercise 6.

Some students may be intimidated by seeing two columns of numbers. Encourage them to find the pattern in each column and then extend the pattern to find how many times per minute a cricket will chirp when the outside temperature is 60°F.

Outside Temperature (°F)	Chirps per Minute
85°F	180
80°F	160
75°F	140
70°F	120
65°F	100
60°F	80

Choosing the Best Strategy

Use before assigning Exercises 7–14.

Prior to assigning Exercises 7–14, read each exercise aloud and discuss with the class which strategy might be best to solve each problem. Possible discussion questions are listed below.

- What question do you need to answer?
- What information is given?
- Is this like any exercises you have done before?
- What strategy would be most effective to solve the problem?
- How could you check your answer to make sure it is reasonable?

Make sure that all students have chosen a strategy for each problem so that they can complete the assignment independently.

Leveled Lesson Resources

Chapter 2 Resource Masters

Study Guide and Intervention*
p. 48 **BL** **OL** **ELL**

NAME _____ DATE _____ PERIOD _____

2-7 Study Guide and Intervention

Problem-Solving Investigation: Look for a Pattern

Looking for a pattern is one strategy that can help you when solving problems. You can use the four-step problem-solving plan along with looking for a pattern to solve problems.

Understand	• Determine what information is given in the problem and what you need to find.
Plan	• Select a strategy including a possible estimate.
Solve	• Solve the problem by carrying out your plan.
Check	• Examine your answer to see if it seems reasonable.

Example MEMBERSHIP The local tennis club started the year with 675 members. In one month they had 690 members. After two months they had 705 members. After three months they had 720 members. When the tennis club reaches 750 members they will close their enrollment. How many months will it take the club to reach their maximum enrollment if they continue adding new members at the same rate?

Understand The club began with 590 members and is adding new members every month. It needs to find out when it reaches its maximum enrollment of 750 members.

Plan Look for a pattern or rule that increases the membership each month. Then use the rule to extend the pattern to find the solution.

Solve After the initial 575 members, 15 new members joined each month. Extend the pattern to find the solution.
675, 690, 705, 720, 735, 750
+15 +15 +15 +15 +15

They will have reached their maximum enrollment in 5 months.

Check They increased by 5 · 15 or 75 members in 5 months which when added to the original 675 members is 675 + 75 = 750. So, 5 months is a reasonable answer.

Exercises

1. PRODUCE A farmer has 42 apples sitting on his front porch. The next day there are only 36 apples left on the porch. After 2 days there are only 30 apples left on the porch and in 3 days 24 apples remain on the porch. After how many days will there be no more apples on the porch if the same amount continue to disappear each day?
7 days

2. TELEPHONE A local phone company charges a standard rate of $3 per call. After one minute the charge is $4.50. In two minutes the charge is $6.00. If Susan only has $10.00, how long can her phone conversation be if the charges per minute stay constant?
4 minutes

Chapter 2   48   Course 2

Skills Practice*
p. 49 **BL** **OL**

NAME _____ DATE _____ PERIOD _____

2-7 Skills Practice

Problem-Solving Investigation: Look for a Pattern

Look for a pattern to solve the problem.

1. NUMBERS What are the next two numbers in the pattern listed below?
7, 21, 63, 189, ..
567, 1701

2. POPULATION The Springfield Zoo is breeding gorillas. They have 3 gorillas, which can mate and give birth. After the first year there are 7 gorillas. After the second year there are 11 gorillas. If the gorillas continue to increase at the same rate, how long will it take for the Springfield Zoo to have 35 gorillas?
8 years

3. ALGEBRA Read the table below to find a pattern relating x and y. Then write an equation to describe the pattern in general.

x	y
1	5
2	8
3	11
4	14
5	17

y is two more than three times x. So, $y = 3x + 2$

4. SAVINGS Maria receives $50 for her birthday. She decides to put the money into a bank account and start saving her money from babysitting in order to buy a television that costs $200. After the first week she has $74. After the second week, she has $98. After the third week she has $122. How many weeks will she have to save at the same rate in order to buy the television?
7 weeks

Chapter 2   49   Course 2

Practice*
p. 50 **OL** **AL**

NAME _____ DATE _____ PERIOD _____

2-7 Practice

Problem-Solving Investigation: Look for a Pattern

Mixed Problem Solving

Use the look for a pattern strategy to solve Exercises 1 and 2.

1. NUMBERS What are the next two numbers in the pattern below?
3, 15, 75, 375, . . .
1,875 and 9,375

2. QUILTING Mrs. Perez is a talented quilter. In the center of the design of her quilt are four identical red squares in the shape of a square. Surrounding these red squares is a border of 12 identical white squares. Surrounding these white squares is a border of 20 identical blue squares. How many squares are in the next border surrounding the 20 blue squares?
28 squares

B	B	B	B	B	B
B	W	W	W	W	B
B	W	R	R	W	B
B	W	R	R	W	B
B	W	W	W	W	B
B	B	B	B	B	B

Use any strategy to solve Exercises 3–6. Some strategies are shown below.

PROBLEM-SOLVING STRATEGIES
• Guess and Check.
• Look for a pattern.

3. TRANSPORTATION A college needs to transport the swim team to a state meet. The large van carries 15 people and each smaller van carries 9 people. How many smaller vans are needed to provide rides for 54 people if the large van is used?
5 smaller vans

4. ALPHABET What are the next three letters in each pattern shown?
D, H, L, P, ... **T and X**
C, F, I, L, ... **O and R**

5. POPULATION The land area of Ebeye, an island in the Pacific, is 90 acres. About 155 persons per acre live on this island. What is the population of Ebeye?
13,950 people

6. ASTRONOMY Earth is 93 million miles from the sun, while Mars is 142 million miles from the sun. Theoretically, what is the closest distance Mars could be to Earth?
49 million miles

Chapter 2   50   Course 2

Word Problem Practice*
p. 51 **OL** **AL**

NAME _____ DATE _____ PERIOD _____

2-7 Word Problem Practice

Problem-Solving Investigation: Look for a Pattern

Solve each problem using any strategy you have learned.

1. COLLECTIONS Brittany received 8 silver dollars on her eighth birthday. After her next birthday she had 15 and after the next she had 22. After her eleventh birthday she had 29 silver dollars. How many silver dollars will she have when her 16th birthday if her collection increases at the same rate every year?
64 silver dollars

2. PATTERNS List the next three terms in the following sequence.
27, 39, 51, 63, ...
75, 87, 99

3. GEOMETRY There are 6 rows of squares stacked upon each other. The first three are shown. How many total squares are needed for the entire pattern?
42 Squares

4. TICKET SALES Madison High School is putting on a school play. They decide to charge $11 for main floor seats and $7 for balcony seats. If the school sold twice as many main floor seats as balcony seats and made $870, how many of each type of seat did they sell?
60 main floor seats,
30 balcony seats

5. EXERCISE The table below shows the distance Katie ran each day this week. If Katie wants to run 3½ a week. How many miles must she run on Sunday?
Katie must run 4 miles on Sunday.

Monday	4 miles
Tuesday	7 miles
Wednesday	5 miles
Thursday	5 miles
Friday	2 miles
Saturday	3 miles

6. AGE Brad is three years more than half of Brandon's age. If their combined age is 93 years, how old is each man?
Brad, 33
Brandon, 60

Chapter 2   51   Course 2

*** Also available in Spanish ELL**

Additional Lesson Resources

Transparencies
• *5-Minute Check Transparency, Lesson 2-7*

Other Print Products
• *Noteables™ Interactive Study Notebook with Foldables™*

Teacher Tech Tools
• *Interactive Classroom CD-ROM, Lesson 2-7*
• *AssignmentWorks, Lesson 2-7*

Student Tech Tools
glencoe.com
• Extra Examples, Chapter 2, Lesson 7
• Self-Check Quiz, Chapter 2, Lesson 7

2-7 Lesson Notes

1 Focus

Look for a Pattern The *look for a pattern* strategy is useful for solving many kinds of problems. Students will work with patterns involving numbers, letters, and geometric figures. It is usually easier to find a pattern if information is organized in a list or a table.

2 Teach

Scaffolding Questions

Tell students that you saw a digital camera on sale for $900.

Ask:
- If I save $100 each month, how many months will it take me to save enough money to buy the camera? 9
- If I save $150 each month, how many months will it take me to save enough money to buy the camera? 6
- If I save $300 each month, how many months will it take me to save enough money to buy the camera? 3

ADDITIONAL EXAMPLE

Solve. Use the *look for a pattern* strategy.

1 **HAIR** Lelani wants to grow an 11-inch ponytail. She has a 3-inch ponytail now, and her hair grows about one inch every two months. How long will it take for her ponytail to reach 11 inches? 16 months

Additional Examples are also in:
- Noteables™ Interactive Study Notebook with Foldables™
- Interactive Classroom PowerPoint® Presentations

2-7 Problem-Solving Investigation

MAIN IDEA: Solve problems by looking for a pattern.

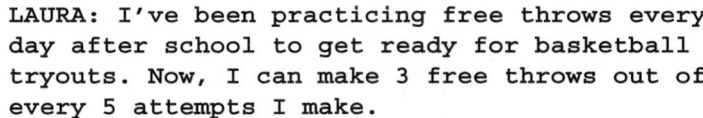

e-Mail: LOOK FOR A PATTERN

LAURA: I've been practicing free throws every day after school to get ready for basketball tryouts. Now, I can make 3 free throws out of every 5 attempts I make.

YOUR MISSION: Look for a pattern to find the number of free throws Laura can make after 30 attempts.

Understand	Laura can make an average of 3 free throws out of every 5 attempts. You need to find the number of free throws she can make after 30 attempts.
Plan	Look for a pattern. Then extend the pattern to find the solution.
Solve	Laura can make 3 free throws out of every 5 she attempts. Extend the pattern.

$$+3 \quad +3 \quad +3 \quad +3 \quad +3$$

Free throws	3	6	9	12	15	18
Attempts	5	10	15	20	25	30

$$+5 \quad +5 \quad +5 \quad +5 \quad +5$$

She can make 18 free throws out of 30 attempts.

Check	She makes free throws a little more than half the time. Since 18 is a little more than 15, the answer is reasonable. ✓

Analyze The Strategy 1–3. See margin.

1. Explain when you would use the *look for a pattern* strategy to solve a problem.

2. Describe how to solve a problem using the *look for a pattern* strategy.

3. **WRITING IN MATH** Write a problem that could be solved by looking for a pattern.

Additional Answers

1. Sample answer: Use the *look for a pattern* strategy when there is a data table, a series of numbers, or a geometric pattern as part of the problem.

2. Sample answer: Look for a rule or pattern in the data or number facts. Then use the rule to extend the pattern, and then find the solution to the problem.

3. Sample answer: Amanda has $2 in change in her bank. If she adds $0.50 each week for 7 weeks, how much money will be in her bank? $5.50

Mixed Problem Solving

EXTRA PRACTICE
See pages 673, 705.

Use the *look for a pattern* strategy to solve Exercises 4–6.

4. **DISPLAYS** A display of cereal boxes is stacked as shown below.

If the display contains 7 rows of boxes and the top three rows are shown, how many boxes are in the display? **70**

5. **MONEY** Peter is saving money to buy an MP3 player. After one month, he has $50. After 2 months, he has $85. After 3 months, he has $120. After 4 months, he has $155. He plans to keep saving at the same rate. How long will it take Peter to save enough money to buy an MP3 player that costs $295? **8 months**

6. **INSECTS** The table shows how many times a cricket chirps at different temperatures. About how many times will a cricket chirp when the temperature is 60°F? **80 times**

Outside Temperature (°F)	Chirps per Minute
85°F	180
80°F	160
75°F	140
70°F	120

Use any strategy to solve Exercises 7–14. Some strategies are shown below.

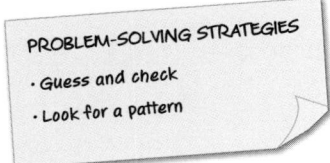

PROBLEM-SOLVING STRATEGIES
· Guess and check
· Look for a pattern

7. **COINS** Adelina has six coins that total $0.86. What are the coins? **See margin.**

8. **ELEVATION** The lowest point in Mexico is Laguna Salada with an elevation of −10 meters. The highest point in Mexico is Volcan Pico de Orizaba with an elevation of 5,700 meters. What is the difference in these elevations? **5,710 m**

9. **MONEY** While on vacation, Edmundo sent postcards and letters to his friends. He spent $3.42 on postage. A stamp for a letter costs 41¢, and a stamp for a postcard costs 26¢. How many postcards and letters did he send? **2 letters and 10 postcards**

10. **GEOMETRY** What is the next figure in the pattern shown? **See margin.**

11. **POPULATION** The total land area of North Carolina is about 48,711 square miles. If an average of 183 persons were living in each square mile of North Carolina in 2007, what was the population of North Carolina in 2007? **8,914,113**

12. **GOLF** Allie's golf scores for the first five holes are given in the table. What is her total score after the first five holes? **+1 over par**

Hole	Score
1	0
2	1
3	−1
4	−2
5	3

13. **FLOWERS** A sunflower grows to be about 252 centimeters tall in 3 months. What is the average rate of growth per month? **84 cm**

14. **NUMBERS** Determine the next three numbers in the pattern below.
48, 42, 36, 30, 24, … **18, 12, 6**

3 Practice

Using the Exercises

Exercises 1–3 can be used to check for understanding.

Exercises 4–6 utilize the look for a pattern strategy.

Exercises 7–14 are structured so that students have the opportunity to practice many different problem solving strategies. You may wish to review some of the strategies they have studied.

- Use the four-step plan (p. 25)
- Guess and check (p. 42)
- Look for a pattern (p. 112)

Choosing Strategies
Tips for New Teachers

You may wish to separate students into pairs. Have the members of each pair work together to find the patterns, choose strategies, and solve the problems.

4 Assess

Name the Math Have students write or tell what mathematical procedure they used to solve one of the exercises.

Additional Answers

7. Sample answer: 3 quarters, 2 nickels, and 1 penny

10.

Dividing Integers

PACING: **Regular:** 1 period, **Block:** 0.5 period

Options for Differentiated Instruction

ELL = English Language Learner   **AL** = Above or Beyond Grade Level   **SS** = Struggling Students   **SN** = Special Needs

Scaffolding the Lesson   **ELL**   **SS**   **SN**

Use before presenting Examples 1–5.

To scaffold this lesson, remind students the relationship between multiplication and division. Display the following example on the board.

Example: Write two multiplication problems related to the division problem $12 \div 6 = 2$.

Solution: $2 \times 6 = 12$ and $6 \times 2 = 12$

To help students see this relationship involving negative integers, have them solve several problems like the ones shown below.

Write two multiplication problems related to each division problem.

1. $8 \div 2 = 4$ $4 \times 2 = 8; 2 \times 4 = 8$
2. $15 \div 3 = 5$ $5 \times 3 = 15; 3 \times 5 = 15$
3. $8 \div (-2) = -4$ $-4 \times (-2) = 8; -2 \times (-4) = 8$
4. $-15 \div 3 = -5$ $-5 \times 3 = -15; 3 \times (-5) = -15$

Write two division problems related to each multiplication problem.

5. $5 \times 2 = 10$ $10 \div 2 = 5; 10 \div 5 = 2$
6. $3 \times 4 = 12$ $12 \div 4 = 3; 12 \div 3 = 4$
7. $5 \times (-2) = -10$ $-10 \div (-2) = 5; -10 \div 5 = -2$
8. $-3 \times (-4) = 12$ $12 \div (-4) = -3; 12 \div (-3) = -4$

Knowing how multiplication and division are related will also help students check their work.

Naturalistic Learning   **ELL**   **AL**   **SS**   **SN**

Use after presenting Example 5.

Have students work in pairs. Assign each pair an animal and have them find their estimated population for both today and 10 years ago. Have students use the expression in Example 5 to determine the average change in number for their animals. On poster board, make a table like the one shown below. Each pair of students should fill in the information on the animal they researched.

Animal	Population Today	Population 10 Years Ago	Average Change in Numbers

Leveled Lesson Resources

Also on
TeacherWorks™
Lesson 2-8

Chapter 2 Resource Masters

BL = Below or Approaching Grade Level **OL** = On Grade Level **AL** = Above or Beyond Grade Level **ELL** = English Language Learner

Lesson Reading Guide
p. 52 BL OL ELL

2-8 Lesson Reading Guide
Dividing Integers

Get Ready for the Lesson
Complete the Mini Lab at the top of page 114 in your textbook.
Write your answers below.
Find each quotient using counters or a drawing.
1. $-6 \div 2$ **−3**
2. $-12 \div 3$ **−4**

Read the Lesson
Write two division sentences related to each of the following multiplication sentences.
3. $-6(-3) = 18$
   $18 \div (-3) = -6;$
   $18 \div (-6) = 3$
4. $-21(-2) = 42$
   $42 \div (-21) = -2;$
   $42 \div (-2) = -21$
5. $-6(3) = -18$
   $-18 \div 3 = -6;$
   $-18 \div (-6) = 3$
6. $2(-21) = -42$
   $-42 \div (-21) = 2;$
   $-42 \div 2 = -21$

7. Complete each of the following sentences with the word *positive* or *negative*.
   a. The quotient of two integers with different signs is _____. **negative**
   b. The quotient of two integers with the same sign is _____. **positive**

8. In the division sentence $-72 \div 8 = -9$, identify the dividend, the divisor, and the quotient. **dividend: −72; divisor: 8; quotient: −9**

Remember What You Learned
9. Describe how the operations of multiplication and division are opposite of each other. Are these operations opposite in all cases? What is the one integer that cannot be a divisor? **Multiplication is the opposite of division in that the product of a quotient and divisor gives the dividend. Even though you can take the product of zero and a number, zero cannot be a divisor.**

Chapter 2   52   Course 2

Study Guide and Intervention*
p. 53 BL OL ELL

2-8 Study Guide and Intervention
Dividing Integers

The quotient of two integers with different signs is negative.
The quotient of two integers with the same sign is positive.

Example 1 Divide $30 \div (-5)$.
$30 \div (-5)$ The integers have different signs.
$30 \div (-5) = -6$ The quotient is negative.

Example 2 Divide $-100 \div (-5)$.
$-100 \div (-5)$ The integers have the same sign.
$-100 \div (-5) = 20$ The quotient is positive.

Exercises
Divide.
1. $-12 \div 4$ **−3**
2. $-14 \div (-7)$ **2**
3. $\frac{18}{-2}$ **−9**
4. $-6 \div (-3)$ **2**
5. $-10 \div 10$ **−1**
6. $\frac{-80}{20}$ **4**
7. $350 \div (-25)$ **−14**
8. $-420 \div (-3)$ **140**
9. $\frac{540}{45}$ **12**
10. $\frac{-256}{16}$ **−16**

ALGEBRA Evaluate each expression if $d = -24$, $e = -4$, and $f = 8$.
11. $12 \div e$ **−3**
12. $40 \div f$ **5**
13. $d \div 6$ **−4**
14. $d \div e$ **6**
15. $f \div e$ **−2**
16. $e^2 \div f$ **2**
17. $\frac{-d}{e}$ **−6**
18. $ef \div 2$ **−16**
19. $\frac{f^2}{e^2}$ **4**
20. $\frac{de}{f}$ **12**

Chapter 2   53   Course 2

Skills Practice*
p. 54 BL OL

2-8 Skills Practice
Dividing Integers

Divide.
1. $-15 \div 3$ **−5**
2. $-24 \div (-8)$ **3**
3. $22 \div (-2)$ **−11**
4. $-49 \div (-7)$ **7**
5. $-8 \div (-8)$ **1**
6. $\frac{36}{-4}$ **−9**
7. $225 \div (-15)$ **−15**
8. $\frac{0}{-9}$ **0**
9. $-38 \div 2$ **−19**
10. $\frac{64}{4}$ **16**
11. $-500 \div (-50)$ **10**
12. $-189 \div (-21)$ **9**

ALGEBRA Evaluate each expression if $m = -32$, $n = 2$, and $p = -8$.
13. $m \div n$ **−16**
14. $p \div 4$ **−2**
15. $p^2 \div m$ **2**
16. $m \div p$ **4**
17. $\frac{-p}{n}$ **4**
18. $p \div n^2$ **−2**
19. $\frac{p^2}{n^2}$ **16**
20. $\frac{18-n}{p}$ **−2**
21. $m \div (np)$ **2**
22. $\frac{m}{p} \div n$ **6**

Chapter 2   54   Course 2

Practice*
p. 55 OL AL

2-8 Practice
Dividing Integers

Divide.
1. $42 \div (-7)$ **−6**
2. $45 \div (-5)$ **−9**
3. $-9 \div 3$ **−3**
4. $-64 \div (-8)$ **8**
5. $-39 \div (-13)$ **3**
6. $-121 \div 11$ **−11**
7. $\frac{-48}{12}$ **−4**
8. $\frac{-35}{7}$ **−5**
9. $\frac{-38}{-2}$ **19**
10. $\frac{32}{-16}$ **−2**
11. $\frac{55}{-5}$ **−11**
12. $(-8)^2$ **64**
13. Divide 75 by -25. **−3**
14. Find the quotient of -30 and -15. **2**

ALGEBRA Evaluate each expression if $f = -15$, $g = 5$, and $h = -45$.
15. $-20 \div g$ **−4**
16. $90 \div h$ **−2**
17. $h \div f$ **3**
18. $fg \div 25$ **−3**
19. $\frac{f-h}{10}$ **3**
20. $\frac{g-5}{-1}$ **0**
21. $-f^2 \div g$ **−45**
22. $\frac{h-3g}{f}$ **4**
23. $\frac{f+h}{-g}$ **12**

ZOOLOGY The table below shows the weight in pounds of large adult males in the cat family.

Cat	Cheetah	Cougar	Leopard	Lion	Tiger
Weight	143	227	200	550	400

Source: www.sandiegozoo.org

For Exercises 24 and 25 use the information in the table.
24. What is the mean weight of these cats? **304 pounds**
25. What is the mean weight of the two largest cats? **475 pounds**

Chapter 2   55   Course 2

Word Problem Practice*
p. 56 OL AL

2-8 Word Problem Practice
Dividing Integers

Divide.
1. **STOCK MARKET** During a 5-day workweek, the stock market decreased by 65 points. Find the average daily change in the market for the week. **−13 points**

2. **MOTION** Mr. Diaz decreased the speed of his car by 30 miles per hour over a period of 13 seconds. Find the average change in speed each second. **−3 mph per second**

3. **WEATHER** Over the past seven days, Mrs. Cho found that the temperature outside had dropped a total of 35 degrees. Find the average change in temperature each day. **−5 degrees per day**

4. **BASKETBALL** The basketball team lost their last 6 games. They lost by a total of 48 points. Find their average number of points relative to their opponents. **−8 points per game**

5. **POPULATION** The enrollment at Davis Middle School dropped by 60 students over a 5-year period. What is the average yearly drop in enrollment? **−12 students annually**

6. **SUBMARINE** A submarine descends at a rate of 60 feet each minute. How long will it take to descend to a depth of 660 feet below the surface? **11 min**

Chapter 2   56   Course 2

Enrichment
p. 57 OL AL

2-8 Enrichment

Division by Zero?
Some interesting things happen when you try to divide by zero. For example, look at these two equations.
$$\frac{5}{0} = x \qquad \frac{0}{0} = x$$
If you can write the equations above, you can also write the two equations below.
$$0 \cdot x = 5 \qquad 0 \cdot y = 0$$
However, there is no number that will make the left equation true. This equation has no solution. For the right equation, every number will make it true. The solutions for this equation are "all numbers."

Because division by zero leads to impossible situations, it is not a "legal" step in solving a problem. People say that division by zero is undefined, or not possible, or simply not allowed.

Describe the solution set for each equation.
1. $4x = 0$ **0**
2. $x \cdot 0 = 0$ **all numbers**
3. $x \cdot 0 = x$ **0**
4. $\frac{0}{0} = 0$ **all numbers but 0**
5. $\frac{0}{x} = x$ **no solution**
6. $\frac{0}{0} = 5$ **no solution**

What values for x must be excluded to prevent division by 0?
7. $\frac{1}{x^2}$ **0**
8. $\frac{1}{x-1}$ **1**
9. $\frac{1}{x+1}$ **−1**
10. $\frac{0}{2x}$ **0**
11. $\frac{1}{2x-2}$ **1**
12. $\frac{1}{3x+6}$ **−2**

Explain what is wrong with this "proof."
13. Step 1 $0 \cdot 1 = 0$ and $0 \cdot (-1) = 0$
    Step 2 Therefore, $\frac{0}{0} = 1$ and $\frac{0}{0} = -1$. **Step 2 involves division by zero.**
    Step 3 Therefore, $1 = -1$.

Chapter 2   57   Course 2

Additional Lesson Resources

*** Also available in Spanish** **ELL**

Transparencies
- *5-Minute Check Transparency,* Lesson 2-8

Other Print Products
- *Noteables™ Interactive Study Notebook with Foldables™*

Teacher Tech Tools
- *Interactive Classroom CD-ROM,* Lesson 2-8
- *AssignmentWorks,* Lesson 2-8

Student Tech Tools
glencoe.com
- Extra Examples, Chapter 2, Lesson 8
- Self-Check Quiz, Chapter 2, Lesson 8

1 Focus

Vertical Alignment

Before Lesson 2-8
Add with negative integers; subtract positive integers from negative integers

Lesson 2-8
Solve division problems, including those arising in concrete situations, that use positive and negative integers

After Lesson 2-8
Divide rational numbers and take positive rational numbers to whole-number powers

2 Teach

▶ **MINI Lab**

You may wish to have students practice evaluating more expressions, such as $-7 \div 1$ and $-15 \div 3$.

Scaffolding Questions

As students answer the following questions, write the expressions on the board.

Ask:

- How can I write a division problem to separate 15 apples into 3 equal groups? $15 \div 3$

- How can I write a division problem to separate 28 pennies into 7 equal groups? $28 \div 7$

- How can I write a division problem to separate 20 into 4 equal groups? $20 \div 4$

- How can I write a division problem to separate -18 into 6 equal groups? $-18 \div 6$

2-8 Dividing Integers

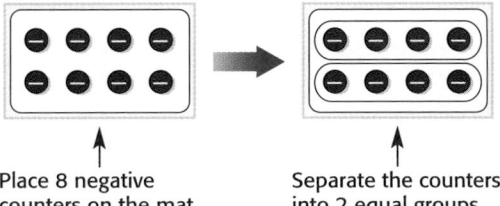

MAIN IDEA

Divide integers.

Math Online

glencoe.com

- Extra Examples
- Personal Tutor
- Self-Check Quiz

▶ **MINI Lab**

You can use counters to model division of integers. Follow these steps to find $-8 \div 2$.

Place 8 negative counters on the mat.

Separate the counters into 2 equal groups.

There are 4 negative counters in each group. So, $-8 \div 2 = -4$.

Find each quotient using counters or a drawing.

1. $-6 \div 2$ **−3** 2. $-12 \div 3$ **−4**

Division of numbers is related to multiplication. When finding the quotient of two integers, you can use a related multiplication sentence.

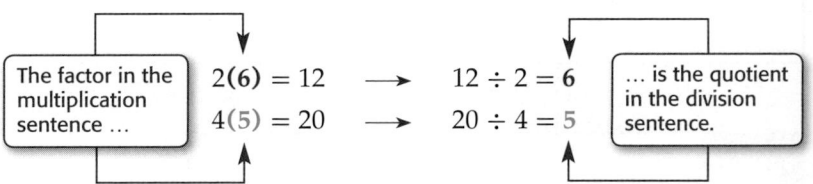

The factor in the multiplication sentence …
$2(6) = 12 \longrightarrow 12 \div 2 = 6$
$4(5) = 20 \longrightarrow 20 \div 4 = 5$
… is the quotient in the division sentence.

Since multiplication and division sentences are related, you can use them to find the quotient of integers with different signs.

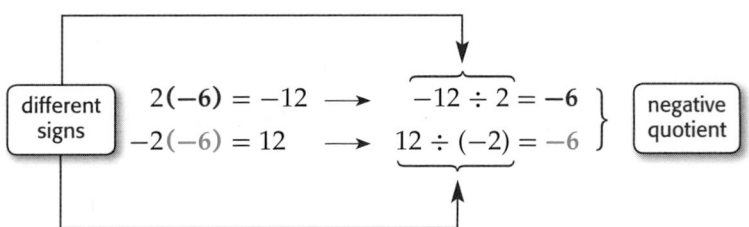

different signs
$2(-6) = -12 \longrightarrow -12 \div 2 = -6$
$-2(-6) = 12 \longrightarrow 12 \div (-2) = -6$
negative quotient

These related sentences lead to the following rule.

Dividing Integers with Different Signs	Key Concept
Words	The quotient of two integers with different signs is negative.
Examples	$33 \div (-11) = -3$ $-64 \div 8 = -8$

Dividing Integers with Different Signs

1 Find $80 \div (-10)$.   The integers have different signs.

$80 \div (-10) = -8$ The quotient is negative.

2 Find $\frac{-55}{11}$.   The integers have different signs.

$\frac{-55}{11} = -5$ The quotient is negative.

✓ **CHECK Your Progress**

a. $20 \div (-4)$ **−5**   b. $\frac{-81}{9}$ **−9**   c. $-45 \div 9$ **−5**

Focus on Mathematical Content

Division is the **inverse operation** of multiplication. You can rewrite a division equation as a multiplication equation. The rules for dividing integers are related to the rules for multiplying integers.

✓ **Formative Assessment**

Use the Check Your Progress exercises after the Examples to determine students' understanding of concepts.

ADDITIONAL EXAMPLES

1 Find $51 \div (-3)$. **−17**

2 Find $\frac{-121}{11}$. **−11**

3 Find $-12 \div (-2)$. **6**

4 **ALGEBRA** Evaluate $-18 \div x$ if $x = -2$. **9**

Additional Examples are also in:

• Noteables™ Interactive Study Notebook with Foldables™

• Interactive Classroom PowerPoint® Presentations

You can also use multiplication and division sentences to find the quotient of integers with the same sign.

Study Tip

Dividing Integers
Dividing integers with same or different signs follow the same rules as the ones for multiplication.

$$\text{same signs} \quad \begin{array}{l} 4(5) = 20 \\ -4(5) = -20 \end{array} \longrightarrow \begin{array}{l} 20 \div 4 = 5 \\ -20 \div (-4) = 5 \end{array} \left. \right\} \text{positive quotient}$$

These related sentences lead to the following rule.

Divide Integers with the Same Sign	**Key Concept**
Words	The quotient of two integers with the same sign is positive.
Examples	$15 \div 5 = 3$ $-64 \div (-8) = 8$

EXAMPLES **Dividing Integers with the Same Sign**

3 Find $-14 \div (-7)$.   The integers have the same sign.

$-14 \div (-7) = 2$ The quotient is positive.

4 **ALGEBRA** Evaluate $-16 \div x$ if $x = -4$.

$-16 \div x = -16 \div (-4)$ Replace x with −4.

$\qquad\quad = 4$ Divide. The quotient is positive.

✓ **CHECK Your Progress**

d. $-24 \div (-4)$ **6**   e. $-9 \div (-3)$ **3**   f. $\frac{-28}{-7}$ **4**

g. **ALGEBRA** Evaluate $a \div b$ if $a = -9$ and $b = -3$. **3**

Real-World Link · · · · ·
An adult koala is 25–30 inches long and weighs 15–30 pounds.
Source: Koala Express

Real-World EXAMPLE

5 **ANIMALS** Ten years ago, the estimated Australian koala population was 1,000,000. Today there are about 100,000 koalas. Use the expression $\frac{N - P}{10}$, where N represents the new population and P the previous population to find the average change in the koala population per year for the 10-year period.

$$\frac{N - P}{10} = \frac{100,000 - 1,000,000}{10} \quad \text{Replace } N \text{ with 100,000 and } P \text{ with 1,000,000.}$$

$$= \frac{-900,000}{10} \text{ or } -90,000 \quad \text{Divide.}$$

The koala population has changed by −90,000 per year.

CHECK Your Progress

h. **WEATHER** The average temperature in January for North Pole, Alaska, is −24.4°C. Use the expression $\frac{9C + 160}{5}$, where C represents the number of degrees Celsius, to find this temperature in degrees Fahrenheit. **about —12°F**

Operations with Integers		Concept Summary
Operation	**Rule**	
Add	**Same Sign:** Add absolute values. The sum has the same sign as the integers.	
	Different Signs: Subtract absolute values. The sum has the sign of the integer with greater absolute value.	
Subtract	To subtract an integer, add its opposite.	
Multiply and Divide	**Same Signs:** The product or quotient is positive.	
	Different Signs: The product or quotient is negative.	

★ indicates multi-step problem

CHECK Your Understanding

Examples 1–3
(p. 115)

Divide.

1. $32 \div (-8)$ **—4**
2. $-16 \div 2$ **—8**
3. $\frac{42}{-7}$ **—6**
4. $-30 \div (-5)$ **6**
5. $55 \div 11$ **5**
6. $\frac{-16}{-4}$ **4**

Example 4
(p. 115)

ALGEBRA Evaluate each expression if $x = 8$ and $y = -5$.

7. $15 \div y$ **—3**
8. $xy \div (-10)$ **4**

Example 5
(p. 116)

9. **TEMPERATURE** The lowest recorded temperature in Wisconsin is −55°F on February 4, 1996. Use the expression $\frac{5(F - 32)}{9}$ to find this temperature in degrees Celsius. Round to the nearest tenth. **—48.3°C**

Practice and Problem Solving

HOMEWORK HELP

For Exercises	See Examples
10–13, 16–19	1, 2
14–15, 20–23	3
24–31	4
32–33	5

Exercise Levels
A: 10–33
B: 34–39
C: 40–44

Divide.

10. $50 \div (-5)$ **−10**
11. $56 \div (-8)$ **−7**
12. $-18 \div 9$ **−2**
13. $-36 \div 4$ **−9**

14. $-15 \div (-3)$ **5**
15. $-100 \div (-10)$ **10**
16. $\frac{22}{-2}$ **−11**
17. $\frac{84}{-12}$ **−7**

18. $\frac{-26}{13}$ **−2**
19. $\frac{-27}{3}$ **−9**
20. $\frac{-21}{-7}$ **3**
21. $\frac{-54}{-6}$ **9**

22. Divide -200 by -100. **2**

23. Find the quotient of -65 and -13. **5**

ALGEBRA Evaluate each expression if $r = 12$, $s = -4$, and $t = -6$.

24. $-12 \div r$ **−1**
25. $72 \div t$ **−12**
26. $r \div s$ **−3**
27. $rs \div 16$ **−3**

28. $\frac{t - r}{3}$ **−6**
29. $\frac{8 - r}{-2}$ **2**
30. $\frac{s + t}{5}$ **−2**
31. $\frac{t + 9}{-3}$ **−1**

32. **MONEY** Last year, Mr. Engle's total income was $52,000, while his total expenses were $53,800. Use the expression $\frac{I - E}{12}$, where I represents total income and E represents total expenses, to find the average difference between his income and expenses each month. **−$150 per month**

33. **SCIENCE** The boiling point of water is affected by changes in elevation. Use the expression $\frac{-2A}{1,000}$, where A represents the altitude in feet, to find the number of degrees Fahrenheit the boiling point of water changes at an altitude of 5,000 feet. **−10°F**

ALGEBRA Evaluate each expression if $d = -9$, $f = 36$, and $g = -6$.

34. $\frac{-f}{d}$ **4**
35. $\frac{12 - (-f)}{-g}$ **8**
36. $\frac{f^2}{d^2}$ **16**
37. $g^2 \div f$ **1**

★ 38. **PLANETS** The temperature on Mars ranges widely from $-207°$F at the winter pole to almost $80°$F on the dayside during the summer. Use the expression $\frac{-207 + 80}{2}$ to find the average of the temperature extremes on Mars. **−63.5°F**

★ 39. **ANALYZE GRAPHS** The *mean* of a set of data is the sum of the data divided by the number of items in the data set. The graph shows the approximate depths where certain fish are found in the Caribbean. What is the mean depth of the fish shown? **−53 ft**

EXTRA PRACTICE
See pages 673, 705.

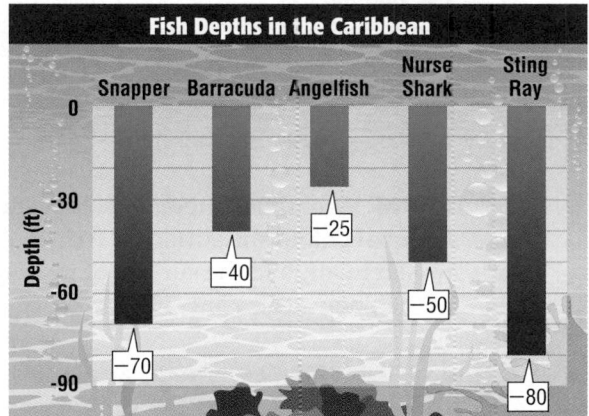

Fish Depths in the Caribbean

Lesson 2-8 Dividing Integers **117**

Odd/Even Assignments

Exercises 10–33 are structured so that students practice the same concepts whether they are assigned odd or even problems.

Differentiated Instruction

Visual/Spatial Learners If students are having difficulty completing the exercises, have them use counters, drawings, or number lines to represent the division of integers. For example, in Exercise 12, students could place 18 negative counters on the mat. Separate the counters into 9 equal groups and count the number of negative counters in each group, resulting in an answer of -2. Remind students to connect this representation with the rule that the quotient of two integers with different signs is negative.

	DIFFERENTIATED HOMEWORK OPTIONS		
Level	**Assignment**	**Two-Day Assignment**	
BL Basic	10–33, 40–42, 44–56	11–33 odd, 45, 46	10–32 even, 40–42, 44, 47–56
OL Core	11–37 odd, 38–42, 44–56	10–33, 45, 46	34–42, 44, 47–56
AL Advanced/Pre-AP	34–56		

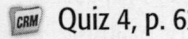 **Formative Assessment**

Check for student understanding of concepts in Lessons 2–7 and 2–8.

CRM Quiz 4, p. 62

 **Foldables™**
Study Organizer **Follow-Up**

Remind students to write what they learn about dividing integers in their Foldables. They may want to consult the Operations with Integers table on page 119 as they update their Foldables.

Additional Answers

44. First evaluate each 2^2 since they are powers. Rewrite the expression as $-2 \cdot (4 + 2) \div 4$. Then add since $4 + 2$ is in parentheses. Rewrite the expression as $-2 \cdot 6 \div 4$. Next, multiply and then divide since multiplication and division occur in order from left to right. Since $-2 \cdot 6 = -12$ and $-12 \div 4 = -3$, the value of the expression is -3.

47.

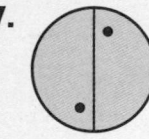

H.O.T. Problems

41. $-32 \div (-4)$ has a positive quotient; the others have negative quotients.

40. OPEN ENDED Write a division sentence with a quotient of -12.
Sample answer: $36 \div (-3) = -12$

41. Which One Doesn't Belong? Identify the expression that does not belong with the other three. Explain your reasoning.

| $-66 \div 11$ | $-32 \div (-4)$ | $16 \div (-4)$ | $-48 \div 4$ |

42. PATTERNS Find the next two numbers in the pattern $729, -243, 81, -27, 9, \ldots$. Explain your reasoning.
$-3, 1$; Divide the previous term by -3.

43. CHALLENGE Order from least to greatest all of the numbers by which -20 is divisible. **$-20, -10, -5, -4, -2, -1, 1, 2, 4, 5, 10, 20$**

44. ◖**WRITING IN** MATH▹ Evaluate $-2 \cdot (2^2 + 2) \div 2^2$. Justify each step in the process. **See margin.**

TEST PRACTICE

45. Find $18 \div (-3)$. **A**

A -6

B $\dfrac{-1}{6}$

C 6

D 15

46. On December 24, 1924, the temperature in Fairfield, Montana, fell from $63°F$ at noon to $-21°F$ at midnight. What was the average temperature change per hour? **G**

F $-3.5°F$

G $-7°F$

H $-42°F$

J $-84°F$

Spiral Review

47. GEOMETRY What is the next figure in the pattern shown at the right? (Lesson 2-7)
See margin.

Multiply. (Lesson 2-6)

48. $14(-2)$ **-28**   **49.** $-20(-3)$ **60**   **50.** $-5(7)$ **-35**   **51.** $(-9)^2$ **81**

52. Find $6 - (-12)$. (Lesson 2-5) **18**

53. DIVING Valentina jumped into 10 feet of water and touched the bottom of the pool before she surfaced. Write an integer to describe where Valentina was in relation to the surface of the water when she touched the bottom of the pool. (Lesson 2-1) **-10**

Find each square root. (Lesson 1-3)

54. $\sqrt{324}$ **18**   **55.** $\sqrt{900}$ **30**   **56.** $\sqrt{196}$ **14**

118 Chapter 2 Integers

Pre-AP Activity **Use after Exercise 44**

Write the following questions on the chalkboard: *Can a square number be negative? Can the square root of a number be negative?* Have students write their answers on a piece of paper. Encourage them to explain their reasoning and give examples.

Study Guide and Review

Math Online > glencoe.com
• STUDY TO GO
• Vocabulary Review

FOLDABLES Study Organizer — GET READY to Study

Be sure the following Big Ideas are noted in your Foldable.

2-1 Integers and Absolute Value

BIG Ideas

Absolute Value (Lesson 2-1)
• The absolute value of a number is the distance the number is from zero on a number line.

Comparing and Ordering Integers (Lesson 2-2)
• When two numbers are graphed on a number line, the number to the left is always less than the number to the right.

Graphing Points (Lesson 2-3)
• On a coordinate plane, the horizontal number line is the x-axis and the vertical number line is the y-axis. The origin is at (0, 0) and is the point where the number lines intersect. The x-axis and y-axis separate the plane into four quadrants.

Integer Operations (Lessons 2-4, 2-5, 2-6, 2-8)
• To add integers with the same sign, add their absolute value. The sum is positive if both integers are positive and negative if both integers are negative.

• The sum of any number and its additive inverse is 0.

• To add integers with different signs, subtract their absolute values. The sum is positive if the positive integer's absolute value is greater and negative if the negative integer's absolute value is greater.

• To subtract an integer, add its opposite.

• The product or quotient of two integers with different signs is negative.

• The product or quotient of two integers with the same sign is positive.

Key Vocabulary

absolute value (p. 81)	origin (p. 88)
additive inverse (p. 96)	positive integer (p. 80)
coordinate plane (p. 88)	quadrant (p. 88)
graph (p. 80)	x-axis (p. 88)
integer (p. 80)	x-coordinate (p. 88)
negative integer (p. 80)	y-axis (p. 88)
opposites (p. 96)	y-coordinate (p. 88)
ordered pair (p. 88)	

Vocabulary Check

State whether each sentence is *true* or *false*. If *false*, replace the underlined word or number to make a true sentence.

1. Integers less than zero are <u>positive</u> integers. **false; negative**

2. The <u>origin</u> is the point where the x-axis and y-axis intersect. **true**

3. The <u>absolute value</u> of 7 is −7. **false; opposite**

4. The sum of two negative integers is <u>positive</u>. **false; negative**

5. The <u>x-coordinate</u> of the ordered pair (2, −3) is −3. **false; y-coordinate**

6. Two integers that are opposites are also called <u>additive inverses</u>. **true**

7. The product of a positive and a negative integer is <u>negative</u>. **true**

8. The x-axis and the y-axis separate the plane into four <u>coordinates</u>. **false; quadrants**

9. The quotient of two negative integers is <u>negative</u>. **false; positive**

Summative Assessment

 Vocabulary Test, p. 64

FOLDABLES Study Organizer — Dinah Zike's Foldables

Have students look through the chapter to make sure they have included notes, key concepts, and examples in their Foldables for each lesson.

Encourage students to refer to their Foldables while completing the Study Guide and Review and while preparing for the Chapter Test.

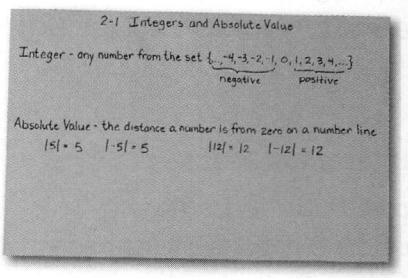

Formative Assessment

Key Vocabulary The page references after each word denote where that term was first introduced. If students have difficulty answering Exercises 1–9, remind them that they can use these page references to refresh their memories about the vocabulary terms.

Math Online > glencoe.com

 Vocabulary PuzzleMaker improves students' mathematics vocabulary using four puzzle formats—crossword, scramble, word search using a word list, and word search using clues. Students can work on a computer screen or from a printed handout.

Lesson-by-Lesson Review
Intervention If the given examples are not sufficient to review the topics covered by the questions, remind students that the page references tell them where to review that topic in their textbooks.

Two-Day Option Have students complete the Lesson-by-Lesson Review on pages 120–122. Then you can use ExamView® Assessment Suite to customize another review worksheet that practices all the objectives of this chapter or only the objectives on which your students need more help.

For more information on ExamView® Assessment Suite, see page 78C.

Differentiated Instruction

Super DVD: MindJogger Plus
Use this DVD as an alternative format of review for the test. For more information on this game show format, see page 78D.

Additional Answer

25. $\{-32, -23, -21, 14, 19, 25\}$

Lesson-by-Lesson Review

2-1 **Integers and Absolute Value** (pp. 80–83)

Write an integer for each situation.
10. a loss of $150 **−$150**
11. 350 feet above sea level **350 ft**
12. a gain of 8 yards **8 yd**
13. 12°F below 0 **−12°F**

Evaluate each expression.
14. $|100|$ **100**
15. $|-32|$ **32**
16. $|-16| + |9|$ **25**

17. **JUICE** Mavis drank 48 milliliters of apple juice before replacing the carton in the refrigerator. Write an integer that shows the change in the volume of juice in the carton. **−48 mL**

Example 1 Write an integer for 8 feet below sea level.

Since this situation represents an elevation *below* sea level, −8 represents the situation.

Example 2 Evaluate $|-10|$.

On the number line, the graph of −10 is 10 units from 0.

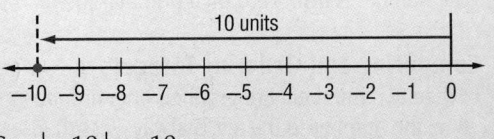

So, $|-10| = 10$.

2-2 **Comparing and Ordering Integers** (pp. 84–87)

Replace each ● with < or > to make a true sentence.

18. $-3 ● -9$ **>** 19. $8 ● -12$ **>**
20. $-3 ● 3$ **<** 21. $|-10| ● |-13|$ **<**
22. $25 ● |8|$ **>** 23. $0 ● |-4|$ **<**

Order each set of integers from least to greatest. **24.** $\{-12, -10, -3, 0, 5, 8, 9\}$
24. $\{-3, 8, -10, 0, 5, -12, 9\}$
25. $\{-21, 19, -23, 14, -32, 25\}$ **See margin.**
26. $\{-17, -18, 18, 15, -16, 16\}$
$\{-18, -17, -16, 15, 16, 18\}$
27. **WEATHER** The high temperatures in degrees Celsius for ten cities were 0, 10, −5, 12, 25, −6, 20, −10, 5 and 2. Order these temperatures from least to greatest. **−10, −6, −5, 0, 2, 5, 10, 12, 20, 25**

Example 3 Replace ● with < or > to make −4 ● −7 a true sentence.

Graph each integer on a number line.

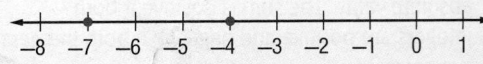

Since −4 is to the right of −7, −4 > −7.

Example 4 Order the integers −4, −3, 5, 3, 0, −2 from least to greatest.

Graph the integers on a number line.

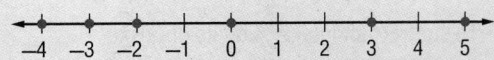

Order the integers by reading from left to right: −4, −3, −2, 0, 3, 5.

Mixed Problem Solving
For mixed problem-solving practice,
see page 705.

CHAPTER
2 **Study Guide and Review**

For mixed problem-solving practice,
see page 705.

2-3 **The Coordinate Plane** (pp. 88–92)

On graph paper, draw a coordinate plane. Then graph and label each point.

28. $E(1, -4)$ **28–31. See margin.**

29. $F(-4, 2)$

30. $G(-2, -3)$

31. $H(4, 0)$

32. **ROUTES** Starting at the school, Pilar walked 1 block east and 3 blocks south. From there, she walked 5 blocks west and 4 blocks north to the park. If the school represents the origin, what is the ordered pair for the park? **(−4, 1)**

Example 5 Graph and label the point $S(3, -1)$.

Draw a coordinate plane. Move 3 units to the right. Then move 1 unit down. Draw a dot and label it $S(3, -1)$.

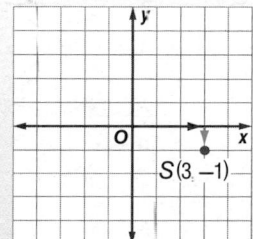

Additional Answers

28–31.

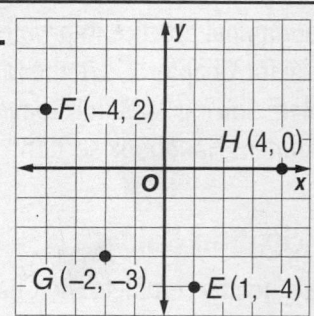

2-4 **Adding Integers** (pp. 95–99)

Add.

33. $-6 + 8$ **2**

34. $-4 + (-9)$ **−13**

35. $7 + (-12)$ **−5**

36. $-18 + 18$ **0**

37. **HIKING** Samuel hiked 75 feet up a mountain. He then hiked 22 feet higher. Then, he descended 8 feet, and finally climbed up another 34 feet. What is Samuel's final elevation? **123 feet**

Example 6 Find $-4 + 3$.

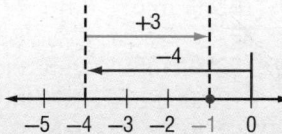

So, $-4 + 3 = -1$.

2-5 **Subtracting Integers** (pp. 103–106)

Subtract.

38. $-5 - 8$ **−13**

39. $3 - 6$ **−3**

40. $5 - (-2)$ **7**

41. $-4 - (-8)$ **4**

42. **GOLF** Owen shot 2 under par while his friend Nathan shot 3 above par. By how many shots was Owen's score better than Nathan's? **5**

Example 7 Find $-3 - 9$.

$-3 - 9 = -3 + (-9)$ To subtract 9, add −9.

$\quad\quad = -12$ Simplify.

Chapter 2 Study Guide and Review   **121**

Problem Solving Review

For additional practice in problem solving for Chapter 2, see the Mixed Problem Solving Appendix, page 716 in the Student Handbook section.

Anticipation Guide

Have students complete the Chapter 2 Anticipation Guide and discuss how their responses have changed now that they have completed Chapter 2.

CRM Anticipation Guide, p. 7

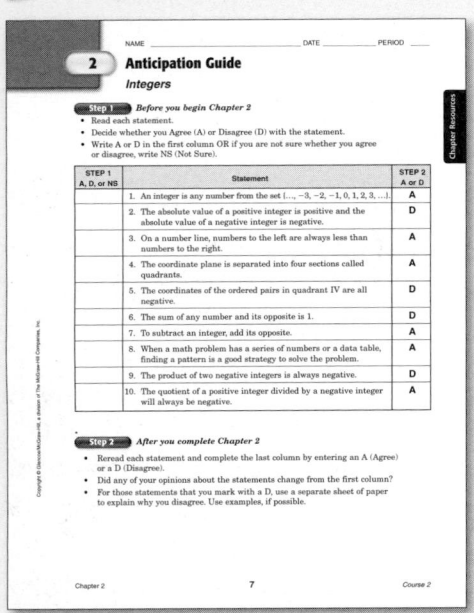

2-6 **Multiplying Integers** (pp. 107–111)

Multiply.

43. $-4(3)$ **−12**
44. $8(-6)$ **−48**
45. $-5(-7)$ **35**
46. $-2(40)$ **−80**

ALGEBRA Evaluate each expression if $a = -4$, $b = -7$, and $c = 5$.

47. ab **28**
48. $-3c$ **−15**
49. bc **−35**
50. abc **140**

Example 8 Find $-5(3)$.

$-5(3) = -15$ The integers have different signs. The product is negative.

Example 9 Evaluate xyz if $x = -6$, $y = 11$, and $z = -10$.

$$xyz$$
$$= (-6)(11)(-10) \quad x = -6, y = 11, z = -10.$$
$$= (-66)(-10) \quad \text{Multiply } -6 \text{ and } 11.$$
$$= 660 \quad \text{Multiply } -66 \text{ and } -10.$$

2-7 **PSI: Look for a Pattern** (pp. 112–113)

Solve. Look for a pattern.

51. **HEALTH** The average person blinks 12 times per minute. At this rate, how many times does the average person blink in one day? **17,280**

52. **SALARY** Suki gets a job that pays $31,000 per year. She is promised a $2,200 raise each year. At this rate, what will her salary be in 7 years? **$46,400**

53. **DOGS** A kennel determined that they need 144 feet of fencing to board 2 dogs, 216 feet to board 3 dogs, and 288 feet to board 4 dogs. If this pattern continues, how many feet of fencing is needed to board 8 dogs? **576 ft**

Example 10 A theater has 18 seats in the first row, 24 seats in the second row, 30 seats in the third row, and so on. If this pattern continues, how many seats are in the sixth row?

Begin with 18 seats and add 6 seats for each additional row. So, there are 48 seats in the sixth row.

Row	Number of Seats
1	18
2	24
3	30
4	36
5	42
6	48

2-8 **Dividing Integers** (pp. 114–118)

Divide.

54. $-45 \div (-9)$ **5**
55. $36 \div (-12)$ **−3**
56. $-12 \div 6$ **−2**
57. $-81 \div (-9)$ **9**

Example 11 Find $-72 \div (-9)$.

$-72 \div (-9) = 8$ The integers have the same sign. The quotient is positive.

Differentiated Instruction

Visual/Spatial Learners If students are having difficulty completing the Exercises, have them use counters, drawings, or number lines to represent the multiplication and division of integers. For example, in Exercise 46, students could display 2 sets of 40 negative counters and count the total number of negative counters, resulting in an answer of −80. Remind students to connect this representation with the rule that the product of two integers with different signs is negative. In Exercise 54, students could display 45 negative counters and then separate the counters into groups so that there are 9 negative counters in each group. Ask students to count the number of groups, resulting in an answer of 5.

Math Online glencoe.com
• Chapter Test

1. **WEATHER** Adam is recording the change in the outside air temperature for a science project. At 8:00 A.M., the high temperature was 42°F. By noon, the outside temperature had fallen 11°F. By mid-afternoon, the outside air temperature had fallen 12°F and by evening, it had fallen an additional 5°F. Write an integer that describes the final change in temperature. **−28**

Evaluate each expression.

2. $|-3|$ **3**
3. $|-18| - |6|$ **12**

Replace each ● with <, >, or = to make a true sentence.

4. -3 ● -9 **>**
5. $|9|$ ● $|-12|$ **<**

6. The Iowa Hawkeyes recorded the following yardage in six plays: 9, −2, 5, 0, 12, and −7. Order these integers from least to greatest. **−7, −2, 0, 5, 9, 12**

7. **MULTIPLE CHOICE** Which of the following coordinates lie within the rectangle graphed below? **D**

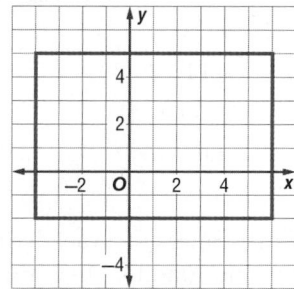

A (5, 6)
B (0, −3)
C (−5, 1)
D (−3, 0)

8. **DEBT** Amanda owes her brother $24. If she plans to pay him back an equal amount from her piggy bank each day for six days, describe the change in the amount of money in her piggy bank each day. **−$4**

Write the ordered pair for each point graphed. Then name the quadrant in which each point is located.

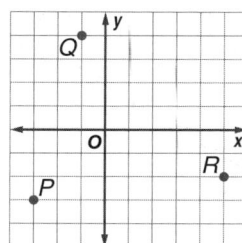

9. P (−3, −3), III
10. Q (−1, 4), II
11. R (5, −2), IV

Add, subtract, multiply, or divide.

12. $12 + (-9)$ **3**
13. $-3 - 4$ **−7**
14. $-7 - (-20)$ **13**
15. $-7(-3)$ **21**
16. $5(-11)$ **−55**
17. $-36 \div (-9)$ **4**
18. $-15 + (-7)$ **−22**
19. $8 + (-6) + (-4)$ **−2**
20. $-9 - 7$ **−16**
21. $-13 + 7$ **−6**

22. **MULTIPLE CHOICE** Kendrick created a 6-week schedule for practicing the piano. If the pattern continues, how many hours will he practice during the sixth week?

The table shows the number of hours he practiced in the first three weeks. **H**

Week	1	2	3
Hours	4	7	10

F 15 hours
G 18 hours
H 19 hours
J 22 hours

Evaluate each expression if $a = -5$, $b = 4$, and $c = -12$.

23. $ac \div b$ **15**
24. $\dfrac{a - b}{3}$ **−3**

25. **−$24 or the stock decreased by $24**

25. **STOCKS** The value of a stock decreased $4 each week for a period of six weeks. Describe the change in the value of the stock at the end of the six-week period.

Data-Driven Decision Making	Exercises	Lesson	State/Local Standards	Resources for Review
Diagnostic Teaching Based on the results of the Chapter 2 Practice Test, use the following to review concepts that students continue to find challenging.	1–11	2–1, 2–2, 2–3		**CRM** Study Guide and Intervention pp. 37, 43, 48, and 53
	12–21, 23–25	2–4, 2–5, 2–6, 2–8		**Math Online** glencoe.com
	22	2–7		• Extra Examples • Personal Tutor • Concepts in Motion

TEST-TAKING TIP

Exercise 5 Have students use mental math to eliminate answer choices. The lower end of Sue's projected spending can be estimated with $6 \times \$200$, or $\$1,200$, so answer choices A and B can be eliminated. Since the original factor (175) was rounded upward, the estimated product is an overestimate, so answer choice D can be eliminated.

 Formative Assessment

You can use these two pages to benchmark student progress.

 Chapter 2 Resource Masters

• Test Practice, pp. 78–80

 Create practice worksheets or tests that align with your state's standrds.

PART 1 Multiple Choice

Read each question. Then fill in the correct answer on the answer document provided by your teacher or on a sheet of paper.

1. The daily low temperatures for Cleveland, Ohio, over the last five days were 15°F, −2°F, 8°F, −6°F, and 5°F. Which expression can be used to find the average daily low temperature during the last five days? **C**

   A $(15 + 2 + 8 + 6 + 5) \div 5$

   B $15 + 2 + 8 + 6 + 5 \div 5$

   C $[15 + (-2) + 8 + (-6) + 5] \div 5$

   D $15 + (-2) + 8 + (-6) + 5 \div 5$

TEST-TAKING TIP

Question 1 Check every answer choice of a multiple-choice question. Each time you find an incorrect answer, cross it off so you remember that you've eliminated it.

2. Marcia runs r miles on Mondays, Tuesdays, and Thursdays. She bicycles for b miles on Wednesday and Saturdays. If she rests on Fridays and Sundays, which equation represents the total number of miles M she exercises each week? **F**

   F $M = 3r + 2b$

   G $M = r + b$

   H $M = 2r + 3b$

   J $M = 5(r + b)$

3. Simplify the expression below. **B**
$$3 + 6(10 - 7) - 3^2$$

   A 0

   B 12

   C 18

   D 74

4. At 8 A.M., the temperature was 13°F below zero. By 1 P.M., the temperature rose 22°F and by 6 P.M. dropped 14°F. What was the temperature at 6 P.M.? **G**

   F 5°F above zero

   G 5°F below zero

   H 21°F above zero

   J 21°F below zero

5. Sue typically spends between $175 and $250 each month on clothes. Which of the following is the best estimate for the amount she spends in 6 months? **C**

   A From $600 to $1,200

   B From $900 to $1,300

   C From $1,050 to $1,500

   D From $1,200 to $1,500

6. On their first play, a football team gained 17 yards. On their next play, they lost 22 yards. On their third play, they gained 14 yards. Which expression represents the total number of yards gained after the third play? **F**

   F $17 + (-22) + 14$

   G $17 + 22 + (-14)$

   H $-17 + (-22) + (-14)$

   J $-17 + 22 + 14$

7. The top four runners of a race were Alicia, Kyle, Drew, and Juanita. Drew finished before Juanita. Alicia finished after both boys, but before Juanita. What information is needed to determine the order of the runners from first to fourth? **A**

   A Did Kyle finish before or after Drew?

   B Did Alicia finish before or after Juanita?

   C Did Drew finish before or after Alicia?

   D Did Kyle finish before or after Alicia?

8. The lowest point in Japan is Hachiro-gata (elevation −4 meters), and the highest point is Mount Fuji (elevation 3,776 meters). What is the difference in elevation between Mount Fuji and Hachiro-gata? **F**

    F   3,780 meters

    G   3,772 meters

    H   3,080 meters

    J   944 meters

9. Which of the following relationships is best represented by the data in the table? **D**

x	y
1	36
2	72
3	108
4	144
5	180

    A   Conversion of feet to inches

    B   Conversion of inches to yards

    C   Conversion of feet to yards

    D   Conversion of yards to inches

10. A storeowner has *n* employees and pays each employee $440 per week. If the owner also pays $*d* weekly to rent the building and $*w* for utilities, which equation below represents the total *E* of these weekly expenses? **H**

    F $E = 440w + n + w$

    G $E = 440n + dw$

    H $E = 440n + d + w$

    J $E = 440(n + d + w)$

PART 2   Short Response/Grid In

Record your answers on the answer sheet provided by your teacher or on a sheet of paper.

11. Nick spends a total of 75 hours per week at work and at the gym. He goes to the gym from 6:45 A.M. to 8:45 A.M., Monday through Friday. Write an equation that can be used to find *t*, the maximum number of hours Nick works at his job each week. $t = 75 − (5 \times 2)$

12. Find $−8 − 17$. **−25**

PART 3   Extended Response

Record your answers on the answer sheet provided by your teacher or a sheet of paper. Show your work.

13. A rectangle and a square are graphed on a coordinate plane. Use the graph below to answer the questions.

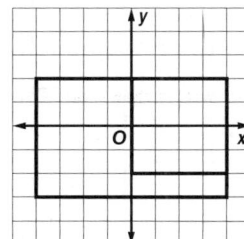

    a. Pick an ordered pair both objects have in common. **Sample answer: (4, 2)**

    b. Find an ordered pair that is inside the rectangle, but not the square. **Sample answer: (−2, 1)**

    c. How could you increase the size of the square so that it still lies within the rectangle? What are the four coordinates?

    d. Draw a graph with the new square inside the rectangle.   **c., d. See margin.**

NEED EXTRA HELP?												
If You Missed Question...	1	2	3	4	5	6	7	8	9	10	11	12	13
Go to Lesson...	1–6	1–7	1–4	2–4	1–1	2–4	1–1	2–5	2–7	1–6	1–7	2–5	2–3

Answer Sheet Practice

Have students simulate taking a standardized test by recording their answers on a practice recording sheet.

CRM Student Recording Sheet, p. 59

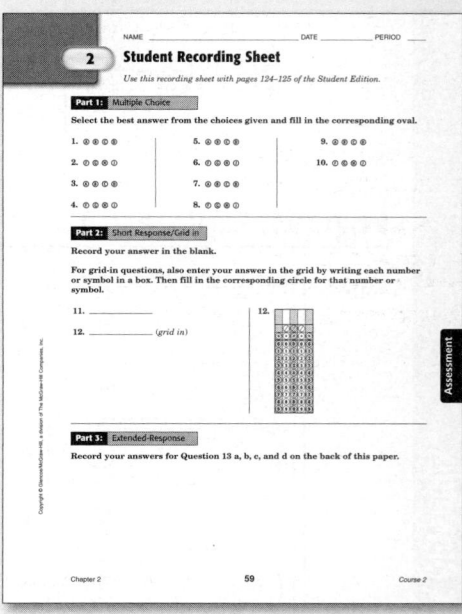

Additional Answers

13c. Make the square 5 × 5; (4, 2), (−1, 2), (−1, −3), and (4, −3).

13d.

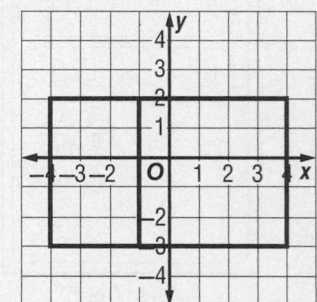

Page 91, Lesson 2-3

23–34.

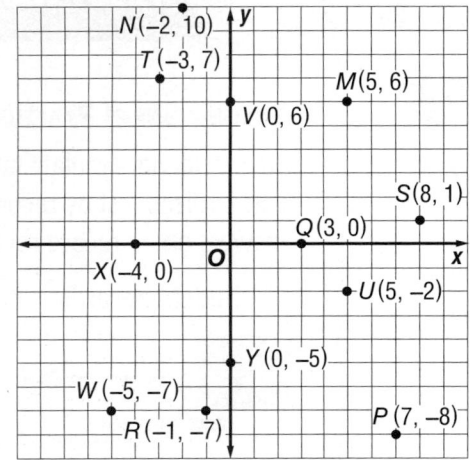

Page 94, Explore 2-4

g.

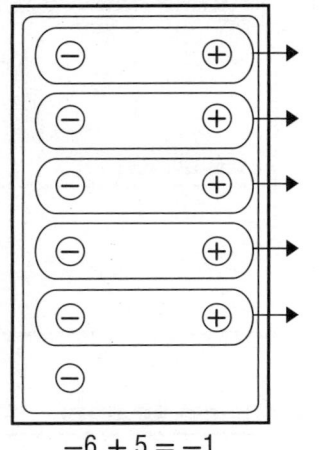

$$-6 + 5 = -1$$

h.

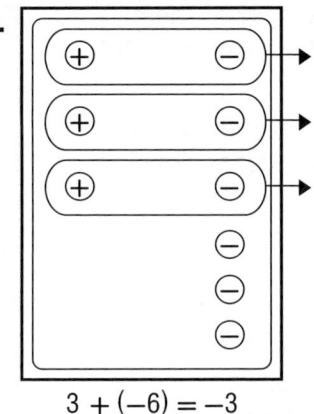

$$3 + (-6) = -3$$

i.

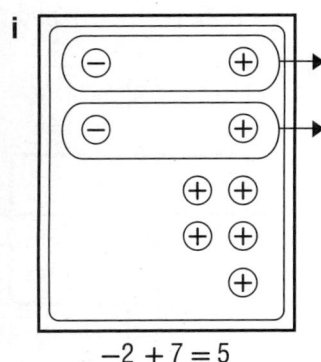

$$-2 + 7 = 5$$

j.

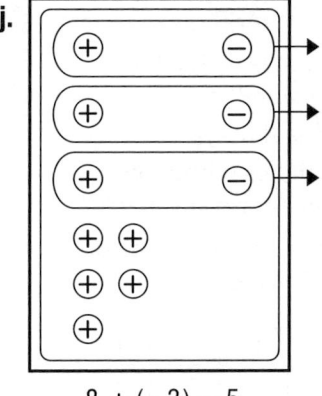

$$8 + (-3) = 5$$

k.

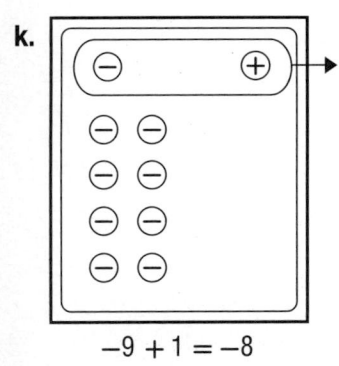

$$-9 + 1 = -8$$

l.

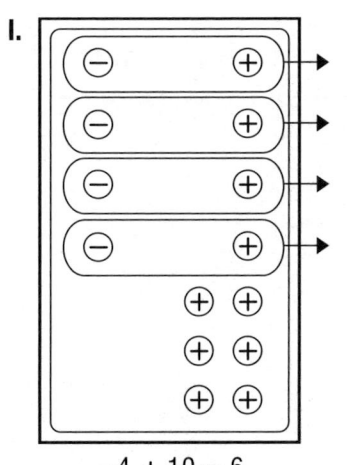

$$-4 + 10 = 6$$

Page 101, Explore 2-5

b.

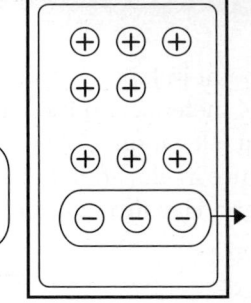

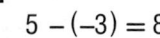

$$5 - (-3) = 8$$

c.

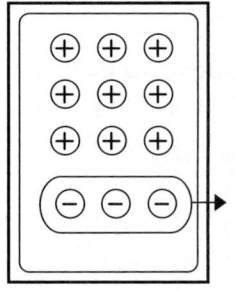

$$6 - (-3) = 9$$

d.

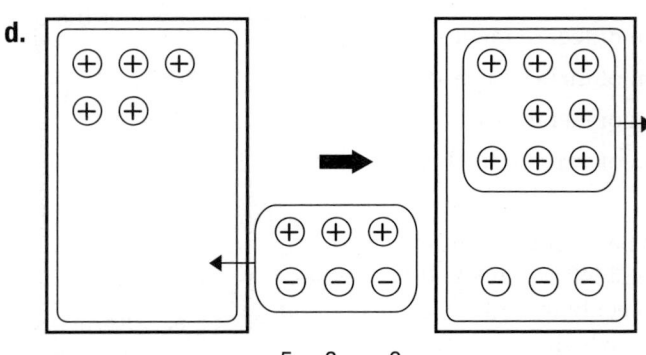

$$5 - 8 = -3$$

Page 102, Explore 2-5

f.

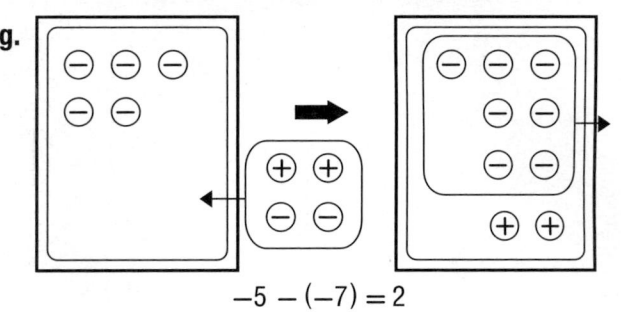

$$-7 - 3 = -10$$

g.

$$-5 - (-7) = 2$$

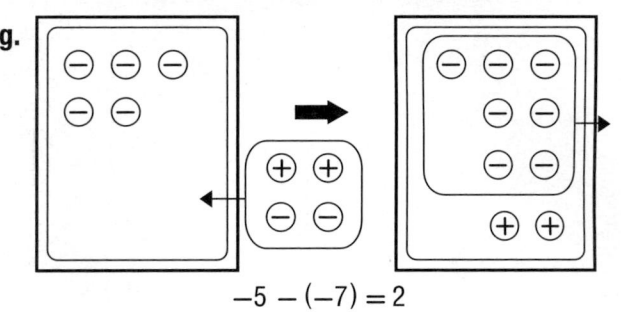

Chapter 2 Answer Appendix

Page 103, Lesson 2-5 (Mini-Lab)

2.

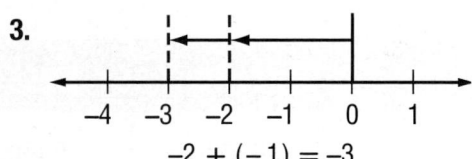

$$1 + (-5) = -4$$

3.

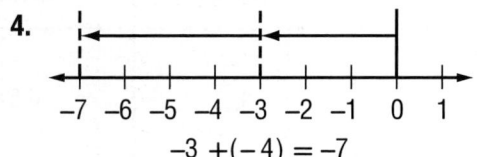

$$-2 + (-1) = -3$$

4.

$$-3 + (-4) = -7$$

5.

$$0 + (-5) = -5$$

Chapter Overview

Algebra: Linear Equations and Functions

Lesson Plan		Pacing Your Lessons	
LESSONS AND OBJECTIVES	State/Local Standards	40–50 Minute Periods	90-Minute Periods
3-1 Writing Expressions and Equations (pp. 128–133) • Write verbal phrases and sentences as simple algebraic expressions and equations.		1	0.5
Explore 3-2 Algebra Lab: Solving Equations Using Models (pp. 134–135) • Solve equations using models. **3-2 Solving Addition and Subtraction Equations** (pp. 136–141) • Solve addition and subtraction equations.		2	1
3-3 Solving Multiplication Equations (pp. 142–146) • Solve multiplication equations.		2	1
3-4 Problem-Solving Investigation: Work Backward (pp. 148–149) • Solve problems using the work backward strategy.		1	0.5
3-5 Solving Two-Step Equations (pp. 151–155) • Solve two-step equations.		1	0.5
3-6 Measurement: Perimeter and Area (pp. 156–161) • Find the perimeters and areas of figures.		1	0.5
Explore 3-7 Measurement Lab: Representing Relationships (p. 162) • Graph data to demonstrate the relationship between the dimensions and the perimeter of a rectangle. **3-7 Functions and Graphs** (pp. 163–167) • Graph data to demonstrate relationships. **Extend 3-7 Graphing Calculator Lab: Graphing Relationships** (p. 168) • Use technology to graph relationships involving conversions of measurement.		2	1
REVIEW		1	0.5
ASSESSMENT		1	0.5*
TOTAL		12	6

*The complete **Assessment Planner** for Chapter 3 is provided on page 127.*

* Begin Chapter 4 in the second half of the period.

Focal Points

G7-FP3 Algebra
For complete wording of the Focal Points for Grade 7, please see page iv.

Professional Development

Vertical Alignment

Before Chapter 3

Related Topics from Grade 6

- use a letter to represent an unknown number; write and evaluate simple algebraic expressions in one variable by substitution.
- differentiate between and use appropriate units of measures for two- and three-dimensional objects
- identify and graph ordered pairs in the four quadrants of the coordinate plane

Chapter 3

Topics from Grade 7

- write and solve one-step linear equations in one variable
- write an algebraic expression for a given situation, using up to three variables
- solve problems involving rates, average speed, distance, and time
- use variables in expressions describing the formulas for the perimeter of a rectangle

After Chapter 3

Preparation for Grade 8

- use variables and appropriate operations to write an expression, an equation, an inequality, or a system of equations
- solve two-step linear equations and inequalities in one variable over the rational numbers
- solve multistep problems involving rate, average speed, distance, and time or a direct variation
- plot the values of quantities whose ratios are always the same. Fit a line to the plot and understand that the slope of the line equals the ratio of the quantities

Backmapping and Vertical Alignment

McGraw-Hill's **Math Connects** program was conceived and developed with the final results in mind: student success in Algebra 1 and beyond. The authors, using the **NCTM Focal Points and Focal Connections** as their guide, developed this brand-new series by backmapping from Algebra 1 concepts and vertically aligning the topics so that they build upon prior skills and concepts and serve as a foundation for future topics.

What the Research Says...

According to the Rand Mathematics Study Panel, connecting algebra with arithmetic, geometry, and statistics helps build student understanding.

- In Lessons 3-2 and 3-3, the Addition, Subtraction, and Division Properties of Equality are shown using arithmetic and using algebra.
- In Lessons 3-2, 3-3, and 3-6, students use algebra to solve problems involving triangles, parallelograms, and area.

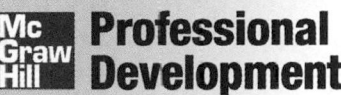

Professional Development

Targeted professional development has been articulated throughout **McGraw-Hill's Math Connects** program. The **McGraw-Hill Professional Development Video Library** provides short videos that support the NCTM Focal Points and Focal Connections. For more information, visit glencoe.com.

| Model Lessons | Instructional Strategies |

TeacherWorks™ All-in-One Planner and Resource Center

All of the print materials from the Classroom Resource Masters are available on your TeacherWorks™ CD-ROM.

BL = Below or Approaching Grade Level   **OL** = On Grade Level   **AL** = Above or Beyond Grade Level   **ELL** = English Language

Chapter Resource Masters					3-1	3-2	3-3	3-4	3-5	3-6	3-7
BL	**OL**		**ELL**	Lesson Reading Guide	9	15	22		32	38	45
BL	**OL**		**ELL**	Study Guide and Intervention*	10	16	23	28	33	39	46
BL	**OL**			Skills Practice*	11	17	24	29	34	40	47
	OL	**AL**		Practice*	12	18	25	30	35	41	48
	OL	**AL**		Word Problem Practice*	13	19	26	31	36	42	49
	OL	**AL**		Enrichment	14	20	27		37	43	50
	OL	**AL**		Calculator and Spreadsheet Activities		21				44	51
	OL	**AL**		Chapter Assessments*	53–76						
BL	**OL**	**AL**		5-Minute Check Transparencies	✓	✓	✓	✓	✓	✓	✓
BL	**OL**			Teaching Mathematics with Manipulatives		✓	✓		✓	✓	✓
BL	**OL**	**AL**		Real-World Investigations for Differentiated Instruction	31–33, 35–36, 37–38, 61–62						

Also available in Spanish.

Graphing Calculator Easy Files

- Timesaving Tech Tools for the TI-Navigator:
- **Quick Checks** to diagnose student progress
- Motivate students with **Concept Launchers**
- Deliver differentiated instruction with **Ready Files**
- **Vocabulary Review**

AssignmentWorks

Differentiated Assignments, Answers, and Solutions

- Print a customized assignment worksheet using the Student Edition exercises along with an answer key or worked-out solutions.
- Use default lesson assignments as outlined in the Differentiated Homework Options in the Teacher Edition.

Interactive Classroom

This CD-ROM is a customizable Microsoft® PowerPoint® presentation that includes:

- In-Class Examples
- Your Turn Exercises*
- 5-Minute Check Transparencies*
- Links to Online Study Tools
- Concepts in Motion

compatible with response pad technology

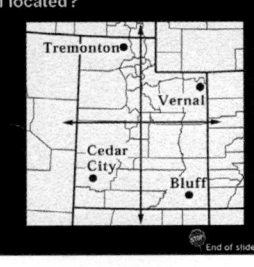

Example 3

GEOGRAPHY Use the map of Utah shown below. In which quadrant is Vernal located?

Vernal is located in the upper right quadrant, quadrant I.

Answer: Quadrant I

ExamView®Assessment Suite

ExamView®
Assessment Suite

- Create, edit, and customize tests and worksheets using QuickTest Wizard.
- Create multiple versions of tests and modify them for a desired level of difficulty.
- Translate from English to Spanish and vice versa.
- Build tests aligned with your state standards.
- Track students' progress using the Teacher Management System.

Student Tools

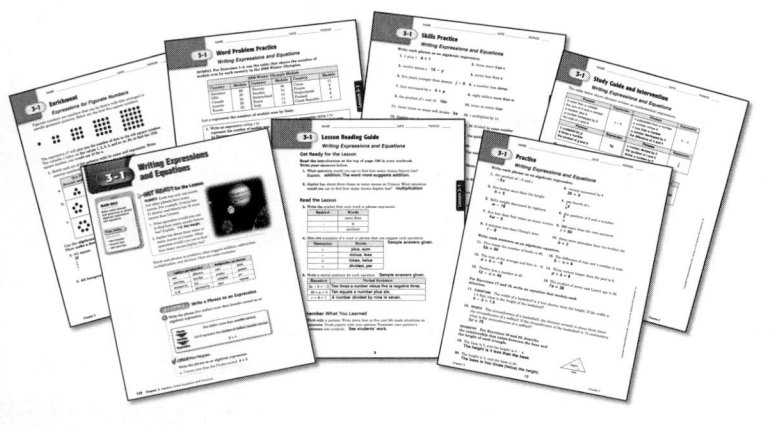

Internet Resources

Math Online > glencoe.com

TEACHER	STUDENT	PARENT	Online Study Tools
	●	●	Online Student Edition
●	●	●	Multilingual Glossary
			Lesson Resources
	●	●	Extra Examples
	●	●	BrainPOPS
	●	●	Self-Check Quizzes
●	●	●	Concepts in Motion
	●	●	Other Calculator Keystrokes
	●	●	Real-World Careers
	●	●	Reading in the Content Area
●			Group Activity Cards
			Chapter Resources
	●	●	Family Letters and Activities
	●		Chapter Readiness Quiz
	●	●	Vocabulary Review
	●	●	Chapter Test
	●	●	Standardized Test Practice
			Unit Resources
●	●		WebQuest Project
			Other Resources
	●		Personal Tutor
●			NAEP Correlations
●			Key Concepts
●	●	●	Meet the Authors
●	●		Game Zone
●	●	●	Math Skills Maintenance
●			National Resources (Professional Organizations)
●			State Resources
●			Vocabulary PuzzleMakers

Reading and Writing in Mathematics

Noteables™ Interactive Study Notebook with Foldables™

This workbook is a study organizer that provides helpful steps for students to follow to organize their notes for Chapter 3.

- Students use Noteables to record notes and to complete their Foldables as you present the material for each lesson.
- Noteables correspond to the Examples in the *Teacher Edition* and *Interactive Classroom CD-ROM*.

Real-World Problem Solving Graphic Novels

Mathematical problem solving is presented in a motivating, graphic novel format. The novels contain real-world problems for each of the following mathematical strands: Number Sense, Algebraic Thinking, Geometry, Measurement, Statistics and Probability, and Mathematical Reasoning.

READING in the Content Area

This online worksheet provides strategies for reading and analyzing Lesson 3-2, Solving Addition and Subtraction Equations. Students are guided through questions about the main idea, subject matter, supporting details, conclusion, clarifying details, and vocabulary of the lesson.

glencoe.com

Recommended Outside Reading for Students

Mathematics and Economics

- *The Toothpaste Millionaire* by Jean Merrill ©1974 [fiction]

The Toothpaste Millionaire is a funny story of how two friends solve real-world mathematics problems involved in starting a toothpaste business and making a profit. They use functions, which students will study in Lesson 3-7.

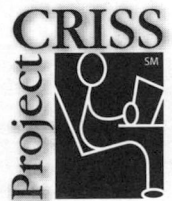

Project CRISS℠

STUDY SKILL

A story frame can help students organize information contained in word problems. They can use story frames either to solve word problems or to help them develop word problems of their own. The sample story frame at the right describes the following word problem: *A car travels 74 miles less than a truck travels in one day. If the truck travels 252 miles, how far has the car traveled?* Have students use story frames to write equation word problems as they work through Chapter 3.

Things Involved:	truck, car
Setting:	truck travels 252 miles; car travels 74 miles less
Goal:	distance traveled by car:
Steps:	1. Write an equation relating the distance taveled by the car to the distance taveled by the truck ($t - 74 = c$)
	2. Insert t, the distance traveled by the truck, 252 miles. ($252 - 74 = c$)
	3. Solve for c, the distance traveled by the car.
Solution:	$c = 178$ miles
Check your solution:	Is it reasonable? Recheck calculations.

CReating **I**ndependence through **S**tudent-owned **S**trategies

Differentiated Instruction

Investigative Approach

MathScape™

This project was supported, in part, by the National Science Foundation

MathScape is a mathematics curriculum for grades 6–8 developed by the Seeing and Thinking Mathematically Project at the Education Development Center.

Equations, Tables, and Graphs
The Language of Algebra

How to Use MathScape with Chapter 3
The unit *The Language of Algebra* can be used to enhance Lessons 3-2 and 3-5.

- **Introduce** ⟶ Before you complete **Lesson 3-2**, you can introduce the idea of solving equations by using the activities on pages 204–205.

- **Enrich** ⟶ After you complete **Lesson 3-5**, you can use the activities on pages 206–207 to challenge students to solve both equations and inequalities.

RTI (Response to Intervention)

1 **On-Level Instruction** Use the *Math Connects* program as instruction for your on-level students.

2 **Strategic Intervention** For options to instruct struggling students, refer to the Diagnostic Assessment table on page 127.

3 **Intensive Intervention** *Math Triumphs* can provide intensive intervention for students who are at risk of not meeting the objectives addressed in Chapter 3.

Diagnose student readiness with the Quick Check and Quick Review on page 127. Then use *Math Triumphs* to accelerate their achievement.

Algebra: Linear Equations and Functions

Prerequisite Skill	Math Triumphs
Translating Verbal Expressions and Sentences	Ch. 4
Solving Equations	Ch. 10

Practice and Review

Quick Review Math Handbook* is Glencoe's mathematical handbook for students and parents.

Hot Words includes a glossary of terms.

Hot Topics consists of two parts:

- explanations of key mathematical concepts

- exercises to check students' understanding.

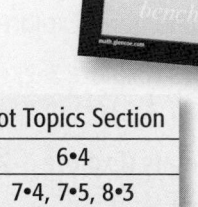

Lesson	Hot Topics Section	Lesson	Hot Topics Section
3-1	6•5	3-5	6•4
3-2	6•1, 6•4	3-6	7•4, 7•5, 8•3
3-3	6•4	3-7	6•7, 6•8

*Also available in Spanish

FOLDABLES™
Study Organizer
Dinah Zike's Foldables

Focus Students write about expressions, equations, functions, and perimeter and area.

Teach After students make their Foldables, discuss note taking with them. Make sure they understand that they should listen or read for main ideas and then record those ideas in a simple form that makes sense to them.

When to Use It Under the tabs of their Foldables, students should take notes about what they learn about expressions, equations, perimeter and area, and functions. Encourage students to also write examples of each concept. *A version of a completed Foldable is shown on p. 169.*

Differentiated Instruction
CRM Student-Built Glossary, p. 1

Students complete the chart by providing the definition for each term and an example as they progress through Chapter 3.

This study tool can be used to review for the chapter test.

Materials Needed for Chapter 3
• cups and counters (Explore 3-2)
• algebra tiles (Explore 3-2, Lessons 3-3, 3-5)
• equation mats (Explore 3-2, Lessons 3-3, 3-5)
• graph paper (Explore 3-7)
• chenille stems or yarn (Explore 3-7)
• scissors (Explore 3-7)
• centimeter rules (Explore 3-7)
• graphing calculator (Extend 3-7)

Algebra: Linear Equations and Functions

BIG Idea
• Solve linear equations in one variable.

Key Vocabulary
formula (p. 144)
linear equation (p. 164)
two-step equation (p. 151)
work backward strategy (p. 148)

🌐 **Real-World Link**
Segways The Segway's top speed is 12.5 miles per hour—two to three times faster than walking. You can use the equation $d = 12.5t$ to find the distance d you can travel in t hours.

FOLDABLES®
Study Organizer

Algebra: Linear Equations and Functions Make this Foldable to help you organize your notes. Begin with a sheet of 11" by 17" paper.

1 **Fold** the short sides toward the middle.

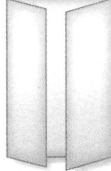

2 **Fold** the top to the bottom.

3 **Open.** Cut along the second fold to make four tabs.

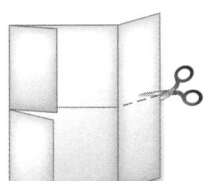

4 **Label** each of the tabs as shown.

GET READY for Chapter 3

Diagnose Readiness You have two options for checking Prerequisite Skills.

Option 1

Take the Quick Quiz below. Refer to the Quick Review for help.

Option 2

Math Online ▷ Take the Online Readiness Quiz at glencoe.com.

QUICK Quiz

(Used in Lessons 3-2, 3-3, and 3-5)
Name the number that is the solution of the given equation. (Lesson 1-6)

1. $a + 15 = 19$; 4, 5, 6 **4**

2. $11k = 77$; 6, 7, 8 **7**

3. $x + 9 = -2$; 7, −11, 11 **−11**

(Used in Lesson 3-7)
Graph each point on a coordinate plane. (Lesson 2-3)

4. $(-4, 3)$ 5. $(-2, -1)$
4–6. See Ch. 3 Answer Appendix.

6. **HIKING** Keith hiked 4 miles north and 2 miles west from the campground before he rested. If the origin represents the campground, graph Keith's resting point. (Lesson 2-3)

(Used in Lessons 3-2 and 3-5)
Add. (Lesson 2-4)

7. $-3 + (-5)$ **−8** 8. $-8 + 3$ **−5**

9. $9 + (-5)$ **4** 10. $-10 + 15$ **5**

(Used in Lessons 3-2 through 3-5)
Subtract. (Lesson 2-5)

11. $-5 - 6$ **−11** 12. $8 - 10$ **−2**

13. $8 - (-6)$ **14** 14. $-3 - (-1)$ **−2**

(Used in Lessons 3-3 and 3-5)
Divide. (Lesson 2-8)

15. $-6 \div (-3)$ **2** 16. $-12 \div 3$ **−4**

17. $10 \div (-5)$ **−2** 18. $-24 \div (-4)$ **6**

QUICK Review

Example 1 Name the number that is the solution of $24 \div a = 3$; 7, 8, or 9.

$24 \div a = 3$	Write the equation.
$24 \div 7 = 3$? No.	Substitute $a = 7$.
$24 \div 8 = 3$? Yes.	Substitute $a = 8$.
$24 \div 9 = 3$? No.	Substitute $a = 9$.

Example 2 Graph the point $(-1, 3)$ on a coordinate plane.

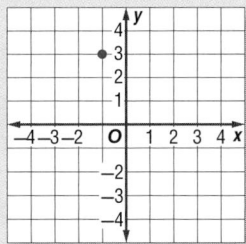

The first number in an ordered pair tells you to move left or right from the origin. The second number tells you to move up or down.

Example 3 Find $-4 + (-2)$.

$-4 + (-2) = -6$ Since −4 and −2 are both negative, add their absolute values. The sum is negative also.

Example 4 Find $9 - (-7)$.

$9 - (-7) = 9 + (7)$ Subtracting −7 is the same as adding 7.
$= 16$ Add.

Example 5 Find $-16 \div 2$.

$-16 \div 2 = -8$ Since −16 and 2 have opposite signs, their quotient is negative.

Diagnostic Assessment

Exercises	State/Local Standards	Strategic Intervention
1–3		SE Review Lesson 1-7, pp. 49–52
4–6		SE Review Lesson 2-3, pp. 88–92
7–14		SE Review Lessons 2-4 and 2–5, pp. 95–99, 103–106
15–18		SE Review Lesson 2-8, pp. 114–118

✔ Formative Assessment

CRM Anticipation Guide, pp. 7–8
Spotting Preconceived Ideas
Students complete this survey to determine prior knowledge about ideas from Chapter 3. Revisit this worksheet after completing the chapter. Also see page 172.

TE Lesson Activities

* Ticket Out the Door, pp. 133, 146, 167
* Crystal Ball, pp. 141, 149
* Name the Math, p. 155
* Yesterday's News, p. 161

Chapter Checkpoints

SE Mid-Chapter Quiz, p. 147

SE Study Guide and Review, pp. 169–172

SE Test Practice, pp. 174–175

CRM Quizzes, pp. 55 and 56

CRM Standardized Test Practice, pp. 72–74

Math Online ▷ glencoe.com

* Self-Check Quizzes
* Practice Test
* Test Practice

✔ Summative Assessment

SE Chapter Practice Test, p. 173

CRM Mid-Chapter Test, p. 57

CRM Vocabulary Test, p. 58

CRM Extended-Response Test, p. 71

CRM Leveled Chapter Tests, pp. 59–70

● ExamView Pro® Assessment Suite

KEY

CRM *Chapter 3 Resource Masters*
SE Student Edition
TE Teacher Edition
● CD-ROM

3-1 Writing Expressions and Equations

PACING: **Regular:** 1 period, **Block:** 0.5 period

Options for Differentiated Instruction

 = English Language Learner   **AL** = Above or Beyond Grade Level   **SS** = Struggling Students   **SN** = Special Needs

Review Vocabulary   **ELL**   **SN**

Use before presenting Lesson 3-1.

Have students review the following vocabulary terms and write their definitions on index cards.
- variable
- equation
- numerical expression
- algebraic expression

Being able to refer to the definitions quickly will allow students to follow along in the lesson more easily and participate in class discussions.

Use Brainstorming   **ELL**   **SS**   **SN**

Use before presenting Lesson 3-1.

Brainstorm a list of words and phrases that indicate each of the four operations. As students make suggestions, write the words and phrases on the board. With help from ELL students, write translations in their primary languages.

Addition	Subtraction	Multiplication	Division
added - sumarlos	difference - diferencia	multiplied - multiplicarlos	quotient - cociente
plus - más		product - producto	
sum - suma			

Match the list that the class generates with the list on page 128.

Use Visual Clues   **ELL**   **SS**   **SN**

Use before assigning the Exercises.

When students translate a verbal phrase into an algebraic expression, have them circle the clue words that indicate the operation and underline the phrase that represents the variable. Have students refer to the list of clue words on page 128.

Examples:

three more than a number   four times the number of years   the length decreased by six meters

Leveled Lesson Resources

Chapter 3 Resource Masters

BL = Below or Approaching Grade Level **OL** = On Grade Level **AL** = Above or Beyond Grade Level **ELL** = English Language Learner

---

Lesson Reading Guide
p. 9 **BL OL ELL**

NAME _____ DATE _____ PERIOD _____

3-1 Lesson Reading Guide
Writing Expressions and Equations

Get Ready for the Lesson
Read the introduction at the top of page 128 in your textbook. Write your answers below.

1. What operation would you use to find how many moons Saturn has? Explain. **addition; The word more suggests addition.**

2. Jupiter has about three times as many moons as Uranus. What operation would you use to find how many moons Jupiter has? **multiplication**

Read the Lesson

3. Write the symbol that each word or phrase represents.

Symbol	Words
+	more than
=	is
÷	quotient

4. Give two examples of a word or phrase that can suggest each operation. **Sample answers given.**

Operation	Words
+	plus, sum
−	minus, less
×	times, twice
÷	divided, per

5. Write a verbal sentence for each equation. **Sample answers given.**

Equation	Verbal Sentence
$2x - 5 = -3$	Two times a number minus five is negative three.
$10 = a + 6$	Ten equals a number plus six.
$r \div 9 = 7$	A number divided by nine is seven.

Remember What You Learned

6. Work with a partner. Write down four or five real life math situations as sentences. Trade papers with your partner. Translate your partner's sentences into symbols. **See students' work.**

Chapter 3   9   Course 2

Study Guide and Intervention*
p. 10 **BL OL ELL**

NAME _____ DATE _____ PERIOD _____

3-1 Study Guide and Intervention
Writing Expressions and Equations

The table below shows phrases written as mathematical expressions.

Phrases	Expression	Phrases	Expression
9 more than a number the sum of 9 and a number a number plus 9 a number increased by 9 the total of x and 9	$x + 9$	4 subtracted from a number a number minus 4 4 less than a number a number decreased by 4 the difference of h and 4	$h - 4$
6 multiplied by g 6 times a number the product of g and 6	$6g$	a number divided by 5 the quotient of t and 5 divide a number by 5	$\frac{t}{5}$

The table below shows sentences written as an equation.

Sentences	Equation
Sixty less than three times the amount is $59. Three times the amount less 60 is equal to 59. 59 is equal to 60 subtracted from three times a number. A number times three minus 60 equals 59.	$3n - 60 = 59$

Exercises

Write each phrase as an algebraic expression.

1. 7 less than m $m - 7$
2. the quotient of 3 and y $\frac{3}{y}$
3. the total of 5 and c $5 + c$
4. the difference of 6 and r $6 - r$
5. n divided by 2 $\frac{n}{2}$
6. the product of k and 9 $9k$

Write each sentence as an algebraic equation.

7. A number increased by 7 is 11. $n + 7 = 11$
8. The price decreased by $4 is $29. $p - 4 = 29$
9. Twice as many points as Bob would be 18 points. $2b = 18$
10. After dividing the money 5 ways, each person got $67. $\frac{m}{5} = 67$
11. Three more than 8 times as many trees is 75 trees. $8t + 3 = 75$
12. Seven less than a number is 15. $n - 7 = 15$

Chapter 3   10   Course 2

Skills Practice*
p. 11 **BL OL**

NAME _____ DATE _____ PERIOD _____

3-1 Skills Practice
Writing Expressions and Equations

Write each phrase as an algebraic expression.

1. b plus 1 $b + 1$
2. three more than x $x + 3$
3. twelve minus y $12 - y$
4. seven less than n $n - 7$
5. five years younger than Jessica $j - 5$
6. a number less eleven $n - 11$
7. four increased by a $4 + a$
8. eight dollars more than m $m + 8$
9. the product of c and 10 $10c$
10. twice as many days $2d$
11. three times as many soft drinks $3s$
12. t multiplied by 14 $14t$
13. Emily's age divided by 3 $\frac{e}{3}$
14. 24 divided by some number $\frac{24}{n}$
15. a number divided by 2 $\frac{n}{2}$
16. the quotient of −15 and w $\frac{-15}{w}$

Write each sentence as an algebraic equation.

17. A number plus three is 9. $n + 3 = 9$
18. The sum of x and 2 is 10. $x + 2 = 10$
19. Four cents more than the price is 93¢. $p + 4 = 93$
20. Fifteen minus y is 7. $15 - y = 7$
21. A number decreased by 5 is 12. $n - 5 = 12$
22. Five dollars less than Yumi's pay is $124. $y - 5 = 124$
23. A number times four is 20. $4n = 20$
24. Twice the number of cars is 40. $2c = 40$
25. The product of z and 6 is 54. $6z = 54$
26. A number divided by 6 is 12. $\frac{n}{6} = 12$
27. 72 divided by y is −9. $\frac{72}{y} = -9$
28. 175 students separated into n classes is 25. $\frac{175}{n} = 25$
29. One more than twice as many CDs is 17. $2c + 1 = 17$
30. Four less than three times a number is 14. $3n - 4 = 14$

Chapter 3   11   Course 2

Practice*
p. 12 **OL AL**

NAME _____ DATE _____ PERIOD _____

3-1 Practice
Writing Expressions and Equations

Write each phrase as an algebraic expression.

1. the product of −5 and x $-5x$
2. twenty increased by k $20 + k$
3. five inches more than the height $h + 5$
4. one fourth of y $\frac{1}{4}y$
5. Bill's weight decreased by eighteen $w - 18$
6. the quotient of 3 and a number $\frac{3}{n}$
7. five less than four times as many women $4w - 5$
8. $60 more than the rent payment $r + 60$
9. 9 minutes less than Chang's time $t - 9$
10. three more pancakes than his brother ate $n + 3$

Write each sentence as an algebraic equation.

11. Five times the number of books is 95. $5b = 95$
12. The difference of nine and a number is nine. $9 - n = 9$
13. The sum of the average and four is −6. $a + 4 = -6$
14. Three meters longer than the pool is 8. $p + 3 = 8$
15. Twelve less a number is 40. $12 - n = 40$
16. The product of seven and Lynn's age is 28. $7a = 28$

For Exercises 17 and 18, write an equation that models each situation.

17. FURNITURE The width of a bookshelf is 2 feet shorter than the height. If the width is 1.5 feet, what is the height of the bookshelf? $h - 2 = 1.5$

18. SPORTS The circumference of a basketball, the distance around, is about three times the circumference of a softball. If the circumference of the basketball is 75 centimeters, what is the circumference of a softball? $3c = 75$

GEOMETRY For Exercises 19 and 20, describe the relationship that exists between the base and the height of each triangle.

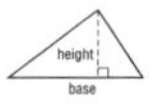

19. The base is b, and the height is b − 4. **The height is 4 less than the base.**

20. The height is h, and the base is 2h. **The base is two times (twice) the height.**

Chapter 3   12   Course 2

Word Problem Practice*
p. 13 **OL AL**

NAME _____ DATE _____ PERIOD _____

3-1 Word Problem Practice
Writing Expressions and Equations

OLYMPICS For Exercises 1–4, use the table that shows the number of medals won by each country in the 2006 Winter Olympics.

2006 Winter Olympic Medals

Country	Medals	Country	Medals	Country	Medals
Germany	29	Norway	19	China	11
USA	25	Sweden	14	France	9
Canada	24	Switzerland	14	Netherlands	9
Austria	23	Korea	11	Finland	9
Russia	22	Italy	11	Czech Republic	4

Let x represent the number of medals won by Italy.

1. Write an expression using x to represent the number of medals won by Norway. $x + 8$

2. Write an expression using x to represent the number of medals won by the Czech Republic. $x - 7$

3. Which country's number of medals can be represented by 2x? **Russia**

4. Which country's number of medals can be represented by 2x + 3? **USA**

5. GEOGRAPHY The Virgin Islands were acquired by the United States in 1927. This is 29 years after Puerto Rico was acquired. Write an equation to model this situation. $y + 29 = 1927$

6. POPULATION According to the Census Bureau, the U.S. population grew from 281.4 million in April 2000 to 284.8 million in July 2001. Write an equation to model this situation. $281.4 + x = 284.8$

Chapter 3   13   Course 2

Enrichment
p. 14 **OL AL**

NAME _____ DATE _____ PERIOD _____

3-1 Enrichment
Expressions for Figurate Numbers

Figurate numbers are numbers which can be shown with dots arranged in specific geometric patterns. Below are the first five square numbers.

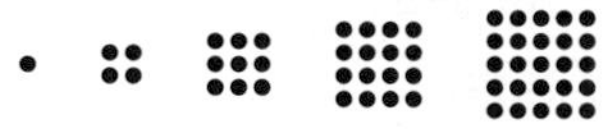

The expression n^2 will give you the number of dots in the nth square number. The variable n takes on the values 1, 2, 3, 4, and so on. So, to find the 10th square number, you would use 10 for n.

1. Match each set of dot patterns with its name and expression. Write exercise numbers in the boxes to show the matchings.

Dot Patterns for Second and Third Numbers	Name of Figurate Number	Expression
a.	pentagonal **b**	$n(2n - 1)$ **c**
b.	hexagonal **c**	$\frac{n(n + 1)}{2}$ **a**
c.	triangular **a**	$\frac{n(3n - 1)}{2}$ **b**

Use the algebraic expressions on this page to compute each number. Then make a drawing of the number on a separate sheet of paper.

2. 6th square 36
3. 4th triangular 10
4. 4th pentagonal 22
5. 4th hexagonal 28
6. 5th triangular 15
7. 5th pentagonal 35

Chapter 3   14   Course 2

Additional Lesson Resources

* Also available in Spanish **ELL**

Transparencies
• *5-Minute Check Transparency,* Lesson 3-1

Other Print Products
• *Noteables™ Interactive Study Notebook with Foldables™*

Teacher Tech Tools
• *Interactive Classroom CD-ROM,* Lesson 3-1
• *AssignmentWorks,* Lesson 3-1

Student Tech Tools
glencoe.com
• Extra Examples, Chapter 3, Lesson 1
• Self-Check Quiz, Chapter 3, Lesson 1

Writing Expressions and Equations

1 Focus

Vertical Alignment

Before Lesson 3-1
Use a letter to represent an unknown number; write and evaluate simple algebraic expressions in one variable by substitution

From Lesson 3-1
Write an algebraic expression for a given situation, using up to three variables

After Lesson 3-1
Use variables and appropriate operations to write an expression, an equation, an inequality, or a system of equations or inequalities

2 Teach

Scaffolding Questions

Write the following expressions on the board.

a. $7 - 2$ **c.** 7×2
b. $7 + 2$ **d.** $7 \div 2$

Ask:

• Which expression represents the phrase *two more than seven?* b

• Which expression represents the phrase *the product of seven and two?* c

• Which expression represents the phrase *seven less two?* a

• Which expression represents the phrase *seven divided by two?* d

• What multiplication expression could you use to find the number of minutes in one day? 24×60

MAIN IDEA

Write verbal phrases and sentences as simple algebraic expressions and equations.

Math Online

glencoe.com

• Extra Examples
• Personal Tutor
• Self-Check Quiz

▶ **GET READY** for the Lesson

PLANETS Earth has only one moon, but other planets have many moons. For example, Uranus has 21 moons, and Saturn has 10 more moons than Uranus.

1. What operation would you use to find how many moons Saturn has? Explain. **1–2. See margin.**

2. Jupiter has about three times as many moons as Uranus. What operation would you use to find how many moons Jupiter has?

Words and phrases in problems often suggest addition, subtraction, multiplication, and division. Here are some examples.

Addition and Subtraction		Multiplication and Division	
sum	difference	each	divide
more than	less than	product	quotient
increased by	less	multiplied	per
in all	decreased by	twice	separate

EXAMPLE Write a Phrase as an Expression

 Write the phrase *five dollars more than Jennifer earned* as an algebraic expression.

Words	five dollars more than Jennifer earned.
Variable	Let *d* represent the number of dollars Jennifer earned.
Expression	$d + 5$

✓ **CHECK** Your Progress

Write the phrase as an algebraic expression.

a. 3 more runs than the Pirates scored $p + 3$

ADDITIONAL EXAMPLE

 Write the phrase *twenty dollars less the price of a movie ticket* as an algebraic expression. $20 - m$

Additional Answers

1. Addition; the word *more* suggests addition.

2. multiplication

Remember, an equation is a sentence in mathematics that contains an equals sign. When you write a verbal sentence as an equation, you can use the equals sign (=) for the words *equals* or *is*.

EXAMPLES Write Sentences as Equations

Write each sentence as an algebraic equation.

2 Six less than a number is 20.

Six less than a number is 20.

Let n represent the number.

$n - 6 = 20$

3 Three times Jack's age equals 12.

Three times Jack's age equals 12.

Let a represent Jack's age.

$3a = 12$

✓ CHECK Your Progress

Write each sentence as an algebraic equation.

b. Seven more than a number is 15. $n + 7 = 15$

c. Five times the number of students is 250. $5s = 250$

Real-World Link . . . .
The tallest waterfall in South Carolina is Raven Cliff Falls, located in Caesars Head State Park.
Source: South Carolina Department of Parks, Recreation, and Tourism

🌐 Real-World EXAMPLE

4 **WATERFALLS** The tallest waterfall in the United States is Yosemite Falls in California with a height of about 739 meters. This height is 617 meters taller than Raven Cliff Falls. What is the height of Raven Cliff Falls? Write an equation that models this situation.

Words	*Yosemite Falls* is 617 meters taller than *Raven Cliff Falls.*
Variable	Let h represent the height of *Raven Cliff Falls.*
Equation	$739 \quad = \quad 617 \quad + \quad h$

The equation is $739 = 617 + h$.

✓ CHECK Your Progress   **d.** $1.5c = 75$

d. **ANIMALS** North American cougars are about 1.5 times as long as cougars found in the tropical jungles of Central America. If North American cougars are about 75 inches long, how long is the tropical cougar? Write an equation that models this situation.

ADDITIONAL EXAMPLE

5 **TEST EXAMPLE** Which problem situation matches the equation $4.9y = 17.3$? D

A After giving away 4.9 kilograms of tomatoes, Harry had 17.3 kilograms left. What is y, the number of kilograms of tomatoes that Harry began with?

B The total length of two toy cars is 17.3 centimeters. One car is 4.9 centimeters long. What is y, the length of the other car?

C A chemist separated a solution into 4 equal quantities of 17.3 milliliters. What is y, the amount of solution she began with?

D Rodrigo spent $17.30 on fishing line. If each meter of line cost $4.90, what is y, the total length of the line?

TEST EXAMPLE

5 Which problem situation matches the equation $x - 5.83 = 3.17$?

A Tyler ran 3.17 kilometers. His friend ran the same distance 5.83 seconds faster than Tyler. What is x, the time in seconds that Tyler ran?

B Lynn and Heather measured the length of worms in science class. Lynn's worm was 5.83 centimeters long, and Heather's worm was 3.17 centimeters long. What is x, the average length of the worms?

C Keisha's lunch cost $5.83. She received $3.17 in change when she paid the bill. What is x, the amount of money she gave the cashier?

D Mr. Carlos paid $3.17 for a notebook that originally cost $5.83. What is x, the amount of money that Mr. Carlos saved?

Read the Item

You need to find which problem situation matches the equation $x - 5.83 = 3.17$.

Solve the Item

- You can eliminate A because you cannot add or subtract different units of measure.

- You can eliminate B because to find an average you add and then divide.

- Act out C. If you gave the cashier x dollars and your lunch cost $5.83, you would subtract to find your change, $3.17. This is the correct answer.

- Check D, just to be sure. To find the amount Mr. Carlos saved, you would calculate $5.83 - 3.17$, not $x - 5.83$.

The solution is C.

CHECK Your Progress

e. Which problem situation matches the equation $4y = 6.76$? **F**

F Mrs. Thomas bought 4 gallons of gas. Her total cost was $6.76. What is y, the cost of one gallon of gas?

G Jordan bought 4 CDs that were on sale for $6.76 each. What is y, the total cost of the CDs?

H The width of a rectangle is 4 meters. The length is 6.76 meters more than the width. What is y, the length of the rectangle?

J The average yearly rainfall is 6.76 inches. What is y, the amount of rainfall you might expect in 4 years?

Example 1
(p. 128)

Write each phrase as an algebraic expression.

1. a number increased by eight
$n + 8$

2. ten dollars more than Grace has
$j + 10$

Examples 2, 3
(p. 129)

Write each sentence as an algebraic equation. 4. $s - 2 = 4$

3. $n - 9 = 24$

3. Nine less than a number equals 24.

4. Two points less than his score is 4.

5. Twice the number of miles is 18.
$2m = 18$

6. One half the regular price is $13.
$p \div 2 = 13$

Example 4
(p. 129)

7. **ALGEBRA** The median age of people living in Arizona is 1 year younger than the median age of people living in the United States. Use this information and the information at the right to write an equation to find the median age in the United States. $x - 1 = 34.3$

Median Age
Arizona   34.3
United States ?

Example 5
(p. 130)

8. **MULTIPLE CHOICE** Which problem situation matches the equation $x - 15 = 46$? **B**

A The original price of a jacket is $46. The sale price is $15 less. What is x, the sale price of the jacket?

B Mark had several baseball cards. He sold 15 of the cards and had 46 left. What is x, the amount of cards Mark had to start with?

C Sonja scored 46 points in last week's basketball game. Talisa scored 15 points less. What is x, the amount of points Talisa scored?

D Katie earned $15 babysitting this week. Last week she earned $46. What is x, her average earnings for the two weeks?

Practice and Problem Solving

HOMEWORK HELP

For Exercises	See Examples
9–16	1
17–22	2, 3
23–24	4
41	5

Exercise Levels
A: 9–24
B: 25–36
C: 37–40

Write each phrase as an algebraic expression.

9. fifteen increased by t $15 + t$

10. five years older than Luis $y + 5$

11. a number decreased by ten $n - 10$

12. three feet less than the length $\ell - 3$

13. the product of r and 8 $8r$

14. twice as many oranges $2f$

15. Emily's age divided by 3 $\dfrac{a}{3}$

16. the quotient of a number and -12 $\dfrac{z}{-12}$

Write each sentence as an algebraic equation.

17. The sum of a number and four is equal to -8. $n + 4 = -8$

18. Two more than the number of frogs is 4. $c + 2 = 4$

19. The product of a number and five is -20. $5d = -20$

20. Ten times the number of students is 280. $10k = 280$

21. Ten inches less than her height is 26. $h - 10 = 26$

22. Five less than a number is 31. $n - 5 = 31$

Lesson 3-1 Writing Expressions and Equations **131**

 Formative Assessment

Use Exercises 1–8 to check for understanding.

Then use the chart at the bottom of this page to customize your assignments for students.

Intervention You may wish to use the Study Guide and Intervention Master on page 10 of the *Chapter 3 Resource Masters* for additional reinforcement.

Odd/Even Assignments

Exercises 9–24 are structured so that students practice the same concepts whether they are assigned odd or even problems.

 **Writing Algebraic Expressions**

After assigning Exercise 11, it may be helpful to have students distinguish between the phrases a number decreased by ten and ten decreased by a number. The first phrase can be represented by the expression $n - 10$, but the second phrase is represented by the expression $10 - n$.

DIFFERENTIATED HOMEWORK OPTIONS

Level	Assignment	Two-Day Option	
BL Basic	9–24, 37, 38, 40–56	9–23 odd, 41, 42	10–24 even, 37, 38, 40, 43–56
OL Core	9–21 odd, 23, 24, 25–33 odd, 35–38, 40–56	9–24, 41, 42	25–38, 40, 43–56
AL Advanced/Pre-AP	25–52 (optional: 53–56)		

🌐 **Real-World Link** · · · ·
A giraffe's heart can pump 16 gallons of blood in one minute.
Source: Woodland Park Zoo

25. the length is 4 times the width

26. the length is 3 more than the width

27. the width is 5 less than the length

For Exercises 23 and 24, write an equation that models each situation.

23. **ANIMALS** A giraffe is 3.5 meters taller than a camel. If a giraffe is 5.5 meters tall, how tall is a camel? $c + 3.5 = 5.5$

24. **FOOTBALL** Carson Palmer led the National Football League with 32 touchdown passes in a season. This was twice as many touchdown passes as Donovan McNabb had. Find the number of touchdown passes for McNabb. $2f = 32$

MEASUREMENT For Exercises 25–28, describe the relationship that exists between the length and width of each rectangle.

25. The width is x, and the length is $4x$.

26. The length is $x + 3$, and the width is x.

27. The length is x, and the width is $x - 5$.

28. The length is x, and the width is $0.5x$.
the width is half the length

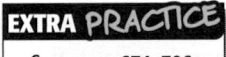

Write each phrase as an algebraic expression.

29. 2 more than twice as many bikes $2b + 2$

30. nine CDs less than three times the number of CDs Margaret owns $3c - 9$

31. 43 dollars off the price of each admission, which is then multiplied by 3 admissions $3(a - 43)$

32. the quotient of a number w and (-8), which is then increased by 7 $\frac{w}{-8} + 7$

33. the square of a number k which is then multiplied by 13 $13k^2$

34. the sum of a number p and 0.4 which is then decreased by the fifth power of the same number $p + 0.4 - p^5$

ANALYZE TABLES For Exercises 35 and 36, use the table. **35. American toad**

The table shows the average lifespan of several types of pets. Let y represent the average lifespan of a gerbil.

35. Which lifespan can be represented by $3y$?

36. Write an expression to represent the lifespan of a cat. **$5y$ or $y + 20$**

Pets	
Type	**Lifespan (years)**
American toad	15
cat	25
dog	22
gerbil	5
rabbit	9

EXTRA PRACTICE
See pages 674, 706.

H.O.T. Problems

38. Candace; "five less than a number" indicates that 5 is subtracted from the variable

37. **OPEN ENDED** Write a verbal sentence for the equation $n - 3 = 6$.
Sample answer: 3 less than a number is 6.

38. **FIND THE ERROR** Sancho and Candace are writing an algebraic expression for the phrase *5 less than a number*. Who is correct? Explain.

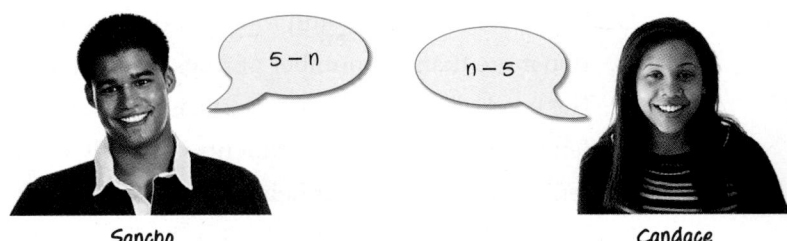

Sancho $5 - n$ $n - 5$ Candace

39. CHALLENGE If x is an odd number, how would you represent the odd number immediately following it? preceding it? **$x + 2$; $x - 2$**

40. WRITING IN MATH Analyze the meaning of the expressions $a + 5$, $a - 3$, $2a$, and $\frac{a}{2}$ if a represents someone's age.
5 years more than someone's age, 3 years less than someone's age, twice someone's age, and half of someone's age

TEST PRACTICE

41. Asha had some change in her purse. After her brother gave her $0.79, Asha had $2.24 altogether. Which equation can she use to find the original amount of money m she had in her purse? **C**

 A $2.24 = m - 0.79$

 B $m = 2.24 \times 0.79$

 C $m + 0.79 = 2.24$

 D $m + 2.24 = 0.79$

42. Which algebraic equation best describes the total distance D traveled in miles after a 6-hour period, if r represents the rate of travel in miles per hour? **H**

 F $D = 6 + r$

 G $D = \frac{r}{6}$

 H $D = 6r$

 J $D = \frac{6}{r}$

Spiral Review

Divide (Lesson 2-8)

43. $-42 \div 6$ **−7** **44.** $36 \div (-3)$ **−12** **45.** $-45 \div (-3)$ **15**

46. MONEY Jordan withdraws $14 per week from his savings account for a period of 7 weeks. Write a multiplication expression to represent this situation. Then find the product and explain its meaning. (Lesson 2-7)
−14(7); −98; Jordan withdraws $98 over the 7 weeks.

Evaluate each expression. (Lesson 1-4)

47. $3 + 7 \cdot 4 - 6$ **25** **48.** $8(16 - 5) - 6$ **82** **49.** $75 \div 3 + 6(5 - 1)$ **49**

ANALYZE DATA For Exercises 50–52, use the table that shows the cost of two different plans for downloading music. (Lesson 1-1) **50. about $1.33 per song**

50. Suppose you download 12 songs in one month. Find the cost per song using Plan B.

51. Which plan is less expensive for downloading 9 songs in one month? **Plan A**

52. When is it less expensive to use Plan B instead of Plan A?
when you download 17 or more songs each month

Music Downloads	
Plan A	$0.99 per song
Plan B	$15.99 per month for unlimited downloads

GET READY for the Next Lesson

PREREQUISITE SKILL Find each sum. (Lesson 2-4)

53. $-8 + (-3)$ **−11** **54.** $-10 + 9$ **−1** **55.** $12 + (-20)$ **−8** **56.** $-15 + 15$ **0**

Lesson 3-1 Writing Expressions and Equations **133**

4 Assess

Ticket Out the Door Write a phrase such as *13 less pennies than 20 pennies times 4* on the board. Have students write what operations the phrase describes and which operation should be performed first.

FOLDABLES Study Organizer **Foldables™ Follow-Up**

Remind students to take notes about writing algebraic expressions and equations under the tabs of their Foldables. Make sure they describe the difference between an expression and an equation. Encourage them to give examples.

1 Focus

Materials
• algebra tiles (optional)

Easy-to-Make Manipulatives
Teaching Mathematics with Manipulatives, templates for:

• algebra tiles, pp. 10–11

2 Teach

Working in Cooperative Groups
You may wish for students to work in groups of 2 or 3. Student 1 can model the equation using algebra tiles. Student 2 can remove tiles from each side of the mat. Student 3 can count the remaining tiles to find the value of *x*.

Activity 1 Make sure students understand that they can represent the variable *x* with a cup, an *x* algebra tile, or a written *x*.

You might wish to emphasize that to solve for *x*, students need to isolate it, so that it is the only term remaining on the left side of the equals sign.

c–d. See Ch. 3 Answer Appendix for drawings.

Algebra Lab
Solving Equations Using Models

MAIN IDEA

Solve equations using models.

In Chapter 2, you used counters to add, subtract, multiply, and divide integers. Integers can also be modeled using algebra tiles. The table shows how these two types of models are related.

Type of Model	Variable *x*	Integer 1	Integer −1
Cups and Counters	cup	+	−
Algebra Tiles	x	1	−1

You can use either type of model to solve equations.

ACTIVITY

1 Solve $x + 2 = 5$ using cups and counters or a drawing.

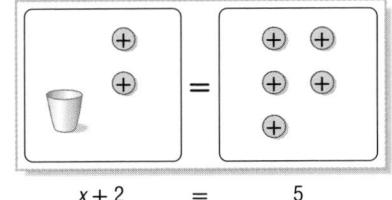

$x + 2 = 5$

Model the equation.

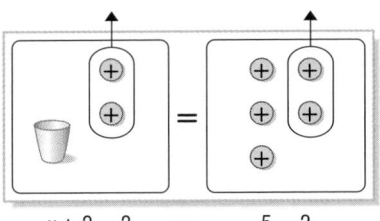

$x + 2 - 2 = 5 - 2$

Remove the same number of counters from each side of the mat until the cup is by itself on one side.

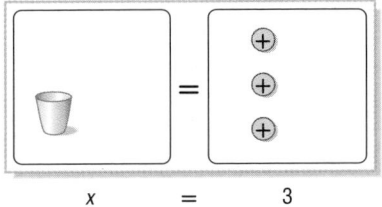

$x = 3$

The number of counters remaining on the right side of the mat represents the value of *x*.

Therefore, $x = 3$. Since $3 + 2 = 5$, the solution is correct.

 **CHECK** Your Progress   **a–b. See margin for drawings.**

Solve each equation using cups and counters or a drawing.

a. $x + 4 = 4$ **0**   b. $5 = x + 4$ **1**   c. $4 = 1 + x$ **3**   d. $2 = 2 + x$ **0**

Additional Answers

a.
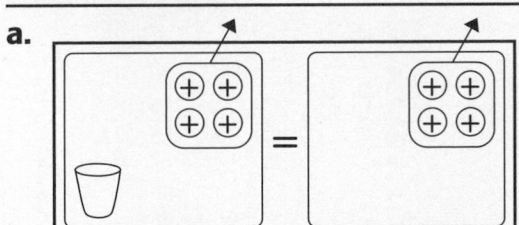

b.
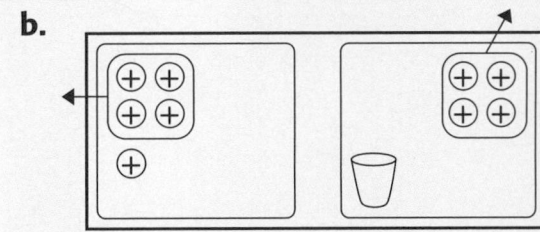

zero pair a number paired with its opposite; Example: 2 and −2. (Explore 2-4)

You can add or subtract a zero pair from either side of an equation without changing its value, because the value of a zero pair is zero.

ACTIVITY

2 Solve $x + 2 = -1$ using models.

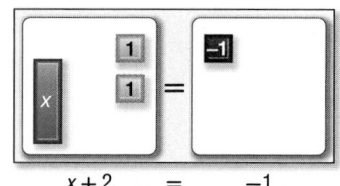

$x + 2 = -1$

Model the equation.

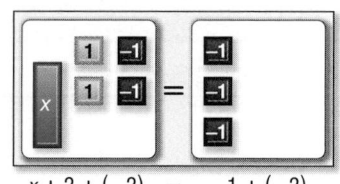

$x + 2 + (-2) = -1 + (-2)$

Add 2 negative tiles to the left side of the mat and add 2 negative tiles to the right side of the mat.

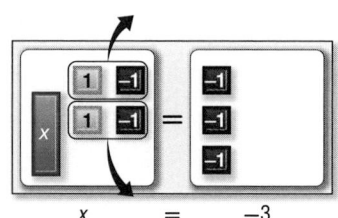

$x = -3$

Remove all of the zero pairs from the left side. There are 3 negative tiles on the right side of the mat.

Therefore, $x = -3$. Since $-3 + 2 = -1$, the solution is correct.

✓ CHECK Your Progress   e–h. See margin for drawings.

e. −3   f. 1   g. −2   h. 6

Solve each equation using models or a drawing.

e. $-2 = x + 1$ f. $x - 3 = -2$ g. $x - 1 = -3$ h. $4 = x - 2$

1. Remove 1 counter from each side of the equation mat; $x = 2$.
2. Add 3 negative tiles to each side of the mat. Remove the zero pairs; $x = -5$.
3. If a number is added to the variable, subtract that number from both sides of the equation. If a number is subtracted from the variable, add that number to both sides of the equation.

ANALYZE THE RESULTS

Explain how to solve each equation using models or a drawing.

1.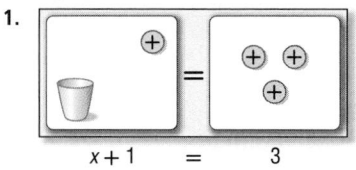

$x + 1 = 3$

2.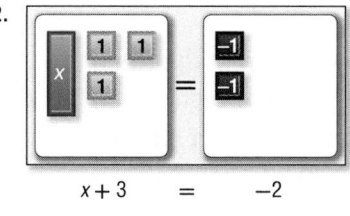

$x + 3 = -2$

3. **MAKE A CONJECTURE** Write a rule that you can use to solve an equation like $x + 3 = 2$ without using models or a drawing.

Explore 3-2 Algebra Lab: Solving Equations Using Models   **135**

Activity 2 Make sure students understand that they cannot simply subtract the two positive tiles from the left side of the equation, since the right side doesn't have any positive tiles to subtract. Remind students that if they add or subtract tiles to or from one side of the equation, they must add or subtract the same tiles to or from the other side (unless, of course, they are adding or subtracting zero pairs).

3 Assess

✓ Formative Assessment

Use Exercises e–h to determine whether students comprehend how to use algebra tiles or drawings to solve equations.

From Concrete to Abstract Use Exercise 4 to bridge the gap between using algebra tiles to solve equations and using an algorithm.

g.

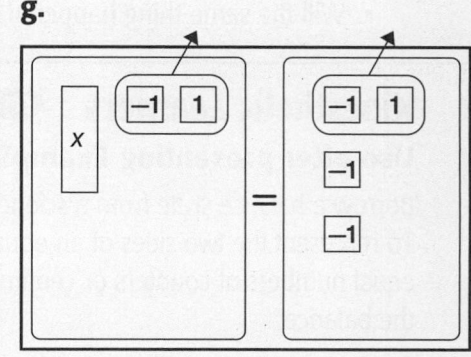

h.

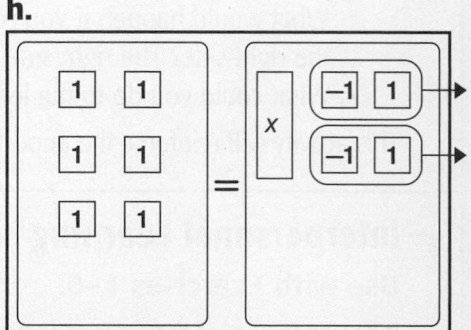

Additional Answers

e.

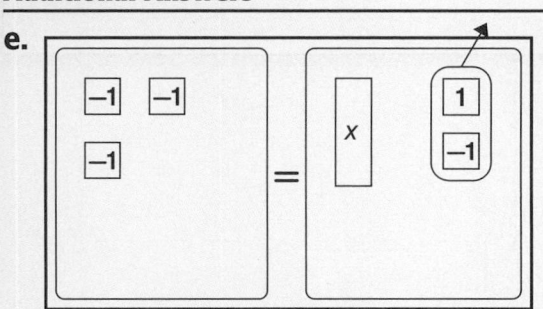

f.

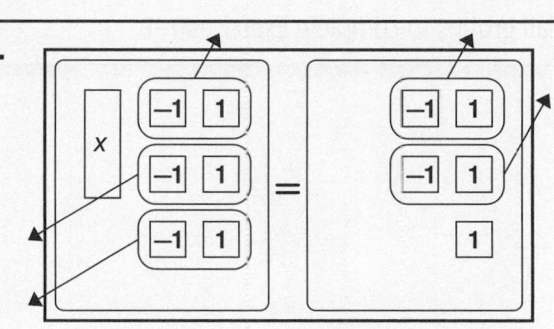

Solving Addition and Subtraction Equations

PACING: **Regular:** 2 periods, **Block:** 1 period

Options for Differentiated Instruction

ELL = English Language Learner ⬛ **AL** = Above or Beyond Grade Level ⬛ **SS** = Struggling Students ⬛ **SN** = Special Needs

Using Mental Math   **SS**   **SN**

Use before presenting Example 1.

Ask students to use mental math to do the following:

1. Choose a number.
2. Add 4 to the number.
3. Subtract 4 from the answer.

Ask:

- What was your final answer? the original number
- Will the same thing happen if you start with a different number? Explain. Yes; subtracting 4 undoes the adding 4.

Kinesthetic Learners   **ELL**   **SS**   **SN**

Use after presenting Examples 1–5.

Borrow a balance scale from a science teacher.
To represent the two sides of an equation, place cups containing equal numbers of counters or centimeter cubes on each side of the balance.

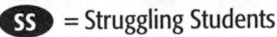

Ask:

- What would happen if you removed two counters from the cup on the right side? The right side of the balance would be higher than the left.
- What could you do to the left side of the scale to make it balanced again? Remove two counters.

This activity will reinforce the importance of doing the same thing to both sides of an equation.

Interpersonal Learning   **ELL**

Use with Exercises 1–8.

It has been shown that language acquisition is a social activity and that ELL students develop the academic language they need by collaborating with other students. To give ELL students practice communicating their ideas orally, have students work in pairs or small groups to complete Exercises 1–8.

Leveled Lesson Resources

Chapter 3 Resource Masters

BL = Below or Approaching Grade Level   **OL** = On Grade Level   **AL** = Above or Beyond Grade Level   **ELL** = English Language Learner

---

Lesson Reading Guide
p. 15 **BL** **OL** **ELL**

NAME _____ DATE ____ PERIOD ____

3-2 Lesson Reading Guide
Solving Addition and Subtraction Equations

Get Ready for the Lesson
Read the introduction at the top of page 136 in your textbook.
Write your answers below.
1. What does x represent in the figure? **number of games initially had**
2. What addition equation is shown in the figure? $x + 2 = 6$
3. Explain how to solve the equation. **Find the number that when added to 2 is 6.**
4. How many games did Max have in the beginning? **4**

Read the Lesson
5. Match the method of solving with the appropriate equation.

$x + 5 = 9$ ___c___   a. add 2 to each side
$-2 + y = 1$ ___a___   b. add 5 to each side
$5 = m - 1$ ___d___   c. subtract 5 from each side
$r + 9 = -7$ ___e___   d. add 1 to each side
$k - 5 = -2$ ___b___   e. subtract 9 from each side

6. Explain in words how to solve each equation.
$a - 10 = 3$ **Add ten to each side and simplify.**
$4 + t = -12$ **Subtract four from each side and simplify.**
$18 = n - 7$ **Add seven to each side and simplify.**

7. Solve each equation.
a. $w + 23 = -11$ **−34**   b. $35 = z - 15$ **50**   c. $42 + c = -9$ **−51**

Remember What You Learned
8. Take turns with a partner explaining the Addition and Subtraction Properties of Equality in your own words. Then each of you write two addition and two subtraction equations. Trade equations and solve. Check your work by explaining to each other the method you used to solve the equations. **See students' answers.**

Chapter 3   15   Course 2

Study Guide and Intervention*
p. 16 **BL** **OL** **ELL**

NAME _____ DATE ____ PERIOD ____

3-2 Study Guide and Intervention
Solving Addition and Subtraction Equations

Remember, equations must always remain balanced. If you subtract the same number from each side of an equation, the two sides remain equal. Also, if you add the same number to each side of an equation, the two sides remain equal.

Example 1 Solve $x + 5 = 11$. Check your solution.

$x + 5 = 11$ Write the equation.
$\underline{-5 \quad -5}$ Subtract 5 from each side.
$x = 6$ Simplify.

Check $x + 5 = 11$ Write the equation.
$6 + 5 \stackrel{?}{=} 11$ Replace x with 6.
$11 = 11$ ✓   This sentence is true.
The solution is 6.

Example 2 Solve $15 = t - 12$. Check your solution.

$15 = t - 12$ Write the equation.
$\underline{+12 \quad +12}$ Add 12 to each side.
$27 = t$ Simplify.

Check $15 = t - 12$ Write the equation.
$15 \stackrel{?}{=} 27 - 12$ Replace t with 27.
$15 = 15$ ✓   This sentence is true.
The solution is 27.

Exercises

Solve each equation. Check your solution.
1. $h + 3 = 14$ **11**   2. $m + 8 = 22$ **14**   3. $p + 5 = 15$ **10**   4. $7 = y + 8$ **9**

5. $w + 4 = -1$ **−5**   6. $k + 5 = -3$ **−8**   7. $25 = 14 + r$ **11**   8. $57 + z = 97$ **40**

9. $h - 3 = 6$ **9**   10. $7 = c - 5$ **12**   11. $j - 12 = 18$ **30**   12. $v - 4 = 18$ **22**

13. $-9 = w - 12$ **3**   14. $y - 8 = -12$ **−4**   15. $14 = f - 2$ **16**   16. $23 = n - 12$ **35**

Chapter 3   16   Course 2

Skills Practice*
p. 17 **BL** **OL**

NAME _____ DATE ____ PERIOD ____

3-2 Skills Practice
Solving Addition and Subtraction Equations

Solve each equation. Check your solution.
1. $x + 2 = 8$ **6**   2. $y + 7 = 9$ **2**   3. $a + 5 = 12$ **7**

4. $16 = n + 6$ **10**   5. $q + 10 = 22$ **12**   6. $m + 9 = 17$ **8**

7. $b - 4 = 9$ **13**   8. $8 = c - 4$ **12**   9. $11 = t - 7$ **18**

10. $d - 10 = 8$ **18**   11. $x - 11 = 9$ **20**   12. $2 = z - 14$ **16**

13. $72 = 24 + w$ **48**   14. $86 + y = 99$ **13**   15. $6 + y = -8$ **−14**

16. $-5 = m + 11$ **−16**   17. $n + 3.5 = 6.7$ **3.2**   18. $x + 1.6 = 0.8$ **−0.8**

19. $98 = t - 18$ **116**   20. $12 = g - 56$ **68**   21. $x - 18 = -2$ **16**

22. $p - 11 = -5$ **6**   23. $a - 1.5 = 4.2$ **5.7**   24. $7.4 = n - 2.6$ **10**

Chapter 3   17   Course 2

Practice*
p. 18 **OL** **AL**

NAME _____ DATE ____ PERIOD ____

3-2 Practice
Solving Addition and Subtraction Equations

Solve each equation. Check your solution.
1. $a + 4 = 11$ $a = 7$ 2. $6 = g + 8$ $g = -2$ 3. $x - 3 = -2$ $x = 1$

4. $h + 8 = 3$ $k = -5$ 5. $j + 0 = 9$ $j = 9$ 6. $12 + y = 15$ $y = 3$

7. $h - 4 = 0$ $h = 4$ 8. $m - 7 = 1$ $m = 8$ 9. $w + 5 = 4$ $w = -1$

10. $b - 28 = 33$ $b = 61$ 11. $45 + f = 48$ $f = 3$ 12. $n + 7.1 = 8.6$ $n = 1.5$

13. $-14 + t = 26$ $t = 40$ 14. $d - 3.03 = 2$ $d = 5.03$ 15. $10 = z + 15$ $z = -5$

16. $c - 5.3 = -6.4$ $c = -1.1$ 17. $39 + p = 77$ $p = 42$ 18. $-15 = -15 + u$ $u = 0$

For Exercises 19 and 20, write an equation. Then solve the equation.
19. **CAFFEINE** A cup of brewed tea has 54 milligrams less caffeine than a cup of brewed coffee. If a cup of tea has 66 milligrams of caffeine, how much caffeine is in a cup of coffee? $c - 54 = 66$; $c = 120$; A cup of coffee has 120 milligrams of caffeine.

20. **GEOMETRY** The sum of the measures of the angles of a trapezoid is 360°. Find the missing measure. $d° + 100° + 110° + 80° = 360°$; $d° = 70°$

Chapter 3   18   Course 2

Word Problem Practice*
p. 19 **OL** **AL**

NAME _____ DATE ____ PERIOD ____

3-2 Word Problem Practice
Solving Addition and Subtraction Equations

ANIMALS For Exercises 1–4, use the table.
The average lifespans of several different types of animals are shown in the table.

Average Lifespans of Animals			
Animal	Lifespan (yr)	Animal	Lifespan (yr)
Black Bear	18	Guinea Pig	4
Dog	12	Puma	?
Giraffe	10	Tiger	16
Gray Squirrel	10	Zebra	?

1. The lifespan of a black bear is 3 years longer than the lifespan of a zebra. Write an addition equation that you could use to find the lifespan of a zebra. $z + 3 = 18$

2. Solve the equation you wrote in Exercise 1. What is the lifespan of a zebra? **15 yr**

3. The lifespan of a guinea pig is 8 years shorter than the lifespan of a puma. Write a subtraction equation that you could use to find the lifespan of a puma. $p - 8 = 4$

4. Solve the equation you wrote in Exercise 3. What is the lifespan of a puma? **12 yr**

5. **TECHNOLOGY** A survey of teens showed that teens in Pittsburgh aged 12-17 spend 15.8 hours per week online. Teens in Miami/Ft. Lauderdale spend 14.2 hours per week online. Write and solve an addition equation to find the difference in time spent online by teens in these cities. $14.2 + d = 15.8$; **1.6 hours per week**

6. **SPORTS** Annika Sorenstam won the 2006 MasterCard Classic with a final score of 8 under par, or -8. Her scores for the first two of the three rounds were -5 and -1. What was Ms. Sorenstam's score for the third round? **−2**

Chapter 3   19   Course 2

Enrichment
p. 20 **OL** **AL**

NAME _____ DATE ____ PERIOD ____

3-2 Enrichment
Equation Hexa-maze

This figure is called a *hexa-maze* because each cell has the shape of a hexagon, or six-sided figure.

To solve the maze, start with the number in the center. This number is the solution to the equation in one of the adjacent cells. Move to that cell. The number in the new cell will then be the solution to the equation in the next cell. At each move, you may only move to an adjacent cell. Each cell is used only once.

Chapter 3   20   Course 2

Additional Lesson Resources

Transparencies
• *5-Minute Check Transparency*, Lesson 3-2

Other Print Products
• *Teaching Mathematics with Manipulatives*
• *Noteables™ Interactive Study Notebook with Foldables™*

Teacher Tech Tools
• *Interactive Classroom CD-ROM*, Lesson 3-2
• *AssignmentWorks*, Lesson 3-2

Student Tech Tools
glencoe.com
• Extra Examples, Chapter 3, Lesson 2
• Self-Check Quiz, Chapter 3, Lesson 2

1 Focus

Vertical Alignment

Before Lesson 3-2
Use a letter to represent an unknown number; write and evaluate simple algebraic expressions in one variable by substitution

Lesson 3-2
Write and solve one-step linear equations in one variable

After Lesson 3-2
Solve two-step linear equations and inequalities in one variable over the rational numbers

2 Teach

Scaffolding Questions

Either show a balance scale with 10 counters on each side or draw one on the board. As you ask the following questions, add or subtract the appropriate number of counters.

Ask:

- If I add 3 counters to the left side, how can I balance the scale? **by adding 3 counters to the right side**

- If I take away 5 counters from the right side, how can I balance the scale? **by taking away 5 counters from the left side**

- When the sides are in balance, how would you compare the number of counters on each side? **The number of counters on the left equals the number of counters on the right.**

3-2 Solving Addition and Subtraction Equations

MAIN IDEA

Solve addition and subtraction equations.

Math Online

glencoe.com

- Extra Examples
- Personal Tutor
- Self-Check Quiz
- Reading in the Content Area

▷ GET READY for the Lesson

VIDEO GAMES Max had some video games, and then he bought two more games. Now he has six games.

He started with an unknown number of games.

He bought two more.

Now he has six games.

1. What does x represent in the figure? **number of games initially had**
2. What addition equation is shown in the figure? $x + 2 = 6$
3. Explain how to solve the equation.
4. How many games did Max have in the beginning? **4**

3. Find the number that when added to 2 is 6.
You can solve the equation $x + 2 = 6$ by *removing*, or subtracting, the same number of positive tiles from each side of the mat. You can also subtract 2 from each side of the equation. The variable is now by itself on one side of the equation.

Use Models

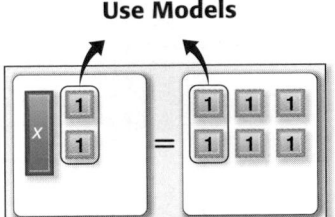

Use Symbols

$$\begin{aligned} x + 2 &= 6 \\ -2 &= -2 \\ \hline x &= 4 \end{aligned}$$

Subtracting 2 from each side of an equation illustrates the Subtraction Property of Equality.

Subtraction Property of Equality   Key Concept

Words	If you subtract the same number from each side of an equation, the two sides remain equal.
Symbols	If $a = b$, then $a - c = b - c$.
Examples	**Numbers** $\quad$ **Algebra**

$$\begin{aligned} 6 &= 6 \\ -2 &= -2 \\ \hline 4 &= 4 \end{aligned} \qquad \begin{aligned} x + 2 &= 6 \\ -2 &= -2 \\ \hline x &= 4 \end{aligned}$$

Tips for New Teachers

Additive Inverses

When solving the addition equation $x + 2 = 6$, you can subtract 2 from each side of the equation. Subtracting 2 is the same as adding -2. Since 2 and -2 are additive inverses, the sum is 0 and the variable x is isolated on the left side of the equation.

EXAMPLES Solve Addition Equations

1 Solve $x + 5 = 8$. Check your solution.

$x + 5 = 8$	Write the equation.
$\underline{-5 = -5}$	Subtract 5 from each side.
$x = 3$	Simplify.

Check

$x + 5 = 8$	Write the original equation.
$3 + 5 \stackrel{?}{=} 8$	Replace x with 3.
$8 = 8 \checkmark$	The sentence is true.

The solution is 3.

Study Tip
Solutions Notice that your new equation, $x = 3$, has the same solution as the original equation, $x + 5 = 8$.

2 Solve $x + 6 = 4$. Check your solution.

$x + 6 = 4$	Write the equation.
$\underline{-6 = -6}$	Subtract 6 from each side.
$x = -2$	Simplify.

The solution is -2.   Check the solution.

 Your Progress

Solve each equation. Check your solution.

a. $y + 6 = 9$ **3** b. $x + 3 = 1$ **−2** c. $-3 = a + 4$ **−7**

Real-World EXAMPLE

3 **MARINE BIOLOGY** Clownfish and angelfish are popular tropical fish. An angelfish can grow to be 12 inches long. If an angelfish is 8.5 inches longer than a clownfish, how long is a clownfish?

Words	An angelfish	is	8.5 inches longer than	a clownfish.
Variable		Let c represent the length of the clownfish.		
Equation	12	=	8.5 +	c

$12 = 8.5 + c$	Write the equation.
$\underline{-8.5 = -8.5}$	Subtract 8.5 from each side.
$3.5 = c$	Simplify.

A clownfish is 3.5 inches long.

Real-World Career ....
How Does a Marine Biologist Use Math?
A marine biologist uses math to analyze data about marine plants, animals, and organisms.

 Math Online
For more information, go to: glencoe.com.

 Your Progress

d. **WEATHER** The highest recorded temperature in Warsaw, Missouri, is 118°F. This is 158° greater than the lowest recorded temperature. Write and solve an equation to find the lowest recorded temperature. $118 = 158 + t$; **−40°F**

Focus on Mathematical Content

The **inverse operation** of addition is subtraction, and the inverse operation of subtraction is addition.

You can use inverse operations to **isolate the variable** in an algebraic equation, thus solving the equation.

Formative Assessment

Use the Check Your Progress exercises after each Example to determine students' understanding of concepts.

ADDITIONAL EXAMPLES

1 Solve $14 + y = 20$. Check your solution. **6**

2 Solve $a + 7 = 6$. Check your solution. **−1**

3 **FRUIT** A grapefruit weighs 11 ounces, which is 6 ounces more than an apple. How much does the apple weigh? **5 ounces**

Additional Examples are also in:
- Noteables™ Interactive Study Notebook with Foldables™
- Interactive Classroom PowerPoint® Presentations

ADDITIONAL EXAMPLES

④ Solve $12 = z - 8$. Check your solution. **20**

⑤ **MUSIC** Vivian practiced the piano for 32 minutes. She practiced 11 minutes less than her brother did. How long did her brother practice the piano? **43 minutes**

Vocabulary Link . . . . .
Inverse
Everyday Use something that is opposite
Math Use undo

∴ Similarly, you can use inverse operations and the Addition Property of Equality to solve equations like $x - 2 = 1$.

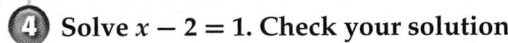

Addition Property of Equality **Key Concept**

Words   If you add the same number to each side of an equation, the two sides remain equal.

Symbols   If $a = b$, then $a + c = b + c$.

Examples

Numbers	Algebra
$5 = 5$	$x - 2 = 4$
$+ 3 = + 3$	$+ 2 = + 2$
$8 = 8$	$x = 6$

 EXAMPLE Solve a Subtraction Equation

④ Solve $x - 2 = 1$. Check your solution.

$$\begin{array}{ll} x - 2 = 1 & \text{Write the equation.} \\ \underline{+2 = +2} & \text{Add 2 to each side.} \\ x = 3 & \text{Simplify.} \end{array}$$

Check the solution. Since $3 - 2 = 1$, the solution is 3.

✓ **CHECK Your Progress**

e. $y - 3 = 4$ **7**   f. $r - 4 = -2$ **2**   g. $q - 8 = -9$ **−1**

 Real-World EXAMPLE

⑤ **SHOPPING** A pair of shoes costs $25. This is $14 less than the cost of a pair of jeans. Find the cost of the jeans.

Study Tip

Check for Reasonableness Ask yourself which costs more: the shoes or the jeans. Then check your answer. Does it show that the jeans cost more than the shoes?

Words	Shoes	are	$14 less than	jeans
▼ Variable		Let j represent the cost of jeans.		
▼ Equation	25	=	j	− 14

$$\begin{array}{ll} 25 = j - 14 & \text{Write the equation.} \\ \underline{+14 = +14} & \text{Add 14 to each side.} \\ 39 = j & \text{Simplify.} \end{array}$$

The jeans cost $39.

✓ **CHECK Your Progress**

h. **ANIMALS** The average lifespan of a tiger is 22 years. This is 13 years less than a lion. Write and solve an equation to find the lifespan of a lion. $x - 13 = 22$; **35 years**

138 Chapter 3 Algebra: Linear Equations and Functions

 Pre-AP Activity Use after Example 5.

Remind students that subtracting an integer is the same as adding its opposite. For example, $2 - 5$ is the same as $2 + (-5)$. Have students use what they know about integers to compare the Subtraction and Addition Properties of Equality.

CHECK Your Understanding

Examples 1, 2
(p. 137)

Solve each equation. Check your solution.

1. $n + 6 = 8$ **2**

2. $7 = y + 2$ **5**

3. $m + 5 = 3$ **−2**

4. $-2 = a + 6$ **−8**

Example 3
(p. 137)

5. **FLYING** Orville and Wilbur Wright made the first airplane flights in 1903. Wilbur's flight was 364 feet. This was 120 feet longer than Orville's flight. Write and solve an equation to find the length of Orville's flight.
   $d + 120 = 364$; **244 ft**

Example 4
(p. 138)

Solve each equation. Check your solution.

6. $x - 5 = 6$ **11**

7. $-1 = c - 6$ **5**

Example 5
(p. 138)

8. **PRESIDENTS** John F. Kennedy was the youngest president to be inaugurated. He was 43 years old. This was 26 years younger than the oldest president to be inaugurated—Ronald Reagan. Write and solve an equation to find how old Reagan was when he was inaugurated.
   $43 = r - 26$; **69 years old**

Practice and Problem Solving

HOMEWORK HELP	
For Exercises	See Examples
9–12	1
13–16	2
17–20	4
21–24	3, 5

Exercise Levels
A: 9–24
B: 25–45
C: 46–48

Solve each equation. Check your solution.

9. $a + 3 = 10$ **7**

10. $y + 5 = 11$ **6**

11. $9 = r + 2$ **7**

12. $14 = s + 7$ **7**

13. $x + 8 = 5$ **−3**

14. $y + 15 = 11$ **−4**

15. $r + 6 = -3$ **−9**

16. $k + 3 = -9$ **−12**

17. $s - 8 = 9$ **17**

18. $w - 7 = 11$ **18**

19. $-1 = q - 8$ **7**

20. $-2 = p - 13$ **11**

For Exercises 21–24, write an equation. Then solve the equation.

21. **MUSIC** Last week Tiffany practiced her bassoon a total of 7 hours. This was 2 hours more than she practiced the previous week. How many hours did Tiffany practice the previous week? $7 = w + 2$; **5**

22. **CIVICS** In the 2004 presidential election, Ohio had 20 electoral votes. This is 14 votes less than Texas had. How many electoral votes did Texas have in 2004? $20 = t - 14$; **34 votes**

23. **AGES** Zack is 15 years old. This is 3 years younger than his brother Tyler. How old is Tyler? $15 = t - 3$; **18 years old**

24. **BASKETBALL** The Miami Heat scored 79 points in a recent game. This was 13 points less than the Chicago Bulls score. How many points did the Chicago Bulls score? $x - 13 = 79$; $x = 92$

Lesson 3-2 Solving Addition and Subtraction Equations **139**

3 Practice

Formative Assessment

Use Exercises 1–8 to check for understanding.

Then use the chart at the bottom of this page to customize your assignments for students.

Intervention You may wish to use the Study Guide and Intervention Master on page 16 of the *Chapter 3 Resource Masters* for additional reinforcement.

Odd/Even Assignments

Exercises 9–24 are structured so that students practice the same concepts whether they are assigned odd or even problems.

Differentiated Instruction

Kinesthetic Learners If students have difficulty, you may wish to have them model Exercises 9–20 with a balance and counters.

DIFFERENTIATED HOMEWORK OPTIONS

Level	Assignment	Two-Day Option	
BL Basic	9–24, 46, 48, 49–57	9–23 odd, 49, 50	10–24 even, 46, 48, 51–57
OL Core	9–19 odd, 21–24, 25–35 odd, 37–46, 48–57	9–24, 49, 50	25–46, 48, 51–57
AL Advanced/Pre-AP	25–53 (optional: 54–57)		

Solve each equation. Check your solution.

25. $34 + r = 95$ **61**
26. $64 + y = 84$ **20**
27. $-23 = x - 18$ **−5**
28. $-59 = m - 11$ **−48**
29. $-18 + c = -30$ **−12**
30. $-34 = t + 9$ **−43**
31. $a - 3.5 = 14.9$ **18.4**
32. $x - 2.8 = 9.5$ **12.3**
33. $r - 8.5 = -2.1$ **6.4**
34. $z - 9.4 = -3.6$ **5.8**
35. $n + 1.4 = 0.72$ **−0.68**
36. $b + 2.25 = 1$ **−1.25**

For Exercises 37–42, write an equation. Then solve the equation.

37. **MONEY** Suppose you have d dollars. After you pay your sister the $5 you owe her, you have $18 left. How much money did you have at the beginning? $d - 5 = 18$; **$23**

38. **MONEY** Suppose you have saved $38. How much more do you need to save to buy a small television that costs $65? $38 + x = 65$; **$27**

39. **GEOMETRY** The sum of the measures of the angles of a triangle is 180°. Find the missing measure.
$35 + 45 + x = 180$; **100°**

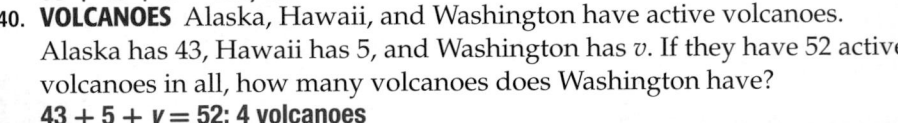

40. **VOLCANOES** Alaska, Hawaii, and Washington have active volcanoes. Alaska has 43, Hawaii has 5, and Washington has v. If they have 52 active volcanoes in all, how many volcanoes does Washington have?
$43 + 5 + v = 52$; **4 volcanoes**

Real-World Link ·····
Cristie Kerr donates $50.00 to breast cancer research for every birdie she makes.
Source: Birdies for Breast Cancer

41. **GOLF** The table shows Cristie Kerr's scores for four rounds of the 2007 U.S. Women's Open. Her total score was −5 (5 under par). What was her score for the third round?
$1 - 1 + s = -5$; **−5**

Round	Score
First	0
Second	+1
Third	s
Fourth	−1

42. **BUSINESS** At the end of the day, the closing price of XYZ Stock was $62.87 per share. This was $0.62 less than the opening price. Find the opening price. $62.87 = p - 0.62$; **$63.49**

ANALYZE TABLES For Exercises 43–45, use the table.

Tallest Wooden Roller Coasters	Height (feet)	Drop (feet)	Speed (mph)
Son of Beast	218	214	s
El Toro	181	176	70
The Rattler	180	d	65
Colossos	h	159	75
Voyage	163	154	67

Source: Coaster Grotto

43. The difference in speeds of Son of Beast and The Rattler is 13 miles per hour. If Son of Beast has the greater speed, write and solve a subtraction equation to find its speed. $s - 65 = 13$; **78 mph**.

44. The Rattler has a drop that is 52 feet less than El Toro. Write and solve an addition equation to find the height of The Rattler. $d + 52 = 176$; **124 ft**

45. Colossos is 13 feet taller than Voyage. Write and solve a subtraction equation to find the height of Colossos. $h - 13 = 163$; **176 ft**

EXTRA PRACTICE
See pages 674, 706.

H.O.T. Problems

46. $b + 5 = -8$;
All of the other equations have solutions of -3. This solution is -13.

46. **Which One Doesn't Belong?** Identify the equation that does not have the same solution as the other three. Explain your reasoning.

| $x - 1 = -4$ | $b + 5 = -8$ | $11 + y = 8$ | $-6 + a = -9$ |

47. **CHALLENGE** Suppose $x + y = 11$ and the value of x increases by 2. If their sum remains the same, what must happen to the value of y?
The value of y decreases by 2.

48. **WRITING IN MATH** Write a problem about a real-world situation that can be represented by the equation $p - 25 = 50$. **See margin.**

TEST PRACTICE

49. The Oriental Pearl Tower in Shanghai, China, is 1,535 feet tall. It is 280 feet shorter than the Canadian National Tower in Toronto, Canada. Which equation can be used to find the height of the Canadian National Tower? **C**

   A $1,535 + h = 280$
   B $h = 1,535 - 280$
   C $1,535 = h - 280$
   D $280 - h = 1,535$

50. Which of the following statements is true concerning the equation $x + 3 = 7$? **J**

   F To find the value of x, add 3 to each side.
   G To find the value of x, add 7 to each side.
   H To find the value of x, find the sum of 3 and 7.
   J To find the value of x, subtract 3 from each side.

Spiral Review

51. **SCIENCE** The boiling point of water is 180° higher than its freezing point. If p represents the freezing point, write an expression that represents the boiling point of water. (Lesson 3-1) **$p + 180$**

52. **ALGEBRA** Evaluate the expression $xy \div (-4)$ if $x = 12$ and $y = -2$. (Lesson 2-8) **6**

53. **ALGEBRA** The table shows the number of pages of a novel Ferguson read each hour. If the pattern continues, how many pages will Ferguson read during the 8th hour? (Lesson 2-7) **46 pages**

Hour	Number of Pages Read
1	11
2	13
3	16
4	20
5	25

▶ **GET READY for the Next Lesson**

PREREQUISITE SKILL Find each quotient.

54. $15.6 \div 13$ **1.2**   55. $8.84 \div 3.4$ **2.6**   56. $75.25 \div 0.25$ **301**   57. $0.76 \div 0.5$ **1.52**

Lesson 3-2 Solving Addition and Subtraction Equations **141**

4 Assess

Crystal Ball Tell students that tomorrow's lesson is about solving multiplication equations. Have students write how they think today's lesson will connect with tomorrow's.

 Formative Assessment

Check for student understanding of concepts in Lessons 3-1 and 3-2.

🔲 **CRM** Quiz 1, p. 55

 **Foldables™ Follow-Up**

Remind students to take notes about today's lesson under the *Equations* tab of their Foldables. Encourage them to record the Addition and Subtraction Properties of Equality and give examples of how to use the properties to solve equations.

Additional Answer

48. Sample answer: An office building is 50 stories tall. Its height is 25 stories less than an apartment building. What is the height of the apartment building?

3-3 Solving Multiplication Equations

PACING: **Regular:** 2 periods, **Block:** 1 period

Options for Differentiated Instruction

 = English Language Learner  = Above or Beyond Grade Level 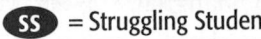 = Struggling Students 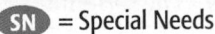 = Special Needs

Scaffolding the Lesson

Use before presenting Lesson 3-3.

Scaffold this lesson by investigating the relationship between multiplication and division.

Ask:
- What is the relationship between multiplication and division? They are inverse operations.
- How is the relationship between multiplication and division like the relationship between addition and subtraction? Give some examples to help explain your reasoning. Like addition and subtraction, multiplication and division "undo" each other. For example, $8 \times 2 \div 2 = 8$ and $15 \div 3 \times 3 = 15$.
- How are addition and subtraction used to solve equations? How might multiplication and division be used to solve equations? To solve addition equations, you subtract; to solve subtraction equations, you add. Similarly, to solve multiplication equations, you divide; to solve division equations, you multiply.
- What division facts are related to the multiplication problem $3 \times 4 = 12$? $12 \div 3 = 4$ and $12 \div 4 = 3$

Students' Self-Monitoring

Use before presenting the Mini Lab.

Have students write the equation given in the beginning of the Mini Lab, $3x = 6$.
- Before beginning the activity, have students write down what they do not yet know about solving an equation like this one. For example, they may not know how to find the value of x.
- After completing the activity, have students look over what they wrote. Are there things they still need to learn?

Visual Clues

Use before assigning the Exercises.

When solving multiplication equations, have students circle the coefficient of the variable as a visual cue of what they will be dividing by. This will be particularly helpful when the variable is not the first term in the equation.

1. $\textcircled{6}c = 18$ **2.** $15 = \textcircled{3}z$ **3.** $\textcircled{-8}x = 24$ **4.** $\textcircled{-9}r = -36$

Leveled Lesson Resources

Chapter 3 Resource Masters

BL = Below or Approaching Grade Level   **OL** = On Grade Level   **AL** = Above or Beyond Grade Level   **ELL** = English Language Learner

---

Lesson Reading Guide
p. 22 BL OL ELL

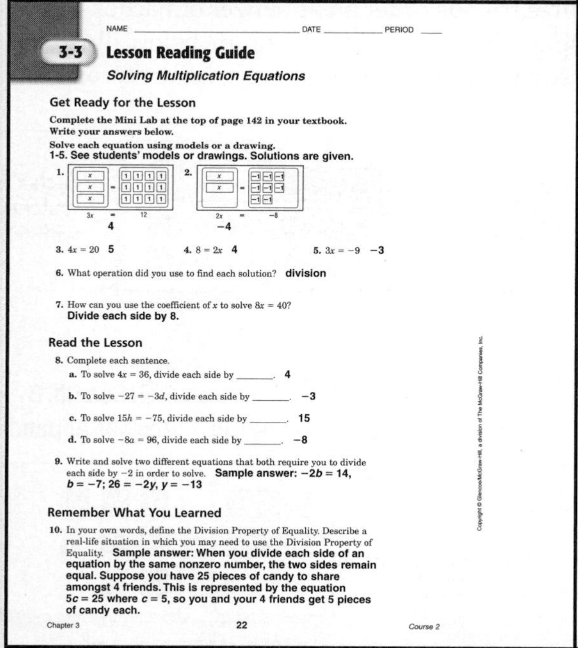

NAME _____ DATE _____ PERIOD _____

3-3 Lesson Reading Guide
Solving Multiplication Equations

Get Ready for the Lesson
Complete the Mini Lab at the top of page 142 in your textbook. Write your answers below.
Solve each equation using models or a drawing.
1–5. See students' models or drawings. Solutions are given.

1. **4**
2. **−4**
3. $4x = 20$ **5**   4. $8 = 2x$ **4**   5. $3x = −9$ **−3**

6. What operation did you use to find each solution? **division**

7. How can you use the coefficient of x to solve $8x = 40$?
Divide each side by 8.

Read the Lesson
8. Complete each sentence.
   a. To solve $4x = 36$, divide each side by _____. **4**
   b. To solve $−27 = −3d$, divide each side by _____. **−3**
   c. To solve $15h = −75$, divide each side by _____. **15**
   d. To solve $−8a = 96$, divide each side by _____. **−8**

9. Write and solve two different equations that both require you to divide each side by −2 in order to solve. **Sample answer: −2b = 14, b = −7; 26 = −2y, y = −13**

Remember What You Learned
10. In your own words, define the Division Property of Equality. Describe a real-life situation in which you may need to use the Division Property of Equality. **Sample answer: When you divide each side of an equation by the same nonzero number, the two sides remain equal. Suppose you have 25 pieces of candy to share amongst 4 friends. This is represented by the equation 5c = 25 where c = 5, so you and your 4 friends get 5 pieces of candy each.**

Chapter 3   22   Course 2

Study Guide and Intervention*
p. 23 BL OL ELL

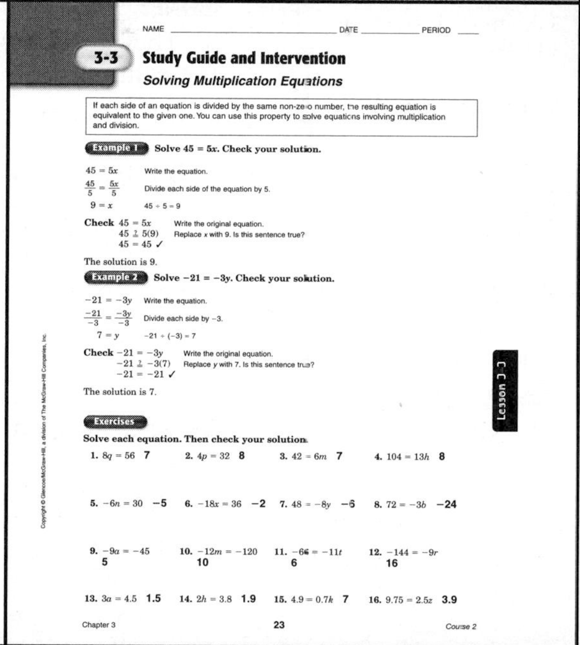

NAME _____ DATE _____ PERIOD _____

3-3 Study Guide and Intervention
Solving Multiplication Equations

If each side of an equation is divided by the same non-zero number, the resulting equation is equivalent to the given one. You can use this property to solve equations involving multiplication and division.

Example 1 Solve $45 = 5x$. Check your solution.

$45 = 5x$ Write the equation.
$\frac{45}{5} = \frac{5x}{5}$ Divide each side of the equation by 5.
$9 = x$ $45 \div 5 = 9$

Check $45 = 5x$ Write the original equation.
$45 \stackrel{?}{=} 5(9)$ Replace x with 9. Is this sentence true?
$45 = 45$ ✓

The solution is 9.

Example 2 Solve $−21 = −3y$. Check your solution.

$−21 = −3y$ Write the equation.
$\frac{−21}{−3} = \frac{−3y}{−3}$ Divide each side by −3.
$7 = y$ $−21 \div (−3) = 7$

Check $−21 = −3y$ Write the original equation.
$−21 \stackrel{?}{=} −3(7)$ Replace y with 7. Is this sentence true?
$−21 = −21$ ✓

The solution is 7.

Exercises
Solve each equation. Then check your solution.

1. $8g = 56$ **7**   2. $4p = 32$ **8**   3. $42 = 6m$ **7**   4. $104 = 13h$ **8**

5. $−6n = 30$ **−5**   6. $−18x = 36$ **−2**   7. $48 = −8y$ **−6**   8. $72 = −3b$ **−24**

9. $−9a = −45$ **5**   10. $−12m = −120$ **10**   11. $−6s = −11t$ **6**   12. $−144 = −9r$ **16**

13. $3a = 4.5$ **1.5**   14. $2h = 3.8$ **1.9**   15. $4.9 = 0.7k$ **7**   16. $9.75 = 2.5z$ **3.9**

Chapter 3   23   Course 2

Skills Practice*
p. 24 BL OL

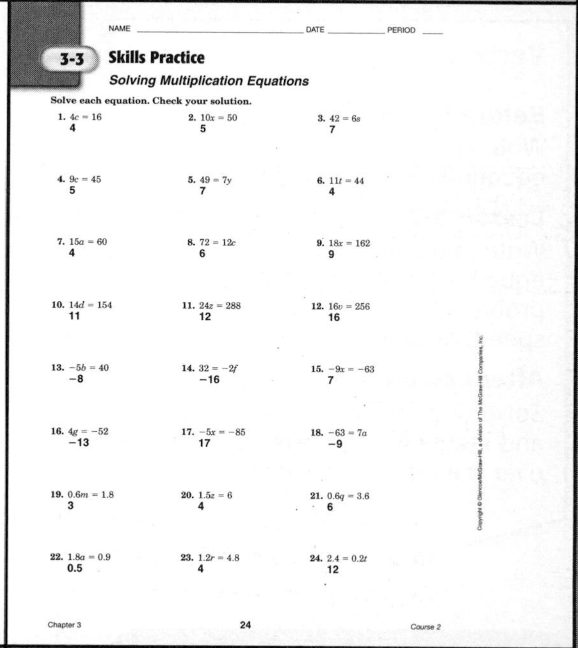

NAME _____ DATE _____ PERIOD _____

3-3 Skills Practice
Solving Multiplication Equations

Solve each equation. Check your solution.

1. $4c = 16$ **4**   2. $10x = 50$ **5**   3. $42 = 6e$ **7**

4. $9c = 45$ **5**   5. $49 = 7y$ **7**   6. $11t = 44$ **4**

7. $15a = 60$ **4**   8. $72 = 12c$ **6**   9. $18x = 162$ **9**

10. $14d = 154$ **11**   11. $24z = 288$ **12**   12. $16c = 256$ **16**

13. $−5b = 40$ **−8**   14. $32 = −2f$ **−16**   15. $−9x = −63$ **7**

16. $4g = −52$ **−13**   17. $−5x = −85$ **17**   18. $−63 = 7a$ **−9**

19. $0.6m = 1.8$ **3**   20. $1.5z = 6$ **4**   21. $0.6q = 3.6$ **6**

22. $1.8a = 0.9$ **0.5**   23. $1.2r = 4.8$ **4**   24. $2.4 = 0.2t$ **12**

Chapter 3   24   Course 2

Practice*
p. 25 OL AL

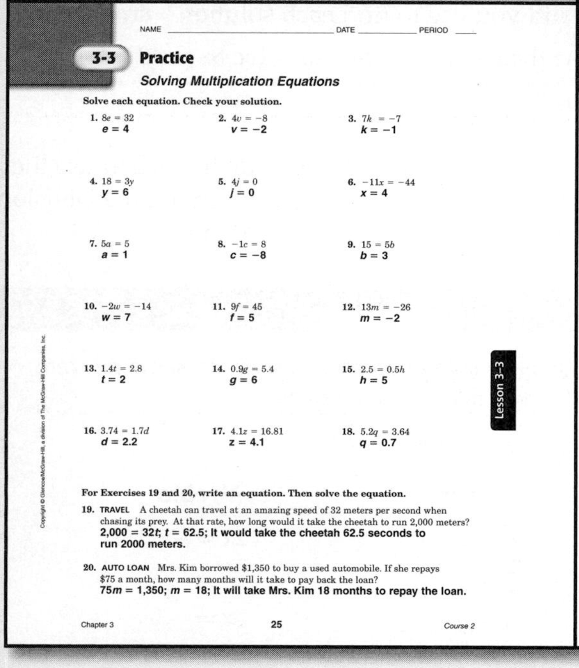

NAME _____ DATE _____ PERIOD _____

3-3 Practice
Solving Multiplication Equations

Solve each equation. Check your solution.

1. $8e = 32$ **e = 4**   2. $4v = −8$ **v = −2**   3. $7k = −7$ **k = −1**

4. $18 = 3y$ **y = 6**   5. $4j = 0$ **j = 0**   6. $−11x = −44$ **x = 4**

7. $5a = 5$ **a = 1**   8. $−1c = 8$ **c = −8**   9. $15 = 5b$ **b = 3**

10. $−2w = −14$ **w = 7**   11. $9f = 45$ **f = 5**   12. $13m = −26$ **m = −2**

13. $1.4t = 2.8$ **t = 2**   14. $0.9g = 5.4$ **g = 6**   15. $2.5 = 0.5h$ **h = 5**

16. $3.74 = 1.7d$ **d = 2.2**   17. $4.1z = 16.81$ **z = 4.1**   18. $5.2q = 3.64$ **q = 0.7**

For Exercises 19 and 20, write an equation. Then solve the equation.

19. TRAVEL A cheetah can travel at an amazing speed of 32 meters per second when chasing its prey. At that rate, how long would it take the cheetah to run 2,000 meters? **2,000 = 32t; t = 62.5; It would take the cheetah 62.5 seconds to run 2000 meters.**

20. AUTO LOAN Mrs. Kim borrowed $1,350 to buy a used automobile. If she repays $75 a month, how many months will it take to pay back the loan? **75m = 1,350; m = 18; It will take Mrs. Kim 18 months to repay the loan.**

Chapter 3   25   Course 2

Word Problem Practice*
p. 26 OL AL

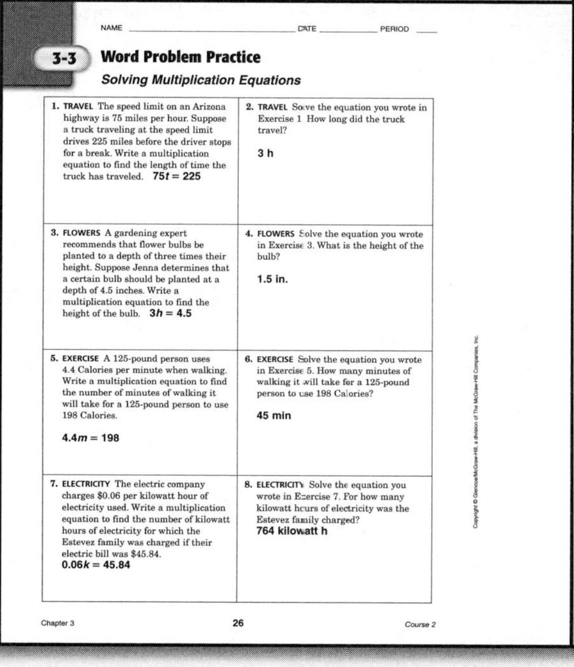

NAME _____ DATE _____ PERIOD _____

3-3 Word Problem Practice
Solving Multiplication Equations

1. TRAVEL The speed limit on an Arizona highway is 75 miles per hour. Suppose a truck traveling at the speed limit drives 225 miles before the driver stops for a break. Write a multiplication equation to find the length of time the truck has traveled. **75t = 225**

2. TRAVEL Solve the equation you wrote in Exercise 1. How long did the truck travel? **3 h**

3. FLOWERS A gardening expert recommends that flower bulbs be planted to a depth of three times their height. Suppose Jenna determines that a certain bulb should be planted at a depth of 4.5 inches. Write a multiplication equation to find the height of the bulb. **3h = 4.5**

4. FLOWERS Solve the equation you wrote in Exercise 3. What is the height of the bulb? **1.5 in.**

5. EXERCISE A 125-pound person uses 4.4 Calories per minute when walking. Write a multiplication equation to find the number of minutes of walking it will take for a 125-pound person to use 198 Calories. **4.4m = 198**

6. EXERCISE Solve the equation you wrote in Exercise 5. How many minutes of walking it will take for a 125-pound person to use 198 Calories? **45 min**

7. ELECTRICITY The electric company charges $0.06 per kilowatt hour of electricity used. Write a multiplication equation to find the number of kilowatt hours of electricity for which the Estevez family was charged if their electric bill was $45.84. **0.06k = 45.84**

8. ELECTRICITY Solve the equation you wrote in Exercise 7. For how many kilowatt hours of electricity was the Estevez family charged? **764 kilowatt h**

Chapter 3   26   Course 2

Enrichment
p. 27 OL AL

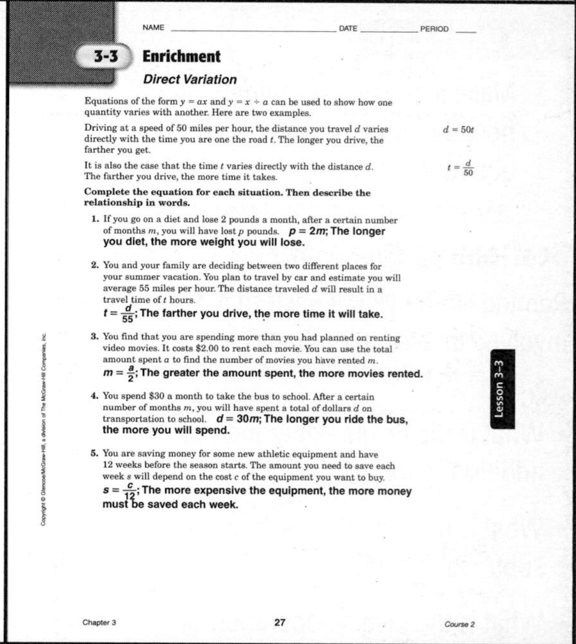

NAME _____ DATE _____ PERIOD _____

3-3 Enrichment
Direct Variation

Equations of the form $y = ax$ and $y = x \div a$ can be used to show how one quantity varies with another. Here are two examples.

Driving at a speed of 50 miles per hour, the distance you travel d varies directly with the time you are one the road t. The longer you drive, the farther you get. $d = 50t$

It is also the case that the time t varies directly with the distance d. The farther you drive, the more time it takes. $t = \frac{d}{50}$

Complete the equation for each situation. Then describe the relationship in words.

1. If you go on a diet and lose 2 pounds a month, after a certain number of months m, you will have lost p pounds. **p = 2m; The longer you diet, the more weight you will lose.**

2. You and your family are deciding between two different places for your summer vacation. You plan to travel by car and estimate you will average 55 miles per hour. The distance traveled d will result in a travel time of t hours. **t = $\frac{d}{55}$; The farther you drive, the more time it will take.**

3. You find that you are spending more than you had planned on renting video movies. It costs $2.00 to rent each movie. You can use the total amount spent a to find the number of movies you have rented m. **m = $\frac{a}{2}$; The greater the amount spent, the more movies rented.**

4. You spend $30 a month to take the bus to school. After a certain number of months m, you will have spent a total of dollars d on transportation to school. **d = 30m; The longer you ride the bus, the more you will spend.**

5. You are saving money for some new athletic equipment. You have 12 weeks before the season starts. The amount you need to save each week s will depend on the cost c of the equipment you want to buy. **s = $\frac{c}{12}$; The more expensive the equipment, the more money must be saved each week.**

Chapter 3   27   Course 2

Additional Lesson Resources

* Also available in Spanish **ELL**

Transparencies
- *5-Minute Check Transparency*, Lesson 3-3

Other Print Products
- *Teaching Mathematics with Manipulatives*
- *Noteables™ Interactive Study Notebook with Foldables™*

Teacher Tech Tools
- *Interactive Classroom CD-ROM*, Lesson 3-3
- *AssignmentWorks*, Lesson 3-3

Student Tech Tools
glencoe.com
- Extra Examples, Chapter 3, Lesson 3
- Self-Check Quiz, Chapter 3, Lesson 3

 **3-3** Solving Multiplication Equations

3-3

1 Focus

Vertical Alignment

Before Lesson 3-3
Write and solve one-step linear equations in one variable

Lesson 3-3
Write and solve one-step linear equations in one variable; solve problems involving rates, average speed, distance, and time

After Lesson 3-3
Solve two-step linear equations and inequalities in one variable over the rational numbers

2 Teach

▶ MINI Lab

Make sure students understand how the model represents the equation $3x = 6$.

Scaffolding Questions

Remind students that yesterday's lesson involved inverse operations.

Ask:

• What is the inverse operation of addition? subtraction

• What is the inverse operation of subtraction? addition

• What is the inverse operation of multiplication? division

• How can you use division to solve a multiplication equation? Sample answer: Since division is the inverse operation of multiplication, you can undo multiplication by dividing.

MAIN IDEA

Solve multiplication equations.

New Vocabulary

formula

Math Online ▶

glencoe.com

• Concepts In Motion
• Extra Examples
• Personal Tutor
• Self-Check Quiz

▶ MINI Lab

MONEY Suppose three friends order an appetizer of nachos that costs $6. They agree to split the cost equally. The figure below illustrates the multiplication equation $3x = 6$, where x represents the amount each friend pays.

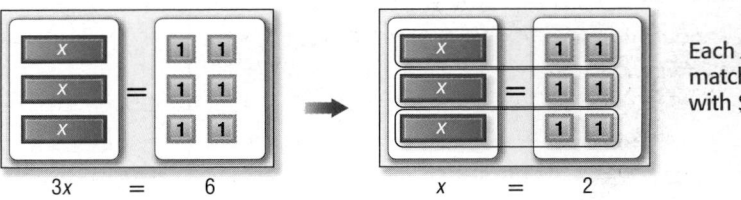

Each x is matched with $2.

Each friend pays $2. The solution of $3x = 6$ is 2.

Solve each equation using models or a drawing. **1–5. See Ch. 3 Answer Appendix.**

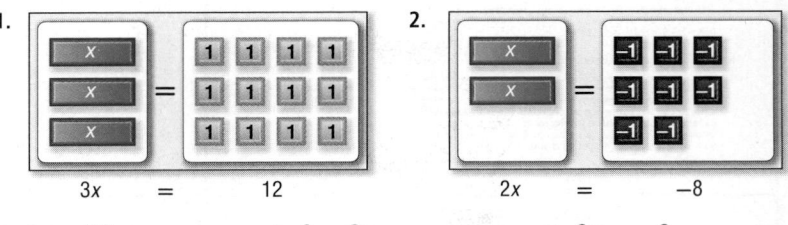

1. $3x = 12$

2. $2x = -8$

3. $4x = 20$ 4. $8 = 2x$ 5. $3x = -9$

6. What operation did you use to find each solution? **division**

7. How can you use the coefficient of x to solve $8x = 40$?

7. divide each side by 8

Equations like $3x = 6$ are called multiplication equations because the expression $3x$ means 3 *times the value of* x. So, you can use the Division Property of Equality to solve multiplication equations.

Division Property of Equality   Key Concept

Words   If you divide each side of an equation by the same nonzero number, the two sides remain equal.

Symbols   If $a = b$ and $c \neq 0$, then $\frac{a}{c} = \frac{b}{c}$.

Examples

Numbers	Algebra
$8 = 8$	$2x = -6$
$\frac{8}{2} = \frac{8}{2}$	$\frac{2x}{2} = \frac{-6}{2}$
$4 = 4$	$x = -3$

---

coefficient the numerical factor for a multiplication expression; *Example*: the coefficient of *x* in the expression 4*x* is 4. (Lesson 1-4)

EXAMPLES Solve Multiplication Equations

① Solve $20 = 4x$. Check your solution.

$20 = 4x$	Write the equation.
$\dfrac{20}{4} = \dfrac{4x}{4}$	Divide each side of the equation by 4.
$5 = x$	$20 \div 4 = 5$
The solution is 5.	Check the solution.

② Solve $-8y = 24$. Check your solution.

$-8y = 24$	Write the equation.
$\dfrac{-8y}{-8} = \dfrac{24}{-8}$	Divide each side by -8.
$y = -3$	$24 \div (-8) = -3$
The solution is -3.	Check the solution.

✓ CHECK Your Progress

Solve each equation. Check your solution.

a. $30 = 6x$ **5** b. $-6a = 36$ **−6** c. $-9d = -72$ **8**

Many real-world situations increase at a constant rate. These can be represented by multiplication equations.

Real-World EXAMPLE

③ **TEXT MESSAGING** It costs $0.10 to send a text message. You can spend a total of $5.00. How many text messages can you send?

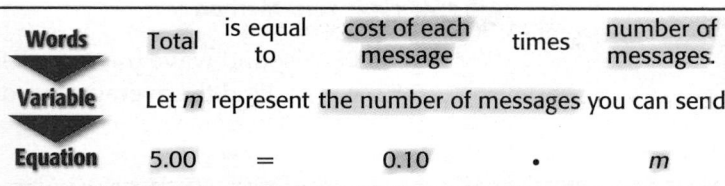

Words	Total	is equal to	cost of each message	times	number of messages.
Variable	Let *m* represent the number of messages you can send.				
Equation	5.00	=	0.10	•	*m*

$5.00 = 0.10m$	Write the equation.
$\dfrac{5.00}{0.10} = \dfrac{0.10m}{0.10}$	Divide each side by 0.10.
$50 = m$	$5.00 \div 0.10 = 50$

At $0.10 per message, you can send 50 text messages for $5.00.

✓ CHECK Your Progress

d. **TRAVEL** Mrs. Acosta's car can travel an average of 24 miles on each gallon of gasoline. Write and solve an equation to find how many gallons of gasoline she will need for a trip of 348 miles.

Real-World Link . . . .
Over 60% of teenagers' text messages are sent from their homes— even when a landline is available.
Source: Xerox

d. $24x = 348$; 14.5 gal

Lesson 3-3 Solving Multiplication Equations **143**

FOLDABLES **Foldables™**
Study Organizer **Follow-Up**

Remind students to take notes about today's lesson under the *Equations* tab of their Foldables. Encourage them to record the Division Property of Equality and give examples of how to use the property to solve equations.

 Focus on Mathematical Content

Dividing each side of an equation by the same nonzero number maintains the equation.

Rate problems can be shown with multiplication equations.

✓ Formative Assessment

Use the Check Your Progress exercises after each Example to determine students' understanding of concepts.

ADDITIONAL EXAMPLES

① Solve $39 = 3y$. Check your solution. 13

② Solve $-4z = 60$. Check your solution. −15

③ **MAIL** Serena went to the post office to mail some party invitations. She had $6.15. If each invitation needed a $0.41 stamp, how many invitations could she mail? 15

Additional Examples are also in:

• Noteables™ Interactive Study Notebook with Foldables™

• Interactive Classroom PowerPoint® Presentations

 **Solving Equations**

Tips for New Teachers

Remind students that to solve an algebraic equation, they need to find a value for the variable that makes the equation true. That is, they need to isolate the variable on one side of the equals sign. They can do this by "undoing" any operation performed with the variable. When students "undo" multiplication by dividing each side of the equation by the same number, they are using the Division Property of Equality.

144 Chapter 3 Algebra: Linear Equations and Functions

ADDITIONAL EXAMPLE

④ **SWIMMING** Ms. Wang swims at a speed of 0.6 mph. At this rate, how long will it take her to swim 3 miles? **5 hours**

Choosing Your Method

Point out to students the benefit of choosing Method 2 in solving Example 4. By solving the equation for t, you can solve similar problems more quickly. Given a distance of 250 miles and a rate of 60 miles per hour, you can quickly substitute d and r into the equation $\frac{d}{r} = t$ to find t.

3 Practice

Formative Assessment

Use Exercises 1–6 to check for understanding.

Then use the chart at the bottom of the next page to customize your assignments for students.

Intervention You may wish to use the Study Guide and Intervention Master on page 23 of the *Chapter 3 Resource Masters* for additional reinforcement.

A **formula** is an equation that shows the relationship among certain quantities. One of the most common formulas is the equation $d = rt$, which gives the relationship among distance d, rate r, and time t.

Reading Math

Speed Another name for *rate* is *speed*.

Real-World EXAMPLE

④ **ANIMALS** The tortoise is one of the slowest land animals, reaching an average top speed of about 0.25 mile per hour. At this speed, how long will it take a tortoise to travel 1.5 miles?

You are asked to find the time t it will take to travel a distance d of 1.5 miles at a rate r of 0.25 mile per hour.

METHOD 1 Substitute, then solve.

$d = rt$	Write the equation.
$1.5 = 0.25t$	Replace d with 1.5 and r with 0.25.
$\dfrac{1.5}{0.25} = \dfrac{0.25t}{0.25}$	Divide each side by 0.25.
$6 = t$	$1.5 \div 0.25 = 6$

METHOD 2 Solve, then substitute.

$d = rt$	Write the equation.
$\dfrac{d}{r} = \dfrac{rt}{r}$	Divide each side by r to solve the equation for t.
$\dfrac{d}{r} = t$	Simplify.
$\dfrac{1.5}{0.25} = t$	Replace d with 1.5 and r with 0.25.
$6 = t$	$1.5 \div 0.25 = 6$

It would take a tortoise 6 hours to travel 1.5 miles.

✓ CHOOSE Your Method

e. SCIENCE A sound wave travels a distance of 700 meters in 2.5 seconds. Find the average speed of the sound wave. **280 m/s**

★ indicates multi-step problem

✓ CHECK Your Understanding

Examples 1, 2 (p. 143)

Solve each equation. Check your solution.

1. $6c = 18$ **3**
2. $15 = 3z$ **5**
3. $-8x = 24$ **−3**
4. $-9r = -36$ **4**

Example 3 (p. 143)

5. **WORKING** Antonia earns $6 per hour helping her grandmother. How many hours does she need to work to earn $48? **8 h**

Example 4 (p. 144)

6. **SWIMMING** A shark can swim at an average speed of about 25 miles per hour. At this rate, how long will it take a shark to swim 60 miles? **2.4 hours**

Practice and Problem Solving

HOMEWORK HELP

For Exercises	See Examples
7–12	1
13–18	2
19–20	3
21–22	4

Exercise Levels
A: 7–22
B: 23–32
C: 33–37

Solve each equation. Check your solution.

7. $7a = 49$ **7**

8. $9e = 27$ **3**

9. $2x = -6$ **—3**

10. $3y = -21$ **—7**

11. $35 = 5v$ **7**

12. $72 = 12r$ **6**

13. $-4j = 36$ **—9**

14. $-12y = 60$ **—5**

15. $-4s = -16$ **4**

16. $-6z = -36$ **6**

17. $48 = -6r$ **—8**

18. $-28 = -7f$ **4**

For Exercises 19–22, write an equation. Then solve the equation.

19. **MONEY** Brandy wants to buy a digital camera that costs $300. If she saves $15 each week, in how many weeks will she have enough money for the camera? **$15w = 300$; 20 weeks**

20. **COMPUTERS** The width of a computer monitor is 1.25 times as long as its height. Find the height of the computer monitor at the right. **$1.25x = 15$; $x = 12$ in.**

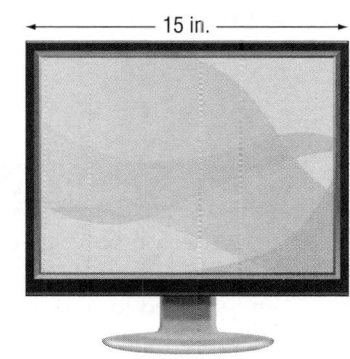

← 15 in. →

21. **SPEED** A racecar can travel at a rate of 205 miles per hour. At this rate, how long would it take to travel 615 miles? **3 h**

22. **INSECTS** A dragonfly, the fastest insect, can fly a distance of 50 feet in about 2 seconds. Find a dragonfly's average speed in feet per second. **$50 = 2r$; 25 feet per second**

Solve each equation. Check your solution.

23. $0.4x = 9.2$ **23**

24. $0.9y = 13.5$ **15**

25. $5.4 = 0.3p$ **18**

26. $9.72 = 1.8a$ **5.4**

27. $3.9y = 18.33$ **4.7**

28. $2.6b = 2.08$ **0.8**

ANALYZE TABLES For Exercises 29 and 30, use the following information.
The table shows women's championship record holders for several track events.

29. Without calculating explain whether Evelyn Ashford or Sanya Richards has the faster average speed.

Name	Race (m)	Time (s)
Evelyn Ashford	200	21.88
Sanya Richards	400	49.27

Source: USA Outdoor Track & Field

30. Find the average speed of each athlete in meters per second. Round to the nearest hundredth.

29. Sample answer: Evelyn Ashford has the faster average speed. Her race is half the distance as Sanya Richards', and it took her less than half the time as Sanya Richards to complete the race.

30. Evelyn Ashford 9.14 m/s; Sanya Richards 8.12 m/s

31. **HURRICANES** A category 3 hurricane reaches speeds up to 20.88 kilometers per hour. The distance from Cuba to Key West is 145 kilometers. Write and solve a multiplication equation to find how long it would take a category 3 hurricane to travel from Cuba to Key West. **$20.88h = 145$; $h \approx 6.94$**

EXTRA PRACTICE
See pages 674, 706.

32. **WATER** A case of water bottles costs $9.48. If there are 12 water bottles in the case, find the cost per bottle. Then find the decrease in cost per bottle if the cost of a case is reduced to $8.64. **$0.79; $0.07**

Odd/Even Assignments

Exercises 7–22 are structured so that students practice the same concepts whether they are assigned odd or even problems.

DIFFERENTIATED HOMEWORK OPTIONS

Level	Assignment	Two-Day Option	
BL Basic	7–22, 33, 35–45	7–21 odd, 38–39	8–22 even, 33, 35–37, 40–45
OL Core	7–17 odd, 19–22, 23–27 odd, 29–33, 35–45	7–22, 38–39	23–33, 35–37, 40–45
AL Advanced/Pre-AP	23–44 (optional: 45)		

Find the Error In Exercise 33, Steve is correct. Becky divided each side of the equation by 6 rather than by −6. Remind students to pay attention to the signs of coefficients when deciding how to solve an equation.

 Assess

Ticket Out the Door Write the rate formula ($d = rt$) on the board. Have students write their own rate problem.

Additional Answers

35. Sample answer: Billie has twice as many cards as Tyree. If Billie has 16 cards, how many does Tyree have?

36. Sample answer: Three coins of the same value are worth 75 cents. How much is each coin worth?

37. Sample answer: If it takes a scuba diver 4 seconds to swim 8 meters below the surface of the water, what is the rate of descent?

45.

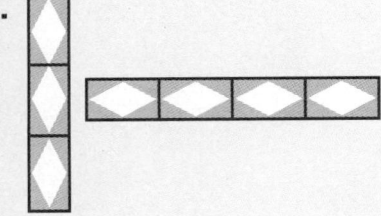

H.O.T. Problems

33. Steve; the variable is multiplied by −6. To solve for x, you need to divide each side of the equation by the entire coefficient, −6.

34. The absolute value of a positive or negative number is always positive. So, $x = 4$ or $x = -4$.

33. FIND THE ERROR Steve and Becky are solving $-6x = 72$. Who is correct? Explain.

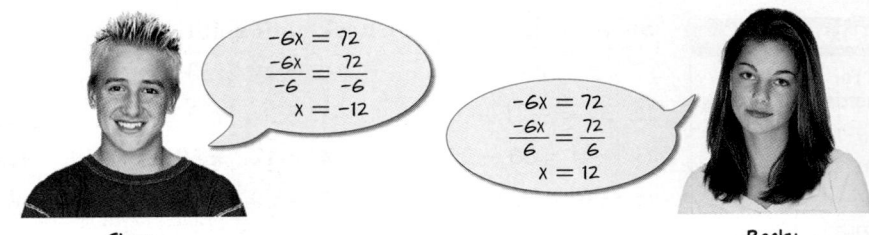

Steve   Becky

34. CHALLENGE Solve $3|x| = 12$. Explain your reasoning.

WRITING IN MATH Write a real-world problem that could be represented by each equation. **35–37. See margin.**

35. $2x = 16$ 36. $3x = 75$ 37. $4x = -8$

TEST PRACTICE

38. A football player can run 20 yards in 3.4 seconds. Which equation could be used to find y, the number of yards the football player can run in a second? **C**

   A $20y = 3.4$

   B $3.4 - y = 20$

   C $3.4y = 20$

   D $20 + y = 3.4$

39. **SHORT RESPONSE** Use the formula $A = bh$ to find the base in inches of a rhombus with a height of 7 inches and an area of 56 square inches. **8**

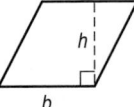

Spiral Review

ALGEBRA Solve each equation. Check your solution. (Lesson 3-2)

40. $y + 8 = -2$ **−10**   41. $x - 7 = -2$ **5**   42. $20 = z + 23$ **−3**

43. **ALGEBRA** Write an algebraic expression for the phrase *the product of −3 and y*. (Lesson 3-1) **−3y**

★ 44. **MONTHS** A lunar month, the time from one new moon to the next, is 29.5 days. How many days longer is our calendar year of 365 days than 12 lunar months? (Lesson 1-1) **11 days**

▷ **GET READY for the Next Lesson**

PREREQUISITE SKILL Draw the next two figures in the pattern. (Lesson 2-7) **See margin.**

45.

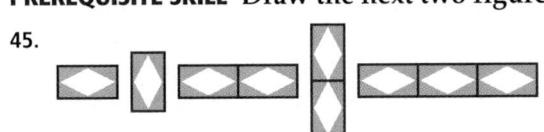

Pre-AP Activity   Use after Exercise 37

Write a two-part equation such as $3x - 4 = 41$ on the board. Have students write what steps they would take to solve it.

Mid-Chapter Quiz
Lessons 3-1 through 3-3

Write each sentence as an algebraic equation.
(Lesson 3-1)

1. The product of a number and 3 is −16. **$3n = -16$**

2. 10 less than a number is 45. **$n - 10 = 45$**

3. **CLIMBING** A rock climber is at an altitude of a feet before she climbs up another 80 feet. Write an expression for her new altitude. (Lesson 3-1) **$a + 80$**

4. **MULTIPLE CHOICE** Stephanie has 5 dollars more than Necie. If Necie has d dollars, which expression represents the number of dollars Stephanie has? (Lesson 3-1) **B**

   A $d - 5$ C $5 - d$

   B $d + 5$ D $5d$

Solve each equation. Check your solution.
(Lesson 3-2)

5. $21 + m = 33$ **12**   6. $a - 5 = -12$ **−7**

7. $p + 1.7 = -9.8$ **−11.5** 8. $56 = k - (-33)$ **23**

9. **GEOMETRY** The sum of the measures of the angles of a triangle is 180°. Write and solve an equation to find the missing measure m. (Lesson 3-2) **$45 + 20 + m = 180; 115°$**

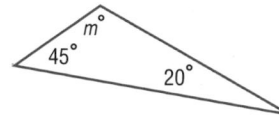

10. **MULTIPLE CHOICE** Trevor's test score was 5 points lower than Ursalina's test score. If Ursalina scored 85 on the test, which equation would give Trevor's score d when solved? (Lesson 3-2) **F**

    F $85 = d + 5$

    G $d - 5 = 85$

    H $80 = d + 5$

    J $d - 5 = 80$

11. **PETS** Cameron has 11 adult Fantail goldfish. This is 7 fewer Fantail goldfish than his friend Julia has. Write and solve a subtraction equation to determine the number of Fantail goldfish g that Julia has. (Lesson 3-2)
    $11 = g - 7$; 18 Fantail goldfish

12. **MEASUREMENT** The Grand Canyon has a maximum depth of almost 5,280 feet. An average four-story apartment building has a height of 66 feet. Write and solve a multiplication equation to determine the number of apartment buildings b, stacked on top of each other, that would fill the depth of the Grand Canyon. (Lesson 3-3)
    $66b = 5,280; b = 80$

Solve each equation. Check your solution.
(Lesson 3-3)

13. $5f = -75$ **−15**   14. $-1.6w = 4.8$ **−3**

15. $63 = 7y$ **9**   16. $-28 = -2d$ **14**

17. $3.7g = -4.44$ **−1.2** 18. $2.25 = 1.5b$ **1.5**

19. **MULTIPLE CHOICE** Michelann drove 44 miles per hour and covered a distance of 154 miles. Which equation accurately describes this situation if h represents the number of hours Michelann drove? (Lesson 3-3) **B**

    A $154 = 44 + h$

    B $44h = 154$

    C $154 = 44 \div h$

    D $h - 44 = 154$

20. **LAWN SERVICE** Trey estimates he will earn $470 next summer cutting lawns in his neighborhood. This amount is 2.5 times the amount a he earned this summer. Write and solve a multiplication equation to find how much Trey earned this summer. (Lesson 3-3) **$2.5a = 470; 188**

 **Formative Assessment**

Use the Mid-Chapter Quiz to assess students' progress in the first half of the chapter.

Have students review the lesson indicated for the problems they answered incorrectly.

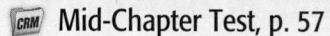 **Summative Assessment**

CRM Mid-Chapter Test, p. 57

ExamView Assessment Suite Customize and create multiple versions of your Mid-Chapter Test and their answer keys.

 **Dinah Zike's Foldables**
Study Organizer

Before students complete the Mid-Chapter Quiz, encourage them to review the information on the first two pages of their Foldables.

Data-Driven Decision Making	Exercises	Lesson	State/Local Standards	Resources for Review
Diagnostic Teaching Based on the results of the Chapter 3 Mid-Chapter Quiz, use the following to review concepts that students continue to find challenging.	1–4	3–1		CRM Study Guide and Intervention pp. 10, 16, and 23 **Math Online** glencoe.com
	5–11	3–2		• Extra Examples
	12–20	3–3		• Personal Tutor • Concepts in Motion

Problem-Solving Investigation
WORK BACKWARD

PACING: **Regular:** 1 period, **Block:** 0.5 period

Options for Differentiated Instruction

ELL = English Language Learner   **AL** = Above or Beyond Grade Level   **SS** = Struggling Students   **SN** = Special Needs

Relating to Everyday Tasks

Use before presenting Lesson 3-4.

Have students list the steps they would take to put on their socks and tennis shoes. Their steps might be similar to those shown to the right.

Ask:

- If you were to work backward to take off your socks and shoes, what would be the first step? List the remaining steps.
- Would it make sense for you to take off your socks before your tennis shoes?
- Would it make a difference if you untied both shoes before taking them off?
- When can the steps of working backward have flexibility and when can they not?

Step	Action
1	Put on my right sock.
2	Put on my left sock.
3	Put on my right tennis shoe.
4	Tie my right tennis shoe.
5	Put on my left tennis shoe.
6	Tie my left tennis shoe.

Organizing Student Work and Thinking   **SN**

Use before assigning the Exercises.

Have students add the work backward strategy to their problem-solving booklets. They should include the following about the strategy:

- a description of the strategy
- an explanation of the best time to use the strategy
- examples of problems that are solved using the strategy
- advantages and disadvantages of using the strategy

Analyzing Problems **ELL** **SS**

Use with Exercises 4–7.

Make sure that students correctly identify the order in which events occur in order to solve problems using the work backward strategy. Stress that they read the problems carefully, as steps are not always presented in order.

Leveled Lesson Resources

Chapter 3 Resource Masters

Study Guide and Intervention*
p. 28 **BL** **OL** **ELL**

NAME _____ DATE _____ PERIOD _____

3-4 Study Guide and Intervention
Problem-Solving Investigation: Work Backward

By working backward from where you end to where you began, you can solve problems. Use the four-step problem solving model to stay organized when working backward.

Example 1 Jonah put half of his birthday money into his savings account. Then he paid back the $10 that he owed his brother for dance tickets. Lastly, he spent $3 on lunch at school. At the end of the day he was left with $12. How much money did Jonah receive for his birthday?

Understand	You know that he had $12 left and the amounts he spent throughout the day. You need to find out how much money he received for his birthday.
Plan	Start with the amount of money he was left with and work backward.
Solve	He had $12 left. 12
	Undo the $3 he spent on lunch. + 3
	15
	Undo the $10 he gave back to his brother + 10
	25
	Undo the half put into his savings account 2
	So, Jonah received $50 for his birthday. 50
Check	Assume that Jonah receive $50 for his birthday. After putting half into his savings account he had $50 ÷ 2 or $25. Then he gave $10 to his brother for dance tickets, so he had $25 − $10 or $15. Lastly, he spent $3 on lunch at school, so he had $15 − $3, or $12. So, our answer of $50 is correct.

Exercises

Solve each problem by using the work backward strategy.

1. On Monday everyone was present in Mr. Miller's class. At 12:00, 5 students left early for doctors' appointments. At 1:15, half of the remaining students went to an assembly. Finally, at 2:00, 6 more students left for a student council meeting. At the end of the day, there were only 5 students in the room. Assuming that no students returned after having left, how many students are in Mr. Miller's class?
27 students

2. Jordan was trading baseball cards with some friends. He gave 15 cards to Tommy and got 3 back. He gave two-thirds of his remaining cards to Elaine and kept the rest for himself. When he got home he counted that he had 25 cards. How many baseball cards did Jordan start with?
87 baseball cards

Chapter 3   28   Course 2

Skills Practice*
p. 29 **BL** **OL**

NAME _____ DATE _____ PERIOD _____

3-4 Skills Practice
Problem-Solving Investigation: Work Backward

Solve. Use the work backward strategy.

1. GOVERNMENT There are 99 members in the Ohio House of Representatives. All of them were present when a vote was taken on a piece of legislation. If 6 of them did not vote, and 13 more voted "yes" than voted "no", how many "no" votes were there?
There were 40 "no" votes.

2. MONEY Jessie and Amar eat lunch at a restaurant and their bill is $21.65. Amar gives the cashier a coupon for $6 off their bill, and also hands the cashier two bills. If he receives $4.35 in change, what were the denominations of the two bills he gave the cashier?
They were both ten dollar bills.

3. AGE Justine is 13 years younger than her uncle Stewart. Stewart is 18 years older than Justine's sister, Julia. Julia's mother is 8 year older than Stewart, and 28 years older than her youngest child, Jared. If Jared is 12 years old, how old is Justine?
Justine is 19 years old.

4. NUMBER THEORY A number is divided by 6. Then 7 is added to the divisor. After dividing by 4, the result is 4. What is the number?
54

5. COMPACT DISCS Carmella borrowed half as many CDs from the library as her friend Ariel. Ariel borrowed 2 more than Juan, but four less than Sierra. Sierra borrowed 12 CDs. How many did each person borrow?
Ariel 8 CDs
Juan 6 CDs
Carmella 4 CDs

6. TIME Ashish needs to leave for the bus stop 15 minutes earlier than his friend Rami. Rami leaves five minutes later than Susan, who leaves 10 minutes earlier than Raphael. If Raphael leaves the bus stop at 8:15, what time does Ashish need to leave?
Ashish needs to leave at 7:50.

Chapter 3   29   Course 2

Practice*
p. 30 **OL** **AL**

NAME _____ DATE _____ PERIOD _____

3-4 Practice
Problem-Solving Investigation: Work Backward

Mixed Problem Solving

Use the work backward strategy to solve Exercises 1 and 2.

1. NUMBER THEORY A number is divided by 5. Then 3 is added to the quotient. After subtracting 10, the result is 30. What is the number?
The number is 185.

2. COUPONS Kendra used 35 cents more in coupons at the store than Leanne. Leanne used 75 cents less than Teresa, who used 50 cents more than Jaclyn. Jaclyn used 40 cents in coupons. What was the value of the coupons Kendra used?
Kendra used 50 cents in coupons.

Use any strategy to solve Exercises 3–6. Some strategies are shown below.

PROBLEM-SOLVING STRATEGIES
• Look for a pattern
• Guess and check.
• Work backward

3. PATTERNS What are the next three numbers in the following pattern?
2, 3, 5, 9, 17, 33, . . .
65, 129, and 257

4. AGES Mr. Gilliam is 3 years younger than his wife. The sum of their ages is 95. How old is Mr. Gilliam?
Mr. Gilliam is 46 years old.

5. GRAND CANYON The elevation of the North Rim of the Grand Canyon is 2,438 meters above sea level. The South Rim averages 304 meters lower than the North Rim. What is the average elevation of the South Rim?
The South Rim averages 2,134 meters above sea level.

6. WATER BILL The water company charges a residential customer $41 for the first 3,000 gallons of water used and $1 for every 200 gallons used over 3,000 gallons. If the water bill was $58, how many gallons of water were used?
6,400 gallons

Chapter 3   30   Course 2

Word Problem Practice*
p. 31 **OL** **AL**

NAME _____ DATE _____ PERIOD _____

3-4 Word Problem Practice
Problem-Solving Investigation: Work Backward

For Exercises 1-3, use the information below.

WEATHER The temperature in Columbus, Ohio on Monday is 35 degrees warmer than it was on Sunday. Saturday's temperature was 7 degrees cooler than Sunday's. At 45 degrees, Friday's temperature was 22 degrees warmer than Saturday's.

For Exercises 4-6, refer to the table below.

MONEY Shelly needs to go to the grocery store to get some items for a dinner party she is hosting with her brother Preston.

Green Pepper	$1.79
Flank Steak	$8.54
Wild Rice	$3.29
Romaine Lettuce	$3.79
Cucumber	$0.99

1. What was the temperature on Monday?
65 degrees.

2. Estimate the average temperature for the time period from Saturday to Monday.
The average temperature from Saturday to Monday is about: 39 degrees.

3. How many degrees cooler was the temperature on Friday than Monday?
20 degrees.

4. How much money should she take to purchase the items contained in the table?
$18.40

5. If Shelly has $24.00 in her purse before she goes to the store, how much will she have left after she shops?
$5.60

6. If Preston pays Shelly for half the cost of the groceries, how much does he pay?
$9.20

7. NUMBER THEORY How many different two-digit numbers can you make using the numbers 3, 7, 9, and 2 if no digit is repeated within a number?
12

8. PATTERNS The following numbers follow a pattern: 2, 8, 32, 128. What would the fifth number in the pattern be?
512

Chapter 3   31   Course 2

---

*Also available in Spanish **ELL**

BL = Below or Approaching Grade Level

OL = On Grade Level

AL = Above or Beyond Grade Level

ELL = English Language Learner

Additional Lesson Resources

Transparencies
• *5-Minute Check Transparency*, Lesson 3-4

Other Print Products
• *Noteables™ Interactive Study Notebook with Foldables™*

Teacher Tech Tools
• *Interactive Classroom CD-ROM*, Lesson 3-4
• *AssignmentWorks*, Lesson 3-4

Student Tech Tools
glencoe.com
• Extra Examples, Chapter 3, Lesson 4
• Self-Check Quiz, Chapter 3, Lesson 4

1 Focus

Work Backward Working backward is not only useful in problem solving but has a strong link to solving equations. Students have used the reverse process when solving addition/subtraction and multiplication equations.

2 Teach

Scaffolding Questions

Write the steps for putting on your shoes on the board: 1) put on your socks, 2) put on your shoes, and 3) tie your shoes. Now tell students that you want to take your shoes off.

Ask:

- If I want to take my shoes off, which step must I undo first? third

- Which step must I undo second? second

- And which step must I undo third? first

ADDITIONAL EXAMPLE

SHOPPING Lucy and Elena went to the mall. Each girl bought a CD for $16.50, a popcorn for $3.50, and a drink for $2.50. Altogether, they had $5.00 left over. How much money did they take to the mall? $50

Additional Examples are also in:

- Noteables™ Interactive Study Notebook with Foldables™
- Interactive Classroom PowerPoint® Presentations

3-4 **P**roblem-**S**olving **I**nvestigation

MAIN IDEA: Solve problems using the work backward strategy.

P.S.I. TEAM +

e-Mail: WORK BACKWARD

MIGUEL: Yesterday, I earned extra money by doing yardwork for my neighbor. Then I spent $5.50 at the convenience store and four times that amount at the bookstore. Now I have $7.75 left.

YOUR MISSION: Work backward to find how much money Miguel had before he went to the convenience store and the bookstore.

Understand	You know he has $7.75 left. You need to find the amount he started with.	
Plan	Start with the end result and work backward.	
Solve	He has $7.75 left. **Undo** the four times $5.50 spent at the bookstore. Since $5.50 × 4 is $22, add $7.75 and $22. **Undo** the $5.50 spent at the convenience store. Add $5.50 and $29.75. So, Miguel had $35.25 to start with.	$7.75 + 22.00 $29.75 + $5.50 $35.25
Check	Assume Miguel started with $35.25. After going to the convenience store, he had $35.25 − $5.50 or $29.75. He spent four times the amount he spent at the convenience store at the bookstore. So, he had $29.75 − 4($5.50) or $7.75 left. So, $35.25 is correct. ✓	

Analyze The Strategy 1–3. See margin.

1. Explain when you would use the work backward strategy to solve a problem.

2. Describe how to solve a problem by working backward.

3. **WRITING IN MATH** Write a problem that could be solved by working backward. Then write the steps you would take to find the solution to your problem.

148 Chapter 3 Algebra: Linear Equations and Functions

Additional Answers

1. When you are given the final result and asked to find an earlier amount.

2. Begin by taking the last value in the problem and perform opposite operations with each subsequent value until you arrive at the initial value.

3. Sample answer: In the first four games, Hannah scored a total of 83 points. In the fourth game she scored 19 points. In game three, she scored 27 points and in the second game she scored 22 points. How many points did she score in the first game? To solve, first subtract 19 from 83, which is 64. Then subtract 27 from 64 to get 37. Finally, subtract 22 from 37. So, Hannah scored 15 points in her first game.

Use the *work backward* strategy to solve
Exercises 4–7.

4. **MONEY** Marisa spent $8 on a movie ticket.
Then she spent $5 on popcorn and one half
of what was left on a drink. She has $2 left.
How much did she have initially? **$17**

5. **NUMBER THEORY** A number is multiplied by
★ −3. Then 6 is subtracted from the product.
After adding −7, the result is −25. What is
the number? **4**

6. **TIME** Timothy's morning schedule is shown.
At what time does Timothy wake up?
7:50 A.M.

Timothy's Schedule	
Activity	**Time**
Wakes up	■
Get ready for school – 45 min	■
Walk to school – 25 min	9:00 A.M.

7. **LOGIC** A small box has 4 tennis balls inside
it. There are 6 of these small boxes inside a
medium box. There are 8 medium boxes
inside each large box, and there are 100 large
boxes shipped in a large truck. How many
tennis balls are on the truck?
19,200 tennis balls

Use any strategy to solve Exercises 8–15.
Some strategies are shown below.

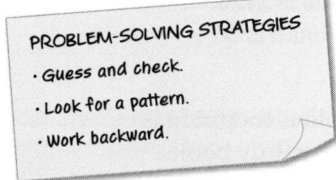
PROBLEM-SOLVING STRATEGIES
· Guess and check.
· Look for a pattern.
· Work backward.

8. **GEOGRAPHY** The land area of North Dakota
is 68,976 square miles. This is about 7 times
the land area of Vermont. Estimate the land
area of Vermont. **about 10,000 mi²**

9. **AGE** Brie is two years older than her sister
★ Kiana. Kiana is 4 years older than their
brother Jeron, who is 8 years younger than
their brother Trey. Trey is 16 years old. How
old is Brie? **Brie is 14 years old.**

10. **ELEVATION** New Orleans, Lousiana, has an
★ elevation of −8 feet related to sea level.
Death Valley, California, is 274 feet lower
than New Orleans. What is the elevation of
Death Valley? **−282 ft**

11. **GEOMETRY** Draw the sixth figure in the
★ pattern shown. **See margin.**

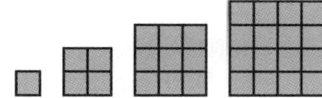

12. **WATERFALLS** Angel Falls in Venezuela, the
★ highest waterfall in the world, is 3,212 feet
high. It is 87 feet higher than 2.5 times the
height of the Empire State Building.
Find the height of the Empire State
Building. **1,250 ft**

13. **AIRCRAFT** An aircraft carrier travels about
★ 6 inches per gallon of fuel. Raquel's car
travels about 28 miles per gallon of fuel.
If there are 5,280 feet in one mile, how many
more inches per gallon would Raquel's car
get than an aircraft carrier? **See margin.**

14. **SCHOOL SUPPLIES** Alexandra wishes to
buy 5 pens, 1 ruler, and 7 folders to start
the school year. The prices are shown in
the table.

Item	Cost
Pens	$2.09
Ruler	$0.99
Folder	$1.19

If there is no tax, is $20 enough to pay for
Alexandra's school supplies? Explain your
reasoning. **See margin.**
1-$10 bill, 2-$5 bills, and 7-$1 bills

15. **MONEY** Antonio has saved $25 in cash to
spend at the arcade. If he has 10 bills, how
many of each kind of bill does he have?

Lesson 3-4 Problem-Solving Investigation: Work Backward **149**

Additional Answers

11.

13. Raquel's car gets 1,774,074 more inches per
gallon than an aircraft carrier.

14. Yes, the total purchase price would be
$19.77 which is less than $20.

---

3 Practice

Using the Exercises

Exercises 1–3 can be used to check
for understanding.

Exercises 4–7 can be used to check
for understanding. Tell students to
first determine which operations the
problem describes. Then students can
use the inverse operations to undo
them, working backward.

Exercises 8–15 are structured so
that students have the opportunity to
practice many different problem-solving
strategies. You may wish to review some
of the strategies they have studied.

- use the four-step plan (p. 25)
- guess and check (p. 42)
- look for a pattern (p. 112)
- work backward (p. 148)

Intervention You may wish to use the
Study Guide and Intervention master on
p. 28 of the *Chapter 3 Resource Masters*
for additional reinforcement.

Tips for New Teachers

Draw a Diagram
Point out that problems do
not always present the steps in order.
Some students may find it helpful to
draw a diagram of the steps and
number them.

4 Assess

Crystal Ball Tell students that
tomorrow's lesson is about solving two-
step equations such as $3x + 5 = 8$. Ask
them to write how the work backward
strategy might help them solve two-step
equations.

✓ Formative Assessment

Check for student understanding of
concepts in Lessons 3-3 and 3-4.

CRM Quiz 2, p. 55

1 Focus

Word problems—like real-world math problems—often contain extra or unneeded information. This activity teaches students to simplify such problems by identifying and selecting the key terms and their relationships.

2 Teach

You may want to have students ask themselves questions such as the following:

- What information am I looking for?
- What information can I use?
- What information is extra?

Some students will be able to skip Step 2, and some may be able to write the problem as a number sentence.

Encourage students to rewrite the problem in as few words as possible, preferably in one sentence. You may also wish to encourage students to use numbers, operation symbols, and variables.

3 Assess

Have students tell what mathematical operations they described for Exercise 1.
multiplication, addition

Simplify the Problem

Have you ever tried to solve a long word problem and didn't know where to start? Try to rewrite the problem using only the most important words. Here's an example.

STEP 1 Read the problem and identify the important words and numbers.

> **CELL PHONES** There is a wide range of cell phone plans available for students. With Janelle's plan, she pays $15 per month for 200 minutes, plus $0.10 per minute once she talks for more than 200 minutes. Suppose Janelle can spend $20 each month for her cell phone. How many minutes can she talk?

STEP 2 Simplify the problem. Keep all of the important words and numbers, but use fewer of them.

> The total monthly cost is the $15 for 200 minutes plus $0.10 times the number of minutes over 200. How many minutes can she talk for $20?

STEP 3 Simplify it again. Use a variable for the unknown.

> The cost of m minutes at $0.10 per minute plus $15 is $20.

PRACTICE

1–4. Sample answers are given.
1. Saving $5 each week for x weeks plus $80 is $125.
3. 40° plus an increase of 5° for each of x hours is 60°.

Use the method above to simplify each problem.

1. **MONEY** Akira is saving money to buy a scooter that costs $125. He has already saved $80 and plans to save an additional $5 each week. In how many weeks will he have enough money for the scooter?

2. **SHOPPING** Online shopping is a popular way to buy books. Cheryl wants to order several books that cost $7 each. In addition, she will pay a shipping fee of $8. How many books can she order with $43? **5 books**

3. **TEMPERATURE** The current temperature is 40°. It is expected to rise 5° each hour for the next several hours. In how many hours will the temperature be 60°?

4. **MONEY** Joaquin wants to buy some DVDs that are each on sale for $10 plus a CD that costs $15. How many DVDs can he buy if he has $75 to spend?

4. The total cost of x DVDs at $10 each plus $15 is $75.

3-5 Solving Two-Step Equations

PACING: **Regular:** 1 period, **Block:** 0.5 period

Options for Differentiated Instruction

ELL = English Language Learner   **AL** = Above or Beyond Grade Level   **SS** = Struggling Students   **SN** = Special Needs

Visual and Kinesthetic Learning **SS** **SN**
Use after presenting Examples 1–5.

Have students work in pairs to write and solve two-step equations. Give each pair an equation on a sheet of paper; for example, $x = 3$.

- Have the first person multiply both sides of the equation by an integer of his or her choice, such as 6.
- The other partner adds or subtracts a number of his or her choice, such as adding 2.
- Then have each pair exchange their final equations with another pair and reverse the steps to solve the equation that they receive.

Given:	$x = 3$
Partner 1:	$6x = 6(3)$
	$6x = 18$
Partner 2:	$6x + 2 = 18 + 2$
	$6x + 2 = 20$

Creating a Template **SS** **SN**
Use before assigning the Exercises.

Create a template for students to organize their work that provides a space for them to check their answers.

Page Number _____ Exercise Number _____	Check

Extending the Concept **AL**
Use after students complete Lesson 3-5.

Display the following equation on the board: $5x - 2 = 3x + 12$

Ask:
- Apply what you have learned about solving two-step equations to solve the equation. 7
- Describe the steps that you used and check your solution. Sample answer: Subtract $3x$ from each side. Add 2 to each side. Divide each side by 2.

Leveled Lesson Resources

Chapter 3 Resource Masters

BL = Below or Approaching Grade Level   **OL** = On Grade Level   **AL** = Above or Beyond Grade Level   **ELL** = English Language Learner

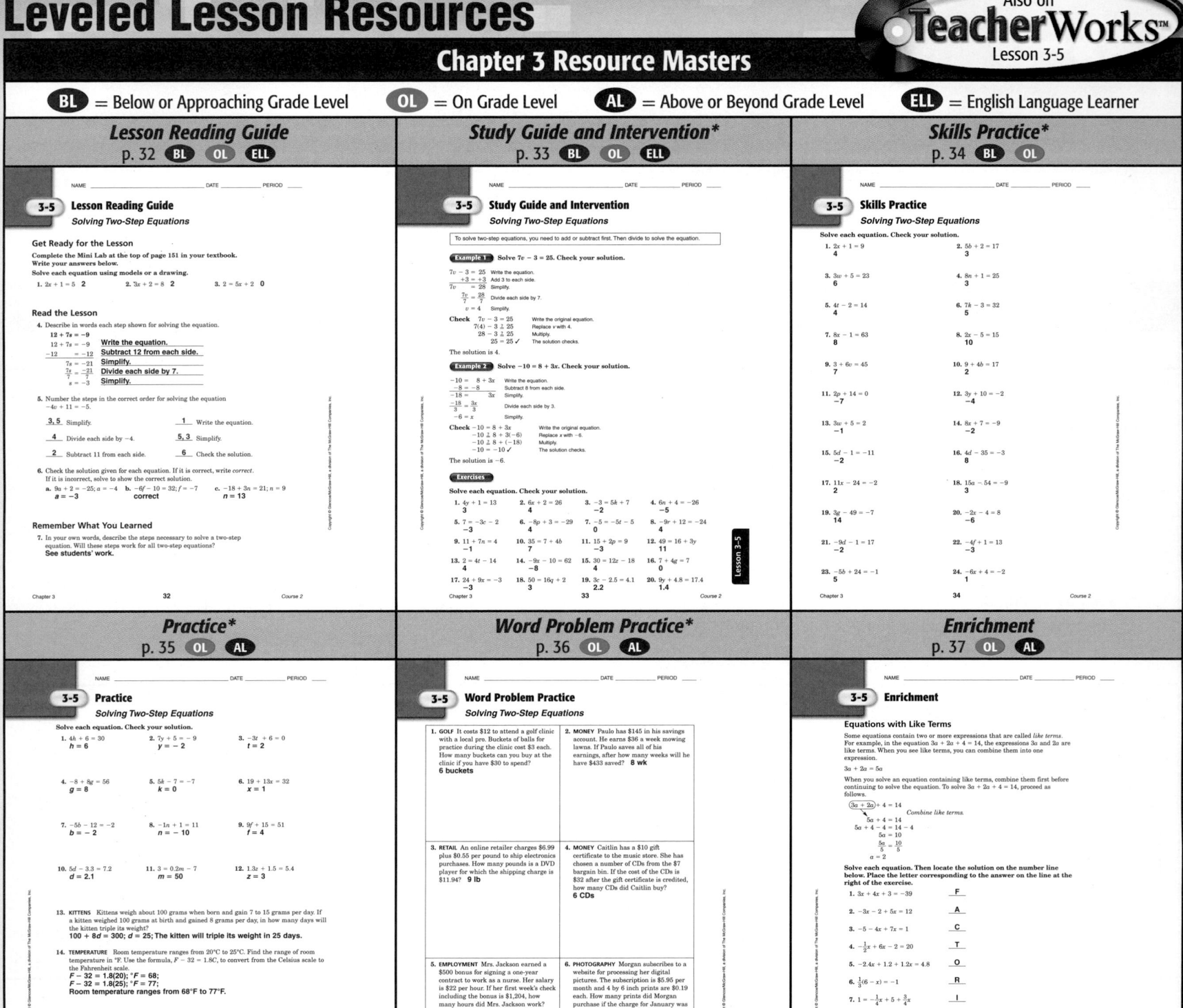

Additional Lesson Resources

Transparencies
- *5-Minute Check Transparency*, Lesson 3-5

Other Print Products
- *Teaching Mathematics with Manipulatives*
- *Noteables™ Interactive Study Notebook with Foldables™*

Teacher Tech Tools
- *Interactive Classroom CD-ROM*, Lesson 3-5
- *AssignmentWorks*, Lesson 3-5

Student Tech Tools
glencoe.com
- Extra Examples, Chapter 3, Lesson 5
- Self-Check Quiz, Chapter 3, Lesson 5

* Also available in Spanish **ELL**

MAIN IDEA

Solve two-step equations.

New Vocabulary

two-step equation

Math Online

glencoe.com
• Concepts In Motion
• Extra Examples
• Personal Tutor
• Self-Check Quiz

▶ MINI Lab

MONEY A florist charges $2 for each balloon in an arrangement and a $3 delivery fee. You have $9 to spend. The model illustrates the equation $2x + 3 = 9$, where x represents the number of balloons.

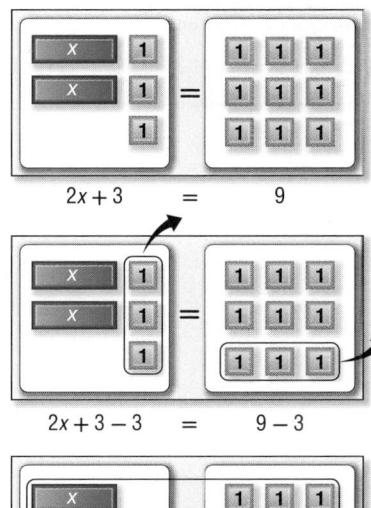

$2x + 3 \quad = \quad 9$

To solve $2x + 3 = 9$, remove three 1-tiles from each side of the mat. Then divide the remaining tiles into two equal groups. The solution of $2x + 3 = 9$ is 3.

$2x + 3 - 3 \quad = \quad 9 - 3$

Solve each equation by using models or a drawing.

1. $2x + 1 = 5$ **2**

2. $3x + 2 = 8$ **2**

3. $2 = 5x + 2$ **0**

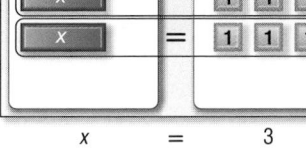

$x \quad = \quad 3$

1–3. See Ch. 3 Answer Appendix for models.

A **two-step equation** has two different operations. To solve a two-step equation, undo the operations in reverse order of the order of operations. You can review the order of operations in Lesson 1-4.

 EXAMPLE **Solve a Two-Step Equation**

① Solve $2x + 3 = 9$. Check your solution.

$2x + 3 =$	9	Write the equation.
$-3 = -3$		Undo the addition first by subtracting 3 from each side.
$2x =$	6	
$\dfrac{2x}{2} =$	$\dfrac{6}{2}$	Next, undo the multiplication by dividing each side by 2.
$x =$	3	Simplify.

Check the solution. Since $2(3) + 3 = 9$, the solution is 3.

✓ **CHECK Your Progress**

Solve each equation. Check your solution.

a. $2x + 4 = 10$ **3**   b. $3x + 1 = 7$ **2**   c. $5 = 2 + 3x$ **1**

Lesson 3-5 Solving Two-Step Equations **151**

---

1 Focus

Vertical Alignment

Before Lesson 3-5
Write and solve one-step linear equations in one variable

Lesson 3-5
Solve two-step linear equations and inequalities in one variable over the rational numbers

After Lesson 3-5
Solve multistep problems involving rate, average speed, distance, and time or a direct variation

2 Teach

▶ MINI Lab

Make sure students understand how to solve one-step equations. Point out that this is just an extension of the modeling tools they already know.

Scaffolding Questions

Write the following expressions on the board: $7 + 3 \cdot (-2)$ and $11 - 10 \div 5$.

Ask:

• Look at the first expression. Which operation should I perform first? multiplication

• Look at the second expression. Which operation should I perform first? division

ADDITIONAL EXAMPLE

① Solve $4x + 3 = 19$. Check your solution. 4

 Tips for New Teachers

Undoing Operations

To solve a two-step equation, students reverse the order of operations. It may be helpful to remind students of the order of operations and to clarify what it means to "undo" an operation. For example, ask students to undo the operation in the expression $4x$. The expression involves the operation of multiplication of 4 by x. To undo this operation, divide the expression $4x$ by 4. In doing so, the expression becomes simply x.

Use the **work backward strategy** to solve two-step equations. Follow the **order of operations** in reverse order. Undo any **addition or subtraction** first. Then undo any **multiplication or division**.

Students should get in the habit of **checking their solutions**.

✓ Formative Assessment

Use the Check Your Progress exercises after each Example to determine students' understanding of concepts.

ADDITIONAL EXAMPLES

2 Solve $6 + 5y = 26$. Check your solution. **4**

3 Solve $-3c + 9 = 3$. Check your solution. **2**

4 Solve $0 = 6 + 3t$. Check your solution. **−2**

Additional Examples are also in:

- Noteables™ Interactive Study Notebook with Foldables™
- Interactive Classroom PowerPoint® Presentations

EXAMPLES Solve Two-Step Equations

Study Tip

Order of Operations
Multiplication comes before addition in the order of operations. To undo these operations, reverse the order. So, undo the addition first by subtracting. Then, undo the multiplication by dividing.

2 Solve $3x + 2 = 23$. Check your solution.

$$
\begin{array}{ll}
3x + 2 = 23 & \text{Write the equation.} \\
\underline{- 2 = -2} & \text{Undo the addition first by subtracting} \\
3x = 21 & \text{2 from each side.} \\
\dfrac{3x}{3} = \dfrac{21}{3} & \text{Divide each side by 3.} \\
x = 7 & \text{Simplify.}
\end{array}
$$

Check $3x + 2 = 23$ Write the original equation.

$3(7) + 2 \overset{?}{=} 23$ Replace x with 7.

$21 + 2 \overset{?}{=} 23$ Simplify.

$23 = 23$ ✓   The sentence is true.

The solution is 7.

3 Solve $-2y - 7 = 3$. Check your solution.

$$
\begin{array}{ll}
-2y - 7 = 3 & \text{Write the equation.} \\
\underline{+ 7 = +7} & \text{Undo the subtraction first by adding 7 to each side.} \\
-2y = 10 & \\
\dfrac{-2y}{-2} = \dfrac{10}{-2} & \text{Divide each side by −2.} \\
y = -5 & \text{Simplify.}
\end{array}
$$

The solution is −5.   Check the solution.

Study Tip

Equations
Remember, solutions of the new equation are also solutions of the original equation.

4 Solve $4 + 5r = -11$. Check your solution.

$$
\begin{array}{ll}
4 + 5r = -11 & \text{Write the equation.} \\
\underline{- 4 = -4} & \text{Undo the addition of 4 first by} \\
5r = -15 & \text{subtracting 4 from each side.} \\
\dfrac{5r}{5} = -\dfrac{15}{5} & \text{Divide each side by 5.} \\
r = -3 & \text{Simplify.}
\end{array}
$$

The solution is −3.   Check the solution.

✓ CHECK Your Progress

Solve each equation. Check your solution.

d. $4x + 5 = 13$ **2**   e. $8y + 15 = 71$ **7**   f. $-3n - 8 = 7$ **−5**

g. $-5s + 8 = -2$ **2**   h. $1 + 2y = -3$ **−2**   i. $-2 + 6w = 10$ **2**

Solving Two-Step Equations	**Key Concept**

To solve a two-step equation like $3x + 4 = 16$ or $2x - 1 = -3$:

Step 1   Undo the addition or subtraction first.

Step 2   Then undo the multiplication or division.

Tips for New Teachers

Solving Two-Step Equations

The guidelines presented in the Concept Summary box are generally valid, but there are exceptions. For example, when solving the equation $4(x + 7) = 26$, students should undo the multiplication prior to undoing the addition. When evaluating the expression $4(x + 7)$ using the order of operations, students should first add 7 to x and then multiply the result by 4. By stressing to students that they should reverse the order of operations when solving the equation $4(x + 7)$, it becomes clear that students should "undo" the multiplication and then undo the addition. Another example that illustrates this exception is the equation $\dfrac{x + 5}{3} = 8$. Students should undo the division prior to undoing the addition.

Some real-world situations start with a given amount and increase at a certain rate.

 Real-World **EXAMPLE**

5 **MOVIES** Aisha wants to have her birthday party at the movies. It costs $27 for pizza and $8.50 per friend for the movie tickets. Since it is Aisha's birthday, she does not have to pay for her movie ticket. How many friends can Aisha have at her party if she has $78 to spend?

Real-World Link . . . .
Most teenagers see more than 7 movies a year.
Source: Gallup News Service

Words	Cost of pizza	plus	cost of 1 friend	times	number of friends	equals $78.

Variable	Let n represent the number of friends.

Equation	27	+	8.50	·	n	=	78

$$27 + 8.50n = 78 \qquad \text{Write the equation.}$$
$$\underline{-27 \qquad\qquad = -27} \qquad \text{Subtract 27 from each side.}$$
$$8.50n = 51$$
$$\frac{8.50n}{8.50} = \frac{51}{8.50} \qquad \text{Divide each side by 8.50.}$$
$$n = 6 \qquad\qquad 51 \div 8.50 = 6$$

Check $\quad 27 + 8.50n = 78 \qquad$ Write the original equation.
$\qquad 27 + 8.50(6) \stackrel{?}{=} 78 \qquad$ Replace n with 6.
$\qquad\qquad 27 + 51 \stackrel{?}{=} 78 \qquad$ Simplify.
$\qquad\qquad\qquad 78 = 78 \checkmark \qquad$ The sentence is true.

Aisha can have 6 friends at her party.

 CHECK Your Progress

j. FITNESS A fitness club is having a special offer where you pay $22 to join plus a $16 monthly fee. You have $150 to spend. Write and solve an equation to find how many months you can use the fitness club. **22 + 16m = 150; 8 months**

 **CHECK Your Understanding**

Examples 1–4 (pp. 151–152)

Solve each equation. Check your solution.

1. $3x + 1 = 7$ **2**
2. $4h - 6 = 22$ **7**
3. $-6r + 1 = -17$ **3**
4. $-3y - 5 = 10$ **−5**
5. $13 = 1 + 4s$ **3**
6. $-7 = 1 + 2n$ **−4**

Example 5 (p. 153)

7. **MONEY** Syreeta wants to buy some CDs, each costing $14, and a DVD that cost $23. She has $65 to spend. Write and solve an equation to find how many CDs she can buy. **14c + 23 = 65; 3 CDs**

Lesson 3-5 Solving Two-Step Equations **153**

Exercises 8–21 are structured so that students practice the same concepts whether they are assigned odd or even problems.

▶ Practice and Problem Solving

HOMEWORK HELP	
For Exercises	See Examples
8–11	1, 2
12–15	3
16–19	4
20–21	5

Exercise Levels
A: 8–21
B: 22–31
C: 32–35

Solve each equation. Check your solution.

8. $3x + 1 = 10$ **3**

9. $5x + 4 = 19$ **3**

10. $2t + 7 = -1$ **−4**

11. $6m + 1 = -23$ **−4**

12. $-4w - 4 = 8$ **−3**

13. $-7y + 3 = -25$ **4**

14. $-8s + 1 = 33$ **−4**

15. $-2x + 5 = -13$ **9**

16. $3 + 8n = -5$ **−1**

17. $5 + 4d = 37$ **8**

18. $14 + 2p = 8$ **−3**

19. $25 + 2y = 47$ **11**

For Exercises 20 and 21, write an equation. Then solve the equation.

20. **BICYCLES** Cristiano is saving money to buy a new bike that costs $189. He has saved $99 so far. He plans on saving $10 each week. In how many weeks will Cristiano have enough money to buy a new bike?
$189 = 10x + 99$; 9 weeks

21. **PETTING ZOOS** It cost $10 to enter a petting zoo. Each cup of food to feed the animals is $2. If you have $14, how many cups of food can you buy?
$2c + 10 = 14$; 2 cups

Solve each equation. Check your solution.

22. $2r - 3.1 = 1.7$ **2.4**

23. $4t + 3.5 = 12.5$ **2.25**

24. $16b - 6.5 = 9.5$ **1**

25. $5w + 9.2 = 19.7$ **2.1**

26. $16 = 0.5r - 8$ **48**

27. $0.2n + 3 = 8.6$ **28**

For Exercises 28 and 29, write an equation. Then solve the equation.

28. **CELL PHONES** A cell phone company charges a monthly fee of $39.99 for unlimited *off-peak* minutes on the nights and weekends but $0.45 for each *peak* minute during the weekday. If Brad's monthly cell phone bill was $62.49, for how many *peak* minutes did he get charged?
$39.99 + 0.45m = 62.49$; 50 *peak* minutes

29. **PLANTS** In ideal conditions, bamboo can grow 47.6 inches each day. At this rate, how many days will it take a bamboo shoot that is 8 inches tall to reach a height of 80 feet? **$8 + 47.6d = 960$; 20 days**

TEMPERATURE For Exercises 30 and 31, use the following information and the table.

Temperature is usually measured on the Fahrenheit scale (°F) or the Celsius scale (°C). Use the formula $F = 1.8C + 32$ to convert from one scale to the other.

Alaska Record Low Temperatures (°F) by Month	
January	−80
April	−50
July	16
October	−48

30. Convert the temperature for Alaska's record low in July to Celsius. Round to the nearest degree. **−9°C**

31. Hawaii's record low temperature is −11°C. Find the difference in degrees Fahrenheit between Hawaii's record low temperature and the record low temperature for Alaska in January. **92.2°F**

EXTRA PRACTICE
See pages 675, 706.

	DIFFERENTIATED HOMEWORK OPTIONS		
Level	**Assignment**	**Two-Day Option**	
BL Basic	8–21, 34–47	9–21 odd, 36, 37	8–20 even, 34, 35, 38–47
OL Core	9–19 odd, 20, 21, 23–27 odd, 28–31, 34–47	8–21, 33, 36, 37	22–31, 34, 35, 38–47
AL Advanced/Pre-AP	22–43 (optional: 44–47)		

H.O.T. Problems

33. $\frac{1}{2}(20x) - 18$ $= 200$; $x = 21.8$; they must sell at least 22 subscriptions

34. Estimation; Bianca doesn't need an exact answer. Sample answer: $50 − 20 = 30. $30 ÷ 0.25 = 120. Bianca can drive for about 120 mi.

32. **CHALLENGE** Refer to Exercises 30 and 31. Is there a temperature at which the number of Celsius degrees is the same as the number of Fahrenheit degrees? If so, find it. If not, explain why not. **No, none of the Fahrenheit temperatures convert to the same temperature in Celsius. Only −40°F = −40°C.**

33. **CHALLENGE** Suppose your school is selling magazine subscriptions. Each subscription costs $20. The company pays the school half of the total sales in dollars. The school must also pay a one-time fee of $18. What is the fewest number of subscriptions that can be sold to earn a profit of $200?

34. **SELECT A TECHNIQUE** Bianca rented a car for a flat fee of $19.99 plus $0.26 per mile. Which of the following techniques might she use to determine the approximate number of miles she can drive for $50? Justify your selection(s). Then use the technique(s) to solve the problem.

Mental Math	Number Sense	Estimation

35. **WRITING IN MATH** Write a real-world problem that would be represented by the equation $2x + 5 = 15$. **See margin.**

4 Assess

Name the Math Have students choose a problem from Exercises 8–19 or 22–27 and tell what procedures they used to solve it.

 **Foldables™ Follow-Up**

Remind students to take notes about today's lesson under the *Equations* tab of their Foldables. Encourage them to include examples of how to solve two-step equations.

Additional Answer

35. Sample answer: A flower shop charges $2 for each flower in a vase and $5 for the vase. How many flowers can you place in a vase if you have $15 to spend?

TEST PRACTICE

36. A rental car company charges $30 a day plus $0.05 a mile. Which expression could be used to find the cost of renting a car for m miles? **C**

   A $30.05m$

   B $30m + 0.05m$

   C $30 + 0.05m$

   D $30m + 0.05$

37. The Rodriguez family went on a vacation. They started with $1,875. If they spent $140 each day, which expression represents how much money they had after d days? **G**

   F $1,735d$

   G $1,875 − 140d$

   H $140d$

   J $1,875 + 140d$

Spiral Review

38. **SCHEDULES** Jaime needs to be at the bus stop by 7:10 A.M. If it takes her 7 minutes to walk to the bus stop and 40 minutes to get ready in the morning, what is the latest time that she can set her alarm in order to be at the bus stop 5 minutes earlier than she needs to be? (Lesson 3-4) **6:18 A.M.**

ALGEBRA Solve each equation. Check your solution. (Lessons 3-2 and 3-3)

39. $4f = 28$ **7**   40. $-3y = -15$ **5**   41. $p − 14 = 27$ **41**   42. $-11 = n + 2$ **−13**

43. **HIKING** Two people are hiking in the Grand Canyon. One is 987 feet below the rim and the other is 1,200 feet below the rim. Find the vertical distance between them (Lesson 2-5) **213 ft**

▷ **GET READY for the Next Lesson**

PREREQUISITE SKILL Multiply or divide.

44. $2.5 × 20$ **50**   45. $3.5 × 4$ **14**   46. $4,200 ÷ 2.1$ **2,000**   47. $104 ÷ 6.5$ **16**

Differentiated Instruction

Interpersonal Learners Separate students into pairs. Have each member of each pair write 3 or 4 two-step equations. Then have the members of each pair exchange equations and solve them.

3-6 Measurement: Perimeter and Area

PACING: **Regular:** 1 period, **Block:** 0.5 period

Options for Differentiated Instruction

ELL = English Language Learner   **AL** = Above or Beyond Grade Level   **SS** = Struggling Students   **SN** = Special Needs

Scaffolding the Lesson   **SS** **SN**

Use before presenting the Key Concept on page 156.

Scaffold this lesson by asking students to find the perimeter of rectangles like the one at the right, where the dimensions of all four sides are labeled. 16 cm

5 cm

3 cm ☐ 3 cm

5 cm

Next, have students find the perimeter of rectangles like the one at the right, where only one length and one width are labeled. 18 in.

Finally, give students the perimeter and one dimension of a rectangle and ask them to find the other dimension. Once students are comfortable with this, then introduce the formula $P = 2\ell + 2w$.

☐ 2 in.

7 in.

Check for Understanding   **ELL** **AL** **SS**

Use after presenting Examples 1–4.

Have each student draw and label a rectangle that has a perimeter of 36 centimeters. Have them calculate the area of the rectangle. Then gather the class data and record the information on the board in a table like the one shown below.

Rectangle	Length (cm)	Width (cm)	Area (cm^2)
1	15	3	45
2	10	8	80
3	9	9	81

Ask:
- Are there any other possible dimensions for a rectangle with a perimeter of 36 centimeters that aren't shown in the table?
- Which rectangle in the table has the greatest area? the least area?

Kinesthetic Learners   **ELL** **AL** **SS** **SN**

Use after presenting Lesson 3-6.

Have students explore the school and grounds, measuring lengths. Suggestions include exterior walls, sidewalks, and sides of rectangular regions bounded by trees, rocks, and so forth. They should record their data, and then calculate perimeter and area for the buildings and regions measured.

Leveled Lesson Resources

Chapter 3 Resource Masters

BL = Below or Approaching Grade Level   **OL** = On Grade Level   **AL** = Above or Beyond Grade Level   **ELL** = English Language Learner

---

Lesson Reading Guide
p. 38 **BL OL ELL**

3-6 Lesson Reading Guide
Measurement: Perimeter and Area

Get Ready for the Lesson
Read the introduction at the top of page 156 in your textbook.
Write your answers below.

1. If the students run around the gym 5 times, how far would they run?
2,180 feet.

2. Explain how you can use both multiplication and addition to find the distance. **Multiply 107 × 2 and 111 × 2. Add the two products together. Multiply the sum by 5.**

Read the Lesson

3. Explain in your own words what the formula $p = 2\ell + 2w$ means?
Answers may vary; you double both the length and width of the figure and add the results together.

4. How is the perimeter of a figure different from the area of the figure?
Sample answer: The perimeter is the distance around the figure. The area is the measure of the surface that is inside the figure.

5. Explain how to find the perimeter and area of a rectangle whose length is 8 feet and whose width is 2 feet. **Sample answer: To find the perimeter, add two times the length and two times the width (20 ft). To find the area, multiply length times width (16 ft²).**

Remember What You Learned

6. The word *perimeter* comes from two Greek words that mean "a measure (*metron*) around (*peri*)." Tell how you can find the perimeter of a rectangle. **Sample answer: The perimeter is the sum of twice the length and twice the width, or $2\ell + 2w$. It is the measure around the rectangle.**

Chapter 3   38   Course 2

Study Guide and Intervention*
p. 39 **BL OL ELL**

3-6 Study Guide and Intervention
Measurement: Perimeter and Area

The distance around a geometric figure is called the **perimeter**.
To find the perimeter of any geometric figure, you can use addition or a formula.
The perimeter of a rectangle is twice the length ℓ plus twice the width w.
$$P = 2\ell + 2w$$

Example 1 Find the perimeter of the figure at right.
$P = 105 + 105 + 35 + 35$ or 280
The perimeter is 280 inches.

The measure of the surface enclosed by a geometric figure is called the **area**.
The area of a rectangle is the product of the length ℓ and width w.
$$A = \ell \cdot w$$

Example 2 Find the area of the rectangle.
$A = \ell \cdot w$
$= 24 \cdot 12$ or 288
The area is 288 square centimeters.

Exercises

Find the perimeter of each figure.
1. **80 cm**   2. **112 m**

Find the perimeter and area of each rectangle.
3. **26 ft; 36 ft²**   4. **28 in.; 33 in²**
5. $\ell = 8$ ft, $w = 5$ ft **26 ft; 40 ft²**   6. $\ell = 3.5$ m, $w = 2$ m **11 m; 7 m²**
7. $\ell = 8$ yd, $w = 4\frac{1}{3}$ yd **$24\frac{2}{3}$ yd; $34\frac{2}{3}$ yd²**   8. $\ell = 29$ cm, $w = 7.3$ cm **72.6 cm; 211.7 cm²**

Chapter 3   39   Course 2

Skills Practice*
p. 40 **BL OL**

3-6 Skills Practice
Measurement: Perimeter and Area

Find the perimeter of each figure.
1. **92 cm**   2. **36 m**
3. **38 yd**   4. **220 in**

Find the perimeter and area of each rectangle.
5. **40 yd; $75\frac{1}{2}$ yd²**   6. **80 cm; 400 cm²**
7. **72 m; 180 m²**   8. **46 cm; 120 cm²**
9. $\ell = 6$ yd, $w = 4$ yd **20 yd; 24 yd²**   10. $\ell = 8.2$ m, $w = 7.1$ m **30.6 m; 58.22 m²**
11. $\ell = 50$ in., $w = 10$ in. **120 in.; 500 in²**   12. $\ell = 10$ cm, $w = 4\frac{1}{2}$ cm **29 cm; 45 cm²**
13. $\ell = 4.5$ ft, $w = 3$ ft **15 ft; 13.5 ft²**   14. $\ell = 7\frac{1}{2}$ mm, $w = 6\frac{5}{8}$ mm **$27\frac{3}{4}$ mm; $47\frac{13}{16}$ mm²**

Chapter 3   40   Course 2

Practice*
p. 41 **OL AL**

3-6 Practice
Measurement: Perimeter and Area

Find the perimeter of each rectangle.
1. **40 m**   2. **11.4 mi**   3. **3 yd**

Find the area of each rectangle.
4. **286 in²**   5. **64.6 ft²**   6. **120 cm²**

Find the missing side.
7. $P = 83.4$ km, $\ell = 27.8$ km $w = $ **13.9 km**   8. $A = 337.68$ yd², $w = 60.3$ yd $\ell = $ **5.6 yd**

LAWN CARE For Exercises 9 and 10, use the following information.
Yuri's dad needs to fertilize the grass in the yard. The back yard measures 55 feet by 30 feet, while the front yard is a square with a length of 42 feet on each side.

9. Yuri's dad needs to rope off the two areas to keep people from disturbing the lawn after he fertilizes the grass. How much rope will he need to go around both areas?
338 feet of rope

10. If a bag of fertilizer covers 600 square feet of lawn, how many bags of fertilizer will Yuri's dad need to fertilize the front and back yards?
6 bags of fertilizer

Chapter 3   41   Course 2

Word Problem Practice*
p. 42 **OL AL**

3-6 Word Problem Practice
Measurement: Perimeter and Area

1. **BUILD A FENCE** Mrs. Chen wants to build a fence around her yard so that her dog, Fluffy, can run free. The yard she wants to fence is 60 feet by 30 feet. The fencing is sold by the linear foot, so in order to figure out how much fencing she needs, Mrs. Chen needs to know the perimeter of the yard. Find the yard's perimeter.
180 feet

2. **WINDOWS** Mrs. Johnson was planning to caulk around the frame of her patio doors that measure 5 feet by $6\frac{1}{2}$ feet. In order to help her to know how much caulk to buy, find the perimeter of the doors. **23 ft**

3. **SOCCER** The dimensions of a field for Men's and Women's NCAA soccer can be no more than 80 yards by 120 yards. If the field has those dimensions what is the perimeter of the field?
400 yards

4. **FENCING** Mr. Lao is planning to build a rectangular cattle pen that measures 50 feet by 75 feet. Find the total length of fencing that he will need to purchase.
250 ft

5. **CARPET** Mr. Yuji plans on buying carpet for his bedroom that measures 12 feet by 12 feet. So he will know how much carpet to buy, find the area of his bedroom. **144 ft²**

6. **BORDER** Mrs. Jackson is going to put up a wallpaper border along the top of the walls in her dining room. If the dining room measures 16 feet by 12 feet, how much border should she buy?
56 ft

7. **LOBBY** A hotel lobby measures 40 yards by 60 yards. Find the area and perimeter of the lobby's floor.
2,400 yd²; 200 yd

8. **MURAL** An artist painted a mural measuring 9 feet by $20\frac{1}{2}$ feet. Find the area and perimeter of the mural.
$184\frac{1}{2}$ ft²; 59 ft

Chapter 3   42   Course 2

Enrichment
p. 43 **OL AL**

3-6 Enrichment
Perimeter and Area

Two shapes can have the same area and different perimeters. Each of these shapes has an area of 16 square units, but their perimeters are different.

$P = 34$ $P = 20$ $P = 20$ $P = 16$

Among rectangles that have an area of 16 square feet, rectangles that are long and thin have the greatest perimeter. Rectangles with the least perimeter are more closely shaped to a square.

The grid shows the basic floor plan of the Smith's house. The side of each box in the grid represents 3 feet. The three bedrooms all have the same area.

1. Which of the rectangular bedrooms has the greater perimeter? What is another dimension that will create a rectangle with the same area? **Tim's bedroom has the greatest perimeter; 3 feet by 36 feet.**

2. Lisa's bedroom has an irregular shape. How does the area of her bedroom compare to the other two bedrooms? How does the perimeter of her bedroom compare to the other two bedrooms? **Lisa's bedroom has the same area as the other two bedrooms. The perimeter of her room is greater than that of Mike's bedroom and the same as that of Tim's bedroom.**

3. The Smith's are moving to a new house. Design two different floor plans for them from which they may choose. Your floor plans must have five rooms including three bedrooms. Each bedroom must have an area of 162 square feet (18 squares) but not the same perimeters. You may add any other features to the house that you want. **See students' work.**

Chapter 3   43   Course 2

Additional Lesson Resources

Also available in Spanish **ELL**

Transparencies
- *5-Minute Check Transparency*, Lesson 3-6

Other Print Products
- *Teaching Mathematics with Manipulatives*
- *Noteables™ Interactive Study Notebook with Foldables™*

Teacher Tech Tools
- *Interactive Classroom CD-ROM*, Lesson 3-6
- *AssignmentWorks*, Lesson 3-6

Student Tech Tools
glencoe.com
- Extra Examples, Chapter 3, Lesson 6
- Self-Check Quiz, Chapter 3, Lesson 6

3-6 Lesson Notes

1 Focus

Vertical Alignment

Before Lesson 3-6
Differentiate between and use appropriate units of measures for two- and three-dimensional objects

Lesson 3-6
Use variables in expressions describing the formulas for the perimeter of a rectangle; express in symbolic form simple relationships arising from geometry

After Lesson 3-6
Use formulas routinely for finding the perimeter and area of basic two-dimensional figures and the surface area and volume of basic three-dimensional figures

2 Teach

Scaffolding Questions

Draw a rectangle on the board.

Ask:

• How many right angles does a rectangle have? four

• How many pairs of parallel sides does a rectangle have? two

• How many pairs of congruent sides does a rectangle have? Two

• Is a square a rectangle? Explain. Yes. A square has 4 right angles, 2 pairs of parallel sides, and 2 pairs of congruent sides.

ADDITIONAL EXAMPLE

① Find the perimeter of the rectangle.
40 ft
2 ft
18 ft

3-6 Measurement: Perimeter and Area

MAIN IDEA

Find the perimeters and areas of figures.

New Vocabulary

perimeter
area

Math Online ▶

glencoe.com

• Extra Examples
• Personal Tutor
• Self-Check Quiz

▷ **GET READY** for the Lesson

MEASUREMENT At the end of gym class, Mrs. Dalton has the students run around the perimeter of the gym.

1. If the students run around the gym 5 times, how far would they run?

2. Explain how you can use both multiplication and addition to find the distance. **See margin.**

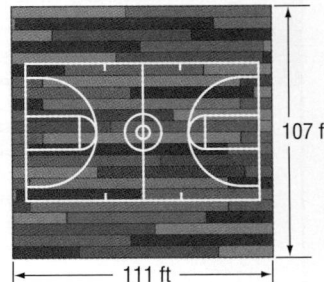

107 ft
111 ft

1. 2,180 feet

The distance around a geometric figure is called the **perimeter**. To find the perimeter of a rectangle, you can use these formulas.

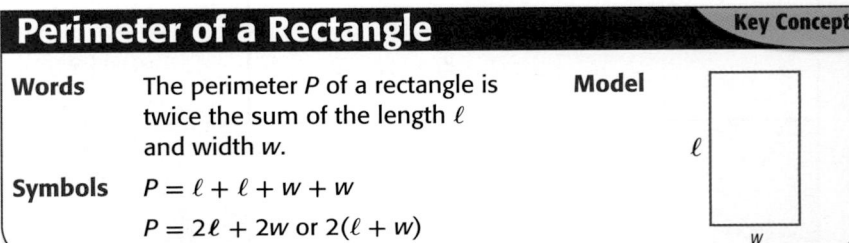

Perimeter of a Rectangle   **Key Concept**

Words	The perimeter P of a rectangle is twice the sum of the length ℓ and width w.	**Model**
Symbols	$P = \ell + \ell + w + w$ $P = 2\ell + 2w$ or $2(\ell + w)$	ℓ
		w

EXAMPLE **Find the Perimeter of a Rectangle**

① Find the perimeter of the rectangle shown at the right.

4 cm
15 cm

$P = 2\ell + 2w$ Perimeter of a rectangle

$P = 2(15) + 2(4)$ Replace ℓ with 15 and w with 4.

$P = 30 + 8$ Multiply.

$P = 38$ Add.

The perimeter is 38 centimeters.

✓ **CHECK** Your Progress

a. Find the perimeter of a rectangle whose length is 14.5 inches and width is 12.5 inches. **54 in.**

156 Chapter 3 Algebra: Linear Equations and Functions

Additional Answer

2. Multiply 107×2 and 111×2. Add the two products together. Multiply the sum by 5.

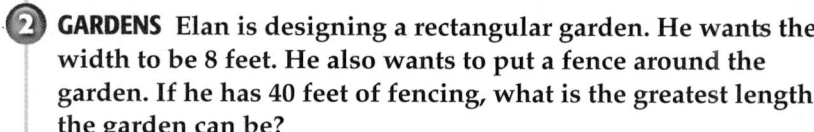 **Real-World EXAMPLE** **Find a Missing Side**

2 **GARDENS** Elan is designing a rectangular garden. He wants the width to be 8 feet. He also wants to put a fence around the garden. If he has 40 feet of fencing, what is the greatest length the garden can be?

$P = 2\ell + 2w$	Perimeter of a rectangle
$40 = 2\ell + 2(8)$	Replace P with 40 and w with 8.
$40 = 2\ell + 16$	Multiply.
$\underline{-16 = \quad -16}$	Subtract 16 from each side.
$24 = 2\ell$	Simplify.
$12 = \ell$	Divide each side by 2.

The greatest length the garden can be is 12 feet.

CHECK Your Progress

b. **FRAMES** Angela bought a frame for a photo of her friends. The width of the frame is 8 inches. If the distance around the frame is 36 inches, what is the length of the frame? **10 inches**

The distance *around* a rectangle is its perimeter. The measure of the surface *enclosed* by a rectangle is its **area**.

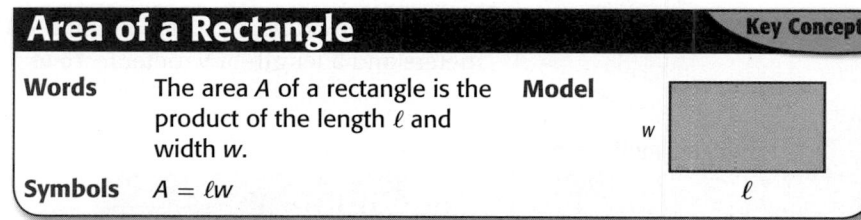

Area of a Rectangle **Key Concept**

Words	The area A of a rectangle is the product of the length ℓ and width w.	Model
Symbols	$A = \ell w$	

Study Tip

Area Units
When finding area, the units are also multiplied. So, area is given in *square* units. Consider a rectangle 2 ft by 3 ft.

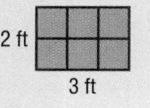

2 ft

3 ft

$A = 2\,ft \cdot 3\,ft$
$A = (2 \cdot 3)(ft \cdot ft)$
$A = 6\,ft^2$

c. 66 in.; 270 in²

EXAMPLE **Find the Area of a Rectangle**

3 **TOYS** Find the area of the top of the wooden train table shown at the right.

$A = \ell w$	Area of a rectangle
$A = 49 \cdot 35$	Replace ℓ with 49 and w with 35.
$A = 1,715$	Multiply.

The area is 1,715 square inches.

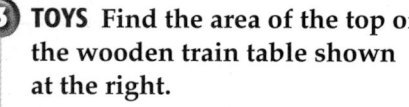

35 in.

49 in.

CHECK Your Progress

c. **VIDEO GAMES** Find the perimeter and area of the top of a video game console that measures 18 inches long and 15 inches wide.

Focus on Mathematical Content

Students can use what they know about solving **two-step equations** to apply the formulas for the perimeter and area of rectangles.

Formative Assessment

Use the Check Your Progress exercises after each Example to determine students' understanding of concepts.

ADDITIONAL EXAMPLES

2 **ART** A painting has a perimeter of 68 inches. If the width of the painting is 13 inches, what is its length? 21 inches

3 **FRESHWATER** Find the area of the surface of the reservoir shown below. 2.5 mi²

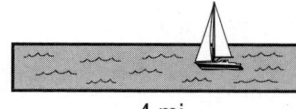

0.625 mi

4 mi

Additional Examples are also in:

• Noteables™ Interactive Study Notebook with Foldables™

• Interactive Classroom PowerPoint® Presentations

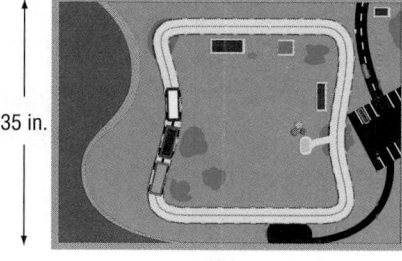

3 Practice

✓ Formative Assessment

Use Exercises 1–6 to check for understanding.

Then use the chart at the bottom of the next page to customize your assignments for students.

Intervention You may wish to use the Study Guide and Intervention Master on page 39 of the *Chapter 3 Resource Masters* for additional reinforcement.

 EXAMPLE **Use Area to Find a Missing Side**

④ The area of a rectangle is 53.94 square feet. If the width is 8.7 feet, find the length.

METHOD 1 **Substitute, then solve.**

$A = \ell w$	Write the equation.
$53.94 = \ell(8.7)$	Replace A with 53.94 and w with 8.7.
$\dfrac{53.94}{8.7} = \dfrac{\ell(8.7)}{8.7}$	Divide each side by 8.7.
$\ell = 6.2$	Simplify.

Study Tip

Check for Reasonableness You know that $53.94 \approx 54$ and that $8.77 \approx 9$. Since $54 \div 9 = 6$, the answer is reasonable.

METHOD 2 **Solve, then substitute.**

$A = \ell w$	Write the equation.
$\dfrac{A}{w} = \dfrac{\ell w}{w}$	Divide each side by w.
$\dfrac{A}{w} = \ell$	Simplify.
$\dfrac{53.94}{8.7} = \ell$	Replace A with 53.94 and w with 8.7.
$\ell = 6.2$	Simplify.

So, the length of the rectangle is 6.2 feet.

✓ CHOOSE Your Method

d. What is the width of a rectangle that has an area of 135 square meters and a length of 9 meters? **15 m**

★ indicates multi-step problem

✓ CHECK Your Understanding

Example 1
(p. 156)

Find the perimeter of each rectangle.

1.

4 yd

5 yd   **18 yd**

2.   4.5 cm

1.9 cm
12.8 cm

Example 2
(p. 157)

3. **PHOTOGRAPHY** A photograph is 5 inches wide. The perimeter of the photograph is 24 inches. What is the length of the photograph? **7 in.**

Example 3
(p. 157)

Find the area of each rectangle.

4.

1 m

3.8 m   **3.8 m²**

5.   5 ft

5.25 ft
26.25 ft²

Example 4
(p. 158)

6. **MEASUREMENT** The area and length of a rectangle are 30 square feet and 6 feet, respectively. What is the width of the rectangle? **5 ft**

Differentiated Instruction

Kinesthetic Learners Separate students into teams of three or four. Have each team measure the length and width of a rectangular surface in the classroom (such as a desktop, chalkboard, book cover, or floor). Then have each team write a perimeter problem and an area problem, each with a missing dimension. Have teams exchange problems and solve them.

41. **CHALLENGE** A rectangle has width w. Its length is one unit more than 3 times its width. Write an expression that represents the perimeter of the rectangle. $P = 2(3w + 1) + 2w$ or $P = 8w + 2$

42. True; The closer a rectangle comes to being a square, the greater the area.

42. **WRITING IN MATH** Decide whether the statement is *true* or *false*. Explain your reasoning and provide examples.

Of all rectangles with a perimeter of 24 square inches, the one with the greatest area is a square.

TEST PRACTICE

43. Oakland Garden Center created a design plan for the Nelson family's rock garden. The shaded areas will hold flowers and the rest of the garden will be rock.

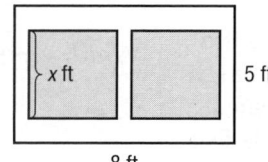

If each shaded area is a square, which expression represents the area of the garden that will be rock? **A**

A $(40 - 2x^2)$ ft²   C $(40 + x)$ ft²
B $(40 - x)$ ft²   D $(40 + x^2)$ ft²

44. The rectangle below has width 4.75 feet and perimeter P feet.

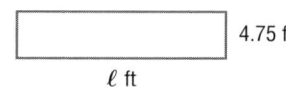

Which of the following could be used to find the length of the rectangle? **H**

F $P = 4.75 + \dfrac{\ell}{2}$
G $P = 4.75 - \ell$
H $P = 9.5 + 2\ell$
J $P = 9.5 - 2\ell$

Spiral Review

Solve each equation. Check your solution. (Lesson 3-5)

45. $5d + 12 = 2$ **−2**   46. $13 - f = 7$ **6**   47. $10 = 2g + 3$ **3.5**   48. $6 = 3 - 3h$ **−1**

49. **ALGEBRA** Anna was charged $11.25 for returning a DVD 5 days late. Write and solve an equation to find how much the video store charges per day for late fees. (Lesson 3-3) $5x = 11.25$; $2.25

Multiply. (Lesson 2-6)

50. $14(-5)$ **−70**   51. $(-3)^3$ **−27**   52. $-10(2)(-8)$ **160**

53. **AGE** The sum of Denise's and Javier's ages is 26 years. If Denise is 4 years older than Javier, find Javier's age. Use the *guess and check* strategy. (Lesson 1-5) **11 years old**

▶ **GET READY for the Next Lesson** 54–57. See margin.

PREREQUISITE SKILL Graph and label each point on a coordinate plane. (Lesson 2-3)

54. $(-4, 2)$ 55. $(3, -1)$ 56. $(-3, -4)$ 57. $(2, 0)$

Lesson 3-6 Measurement: Perimeter and Area   **161**

4 Assess

Yesterday's News Remind students that yesterday's lesson was about solving two-step equations. Have them write how yesterday's concepts helped them with today's material.

Formative Assessment

Check for student understanding of concepts in Lessons 3-5 and 3-6.

CRM Quiz 3, p. 56

Additional Answers

54.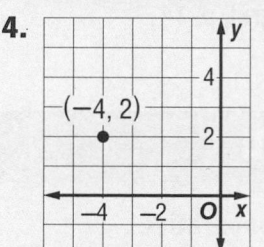

55.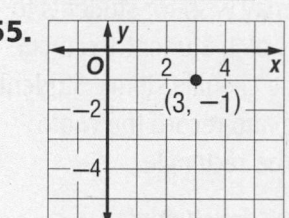

56.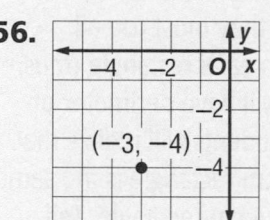

57.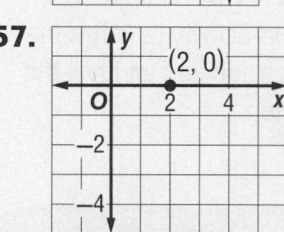

① Focus

Materials

- chenille stems
- scissors
- centimeter rulers
- graph paper

Easy-to-Make Manipulatives

Teaching Mathematics with Manipulatives, templates for:

- quarter-inch grid, p. 14

② Teach

Working in Cooperative Groups

You may wish for students to work in groups of 2. Student 1 can cut and arrange the chenille stems. Student 2 can measure and record the width and length of the rectangle.

Activity Make sure students understand that they must use all 10 stems to form each rectangle (thus, each rectangle will have perimeter of 24 cm). Some students will realize that a 2.4 cm × 9.6 cm rectangle is the same as a 9.6 cm × 2.4 cm rectangle. Tell them that for this activity length is the horizontal dimension and width is the vertical dimension.

③ Assess

Formative Assessment

Use Exercises 1 and 2 to determine whether students understand the relationship between a rectangle's perimeter and its dimensions.

From Concrete to Abstract Use Exercise 7 to bridge the gap between using models of rectangles' dimensions to explore the relationship (between a rectangle's perimeter and its dimensions) and making predictions about other rectangles.

Explore 3-7

Measurement Lab
Representing Relationships

MAIN IDEA

Graph data to demonstrate the relationship between the dimensions and the perimeter of a rectangle.

In this lab, you will investigate the relationships between the dimensions and the perimeter of a rectangle.

ACTIVITY

STEP 1 Use 10 chenille stems, 24 centimeters in length, to form 10 rectangles with different dimensions.

STEP 2 Measure and record the width and length of each rectangle to the nearest centimeter in a table like the one at the right.

Width (cm)	Length (cm)

ANALYZE THE RESULTS 1–7. See Ch. 3 Answer Appendix.

1. What rectangle measure does 24 centimeters represent?

2. Find the sum of the width and length for each of your rectangles. Write a sentence that describes the relationship between this sum and the measure of the length of the stem for each rectangle. Then write a rule that describes this relationship for a rectangle with a width w and length ℓ.

3. In this activity, if a rectangle has a length of 4.5 centimeters, what is its width? Explain your reasoning. Write a rule that can be used to find w when ℓ is known for any rectangle in this Activity.

4. **GRAPH THE DATA** Graph the data in your table on a coordinate plane like the one at the right.

5. Describe what the ordered pair (w, ℓ) represents. Describe how these points appear on the graph.

6. Use your graph to find the width of a rectangle with a length of 7 centimeters. Explain your method.

7. **MAKE A CONJECTURE** If the length of each chenille stem was 20 centimeters, how would this affect the data in your table? the rule you wrote in Exercise 3? the appearance of your graph?

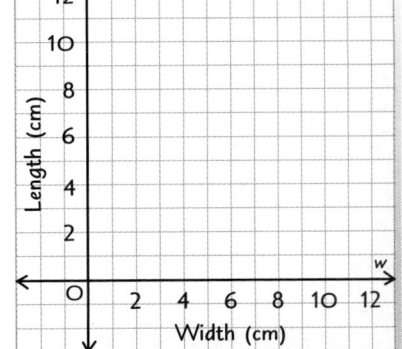

162 Chapter 3 Algebra: Linear Equations and Functions

3-7 Functions and Graphs

PACING: **Regular:** 2 periods, **Block:** 1 period

Options for Differentiated Instruction

 = English Language Learner    = Above or Beyond Grade Level   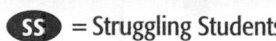 = Struggling Students    = Special Needs

Reviewing Concepts

Use before presenting Lesson 3-7.

Review vocabulary terms related to the coordinate plane. Review how to graph points on a coordinate plane.

- *x*-axis
- *x*-coordinate
- *y*-axis
- *y*-coordinate
- origin

Creating a Template

Use before assigning the Exercises.

Create a template that students can use to organize work, evaluate expressions, and determine the specific points to be plotted.

x	Evaluate Expression:	y	(x, y)

Extensions and Challenges

Use after students complete Lesson 3-7.

Display the pairs of lines shown on the board or overhead.

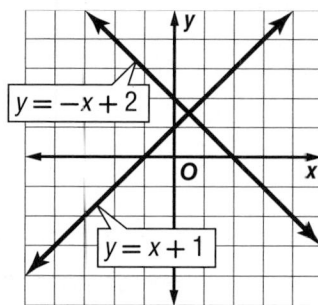   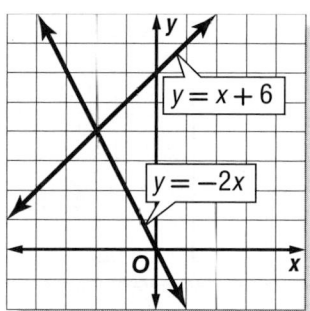

Ask:

- What can you conclude about the point of intersection for two lines? The point of intersection for two lines is a solution to the equations of each of the two lines.
- Test your hypothesis with two more equations. Were you correct? Explain your results. See students' work.

Leveled Lesson Resources

Chapter 3 Resource Masters

BL = Below or Approaching Grade Level   **OL** = On Grade Level   **AL** = Above or Beyond Grade Level   **ELL** = English Language Learner

---

Lesson Reading Guide
p. 45 **BL** **OL** **ELL**

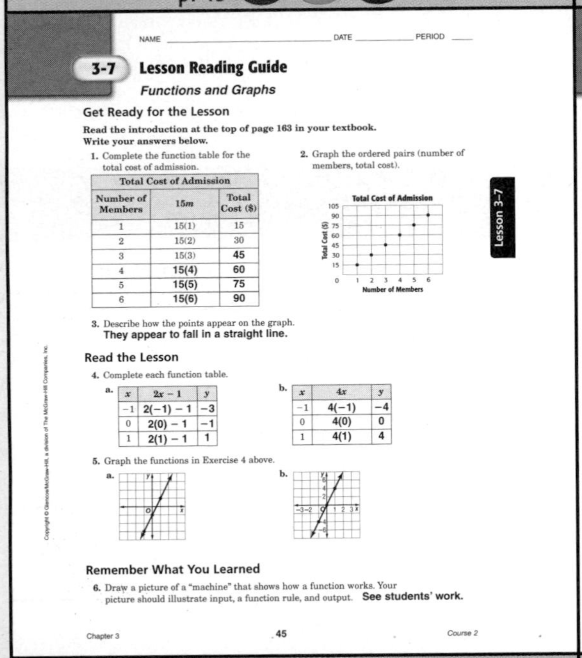

NAME _____ DATE _____ PERIOD _____

3-7 Lesson Reading Guide
Functions and Graphs

Get Ready for the Lesson
Read the introduction at the top of page 163 in your textbook.
Write your answers below.

1. Complete the function table for the total cost of admission.

Total Cost of Admission

Number of Members	$15m$	Total Cost ($)
1	15(1)	15
2	15(2)	30
3	15(3)	45
4	15(4)	60
5	15(5)	75
6	15(6)	90

2. Graph the ordered pairs (number of members, total cost).

Total Cost of Admission

3. Describe how the points appear on the graph.
They appear to fall in a straight line.

Read the Lesson
4. Complete each function table.

a.
x	$2x - 1$	y
-1	2(-1) - 1	-3
0	2(0) - 1	-1
1	2(1) - 1	1

b.
x	$4x$	y
-1	4(-1)	-4
0	4(0)	0
1	4(1)	4

5. Graph the functions in Exercise 4 above.
a.   b.

Remember What You Learned
6. Draw a picture of a "machine" that shows how a function works. Your picture should illustrate input, a function rule, and output. **See students' work.**

Chapter 3   45   Course 2

Study Guide and Intervention*
p. 46 **BL** **OL** **ELL**

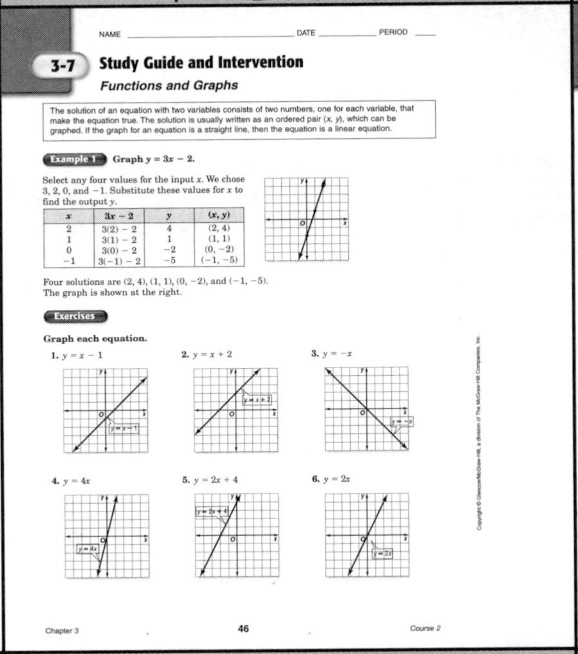

NAME _____ DATE _____ PERIOD _____

3-7 Study Guide and Intervention
Functions and Graphs

The solution of an equation with two variables consists of two numbers, one for each variable, that make the equation true. The solution is usually written as an ordered pair (x, y), which can be graphed. If the graph for an equation is a straight line, then the equation is a linear equation.

Example 1 Graph $y = 3x - 2$.

Select any four values for the input x. We chose 3, 2, 0, and -1. Substitute these values for x to find the output y.

x	$3x - 2$	y	(x, y)
2	3(2) - 2	4	(2, 4)
1	3(1) - 2	1	(1, 1)
0	3(0) - 2	-2	(0, -2)
-1	3(-1) - 2	-5	(-1, -5)

Four solutions are (2, 4), (1, 1), (0, -2), and (-1, -5).
The graph is shown at the right.

Exercises
Graph each equation.

1. $y = x - 1$ 2. $y = x + 2$ 3. $y = -x$

4. $y = 4x$ 5. $y = 2x + 4$ 6. $y = 2x$

Chapter 3   46   Course 2

Skills Practice*
p. 47 **BL** **OL**

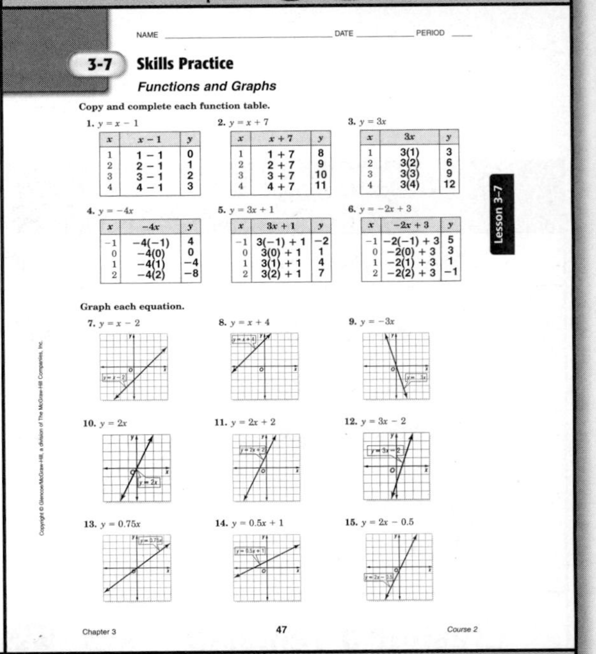

NAME _____ DATE _____ PERIOD _____

3-7 Skills Practice
Functions and Graphs

Copy and complete each function table.

1. $y = x - 1$

x	$x - 1$	y
1	1 - 1	0
2	2 - 1	1
3	3 - 1	2
4	4 - 1	3

2. $y = x + 7$

x	$x + 7$	y
1	1 + 7	8
2	2 + 7	9
3	3 + 7	10
4	4 + 7	11

3. $y = 3x$

x	$3x$	y
1	3(1)	3
2	3(2)	6
3	3(3)	9
4	3(4)	12

4. $y = -4x$

x	$-4x$	y
-1	-4(-1)	4
0	-4(0)	0
1	-4(1)	-4
2	-4(2)	-8

5. $y = 3x + 1$

x	$3x + 1$	y
-1	3(-1) + 1	-2
0	3(0) + 1	1
1	3(1) + 1	4
2	3(2) + 1	7

6. $y = -2x + 3$

x	$-2x + 3$	y
-1	-2(-1) + 3	5
0	-2(0) + 3	3
1	-2(1) + 3	1
2	-2(2) + 3	-1

Graph each equation.

7. $y = x - 2$ 8. $y = x + 4$ 9. $y = -3x$

10. $y = 2x$ 11. $y = 2x + 2$ 12. $y = 3x - 2$

13. $y = 0.75x$ 14. $y = 0.5x + 1$ 15. $y = 2x - 0.5$

Chapter 3   47   Course 2

Practice*
p. 48 **OL** **AL**

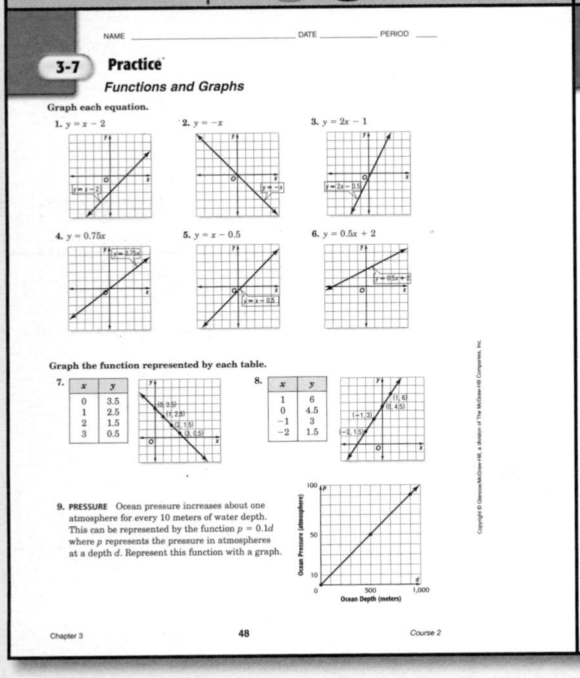

NAME _____ DATE _____ PERIOD _____

3-7 Practice
Functions and Graphs

Graph each equation.

1. $y = x - 2$ 2. $y = -x$ 3. $y = 2x - 1$

4. $y = 0.75x$ 5. $y = x - 0.5$ 6. $y = 0.5x + 2$

Graph the function represented by each table.

7.
x	y
0	3.5
1	2.5
2	1.5
3	0.5

8.
x	y
-2	6
0	4.5
-1	3
-2	1.5

9. **PRESSURE** Ocean pressure increases about one atmosphere for every 10 meters of water depth. This can be represented by the function $p = 0.1d$ where p represents the pressure in atmospheres at a depth d. Represent this function with a graph.

Chapter 3   48   Course 2

Word Problem Practice*
p. 49 **OL** **AL**

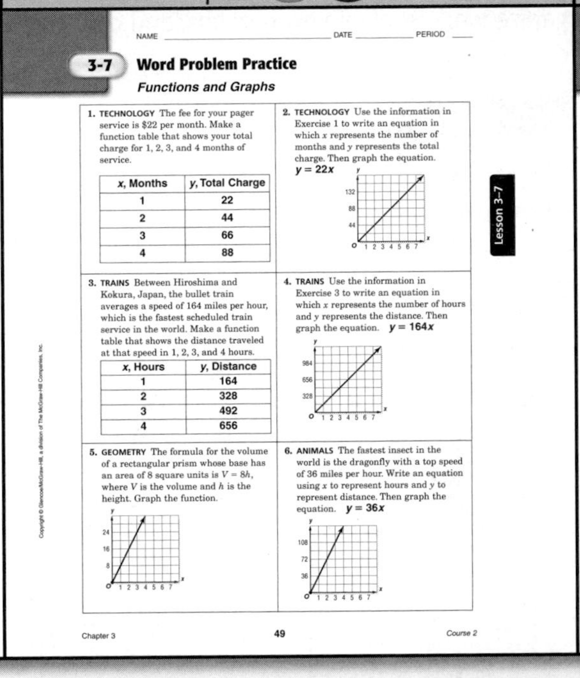

NAME _____ DATE _____ PERIOD _____

3-7 Word Problem Practice
Functions and Graphs

1. **TECHNOLOGY** The fee for your pager service is $22 per month. Make a function table that shows your total charge for 1, 2, 3, and 4 months of service.

x, Months	y, Total Charge
1	22
2	44
3	66
4	88

2. **TECHNOLOGY** Use the information in Exercise 1 to write an equation in which x represents the number of months and y represents the total charge. Then graph the equation.
$y = 22x$

3. **TRAINS** Between Hiroshima and Kokura, Japan, the bullet train averages a speed of 164 miles per hour, which is the fastest scheduled train service in the world. Make a function table that shows the distance traveled at that speed in 1, 2, 3, and 4 hours.

x, Hours	y, Distance
1	164
2	328
3	492
4	656

4. **TRAINS** Use the information in Exercise 3 to write an equation in which x represents the number of hours and y represents the distance. Then graph the equation. $y = 164x$

5. **GEOMETRY** The formula for the volume of a rectangular prism whose base has an area of 8 square units is $V = 8h$, where V is the volume and h is the height. Graph the function.

6. **ANIMALS** The fastest insect in the world is the dragonfly with a top speed of 36 miles per hour. Write an equation using x to represent hours and y to represent distance. Then graph the equation. $y = 36x$

Chapter 3   49   Course 2

Enrichment
p. 50 **OL** **AL**

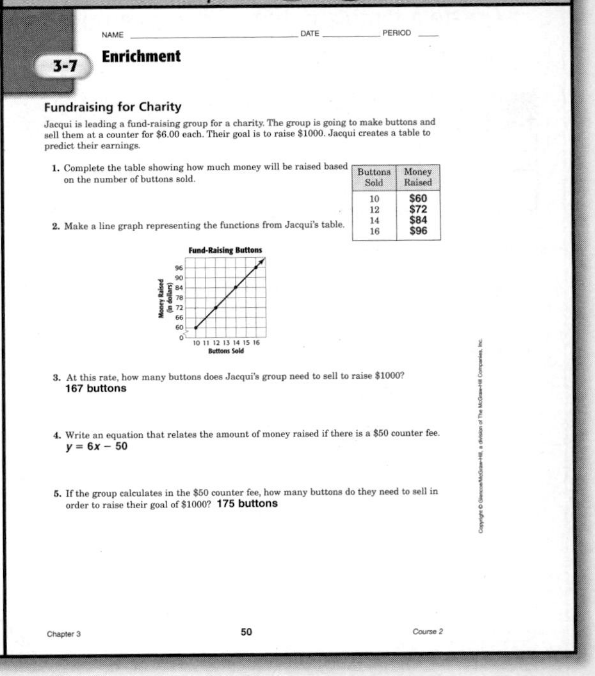

NAME _____ DATE _____ PERIOD _____

3-7 Enrichment

Fundraising for Charity
Jacqui is leading a fund-raising group for a charity. The group is going to make buttons and sell them at a counter for $6.00 each. Their goal is to raise $1000. Jacqui creates a table to predict their earnings.

1. Complete the table showing how much money will be raised based on the number of buttons sold.

Buttons Sold	Money Raised
10	$60
12	$72
14	$84
16	$96

2. Make a line graph representing the functions from Jacqui's table.

Fund-Raising Buttons

3. At this rate, how many buttons does Jacqui's group need to sell to raise $1000?
167 buttons

4. Write an equation that relates the amount of money raised if there is a $50 counter fee.
$y = 6x - 50$

5. If the group calculates in the $50 counter fee, how many buttons do they need to sell in order to raise their goal of $1000? **175 buttons**

Chapter 3   50   Course 2

*** Also available in Spanish ELL**

Additional Lesson Resources

Transparencies
• *5-Minute Check Transparency*, Lesson 3-7

Other Print Products
• *Teaching Mathematics with Manipulatives*
• *Noteables™ Interactive Study Notebook with Foldables™*

Teacher Tech Tools
• *Interactive Classroom CD-ROM*, Lesson 3-7
• *AssignmentWorks*, Lesson 3-7

Student Tech Tools
glencoe.com
• Extra Examples, Chapter 3, Lesson 7
• Self-Check Quiz, Chapter 3, Lesson 7

MAIN IDEA

Graph data to demonstrate relationships.

New Vocabulary

linear equation

Math Online

glencoe.com
• Extra Examples
• Personal Tutor
• Self-Check Quiz

▷ **GET READY** for the Lesson

MONEY The Westerville Marching Band is going on a year-end trip to an amusement park. Each band member must pay an admission price of $15. In the table, this is represented by $15m$.

Total Cost of Admission		
Number of Members	15m	Total Cost ($)
1	15(1)	15
2	15(2)	30
3	15(3)	45
4	15(4)	60
5	15(5)	75
6	15(6)	90

1. Copy and complete the function table for the total cost of admission.

2. Graph the ordered pairs (number of members, total cost). **See Ch. 3 Answer Appendix.**

3. Describe how the points appear on the graph.

3. They appear to fall in a straight line.

If you are given a function, ordered pairs in the form (input, output), or (x, y), provide useful information about that function. These ordered pairs can then be graphed on a coordinate plane and form part of the graph of the function. The graph of the function consists of the points in the coordinate plane that correspond to *all* the ordered pairs of the form (input, output).

Real-World EXAMPLE

1 **TEMPERATURE** The table shows temperatures in Celsius and the corresponding temperatures in Fahrenheit. Make a graph of the data to show the relationship between Celsius and Fahrenheit.

The ordered pairs (5, 41), (10, 50), (15, 59), (20, 68), (25, 77), and (30, 86) represent this function. Graph the ordered pairs.

Celsius (input)	Fahrenheit (output)
5	41
10	50
15	59
20	68
25	77
30	86

Celsius to Fahrenheit

Lesson 3-7 Functions and Graphs **163**

Focus on Mathematical Content

Discrete Functions Some of the functions described in this lesson are *not* continuous but are drawn with a line connecting the points. This is intentional to prepare students to make predictions from line and other graphs in Chapter 8.

1 Focus

Vertical Alignment

Before Lesson 3-7
Identify and graph ordered pairs in the four quadrants of the coordinate plane

Lesson 3-7
Solve problems involving rates, average speed, distance, and time; use a variety of methods, such as words, numbers, symbols, graphs, and tables to explain mathematical reasoning

After Lesson 3-7
Plot the values of quantities whose ratios are always the same; fit a line to the plot and understand that the slope of the line equals the ratio of the quantities

2 Teach

Scaffolding Questions

Tell students that a cheeseburger costs $2 at a local restaurant. After students answer each of the following questions, write an ordered pair (number of cheeseburgers, cost).

Ask:
• How much will 1 cheeseburger cost? (1, $2)

• How much will 2 cheeseburgers cost? (2, $4)

• How much will 3 cheeseburgers cost? (3, $6)

• How much will 4 cheeseburgers cost? (4, $8)

• How could you use this information to make a line graph? Sample answer: Show the number of cheeseburgers on the x-axis and the cost on the y-axis.

Focus on Mathematical Content

Functions can be graphed on a **coordinate plane**.

To find **solutions** to a function, substitute values for the input variable, *x*, and then solve to get the corresponding values for the output variable, *y*. Each solution is an **ordered pair** (*x*, *y*).

To show a function on a coordinate plane, **graph several ordered pairs** that represent it, and then connect the points.

The graph of a **linear function** is a line.

Formative Assessment

Use the Check Your Progress exercises after each Example to determine students' understanding of concepts.

ADDITIONAL EXAMPLES

1 **WORK** The table shows the number of hours Abby worked and her corresponding earnings. Make a graph of the data to show the relationship between the number of hours Abby worked and her earnings.

Number of Hours	Earnings ($)
1	6
2	12
3	18
4	24

Hours Worked and Earnings

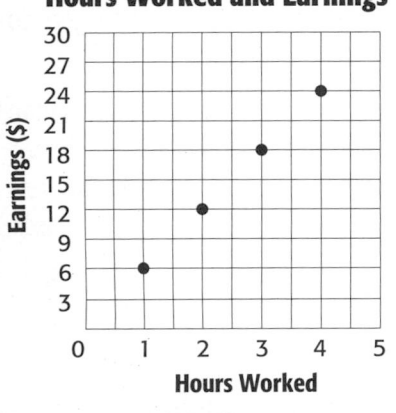

Review Vocabulary

function a relation in which each element of the input is paired with exactly one element of the output according to a specified rule (Lesson 1-10)

 CHECK Your Progress

a. **MUSIC** The table shows the money remaining on a $75 gift certificate after a certain number of CDs are bought. Make a graph to show how the number of CDs bought and the remaining balance are related.
See Ch. 3 Answer Appendix.

$75 Music Gift Certificate	
Number of CDs	**Balance ($)**
1	63
2	51
3	39
4	27
5	15

The solution of an equation with two variables consists of two numbers, one for each variable, that make the equation true. The solution is usually written as an ordered pair (*x*, *y*).

EXAMPLE **Graph Solutions of Linear Equations**

2 Graph $y = 2x + 1$.

Select any four values for the input *x*. We chose 2, 1, 0, and −1. Substitute these values for *x* to find the output *y*.

x	2*x* + 1	*y*	(*x*, *y*)
2	2(2) + 1	5	(2, 5)
1	2(1) + 1	3	(1, 3)
0	2(0) + 1	1	(0, 1)
−1	2(−1) + 1	−1	(−1, −1)

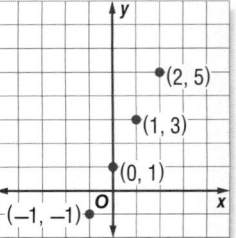

The four inputs correspond to the solutions (2, 5), (1, 3), (0, 1), and (−1, −1). By graphing these ordered pairs, you can create the graph of $y = 2x + 1$.

 CHECK Your Progress   Graph each equation.
b–d. See Ch. 3 Answer Appendix.

b. $y = x - 3$ **c.** $y = -3x$ **d.** $y = -3x + 2$

Study Tip

Graphing Equations
Only two points are needed to graph the line. However, graph more points to check accuracy.

Notice that all four points in the graph lie on the same straight line. Draw a line through the points to graph *all* solutions of the equation $y = 2x + 1$. Note that the point (3, 7) is also on this line.

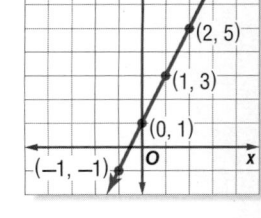

$y = 2x + 1$ Write the equation.
$7 \overset{?}{=} 2(3) + 1$ Replace *x* with 3 and *y* with 7.
$7 = 7$ ✓   This sentence is true.

So, (3, 7) is also a solution of $y = 2x + 1$. An equation like $y = 2x + 1$ is called a **linear equation** because its graph is a straight line.

2 Graph $y = x + 3$.

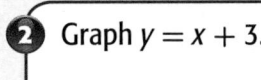

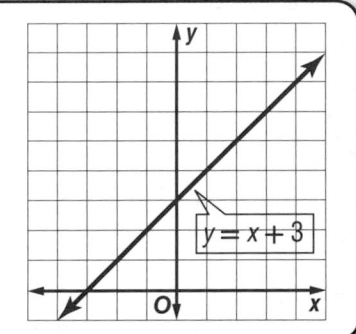

③ SWIMMING Michael Phelps swims the 400-meter individual medley at an average speed of 100 meters per minute. The equation $d = 100t$ describes the distance d that he can swim in t minutes at this speed. Represent the function by a graph.

Step 1   Select any four values for t. Select only positive numbers because t represents time. Make a function table.

t	$100t$	d	(t, d)
1	100(1)	100	(1, 100)
2	100(2)	200	(2, 200)
3	100(3)	300	(3, 300)
4	100(4)	400	(4, 400)

Step 2   Graph the ordered pairs and draw a line through the points.

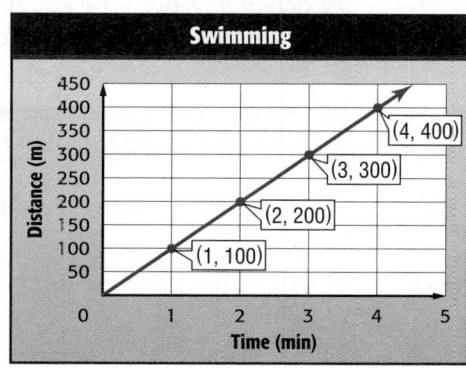

✔ CHECK Your Progress

e. **JOBS** Sandi makes $6 an hour babysitting. The equation $m = 6h$ describes how much money m she earns babysitting for h hours. Represent this function by a graph. **See Ch. 3 Answer Appendix.**

Representing Functions   Key Concept

Words   There are 12 inches in one foot.

Table

Feet	Inches
1	12
2	24
3	36
4	48

Graph

Convert Feet to Inches

Equation $f = 12n$, where f represents the number of feet and n represents the number of inches.

---

③ ANIMALS Blue whales can reach a top speed of 30 miles per hour. The equation $d = 30t$ describes the distance d that a whale swimming at that speed can travel in time t. Assuming that a whale can maintain the speed, represent the function with a graph.

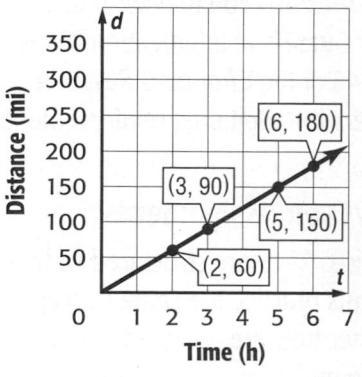

Blue Whales

Additional Examples are also in:

- Noteables™ Interactive Study Notebook with Foldables™

- Interactive Classroom PowerPoint® Presentations

3 Practice

Formative Assessment

Use Exercises 1–6 to check for understanding.

Then use the chart at the bottom of this page to customize your assignments for students.

Intervention You may wish to use the Study Guide and Intervention Master on page 46 of the *Chapter 3 Resource Masters* for additional reinforcement.

Odd/Even Assignments

Exercises 7–16 are structured so that students practice the same concepts whether they are assigned odd or even problems.

 **Graphs**

Some students may wonder why some of the directions say to "graph the equation" while others say to "graph the function." Remind them that functions can be shown in tables and written as equations. You may wish to have students review Lesson 1-10 to see how functions can be written as equations.

Example 1 (p. 163)

1–6. See Ch. 3 Answer Appendix.

Graph the function represented by each table.

1.
Total Cost of Baseballs	
Baseball	Total Cost ($)
1	4
2	8
3	12
4	16

2.
Convert Minutes to Seconds	
Minutes	Seconds
1	60
2	120
3	180
4	240

Example 2 (p. 164)

Graph each equation.

3. $y = x - 1$ 4. $y = -1x$ 5. $y = -2x + 3$

Example 3 (p. 165)

6. **MEASUREMENT** The perimeter of a square is 4 times greater than the length of one of its sides. The equation $p = 4s$ describes the perimeter p of a square with sides s units long. Represent this function by a graph.

HOMEWORK HELP

For Exercises	See Examples
7–8	1
9–14	2
15–16	3

Exercise Levels
A: 7–16
B: 17–20
C: 21–24

Graph the function represented by each table. **7–20. See Ch. 3 Answer Appendix.**

7.
Total Phone Bill	
Time (min)	Total (¢)
1	8
2	16
3	24
4	32

8.
Calories in Fruit Cups	
Servings	Total Calories
1	70
3	210
5	350
7	490

Graph each equation.

9. $y = x + 1$ 10. $y = x + 3$ 11. $y = x$

12. $y = -2x$ 13. $y = 2x + 3$ 14. $y = 3x - 1$

For Exercises 15 and 16, represent each function by a graph.

15. **CARS** A car averages 36 miles per gallon of gasoline. The function $m = 36g$ represents the miles m driven using g gallons of gasoline.

16. **FITNESS** A health club charges $35 a month for membership fees. The equation $c = 35m$ describes the total charge c for m months of membership.

Graph each equation.

17. $y = 0.25x$ 18. $y = x + 0.5$ 19. $y = 0.5x - 1$

EXTRA PRACTICE
See pages 676, 706.

20. **SHOPPING** You buy a DVD for $14 and CDs for $9 each. The equation $t = 14 + 9c$ represents the total amount t that you spend if you buy 1 DVD and c CDs. Represent this function by a graph.

166   **Chapter 3** Algebra: Linear Equations and Functions

DIFFERENTIATED HOMEWORK OPTIONS			
Level	Assignment	Two-Day Option	
BL Basic	7–16, 21, 24–31	7–15 odd, 25	8–16 even, 21, 24, 26–31
OL Core	7–13 odd, 15–17, 19–21, 24–31	7–16, 25	17–21, 24, 26–31
AL Advanced/Pre-AP	17–31		

H.O.T. Problems

21. **OPEN ENDED** Draw the graph of a linear function. Name three ordered pairs in the function. **See students' work.**

   CHALLENGE For Exercises 22 and 23, let *x* represent the first number and let *y* represent the second number. Draw a graph of each function.

22. The second number is three more than the first number. **22–23. See margin.**

23. The second number is the product of −3 and the first number.

24. **WRITING IN MATH** Describe how you use a function table to create the graph of a function. **See Ch. 3 Answer Appendix.**

TEST PRACTICE

25. The graph shows the relationship between the number of hours Jennifer spent jogging and the total number of miles she jogged. Which table best represents the data in the graph? **C**

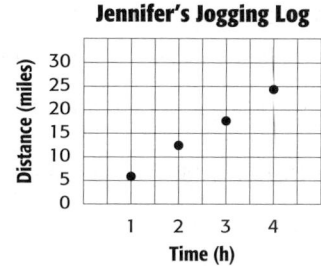

Jennifer's Jogging Log

A	Time (h)	Distance (mi)
	6	4
	12	3
	18	2
	24	1

B	Time (h)	Distance (mi)
	2	6
	3	12
	4	18
	5	24

C	Time (h)	Distance (mi)
	1	6
	2	12
	3	18
	4	24

D	Time (h)	Distance (mi)
	4	6
	3	6
	2	6
	1	6

Spiral Review

26. **MEASUREMENT** The area and width of a rug are 323 square inches and 17 inches respectively. What is the perimeter of the rug? (Lesson 3-6) **72 in.**

Solve each equation. Check your solution. (Lesson 3-5)

27. $4y + 19 = 7$ **−3**   28. $10x + 2 = 32$ **3**   29. $48 - 8j = 16$ **4**   30. $14 = 2 - 6d$ **−2**

31. Evaluate $|5| + |-10|$. (Lesson 2-1) **15**

Problem Solving in Social Studies

Real-World Unit Project

Stand Up and Be Counted! It's time to complete your project. Use the data you have gathered about how the U.S. Census affects the House of Representatives to prepare a poster. Be sure to include a map, frequency table, and paragraph discussing the changes in the House of Representatives.

Math Online Unit Project at glencoe.com

Pre-AP Activity   Use after Exercise 19

Have students describe the functions they graphed for Exercises 17–19. Do the lines slope upward or downward? How steep are the lines? Where do the lines intersect the *y*-axis?

---

4 Assess

Ticket Out the Door Have students describe the functions they graphed for one of the following exercises: 11, 12, or 19. Are the functions linear? Do the functions rise or fall?

 Formative Assessment

Check for student understanding of concepts in Lesson 3-7.

 Quiz 4, p. 56

FOLDABLES Study Organizer **Foldables™ Follow-Up**

Remind students to take notes about today's lesson under the *Functions* tab of their Foldables. Encourage them to write a linear function from the lesson, complete a function table, and graph the function.

Additional Answers

22.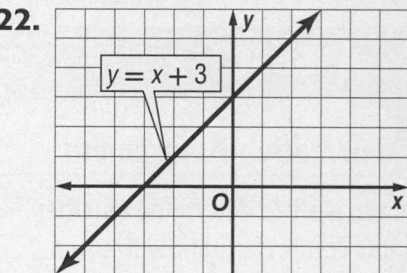

$y = x + 3$

23.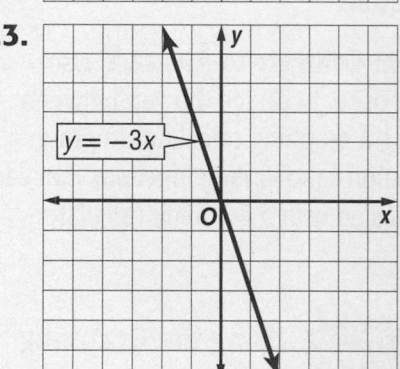

$y = -3x$

 **Focus**

Materials

• graphing calculator

Teaching Tip

If your class does not have enough graphing calculators for every student, have students work in pairs or groups of three, sharing calculators.

② Teach

Activity When typing fractions into the graphing calculator, place parentheses around the fraction and use the division button to denote the fraction bar. For example, type (1/3) to represent the fraction $\frac{1}{3}$.

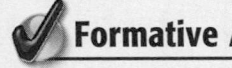 **Assess**

✓ Formative Assessment

Use Exercise 1 to determine whether students comprehend how to use a graphing calculator to graph the relationship between different units of measure.

From Concrete to Abstract Use Exercise 5 to bridge the gap between using a graphing calculator to graph functions and writing functions that can be tested with a graphing calculator.

 **Using the Graphing Calculator**

The first function key under the MATH key is ▶Frac. Use this function key to convert a terminating decimal to a fraction. For example, to convert the decimal 0.356 to a fraction, enter 0.356 on your calculator. Press the MATH key and then press 1 (or ENTER). The

---

Extend 3-7

Graphing Calculator Lab
Graphing Relationships

MAIN IDEA

Use technology to graph relationships involving conversions of measurement.

You can use a graphing calculator to graph relationships.

ACTIVITY

1 **MEASUREMENT** Use the table at the right to write a function that relates the number of yards x to the number of feet y. Then graph your function.

Yards (x)	Feet (y)
1	3
2	6
3	9
4	12

STEP 1 By examining the table, you can see that the number of feet is 3 times the number of yards. Write a function.

The number of feet	is	3 times	the number of yards.
y	$=$	3	x

STEP 2 Press Y= and enter the function $y = 3x$ into Y₁.

STEP 3 Adjust your viewing window. Press WINDOW and change the values to reflect the range of values in the table.

STEP 4 Finally, graph the function by pressing Graph.

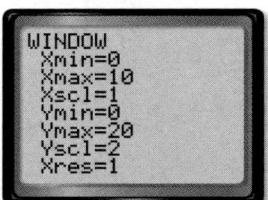

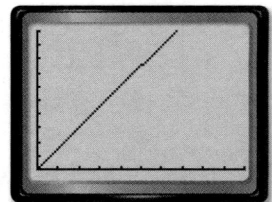

ANALYZE THE RESULTS 1–5. See Ch. 3 Answer Appendix.

1. Test the function above using one of the values from the table and the CALC feature on your calculator. Press 2nd [CALC] 1 and then enter an x-value of 3. What y-value is displayed? What do each of these values represent and how are they represented on the graph?

2. Use your graph to convert 7 yards into feet. Explain your method.

3. **MAKE A CONJECTURE** Write a function that could be used to convert feet into yards. What is an appropriate window for a graph of this function? Graph and test your function.

4. Use your function from Exercise 3 to convert 16 feet into yards.

5. Write a function that could be used to convert 36 ounces to pounds. Indicate an appropriate window, then use a graph of the function to convert 36 ounces to pounds. (*Hint*: 1 pound = 16 ounces)

---

screen displays the conversion of 0.356 as 89/250. You can also use this function key to convert a repeating decimal as a fraction as long as you type in several of the repeating digits.

CHAPTER
3 **Study Guide and Review**

Math Online ▷ glencoe.com
• STUDY *TO GO*
• Vocabulary Review

CHAPTER
3 Study Guide and Review

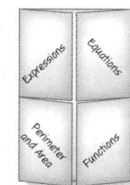

FOLDABLES
Study Organizer ▷ **GET READY to Study**

Be sure the following Big Ideas are noted in your Foldable.

BIG Ideas

Solving Equations (Lessons 3-2, 3-3, and 3-5)
• If you add or subtract the same number from each side of an equation, the two sides remain equal.

• If you divide each side of an equation by the same nonzero number, the two sides remain equal.

• To solve a two-step equation like $3x + 4 = 19$ or $2x - 1 = -5$:

Step 1 Undo the addition or subtraction first.

Step 2 Then undo the multiplication or division.

Perimeter and Area Formulas (Lesson 3-6)
• The perimeter P of a rectangle is twice the sum of the length ℓ and width w.

• The area A of a rectangle is the product of the length ℓ and width w.

Linear Functions (Lesson 3-7)
• The graph of a linear function is a straight line. Ordered pairs in the form (x, y) can be used to represent a function and graphed on the coordinate plane as part of the graph of the function.

2. false; addition
7. False; subtract 3 from each side.
10. false; 5 times the value of x

Key Vocabulary

formula (p. 144)
linear equation (p. 164)
two-step equation (p. 151)
work backward strategy (p. 148)

Vocabulary Check

State whether each sentence is *true* or *false*. If *false*, replace the underlined word or number to make a true sentence.

1. The expression $\frac{1}{3}y$ means <u>one third of y</u>. **true**

2. The words *more than* sometimes suggest the operation of <u>multiplication</u>.

3. The formula <u>$d = rt$</u> gives the distance d traveled at a rate of r for t units of time. **true**

4. The algebraic expression representing the words *six less than m* is <u>$6 - m$</u>. **false; $m - 6$**

5. Use the <u>work backward</u> strategy when you are given a final result and asked to find an earlier amount. **true**

6. The word *each* sometimes suggests the operation of <u>division</u>. **false; multiplication**

7. In solving the equation $4x + 3 = 15$, first <u>divide each side by 4</u>.

8. The solution to the equation $p + 4.4 = 11.6$ is <u>7.2</u>. **true**

9. The process of solving a <u>two-step equation</u> uses the work backward strategy. **true**

10. The expression $5x$ means <u>5 more than x</u>.

11. To find the distance around a rectangle, use the formula for its <u>area</u>. **false; perimeter**

12. The word *per* sometimes suggests the operation of <u>subtraction</u>. **false; division**

FOLDABLES™
Study Organizer **Dinah Zike's Foldables**

Have students look through the chapter to make sure they have included notes, key concepts, and examples in their Foldables for each lesson.

Encourage students to refer to their Foldables while completing the Study Guide and Review and while preparing for the Chapter Test.

 Formative Assessment

Key Vocabulary The page references after each word in the Key Vocabulary denote where that term was first introduced. If students have difficulty answering Exercises 1–12, remind them that they can use these page references to refresh their memories about the vocabulary terms.

 glencoe.com

Vocabulary PuzzleMaker improves students' mathematics vocabulary using four puzzle formats—crossword, scramble, word search using a word list, and word search using clues. Students can work online or from a printed worksheet.

✓ **Summative Assessment**

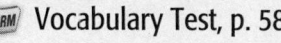 Vocabulary Test, p. 58

Lesson-by-Lesson Review

Intervention If the given examples are not sufficient to review the topics covered by the questions, remind students that the page references tell them where to review that topic in their textbooks.

Two-Day Option Have students complete the Lesson-by-Lesson Review on pages 170–172. Then you can use ExamView® Assessment Suite to customize another review worksheet that practices all the objectives of this chapter or only the objectives on which your students need more help.

For more information on ExamView® Assessment Suite, see page 126C.

Differentiated Instruction

Super DVD: MindJogger Plus
Use this DVD as an alternative format of review for the test. For more information on this game show format, see page 126D.

Lesson-by-Lesson Review

3-1 **Writing Expressions and Equations** (pp. 128–133)

Write each phrase as an algebraic expression.

13. the sum of a number and 5 $x + 5$

14. six inches less than her height $h - 6$

15. twice as many apples $2a$

Write each sentence as an algebraic equation.

16. Ten years older than Theresa's age is 23. $10 + t = 23$

17. Four less than a number is 19.
$n - 4 = 19$

18. The quotient of 56 and a number is 14.
$\frac{56}{n} = 14$

19. **AMUSEMENT PARKS** This year, admission to a popular amusement park is $8.75 more than the previous year's admission fee. Write an expression describing the cost of this year's admission. $f + \$8.75$

Example 1 Write the phrase as an algebraic expression.

four times the price

Let p represent the price.
The algebraic expression is $4p$.

Example 2 Write the sentence as an algebraic equation.

Six less than the number of cookies is 24.

Let c represent the number of cookies.
The equation is $c - 6 = 24$.

3-2 **Solving Addition and Subtraction Equations** (pp. 136–141)

Solve each equation. Check your solution.

20. $x + 5 = 8$ **3**   21. $r + 8 = 2$ **−6**

22. $p + 9 = -4$ **−13**   23. $s - 8 = 15$ **23**

24. $n - 1 = -3$ **−2**   25. $w - 9 = 28$ **37**

26. **COOKIES** Marjorie baked some chocolate chip cookies for her and her sister. Her sister ate 6 of these cookies. If there were 18 cookies left, write and solve an equation to find how many cookies c Marjorie baked.

26. $c - 6 = 18$; 24 cookies

Example 3 Solve $x + 6 = 4$.
$$x + 6 = 4$$
$$\underline{-6 = -6} \quad \text{Subtract 6 from each side.}$$
$$x \quad = -2$$

Example 4 Solve $y - 3 = -2$.
$$y - 3 = -2$$
$$\underline{+3 = +3} \quad \text{Add 3 to each side.}$$
$$y \quad = 1$$

Mixed Problem Solving
For mixed problem-solving practice,
see page 706.

CHAPTER
3 Study Guide
and Review

3-3 **Solving Multiplication Equations** (pp. 142–146)

Solve each equation. Check your
solution.

27. $7c = 28$ **4**   28. $-8w = 72$ **−9**

29. $10y = -90$ **−9**   30. $-12r = -36$ **3**

31. **MONEY** Matt borrowed $98 from his
father. He plans to repay his father at
$14 per week. Write and solve an
equation to find the number of weeks
w required to pay back his father.

31. $14w = 98$; **7 weeks**

Example 5 Solve $-4b = 32$.

$$-4b = 32$$
$$\frac{-4b}{-4} = \frac{32}{-4} \qquad \text{Divide each side by } -4.$$
$$b = -8$$

3-4 **PSI: Work Backward** (pp. 148–149)

Solve. Use the *work backward* strategy.

32. **BASEBALL** Last baseball season, Nelson
had four less than twice the number of
hits Marcus had. Nelson had 48 hits.
How many hits did Marcus have last
season? **26 hits**

33. **CREDIT CARDS** Alicia paid off $119 of
her credit card balance and made an
additional $62.75 in purchases. If she
now owes $90.45, what was her
starting balance? **$146.70**

Example 6 A number is divided by 2.
Then 4 is added to the quotient. After
subtracting 3, the result is 18. What is
the number?

Start with the final value and work
backward with each resulting value
until you arrive at the starting value.

$18 + 3 = 21$ Undo subtracting 3.

$21 - 4 = 17$ Undo adding 4.

$17 \cdot 2 = 34$ Undo dividing by 2.

The number is 34.

3-5 **Solving Two-Step Equations** (pp. 151–155)

Solve each equation. Check your
solution.

34. $3y - 12 = 6$ **6**   35. $6x - 4 = 20$ **4**

36. $2x + 5 = 3$ **−1**   37. $5m + 6 = -4$ **−2**

38. $10c - 8 = 90$ **9.8** 39. $3r - 20 = -5$ **5**

40. **ALGEBRA** Ten more than five times
a number is 25. Find the number. **3**

Example 7 Solve $3p - 4 = 8$.

$$3p - 4 = \quad 8$$
$$\underline{+ 4 = + 4} \qquad \text{Add 4 to each side.}$$
$$3p \quad = \quad 12$$
$$\frac{3p}{3} = \frac{12}{3} \qquad \text{Divide each side by 3.}$$
$$p = 4$$

Chapter 3 Study Guide and Review **171**

Problem Solving Review

For additional practice in problem solving for Chapter 3, see the Mixed Problem Solving Appendix, page 706 in the Student Handbook section.

Anticipation Guide

Have students complete the Chapter 3 Anticipation Guide and discuss how their responses have changed now that they have completed Chapter 3.

[CRM] Anticipation Guide, pp. 7–8

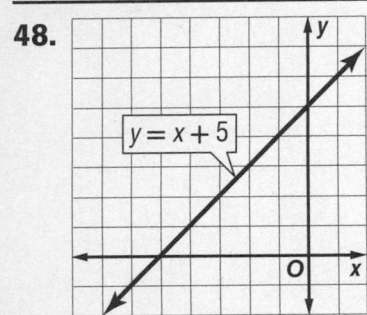

Additional Answers

48.

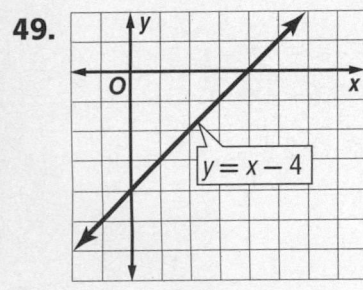

3-6 Measurement: Perimeter and Area (pp. 156–161)

Find the perimeter and area of each rectangle.

41.

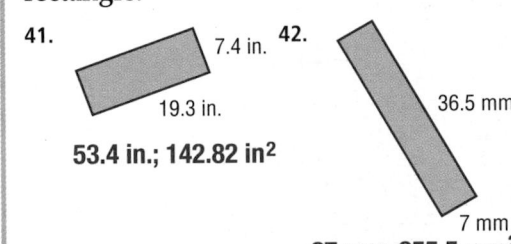

7.4 in.

19.3 in.

53.4 in.; 142.82 in²

42.

36.5 mm

7 mm

87 mm; 255.5 mm²

Find the missing measure.

43. $P = 56$ mi, $\ell = 21$ mi **7 mi**

44. $A = 10.26$ ft², $w = 2.7$ ft **3.8 ft**

45. $A = 272$ yd², $\ell = 17$ yd **16 yd**

46. $P = 14.2$ cm, $w = 2.6$ cm **4.5 cm**

47. **CARPET** In order to carpet her rectangular living room, Flora needs 192 square feet of carpet. If the length of her living room is 16 feet, find the width. **12 ft**

Example 8 The perimeter of a rectangle is 38 meters. If the length is 7 meters, find the width.

$P = 2\ell + 2w$	Perimeter formula
$38 = 2(7) + 2w$	Replace P with 38 and ℓ with 7.
$38 = 14 + 2w$	Simplify.
$24 = 2w$	Subtract 14 from each side.
$\dfrac{24}{2} = \dfrac{2w}{2}$	Divide each side by 2.
$12 = w$	Simplify.

The width is 12 meters.

Example 9 The area of a rectangle is 285 square inches. If the width is 15 inches, find the length.

$A = \ell w$	Area formula
$285 = \ell(15)$	Replace A with 285 and w with 15.
$\dfrac{285}{15} = \dfrac{15\ell}{15}$	Divide each side by 15.
$19 = \ell$	Simplify.

The length is 19 inches.

3-7 Functions and Graphs (pp. 163–167)

Graph each equation. **48–51. See margin.**

48. $y = x + 5$

49. $y = x - 4$

50. $y = 2x$

51. $y = -1x$

52. $y = 3x + 2$

53. $y = -2x + 3$

52–53. See Ch. 3 Answer Appendix.

MONEY For Exercises 54–56, use the following information.

Clara earns $9 per hour mowing lawns.

54. Make a table that shows her total earnings for 2, 4, 6, and 8 hours.

55. Write an equation in which x represents the number of hours and y represents Clara's total earnings. **$y = 9x$**

56. Graph the equation.

54, 56. See Ch. 3 Answer Appendix.

Example 10 Graph $y = x + 3$.

Select four values for x. Substitute these values for x to find values for y.

x	$x + 3$	y
-1	$-1 + 3$	2
0	$0 + 3$	3
1	$1 + 3$	4
2	$2 + 3$	5

Four solutions are $(-1, 2)$, $(0, 3)$, $(1, 4)$, and $(2, 5)$. The graph is shown below.

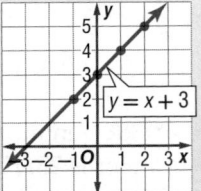

49.

50.

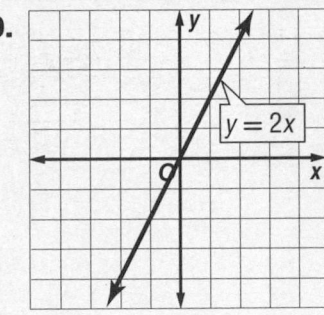

51.

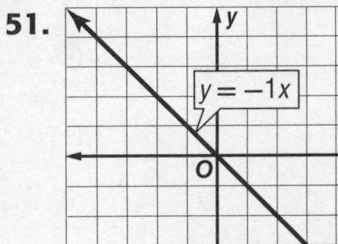

CHAPTER
3
Practice Test

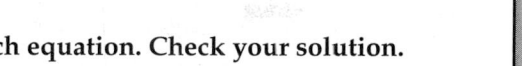
Math Online glencoe.com
• Chapter Test

CHAPTER
3 Practice Test

Write each phrase as an algebraic expression or equation.

1. $5 less than Tomasita has **$t - 5$**

2. 4 years older than Hana **$h + 4$**

3. 56 inches is 9 inches shorter than Jacob's height. **$56 = j - 9$**

4. Twice the distance from the park to the post office is 5 miles. **$2d = 5$**

5. **FLOWERS** The number of tulips in Paula's garden is 8 less than the number of marigolds. If there are 16 tulips, write and solve an equation to determine the number of marigolds m. **$16 = m - 8$; 24**

6. **MULTIPLE CHOICE** If you divide a number by 8 and subtract 11 from the result, the answer is 4. Which equation matches this relationship? **B**

   A $\frac{n - 11}{8} = 4$ C $\frac{n}{8} = 11 - 4$

   B $4 = \frac{n}{8} - 11$ D $4 = 11 - \frac{n}{8}$

ANALYZE TABLES For Exercises 7–9, use the table below. It shows how Jared's age and his sister Emily's are related. **7. $y = x + 6$**

Jared's age (yr)	1	2	3	4	5
Emily's age (yr)	7	8	9	10	11

7. Write an equation in which x represents Jared's age, and y represents Emily's age.

8. Graph the equation. **See margin.**

9. Predict how old Emily will be when Jared is 10 years old. **16 yr**

                             $x - 835 = 151$; 986 ft

10. **TOURISM** The Statue of Liberty is 151 feet tall. It is 835 feet shorter than the Eiffel Tower. Write and solve an equation to find the height of the Eiffel Tower.

Solve each equation. Check your solution.

11. $x + 5 = -8$ **−13**

12. $y - 11 = 15$ **26**

13. $9z = -81$ **−9**

14. $-6k + 4 = -38$ **7**

15. $3z - 7 = 17$ **8**

16. $2g - 9 = -5$ **2**

17. **PIZZA** Chris and Joe shared a pizza. Chris ate two more than twice as many pieces as Joe, who ate 3 pieces. If there were 3 pieces left, how many pieces were there initially? Use the *work backward* strategy. **14 pieces**

18. **MULTIPLE CHOICE** A giant cake in the shape of and decorated as an American flag was 60 feet in length. If it took A square feet of icing to cover the top of the cake, which of the following would represent the cake's perimeter? **F**

   F $P = 120 + 2 \cdot \frac{A}{60}$ H $P = 60 + \frac{A}{60}$

   G $P = 120 + 2A$ J $P = 60 + 2A$

Find the perimeter and area of each rectangle.

19.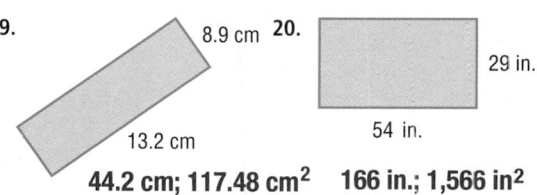
8.9 cm

13.2 cm

44.2 cm; 117.48 cm²

20.
29 in.

54 in.

166 in.; 1,566 in²

Graph each equation. **21–24. See Ch. 3 Answer Appendix.**

21. $y = x + 1$

22. $y = 2x$

23. $y = 2x - 3$

24. $y = -x + 1$

            25. See Ch. 3 Answer Appendix.

25. **MOVIES** A student ticket to the movies costs $6. The equation $c = 6t$ describes the total cost c for t tickets. Make a function table that shows the total cost for 1, 2, 3, and 4 tickets and then graph the equation.

✓ **Summative Assessment**

CRM **Chapter 3 Resource Masters**

Leveled Chapter 3 Tests			
Form	Type	Level	Pages
1	MC	BL	59–60
2A	MC	OL	61–62
2B	MC	OL	63–64
2C	FR	OL	65–66
2D	FR	OL	67–68
3	FR	AL	69–70

MC = multiple-choice questions
FR = free-response questions
BL = below or approaching grade level
OL = on grade level
AL = above or beyond grade level

• Vocabulary Test, p. 58
• Extended-Response Test, p. 71
• Unit 1 Test, pp. 75–76

ExamView Assessment Suite Customize and create multiple versions of your chapter test and the answer key. All of the questions from the leveled chapter tests in the *Chapter 3 Resource Masters* are also available on ExamView® Assessment Suite.

Additional Answer

8.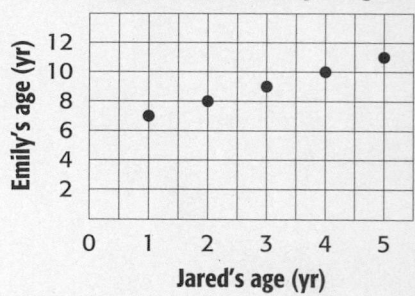
Jared's and Emily's Ages

Data-Driven Decision Making	Exercises	Lesson	State/Local Standards	Resources for Review
Diagnostic Teaching Based on the results of the Chapter 3 Practice Test, use the following to review concepts that students continue to find challenging.	1–5, 10–12	3-1, 3-2		CRM Study Guide and Intervention pp. 10, 16, 23, 28, 33, 39, and 46
	6, 13, 17	3-3, 3-4		**Math Online** glencoe.com
	14–16, 18–20	3-5, 3-6		• Extra Examples • Personal Tutor
	7–9, 21–25	3-7		• Concepts in Motion

TEST-TAKING TIP

Exercise 3 Remind students that they can eliminate incorrect answer choices by substituting one of the given positions, say 3, for n and using mental math to perform the described operations. Is the result 13? Using this procedure, students can eliminate answer choices A, B, and C.

✓ **Formative Assessment**

You can use these two pages to benchmark student progress.

CRM *Chapter 3 Resource Masters*

• Standardized Test Practice, pp. 72–74

ExamView Assessment Suite Create practice worksheets or tests that align to your state's standards, as well as TIMSS and NAEP tests.

PART 1   Multiple Choice

Read each question. Then fill in the correct answer on the answer sheet provided by your teacher or on a sheet of paper.

1. During a bike-a-thon, Shalonda cycled at a constant rate. The table shows the distance she covered in half-hour intervals.

Time (h)	Distance (mi)
$\frac{1}{2}$	6
1	12
$1\frac{1}{2}$	18
2	24

Which of the following equations represents the distance d Shalonda covered after h hours? **D**

A $d = 6 + h$

B $d = 6h$

C $d = 12 + h$

D $d = 12h$

2. Which line contains the ordered pair $(-2, 4)$? **H**

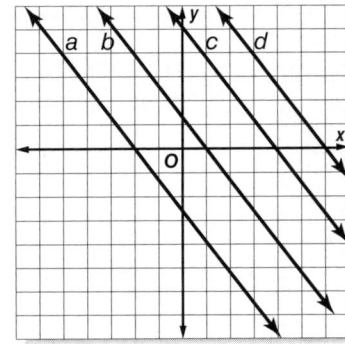

F line a H line b
G line c J line d

3. The table gives the value of several terms and their positions in a sequence.

Position	3	4	5	6	7	n
Value of Term	13	17	21	25	29	

Which description shows the relationship between a term and n, its position in the sequence? **D**

A Add 4 to n.

B Multiply n by 5 and add 1.

C Multiply n by 3 and add 2.

D Multiply n by 4 and add 1.

4. Mr. McDowell owes $1,750 on his car loan and pays off $185 each month towards the loan balance. Which expression represents how much money in dollars he still owes after x months? **J**

F $1,750x$

G $1,750x + 185$

H $1,750x - 185$

J $1,750 - 185x$

5. Which of the following problems can be solved by solving the equation $x - 9 = 15$? **A**

A Allison is nine years younger than her sister Pam. Allison is 15 years old. What is x, Pam's age?

B David's portion of the bill is $9 more than Sam's portion of the bill. If Sam pays $9, find x, the amount in dollars that David pays.

C The sum of two numbers is 15. If one of the numbers is 9, what is x, the other number?

D Pedro owns 15 CDs. If he gave 9 of them to a friend, what is x, the number of CDs he has left?

Preparing for Standardized Tests
For test-taking strategies and practice,
see pages 716–733.

CHAPTER
3 Test Practice

6. The table below shows values for x and corresponding values for y.

x	y
18	2
27	3
9	1
36	4

Which of the following represents the relationship between x and y? **H**

F $y = x + 16$

G $y = 9x$

H $y = \frac{1}{9}x$

J $y = x + 9$

TEST-TAKING TIP

Question 7 Read the question carefully to check that you answered the question that was asked. In question 7, you are asked to pick which coordinates lie within the triangle, not to identify a vertex.

7. Which of the following coordinates lies within the triangle graphed below? **D**

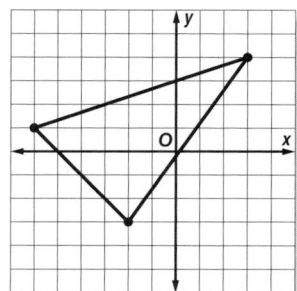

A $(3, 4)$ C $(-3, 6)$

B $(2, 0)$ D $(-1, -1)$

NEED EXTRA HELP?										
If You Missed Question...	1	2	3	4	5	6	7	8	9	10
Go to Lesson...	3-7	3-7	1-9	3-1	3-1	3-7	3-7	2-8	1-7	3-7

PART 2 Short Response/Grid In

Record your answers on the answer sheet provided by your teacher or on a sheet of paper.

8. Write an expression that can be used to find the maximum number of 3-foot pieces of lumber than can be cut from a 12-foot length of lumber. **12 ÷ 3**

9. Tonya bought p pounds of sand. Each pound of sand costs $0.40. How many pounds of sand could Tonya buy with $3.20? **8**

PART 3 Extended Response

Record your answers on the answer sheet provided by your teacher or on a sheet of paper. Show your work.

10. The distances traveled by cars traveling at 40 miles per hour and at 60 miles per hour are given in the table. **10a–c. See margin.**

Time (hours)	Distance (miles) at 40 mph	Distance (miles) at 60 mph
0	0	0
1	40	60
2	80	120
3	120	180
4	160	240

a. Graph the ordered pairs (time, distance) for 40 miles per hour.

b. Graph the ordered pairs (time, distance) for 60 miles per hour.

c. Predict where the ordered pairs for 50 miles per hour would be graphed. Explain how you know.

Answer Sheet Practice

Have students simulate taking a standardized test by recording their answers on a practice recording sheet.

CRM Student Recording Sheet, p. 53

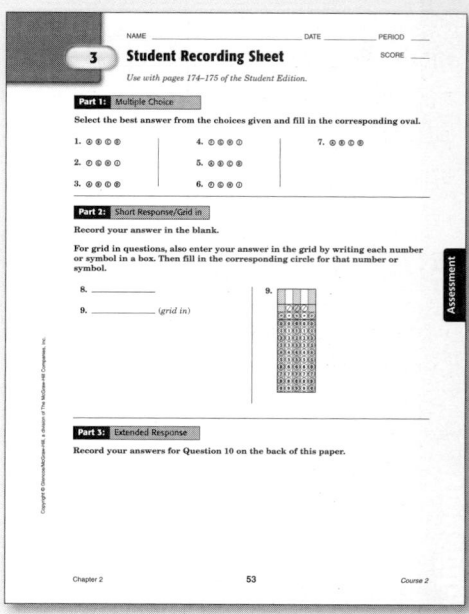

Additional Answers

10a.

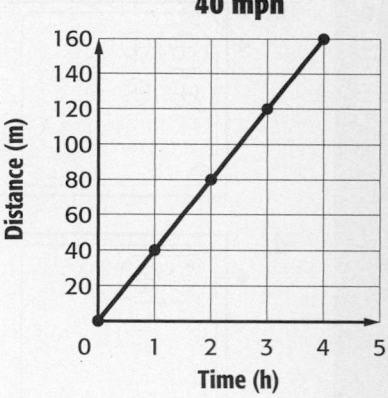

10b.

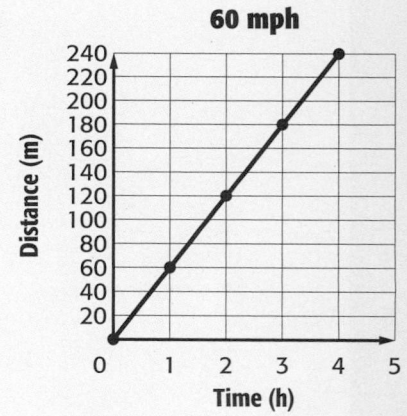

10c. The line for 50 miles per hour would be between the 40 miles per hour and 60 miles per hour lines, because 50 is between 40 and 60.

Page 127, Get Ready for Chapter 3

4.

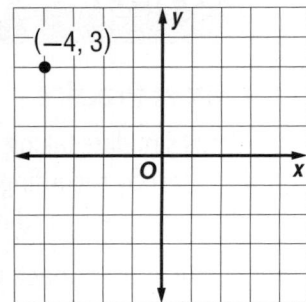

5.

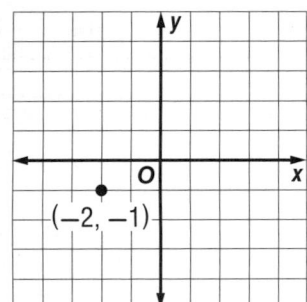

6.

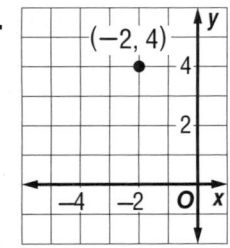

Page 134, Explore 3-2

c.

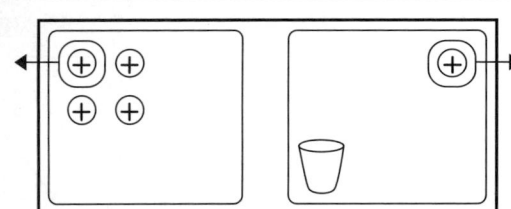

d.

Page 142, Lesson 3-3 (Mini Lab)

1.

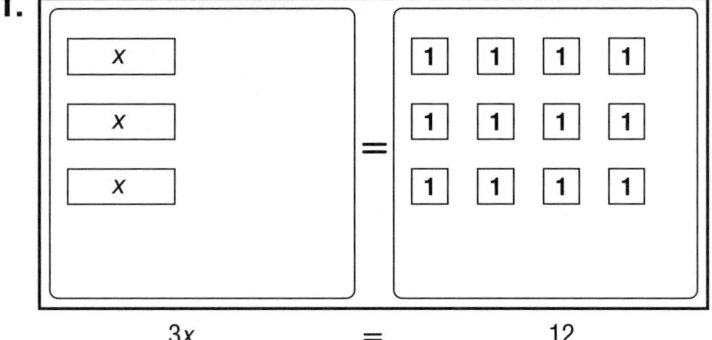

$$3x \quad = \quad 12$$

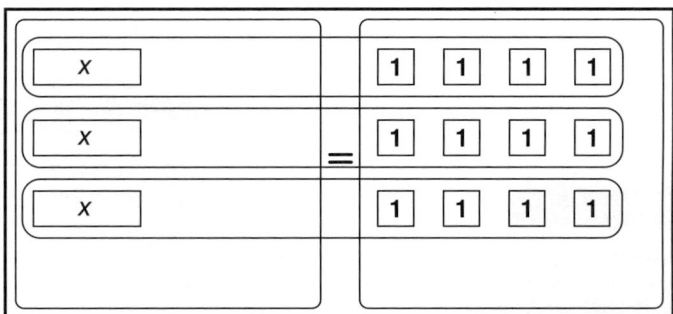

$$x \quad = \quad 4$$

2.

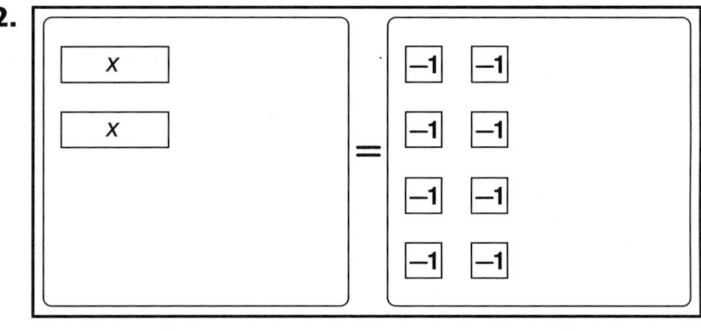

$$2x \quad = \quad -8$$

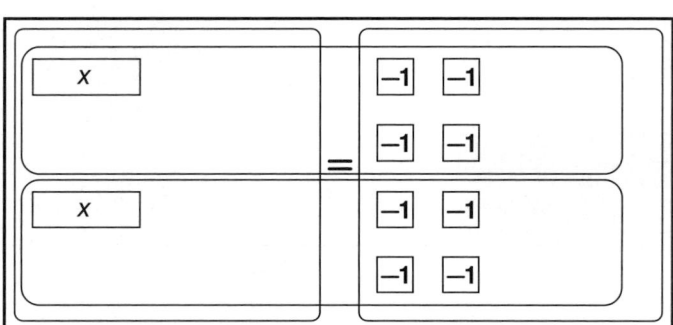

$$x \quad = \quad -4$$

3.

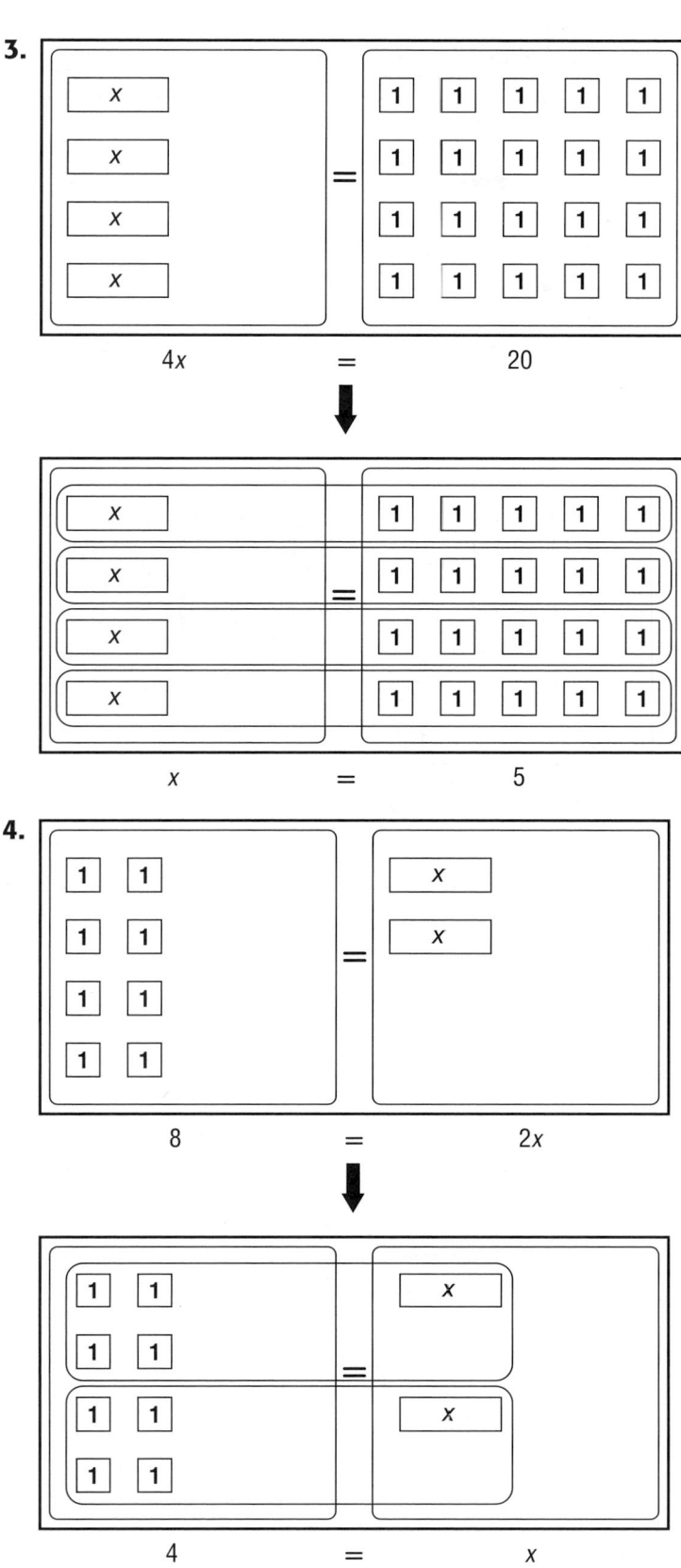

$4x = 20$

$x = 5$

4.

$8 = 2x$

$4 = x$

5.

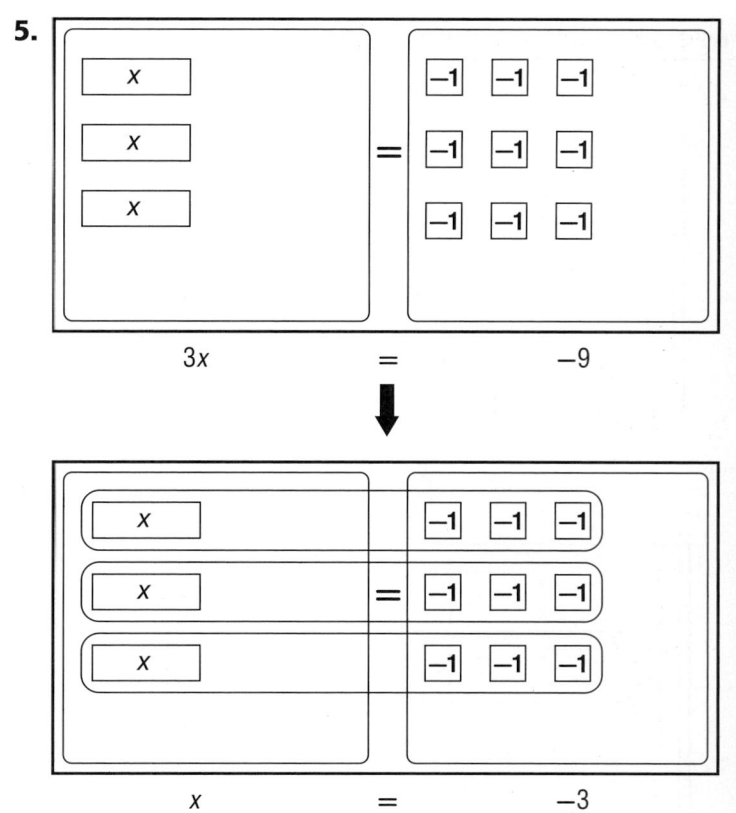

$3x = -9$

$x = -3$

Page 151, Lesson 3-5 (Mini Lab)

1.

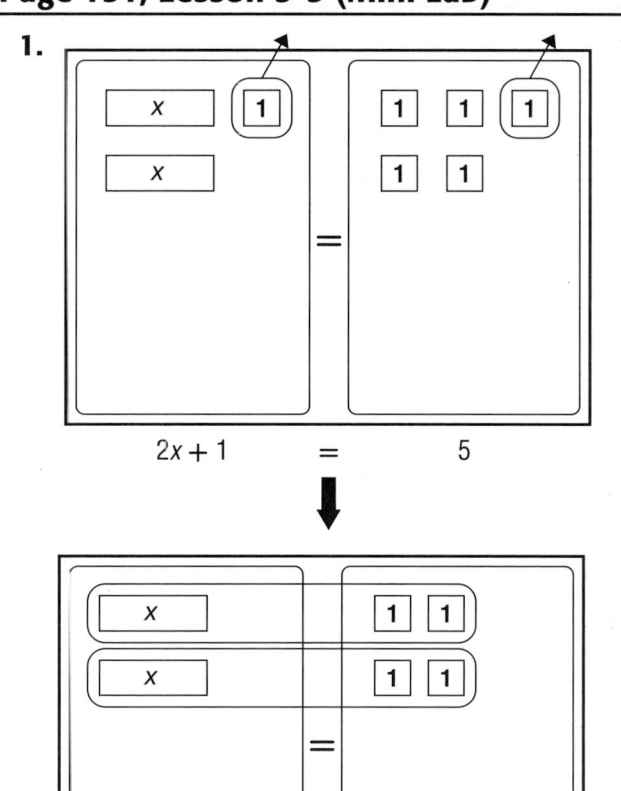

$2x + 1 = 5$

$x = 2$

2.

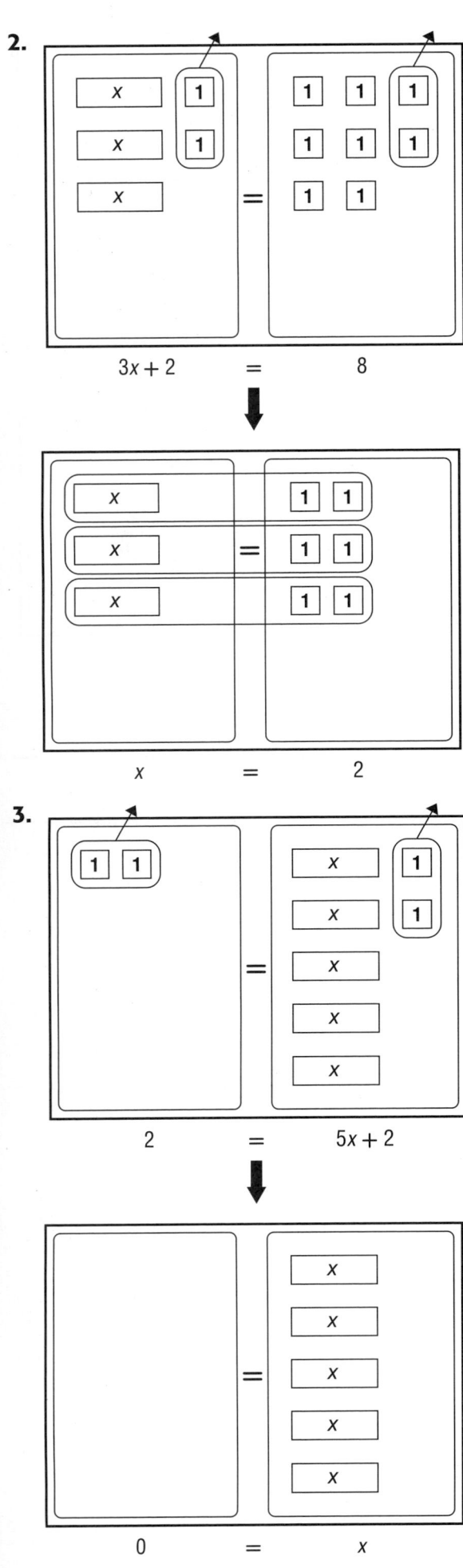

$3x + 2 = 8$

$x = 2$

3.

$2 = 5x + 2$

$0 = x$

34. Sample answers:

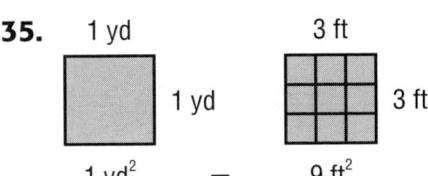

2 cm   12 cm   3 cm   8 cm   4 cm   6 cm

35.

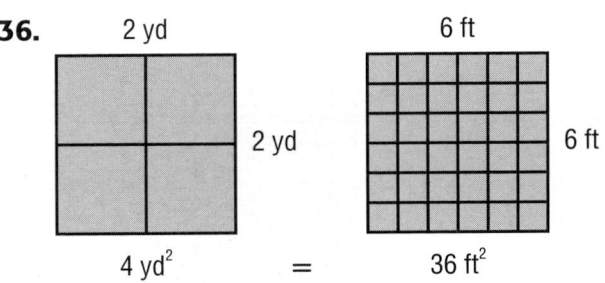

1 yd   1 yd   3 ft   3 ft

$1 \text{ yd}^2 \quad = \quad 9 \text{ ft}^2$

36.

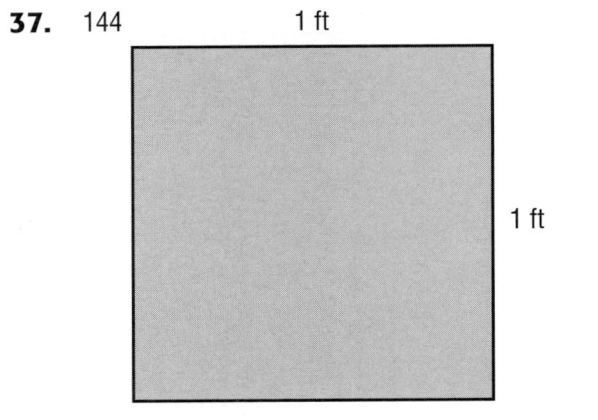

2 yd   2 yd   6 ft   6 ft

$4 \text{ yd}^2 \quad = \quad 36 \text{ ft}^2$

37. 144

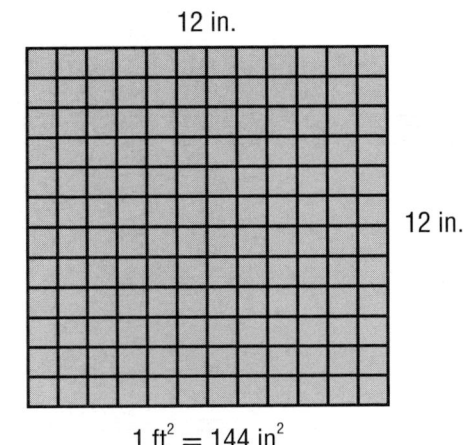

1 ft   1 ft

12 in.   12 in.

$1 \text{ ft}^2 = 144 \text{ in}^2$

38. 288

1 ft   1 ft

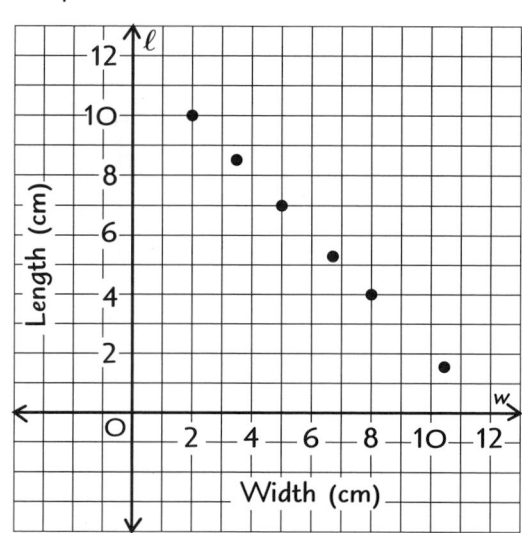

1ft

12 in.   12 in.

12 in.

$2 \text{ ft}^2 = 288 \text{ in}^2$

39. When the width of a rectangle is doubled, the perimeter becomes $2\ell + 4w$ and the area becomes $2\ell w$, or in other words, the area is doubled.

Page 162, Explore 3-7

1. The perimeter of the rectangle is 24 cm.

2. The sum of the length and width of each rectangle is 12; Sample answer: The sum of the length and width of each rectangle is half the length of each stem; $\ell + w = \frac{1}{2}(24)$ or $\ell + w = 12$.

3. 7.5 cm; Sample answer: Since the sum of the two measures must be 12, the length of the rectangle is $12 - 4.5$ or 7.5 cm; $w = 12 - \ell$.

4. Sample answer:

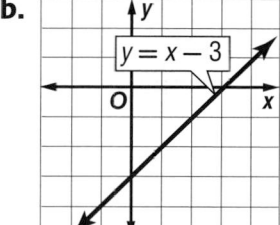

5. The data appear to fall on a line; the width w and length ℓ of a rectangle whose perimeter is 24 cm.

6. Draw the line that goes through the data points. Then find the point on the graph whose ℓ-value is 7. Move down from that point to determine the w-value of the point. The w-value that corresponds to an ℓ-value of 7 is 5.

7. The sum of the data in each row of the table would be 10 centimeters, instead of 12; the rule would become $w = 10 - \ell$; the line on the graph would start at (0, 10) and end at (10, 0).

Page 163, Lesson 3-7 (Get Ready for the Lesson)

2.

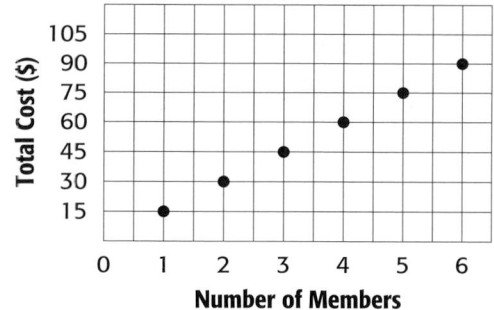

Page 164, Lesson 3-7

a.

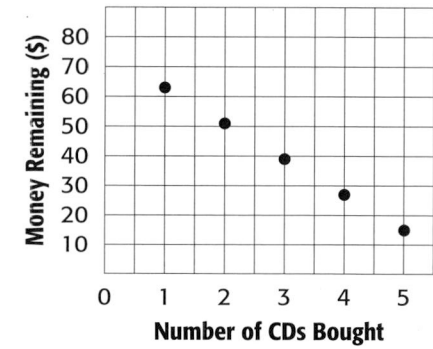

b.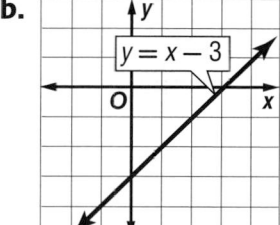

$y = x - 3$

c.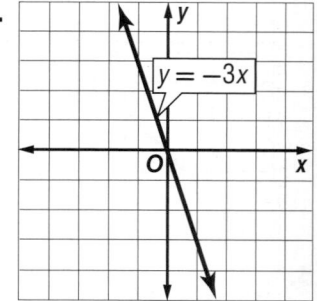

$y = -3x$

d.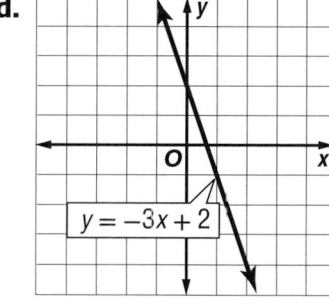

$y = -3x + 2$

Page 165, Lesson 3-7

e.

Babysitting Money

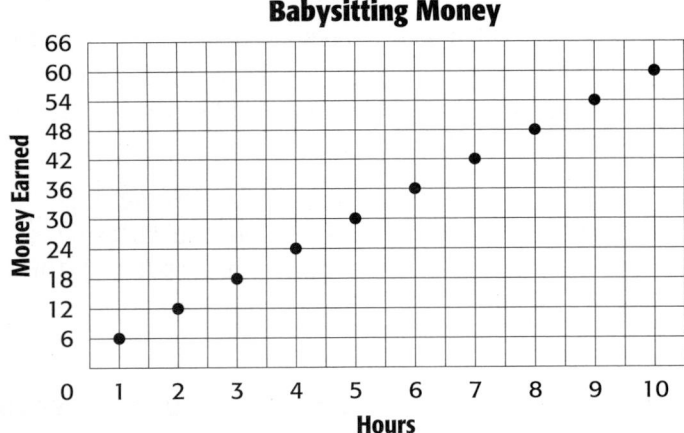

Page 166, Lesson 3-7

1.

Total Cost of Baseballs

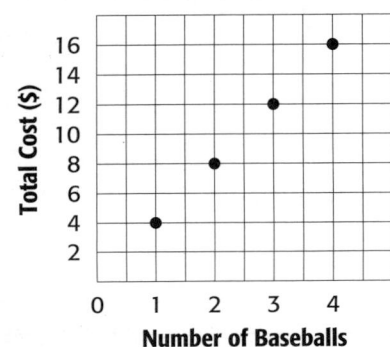

2.

Minutes to Seconds

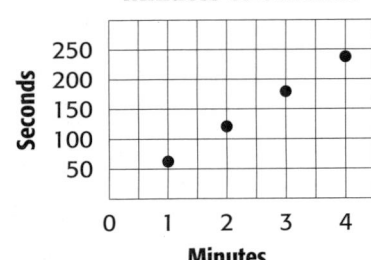

3.

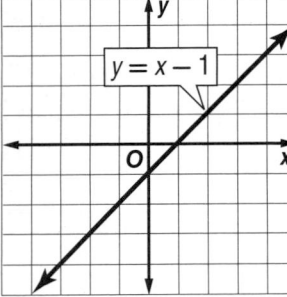

$y = x - 1$

4.

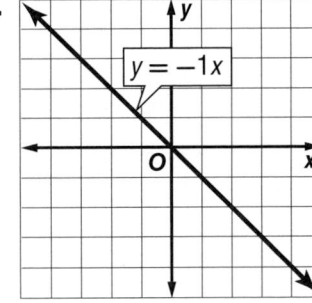

$y = -1x$

5.

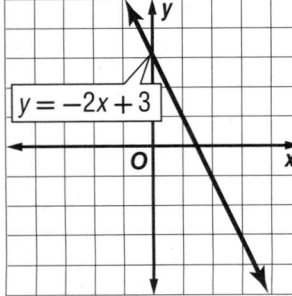

$y = -2x + 3$

6.

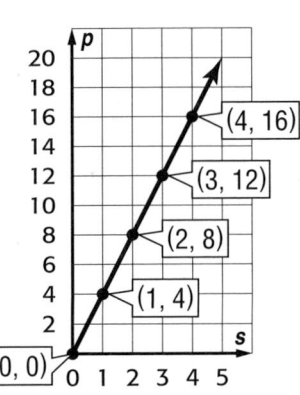

(4, 16)
(3, 12)
(2, 8)
(1, 4)
(0, 0)

7.

Total Phone Bill

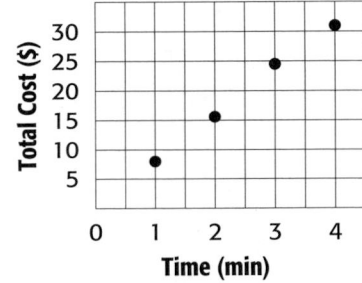

8.

Calories in Fruit Cups

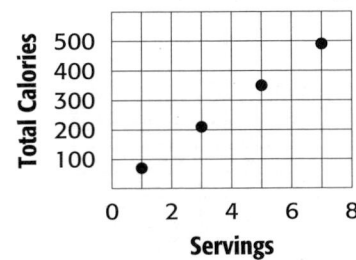

9.

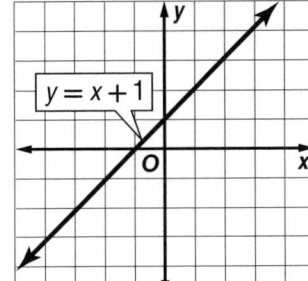

$y = x + 1$

10.

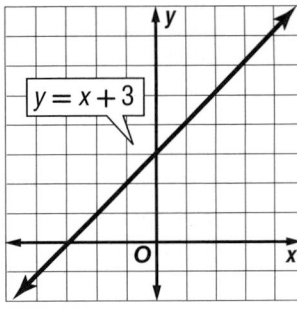

$y = x + 3$

11.

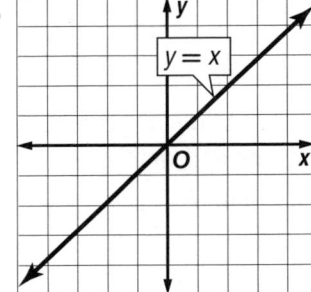

$y = x$

12.

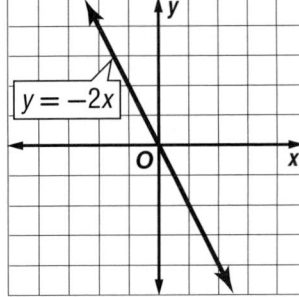

$y = -2x$

13.

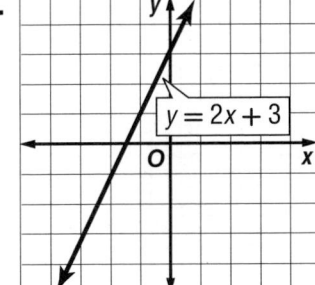

$y = 2x + 3$

14.

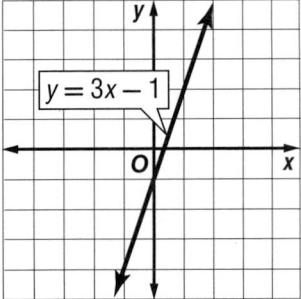

$y = 3x - 1$

175E **Chapter 3** Algebra: Linear Equations and Functions

15.

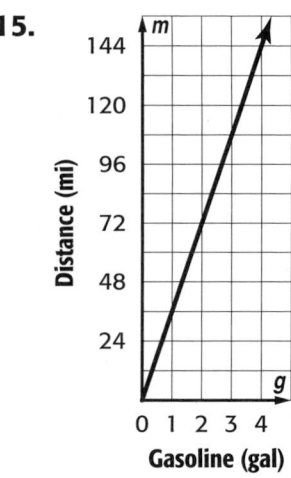

16.

Health Club Fees

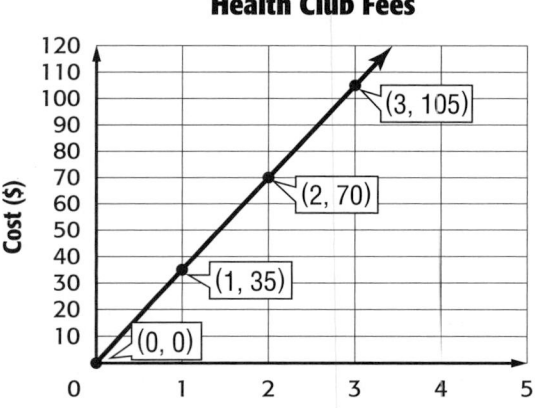

17.

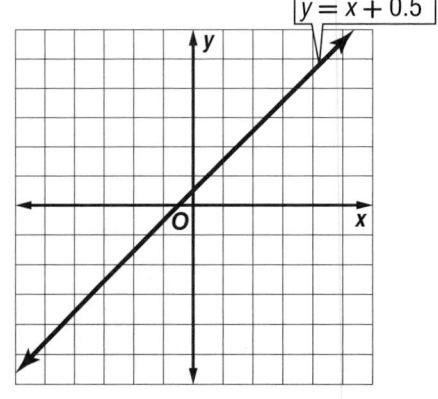

$y = 0.25x$

18.

$y = x + 0.5$

19.

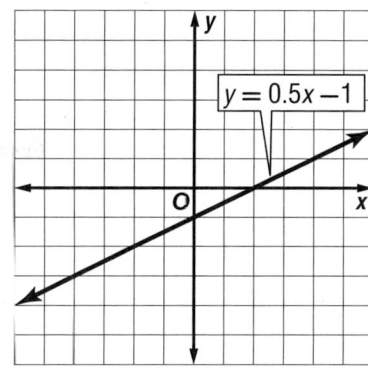

$y = 0.5x - 1$

20.

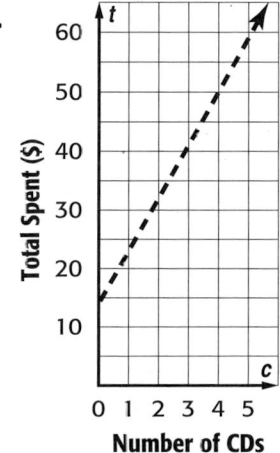

Number of CDs

Page 167, Lesson 3-7

24. Sample answer; Once the function table has been completed, plot the coordinates of each point represented in the table. The *x*-coordinate of each point is usually the number in the first column and the *y*-coordinate of each point is usually the number in the second column.

Page 168, Extend 3-7

1. 9; These values represent a conversion of 3 yd to 9 ft and they are represented on the graph by a point on the line with coordinates (3, 9).

2. 21 ft; Use the CALC feature of the calculator to find the *y*-value that corresponds to an *x*-value of 7.

3. $y = \frac{1}{3}x$; Sample answer: Xmin = 0, Xmax = 20, Xscl = 2, Ymin = 0, Ymax = 10, Ysel = 1;

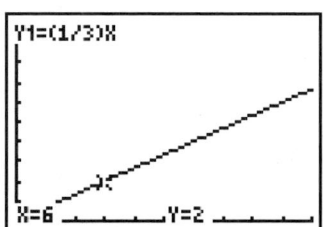

4. $16 \text{ ft} = 5\frac{1}{3} \text{ yd}$;

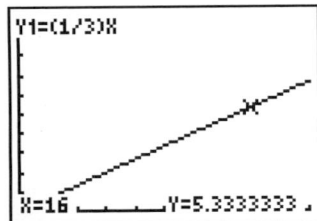

5. $y = \frac{1}{16}x$; Sample answer: Xmin = 0, Xmax = 40, Xscl = 5, Ymin = 0, Ymax = 5, Yscl = 1; 36 oz = 2.25 lbs;

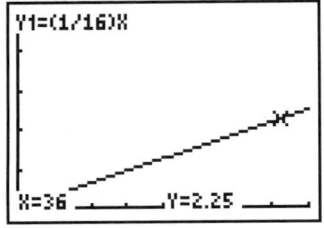

Page 172, Study Guide and Review

52.

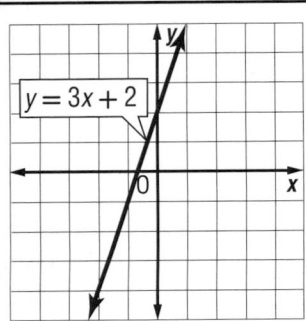

$y = 3x + 2$

53.

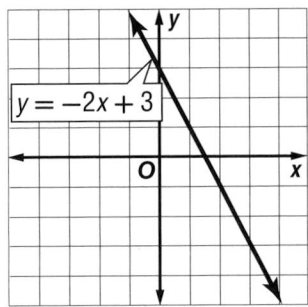

$y = -2x + 3$

54.

Hours Worked	Dollars Earned
2	$18
4	$36
6	$54
8	$72

56.

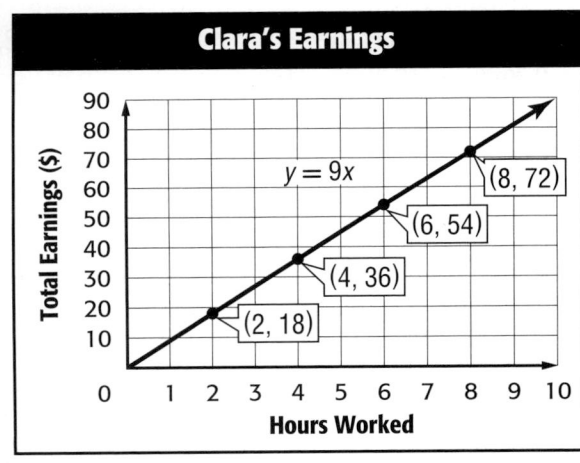

Clara's Earnings

$y = 9x$
(8, 72)
(6, 54)
(4, 36)
(2, 18)

Page 173, Practice Test

21.

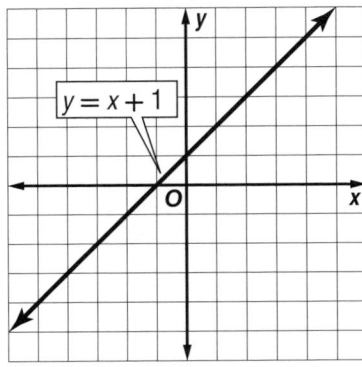

$y = x + 1$

22.

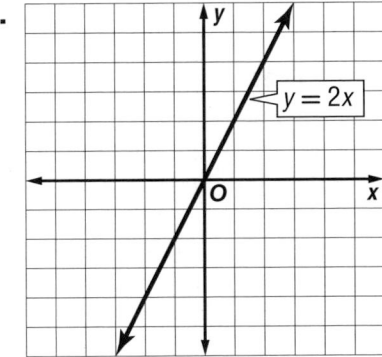

$y = 2x$

23.

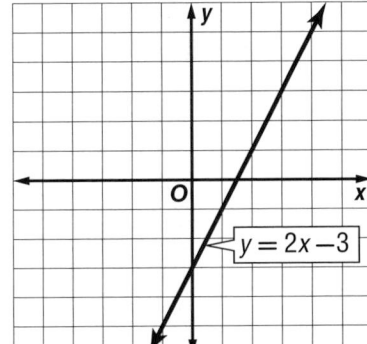

$y = 2x - 3$

24.

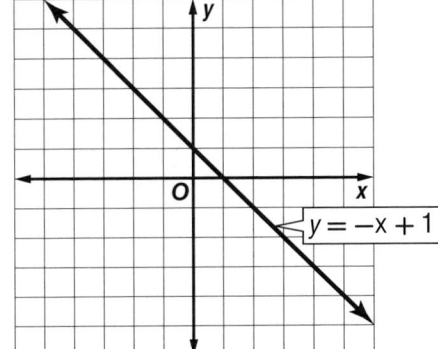

$y = -x + 1$

25.

t	$c = 6t$
1	6
2	12
3	18
4	24

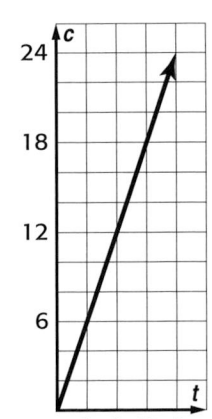

NOTES

Introduction

In this unit, students will learn to simplify fractions using the greatest common factor (GCF) of the numerator and denominator and by using prime factorization. They will also learn to express fractions as decimals that either terminate or repeat. In addition, students will learn to convert fractions to decimals and percents and vice versa. They then will use the least common denominator (LCD) of a set of fractions to compare and order fractions and other rational numbers.

Students will apply their knowledge of fractions by adding, subtracting, multiplying, and dividing fractions and mixed numbers.

Assessment Options

Unit 2 Test Pages 73–74 of the *Chapter 5 Resource Masters* may be used as a test or a review for Unit 2. This assessment contains both multiple-choice and short-response items.

Create additional customized Unit Tests and review worksheets for differentiated instruction.

Unit 2
Number Sense: Fractions

Focus

Represent and use numbers in a variety of equivalent forms and apply addition, subtraction, multiplication, and division of fractions.

CHAPTER 4
Fractions, Decimals, and Percents

BIG Idea Represent and use numbers in a variety of forms.

CHAPTER 5
Applying Fractions

BIG Idea Extend understandings of operations. Add, subtract, multiply, and divide to solve fraction problems.

176

What's MATH Got To Do With It? DVD

Real-Life Math Videos engage students, showing them how math is used in everyday situations. Use Video 2 with this unit to discuss how fractions and percents are used in amusement parks and in movie concessions (also available on one Super DVD combined with MindJogger Videoquizzes).

Problem Solving in Geography

A Traveling We Will Go You're about to embark on a journey to your favorite vacation spot in the United States. In your role as a travel agent, you will plan a vacation for you and your family. You will calculate the total cost including transportation, lodging, and tourist attractions. So bring your sense of adventure and get ready to set off on your trip!

Math Online > Log on to glencoe.com to begin.

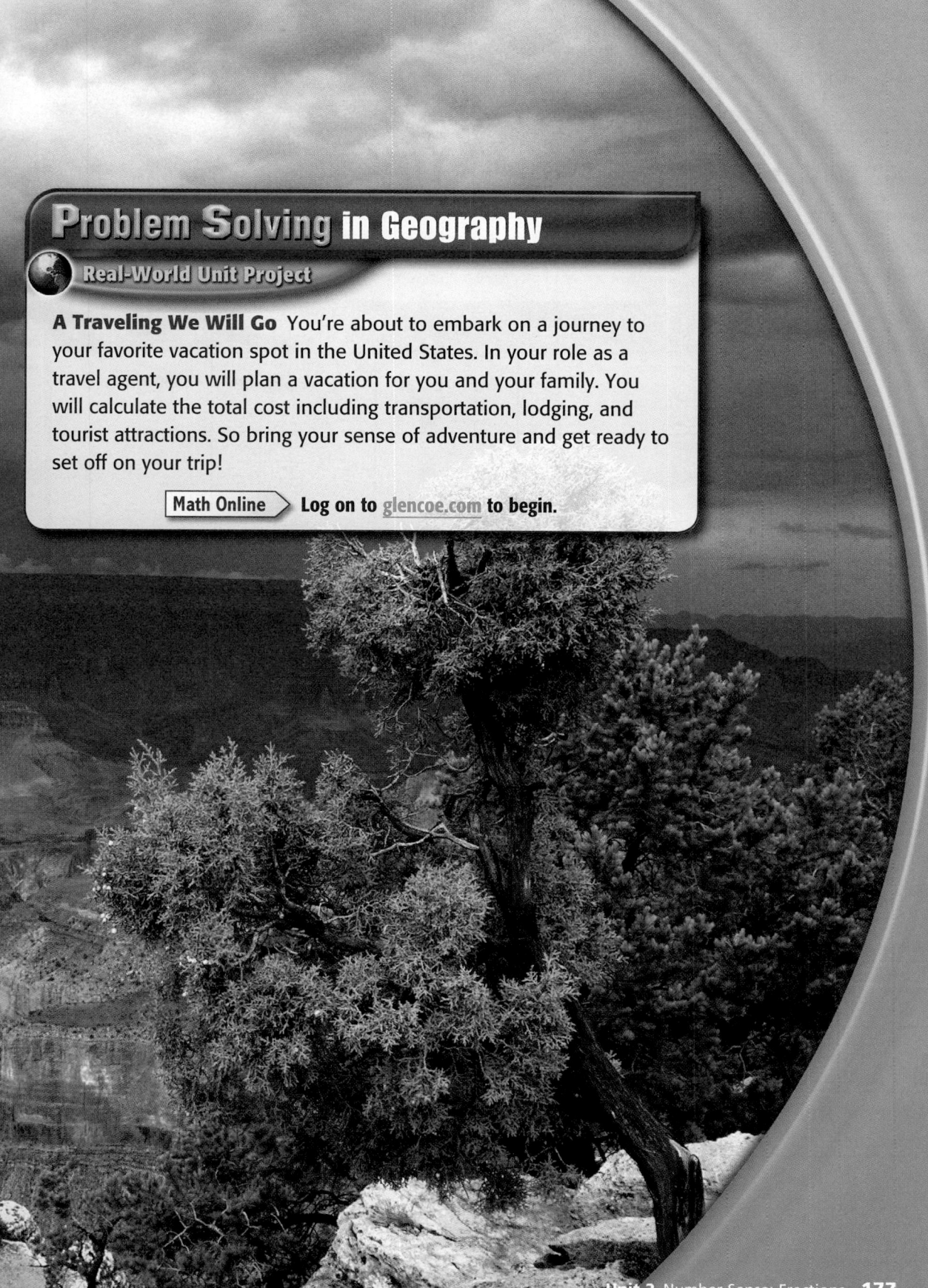

A Traveling We Will Go

This cross-curricular project is an online project in which students do research on the Internet, gather data, and make presentations using word processing, graphing, page-making, or presentation software. In each chapter, students advance to the next step in their project. At the end of Chapter 6, the project culminates with a presentation of their findings.

Math Online >

glencoe.com Log on for teaching suggestions and sample answers for this project.

Team Teaching You can use this project with your students' geography teacher to make the connection from mathematics to the geography topics your students are studying.

Unit 2 Number Sense: Fractions **177**

More Cross-Curricular Connections

You may wish to share these suggestions with your students' other teachers.

Math and Life Skills

Imagine that you will be driving a rental car to your favorite vacation spot. Research and find the distance between your home and your destination. If you are able to get 25 miles to the gallon, how many gallons of gas will be used? If gas is $2.50 a gallon, how much will it cost?

Math and Language Arts

Write a paragraph about some of the main attractions found at your favorite vacation spot. Promote your vacation spot to try and attract more tourists. How much does it cost? What makes this location fun? Why would you want to go there?

Lesson Plan		Pacing Your Lessons	
LESSONS AND OBJECTIVES	State/Local Standards	40–50 Minute Periods	90-Minute Periods
Explore 4-1 **Math Lab: Exploring Factors** (p. 180) Discover factors of whole numbers. **4-1** **Prime Factorization** (pp. 181–184) • Find the prime factorization of a composite number.		2	1
4-2 **Greatest Common Factor** (pp. 186–189) • Find the greatest common factor of two or more numbers.		2	1
4-3 **Problem-Solving Investigation: Make an Organized List** (pp. 190–191) • Solve problems by making an organized list.		1	0.5
4-4 **Simplifying Fractions** (pp. 192–195) • Write fractions in simplest form.		2	1
4-5 **Fractions and Decimals** (pp. 196–200) • Write fractions as terminating or repeating decimals and write decimals as fractions.		1	0.5
4-6 **Fractions and Percents** (pp. 202–205) • Write fractions as percents and percents as fractions.		1	0.5
4-7 **Percents and Decimals** (pp. 206–210) • Write percents as decimals and decimals as percents.		1	0.5
4-8 **Least Common Multiple** (pp. 211–214) • Find the least common multiple of two or more numbers.		2	1
4-9 **Comparing and Ordering Rational Numbers** (pp. 215–220) • Compare and order fractions, decimals, and percents.		1	0.5
REVIEW		1	0.5
ASSESSMENT		1	0.5*
TOTAL		15	7.5

*The complete **Assessment Planner** for Chapter 4 is provided on page 179.*

* Begin Chapter 5 in the second half of the period.

Focal Points

G7-FP3 Number and Operations,
G7-FP5C Number and Operations
For the complete wording of the Focal Points for Grade 7, please see page iv.

Professional Development

Vertical Alignment

Before Chapter 4

Related Topics from Grade 6

- determine the prime factors of all numbers through 50 and write the numbers as the product of their prime factors by using exponents to show multiples of a factor
- identify and represent on a number line decimals, fractions, mixed numbers, and positive and negative numbers

Chapter 4

Topics from Grade 7

- determine the least common multiple and the greatest common divisor of whole numbers; use them to solve problems with fractions
- compare and order positive and negative fractions, decimals, and mixed numbers and place them on a number line

After Chapter 4

Preparation for Grade 8

- compare rational numbers
- convert fractions to decimals and percents and use these representations in estimations, computations, and applications
- know that every rational number is either a terminating or repeating decimal and be able to convert terminating decimals into reduced fractions
- add and subtract fractions by using factoring to find common denominators

Backmapping and Vertical Alignment

McGraw-Hill's *Math Connects* program was conceived and developed with the final results in mind: student success in Algebra 1 and beyond. The authors, using the **NCTM Focal Points and Focal Connections** as their guide, developed this brand-new series by backmapping from Algebra 1 concepts, and vertically aligning the topics so that they build upon prior skills and concepts and serve as a foundation for future topics.

What the Research Says...

Through twenty years of research, the Rational Number Project has found that the optimum curriculum for learning fractions includes active involvement with multiple concrete models.

- In Lesson 4-4, students use area models to help them simplify fractions.
- In Lesson 4-6, students use decimal models to write fractions as percents.

Professional Development

Targeted professional development has been articulated throughout **McGraw-Hill's *Math Connects*** program. The **McGraw-Hill Professional Development Video Library** provides short videos that support the NCTM Focal Points and Focal Connections. For more information, visit glencoe.com.

| Model Lessons | Instructional Strategies |

CHAPTER 4
Technology Solutions

Teacher Resources

TeacherWorks™ All-in-One Planner and Resource Center

All of the print materials from the Classroom Resource Masters are available on your TeacherWorks™ CD-ROM.

BL = Below or Approaching Grade Level   **OL** = On Grade Level   **AL** = Above or Beyond Grade Level   **ELL** = English Language Learner

Chapter Resource Masters		4-1	4-2	4-3	4-4	4-5	4-6	4-7	4-8	4-9
BL **OL** **ELL**	Lesson Reading Guide	9	16		26	32	39	45	51	58
BL **OL** **ELL**	Study Guide and Intervention*	10	17	22	27	33	40	46	52	59
BL **OL**	Skills Practice*	11	18	23	28	34	41	47	53	60
OL **AL**	Practice*	12	19	24	29	35	42	48	54	61
OL **AL**	Word Problem Practice*	13	20	25	30	36	43	49	55	62
OL **AL**	Enrichment	14	21		31	37	44	50	56	63
OL **AL**	Calculator and Spreadsheet Activities	15				38			57	
OL **AL**	Chapter Assessments*	65–86								
BL **OL** **AL**	5-Minute Check Transparencies	✓	✓	✓	✓	✓	✓	✓	✓	✓
BL **OL**	Teaching Mathematics with Manipulatives	✓					✓			
BL **OL** **AL**	Real-World Investigations for Differentiated Instruction	39								

Also available in Spanish.

Graphing Calculator Easy Files

Timesaving Tech Tools for the TI-Navigator:

- **Quick Checks** to diagnose student progress
- Motivate students with **Concept Launchers**
- Deliver differentiated instruction with **Ready Files**
- **Vocabulary Review**

AssignmentWorks

Differentiated Assignments, Answers, and Solutions

- Print a customized assignment worksheet using the Student Edition exercises along with an answer key or worked-out solutions.
- Use default lesson assignments as outlined in the Differentiated Homework Options in the Teacher Edition.

Interactive Classroom

This CD-ROM is a customizable Microsoft® PowerPoint® presentation that includes:

- In-Class Examples
- Your Turn Exercises*
- 5-Minute Check Transparencies*
- Links to Online Study Tools
- Concepts in Motion

compatible with response pad technology

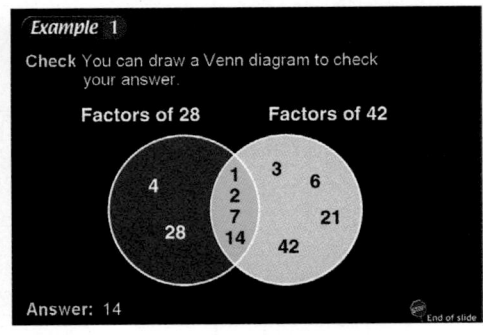

ExamView®Assessment Suite

ExamView®
Assessment Suite

- Create, edit, and customize tests and worksheets using QuickTest Wizard.
- Create multiple versions of tests and modify them for a desired level of difficulty.
- Translate from English to Spanish and vice versa.
- Build tests aligned with your state standards.
- Track students' progress using the Teacher Management System.

Student Tools

StudentWorks™ Plus

Textbook, Audio, Workbooks, and more

This CD-ROM is a valuable resource for students to access content online and use online resources to continue learning Chapter 4 concepts. Includes:

- Complete Student Editions in both English and Spanish
- English audio integrated throughout the text
- Links to Concepts in Motion, Personal Tutor, and other online resources
- Access to all student worksheets
- Daily Assignments and Grade Log

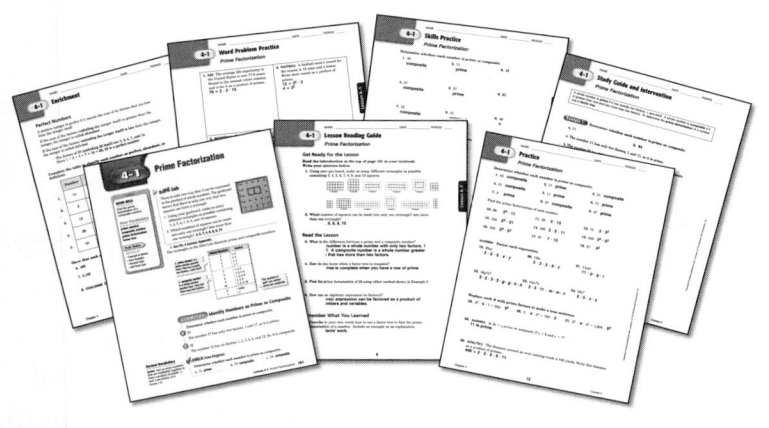

Super DVD

The Super DVD contains two Glencoe multimedia products.

MindJogger Plus An alternative review of concepts in which students work as teams in a game show format to gain points for correct answers.

What's Math Got to Do With It? Real-Life Math Videos Engaging video that shows students how math is used in everyday situations.

Internet Resources

Math Online ▶ glencoe.com

TEACHER	STUDENT	PARENT	Online Study Tools
	●	●	Online Student Edition
●	●	●	Multilingual Glossary
			Lesson Resources
	●	●	BrainPOP®
●	●	●	Concepts in Motion
●	●	●	Extra Examples
●			Group Activity Cards
●	●		Other Calculator Keystrokes
●	●		Reading in the Content Area
●	●		Real-World Careers
●	●		Self-Check Quizzes
			Chapter Resources
	●	●	Chapter Readiness
	●	●	Chapter Test
	●	●	Family Letters and Activities
	●	●	Standardized Test Practice
	●	●	Vocabulary Review/Chapter Review Activities
			Unit Resources
●	●		Cross-Curricular Internet Project
			Other Resources
●			Dinah Zike's Foldables
●	●		Game Zone Games and Recording Sheets
	●	●	Hotmath Homework Help
●			Key Concepts
●	●	●	Math Skills Maintenance
●	●	●	Meet the Authors
●			NAEP Correlations
	●	●	Personal Tutor
●			Project CRISS℠
	●	●	Scavenger Hunts and Answer Sheets
●			Vocabulary PuzzleMakers

CHAPTER 4 Reading and Writing in Mathematics

Noteables™ Interactive Study Notebook with Foldables™

This workbook is a study organizer that provides helpful steps for students to follow to organize their notes for Chapter 4.

- Students use Noteables to record notes and to complete their Foldables as you present the material for each lesson.
- Noteables correspond to the Examples in the *Teacher Edition* and *Interactive Classroom* CD-ROM.

Real-World Problem Solving Graphic Novels

Mathematical problem solving is presented in a motivating, graphic novel format. The novels contain real-world problems for each of the following mathematical strands: Number Sense, Algebraic Thinking, Geometry, Measurement, Statistics and Probability, and Mathematical Reasoning.

READING in the Content Area

This online worksheet provides strategies for reading and analyzing Lesson 4-2, Greatest Common Factor. Students are guided through questions about the main idea, subject matter, supporting details, conclusion, clarifying details, and vocabulary of the lesson.

glencoe.com

Recommended Outside Reading for Students

Mathematics and Games

- *Math Games for Middle School: Challenges and Skill Builders for Students at Every Level* by Joseph Wright and Mario Salvadori ©1998 [nonfiction]

This book uses activities and games to reinforce middle school mathematics concepts. Fractions and decimals are among the topics addressed in the book.

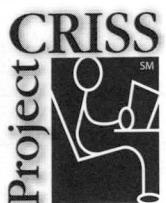

Project CRISS℠

STUDY SKILL

showing how to write fractions as percents, percents as fractions, percents as decimals, and decimals as percents.

A comparison map can help students understand the differences in two or more similar concepts. Show students the sample map at the right that compares the way prime factorization can be used to find the greatest common factor (GCF) and least common multiple (LCM) of two numbers. While studying Chapter 4, have students work in small cooperative groups to design comparison maps

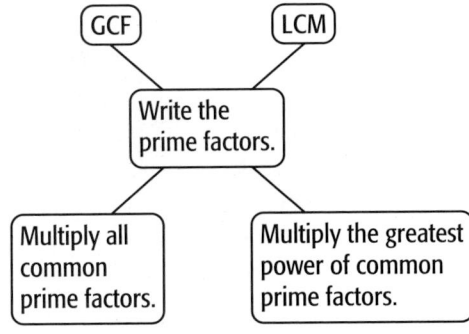

CReating **I**ndependence through **S**tudent-owned **S**trategies

Differentiated Instruction

Investigative Approach

MathScape™

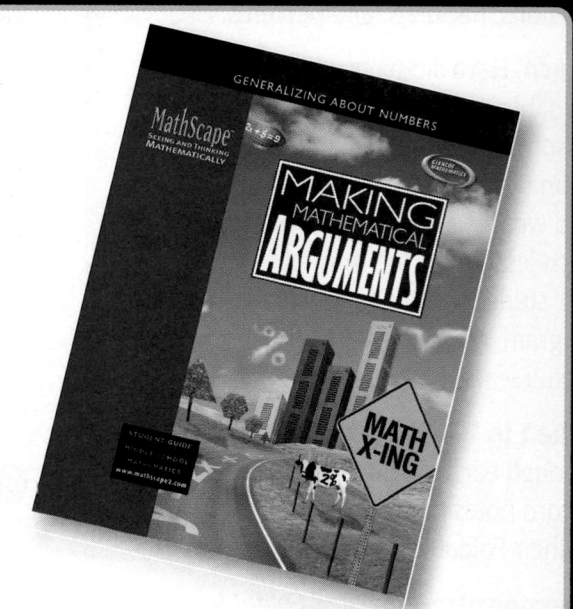

This project was supported, in part, by the National Science Foundation

MathScape is a mathematics curriculum for grades 6–8 developed by the Seeing and Thinking Mathematically Project at the Education Development Center.

> Generalizing About Numbers
>
> Making Mathematical Arguments

How to Use *MathScape* with Chapter 4
The unit *The Language of Algebra* can be used to enhance Lesson 4-1.

- **Introduce** ⟶ Before you begin **Lesson 4-1**, you can introduce prime numbers and prime factorization by using pages 118–119.

- **Enrich** ⟶ After you complete **Lesson 4-1**, you can use the activities on pages 120–123 to challenge students to make generalizations about factors of various types of numbers.

RTI (Response to Intervention)

TIER 1 On-Level Instruction Use the *Math Connects* program as instruction for your on-level students.

TIER 2 Strategic Intervention For options to instruct struggling students, refer to the Diagnostic Assessment table on page 179.

TIER 3 Intensive Intervention *Math Triumphs* can provide intensive intervention for students who are at risk of not meeting the objectives addressed in Chapter 4.

Diagnose student readiness with the Quick Check and Quick Review on page 179. Then use *Math Triumphs* to accelerate their achievment.

Fractions, Decimals, and Percents

Prerequisite Skill	Math Triumphs
Fractions: Representing, Ordering	Chapter 1
Percentages	Chapter 3

Practice and Review

Quick Review Math Handbook* is Glencoe's mathematical handbook for students and parents.

Hot Words includes a glossary of terms.

Hot Topics consists of two parts:

- explanations of key mathematical concepts
- exercises to check students' understanding.

Lesson	Hot Topics Section	Lesson	Hot Topics Section
4-1	1•4	4-6	2•9
4-2	1•4	4-7	2•9
4-4	2•1	4-8	1•4
4-5	2•5, 2•9	4-9	2•2, 2•5

*Also available in Spanish

Notes

FOLDABLES™ Dinah
Study Organizer Zike's
Foldables

Focus This Foldable is designed to help students organize their notes about fractions, decimals, and percents.

Teach Have students make the Foldable and label the tab for each lesson. Tell students that they should define terms, record key concepts, and write examples under the tab for each lesson. On the front of each tab, students should draw a graph, diagram, or picture that presents the main idea(s) of the lesson.

When to Use It As students work through each lesson, remind them to record notes under the appropriate tab of their Foldables.

A version of a completed Foldable is shown on p. 221.

Differentiated Instruction

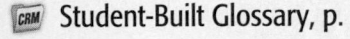 Student-Built Glossary, p. 1

Students complete the chart by providing a definition for each term and an example as they progress through Chapter 4.

This study tool can be used to review for the chapter test.

Materials Needed for Chapter 4

- index cards (Explore 4-1)
- geoboard (Lesson 4-1)
- grid paper (Lessons 4-1, 4-4, 4-6)
- colored pencils (Lessons 4-4, 4-6)
- centimeter cubes (Lesson 4-8)

CHAPTER
4

Fractions, Decimals, and Percents

BIG Idea

- Represent and use numbers in a variety of equivalent forms.

Key Vocabulary

equivalent fractions (p. 192)
percent (p. 202)
ratio (p. 202)
simplest form (p. 192)

🌐 Real-World Link

Reptiles North Carolina's state reptile is the Eastern Box Turtle. Adults range in size from $4\frac{1}{2}$ inches to $5\frac{9}{10}$ inches. You can write these fractions as 4.5 and 5.9, respectively.

FOLDABLES®
Study Organizer

Fractions, Decimals, and Percents Make this Foldable to help you organize your notes. Begin with five sheets of $8\frac{1}{2}" \times 11"$ paper.

❶ **Stack** five sheets of paper $\frac{3}{4}$ inch apart.

❷ **Roll** up bottom edges so that all tabs are the same size.

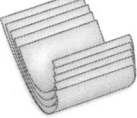

❸ **Crease** and staple along the fold.

❹ **Write** the chapter title on the front. Label each tab with a lesson number and title.

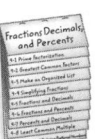

GET READY for Chapter 4

Diagnose Readiness You have two options for checking Prerequisite Skills.

Option 2

Math Online Take the Online Readiness Quiz at glencoe.com.

Option 1

Take the Quick Quiz below. Refer to the Quick Review for help.

QUICK Quiz

(Used in Lesson 4-9)
State which decimal is greater. (Prior Grade)

1. 0.6, 0.61 **0.61**   2. 1.25, 1.52 **1.52**

3. 0.33, 0.13 **0.33**   4. 1.08, 10.8 **10.8**

5. **LUNCH** Kirsten spent $4.21 on lunch while Almanzo spent $4.12. Who spent the greater amount? (Lesson 3-9) **Kirsten**

(Used in Lessons 4-1 and 4-2)
Use divisibility rules to determine whether each number is divisible by 2, 3, 5, 6, or 10. (Prior Grade)

6. 125 **5**   7. 78 **2, 3, 6**   8. 37 **none**

9. **MUFFINS** Without calculating, determine whether 51 banana nut muffins can be evenly distributed among 3 persons. Explain. (Prior Grade) **Yes; the sum of the digits, 6, is divisible by 3.**

(Used in Lessons 4-4, 4-5, 4-6, and 4-7)
Divide. (Prior Grade)

10. $12 \div 6$ **2**   11. $18 \div 3$ **6**

12. $2 \div 5$ **0.4**   13. $3 \div 4$ **0.75**

(Used in Lesson 4-1)
Write each power as a product of the same factor. (Lesson 1-2)

14. 2^3 **$2 \times 2 \times 2$**   15. 5^5 **$5 \times 5 \times 5 \times 5 \times 5$**

16. 7^2 **7×7**   17. 9^4 **$9 \times 9 \times 9 \times 9$**

QUICK Review

Example 1
State which decimal is greater, 7.4 or 7.04.

7.4
7.04

Line up the decimal points and compare place value. The 4 in the tenths place is greater than the 0 in the tenths place.

7.4 is greater.

Example 2
Use divisibility rules to determine whether 84 is divisible by 2, 3, 5, 6, or 10.

2: Yes, the ones digit, 4, is divisible by 2.
3: Yes, the sum of the digits, 12, is divisible by 3.
5: No, the ones digit is neither 0 nor 5.
6: Yes, the number is divisible by both 2 and 3.
10: No, the ones digit is not 0.

Example 3
Find $1 \div 5$.

$$\begin{array}{r} 0.2 \\ 5\overline{)1.0} \\ -10 \\ \hline 0 \end{array}$$

Divide 1 by 5 until there is a remainder of 0 or a repeating pattern.

Example 4
Write 4^3 as a product of the same factor.

$4^3 = 4 \times 4 \times 4$

Chapter 4 Get Ready for Chapter 4 **179**

Diagnostic Assessment

Exercises	State/Local Standards	Intervention
1–5		SE Review Lesson 2-2, pp. 84–87
6–9		SE Concepts and Skills Bank, p. 734
10–13		*Math Skills Maintenance Masters,* pp. 11–12
14–16		SE Review Lesson 1-2, pp. 30–33

ASSESSMENT PLANNER

CHAPTER **4**

✓ Formative Assessment

CRM Anticipation Guide, pp. 7–8
Spotting Preconceived Ideas
Students complete this survey to determine prior knowledge about ideas from Chapter 4. Revisit this worksheet after completing the chapter. Also see page 224.

TE Lesson Activities

- Ticket Out the Door, pp. 184, 195, 210
- Crystal Ball, pp. 205, 214
- Name the Math, pp. 191, 220
- Yesterday's News, pp. 189, 200

Chapter Checkpoints

SE Mid-Chapter Quiz, p. 201

SE Study Guide and Review, pp. 221–224

SE Test Practice, pp. 226–227

CRM Quizzes, pp. 67 and 68

CRM Standardized Test Practice, pp. 84–86

Math Online glencoe.com

- Self-Check Quizzes
- Practice Test
- Test Practice

✓ Summative Assessment

SE Chapter Practice Test, p. 225

CRM Mid-Chapter Test, p. 69

CRM Vocabulary Test, p. 70

CRM Extended-Response Test, p. 83

CRM Leveled Chapter Tests, pp. 71–82

💿 ExamView Pro® Assessment Suite

KEY

CRM *Chapter 4 Resource Masters*

SE Student Edition

TE Teacher Edition

💿 CD-ROM

1 Focus

Teaching Tip
You may want to provide students with index cards, representing locker doors, for students to flip as a way of showing whether a locker door is open or closed. You may also want to group students into pairs of varying abilities to complete the activity.

2 Teach

Activity For Step 4, make sure students understand that some lockers (with odd numbers that are multiples of 3) will be closed, while other lockers (with even numbers that are multiples of 3) will be opened. All other lockers will stay the same. Students should realize that as they continue past student 15, only one locker will be opened or shut.

3 Assess

 Formative Assessment

Use Exercise 2 to determine whether students understand the effect that the number of factors a number in the exercise had determined the final state of the locker door.

From Concrete to Abstract Use Exercise 3 to bridge the gap between modeling factors and analyzing the difference between prime numbers and composite numbers.

Extending the Concept Ask students to predict numbers greater than 30 that only have two factors, 1 and the number itself.

Explore 4-1

Math Lab
Exploring Factors

MAIN IDEA

Discover factors of whole numbers.

The students in Mrs. Faccinto's homeroom have lockers numbered 1–30, located down a long hallway. One day the class did an experiment.

ACTIVITY

STEP 1 The first student, Student 1, walked down the hall and opened every locker.

STEP 2 Student 2 closed Locker 2 and every second locker after it.

STEP 3 Student 3 closed Locker 3 and changed the state of every third locker after it. This means that if the locker was open, Student 3 closed it; if the locker was closed, Student 3 opened it.

STEP 4 Student 4 changed the state of every fourth locker, starting with Locker 4. The student continued this pattern until all 30 students had a turn.

1, 2. See Ch. 4 Answer Appendix.

ANALYZE THE RESULTS 4. 24 and 30, both were opened or closed 8 times

1. Which lockers were open after Student 30 took a turn? What do the numbers on the open lockers have in common?

2. Explain why the lockers you listed in Exercise 1 were open after Student 30 took a turn.

3. Suppose there were 100 lockers. Which lockers would be open after Student 100 took a turn? **1, 4, 9, 16, 25, 36, 49, 64, 81, 100**

4. **CHALLENGE** Which lockers were touched the greatest number of times?

5. What are the fewest lockers and students needed for 31 lockers to be open at the end of the experiment? **961**

180   Chapter 4 Fractions, Decimals, and Percents

Prime Factorization

PACING: **Regular:** 2 periods, **Block:** 1 period

Options for Differentiated Instruction

ELL = English Language Learner   **AL** = Above or Beyond Grade Level   **SS** = Struggling Students   **SN** = Special Needs

Using Manipulatives **SN**

Use with the Mini Lab.

Have students use blocks or centimeter cubes to build the rectangles. Examples of rectangles containing 4 "squares" would be a 2 × 2 rectangle, a 4 × 1 rectangle, and a 1 × 4 rectangle.

- Explain to students that each rectangle must use all the blocks. Once students have found the dimensions, have them transfer the rectangles to grid paper.
- Make sure that students understand that a 1 × 2 rectangle is the same as a 2 × 1 rectangle.

Kinesthetic Learners **ELL** **SS** **SN**

Use after presenting Examples 1 and 2.

Have students use a 100 chart like the one shown to help them find all the prime numbers that are less than 100:

1. Cross off 1, since a prime number is a whole number greater than 1.
2. Circle the first prime number found in the Mini Lab, 2. Since multiples of 2 are not prime numbers, cross off every even number.
3. Circle the next prime number, 3. Cross off every multiple of 3.
4. Continue the process until every number on the chart is either crossed off or circled.

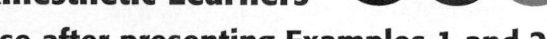

Ask:

- Do you need to count and cross off the multiples of 4? Explain. Since every other multiple of 2 is a multiple of 4, multiples of 4 are already crossed off.
- Do you need to count and cross off the multiples of 6? Explain. Since all the multiples of 2 and 3 were crossed off, the multiples of 6 are already crossed off.
- What is a quick way to find the multiples of 11? Sample answer: Find every number on the same diagonal as 11.

Once all the prime numbers less than 100 have been circled, post them on the word wall.

Leveled Lesson Resources

Also on TeacherWorks™
Lesson 4-1

Chapter 4 Resource Masters

BL = Below or Approaching Grade Level   **OL** = On Grade Level   **AL** = Above or Beyond Grade Level   **ELL** = English Language Learner

Lesson Reading Guide
p. 9 **BL** **OL** **ELL**

NAME _____ DATE _____ PERIOD _____

4-1 Lesson Reading Guide
Prime Factorization

Get Ready for the Lesson
Read the introduction at the top of page 181 in your textbook.
Write your answers below.
1. Using your geo board, make as many different rectangles as possible containing 3, 4, 5, 6, 7, 8, 9, and 10 squares.

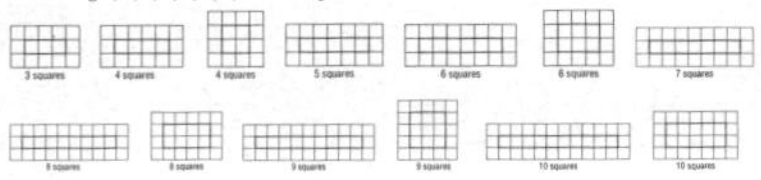

2. Which number of squares can be made into only one rectangle? into more than one rectangle?
3, 5, 7; 4, 6, 8, 9, 10

Read the Lesson
3. What is the difference between a prime and a composite number?
A prime number is a whole number with only two factors, 1 and itself. A composite number is a whole number greater than one that has more than two factors.

4. How do you know when a factor tree is complete?
A factor tree is complete when you have a row of prime factors.

5. Find the prime factorization of 28 using either method shown in Example 3.
7 · 2 · 2

6. How can an algebraic expression be factored?
An algebraic expression can be factored as a product of prime numbers and variables.

Remember What You Learned
7. Describe in your own words how to use a factor tree to find the prime factorization of a number. Include an example as an explanation.
See students' work.

Chapter 4   9   Course 2

Study Guide and Intervention*
p. 10 **BL** **OL** **ELL**

NAME _____ DATE _____ PERIOD _____

4-1 Study Guide and Intervention
Prime Factorization

A whole number is **prime** if it has exactly two factors, 1 and itself. A whole number is **composite** if it is greater than one and has more than two factors. To determine the **prime factorization** of a number, use a **factor tree**.

Example 1 Determine whether each number is *prime* or *composite*.
a. 11   b. 24

a. The number 11 has only two factors, 1 and 11, so it is prime.

b. The number 24 has 8 factors, 1, 2, 3, 4, 6, 8, 12, and 24. So, it is composite.

Example 2 Determine the prime factorization of 48.
Use a factor tree.

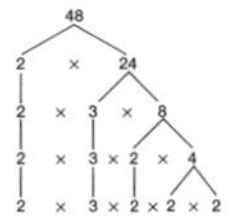

The prime factorization of 48 is $2 \times 2 \times 2 \times 2 \times 3$ or $2^3 \cdot 3$

Exercises

Determine whether each number is *prime* or *composite*.
1. 27 **composite**   2. 31 **prime**   3. 46 **composite**   4. 53 **prime**

5. 11 **prime**   6. 72 **composite**   7. 17 **prime**   8. 51 **composite**

Determine the prime factorization of the following numbers.
9. 64 **2^6**   10. 100 **$2^2 \times 5^2$**   11. 45 **$3^2 \times 5$**   12. 81 **3^4**

Chapter 4   10   Course 2

Skills Practice*
p. 11 **BL** **OL**

NAME _____ DATE _____ PERIOD _____

4-1 Skills Practice
Prime Factorization

Determine whether each number is *prime* or *composite*.
1. 36 **composite**   2. 71 **prime**   3. 18 **composite**

4. 27 **composite**   5. 37 **prime**   6. 61 **prime**

7. 32 **composite**   8. 21 **composite**   9. 40 **composite**

Find the prime factorization of each number.
10. 425 **$5^2 \cdot 17$**   11. 82 **$41 \cdot 2$**   12. 93 **$31 \cdot 3$**

13. 142 **$71 \cdot 2$**   14. 45 **$3^2 \cdot 5$**   15. 56 **$2^3 \cdot 7$**

16. 63 **$3^2 \cdot 7$**   17. 236 **$2^2 \cdot 59$**   18. 12 **$2^2 \cdot 3$**

19. 110 **$2 \cdot 11 \cdot 5$**   20. 46 **$2 \cdot 23$**   21. 84 **$2^2 \cdot 3 \cdot 7$**

Chapter 4   11   Course 2

Practice*
p. 12 **OL** **AL**

NAME _____ DATE _____ PERIOD _____

4-1 Practice
Prime Factorization

Determine whether each number is *prime* or *composite*.
1. 45 **composite**   2. 17 **prime**   3. 21 **composite**

4. 51 **composite**   5. 11 **prime**   6. 71 **prime**

7. 3 **prime**   8. 27 **composite**   9. 47 **prime**

Find the prime factorization of each number.
10. 88 **$2^3 \cdot 11$**   11. 39 **$3 \cdot 13$**   12. 75 **$3 \cdot 5^2$**

13. 124 **$2^2 \cdot 31$**   14. 165 **$3 \cdot 5 \cdot 11$**   15. 225 **$3^2 \cdot 5^2$**

16. 100 **$2^2 \cdot 5^2$**   17. 91 **$7 \cdot 13$**   18. 27 **3^3**

ALGEBRA Factor each expression.
19. $20xy$ 20. $18bc$ 21. $11pqr$
$2 \cdot 2 \cdot 5 \cdot x \cdot y$ **$2 \cdot 3 \cdot 3 \cdot b \cdot c$**   **$11 \cdot p \cdot q \cdot r$**

22. $36g^2h^2$ 23. $44m^2n$ 24. $25c^2$
$2 \cdot 2 \cdot 3 \cdot 3 \cdot g \cdot g \cdot h \cdot h$ **$2 \cdot 2 \cdot 11 \cdot m \cdot m \cdot n$**   **$5 \cdot 5 \cdot z \cdot z$**

Replace each ● with prime factors to make a true sentence.
25. $2^2 \cdot ● \cdot 7 = 252$ **3^2**   26. $2 \cdot ● \cdot 5^2 = 750$ **3**   27. $2^3 \cdot ● \cdot 3^2 = 1,800$ **5^2**

28. **ALGEBRA** Is $2x + y$ *prime* or *composite* if $x = 2$ and $y = 7$?
11 is prime.

29. **ATHLETICS** The distance around an oval running track is 440 yards. Write this distance as a product of primes.
$440 = 2 \cdot 2 \cdot 2 \cdot 5 \cdot 11$

Chapter 4   12   Course 2

Word Problem Practice*
p. 13 **OL** **AL**

NAME _____ DATE _____ PERIOD _____

4-1 Word Problem Practice
Prime Factorization

1. **AGE** The average life expectancy in the United States is now 77.6 years. Round to the nearest whole number, and write it as a product of primes
$78 = 2 \cdot 3 \cdot 13$

2. **FOOTBALL** A football team's record for the season is 12 wins and 4 losses. Write their record as a product of primes.
$12 = 2^2 \cdot 3$
$4 = 2^2$

3. **BASKETBALL** The average height of players in the NBA is 6 feet 7 inches. Write this height in inches as a product of primes.
$1 \cdot 79$

4. **TRAVELING** The distance between Washington, D.C. and Chicago, IL is about 590 miles by air. Write this distance as a product of primes.
$2 \cdot 5 \cdot 59$

5. **SCIENCE** There are 118 elements in the Periodic Table. List all the factors of 118. What type of number is this?
1, 2, 59, 118
composite

6. **READING** A copy of *A Tale of Two Cities*, the classic written by Charles Dickens, has about 530 pages. Write this as a product of primes.
$2 \cdot 5 \cdot 53$

Chapter 4   13   Course 2

Enrichment
p. 14 **OL** **AL**

NAME _____ DATE _____ PERIOD _____

4-1 Enrichment

Perfect Numbers

A positive integer is *perfect* if it equals the sum of its factors that are less than the integer itself.

If the sum of the factors (excluding the integer itself) is greater than the integer, the integer is called *abundant*.

If the sum of the factors (excluding the integer itself) is less than the integer, the integer is called *deficient*.

The factors of 28 (excluding 28 itself) are 1, 2, 4, 7, and 14.
Since $1 + 2 + 4 + 7 + 14 = 28$, 28 is a perfect number.

Complete the table to classify each number as perfect, abundant, or deficient.

	Number	Divisors (Excluding the Number Itself)	Sum	Classification
1.	14	1, 2, 7	10	deficient
2.	6	1, 2, 3	6	perfect
3.	12	1, 2, 3, 4, 6	16	abundant
4.	20	1, 2, 4, 5, 10	22	abundant
5.	10	1, 2, 5	8	deficient

Show that each number is perfect.
6. 496 $1 + 2 + 4 + 8 + 16 + 31 + 62 + 124 + 248 = 496$

7. 8,128 $1 + 2 + 4 + 8 + 16 + 32 + 64 + 127 + 254 + 508 + 1,016 + 2,032 + 4,064 = 8,128$

8. **CHALLENGE** 33,550,336 $1 + 2 + 4 + 8 + 16 + 32 + 64 + 128 + 256 + 512 + 1,024 + 2,048 + 4,096 + 8,191 + 16,382 + 32,764 + 65,528 + 131,056 + 262,112 + 524,224 + 1,048,448 + 2,096,896 + 4,193,792 + 8,387,584 + 16,775,168 = 33,550,336$

Chapter 4   14   Course 2

***Also available in Spanish* ELL**

Additional Lesson Resources

Transparencies
• *5-Minute Check Transparency*, Lesson 4-1

Other Print Products
• *Teaching Mathematics with Manipulatives*
• *Noteables™ Interactive Study Notebook with Foldables™*

Teacher Tech Tools
• *Interactive Classroom CD-ROM*, Lesson 4-1
• *AssignmentWorks*, Lesson 4-1

Student Tech Tools
glencoe.com
• Extra Examples, Chapter 4, Lesson 1
• Self-Check Quiz, Chapter 4, Lesson 1

Prime Factorization

MAIN IDEA

Find the prime factorization of a composite number.

New Vocabulary

prime number
composite number
prime factorization
factor tree

Math Online

glencoe.com

- Concepts In Motion
- Extra Examples
- Personal Tutor
- Self-Check Quiz

▷ MINI Lab

There is only one way that 2 can be expressed as the product of whole numbers. The geoboard shows that there is only one way that two squares can form a rectangle.

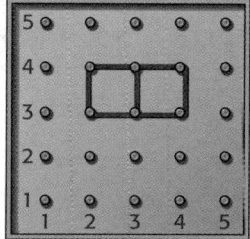

1. Using your geoboard, make as many different rectangles as possible containing 3, 4, 5, 6, 7, 8, 9, and 10 squares.

2. Which numbers of squares can be made into only one rectangle? Into more than one rectangle? **3, 5, 7; 4, 6, 8, 9, 10**

1. See Ch. 4 Answer Appendix.

The rectangles in the Mini Lab illustrate prime and composite numbers.

A **prime number** is a whole number greater than 1 that has exactly two factors, 1 and itself.

A **composite number** is a whole number greater than 1 that has more than two factors.

Whole Numbers	Factors
2	1, 2
3	1, 3
5	1, 5
7	1, 7
4	1, 2, 4
6	1, 2, 3, 6
8	1, 2, 4, 8
9	1, 3, 9
10	1, 2, 5, 10
0	many
1	1

The numbers 0 and 1 are neither prime nor composite.

EXAMPLES Identify Numbers as Prime or Composite

Determine whether each number is *prime* or *composite*.

① 17

The number 17 has only two factors, 1 and 17, so it is prime.

② 12

The number 12 has six factors: 1, 2, 3, 4, 6, and 12. So, it is composite.

Review Vocabulary

factor two or more numbers that are multiplied together to form a product; *Example:* 2 and 3 are factors of 6. (Lesson 1-2)

✓ CHECK Your Progress

Determine whether each number is *prime* or *composite*.

a. 11 **prime**   b. 15 **composite**   c. 24 **composite**

ADDITIONAL EXAMPLES

Determine whether each number is *prime* or *composite*.

① 63 composite

② 29 prime

- What are the factors of 18? 1, 2, 3, 6, 9, and 18

- What are some examples of numbers with only two factors? 2, 3, and 7

① Focus

Vertical Alignment

Before Lesson 4-1

Determine the prime factors of all numbers through 50 and write the numbers as the product of their prime factors by using exponents to show multiples of a factor

Lesson 4-1

Determine the least common multiple and the greatest common divisor of whole numbers; use them to solve problems with fractions

After Lesson 4-1

Add and subtract fractions by using factoring to find common denominators

② Teach

▷ MINI Lab

You may need to point out that a 1×2 rectangle and a 2×1 rectangle are considered the same rectangle. They are just drawn differently. Students should realize that with 4 squares they can create multiple rectangles (1×4 and 2×2), but with 3 squares they can create only one rectangle (1×3).

Scaffolding Questions

Remind students that factors are numbers that are multiplied together to get a product.

Ask:

- What are the factors of 6? 1, 2, 3, and 6

- What are the factors of 10? 1, 2, 5, and 10

Use the Check Your Progress exercises after the Examples to determine students' understanding of concepts.

ADDITIONAL EXAMPLES

3 Find the prime factorization of 100. $2^2 \cdot 5^2$

4 **ALGEBRA** Factor $21m^2n$.
$3 \cdot 7 \cdot m \cdot m \cdot n$

Additional Examples are also in:
- Noteables™ Interactive Study Notebook with Foldables™
- Interactive Classroom PowerPoint® Presentations

Focus on Mathematical Content

The **prime factorization** of a composite number shows the number as a product of prime numbers.

Factor trees are a good way to find the prime factorization of a number.

Every composite number can be written as a product of prime numbers. This product is the **prime factorization** of the number. You can use a **factor tree** to find the prime factorization. The following two factor trees show the prime factorization of 60.

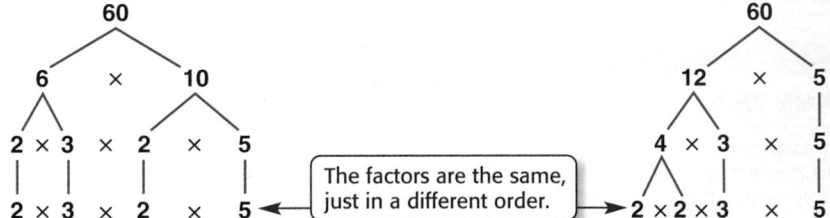

Study Tip

Factors You can also choose any other pair of whole-number factors of 60 such as 3 × 20 or 4 × 15.

The factors are the same, just in a different order.

The prime factorization of 60 is $2 \times 2 \times 3 \times 5$, or $2^2 \times 3 \times 5$.

EXAMPLE **Find the Prime Factorization**

3 Find the prime factorization of 24.

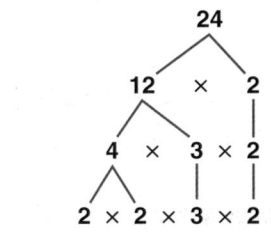

METHOD 1	METHOD 2
Use a factor tree.	**Divide by prime numbers.**

METHOD 1:
24
12 × 2
4 × 3 × 2
2 × 2 × 3 × 2

METHOD 2:
2)24
2)12
2) 6
   3

The divisors are 2, 2, 2, and 3.

The prime factorization of 24 is $2 \times 2 \times 3 \times 2$ or $2^3 \times 3$.

**CHOOSE Your Method**

Find the prime factorization.

d. 18 2×3^2 e. 28 $2^2 \times 7$ f. 16 2^4

Algebraic expressions like $6ab$ can also be factored as the product of prime numbers and variables.

EXAMPLE **Factor an Algebraic Expression**

4 **ALGEBRA** Factor $6ab$.

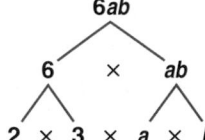
6ab
6 × ab
2 × 3 × a × b

$6ab = 2 \cdot 3 \cdot a \cdot b$

CHECK Your Progress

g. **ALGEBRA** Factor $18xy$. $2 \cdot 3 \cdot 3 \cdot x \cdot y$ or $2 \cdot 3^2 \cdot x \cdot y$

★ indicates multi-step problem

CHECK Your Understanding

Examples 1, 2
(p. 181)

Determine whether each number is *prime* or *composite*.

1. 7 **prime**
2. 50 **composite**
3. 67 **prime**

4. **GARDENING** Louisa has 72 flowers to plant in rows in a flower bed. How many different ways can she plant the flowers? Justify your answer. **See margin.**

Example 3
(p. 182)

Find the prime factorization of each number.

5. 34 2×17
6. 30 $2 \times 3 \times 5$
7. 12 $2^2 \times 3$

Example 4
(p. 182)

ALGEBRA Factor each expression.

8. $10ac$ $2 \cdot 5 \cdot a \cdot c$
9. $16x^2$ $2 \cdot 2 \cdot 2 \cdot 2 \cdot x \cdot x$
10. $11g^3$ $11 \cdot g \cdot g \cdot g$

Practice and Problem Solving

HOMEWORK HELP	
For Exercises	See Examples
11–18	1, 2
19–28	3
29–34	4

Exercise Levels
A: 11–34
B: 35–43
C: 44–47

Determine whether each number is *prime* or *composite*.

11. 22 **composite**
12. 44 **composite**
13. 13 **prime**
14. 39 **composite**
15. 81 **composite**
16. 31 **prime**
17. 97 **prime**
18. 43 **prime**

Find the prime factorization of each number.

19. 96 $2^5 \times 3$
20. 42 $2 \times 3 \times 7$
21. 99 $3^2 \times 11$
22. 64 2^6
23. 210 $2 \times 3 \times 5 \times 7$
24. 180 $2^2 \times 3^2 \times 5$
25. 126 $2 \times 3^2 \times 7$
26. 375 3×5^3

27. **LOBSTERS** Lobsters can live up to 50 years. What is this amount expressed as a product of primes? $2 \cdot 5^2$

28. **DOGS** Greyhounds can jump a distance of 27 feet. Write this distance as a product of primes. 3^3

ALGEBRA Factor each expression.

29. $15mn$ $3 \cdot 5 \cdot m \cdot n$
30. $20pq$ $2 \cdot 2 \cdot 5 \cdot p \cdot q$
31. $34jkm$ $2 \cdot 17 \cdot j \cdot k \cdot m$
32. $49y^2$ $7 \cdot 7 \cdot y \cdot y$
33. $52gh^2$ $2 \cdot 2 \cdot 13 \cdot g \cdot h \cdot h$
34. $48a^2b^2$ $2 \cdot 2 \cdot 2 \cdot 2 \cdot 3 \cdot a \cdot a \cdot b \cdot b$

Replace each ▓ with prime factors to make a true sentence.

35. $2^3 \cdot ▓ \cdot 11 = 616$ **7**
36. $2 \cdot ▓ \cdot 5^2 = 450$ **3^2**
37. $3 \cdot 2^4 \cdot ▓ = 1,200$ **5^2**
38. $2^2 \cdot ▓ \cdot 3 = 1,500$ **5^3**

39. **RIVERS** The Colorado River is 1,450 miles long. Write 1,450 as a product of primes. $2 \times 5^2 \times 29$

ALGEBRA For Exercises 40 and 41, determine whether the value of each expression is *prime* or *composite* if $a = 1$ and $b = 5$.

40. $3a + 6b$ **composite**
41. $7b - 4a$ **prime**

---

3 Practice

✓ Formative Assessment

Use Exercises 1–10 to check for understanding.

Then use the chart at the bottom of this page to customize your assignments for students.

Intervention You may wish to use the Study Guide and Intervention Master on page 10 of the *Chapter 4 Resource Masters* for additional reinforcement.

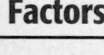

Factors

Make sure students understand that *factoring* an algebraic expression is like finding the prime factorization of a number—except that the variables may or may not represent prime numbers.

Odd/Even Assignments

Exercises 11–34 are structured so that students practice the same concepts whether they are assigned odd or even problems.

Additional Answer

4. 12 ways; 1 row of 72, 2 rows of 36, 3 rows of 24, 4 rows of 18, 6 rows of 12, 8 rows of 9, 9 rows of 8, 12 rows of 6, 18 rows of 4, 24 rows of 3, 36 rows of 2, and 72 rows of 1

DIFFERENTIATED HOMEWORK OPTIONS

Level	Assignment	Two-Day Option	
BL Basic	11–34, 44, 46, 59	11–33 odd, 48, 49	12–34 even, 44, 46–59
OL Core	11–27 odd, 28, 29–39 odd, 42–46, 47–59	11–34, 48, 49	35–44, 46, 47, 50–59
AL Advanced/Pre-AP	35–55 (optional: 56–59)		

Ticket Out the Door Have students write the prime factorization of 1,000 on a piece of paper. You might want to point out that they already found the prime factorization of 50 (in Exercise 2), and ask: Can this help you find the prime factorization of 1,000?

FOLDABLES **Foldables™**
Study Organizer **Follow-Up**

Remind students to write–under the tab for this lesson of their Foldable–a question about prime factorization. As students progress through the lesson, encourage them to take notes and record information that answers the question.

Additional Answer

50.

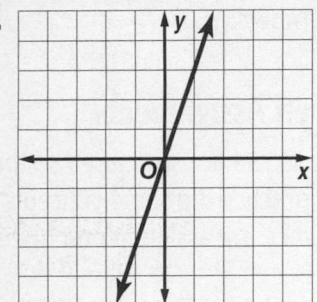

---

43. Sample answer: 81: 9 × 9, 3 × 27; 225: 9 × 25, 5 × 45; 441: 9 × 49; 7 × 63

EXTRA PRACTICE
See pages 676, 707.

H.O.T. Problems
44. See Ch. 4 Answer Appendix.

47. If $n = 1$, $2n$ is a prime number. If $n > 1$, $2n$ is a composite number with at least three factors.

CONTESTS For Exercises 42 and 43, use the following information.

Sandcastle Day at Cannon Beach, Oregon, is one of the largest sandcastle contests on the west coast. Entrants from each age division are given lots measuring 81 square feet, 225 square feet, or 441 square feet, on which to build their castles.

42. Find the prime factorization of 81, 225, and 441. 3^4, $3^2 \times 5^2$, $3^2 \times 7^2$

43. Use the prime factors to determine two possible dimensions for each plot.

44. RESEARCH Use the Internet or another source to make a Sieve of Eratosthenes to determine the prime numbers up to 100.

45. CHALLENGE This whole number is between 30 and 40. It has only two prime factors whose sum is 5. What is the number? **36**

46. OPEN ENDED Primes that differ by two are called *twin primes*. For example, 59 and 61 are twin primes. Give three examples of twin primes that are less than 50. **Sample answer: 5 and 7, 11 and 13, and 17 and 19**

47. **WRITING IN MATH** Suppose n represents a whole number. Is $2n$ prime or composite? Explain.

TEST PRACTICE

48. Which number is a prime factor of both 63 and 140? **D**

   A 2   **C** 5

   B 3   **D** 7

49. Which of the following numbers is *not* a prime number? **H**

   F 2   **H** 16

   G 11   **J** 31

Spiral Review

50. ALGEBRA Graph $y = 3x$. (Lesson 3-7) **See margin.**

51. MEASUREMENT Find the perimeter and area of a rectangle with a length of 13 feet and width of 5 feet. (Lesson 3-6) **36 feet; 65 ft²**

Add. (Lesson 2-4)

52. $6 + (-4)$ **2**   **53.** $-13 + 9$ **−4**   **54.** $25 + (-26)$ **−1**   **55.** $-5 + 5$ **0**

GET READY for the Next Lesson

PREREQUISITE SKILL State whether each number is divisible by 2, 3, 5, 6, 9, or 10. (Page 668)

56. 24 **2, 3, 6**   **57.** 70 **2, 5, 10**   **58.** 120 **2, 3, 5, 6, 10**   **59.** 99 **3, 9**

184 Chapter 4 Fractions, Decimals, and Percents

Pre-AP Activity **Use after Exercise 47**

Have students answer the following questions: If x represents a whole number, can x^2 be prime? composite? neither? Make sure students explain their reasoning and give examples.

READING to SOLVE PROBLEMS

Everyday Meaning

The key to understanding word problems is to understand the meaning of the mathematical terms in the problem. Many words used in mathematics are also used in everyday language.

For example, you will use the terms *factor* and *multiple* in this chapter. Here are two sentences that show their everyday meanings.

- Weather was a *factor* in their decision to postpone the picnic.
- The star quarterback won *multiple* post-season awards.

The table below shows how the everyday meaning is connected to the mathematical meaning.

Term	Everyday Meaning	Mathematical Meaning	Connection
factor from the Latin *factor,* meaning doer	something that actively contributes to a decision or result	2 and 3 are *factors* of 6.	A *factor* helps to make a decision, and in mathematics, factors "make up" a product.
multiple from the Latin *multi-,* meaning many, and *plex,* meaning fold	consisting of more than one or shared by many	The *multiples* of 2 are 0, 2, 4, 6, … .	*Multiple* means many, and in mathematics, a number has infinitely many multiples.

1. Sample answer: *fact-*: fact, faction, factory; *multi-*: multiplex, multimedia, multicultural. The words beginning with *fact-* all refer to parts of something; the words beginning with *multi-* all refer to more than one.

1. Make a list of other words that have the prefixes *fact-* or *multi-*. Determine what the words in each list have in common.

2. **WRITING IN MATH** Write your own rule for remembering the difference between *factor* and *multiple*. **See students' work.**

RESEARCH Use a dictionary to find the everyday meanings of *least*, *greatest*, and *common*. Then use the definitions to determine how to find each number. Do not solve.

3. the greatest common factor of 10 and 15

4. the least common multiple of 2 and 3.

3. Greatest: largest in size; common: belonging to or shared by two or more individuals or things; the greatest common factor of 10 and 15 is the largest factor common to both 10 and 15.

4. Least: smallest in size; the least common multiple of 2 and 3 is the smallest multiple common to both 2 and 3.

Chapter 4 Reading to Solve Problems: Everyday Meaning **185**

 **Greatest Common Factor**

PACING: **Regular:** 2 periods, **Block:** 1 period

Options for Differentiated Instruction

ELL = English Language Learner · **AL** = Above or Beyond Grade Level · **SS** = Struggling Students · **SN** = Special Needs

Visual Learners **ELL** **AL** **SS**

Use with Example 1.

Display the Venn diagram at the right, which shows the common factors of 18 and 48.

Ask:

- How can you tell from looking at the diagram what the GCF of 18 and 48 is? It is 6, the greatest number in the area where the circles overlap.

If you were to display the common factors of 20 and 24, what would be the numbers in the area where the circles overlap? 1, 2, 4

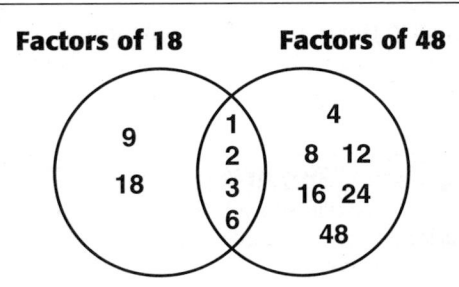

Alternative Methods **AL**

Use with the Examples.

Have students solve the Examples using a hundreds chart and colored chips to cover factors of the numbers. Have students mark all factors of the first number with one color and all factors of the second number in another color.

Ask:

- What factors do they have in common?
- What is the GCF?

Organizing Student Work and Thinking **ELL** **SS** **SN**

Use before assigning the Exercises.

Have students use index cards to create a factor card for each of the numbers from 1 to 30. On each card, write the following:

- the number
- a list of all the factors
- a factor tree
- the prime factorization

Have students fasten the cards together by hole-punching the corner of each card and placing a ring through it.

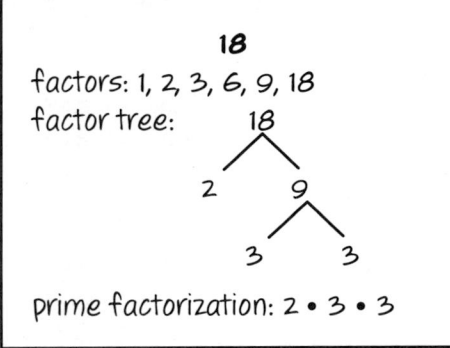

Leveled Lesson Resources

Chapter 4 Resource Masters

BL = Below or Approaching Grade Level   **OL** = On Grade Level   **AL** = Above or Beyond Grade Level   **ELL** = English Language Learner

---

Lesson Reading Guide
p. 16 **BL** **OL** **ELL**

NAME _____ DATE _____ PERIOD _____

4-2 Lesson Reading Guide
Greatest Common Factor

Get Ready for the Lesson

Read the introduction at the top of page 186 in your textbook. Write your answers below.

1. Which factors are in the overlapping section? What does this mean?
   2, 3; 2 and 3 are prime factors of both 12 and 18.

2. Is the product of 2 and 3 also a factor of 12 and 18?
   Yes; since each prime factor divides the number, the product of factors will also divide the number.

3. Make a Venn diagram showing the prime factors of 12 and 20. Identify the common factors and find their product. **2, 2; 4**

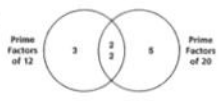

Read the Lesson

4. What does a Venn diagram show? **how elements among sets of numbers or objects are related**

5. How does a Venn diagram show relationships between elements? **Sample answer: The common elements are within the overlapping part of the circles.**

6. You can find the GCF by using common factors or using common prime factors. What is the difference? **Sample answer: In one method you list all factors of both numbers then find the greatest common factor. In the other method, the prime factorizations are compared, and the GCF is the product of those common factors.**

7. Find the prime factors of 20 and 24. What are the prime factors that are common to both numbers? What is the GCF? **20 = 2² · 5; 24 = 2³ · 3; The common prime factors are 2 and 2; the GCF is 4.**

8. How is the GCF of two numbers found if you know the prime factors common to the numbers? **Multiply the common prime factors to find the GCF.**

Remember What You Learned

9. In your own words, describe what the GCF of two numbers is and explain one way to find it. **Sample answer: The greatest common factor (GCF) of two numbers is the greatest number among the factors common to both numbers; for small numbers you can list the factors easily, and for large numbers find the prime factorization or use division.**

Chapter 4   16   Course 2

Study Guide and Intervention*
p. 17 **BL** **OL** **ELL**

NAME _____ DATE _____ PERIOD _____

4-2 Study Guide and Intervention
Greatest Common Factor

The **greatest common factor (GCF)** of two or more numbers is the largest number that is a factor of each number. The GCF of prime numbers is 1.

Example 1 Find the GCF of 72 and 108 by listing factors.

factors of 72: 1, 2, 3, 4, 6, 8, 9, 12, 18, 24, 36, 72
factors of 108: 1, 2, 3, 4, 6, 9, 12, 18, 27, 36, 54, 108
common factors: 1, 2, 3, 4, 6, 9, 12, 18, 36
The GCF of 72 and 108 is 36.

Example 2 Find the GCF of 42 and 60 using prime factors.

Method 1 Write the prime factorization.
60 = 2 × 2 × 3 × 5
42 = 2 × 3 × 7

Method 2 Divide by prime numbers.
Divide both 42 and 60 by 2.
Then divide the quotients by 3.
7   10
3)21 30
2)42 60 ← Start here

The common prime factors are 2 and 3. The GCF of 42 and 60 is 2 × 3, or 6.

Exercises

Find the GCF of each set of numbers.

1. 18, 30 **6**
2. 60, 45 **15**
3. 24, 72 **24**
4. 32, 48 **16**
5. 100, 30 **10**
6. 54, 36 **18**
7. 3, 97, 5 **1**
8. 4, 20, 24 **4**
9. 36, 9, 45 **9**

Chapter 4   17   Course 2

Skills Practice*
p. 18 **BL** **OL**

NAME _____ DATE _____ PERIOD _____

4-2 Skills Practice
Greatest Common Factor

Find the GCF of each set of numbers.

1. 14, 20 **2**
2. 16, 42 **2**
3. 8, 18 **2**
4. 24, 36 **12**
5. 72, 22 **2**
6. 77, 15 **1**
7. 32, 80 **16**
8. 90, 120 **30**
9. 45, 30 **15**
10. 12, 62 **2**
11. 15, 27 **3**
12. 21, 28 **7**
13. 12, 20, 26 **2**
14. 15, 20, 25 **5**
15. 60, 72, 36 **12**
16. 32, 48, 64 **16**
17. 36, 48, 30 **6**
18. 28, 56, 42 **14**
19. 80, 110, 90 **10**
20. 9, 25, 49 **1**

Find the GCF of each set of algebraic expressions.

21. 21ab, 14b **7b**
22. 20a², 36a **4a**
23. 15ab, 5b² **5b**
24. 35a², 85ab **5a**

25. Find the GCF of 2³ × 3² × 5 and 2² × 3 × 5². **2² × 3 × 5 or 60**

Chapter 4   18   Course 2

Practice*
p. 19 **OL** **AL**

NAME _____ DATE _____ PERIOD _____

4-2 Practice
Greatest Common Factor

Find the GCF of each set of numbers.

1. 16, 44 **4**
2. 15, 35 **5**
3. 24, 32 **8**
4. 27, 63 **9**
5. 20, 80 **20**
6. 18, 38 **2**
7. 14, 49 **7**
8. 66, 99 **33**
9. 9, 35 **1**
10. 6, 24, 42 **6**
11. 30, 50, 70 **10**
12. 32, 48, 96 **16**
13. 10w, 5w **5w**
14. 16xy, 24xy **8xy**
15. 21ab, 35a **7a**
16. 10jk, 15k **5k**
17. 3mn, 9mn, 12mn **3mn**
18. 6xy, 9x, 3y **3**

19. 4 inches, 1 foot, 6 inches, 2 feet **2 inches**

20. 10 gallons, 55 gallons, 35 gallons, 20 gallons **5 gallons**

Find two numbers whose GCF is the given number.

21. 10 **Sample answer: 20, 50**
22. 8 **Sample answer: 24, 32**
23. 14 **Sample answer: 56, 70**

24. **SPORTS CARDS** Jason wants to organize his sports cards in packets for each type of sport. Each packet has the same number of cards. If he has 24 baseball cards, 60 hockey cards, and 48 football cards, find the greatest number of cards in each packet. **12 cards**

25. **FORESTRY** A forest ranger needs to remove three tree trunks by cutting the trunks into equal lengths. If the lengths of the tree trunks are 6 feet, 8 feet, and 12 feet, what is the length of the longest log that can be cut? **2 feet**

Chapter 4   19   Course 2

Word Problem Practice*
p. 20 **OL** **AL**

NAME _____ DATE _____ PERIOD _____

4-2 Word Problem Practice
Greatest Common Factor

1. **TABLE TENNIS** Rebecca has 20 table tennis balls and 16 table tennis paddles. She wants to sell packages of balls and paddles bundled together. What is the greatest number of packages she can sell with no leftover balls or paddles? **4**

2. **TUMBLING** Mr. Nicolet wants to organize equal-sized groups of boys and girls for tumbling exercises. If there are 12 boys and 18 girls and each group is all boys or all girls, what is the largest size group he can organize? **6**

3. **BAKE SALE** Volunteers at a bake sale want to sell slices of banana nut bread and raisin bread packaged together. They have 63 slices of banana nut bread and 45 slices of raisin bread, and they plan to use all the bread. What is the greatest number of packages they can put together? How many slices of each type of bread are in a package? **9; 7 slices of banana nut bread and 5 slices of raisin bread**

4. **DOG TREATS** Krista wants to give her dog a special treat. She has 81 dog bones and 54 pieces of beef jerky. If she wants to give her dog the same number of treats every day, what is the greatest number of days she can feed the dog these treats? How many of each type should she give the dog? **27; 3 dog bones and 2 pieces of beef jerky**

5. **FRUIT TREES** Mr. Farber has 84 pear trees and 180 apple trees. He wants to plant the trees in rows of equal width. Find the most trees that can be planted in a row if each row has only one type of tree. **12**

6. **BOARDS** A scouting troop has three boards of lengths 14 feet, 28 feet, and 21 feet. If the boards must be cut to produce equal-sized pieces, what is the longest piece that can be cut with no waste? **7 ft**

Chapter 4   20   Course 2

Enrichment
p. 21 **OL** **AL**

NAME _____ DATE _____ PERIOD _____

4-2 Enrichment

Sundaram's Sieve

This arrangement of numbers is called Sundaram's Sieve. Like the Sieve of Eratosthenes, Sundaram's arrangement can be used to find prime numbers.

4	7	10	13	16	19	22	25	28	31
7	12	17	22	27	32	37	42	47	52
10	17	24	31	38	45	52	59	66	73
13	22	31	40	49	58	67	76	85	94
16	27	38	49	60	71	82	93	104	115

Here's how to use Sundaram's Sieve to find prime numbers. If a number, *n*, is not in the Sieve, then 2*n* + 1 is a prime number. If a number, *n*, is in the Sieve, then 2*n* + 1 is not a prime number.

32 is in the sieve.   2 × 32 + 1 = 65   65 is not prime.
35 is not in the sieve.   2 × 35 + 1 = 71   71 is prime.

1. Does the sieve give all primes up to 99? all the composites? **all primes except 2; only 22 of the composites**

2. Sundaram's Sieve is constructed from arithmetic sequences. Describe the pattern used to make the first row. **Start with 4 and add 3 each time.**

3. How is the first column constructed? **It is the same as the first row.**

4. How are the second through fifth rows constructed? **arithmetic sequences using 5, 7, 9, and 11**

5. How would you add a sixth row to the sieve? **Start with 19 and add 13 each time.**

6. Use Sundaram's Sieve to find 5 four-digit prime numbers. You will need to add more numbers to the sieve to do this. **See students' work.**

Chapter 4   21   Course 2

Additional Lesson Resources

* Also available in Spanish **ELL**

Transparencies
- *5-Minute Check Transparency*, Lesson 4-2

Other Print Products
- *Noteables™ Interactive Study Notebook with Foldables™*

Teacher Tech Tools
- *Interactive Classroom CD-ROM*, Lesson 4-2
- *AssignmentWorks*, Lesson 4-2

Student Tech Tools
glencoe.com
- Extra Examples, Chapter 4, Lesson 2
- Self-Check Quiz, Chapter 4, Lesson 2

4-2 Greatest Common Factor

MAIN IDEA

Find the greatest common factor of two or more numbers.

New Vocabulary

Venn diagram
greatest common factor (GCF)

Math Online

glencoe.com
• Extra Examples
• Personal Tutor
• Self-Check Quiz
• Reading in the Content Area

▷ **GET READY** for the Lesson

VENN DIAGRAM The Venn diagram shows the prime factors of 12 and 18.

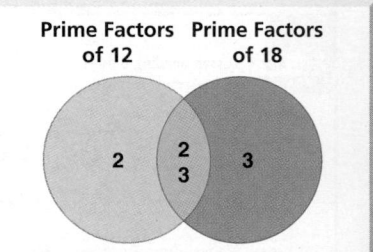

Prime Factors of 12   Prime Factors of 18

1. Which factors are in the overlapping section? What does this mean?

2. Is the product of 2 and 3 also a factor of 12 and 18?

3. Make a Venn diagram showing the prime factors of 12 and 20. Identify the common factors and find their product. **1–3. See margin.**

As shown above, **Venn diagrams** use overlapping circles to show how common elements among sets of numbers or objects are related. They can also show common factors. The greatest of the common factors of two or more numbers is the **greatest common factor, or GCF**.

EXAMPLE **Find the Greatest Common Factor**

① Find the GCF of 18 and 48.

METHOD 1   **List the factors of the numbers.**

factors of 18: **1, 2, 3, 6,** 9, 18
factors of 48: **1, 2, 3,** 4, **6,** 8, 12, 16, 24, 48

List the factors of 18 and 48.

The common factors of 18 and 48 are 1, 2, 3, and 6. So, the greatest common factor or GCF is 6.

METHOD 2   **Use prime factorization.**

Write the prime factorization. Circle the common prime factors.

$18 = ②\times 3 \times ③$
$48 = ②\times 2 \times 2 \times 2 \times ③$

Write the prime factorizations of 18 and 48.

The greatest common factor or GCF is 2×3 or 6.

✔ **CHOOSE Your Method**

Find the GCF of each pair of numbers.

a. 8, 10 **2**   b. 6, 12 **6**   c. 10, 17 **1**

186   Chapter 4 Fractions, Decimals, and Percents

Additional Answers

1. 2, 3; 2 and 3 are prime factors of both 12 and 18.

2. Yes; Since each prime factor divides the number, the product of factors will also divide the number.

EXAMPLE **Find the GCF of Three Numbers**

2 **Find the GCF of 12, 24, and 60.**

Write the prime factorization. Circle the common prime factors.

$12 = 2 \times 2 \times 3$
$24 = 2 \times 2 \times 2 \times 3$ Write the prime factorization of 12, 24, and 60.
$60 = 2 \times 2 \times 3 \times 5$

The common prime factors are 2, 2, and 3. So, the GCF is $2 \times 2 \times 3$, or 12.

✓ CHECK Your Progress

Find the GCF of each set of numbers.

d. 30, 45, 75 **15**   e. 42, 70, 84 **14**

🌐 Real-World EXAMPLES

3 **SCHOOL SPIRIT** The cheerleaders are making spirit ribbons. Blue ribbon comes in a 24 inch spool, red ribbon comes in a 30 inch spool, and gold ribbon comes in a 36 inch spool. The cheerleaders want to cut strips of equal length and use the entire spool of each ribbon. What is the length of the longest piece of ribbon that can be cut from each spool?

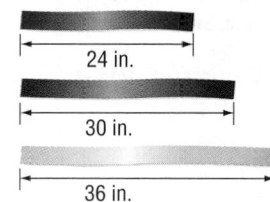

24 in.

30 in.

36 in.

The length of the longest ribbon that can be cut from each spool is the GCF of the three lengths.

$24 = 2 \times 2 \times 2 \times 3$
$30 = 2 \qquad \times 3 \times 5$ Write the prime factorization of 24, 30, and 36.
$36 = 2 \times 2 \qquad \times 3 \times 3$

The GCF of 24, 30, and 36 is 2×3 or 6. So, the ribbons should be 6 inches long.

4 **How many spirit ribbons can be made if the ribbons are cut into 6-inch pieces?**

There is a total of $24 + 30 + 36$, or 90 inches of ribbon. So, $90 \div 6$, or 15 spirit ribbons can be made.

Study Tip

Prime Numbers
The GCF of a group of prime numbers is 1.

✓ CHECK Your Progress

f. **CARPENTRY** Mr. Glover wants to make shelves for his garage using an 18-foot board and a 36-foot board. He will cut the boards to make shelves of the same length and wants to use all of both boards. Find the longest possible length of each shelf. How many shelves can he make? **18 ft, 3**

Lesson 4-2 Greatest Common Factor   **187**

Additional Answer

3. 2, 2; 4

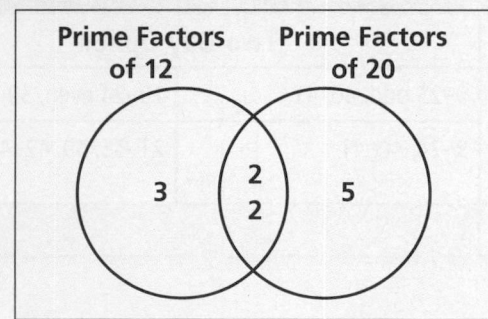

Prime Factors of 12   Prime Factors of 20

3   2 2   5

Formative Assessment

Use Exercises 1–8 to check for understanding.

Then use the chart at the bottom of this page to customize your assignments for students.

Intervention You may wish to use the Study Guide and Intervention Master on page 17 of the *Chapter 4 Resource Masters* for additional reinforcement.

Odd/Even Assignments

Exercises 9–24 are structured so that students practice the same concepts whether they are assigned odd or even problems.

Tips for New Teachers **Working in Groups**

If students have difficulty finding the GCF of sets of numbers, you may want to separate them into pairs or groups. Let the members of each pair or group discuss the problems and possible solution methods. Each member can find the factors (or prime factorization) of one number, and then all of the members could compare their lists of factors.

Tips for New Teachers **Greatest Common Divisor**

Be sure that your students understand that the terms *greatest common factor* (GCF) and the *greatest common divisor* can be used interchangeably.

★ indicates multi-step problem

CHECK Your Understanding

Examples 1, 2 (pp. 186–187)

Find the GCF of each set of numbers.
1. 18, 30 **6**   2. 45, 60 **15**   3. 20, 50 **10**
4. 6, 8, 12 **2**   5. 8, 20, 40 **4**   6. 18, 42, 60 **6**

JOBS For Exercises 7 and 8, use the following information.
A store manager wants to display the inventory of three styles of bicycle helmets in rows with the same number of each style in each row.

Bike Helmets	
Style	**Inventory**
Sport	36
Road	72
Mountain	45

Examples 3, 4 (p. 187)

7. Find the greatest number of helmets that can be placed in each row. **9**

8. How many rows of each helmet are there? **4, 8, 5**

Practice and Problem Solving

HOMEWORK HELP

For Exercises	See Examples
9–16	1
17–20	2
21–24	3, 4

Find the GCF of each set of numbers.
9. 12, 78 **6**   10. 40, 50 **10**   11. 20, 45 **5**
12. 32, 48 **16**   13. 24, 48 **24**   14. 45, 75 **15**
15. 56, 96 **8**   16. 40, 125 **5**   17. 18, 24, 30 **6**
18. 36, 60, 84 **12**   19. 35, 49, 84 **7**   20. 36, 50, 130 **2**

Exercise Levels
A: 9–24
B: 25–35
C: 36–39

BANDS For Exercises 21 and 22, use the following information.
In a marching band, there are 64 woodwinds, 88 brass, and 16 percussion players. When they march in a parade, there is the same number of students in each row.

21. Find the greatest number of students in each row. **8 students**

22. How many rows of each group are there? **8, 11, 2**

COMMUNITY SERVICE For Exercises 23 and 24, use the following information.
You want to make care packages for a local shelter. You have 18 toothbrushes, 30 combs, and 12 bars of soap. Each package has the same number of each item.

23. What is the greatest number of care packages you can make using all the items? **6 care packages**

24. How many of each item are in each package? **3 toothbrushes, 5 combs, and 2 bars of soap**

30. Sample answer: 18 and 81
31. Sample answer: 24 and 36
32. Sample answer: 15 and 45
33. Sample answer: 60 and 90

Find the GCF of each set of numbers.
25. 25¢, $1.50, 75¢, $3.00 **25¢**   26. 6 feet, 15 feet, 21 feet, 9 feet **3 ft**

ALGEBRA Find the greatest common divisor of each set of expressions.
27. $24a$, $6a$ **$6a$**   28. $30mn$, $40mn$ **$10mn$**   29. $15xy$, $55y$ **$5y$**

Find two numbers whose greatest common divisor is the given number.
30. 9   31. 12   32. 15   33. 30

DIFFERENTIATED HOMEWORK OPTIONS

Level	Assignment	Two-Day Option	
BL Basic	9–24, 34–47	9–23 odd, 40, 41	10–24 even, 39, 42–47
OL Core	9–21 odd, 23–25, 27–33 odd, 34–35, 39–47	9–24, 40, 41	21–35, 39, 42–47
AL Advanced/Pre-AP	25–46, (optional: 47)		

35. Sample answer: The first prism is 8 in. high, 3 in. long, and 4 in. wide. The second prism is 8 in. high, 6 in. long, and 5 in. wide. The third prism is 8 in. high, 5 in. long, and 5 in. wide.

EXTRA PRACTICE
See pages 676, 707.

GEOMETRY For Exercises 34 and 35, use the following information.

Jeremy is building rectangular prisms using one-inch cubes. He is planning to build three prisms, the first with 96 blue cubes, the second with 240 red cubes, and the third with 200 yellow cubes. All of prisms must be the same height, but not necessarily the same length and width.

34. What is the maximum height of each prism Jeremy can build? **8 in.**

35. What are the dimensions of all three prisms?
★

H.O.T. Problems **CHALLENGE** Determine whether each statement is *sometimes*, *always*, or *never* true.

36. The GCF of two numbers is greater than both numbers. **never**

37. If two numbers have no common prime factors, the GCF is 1. **always**

38. The GCF of two numbers is one of the numbers. **sometimes**

39. **WRITING IN MATH** Using the words *factor* and *greatest common factor*, explain the relationship between the numbers 4, 12, and 24. **Sample answer: 4 and 12 are factors of 24. The greatest common factor of 4, 12, and 24 is 4.**

TEST PRACTICE

40. Student Council earned $26 selling bottled water, $32 selling oranges, and $28 selling energy bars. If all items cost the same, what is the greatest possible price per item? **A**

A $2 **C** $7

B $4 **D** $8

41. Which set of numbers has the greatest GCF? **G**

F 4, 5, 20

G 18, 36

H 18, 36, 45

J 23, 29

Spiral Review

42. What is the prime factorization of 75? (Lesson 4-1) **3 × 5 × 5**

ALGEBRA Graph each equation. (Lesson 3-7) **43–45. See margin.**

43. $y = -x$ **44.** $y = x + 3$ **45.** $y = 2x - 1$

46. ALGEBRA Solve the equation $-7y + 18 = 39$. Check your solution. (Lesson 3-5) **−3**

▷ **GET READY for the Next Lesson**

47. PREREQUISITE SKILL Serena received a gift card to download music from the Internet. She downloaded 3 songs on Monday, 5 songs on Tuesday, and one half of what was left on Wednesday. She has 6 songs left. How many songs were initially on the gift card? Use the *work backward* strategy. (Lesson 3-4) **20 songs**

---

4 Assess

Yesterday's News Remind students that yesterday's lesson was about finding prime factorizations. Ask them to write how yesterday's concepts helped them with today's material.

Additional Answers

43.

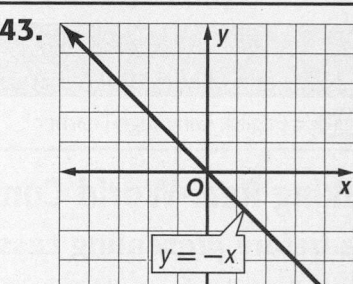
$y = -x$

44.

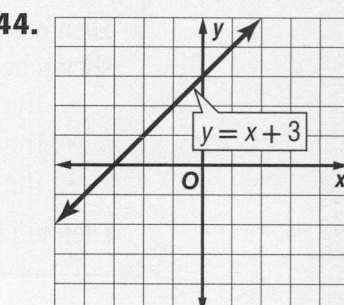
$y = x + 3$

45.

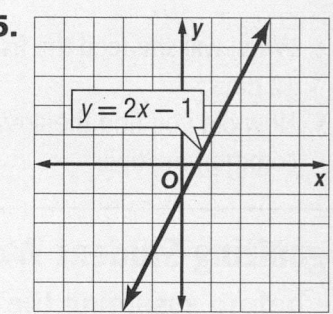
$y = 2x - 1$

Problem-Solving Investigation
MAKE AN ORGANIZED LIST

PACING: **Regular:** 1 period, **Block:** 0.5 period

Options for Differentiated Instruction

ELL = English Language Learner   **AL** = Above or Beyond Grade Level   **SS** = Struggling Students   **SN** = Special Needs

Making Real-World Connections

Use before presenting Lesson 4-3.

Present the following problem to students.

> Ellen has three different fish tanks. The feeding schedule for the fish in each is shown below.
> - The fish in tank A need to be fed every 2 days.
> - The fish in tank B need to be fed every 3 days.
> - The fish in tank C need to be fed every 4 days.
>
> Ellen fed the fish in all three tanks today.

Ask:
- When will she feed the fish in all three tanks on the same day again? How often will that happen? in 12 days; every 12 days
- How did you find the answer? Explain. Sample answer: List the multiples of 2, 3, and 4, and find the first common multiple.

Organizing Student Work and Thinking

Use before assigning the Exercises.

Have students add the strategy of making an organized list to their problem-solving booklets. They should include the following about the strategy:
- a description of the strategy
- an explanation of the best time to use the strategy
- examples of problems that are solved using the strategy
- advantages and disadvantages of using the strategy

Leveled Lesson Resources

Chapter 4 Resource Masters

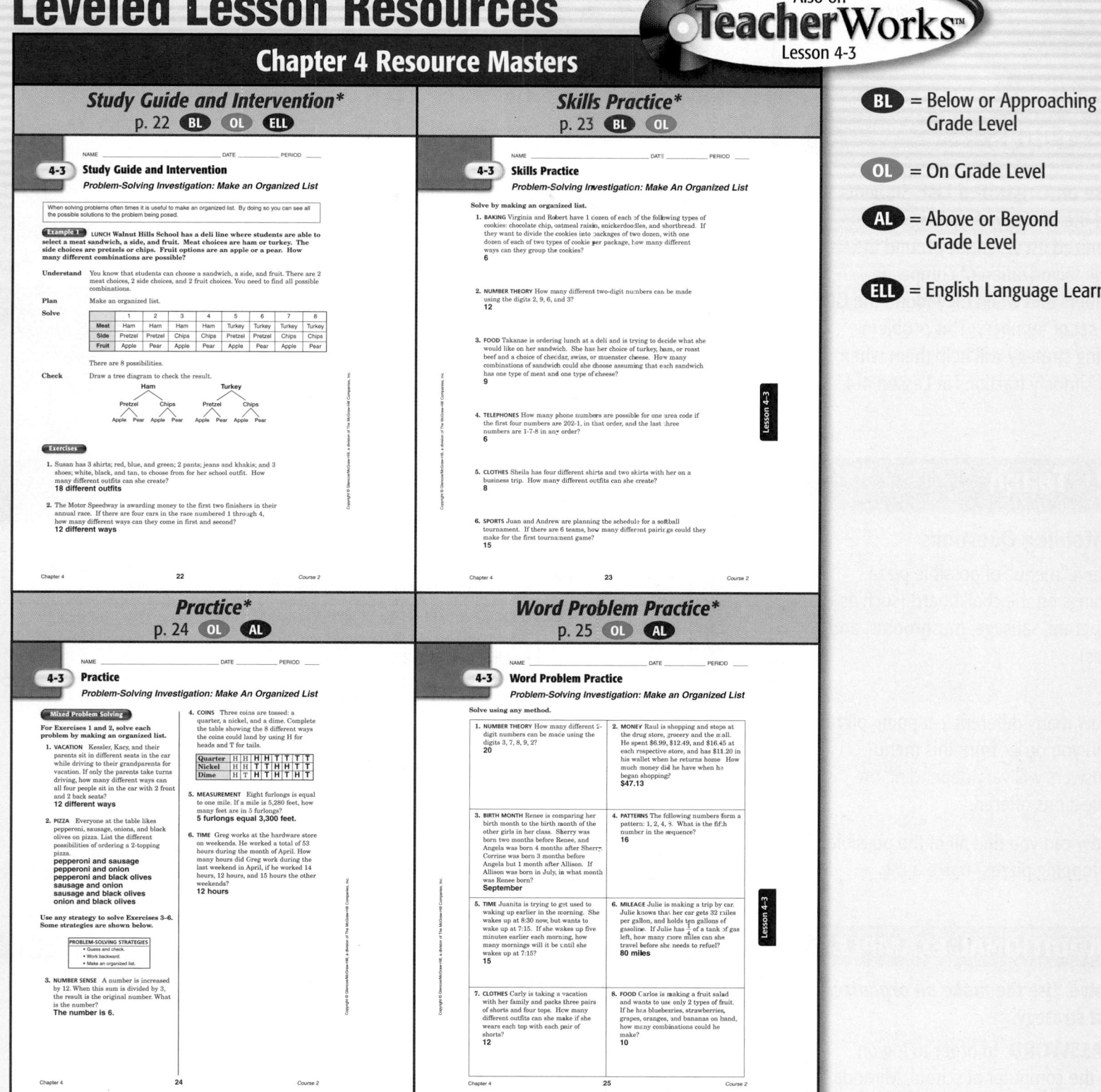

Study Guide and Intervention*
p. 22 BL OL ELL

Skills Practice*
p. 23 BL OL

Practice*
p. 24 OL AL

Word Problem Practice*
p. 25 OL AL

BL = Below or Approaching Grade Level

OL = On Grade Level

AL = Above or Beyond Grade Level

ELL = English Language Learner

Also available in Spanish ELL

Additional Lesson Resources

Transparencies
- *5-Minute Check Transparency*, Lesson 4-3

Other Print Products
- *Noteables™ Interactive Study Notebook with Foldables™*

Teacher Tech Tools
- *Interactive Classroom CD-ROM*, Lesson 4-3
- *AssignmentWorks*, Lesson 4-3

Student Tech Tools
glencoe.com
- Extra Examples, Chapter 4, Lesson 3
- Self-Check Quiz, Chapter 4, Lesson 3

1 Focus

Make an Organized List Students used the strategy of making an organized list when they found the prime factorization of composite numbers and when they found the GCF of a set of numbers. This problem-solving strategy will help them when they simplify fractions in Lesson 4-4.

2 Teach

Scaffolding Questions

Write a "menu" of possible pizza toppings on the chalkboard (such as pepperoni, sausage, mushrooms, and olives).

Ask:

• How many different 2-topping pizzas can you order from this menu? Answers will vary depending on selections offered.

• How can you find all of the possible 2-topping pizzas? make a list

ADDITIONAL EXAMPLE

Solve. Use the *make an organized list* strategy.

PASSWORD In order to log on to the computer at school, Miranda must use a password. The password is 2 characters. The first character is the letter A or B followed by a single numeric digit. How many passwords does Miranda have to choose from? 20

Additional Examples are also in:

• Noteables™ Interactive Study Notebook with Foldables™

• Interactive Classroom PowerPoint® Presentations

4-3 Problem-Solving Investigation

MAIN IDEA: Solve problems by making an organized list.

P.S.I. TEAM +

e-Mail: MAKE AN ORGANIZED LIST

NIKKI: I am ordering a pizza. The crust choices are thin or hand-tossed. The meat choices are pepperoni or sausage. The vegetable choices are olives, mushrooms, or banana peppers.

YOUR MISSION: Nikki chooses from one crust, one meat, and one vegetable choice. Make an organized list to find how many different types of pizza Nikki can order.

Understand	You know the crust, meat, and vegetable options for the pizza. You need to find all the possible pizza combinations that can be made.
Plan	Make an organized list of all the possible combinations. Use T for thin, H for hand-tossed, P for pepperoni, S for sausage, O for olives, M for mushrooms, and B for banana peppers.
Solve	**Choosing thin crust:** T P O T P M T P B T S O T S M T S B **Choosing hand-tossed crust:** H P O H P M H P B H S O H S M H S B There are 12 different combinations of pizza that can be ordered.
Check	Draw a tree diagram to check the result.

Analyze The Strategy

1. Explain why making an organized list was a useful strategy in solving this problem. **1, 2. See margin.**

2. **WRITING IN MATH** Write a problem that can be solved by making an organized list. Then explain how to solve the problem using this strategy.

190 Chapter 4 Fractions, Decimals, and Percents

Additional Answers

1. Sample answer: By making an organized list, you can show all the possible pizza combinations. Count the number of pizzas to determine the answer.

2. How many different ways can a woodwind trio be made if the first position needs to be either a bass clarinet or a bassoon? The other two positions should be filled by a clarinet, oboe, or flute. Using an organized list, there will be 6 different possibilities.

For Exercises 3–6, solve each problem by making an organized list.

3. **SHOPPING** Charmaine went to the store and bought a yellow shirt, a blue shirt, and a red shirt. She also bought a pair of jeans and a pair of khaki dress pants. How many different outfits can be made using one shirt and one pair of pants? **6 outfits**

4. **WORK** The following four numbers are used for employee identification numbers at a small company: 0, 1, 2, and 3. How many different employee identification numbers can be made using each digit once? **24 numbers**

5. **PHOTOS** Joshua, Diego, and Audri stand side-by-side for a photo. How many different ways can the three friends stand next to each other? **6 ways**

6. **CELL PHONES** How many phone numbers are possible for one area code if the first three numbers are 268, in that order, and the last four numbers are 0, 9, 7, 1 in any order? **24**

Use any strategy to solve Exercises 7–14. Some strategies are shown below.

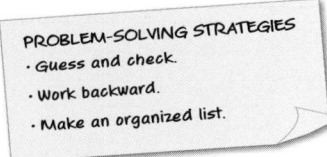

PROBLEM-SOLVING STRATEGIES
· Guess and check.
· Work backward.
· Make an organized list.

7. **ALGEBRA** Consecutive odd numbers are numbers like 1, 3, 5, and 7. Find two consecutive odd numbers whose sum is 56 and whose product is 783. **27, 29**

8. **FOOD** The table shows the choices for ordering a deli sandwich. How many different subs can be ordered if you choose only one kind of bread and one kind of meat? **9 subs**

The Sandwich Shop	
Bread	White, Wheat, Whole Grain
Meat	Ham, Turkey, Roast Beef
Cheese	American, Swiss
Dressing	Italian, Ranch

9. **DVDS** Paul rented 2 times as many DVDs as Angelina last month. Angelina rented 4 fewer than Bret, but 4 more than Jill. Bret rented 9 DVDs. How many DVDs did each person rent? **Paul: 10; Angelina: 5; Bret: 9; Jill: 1**

10. **CLOTHES** Jeffrey owns 3 shirts, 2 pairs of pants, and 2 pairs of shoes. How many different outfits can he create? **12 outfits**

11. **SNOWFALL** A total of 17 inches of snow fell in a 72-hour period. In the last 24 hours, 6 inches fell, and in the previous 24 hours, 4 inches fell. How many inches fell in the first 24 hours? **7 in.**

12. **GAS MILEAGE** Mrs. Acosta travels 44 miles in her car and uses 2 gallons of gas. If her gas mileage continues at the same rate, how many gallons of gas would she use to travel 528 miles? **24 gallons**

13. **SCIENCE** Hydrothermal vents are similar to geysers, but are found on the ocean floor. A hydrothermal vent chimney can grow at an average rate of 9 meters in 18 months. What is the average rate of growth per month? **0.5 m**

14. **CRAFTS** Paul makes three different sizes of birdhouses. He can paint each style in red, brown, or yellow. How many different birdhouses can Paul make? **9**

Lesson 4-3 Problem-Solving Investigation: Make an Organized List   **191**

Simplifying Fractions

PACING: **Regular:** 2 periods, **Block:** 1 period

Options for Differentiated Instruction

 = English Language Learner   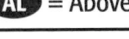 = Above or Beyond Grade Level   **SS** = Struggling Students   **SN** = Special Needs

Connecting to Prior Knowledge   **SS** **SN**

Use before presenting Lesson 4-4.

Display the following fractions on the board and ask students what is true about them. They are equal.

$$\frac{1}{2} \qquad \frac{2}{4} \qquad \frac{3}{6}$$

Have students recall how to find equivalent fractions. Build on what they know about identifying or finding equivalent fractions. Have them use these skills to show that simplifying fractions is working the process backward.

Creating a Checklist   **SS** **SN**

Use before assigning the Exercises.

Have students create a checklist of the steps they need to follow to simplify a fraction. Have them include an example next to the steps.

Step 1 Find the greatest common factor of the numerator and the denominator.

Step 2 Divide BOTH the numerator and the denominator by the GCF.

Step 3 Check that the new fraction is in simplest form.

> **Example** Simplify $\frac{12}{15}$.
>
> **Step 1:** The GCF of 12 and 15 is 3.
>
> **Step 2:** $\frac{12 \div 3}{15 \div 3} = \frac{4}{5}$
>
> **Step 3:** 4 and 5 have no common factors greater than 1, so $\frac{4}{5}$ is in simplest form.

Find the Error   **AL**

Use after presenting Lesson 4-4.

Present the following statement to students:

> "When a fraction has a prime number in its numerator or denominator, it cannot be simplified since prime numbers have no other factors."

Ask students to explain whether the statement is correct. Have them use examples to reinforce their reasoning.

Sample answer: It is not correct because a fraction like $\frac{3}{12}$ contains the prime number 3, but it can be simplified as $\frac{1}{4}$.

Leveled Lesson Resources

Chapter 4 Resource Masters

BL = Below or Approaching Grade Level　　**OL** = On Grade Level　　**AL** = Above or Beyond Grade Level　　**ELL** = English Language Learner

---

Lesson Reading Guide
p. 26 **BL** **OL** **ELL**

NAME _____ DATE _____ PERIOD _____

4-4 Lesson Reading Guide
Simplifying Fractions

Get Ready for the Lesson
Complete the Mini Lab at the top of page 192 in your textbook.
Write your answers below.
Show your shading.

1. Write a fraction to describe each figure: number of shaded parts / total number of parts
$\frac{4}{10}, \frac{2}{5}$

2. Based on the figures, what can you conclude about the fractions?
They represent the same number.

Read the Lesson
3. How do you find the simplest form of a fraction? Sample answer:
1) Find the GCF of the numerator and denominator. 2) Divide the numerator and denominator by the GCF.
4. When you find the simplest form of a fraction, how can you check to make sure your answer is correct? Multiply the numerator and denominator of the answer by the GCF of the original numerator and denominator. If you get the original fraction, your answer is correct.
5. Use canceling to simplify the fraction $\frac{2 \times 3 \times 7 \times 11}{3 \times 11 \times 17} = \frac{2 \times 7}{17} = \frac{14}{17}$

Remember What You Learned
6. Use a collection of rectangles like the one in the Mini Lab to show how to write $\frac{15}{25}$ in simplest form.
$\frac{15}{25} = \frac{3}{5}$

Chapter 4　　26　　Course 2

Study Guide and Intervention*
p. 27 **BL** **OL** **ELL**

NAME _____ DATE _____ PERIOD _____

4-4 Study Guide and Intervention
Simplifying Fractions

Fractions that have the same value are called **equivalent fractions**. A fraction is in **simplest form** when the GCF of the numerator and denominator is 1.

Example 1 Write $\frac{36}{54}$ in simplest form.

First, find the GCF of the numerator and denominator.
factors of 36: 1, 2, 3, 4, 6, 9, 12, 18, 36
factors of 54: 1, 2, 3, 6, 9, 18, 27, 54
The GCF of 36 and 54 is 18.
Then, divide the numerator and the denominator by the GCF.
$\frac{36}{54} = \frac{36 \div 18}{54 \div 18} = \frac{2}{3}$　So, $\frac{36}{54}$ written in simplest form is $\frac{2}{3}$.

Example 2 Write $\frac{8}{12}$ in simplest form.

Find the GCF of the numerator and the denominator.
factors of 8 = 2 · 2 · 2
factors of 12 = 2 · 2 · 3
The GCF of 8 and 12 is 2 · 2 or 4.
$\frac{8}{12} = \frac{8 \div 4}{12 \div 4} = \frac{2}{3}$
So, $\frac{8}{12}$ written in simplest form is $\frac{2}{3}$.

Exercises

Write each fraction in simplest form.
1. $\frac{42}{72}$　$\frac{7}{12}$
2. $\frac{40}{64}$　$\frac{5}{8}$
3. $\frac{21}{35}$　$\frac{3}{5}$
4. $\frac{25}{100}$　$\frac{1}{4}$
5. $\frac{99}{132}$　$\frac{3}{4}$
6. $\frac{17}{85}$　$\frac{1}{5}$

Chapter 4　　27　　Course 2

Skills Practice*
p. 28 **BL** **OL**

NAME _____ DATE _____ PERIOD _____

4-4 Skills Practice
Simplifying Fractions

Write each fraction in simplest form.
1. $\frac{49}{70}$　$\frac{7}{10}$
2. $\frac{5}{30}$　$\frac{1}{6}$
3. $\frac{6}{14}$　$\frac{3}{7}$
4. $\frac{14}{28}$　$\frac{1}{2}$
5. $\frac{72}{72}$　1
6. $\frac{18}{21}$　$\frac{6}{7}$
7. $\frac{45}{75}$　$\frac{3}{5}$
8. $\frac{50}{200}$　$\frac{1}{4}$
9. $\frac{32}{50}$　$\frac{16}{25}$
10. $\frac{56}{64}$　$\frac{7}{8}$
11. $\frac{14}{35}$　$\frac{2}{5}$
12. $\frac{39}{45}$　$\frac{13}{15}$
13. $\frac{48}{66}$　$\frac{8}{11}$
14. $\frac{42}{45}$　$\frac{14}{15}$
15. $\frac{78}{130}$　$\frac{3}{5}$

Write two fractions that are equivalent to each fraction.
16-21 Sample answers given.
16. $\frac{3}{4}$　$\frac{6}{8}, \frac{9}{12}$
17. $\frac{7}{9}$　$\frac{14}{18}, \frac{21}{27}$
18. $\frac{7}{11}$　$\frac{14}{22}, \frac{21}{33}$
19. $\frac{14}{17}$　$\frac{28}{34}, \frac{42}{51}$
20. $\frac{21}{23}$　$\frac{42}{46}, \frac{63}{69}$
21. $\frac{11}{17}$　$\frac{22}{34}, \frac{33}{51}$

Chapter 4　　28　　Course 2

Practice*
p. 29 **OL** **AL**

NAME _____ DATE _____ PERIOD _____

4-4 Practice
Simplifying Fractions

Write each fraction in simplest form.
1. $\frac{12}{15}$　$\frac{4}{5}$
2. $\frac{20}{45}$　$\frac{4}{9}$
3. $\frac{8}{24}$　$\frac{1}{3}$
4. $\frac{22}{30}$　$\frac{11}{15}$
5. $\frac{30}{90}$　$\frac{1}{3}$
6. $\frac{29}{29}$　1
7. $\frac{77}{88}$　$\frac{7}{8}$
8. $\frac{32}{48}$　$\frac{2}{3}$
9. $\frac{21}{35}$　$\frac{3}{5}$
10. $\frac{63}{99}$　$\frac{7}{11}$
11. $\frac{18}{36}$　$\frac{1}{2}$
12. $\frac{24}{30}$　$\frac{4}{5}$
13. $\frac{30}{75}$　$\frac{2}{5}$
14. $\frac{12}{60}$　$\frac{1}{5}$
15. $\frac{16}{36}$　$\frac{4}{9}$
16. $\frac{42}{49}$　$\frac{6}{7}$
17. $\frac{55}{100}$　$\frac{11}{20}$
18. $\frac{150}{180}$　$\frac{5}{6}$
19. $\frac{35}{140}$　$\frac{1}{4}$
20. $\frac{90}{135}$　$\frac{2}{3}$

21. STATES Eight states in the United States start with the letter M. What fraction of states, in simplest form, begins with the letter M?
$\frac{4}{25}$

22. MEASUREMENT Fifteen inches is what fraction, in simplest form, of a yard?
$\frac{5}{12}$

23. PERIMETER A rectangle has length 7 centimeters and width 4 centimeters. What fraction of the perimeter, in simplest form, is the width?
$\frac{2}{11}$

24. MONEY Thirty-five cents is what fraction, in simplest form, of a dollar?
$\frac{7}{20}$

25. AGE Angie is 6 years old. Her dad is 30 years old. Angie's age is what fraction, in simplest form, of her dad's age?
$\frac{1}{5}$

Chapter 4　　29　　Course 2

Word Problem Practice*
p. 30 **OL** **AL**

NAME _____ DATE _____ PERIOD _____

4-4 Word Problem Practice
Simplifying Fractions

1. EXAM Mr. Bonilla gave an exam and 20 out of 25 students passed the exam. What fraction of the students passed the exam? Write the answer in simplest form.
$\frac{4}{5}$

2. GASOLINE Aisha filled her car's 24-gallon gas tank. She took a short trip and used 8 gallons of gas. What fraction of the full gas tank was used on the trip? Write the answer in simplest form.
$\frac{1}{3}$

3. BICYCLES A local community college has 860 students. Of these 860 students, 220 ride bicycles. Write the number of bike riders as a fraction of the number of students at the college in simplest form.
$\frac{11}{43}$

4. PRESIDENTS Of the first 22 presidents, 8 were from New York. Write the number of presidents from New York as a fraction of the first 22 presidents in simplest form.
$\frac{4}{11}$

5. TIME Ten hours is what part of a day? Write the fraction in simplest form.
$\frac{5}{12}$

6. MEASUREMENT Eighteen inches is what part of a yard? Write the fraction in simplest form.
$\frac{1}{2}$

Chapter 4　　30　　Course 2

Enrichment
p. 31 **OL** **AL**

NAME _____ DATE _____ PERIOD _____

4-4 Enrichment

Parts of the World
It can be difficult to understand comparisons of different continents and their populations because the numbers are so large. You can make these comparisons easier to understand by writing them as fractions and using rounding to find an estimated ratio.

Continent	Area (km2)	Population (2005 estimate)
Asia	44,529,000	3,879,000,000
Africa	30,065,000	877,500,000
North America	24,256,000	501,500,000
South America	17,819,000	379,500,000
Antarctica	13,209,000	0
Europe	9,938,000	727,000,000
Australia/Oceania	7,687,000	32,000,000
Total	147,503,000	6,396,500,000

Source: World Atlas

For example, the ratio of North America's population to Asia's population is
$\frac{501,500,000}{3,879,000,000}$ or $\frac{5,015}{38,790}$. If you divide both the numerator and the denominator by 1,000, you get $\frac{5,015}{38.79}$, which can be approximated as $\frac{5}{40}$ or about $\frac{1}{8}$.

1. Approximately what fraction of the world's land area is found in South America?
$\frac{17,819,000}{147,503,000}$　$\frac{3}{25}$

2. Approximately what fraction of the world's population is found in South America?
$\frac{379,500,000}{6,396,500,000}$　$\frac{1}{160}$

3. Approximately what fraction of Asia's land area does the North America fill? What percentage is this?
$\frac{24,256,000}{44,529,000}$　$\frac{8}{15}$, 53%

4. Which continent is more crowded, Asia or North America? Explain. Hint: Use the example at the top of the page and your answer to Exercise 3.
Asia is more crowded because while it has about twice as much land area, it has about eight times as many people living there.

5. Which continent has the largest population per square kilometer? Explain.
Asia; if you find the fraction of $\frac{population}{area}$ for each continent, Asia has the most with 87 people per km².

Chapter 4　　31　　Course 2

Additional Lesson Resources

Also available in Spanish **ELL**

Transparencies
- *5-Minute Check Transparency*, Lesson 4-4

Other Print Products
- *Noteables™ Interactive Study Notebook with Foldables™*

Teacher Tech Tools
- *Interactive Classroom CD-ROM*, Lesson 4-4
- *AssignmentWorks*, Lesson 4-4

Student Tech Tools
glencoe.com
- Extra Examples, Chapter 4, Lesson 4
- Self-Check Quiz, Chapter 4, Lesson 4

1 Focus

Vertical Alignment

Before Lesson 4-4
Determine the prime factors of all numbers through 50 and write the numbers as the product of their prime factors by using exponents to show multiples of a factor

Lesson 4-4
Determine the greatest common divisor of whole numbers; use them to solve problems with fractions or to find the reduced form for a fraction

After Lesson 4-4
Know that every rational number is either a terminating or repeating decimal and be able to convert terminating decimals into reduced fractions

2 Teach

▶ MINI Lab

Make sure students see that the two figures—and their shaded regions—are congruent. The difference is that each figure has been separated into a different number of parts.

Scaffolding Questions

As you ask the following questions, write each pair of numbers on the chalkboard.

Ask:
• What is the greatest common factor of 4 and 6? 2
• What is the greatest common factor of 5 and 10? 5
• What is the greatest common factor of 8 and 9? 1

4-4 Simplifying Fractions

▶ MINI Lab

On grid paper, draw the two figures shown. Shade 4 out of the 10 squares in one figure. Shade 2 out of the 5 rectangles in the other.

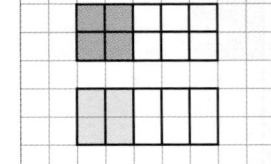

1. Write a fraction to describe each figure:

$$\frac{\text{number of shaded parts}}{\text{total number of parts}} \quad \frac{4}{10}, \frac{2}{5}$$

2. Based on the figures, what can you conclude about the fractions? **They represent the same number.**

Equivalent fractions have the same value. A fraction is in **simplest form** when the GCF of the numerator and denominator is 1.

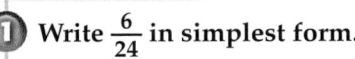 **Write a Fraction in Simplest Form**

① Write $\frac{6}{24}$ in simplest form.

METHOD 1 Divide by common factors.

$$\frac{6}{24} = \frac{6 \div 2}{24 \div 2} = \frac{3}{12}$$
2 is a common factor of 6 and 24, so divide by 2.

$$\frac{3}{12} = \frac{3 \div 3}{12 \div 3} = \frac{1}{4}$$
3 is a common factor of 3 and 12, so divide by 3.

The fraction $\frac{1}{4}$ is in simplest form since 1 and 4 have no common factors greater than 1.

METHOD 2 Divide by the GCF.

First, find the GCF of the numerator and denominator.

factors of 6: 1, 2, 3, **6**

factors of 24: 1, 2, 3, 4, **6**, 8, 12, 24

The GCF of 6 and 24 is 6.

Then, divide the numerator and denominator by the GCF, 6.

$$\frac{6}{24} = \frac{6 \div 6}{24 \div 6} = \frac{1}{4}$$
Divide the numerator and denominator by the GCF, 6.

So, $\frac{6}{24}$ written in simplest form is $\frac{1}{4}$.

② Write $\frac{36}{45}$ in simplest form.

First, find the GCF of the numerator and denominator.

factors of 36: 1, 2, 3, 4, 6, **9**, 12, 18, 36   The GCF of
factors of 45: 1, 3, 5, **9**, 15, 45   36 and 45 is 9.

Then, divide the numerator and denominator by the GCF, 9.

$$\frac{36}{45} = \frac{36 \div 9}{45 \div 9} = \frac{4}{5}$$ Divide the numerator and denominator by the GCF, 9.

So, $\frac{36}{45}$ written in simplest form is $\frac{4}{5}$.

✓ CHOOSE Your Method

Write each fraction in simplest form.

a. $\frac{7}{28}$ **$\frac{1}{4}$**   b. $\frac{8}{20}$ **$\frac{2}{5}$**   c. $\frac{27}{36}$ **$\frac{3}{4}$**

Real-World EXAMPLE

③ **SCIENCE** Lauren measured a grasshopper for her science project. Each line on her ruler represents $\frac{1}{16}$ inch. Find the length of the grasshopper in simplest form.

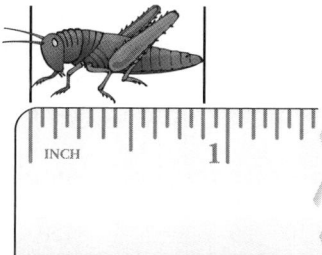

$$\frac{14}{16} = \frac{\overset{1}{\cancel{2}} \cdot 7}{\underset{1}{\cancel{2}} \cdot 2 \cdot 2 \cdot 2}$$

> The slashes mean that part of the numerator and part of the denominator are both divided by the same number. For example, 2 ÷ 2 = 1.

$$= \frac{7}{8}$$

So, $\frac{14}{16}$ written in simplest form is $\frac{7}{8}$.

✓ CHECK Your Progress

d. **CARPENTRY** A carpenter measured a shelf and found it to be $\frac{10}{16}$ inch thick. Find the simplified fraction. $\frac{5}{8}$

e. **CARPENTRY** A carpenter measured a board to be $\frac{8}{16}$ inch thick. Find the simplified fraction. $\frac{1}{2}$

Study Tip

More Than One Way
To write in simplest form, you can also divide by common factors.

$$\frac{36}{45} = \frac{36 \div 3}{45 \div 3} = \frac{12}{15}$$
$$\downarrow$$
$$\frac{12}{15} = \frac{12 \div 3}{15 \div 3} = \frac{4}{5}$$

So, $\frac{36}{45} = \frac{4}{5}$.

Real-World Career····
How Does a Carpenter Use Math?
Carpenters use fractions when they measure and cut boards.

Math Online
For more information visit: glencoe.com

✓ Formative Assessment

Use the Check Your Progress exercises after each Example to determine students' understanding of concepts.

ADDITIONAL EXAMPLES

❶ Write $\frac{12}{45}$ in simplest form. $\frac{4}{15}$

❷ Write $\frac{40}{64}$ in simplest form. $\frac{5}{8}$

❸ **MUSIC** Two notes form a *perfect fifth* if the simplified fraction of the frequencies of the notes equals $\frac{3}{4}$. If note D = 294 Hertz and note G = 392 Hertz, do they form a *perfect fifth?* yes

Additional Examples are also in:
- Noteables™ Interactive Study Notebook with Foldables™
- Interactive Classroom PowerPoint® Presentations

Focus on Mathematical Content

One way to write a fraction in simplest form is to **divide the numerator and denominator by common factors.**

Another way to write a fraction in simplest form is to **divide the numerator and denominator by the GCF.**

3 Practice

Tips for New Teachers

Greatest Common Factor

You may wish to point out to students that the two methods of writing a fraction in simplest form are essentially the same. Dividing the numerator and denominator by common factors may take several steps, but the product of the common factors is the GCF. Have students use both methods to write the fraction $\frac{24}{30}$ in simplest form. What is the GCF? 6 What is the product of the common factors? $2 \times 3 = 6$

✔ Formative Assessment

Use Exercises 1–5 to check for understanding.

Then use the chart at the bottom of this page to customize your assignments for students.

Intervention You may wish to use the Study Guide and Intervention Master on page 27 of the *Chapter 4 Resource Masters* for additional reinforcement.

Odd/Even Assignments

Exercises 6–19 are structured so that students practice the same concepts whether they are assigned odd or even problems.

★ indicates multi-step problem

✔ CHECK Your Understanding

Examples 1, 2
(pp. 192–193)

Write each fraction in simplest form.

1. $\frac{3}{9}$ $\frac{1}{3}$ 2. $\frac{4}{18}$ $\frac{2}{9}$ 3. $\frac{10}{25}$ $\frac{2}{5}$ 4. $\frac{36}{40}$ $\frac{9}{10}$

Example 3
(p. 193)

5. **ALLOWANCE** Mary received $15 for her weekly allowance. She spent $10 at the movie theater with her friends. What fraction of the money, in simplest form, was spent at the theater? $\frac{2}{3}$

▶ Practice and Problem Solving

HOMEWORK HELP

For Exercises	See Examples
6–17	1,2
18–19	3

Exercise Levels
A: 6–19
B: 20–29
C: 30–33

Write each fraction in simplest form.

6. $\frac{9}{12}$ $\frac{3}{4}$ 7. $\frac{25}{35}$ $\frac{5}{7}$ 8. $\frac{16}{32}$ $\frac{1}{2}$ 9. $\frac{14}{20}$ $\frac{7}{10}$

10. $\frac{10}{20}$ $\frac{1}{2}$ 11. $\frac{12}{21}$ $\frac{4}{7}$ 12. $\frac{15}{25}$ $\frac{3}{5}$ 13. $\frac{24}{28}$ $\frac{6}{7}$

14. $\frac{48}{64}$ $\frac{3}{4}$ 15. $\frac{32}{32}$ 1   16. $\frac{20}{80}$ $\frac{1}{4}$ 17. $\frac{45}{54}$ $\frac{5}{6}$

18. **PRESIDENTS** Of the 43 U.S. presidents, 15 were elected to serve two terms. What fraction of the U.S. presidents, in simplest form, was elected to serve two terms? $\frac{15}{43}$

19. **TV SHOWS** A television station has 28 new TV shows scheduled to air this week. What fraction of the television shows, in simplest form, are 30-minute programs? $\frac{5}{7}$

WYTB Programming	
30-minute	60-minute
20	8

Write each fraction in simplest form.

20. $\frac{45}{100}$ $\frac{9}{20}$ 21. $\frac{60}{150}$ $\frac{2}{5}$ 22. $\frac{16}{120}$ $\frac{2}{15}$ 23. $\frac{35}{175}$ $\frac{1}{5}$

24. **TIME** Fifteen minutes is what part of one hour? $\frac{1}{4}$

25. **MEASUREMENT** Nine inches is what part of one foot? $\frac{3}{4}$

26. **CALENDAR** Four days is what part of the month of April? $\frac{2}{15}$

27. **SLEEP** Marcel spends 8 hours each day sleeping. What fraction of a week, written in simplest form, does Marcel spend sleeping? $\frac{1}{3}$

28. **MONEY** Each week, Lorenzo receives a $10 allowance. What fraction of his yearly allowance, in simplest form, does he receive each week? $\frac{10}{520}$ or $\frac{1}{52}$

29. **FIND THE DATA** Refer to the Data File on pages 16–19 of your book. Choose some data and write a real-world problem in which you would simplify fractions. **See students' work.**

EXTRA PRACTICE
See pages 677, 707.

30. **OPEN ENDED** Select a fraction in simplest form. Then, write two fractions that are equivalent to it. $\frac{1}{4}, \frac{2}{8}, \frac{4}{16}$

DIFFERENTIATED HOMEWORK OPTIONS

Level	Assignment	Two-Day Option	
BL Basic	6–19, 32–44	7–19 odd, 34, 35	6–18 even, 32, 33, 36–44
OL Core	7–17 odd, 18, 19–23 odd, 24–30, 32–44	6–19, 34, 35	20–30, 32, 33, 36–44
AL Advanced/Pre-AP	20–40, (optional: 41–44)		

31. No, because both the numerator and denominator can be divided by 2.
32. Nhu; Booker did not divide the numerator and denominator by the GCF.

31. **CHALLENGE** Both the numerator and denominator of a fraction are even. Is the fraction in simplest form? Explain your reasoning.

32. **FIND THE ERROR** Nhu and Booker both wrote $\frac{16}{36}$ in simplest form. Who is correct? Explain.

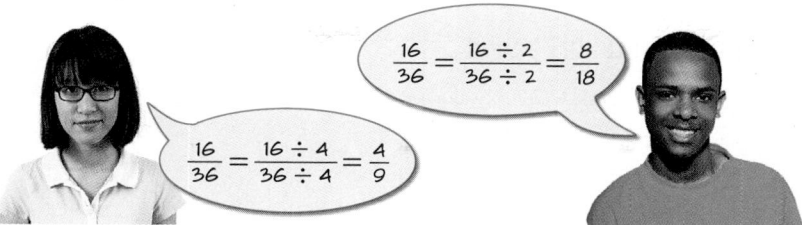

Booker: $\frac{16}{36} = \frac{16 \div 2}{36 \div 2} = \frac{8}{18}$

Nhu: $\frac{16}{36} = \frac{16 \div 4}{36 \div 4} = \frac{4}{9}$

Nhu   Booker

33. **WRITING IN MATH** Explain how to determine whether a fraction is in simplest form. **Sample answer: A fraction is in simplest form if the GCF of the numerator and denominator is 1.**

TEST PRACTICE

34. It takes Benito 12 minutes to walk to school. What fraction represents the part of an hour it takes Benito to walk to school? **D**

   A $\frac{12}{1}$ C $\frac{5}{30}$

   B $\frac{4}{15}$ D $\frac{1}{5}$

35. What fraction of a foot is 2 inches? **F**

   F $\frac{1}{6}$ H $\frac{1}{3}$

   G $\frac{1}{4}$ J $\frac{1}{2}$

Spiral Review

36. **SANDWICHES** A deli offers sandwiches with ham, turkey, or roast beef with American, provolone, Swiss, or mozzarella cheese. How many different types of sandwiches can be made if you choose one meat and one cheese? Use the *make an organized list* strategy. (Lesson 4-3) **12**

Find the GCF of each set of numbers. (Lesson 4-2)

37. 27, 36 **9**   38. 16, 28 **4**   39. 20, 50, 65 **5**

★ 40. **ANALYZE GRAPHS** Refer to the graph. At these rates, about how much longer would it take a blue shark to swim 280 miles than it would a sailfish? Use the formula $d = rt$. Justify your answer. (Lesson 3-3) **3 h; See margin for justification.**

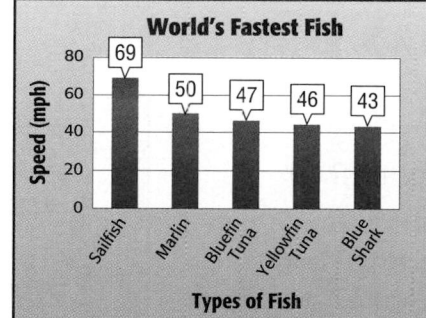

World's Fastest Fish

Source: *Top Ten of Everything*

GET READY for the Next Lesson

PREREQUISITE SKILL Divide. (Page 676)

41. $2\overline{)1.0}$ **0.5**   42. $4\overline{)1.00}$ **0.25**

43. $10\overline{)7.0}$ **0.7**   44. $8\overline{)3.000}$ **0.375**

Find the Error In Exercise 32, Nhu is correct. Booker correctly divided the numerator and denominator by a common factor, 2, but then failed to see that he could divide them again by another common factor, 2. Remind students to check whether the GCF of the numerator and denominator of a fraction is 1. If it isn't, then the fraction is not in simplest form.

4 Assess

Ticket Out the Door Write a fraction such as $\frac{125}{1,000}$ or $\frac{250}{1,000}$ on the chalkboard. Have students write the fraction in simplest form on a piece of paper.

FOLDABLES Study Organizer **Foldables™ Follow-Up**

Remind students to write—under the tab for this lesson of their Foldables—the answer to the question they wrote about the lesson.

Additional Answer

40. Sample answer: A blue shark swims at about 40 mph while a sailfish swims at about 70 mph. To swim 280 miles, a blue shark would take about $280 \div 40$ or 7 hours while a sailfish would take about $280 \div 70$ or 4 hours.

Fractions and Decimals

PACING: **Regular:** 1 period, **Block:** 0.5 period

Options for Differentiated Instruction

 = English Language Learner 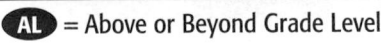 = Above or Beyond Grade Level **SS** = Struggling Students **SN** = Special Needs

Creating a Resource Sheet **SS** **SN**

Use before presenting the Examples.

Many students would benefit from creating a resource sheet listing some commonly used fraction-decimal equivalencies. Some examples are here.

$\frac{1}{2} = 0.5$	$\frac{1}{3} = 0.\overline{3}$	$\frac{2}{3} = 0.\overline{6}$	$\frac{1}{4} = 0.25$
$\frac{3}{4} = 0.75$	$\frac{1}{5} = 0.2$	$\frac{1}{8} = 0.125$	$\frac{1}{10} = 0.1$

Alternate Examples **SS** **SN**

Use with Example 3.

It may be helpful to use a common fraction such as $\frac{3}{4}$ when showing students how to write a fraction as a decimal by long division. Using a fraction whose decimal equivalent they already know will allow students to feel confident with the long division steps and to make connections about where the numbers are coming from.

Also, prevent students from dividing $4 \div 3$ when writing $\frac{3}{4}$ as a decimal. This is a common mistake and students need to think about the fact that $\frac{3}{4}$ is less than 1. Therefore, the decimal should not have a digit in the ones place.

Use Reasoning **AL**

Use after students complete Lesson 4-5.

Have students examine the pattern at the right.

Ask:

- What should $\frac{9}{9}$ equal according to the pattern? $0.\overline{9}$
- Any number divided by itself equals 1. How can you explain the contradiction? Sample answer: Since the digits of $0.\overline{9}$ repeat forever, the difference between $0.\overline{9}$ and 1 is negligible.

$\frac{1}{9} = 0.\overline{1}$	$\frac{5}{9} = 0.\overline{5}$
$\frac{2}{9} = 0.\overline{2}$	$\frac{6}{9} = 0.\overline{6}$
$\frac{3}{9} = 0.\overline{3}$	$\frac{7}{9} = 0.\overline{7}$
$\frac{4}{9} = 0.\overline{4}$	$\frac{8}{9} = 0.\overline{8}$

Leveled Lesson Resources

Chapter 4 Resource Masters

BL = Below or Approaching Grade Level   **OL** = On Grade Level   **AL** = Above or Beyond Grade Level   **ELL** = English Language Learner

Lesson Reading Guide
p. 32 **BL OL ELL**

4-5 Lesson Reading Guide
Fractions and Decimals

Get Ready for the Lesson
Read the introduction at the top of page 196 in your textbook. Write your answers below.

1. What fraction of the speeds are between 130 and 145 miles per hour?
$\frac{4}{10}$

2. Express this fraction using words and then as a decimal.
four tenths; 0.4

3. What fraction of the speeds are between 145 and 160 miles per hour? Express this fraction using words and then as a decimal.
$\frac{4}{10}$; **four tenths; 0.4**

Read the Lesson

4. What is meant by the term *place value*?
Sample answer: the value of the place of a digit in a numeral

5. In place value, what serves as the divider between ones and tenths?
the decimal point

6. What is the difference between a terminating decimal and a repeating decimal? Give an example of each. **Sample answer: A terminating decimal has an ending, and a repeating decimal does not; 6.25 is a terminating decimal, and 0.7777... is a repeating decimal.**

Remember What You Learned

7. Work with a partner. Use a local newspaper, a favorite magazine, or the Internet. Find real-world situations that use fractions or decimals. Convert the fractions to decimals and the decimals to fractions. Exchange papers with your partner and correct each other's work. **See students' work.**

Chapter 4   32   Course 2

Study Guide and Intervention*
p. 33 **BL OL ELL**

4-5 Study Guide and Intervention
Fractions and Decimals

To write a decimal as a fraction, divide the numerator of the fraction by the denominator. Use a power of ten to change a decimal to a fraction.

Example 1 Write $\frac{5}{9}$ as a decimal.

Method 1 Use pencil and paper.
0.555...
$9\overline{)5.000}$
The remainder after each step is 5.

Method 2 Use a calculator.
5 ÷ 9 = 0.55555556
You can use bar notation $0.\overline{5}$ to indicate that 5 repeats forever. So, $\frac{5}{9} = 0.\overline{5}$.

Example 2 Write 0.32 as a fraction in simplest form.
$0.32 = \frac{32}{100}$ The 2 is in the hundredths place.
$= \frac{8}{25}$ Simplify.

Exercises

Write each fraction or mixed number as a decimal. Use bar notation if the decimal is a repeating decimal.

1. $\frac{8}{10}$ **0.8**   2. $\frac{3}{5}$ **0.6**   3. $\frac{7}{11}$ **0.$\overline{63}$**

4. $4\frac{7}{8}$ **4.875**   5. $\frac{13}{15}$ **0.8$\overline{6}$**   6. $3\frac{47}{99}$ **3.$\overline{47}$**

Write each decimal as a fraction in simplest form.

7. 0.14 $\frac{7}{50}$ 8. 0.3 $\frac{3}{10}$ 9. 0.94 $\frac{47}{50}$

Chapter 4   33   Course 2

Skills Practice*
p. 34 **BL OL**

4-5 Skills Practice
Fractions and Decimals

Write each repeating decimal using bar notation.
1. 0.7353535... **0.7$\overline{35}$**   2. 0.424242... **0.$\overline{42}$**   3. 5.126126126... **5.$\overline{126}$**

Write each fraction or mixed number as a decimal. Use bar notation if the decimal is a repeating decimal.

4. $\frac{3}{5}$ **0.6**   5. $\frac{19}{20}$ **0.95**   6. $3\frac{4}{5}$ **3.8**

7. $\frac{23}{50}$ **0.46**   8. $1\frac{5}{8}$ **1.625**   9. $\frac{19}{25}$ **0.76**

10. $4\frac{17}{37}$ **4.$\overline{459}$**   11. $5\frac{3}{11}$ **5.$\overline{27}$**   12. $\frac{17}{24}$ **0.708$\overline{3}$**

13. $6\frac{7}{32}$ **6.21875**   14. $7\frac{9}{22}$ **7.40$\overline{9}$**   15. $1\frac{17}{48}$ **1.3541$\overline{6}$**

Write each decimal as a fraction in simplest form.

16. 0.8 $\frac{4}{5}$ 17. 0.52 $\frac{13}{25}$ 18. 0.92 $\frac{23}{25}$

19. 0.48 $\frac{12}{25}$ 20. 0.86 $\frac{43}{50}$ 21. 0.76 $\frac{19}{25}$

Chapter 4   34   Course 2

Practice*
p. 35 **OL AL**

4-5 Practice
Fractions and Decimals

Write each fraction or mixed number as a decimal. Use bar notation if the decimal is a repeating decimal.

1. $\frac{5}{8}$ **0.625**   2. $\frac{2}{9}$ **0.$\overline{2}$**   3. $\frac{37}{16}$ **2.3125**

4. $\frac{3}{4}$ **0.75**   5. $\frac{27}{50}$ **0.54**   6. $\frac{121}{25}$ **4.84**

7. $\frac{5}{6}$ **0.8$\overline{3}$**   8. $\frac{1}{33}$ **0.$\overline{03}$**   9. $\frac{62}{11}$ **5.$\overline{63}$**

10. $\frac{2}{3}$ **0.$\overline{6}$**   11. $\frac{11}{40}$ **0.275**   12. $\frac{13}{20}$ **0.65**

13. $\frac{83}{5}$ **16.6**   14. $\frac{3}{10}$ **0.3**   15. $\frac{1}{9}$ **0.$\overline{1}$**

16. $\frac{3}{7}$ **0.$\overline{428571}$**   17. $\frac{111}{24}$ **4.625**   18. $\frac{7}{32}$ **0.21875**

Write each decimal as a fraction or mixed number in simplest form.

19. 0.4 $\frac{2}{5}$ 20. 0.83 $\frac{83}{100}$ 21. 3.75 $3\frac{3}{4}$

22. 2.42 $2\frac{21}{50}$ 23. 0.16 $\frac{4}{25}$ 24. 0.65 $\frac{13}{20}$

25. **KILOMETERS** One kilometer is approximately 0.62 mile. What fraction represents this length?
$\frac{31}{50}$

26. **MARATHON** Jake completed a marathon race in 3 hours and 12 minutes. Write Jake's running time as a decimal.
3.2

Chapter 4   35   Course 2

Word Problem Practice*
p. 36 **OL AL**

4-5 Word Problem Practice
Fractions and Decimals

1. **BOYS AND GIRLS** There were 6 girls and 18 boys in Mrs. Johnson's math class. Write the number of girls as a fraction of the number of boys. Then write the fraction as a repeating decimal.
$\frac{6}{18}$; $0.\overline{3}$

2. **CATS** In a neighborhood of 72 families, 18 families own one or more cats. Write the number of families who own one or more cats as a fraction. Then write the fraction as a decimal.
$\frac{18}{72}$; 0.25

3. **CELLULAR PHONES** In Italy, about 74 of every 100 people use cellular telephones. Write the fraction of cellular phone users in Italy. Then write the fraction as a decimal.
$\frac{74}{100}$; 0.74

4. **FRUITS** Ms. Rockwell surveyed her class and found that 12 of the 30 students chose peaches as their favorite fruit. Write the number of students who chose peaches as a fraction in simplest form. Then write the fraction as a decimal.
$\frac{2}{5}$; 0.4

5. **TRAVEL** Tora took a short trip of 320 miles. He stopped to have lunch after he had driven 120 miles. Write the fraction of the trip he had completed by lunch in simplest form. Then write the fraction as a decimal.
$\frac{3}{8}$; 0.375

6. **VOTING** In a recent school election, 208 of the 325 freshmen voted in their class election. Write the fraction of freshmen who voted. Then write the fraction as a decimal.
$\frac{208}{325}$; 0.64

Chapter 4   36   Course 2

Enrichment
p. 37 **OL AL**

4-5 Enrichment

Writing Repeating Decimals as Fractions

All fractions can be written as decimals that either terminate or repeat. You have learned how to use a power of 10 to write a terminating decimal as a fraction. Below, you will study a strategy to write a repeating decimal as a fraction.

For Exercises 1–4, write each fraction as a decimal. Use bar notation if the decimal is a repeating decimal.

1. $\frac{1}{9}$ **0.$\overline{1}$**   2. $\frac{2}{9}$ **0.$\overline{2}$**

3. $\frac{3}{9}$ **0.$\overline{3}$**   4. $\frac{5}{9}$ **0.$\overline{5}$**

5. Describe the relationship between the numerator of each fraction and its decimal equivalent.
The numerator is the same as the repeating part of the decimal.

For Exercises 6–9, write each fraction as a decimal. Use bar notation if the decimal is a repeating decimal.

6. $\frac{7}{99}$ **0.$\overline{07}$**   7. $\frac{24}{99}$ **0.$\overline{24}$**

8. $\frac{37}{99}$ **0.$\overline{37}$**   9. $\frac{82}{99}$ **0.$\overline{82}$**

10. Describe the relationship between the numerator of each fraction and its decimal equivalent.
The repeating part of the decimal is the same as the numerator, with a zero added if the numerator is a single digit.

11. Use the relationship from Exercise 10 to write the decimal $0.\overline{52}$ as a fraction. Check your work using long division.
$\frac{52}{99}$

12. Using your observations from Exercises 5 and 11, make a prediction about the decimal equivalent of $\frac{127}{999}$. Check to see if your prediction was correct by using long division.
0.$\overline{127}$

13. How are the decimal equivalents of $\frac{4}{9}$, $\frac{4}{99}$, and $\frac{4}{999}$ different? Explain.
They differ in the number of digits that repeat. Extra zeros are added in front of the four depending on how many digits repeat.

For Exercises 14–19, write each decimal as a fraction. Check your answers with a calculator.

14. 0.47474747... $\frac{47}{99}$ 15. 0.$\overline{22}$ $\frac{22}{99} = \frac{2}{9}$ 16. 0.$\overline{530}$ $\frac{530}{999}$

17. 0.010010010... $\frac{10}{999}$ 18. 0.$\overline{3266}$ $\frac{3266}{9999}$ 19. 0.$\overline{00328}$ $\frac{328}{99999}$

Chapter 4   37   Course 2

Additional Lesson Resources

Transparencies
- *5-Minute Check Transparency*, Lesson 4-5

Other Print Products
- *Noteables™ Interactive Study Notebook with Foldables™*

Teacher Tech Tools
- *Interactive Classroom CD-ROM*, Lesson 4-5
- *AssignmentWorks*, Lesson 4-5

Student Tech Tools
glencoe.com
- Extra Examples, Chapter 4, Lesson 5
- Self-Check Quiz, Chapter 4, Lesson 5

4-5 Fractions and Decimals

1 Focus

Vertical Alignment

Before Lesson 4-5
Identify and represent on a number line decimals, fractions, mixed numbers, and positive and negative numbers

Lesson 4-5
Compare and order positive and negative fractions, decimals, and mixed numbers and place them on a number line

After Lesson 4-5
Convert fractions to decimals and percents and use these representations in estimations, computations, and applications

2 Teach

Scaffolding Questions

As you ask the following questions, write each money amount on the board.

Ask:

- What fraction of a dollar is ten cents? (Write: $0.10) $\frac{1}{10}$

- What fraction of a dollar is twenty-five cents? (Write: $0.25) $\frac{1}{4}$

- What fraction of a dollar is fifty cents? (Write: $0.50) $\frac{1}{2}$

- What fraction of a dollar is seventy-five cents? (Write: $0.75) $\frac{3}{4}$

- If you are given an amount of money in cents, how can you find the fraction of a dollar it represents in simplest form? Write the amount as the numerator of a fraction with a denominator of 100, and then write the fraction in simplest form.

MAIN IDEA

Write fractions as terminating or repeating decimals and write decimals as fractions.

New Vocabulary

terminating decimals
repeating decimals
bar notation

Math Online

glencoe.com

- Extra Examples
- Personal Tutor
- Self-Check Quiz

▷ GET READY for the Lesson

NASCAR The table shows the winning speeds for a 10-year-period at the Daytona 500.

1. What fraction of the speeds are between 130 and 145 miles per hour? $\frac{4}{10}$

2. Express this fraction using words and then as a decimal. **four tenths; 0.4**

3. What fraction of the speeds are between 145 and 165 miles per hour? Express this fraction using words and then as a decimal.

Daytona 500		
Year	Winner	Speed (mph)
1998	D. Earnhardt	172.712
1999	J. Gordon	148.295
2000	D. Jarrett	155.669
2001	M. Waltrip	161.783
2002	W. Burton	142.971
2003	M. Waltrip	133.870
2004	D. Earnhardt Jr.	156.345
2005	J. Gordon	135.173
2006	J. Johnson	142.667
2007	K. Harvick	149.335

Source: ESPN Sports Almanac

3. $\frac{5}{10}$; five tenths; 0.5

Our decimal system is based on powers of 10. So, if the denominator of a fraction is a power of 10, you can use place value to write the fraction as a decimal. For example, to write $\frac{7}{10}$ as a decimal, place a 7 in the tenths place.

Words	Fraction	Decimal
seven tenths	$\frac{7}{10}$	0.7

If the denominator of a fraction is a *factor* of 10, 100, 1,000, or any higher power of ten, you can use mental math and place value.

EXAMPLES Use Mental Math

Write each fraction or mixed number as a decimal.

1 $\frac{7}{20}$

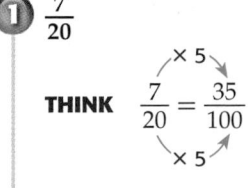

THINK

So, $\frac{7}{20} = 0.35$.

2 $5\frac{3}{4}$

$5\frac{3}{4} = 5 + \frac{3}{4}$ Think of it as a sum.

$= 5 + 0.75$ You know that $\frac{3}{4} = 0.75$.

$= 5.75$ Add mentally.

So, $5\frac{3}{4} = 5.75$.

✓ CHECK Your Progress

a. $\frac{3}{10}$ **0.3**   b. $\frac{3}{25}$ **0.12**   c. $6\frac{1}{2}$ **6.5**

196 Chapter 4 Fractions, Decimals, and Percents

Study Tip

Mental Math It will be helpful to memorize the following fraction-decimal equivalencies.

$\frac{1}{2} = 0.5$

$\frac{1}{3} = 0.\overline{3}$ $\frac{2}{3} = 0.\overline{6}$

$\frac{1}{4} = 0.25$ $\frac{3}{4} = 0.75$

$\frac{1}{5} = 0.2$ $\frac{1}{10} = 0.1$

$\frac{1}{8} = 0.125$

Any fraction can be written as a decimal by dividing its numerator by its denominator. Division ends when the remainder is zero.

EXAMPLES Use Division

3 Write $\frac{3}{8}$ as a decimal.

$$
\begin{array}{r}
0.375 \\
8\overline{)3.000} \\
-24 \\
\hline
60 \\
-56 \\
\hline
40 \\
-40 \\
\hline
0
\end{array}
$$

Divide 3 by 8.

Division ends when the remainder is 0.

So, $\frac{3}{8} = 0.375$.

4 Write $\frac{1}{40}$ as a decimal.

$$
\begin{array}{r}
0.025 \\
40\overline{)1.000} \\
-80 \\
\hline
200 \\
-200 \\
\hline
0
\end{array}
$$

Divide 1 by 40.

So, $\frac{1}{40} = 0.025$.

✓ CHECK Your Progress

Write each fraction or mixed number as a decimal.

d. $\frac{7}{8}$ **0.875**   e. $2\frac{1}{8}$ **2.125**   f. $7\frac{9}{20}$ **7.45**

Vocabulary Link · · · ·
Terminate

Everyday Use coming to an end, as in terminate a game

Math Use a decimal whose digits end

In Examples 1–4, the decimals 0.35, 5.75, 0.375, and 0.025 are called terminating decimals. A **terminating decimal** is a decimal whose digits end.

Repeating decimals have a pattern in their digits that repeats forever. Consider $\frac{1}{3}$.

$$
\begin{array}{r}
0.333\ldots \\
3\overline{)1.000} \\
-9 \\
\hline
10 \\
-9 \\
\hline
10 \\
-9 \\
\hline
1
\end{array}
$$

The number 3 repeats. The repetition of 3 is represented by three dots.

You can use **bar notation** to indicate that a number pattern repeats indefinitely. A bar is written only over the digits that repeat.

$0.33333\ldots = 0.\overline{3}$ $0.121212\ldots = 0.\overline{12}$ $11.3858585\ldots = 11.3\overline{85}$

Lesson 4-5 Fractions and Decimals **197**

Focus on Mathematical Content

When the denominator of a fraction is a factor or a multiple of 10, the fraction can be written as a decimal by using **mental math** and **place value**.

Formative Assessment

Use the Check Your Progress exercises after the Examples to determine students' understanding of concepts.

ADDITIONAL EXAMPLES

Write each fraction or mixed number as a decimal.

1 $\frac{9}{10}$ 0.9

2 $7\frac{3}{5}$ 7.6

3 $\frac{1}{8}$ 0.125

4 $\frac{1}{25}$ 0.04

Additional Examples are also in:

• Noteables™ Interactive Study Notebook with Foldables™

• Interactive Classroom PowerPoint® Presentations

Tips for New Teachers

Mental Math

Encourage students to use mental math whenever possible when writing fractions as decimals. Have them first ask themselves whether the denominator of a fraction is a factor of 10 (or of 100 or 1,000). If it is, what number can they multiply the denominator by to get a power of ten? Once they multiply the numerator and denominator by that number, they will have an equivalent fraction that can be written as a decimal by using place value.

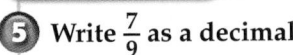

EXAMPLE Write Fractions as Repeating Decimals

5 Write $\frac{7}{9}$ as a decimal.

$$
\begin{array}{r}
0.777\ldots \\
9\overline{)7.000} \\
\underline{-63} \\
70 \\
\underline{-63} \\
70 \\
\underline{-63} \\
7
\end{array}
$$

Divide 7 by 9.

Notice that the remainder will never be zero. That is, the division never ends.

So, $\frac{7}{9} = 0.777\ldots$ or $0.\overline{7}$.

✓ CHECK Your Progress

Write each fraction or mixed number as a decimal. Use bar notation if the decimal is a repeating decimal.

g. $\frac{2}{3}$ $0.\overline{6}$ h. $\frac{3}{11}$ $0.\overline{27}$ i. $8\frac{1}{3}$ $8.\overline{3}$

Every terminating decimal can be written as a fraction with a denominator of 10, 100, 1,000, or a higher power of ten. Place the digits that come after the decimal point in the numerator. Use the place value of the final digit as the denominator.

numerator

$$0.25 = \frac{25}{100}$$

hundredths place

Real-World Link . . . .
The recommended water temperature for goldfish is 65–72°F.
Source: Animal-World

Real-World EXAMPLE Use a Power of 10

6 **FISH** Use the table to find what fraction of the fish in an aquarium are goldfish. Write in simplest form.

$0.15 = \frac{15}{100}$ The final digit, 5, is in the hundredths place.

$= \frac{3}{20}$ Simplify.

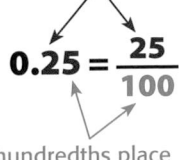

Fish	Amount
Guppy	0.25
Angel Fish	0.4
Goldfish	0.15
Molly	0.2

✓ CHECK Your Progress

Determine the fraction of the aquarium made up by each fish. Write the answer in simplest form.

j. molly $\frac{1}{5}$ k. guppy $\frac{1}{4}$ l. angel fish $\frac{2}{5}$

★ indicates multi-step problem

CHECK Your Understanding

Examples 1–5
(pp. 196–198)

Write each fraction or mixed number as a decimal. Use bar notation if the decimal is a repeating decimal.

1. $\frac{2}{5}$ **0.4**
2. $\frac{9}{10}$ **0.9**
3. $7\frac{1}{2}$ **7.5**
4. $4\frac{3}{20}$ **4.15**

5. $\frac{1}{8}$ **0.125**
6. $3\frac{5}{8}$ **3.625**
7. $\frac{5}{9}$ **0.$\overline{5}$**
8. $1\frac{5}{6}$ **1.8$\overline{3}$**

Example 6
(p. 198)

Write each decimal as a fraction or mixed number in simplest form.

9. 0.22 $\frac{11}{50}$
10. 0.1 $\frac{1}{10}$
11. 4.6 $4\frac{3}{5}$

12. **HOCKEY** During a hockey game, an ice resurfacer travels 0.75 mile during each ice resurfacing. What fraction represents this distance? $\frac{3}{4}$ mi

Practice and Problem Solving

Write each fraction or mixed number as a decimal. Use bar notation if the decimal is a repeating decimal.

13. $\frac{4}{5}$ **0.8**
14. $\frac{1}{2}$ **0.5**
15. $4\frac{4}{25}$ **4.16**
16. $7\frac{1}{20}$ **7.05**

17. $\frac{5}{16}$ **0.3125**
18. $\frac{3}{16}$ **0.1875**
19. $\frac{33}{50}$ **0.66**
20. $\frac{17}{40}$ **0.425**

21. $5\frac{7}{8}$ **5.875**
22. $9\frac{3}{8}$ **9.375**
23. $\frac{4}{9}$ **0.$\overline{4}$**
24. $\frac{8}{9}$ **0.$\overline{8}$**

25. $\frac{1}{6}$ **0.1$\overline{6}$**
26. $\frac{8}{11}$ **0.$\overline{72}$**
27. $5\frac{1}{3}$ **5.$\overline{3}$**
28. $2\frac{6}{11}$ **2.$\overline{54}$**

Write each decimal as a fraction or mixed number in simplest form.

29. 0.2 $\frac{1}{5}$
30. 0.9 $\frac{9}{10}$
31. 0.55 $\frac{11}{20}$

32. 0.34 $\frac{17}{50}$
33. 5.96 $5\frac{24}{25}$
34. 2.66 $2\frac{33}{50}$

35. **INSECTS** The maximum length of a praying mantis is 30.5 centimeters. What mixed number represents this length? $30\frac{1}{2}$ cm

36. **GROCERIES** Suppose you buy a 1.25 pound package of ham for $4.99. What fraction of a pound did you buy? $\frac{5}{4}$

37. **FIND THE DATA** Refer to the Data File on page 16–19 of your book. Choose some data and write a real-world problem in which you would write a percent as a decimal. **See students' work.**

Write each of the following as an integer over a whole number.

38. -13 $\frac{-13}{1}$
39. $7\frac{1}{3}$ $\frac{22}{3}$
40. -0.028 $\frac{-7}{250}$
41. -3.2 $\frac{-16}{5}$

42. **MUSIC** Nicolás practiced playing the cello for 2 hours and 18 minutes. Write the time Nicolás spent practicing as a decimal. **2.3 h**

Yesterday's News Remind students that yesterday's lesson was about simplifying fractions, or finding equivalent fractions in simplest form. Ask students to write how yesterday's concepts helped them with today's material.

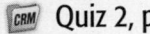 **Formative Assessment**

Check for student understanding of concepts in Lessons 4-4 and 4-5.

CRM Quiz 2, p. 67

 **Foldables™ Follow-Up**

Remind students to write—under the tab for this lesson of their Foldables—the answer to the question they wrote about the lesson.

Additional Answers

43. Felisa; Sample answer: Felisa's batting average is about 0.286. Harmony's batting average is about 0.263. 0.286 > 0.263, so, Felisa's average is better than Harmony's.

46. Sample answer: The first set of numbers can be factored into primes of 2s. The second set of numbers can be factored into primes of 2s and 3s; the factor of 3 produces the repeating decimal.

★ **43. SOFTBALL** The batting average of a softball player is the number of hits divided by the number of at-bats. If Felisa had 50 hits in 175 at-bats and Harmony had 42 hits in 160 at-bats, who had the better batting average? Justify your answer. **See margin.**

H.O.T. Problems

45. Sample answer: $3\frac{1}{7} \approx 3.14286$ and $3\frac{10}{71} \approx 3.14085$; Since 3.1415927... is between $3\frac{1}{7}$ and $3\frac{10}{71}$, Archimedes was correct.

44. OPEN ENDED Write a fraction that is equivalent to a terminating decimal between 0.5 and 0.75. **Sample answer:** $\frac{3}{5}$

45. CHALLENGE The value of pi (π) is 3.1415926… . The mathematician Archimedes believed that π was between $3\frac{1}{7}$ and $3\frac{10}{71}$. Was Archimedes correct? Explain your reasoning.

46. WRITING IN MATH Fractions with denominators of 2, 4, 8, 16, and 32 produce terminating decimals. Fractions with denominators of 6, 12, 18, and 24 produce repeating decimals. What causes the difference? Explain. **See margin.**

TEST PRACTICE

47. Which decimal represents the shaded region of the model? **B**

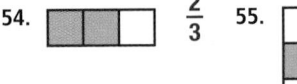

A 0.666   C 0.667
B $0.\overline{6}$ D $0.66\overline{7}$

48. Based on the information given in the table, what fraction represents $0.\overline{8}$? **J**

F $\frac{4}{5}$
G $\frac{80}{99}$
H $\frac{5}{6}$
J $\frac{8}{9}$

Decimal	Fraction
$0.\overline{3}$	$\frac{3}{9}$
$0.\overline{4}$	$\frac{4}{9}$
$0.\overline{5}$	$\frac{5}{9}$
$0.\overline{6}$	$\frac{6}{9}$

Spiral Review

Write each fraction in simplest form. (Lesson 4-4)

49. $\frac{10}{24}$ $\frac{5}{12}$ **50.** $\frac{39}{81}$ $\frac{13}{27}$ **51.** $\frac{28}{98}$ $\frac{2}{7}$ **52.** $\frac{51}{68}$ $\frac{3}{4}$

53. PIZZA How many different pizzas can Alfonso order if he can choose thick, thin, or deep dish crust and one topping from either pepperoni, sausage, or mushrooms? Use the *make an organized list* strategy. (Lesson 4-3) **9 pizzas**

▷ **GET READY for the Next Lesson**

PREREQUISITE SKILL Write a fraction for the number of shaded squares to the total number of squares.

54. $\frac{2}{3}$ **55.** $\frac{3}{9}$ or $\frac{1}{3}$ 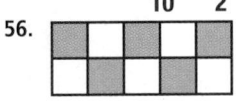   **56.** $\frac{5}{10}$ or $\frac{1}{2}$ 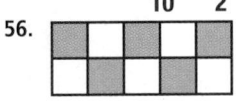   **57.** $\frac{4}{12}$ or $\frac{1}{3}$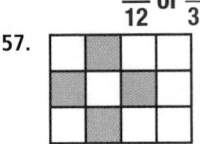

Pre-AP Activity **Use after Exercise 45**

The Rhind Papyrus states that the Egyptians used $\frac{256}{81}$ for π. Have students write the fraction as a decimal rounded to the nearest hundred-thousandth. Then ask them which is closer to the actual value of π, Archimedes' value or the Egyptians' value? **3.16049; Archimedes'**

Determine whether each number is *prime* **or** *composite.* (Lesson 4-1)

1. 24 **composite**   2. 61 **prime**   3. 2 **prime**

4. **AGE** Kevin just turned 13 years old. How old will he be the next time his age is a prime number? (Lesson 4-1) **17 years old**

Find the prime factorization of each number. (Lesson 4-1)

5. 30 $2 \times 3 \times 5$ 6. 120 $2^3 \times 3 \times 5$

Factor each expression. (Lesson 4-1)

7. $14x^2y$ **$2 \cdot 7 \cdot x \cdot x \cdot y$**   8. $50mn$ **$2 \cdot 5 \cdot 5 \cdot m \cdot n$**

Find the GCF of each set of numbers. (Lesson 4-2)

9. 16, 40 **8**   10. 65, 100 **5**

11. **MULTIPLE CHOICE** Lakeesha wants to cut a 14-inch by 21-inch poster board into equal-size squares for an art project. She does not want to waste any of the poster board, and she wants the largest squares possible. What is the length of the side of the largest squares she can cut? (Lesson 4-2) **B**

A 14   C 6

B 7   D 2

12. **MULTIPLE CHOICE** Lynne cannot remember her password to check the messages on her cell phone. She knows that it is a three-digit number consisting of the numbers 1, 4, and 7, but she cannot remember the order. Which list shows all the different possibilities for her password? (Lesson 4-3) **G**

F   147, 174, 417, 714, 741

G   147, 174, 417, 471, 714, 741

H   417, 471, 714, 741

J   147, 174, 74, 417, 17, 471, 714, 741

13. **PIANO** Evelina spends 40 minutes practicing the flute each afternoon after school. What part of one hour does she spend practicing? Write as a fraction in simplest form. (Lesson 4-4) $\frac{2}{3}$

Write each fraction in simplest form. (Lesson 4-4)

14. $\frac{20}{36}$ **$\frac{5}{9}$**

15. $\frac{45}{60}$ **$\frac{3}{4}$**

16. $\frac{63}{108}$ **$\frac{7}{12}$**

17. $\frac{60}{72}$ **$\frac{5}{6}$**

18. **VOTING** In the 2004 presidential election, Kentucky had 8 out of 538 total electoral votes. Write Kentucky's portion of the electoral votes as a fraction in simplest form. (Lesson 4-4) $\frac{4}{269}$

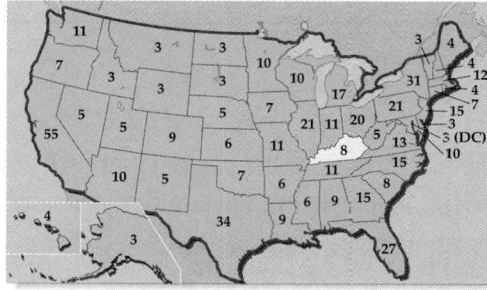

Write each fraction or mixed number as a decimal. Use bar notation if the decimal is a repeating decimal. (Lesson 4-5)

19. $\frac{7}{8}$ **0.875**   20. $\frac{2}{9}$ **$0.\overline{2}$**   21. $3\frac{13}{20}$ **3.65**

Write each decimal as a fraction in simplest form. (Lesson 4-5)

22. 0.6 **$\frac{3}{5}$**   23. 0.48 **$\frac{12}{25}$**   24. 7.02 **$7\frac{1}{50}$**

25. **ANIMALS** The maximum height of an Asian elephant is 9.8 feet. What mixed number represents this height? (Lesson 4-5) $9\frac{4}{5}$

Chapter 4 Mid-Chapter Quiz **201**

CHAPTER 4 Mid-Chapter Quiz

 Formative Assessment

Use the Mid-Chapter Quiz to assess students' progress in the first half of the chapter.

Have students review the lesson indicated for the problems they answered incorrectly.

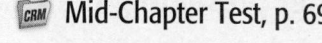 **Summative Assessment**

CRM Mid-Chapter Test, p. 69

ExamView Assessment Suite  Customize and create multiple versions of your Mid-Chapter Test and their answer keys.

FOLDABLES Study Organizer  **Dinah Zike's Foldables**

Before students complete the Mid-Chapter Quiz, encourage them to review the questions and answers they recorded on the first five tabs of their Foldables.

Data-Driven Decision Making	Exercises	Lesson	State/Local Standards	Resources for Review
Diagnostic Teaching Based on the results of the Chapter 4 Mid-Chapter Quiz, use the following to review concepts that students continue to find challenging.	1–8	4–1		**CRM** Study Guide and Intervention pp. 10, 17, 22, 27, and 33
	9–11	4–2		
	12	4–3		**Math Online** ▶ glencoe.com
	13–18	4–4		• Extra Examples • Personal Tutor
	19–25	4–5		• Concepts in Motion

PACING: **Regular:** 1 period, **Block:** 0.5 period

Options for Differentiated Instruction

ELL = English Language Learner   **AL** = Above or Beyond Grade Level   **SS** = Struggling Students   **SN** = Special Needs

Visual Learners **ELL** **AL** **SS**

Use after presenting the Examples.

Provide students with a 10 × 10 array of dots in which you have drawn
a triangle and a square that intersect, like those shown at the right.
- Ask students to write a percent that expresses the fraction of dots
  inside both the triangle and the square. 3%
- Have students make up similar problems for classmates to solve.

Investigating Literature **ELL** **AL** **SS**

Use after assigning the Exercises.

Have students choose a paragraph in a literature book and record the percent that each vowel is of the total
number of vowels. Have students record their findings in a table like the one shown below.

Vowel	Tally	Frequency	Percent
a			
e			
i			
o			
u			
Total			100%

Have students determine the most common vowel. The most common vowel is "e."

Research **AL**

Use after presenting Lesson 4-6.

Have students use newspaper or magazines to find real-world examples of fractions and percents. Have them cut
out or make a copy of the articles or graphs and make a poster. The posters should include the following:
- a graph or diagram showing the relationship of fractions and percents
- an explanation of what the fractions and percents represent

Have students share their posters with the entire class, demonstrating the usefulness of using fractions or percents
in each situation.

Leveled Lesson Resources

Also on TeacherWorks™
Lesson 4-6

Chapter 4 Resource Masters

BL = Below or Approaching Grade Level   **OL** = On Grade Level   **AL** = Above or Beyond Grade Level   **ELL** = English Language Learner

---

Lesson Reading Guide
p. 39 **BL** **OL** **ELL**

4-6 Lesson Reading Guide
Fractions and Percents

Get Ready for the Lesson
Read the introduction at the top of page 202 in your textbook.
Write your answers below.

1. For each sport, shade a 10 × 10 grid that represents the number of students that chose the sport.

3 out of 20   3 out of 25   1 out of 20   9 out of 100

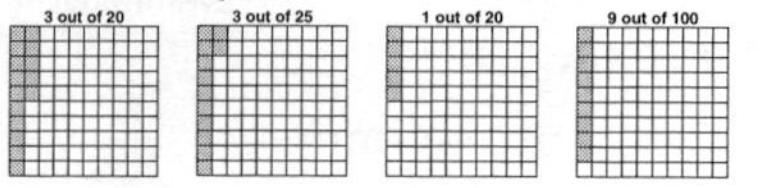

2. What fraction of the students chose swimming?
$\frac{9}{100}$

Read the Lesson

3. There is more than one way to write a ratio. Write the ratio that compares 4 to 25 in three different ways.
Sample answer: 4 out of 25, 4:25, and $\frac{4}{25}$

4. Write the ratio in Exercise 3 as a percent.
16%

5. How does having ratio written as percents make it easier to compare amounts? Sample answer: Percents have the same denominator (100), so all you need to do to compare ratios is compare the numerators.

Remember What You Learned

6. Work with a partner. Explain to your partner how to convert a ratio that does *not* compare a number to 100 as a percent. Then have your partner explain to you how to change from a percent to a fraction in simplest form. Both of you should use examples as well as general explanations.
See students' work.

Chapter 4   39   Course 2

Study Guide and Intervention*
p. 40 **BL** **OL** **ELL**

4-6 Study Guide and Intervention
Fractions and Percents

A **ratio** is a comparison of two numbers by division. When a ratio compares a number to 100, it can be written as a **percent**. To write a ratio or fraction as a percent, find an equivalent fraction with a denominator of 100. You can also use the meaning of percent to change percents to fractions.

Example 1 Write $\frac{19}{20}$ as a percent.

$\frac{19}{20} = \frac{95}{100} = 95\%$ Since $100 \div 20 = 5$, multiply the numerator and denominator by 5.

Example 2 Write 92% as a fraction in simplest form.

$92\% = \frac{92}{100}$ Definition of percent
$= \frac{23}{25}$ Simplify.

Exercises

Write each ratio as a percent.

1. $\frac{14}{100}$ 14%   2. $\frac{27}{100}$ 27%   3. 34.5 per 100 34.5%

4. 18 per 100 18%   5. 21:100 21%   6. 96:100 96%

Write each fraction as a percent.

7. $\frac{3}{100}$ 3%   8. $\frac{7}{50}$ 14%   9. $\frac{2}{5}$ 40%

10. $\frac{1}{20}$ 5%   11. $\frac{13}{25}$ 52%   12. $\frac{4}{10}$ 40%

Write each percent as a fraction in simplest form.

13. 35% $\frac{7}{20}$ 14. 18% $\frac{9}{50}$ 15. 75% $\frac{3}{4}$

16. 80% $\frac{4}{5}$ 17. 16% $\frac{4}{25}$ 18. 15% $\frac{3}{20}$

Chapter 4   40   Course 2

Skills Practice*
p. 41 **BL** **OL**

4-6 Skills Practice
Fractions and Percents

Write each ratio as a percent.

1. 26 out of 100 26%   2. 5 per 100 5%   3. 13:100 13%

4. $\frac{39}{100}$ 39%   5. 12.5 per 100 12.5%   6. 51 out of 100 51%

Write each fraction as a percent.

7. $\frac{7}{10}$ 70%   8. $\frac{6}{50}$ 12%   9. $\frac{13}{20}$ 65%

10. $\frac{30}{50}$ 60%   11. $\frac{7}{20}$ 35%   12. $\frac{12}{20}$ 60%

13. $\frac{23}{25}$ 92%   14. $\frac{3}{10}$ 30%   15. $\frac{17}{50}$ 34%

Write each percent as a fraction in simplest form.

16. 15% $\frac{3}{20}$ 17. 85% $\frac{17}{20}$ 18. 1% $\frac{1}{100}$

19. 70% $\frac{7}{10}$ 20. 25% $\frac{1}{4}$ 21. 19% $\frac{19}{100}$

22. 33% $\frac{33}{100}$ 23. 22% $\frac{11}{50}$ 24. 95% $\frac{19}{20}$

Chapter 4   41   Course 2

Practice*
p. 42 **OL** **AL**

4-6 Practice
Fractions and Percents

Write each ratio as a percent.

1. 56 out of 100 CDs sold 56%   2. 75 per 100 adults 75%

3. 89.2 out of 100 hours worked 89.2%   4. 26.5:100 Calories 26.5%

5. $45\frac{7}{8}$ out of 100 meters 45.875%   6. $33\frac{1}{3}$:100 minutes 33.3%

Write each fraction as a percent.

7. $\frac{6}{10}$ 60%   8. $\frac{7}{20}$ 35%   9. $\frac{21}{25}$ 84%   10. $\frac{12}{50}$ 24%

11. $\frac{1}{2}$ 50%   12. $\frac{4}{5}$ 80%   13. $\frac{20}{90}$ 22.2%   14. $\frac{24}{25}$ 96%

Write each percent as a fraction in simplest form.

15. 40% $\frac{2}{5}$ 16. 35% $\frac{7}{20}$ 17. 72% $\frac{18}{25}$ 18. 44% $\frac{11}{25}$

19. 90% $\frac{9}{10}$ 20. 17% $\frac{17}{100}$ 21. 5% $\frac{1}{20}$ 22. 26% $\frac{13}{50}$

Replace each ● with >, <, or = to make a true sentence.

23. $\frac{1}{10}$ ● 15% <   24. $\frac{4}{5}$ ● 72% >   25. 85% ● $\frac{17}{20}$ =

26. $\frac{21}{25}$ ● 21% >   27. 27% ● $\frac{27}{50}$ <   28. $\frac{3}{5}$ ● 60% >

29. SPORTS If twenty-seven out of every 50 sports fans attend at least one professional game every year, what percent of sports fans attend at least one professional game every year? 54%

30. WEATHER It rained 18 days during the month of April. What percent of the days during the month of April did it not rain? 40%

Chapter 4   42   Course 2

Word Problem Practice*
p. 43 **OL** **AL**

4-6 Word Problem Practice
Fractions and Percents

1. LUNCHES Three out of every 10 students in Mr. Chan's class bring their lunch to school. Write this ratio as a percent. 30%

2. COMPUTERS In 2007, 57 out of every 100 school age children (ages 6 to 17 years) had access to a computer both at home and at school. Write this ratio as a percent. 57%

3. SALES TAX In one town, the sales tax is 8%. Write this percent as a fraction in simplest form. $\frac{2}{25}$

4. HYGIENE Ms. Agosto surveyed her class and found that 15 out of 30 students brushed their teeth more than twice a day. What percent of students brushed more than twice a day? 50%

5. DISCOUNT A local retail store was having a sale and offered all their merchandise at a 25% discount. Write this percent as a fraction in simplest form. $\frac{1}{4}$

6. SPACE FLIGHT About 64% of all individuals who have flown in space from 1961 to 2001 are from the United States. Write this percent as a fraction in simplest form. $\frac{16}{25}$

Chapter 4   43   Course 2

Enrichment
p. 44 **OL** **AL**

4-6 Enrichment

Margarita Colmenares

Margarita Colmenares is an environmental engineer. She is a native of Los Angeles and a 1981 graduate of Stanford University. In 1989, she became the first woman president of the Society of Hispanic Professional Engineers. Ms. Colmenares was recently appointed to direct an office at the U.S. Department of Education. She has a special interest in education and has traveled extensively to talk to student groups about careers in engineering.

Environmental engineers like Colmenares use mathematics to predict the effect that our actions will have on our environment. They may also recommend ways to protect the environment. On this page, you will consider some data and recommendations concerning water usage.

Daily Water Usage in the United States (Per Person)

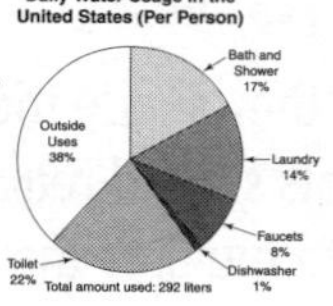

(Bath and Shower 17%, Laundry 14%, Faucets 8%, Dishwasher 1%, Toilet 22%, Outside Uses 38%)
Total amount used: 292 liters

Refer to the graph above.

1. Which one category accounts for more than $\frac{1}{3}$ of the water usage? outside uses

2. Estimate the fraction of a person's daily water usage that is for bath and shower. about $\frac{1}{5}$

Use the graph above. Estimate the amount of water used in each category. Sample answers are given.

3. outside uses $\frac{2}{5}$ × 300 = 120 liters   4. bath and shower $\frac{1}{5}$ × 300 = 60 liters

5. toilet $\frac{1}{5}$ × 300 = 60 liters   6. laundry $\frac{3}{20}$ × 300 = 45 liters

7. dishwasher $\frac{1}{100}$ × 300 = 3 liters   8. faucets $\frac{1}{10}$ × 300 = 30 liters

In each situation, what percent of the water used can be saved by following the recommendation?

9. Using a water-saving shower head can save 65 liters of water out of the 130 liters normally used in a five-minute shower. 50%

10. Turning off the water while brushing your teeth can reduce the water used from 20 liters to 2 liters. 90%

Chapter 4   44   Course 2

Additional Lesson Resources

* Also available in Spanish **ELL**

Transparencies
- *5-Minute Check Transparency*, Lesson 4-6

Other Print Products
- *Teaching Mathematics with Manipulatives*
- *Noteables™ Interactive Study Notebook with Foldables™*

Teacher Tech Tools
- *Interactive Classroom CD-ROM*, Lesson 4-6
- *AssignmentWorks*, Lesson 4-6

Student Tech Tools
glencoe.com
- Extra Examples, Chapter 4, Lesson 6
- Self-Check Quiz, Chapter 4, Lesson 6

4-6 Fractions and Percents

Vertical Alignment

Before Lesson 4-6 Identify and represent on a number line decimals, fractions, mixed numbers, and positive and negative numbers

Lesson 4-6
Compare and order positive and negative fractions, decimals, and mixed numbers and place them on a number line

After Lesson 4-6
Convert fractions to decimals and percents and use these representations in estimations, computations, and applications

2 Teach

▷ GET READY

When they shade the grids, students should realize that they need to multiply the number of students who chose each sport by the same number that, when multiplied by the size of the sample, gives a product of 100.

Scaffolding Questions

Tell the class that you have 100 pennies.

Ask:

• If 17 of the pennies are from the 1980s, what fraction of the pennies is that? $\frac{17}{100}$

• If 29 of the pennies are from the 1990s, what fraction of the pennies is that? $\frac{29}{100}$

• If 4 of the pennies are from the 1960s, what fraction of the pennies is that? $\frac{1}{25}$

MAIN IDEA

Write fractions as percents and percents as fractions.

New Vocabulary

ratio
equivalent ratios

Math Online ⟩

glencoe.com

• Extra Examples
• Personal Tutor
• Self-Check Quiz

▷ GET READY for the Lesson

In a recent survey, students were asked to choose their favorite sport to play. The results are shown in the table.

1. For each sport, shade a 10 × 10 grid that represents the number of students that chose the sport. **See margin.**

2. What fraction of the students chose swimming? $\frac{9}{100}$

Sport	Number of Students
Basketball	3 out of 20
Football	3 out of 25
Gymnastics	1 out of 20
Swimming	9 out of 100

A **ratio** is a comparison of two quantities by division. Ratios like 9 out of 100 can also be written as 9:100 or $\frac{9}{100}$. When a ratio compares a number to 100, it can be written as a **percent.**

Percent		**Key Concept**
Words	A percent is a part to whole ratio that compares a number to 100.	**Example** 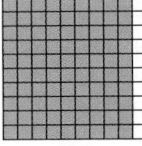
Symbols	$\frac{n}{100} = n\%$	**9 out of 100 = 9%**

EXAMPLES Write Ratios as Percents

Write each ratio as a percent.

1 Annie answered 90 out of 100 questions correctly.

$\frac{90}{100} = 90\%$

Annie answered 90% of the questions correctly.

90%

2 On average, 50.5 out of 100 students own a pet.

$\frac{50.5}{100} = 50.5\%$

On average, 50.5% of the students own a pet.

Reading Math

Percent *Percent* means per *hundred* or *hundredths*. The symbol % means percent.

✓ CHECK Your Progress

a. 45 out of 100 cars sold **45%**   b. $3.30 : $100 spent on soft drinks **3.3%**

202 Chapter 4 Fractions, Decimals, and Percents

Additional Answer

1. 3 out of 20 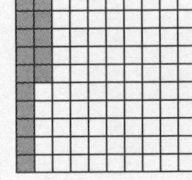   3 out of 25   1 out of 20   9 out of 100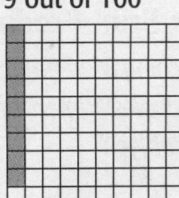

Fractions and percents are ratios that can represent the same number. You can write a fraction as a percent by finding an equivalent fraction with a denominator of 100.

EXAMPLE **Write a Fraction as a Percent**

3 Write $\frac{3}{20}$ as a percent.

First, find an equivalent fraction with a denominator of 100. Then write the fraction as a percent.

$$\frac{3}{20} = \frac{3 \times 5}{20 \times 5} = \frac{15}{100} \text{ or } 15\%$$

So, $\frac{3}{20} = 15\%$.

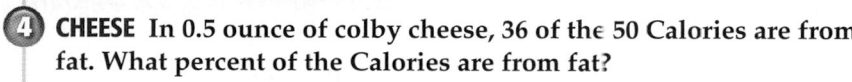

$$\frac{3}{20} \quad = \quad \frac{15}{100}$$

CHECK Your Progress

Write each fraction as a percent.

c. $\frac{17}{20}$ **85%**   d. $\frac{3}{5}$ **60%**   e. $\frac{2}{25}$ **8%**

Real-World EXAMPLE

4 **CHEESE** In 0.5 ounce of colby cheese, 36 of the 50 Calories are from fat. What percent of the Calories are from fat?

$\frac{36}{50} = \frac{72}{100}$ Write an equivalent fraction with a denominator of 100.

$\phantom{\frac{36}{50}} = 72\%$ $\frac{72}{100} = 72\%$

About 72% of the Calories are from fat.

CHECK Your Progress

f. **CHEESE** In a small piece of mozzarella cheese, 17 of the 25 Calories come from fat. What percent of the Calories come from fat? **68%**

EXAMPLE **Write a Percent as a Fraction**

5 Write 48% as a fraction in simplest form.

$48\% = \frac{48}{100}$ Definition of percent

$ = \frac{12}{25}$ Simplify.

CHECK Your Progress

Write each percent as a fraction in simplest form.

g. 40% $\frac{2}{5}$ h. 6% $\frac{3}{50}$. 24% $\frac{6}{25}$

Lesson 4-6 Fractions and Percents **203**

★ indicates multi-step problem

CHECK Your Understanding

Examples 1, 2 (p. 202)   Write each ratio as a percent.

1. 57:100 insects are spiders **57%**   2. $29.20 per $100 **29.2%**

Example 3 (p. 203)   Write each fraction as a percent.

3. $\frac{1}{4}$ **25%**   4. $\frac{6}{10}$ **60%**   5. $\frac{17}{20}$ **85%**

Example 4 (p. 203)   6. **TECHNOLOGY** Tansy used $\frac{2}{5}$ of the memory available on her flash drive. What percent of the memory did she use? **40%**

Example 5 (p. 203)   Write each percent as a fraction in simplest form.

7. 90% $\frac{9}{10}$ 8. 75% $\frac{3}{4}$ 9. 22% $\frac{11}{50}$

HOMEWORK HELP

For Exercises	See Examples
10–15	1, 2
16–23	3
24–25	4
26–33	5

Exercise Levels
A: 10–33
B: 34–40
C: 41–44

Write each ratio as a percent.

10. 87 out of 100 books read **87%**   11. 42 per 100 teenagers **42%**

12. 12.2 out of 100 points earned **12.2%**   13. 99.9:100 miles driven **99.9%**

14. $11\frac{3}{4}$ out of 100 feet **$11\frac{3}{4}$%**   15. $66\frac{2}{3}$:100 yards run **$66\frac{2}{3}$%**

Write each fraction as a percent.

16. $\frac{7}{10}$ **70%**   17. $\frac{16}{20}$ **80%**   18. $\frac{15}{25}$ **60%**   19. $\frac{13}{50}$ **26%**

20. $\frac{1}{5}$ **20%**   21. $\frac{3}{5}$ **60%**   22. $\frac{19}{20}$ **95%**   23. $\frac{10}{10}$ **100%**

24. **PETS** Twenty out of every 25 households own one dog. What percent of households own one dog? **80%**

25. **SPORTS** If 15 out of every 50 teens like to ski, what percent of teens like to ski? **30%**

Write each percent as a fraction in simplest form.

26. 45% $\frac{9}{20}$ 27. 30% $\frac{3}{10}$ 28. 62% $\frac{31}{50}$ 29. 88% $\frac{22}{25}$

30. 68% $\frac{17}{25}$ 31. 13% $\frac{13}{100}$ 32. 2% $\frac{1}{50}$ 33. 300% **3**

Replace each ● with >, <, or =.

34. $\frac{1}{4}$ ● 25% **=**   35. $\frac{9}{20}$ ● 55% **<**   36. 78% ● $\frac{3}{5}$ **>**

37. 38% ● $\frac{19}{50}$ **=**   38. 12% ● $1\frac{1}{5}$ **<**   39. $2\frac{2}{5}$ ● 24% **>**

EXTRA PRACTICE
See pages 678, 708.

40. **VOLUNTEERING** A Girl Scouts event is expecting 40 out of 50 people to
★ volunteer at a charity auction. So far 30 volunteers have arrived at the auction. What percent of the volunteers have not yet arrived? **25%**

204   Chapter 4 Fractions, Decimals, and Percents

DIFFERENTIATED HOMEWORK OPTIONS

Level	Assignment	Two-Day Option	
BL Basic	10–33, 41, 43–57	11–33 odd, 45, 46	10–32 even, 41, 43, 44, 47–57
OL Core	11–23 odd, 24, 25–39 odd, 40, 41, 43–57	10–33, 45, 46	34–41, 43, 44, 47–57
AL Advanced/Pre-AP	34–53, (optional: 54–57)		

---

3 Practice

✔ **Formative Assessment**

Use Exercises 1–9 to check for understanding.

Then use the chart at the bottom of this page to customize your assignments for students.

Intervention You may wish to use the Study Guide and Intervention Master on page 40 of the *Chapter 4 Resource Masters* for additional reinforcement.

Odd/Even Assignments

Exercises 10–33 are structured so that students practice the same concepts whether they are assigned odd or even problems.

H.O.T. Problems

41. GEOMETRY What percent of the larger rectangle shown is *not* shaded? **64%**

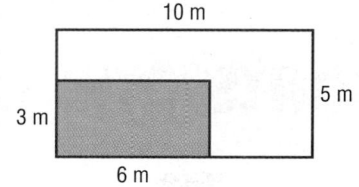

10 m
5 m
3 m
6 m

42. You know that $12\frac{1}{2}\% = \dfrac{12\frac{1}{2}}{100}$ **and that** $\dfrac{12\frac{1}{2}}{100} = \dfrac{12.5}{100}$ **or 0.125.**
Write 0.125 as $\dfrac{125}{1,000}$ **and simplify** $\dfrac{125}{1,000}$ **to get** $\dfrac{1}{8}$. **So,** $12\frac{1}{2}\% = \dfrac{1}{8}$

42. CHALLENGE Apply what you know about percents, fractions, and decimals to write $12\frac{1}{2}\%$ as a fraction. Justify your answer.

43. Which One Doesn't Belong? Identify the ratio that does not have the same value as the other three. Explain your reasoning.

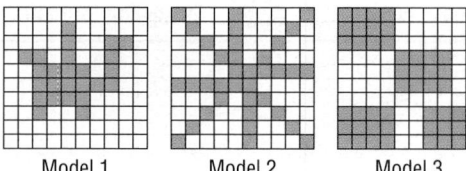

$\dfrac{5}{20}$ 5% $\dfrac{1}{4}$ 50 out of 200

43. 5%; the other ratios equal 25%

44. WRITING IN MATH Explain how you know which model represents 36%. Then explain why that model also represents $\dfrac{9}{25}$. **See margin.**

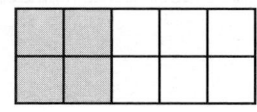

Model 1   Model 2   Model 3

TEST PRACTICE

45. What percent of the model is shaded? **C**

A 25%   C 40%
B 30%   D 60%

46. Cats spend about $\dfrac{3}{10}$ of their time awake grooming themselves. Which number is equivalent to $\dfrac{3}{10}$? **G**

F 3%   H 33.3%
G 30%   J 300%

Spiral Review

Write each decimal as a fraction or mixed number in simplest form. (Lesson 4-5)

47. 0.6 $\dfrac{3}{5}$ **48.** 0.15 $\dfrac{3}{20}$ **49.** 2.8 $2\dfrac{4}{5}$

50. TIME The drive to a football game took 56 minutes. Twenty-four minutes of the time was spent stopped in traffic. What fraction of the drive, in simplest form, was spent in stopped traffic? (Lesson 4-4) $\dfrac{3}{7}$

Solve each equation. (Lesson 3-2)

51. $x + 7 = 10$ **3**   **52.** $m - 2 = 8$ **10**   **53.** $12 + a = 16$ **4**

GET READY for the Next Lesson

PREREQUISITE SKILL Multiply or divide. (Pages 675, 676)

54. 16.2×10 **162**   **55.** 0.71×100 **71**   **56.** $14.4 \div 100$ **0.144**   **57.** $791 \div 1,000$ **0.791**

Lesson 4-6 Fractions and Percents **205**

Differentiated Instruction

Verbal/Linguistic Learners Have students work in pairs or groups to choose a section in a novel. Have each pair or group make a tally chart of the first 50 vowels in the section. Then have them write each vowel's fraction of the total vowels. Finally, have them convert the fractions to percents. Have each group present its data. Which vowel is most common?

4-7 Percents and Decimals

Options for Differentiated Instruction

ELL = English Language Learner   **AL** = Above or Beyond Grade Level   **SS** = Struggling Students   **SN** = Special Needs

Clarifying the Concept **SS**

Use after presenting Example 1.

Students may become confused when percents have a decimal component, such as 55.8%. Remind students that such a percent can be converted to a decimal in the standard way: removing the % symbol, dividing by 100, and moving the decimal two places to the left.

$$55.8\% = 0.558$$

Kinesthetic Learners **ELL** **AL**

Use after presenting the Examples.

Have students find six numbers that are between 0 and 1, of which two are decimals, two are fractions, and two are percents. Examples of six such numbers are shown below.

0.65	0.08	$\frac{3}{8}$	$\frac{1}{2}$	15%	42%

Have them write the numbers in order from least to greatest on a separate sheet of paper. Then have them write each number on a separate index card and shuffle the cards. Students should exchange sets of cards with a classmate, and order each other's set.

Relating to Everyday Concepts **ELL** **AL**

Use after presenting Lesson 4-7.

Use the concept that coins are percents of a dollar to reinforce the relationship among decimals, fractions, and percents.

• Have students use combinations of coins to make different money amounts.
• Help students write these amounts in dollar-and-cents notation, as fractions of a dollar, and as percents of a dollar.
• Have them organize their work in a table like the one below.

Coins	Dollars/Cents ($)	Fraction of a Dollar	Percent of a Dollar
2 dimes, 2 pennies	0.22	$\frac{22}{100}$	22%

Leveled Lesson Resources

Chapter 4 Resource Masters

BL = Below or Approaching Grade Level   **OL** = On Grade Level   **AL** = Above or Beyond Grade Level   **ELL** = English Language Learner

---

Lesson Reading Guide
p. 45 BL OL ELL

NAME _____ DATE _____ PERIOD _____

4-7 Lesson Reading Guide
Percents and Decimals

Get Ready for the Lesson
Read the introduction at the top of page 206 in your textbook. Write your answers below.

1. Write the percent of students who chose black as a fraction. $\frac{36}{100}$ or $\frac{9}{25}$

2. Write the fraction as a decimal. **0.36**

3. What do you notice about the percent and decimal forms for students who chose black? **Sample answer: They include the same digits.**

Read the Lesson

4. Describe each step in changing a percent to a decimal. **Sample answer: 1) Write the percent as a fraction with the denominator equal to 100. 2) Write the fraction as a decimal, moving the decimal point two places to the left.**

5. Describe each step in changing a percent to a decimal by first writing the percent as a fraction. **Sample answer: 1) Write the percent as a fraction with the denominator equal to 100. 2) If necessary, multiply the numerator and denominator by a power of 10 to remove a decimal in the numerator. Then simplify. 3) Write the fraction as a decimal.**

6. Describe how to write a percent as a decimal without writing the percent as a fraction. **Sample answer: 1) Write any fractions as decimals. 2) Divide by 100 (move the decimal point two places to the left). 3) Remove the % symbol.**

Remember What You Learned

7. Work with a partner. Think of a way that will help you remember which way to move the decimal when you go from a percent to a decimal and which way to move it when you go from a decimal to a percent. **See students' work.**

Chapter 4   45   Course 2

Study Guide and Intervention*
p. 46 BL OL ELL

NAME _____ DATE _____ PERIOD _____

4-7 Study Guide and Intervention
Percents and Decimals

To write a percent as a decimal, divide the percent by 100 and remove the percent symbol. To write a decimal as a percent, multiply the decimal by 100 and add the percent symbol.

Example 1 Write 42.5% as a decimal.

$42.5\% = \frac{42.5}{100}$ Write the percent as a fraction.

$= \frac{42.5 \times 10}{100 \times 10}$ Multiply by 10 to remove the decimal in the numerator.

$= \frac{425}{1,000}$ Simplify.

$= 0.425$ Write the fraction as a decimal.

Example 2 Write 0.625 as a percent.

$0.625 = 0\underset{\smile}{62.5}$ Multiply by 100.

$= 62.5\%$ Add the % symbol.

Exercises

Write each percent as a decimal.

1. 6% **0.06**   2. 28% **0.28**
3. 81% **0.81**   4. 84% **0.84**
5. 35.5% **0.355** 6. 12.5% **0.125**
7. 14.2% **0.142** 8. 11.1% **0.111**

Write each decimal as a percent.

9. 0.47 **47%**   10. 0.03 **3%**
11. 0.075 **7.5%** 12. 0.914 **91.4%**

Chapter 4   46   Course 2

Skills Practice*
p. 47 BL OL

NAME _____ DATE _____ PERIOD _____

4-7 Skills Practice
Percents and Decimals

Write each percent as a decimal.

1. 5% **0.05**   2. 20% **0.2**
3. 21% **0.21**   4. 83% **0.83**
5. 7% **0.07**   6. 56% **0.56**
7. 16% **0.16**   8. 45% **0.45**
9. 27.3% **0.273** 10. 14.9% **0.149**
11. 91.5% **0.915** 12. 29.3% **0.293**
13. 14.4% **0.144** 14. 80% **0.8**
15. 7.5% **0.075** 16. $10\frac{1}{2}\%$ **0.105**

Write each decimal as a percent.

17. 0.06 **6%**   18. 0.13 **13%**
19. 0.5 **50%**   20. 0.74 **74%**
21. 0.14 **14%**   22. 0.92 **92%**
23. 0.54 **54%**   24. 0.66 **66%**
25. 0.192 **19.2%** 26. 0.295 **29.5%**
27. 0.911 **91.1%** 28. 0.247 **24.7%**
29. 0.4165 **41.65%** 30. 0.2199 **21.99%**
31. 0.7601 **76.01%** 32. 0.4833 **48.33%**

Chapter 4   47   Course 2

Practice*
p. 48 OL AL

NAME _____ DATE _____ PERIOD _____

4-7 Practice
Percents and Decimals

Write each percent as a decimal.

1. 35% **0.35**   2. 90% **0.90**   3. 5% **0.05**   4. 1% **0.01**
5. 21.8% **0.218** 6. 64.8% **0.648** 7. 4.1% **0.041** 8. 8.5% **0.085**
9. $39\frac{21}{50}\%$ **0.3942** 10. $17\frac{2}{5}\%$ **0.174** 11. $40\frac{3}{4}\%$ **0.4075** 12. $88\frac{3}{5}\%$ **0.886**

Write each decimal as a percent.

13. 0.4 **40%**   14. 0.8 **80%**   15. 3.7 **370%**   16. 9.1 **910%**
17. 0.77 **77%**   18. 0.03 **3%**   19. 0.25 **25%**   20. 0.59 **59%**
21. 0.375 **37.5%** 22. 0.123 **12.3%** 23. 0.005 **0.5%** 24. 0.6019 **60.19%**

Replace each ● with >, <, or = to make a true sentence.

25. 1.5 ● 15% **>**   26. 0.88 ● 8.8% **>**   27. 33% ● 0.33 **=**
28. 90% ● 0.09 **>**   29. 0.26 ● 27% **<**   30. 65.4% ● 0.645 **>**

ANALYZE TABLES For Exercises 31–33, use the table and the information given.

The table lists the approximate milk fat content of 5 types of milk products.

31. Which product has the highest milk fat content? **heavy cream**

32. Find the approximate number of grams of milk fat in a 200-gram serving of whole milk. **7 grams**

33. Which milk product will have approximately 15.36 grams of milk fat in an 80-gram serving? **light cream**

Milk Product	Percent Milk Fat
Heavy Cream	36.7%
Light Cream	19.2%
Whole Milk	3.5%
Low-Fat Milk	1.5%
Skim Milk	0.05%

Chapter 4   48   Course 2

Word Problem Practice*
p. 49 OL AL

NAME _____ DATE _____ PERIOD _____

4-7 Word Problem Practice
Percents and Decimals

1. **AREA** New Mexico's land area is about 0.03 of the total area of the United States. What percent is New Mexico's land area of the total area of the United States? **3%**

2. **SCALE MODEL** A scale model of a building is 0.25 the actual size. What percent of the actual size of the building is the model? **25%**

3. **NFL COACHES** Don Shula ranks among the most successful coaches in the National Football League. In his career, he won 0.665 of his games. Write the decimal as a percent. **66.5%**

4. **SOFTBALL** Jenny's batting average is 0.346. Write the decimal as a percent. **34.6%**

5. **VITAMINS** A multiple vitamin contains 450 milligrams of calcium. This is 45% of the recommended daily allowance. Write the percent as a decimal. **0.45**

6. **BASKETBALL** Tao makes 74% of his free throws. Write the percent as a decimal. **0.74**

7. **SALES TAX** The sales tax in a town is 7.25%. Write the percent as a decimal. **0.0725**

8. **FIELD TRIP** In Ms. Silver's English class, $20\frac{1}{4}\%$ of the students signed up to visit a local museum. Write the percent as a decimal. **0.2025**

Chapter 4   49   Course 2

Enrichment
p. 50 OL AL

NAME _____ DATE _____ PERIOD _____

4-7 Enrichment

African-American Scientists and Inventors

When you buy a pair of shoes, you usually have a wide variety of styles, sizes, and prices to choose from. It is the work of an African-American inventor, Jan Matzeliger (1852–1889), that makes this possible. In 1882, Matzeliger patented a *lasting machine* that could shape the upper portion of a shoe and attach it to the sole in a fraction of the time it took to do the job by hand. Using this machine, shoe manufacturers were able to increase production and reduce prices dramatically.

African Americans have made many significant contributions to mathematics, science, and invention. By solving the percent problems and matching the problem and the correct solution, you will learn more about just a few of them.

Solutions
A. 20   Benjamin Banneker
B. 21   Majorie Lee Browne
C. 18   Lewis Latimer
D. 17.5 Jane Cooke Wright

1. 35% of 50 is what number?
This physician researched and tested chemotherapy as a method of treating cancer. In 1952, she became head of the Cancer Research Foundation at Harlem Hospital. **D**

2. What percent of 75 is 15?
This mathematician was part of the team of surveyors who created the street plan for Washington, D.C. in the late eighteenth century. **A**

3. 4.5% of 400 is what number?
In 1876, this engineer drew up the plans that accompanied Alexander Graham Bell's application for a patent on the telephone. **A**

4. 120% of what number is 25.2?
In 1949, she became one of the first two African-American women to earn a doctorate in mathematics. She was head of the mathematics department at North Carolina Central University from 1951 to 1970. **B**

Chapter 4   50   Course 2

Additional Lesson Resources

* Also available in Spanish **ELL**

Transparencies
- *5-Minute Check Transparency*, Lesson 4-7

Other Print Products
- *Noteables™ Interactive Study Notebook with Foldables™*

Teacher Tech Tools
- *Interactive Classroom CD-ROM*, Lesson 4-7
- *AssignmentWorks*, Lesson 4-7

Student Tech Tools
glencoe.com
- Extra Examples, Chapter 4, Lesson 7
- Self-Check Quiz, Chapter 4, Lesson 7

Lesson Notes

4-7

1 Focus

Vertical Alignment

Before Lesson 4-7
Identify and represent on a number line decimals, fractions, mixed numbers, and positive and negative numbers

Lesson 4-7
Compare and order positive and negative fractions, decimals, and mixed numbers and place them on a number line

After Lesson 4-7
Convert fractions to decimals and percents and use these representations in estimations, computations, and applications

2 Teach

Scaffolding Questions

Ask:
• What fraction, in simplest form, is equivalent to 50%? $\frac{1}{2}$

• What fraction, in simplest form, is equivalent to 25%? $\frac{1}{4}$

• What fraction, in simplest form, is equivalent to 80%? $\frac{4}{5}$

ADDITIONAL EXAMPLE

① Write 47.8% as a decimal. 0.478

Additional Examples are also in:
• Noteables™ Interactive Study Notebook with Foldables™
• Interactive Classroom PowerPoint® Presentations

MAIN IDEA

Write percents as decimals and decimals as percents.

Math Online

glencoe.com
• Concepts in Motion
• Extra Examples
• Personal Tutor
• Self-Check Quiz

▷ **GET READY for the Lesson**

SCHOOL UNIFORMS The graph shows students' favorite school uniform colors.

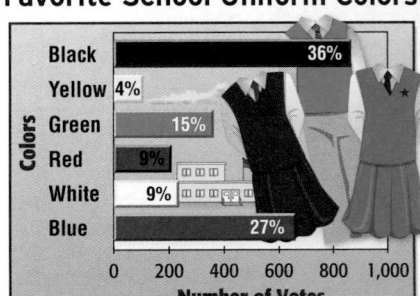

Favorite School Uniform Colors

Source: *Kids USA Survey*

1. Write the percent of students who chose black as a fraction. $\frac{36}{100}$ or $\frac{9}{25}$

2. Write the fraction as a decimal. **0.36**

3. What do you notice about the percent and decimal form for students who chose black? **Sample answer: They include the same digits.**

Any percent can be written as a fraction with the percent as the numerator and 100 as the denominator. Use this fact to help write percents as decimals.

EXAMPLE **Write Percents as Decimals**

① Write 7% as a decimal.

METHOD 1 Write the percent as a fraction.

$7\% = \frac{7}{100}$ Write the percent as a fraction.

$= 0.07$ Write the fraction as a decimal.

METHOD 2 Divide mentally.

The % symbol means to divide by 100. So, remove the % symbol and divide by 100.

$7\% = .07$ Remove the % symbol and divide by 100. Add placeholder zero.

$= 0.07$ Add leading zero.

So, 7% = 0.07.

✓ **CHOOSE Your Method**

Write each percent as a decimal.

a. 8% **0.08**   b. 54% **0.54**   c. 85.2% **0.852**

206 **Chapter 4** Fractions, Decimals, and Percents

 Formative Assessment

Use the Check Your Progress exercises after each Example to determine students' understanding of concepts.

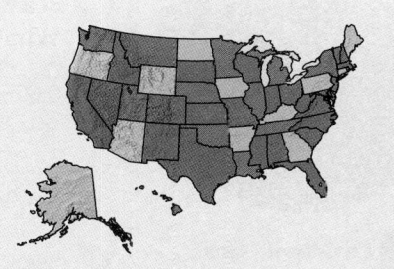

Real-World EXAMPLE

2 **GEOGRAPHY** Alaska is the largest state, making up about $16\frac{1}{10}\%$ of the land area of the United States. Write this amount as a decimal.

$16\frac{1}{10}\% = 16.1\%$ Write $\frac{1}{10}$ as 0.1.

$\phantom{16\frac{1}{10}\%} = 16.1$ Remove the % symbol and divide by 100.

$\phantom{16\frac{1}{10}\%} = 0.161$ Add leading zero.

So, $16\frac{1}{10}\% = 0.161$.

✔ CHECK Your Progress

d. **GEOGRAPHY** About $6\frac{4}{5}\%$ of the total area of the United States is water. What decimal represents this amount? **0.068**

e. **GEOGRAPHY** The total area of Australia is about $38\frac{11}{20}\%$ of the total area of North America. Write the amount as a decimal. **0.3855**

EXAMPLE   Write Decimals as Percents

3 Write 0.4 as a percent.

METHOD 1   Write the decimal as a fraction.

$0.4 = \frac{4}{10}$ or $\frac{40}{100}$ Write the decimal as a fraction.

$ = 40\%$ Write the fraction as a percent.

METHOD 2   Multiply mentally.

Multiply by 100 and add the % symbol.

$0.4 = 0.40$ Multiply by 100. Add a placeholder zero.

$ = 40\%$ Add the % symbol.

So, $0.4 = 40\%$.

✔ CHOOSE Your Method

Write each decimal as a percent.

f. 0.5 **50%**   g. 0.34 **34%**   h. 0.98 **98%**

Study Tip

Multiplication When multiplying by 100, the decimal point moves two places right.

Lesson 4-7 Percents and Decimals   **207**

2 **POPULATION** According to the Administration on Aging, about $28\frac{1}{5}\%$ of the population of the United States is 19 years of age or younger. Write $28\frac{1}{5}\%$ as a decimal. **0.282**

3 Write 0.33 as a percent. **33%**

Focus on Mathematical Content

Any **percent** can be written as a fraction, and any fraction can be written as a **decimal**.

To **write a decimal as a percent**, multiply by 100, which is the same as moving the decimal two places to the right.

3 Practice

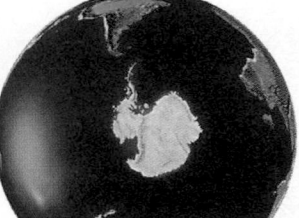

Real-World EXAMPLE

4 **SCIENCE** About 0.875 of an iceberg's mass is underwater. What percent of an iceberg's mass is underwater?

$0.875 = 0.875$ Multiply by 100.

$ = 87.5\%$ Add the % symbol.

So, 87.5% of an iceberg's mass is underwater.

Real-World Link . . . .
Of the world's icebergs, 93% are found surrounding the Antarctic.
Source: JPL Polar Oceanography Group

✓ CHECK Your Progress

i. EXERCISE Each day, Rico and his dog walk 0.625 mile. What percent of a mile do they walk? **62.5%**

Percent as a Decimal   Key Concept

To write a percent as a decimal, divide the percent by 100 and remove the percent symbol.

$$25\% = .25 \quad \text{or } 0.25$$

Decimal as a Percent   Key Concept

To write a decimal as a percent, multiply the percent by 100 and add the percent symbol.

$$0.58 = 0.58 = 58\%$$

★ indicates multi-step problem

✓ CHECK Your Understanding

Example 1 (p. 206)   Write each percent as a decimal.

1. 68% **0.68**   2. 5% **0.05**   3. 27.6% **0.276**

Example 2 (p. 207)   4. **SPENDING** A family spends about $33\frac{2}{5}\%$ of their annual income on housing. What decimal represents the amount spent on housing? **0.334**

Example 3 (p. 207)   Write each decimal as a percent.

5. 0.09 **9%**   6. 0.3 **30%**   7. 0.73 **73%**

Example 4 (p. 208)   8. **BASKETBALL** The table shows the top five WNBA players with the highest free throw averages. What percent of the time does Sue Bird make a free throw? **87.8%**

Player	Average
Eva Nemcova	0.897
Seimone Augustus	0.897
Elena Tornikidou	0.882
Sue Bird	0.878
Cynthia Cooper	0.871

Source: Women's National Basketball Association

Practice and Problem Solving

HOMEWORK HELP

For Exercises	See Examples
9–20	1
21–22	2
23–34	3
35–37	4

Write each percent as a decimal.

9. 27% **0.27**   10. 70% **0.7**   11. 6% **0.06**   12. 4% **0.04**

13. 18.5% **0.185**   14. 56.4% **0.564**   15. 2.2% **0.022**   16. 3.8% **0.038**

17. $27\frac{7}{10}$% **0.277**   18. $15\frac{1}{2}$% **0.155**   19. $30\frac{1}{4}$% **0.3025**   20. $46\frac{2}{5}$% **0.464**

21. **BONES** An adult human body has $68\frac{3}{5}$% of the number of bones it had at birth. What decimal represents this amount? **0.686**

Exercise Levels
A: 9–37
B: 38–48
C: 49–54

22. **VIDEO GAMES** Brian reaches the sixth level of a video game $92\frac{3}{4}$% of the time he plays. What decimal represents this percent? **0.9275**

Write each decimal as a percent.

23. 0.7 **70%**   24. 0.6 **60%**   25. 5.8 **580%**   26. 8.2 **820%**

27. 0.95 **95%**   28. 0.08 **8%**   29. 0.17 **17%**   30. 0.78 **78%**

31. 0.675 **67.5%**   32. 0.145 **14.5%**   33. 0.012 **1.2%**   34. 0.7025 **70.25%**

BASEBALL The table shows the top five Major League Baseball players with the highest batting averages in a recent year. Express each player's batting average as a percent.

Player	Average
Joe Mauer	0.347
Freddy Sanchez	0.344
Derek Jeter	0.344
Robinson Cano	0.342
Miguel Cabrera	0.339

Source: Major League Baseball

35. Joe Mauer **34.7%**

36. Derek Jeter **34.4%**

37. Miguel Cabrera **33.9%**

Replace each ● with >, <, or = to make a true sentence.

38. 0.25% ● 0.125 **<**   39. 0.76 ● 76.5% **<**   40. 500% ● 50 **<**

41. 99% ● 0.985 **>**   42. 0.325 ● 30% **>**   43. 56% ● 0.5625 **<**

★ 44. **SPORTS** A tennis player won 0.805 of the matches she played. What percent of the matches did she lose? **19.5%**

ANALYZE TABLES For Exercises 45–48, use the table and the information given.

Model airplane measurements are based on a scale of the life-size original. For example, a scale of $\frac{1}{72}$ is about 1% of the size of the original. Percents are rounded to the nearest thousandth.

Scale	Percent Equivalent
$\frac{1}{72}$	1.389%
$\frac{1}{24}$	4.167%
$\frac{1}{48}$	2.083%
$\frac{1}{20}$	5%
$\frac{1}{32}$	3.125%

45. 0.01389, 0.04167, 0.02083, 0.05, 0.03125

45. Find the decimal equivalents for each scale.

46. Which scale is the smallest? $\frac{1}{72}$

47. About how long is a model of an actual 88.5-foot C-119 boxcar plane using a $\frac{1}{72}$ scale? **1.2 ft**

48. Which scale is used if a model of an 88.5-foot C-119 boxcar plane is about 33.1875 inches long? $\frac{1}{32}$

EXTRA PRACTICE

See pages 678, 708.

Odd/Even Assignments

Exercises 9–37 are structured so that students practice the same concepts whether they are assigned odd or even problems.

Tips for New Teachers

Percents

You may need to remind students that when a percent is written as a mixed number (such as $4\frac{1}{5}$%), they should first rewrite the fractional part as a decimal (such as 4.2%).

DIFFERENTIATED HOMEWORK OPTIONS

Level	Assignment	Two-Day Option	
BL Basic	9–37, 49–50, 54–66	9–37 odd, 55, 56	10–36 even, 49–50, 54, 57–66
OL Core	9–21 odd, 22, 23–33 odd, 35–37, 39–43 odd, 44–50, 54–66	9–37, 55, 56	38–50, 54, 57–66
AL Advanced /Pre-AP	38–62 (optional: 63–66)		

Assess

Ticket Out the Door Have students invent a real-world ratio (such as red cars:total cars in a parking lot) and then write the equivalent fraction, decimal, and percent.

 Formative Assessment

Check for student understanding of concepts in Lessons 4-6 and 4-7.

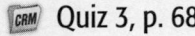 Quiz 3, p. 68

 **Foldables™ Follow-Up**

Remind students to write—under the tab for this lesson of their Foldables—the answer to the question they wrote about the lesson.

Additional Answer

64. $2 \times 2 \times 2 \times 2 \times 2$

H.O.T. Problems

49. OPEN ENDED Write any decimal between 0 and 1. Then write it as a fraction in simplest form and as a percent. **Sample answer:** $0.25, \frac{1}{4}, 25\%$

50. Emilio; Janelle divided by 100 instead of multiplying by 100.

50. FIND THE ERROR Emilio and Janelle both wrote 0.992 as a percent. Who is correct? Explain.

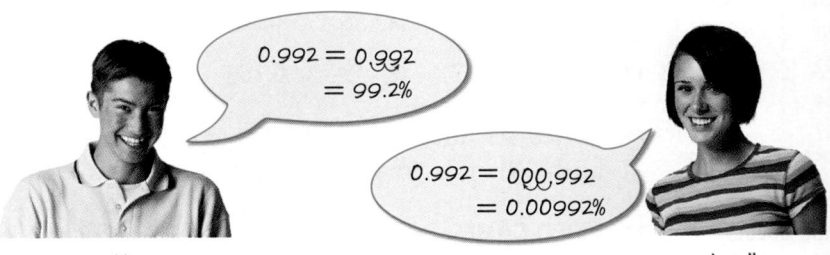

Emilio   Janelle

54. Sample answer: Amelia received a 0.95 on her quiz. What percent is this?

CHALLENGE Write each fraction as a percent.

51. $\frac{3}{8}$ **37.5%**   **52.** $\frac{1}{40}$ **2.5%**   **53.** $\frac{1}{32}$ **3.125%**

54. **WRITING IN MATH** Write a word problem about a real-world situation in which you would change a decimal to a percent.

TEST PRACTICE

55. It is estimated that 13.9% of the population of Texas was born outside the United States. Which number is *not* equivalent to 13.9%? **D**

A $\frac{139}{1,000}$ **C** 0.139

B $\frac{13.9}{100}$ **D** 1.39

56. Which of the following is ordered from least to greatest? **G**

F $0.42, \frac{2}{5}, 50\%, \frac{3}{4}$

G $\frac{2}{5}, 0.42, 50\%, \frac{3}{4}$

H $\frac{3}{4}, \frac{2}{5}, 0.42\%, 50\%$

J $\frac{3}{4}, 0.42, \frac{2}{5}, 50\%$

Spiral Review

Write each ratio as a percent. (Lesson 4-6)

57. 72 out of 100 animals **72%** **58.** $9.90:$100 **9.9%** **59.** 3.1 out of 100 households **3.1%**

60. Write $9\frac{3}{8}$ as a decimal. (Lesson 4-5) **9.375**

61. AIRPLANES Write an integer that represents an airplane descending 125 feet. (Lesson 2-1) **−125**

★ **62. MONEY** Marina earned $187.50 by working 30 hours. If she works 35 hours at this rate, how much will she earn? (Lesson 1-1) **$218.75**

▷ **GET READY for the Next Lesson**

PREREQUISITE SKILL Write the prime factorization of each number. (Lesson 4-1)

63. 50 **2 × 5 × 5**   **64.** 32 **See margin.**   **65.** 76 **2 × 2 × 19**   **66.** 105 **3 × 5 × 7**

Least Common Multiple

PACING: **Regular:** 2 periods, **Block:** 1 period

Options for Differentiated Instruction

ELL = English Language Learner   **AL** = Above or Beyond Grade Level   **SS** = Struggling Students   **SN** = Special Needs

Organizing Student Work and Thinking **ELL** **SS** **SN**

Use before assigning the Exercises.

Have students get out the ring of factor cards that they made in Lesson 4-2. On the blank side of each card, have students list the first ten multiples of the number that is written on the front of the card.

Multiples of 8
8, 16, 24, 32, 40, 48, 56, 64, 72, 80

Making Conjectures **AL**

Use after presenting Lesson 4-8.

Have students find the LCM and GCF for two numbers, the product of the two numbers, and the product of their GCF and LCM.

Ask:

What do you notice? **Both products are equal.**

Repeat, using other pairs of numbers.

Ask:

What conclusions, if any, can you make? **The product of any two numbers equals the product of their GCF and LCM.**

Kinesthetic Learners **ELL** **SS**

Use after presenting Lesson 4-8.

Write the numbers 3, 5, 10, and 15 on index cards, one number per card. Have students in groups of four each take a card. Looking at a clock with a second hand, have students tap their pencils at 3, 5, 10, or 15 seconds, depending on their card. Stop when all four members tap their pencils at the same time.

Ask:

• How many seconds did this take? **30 s**
• What is the LCM of 3, 5, 10, and 15? **30**

Leveled Lesson Resources

Chapter 4 Resource Masters

BL = Below or Approaching Grade Level **OL** = On Grade Level **AL** = Above or Beyond Grade Level **ELL** = English Language Learner

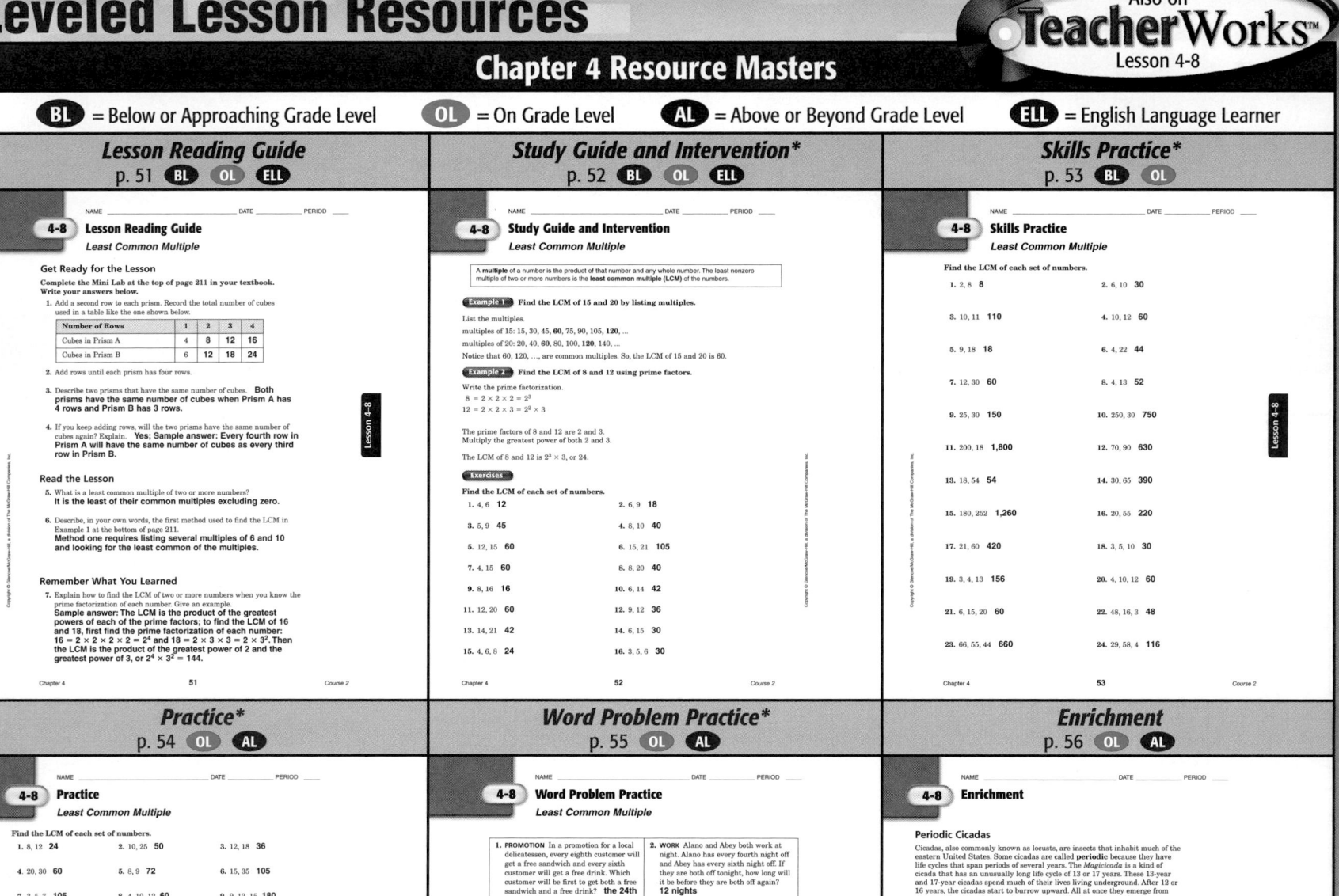

Lesson Reading Guide p. 51 BL OL ELL

Study Guide and Intervention* p. 52 BL OL ELL

Skills Practice* p. 53 BL OL

Practice* p. 54 OL AL

Word Problem Practice* p. 55 OL AL

Enrichment p. 56 OL AL

Additional Lesson Resources

* Also available in Spanish ELL

Transparencies
- *5-Minute Check Transparency*, Lesson 4-8

Other Print Products
- *Noteables™ Interactive Study Notebook with Foldables™*

Teacher Tech Tools
- *Interactive Classroom CD-ROM*, Lesson 4-8
- *AssignmentWorks*, Lesson 4-8

Student Tech Tools
glencoe.com
- Extra Examples, Chapter 4, Lesson 8
- Self-Check Quiz, Chapter 4, Lesson 8

▷ **MINI Lab**

Use cubes to build the first row of each prism as shown.

1. Add a second row to each prism. Record the total number of cubes used in a table like the one shown below.

Prism A

Number of Rows	1	2	3	4
Cubes in Prism A	4	■ 8	■ 12	■ 16
Cubes in Prism B	6	■ 12	■ 18	■ 24

Prism B

2. Add rows until each prism has four rows.

3. Describe two prisms that have the same number of cubes. **See margin.**

4. If you keep adding rows, will the two prisms have the same number of cubes again? **See margin.**

A **multiple** is the product of a number and any whole number. The **least common multiple**, or **LCM**, of two or more numbers is the least of their common multiples, excluding zero.

EXAMPLES Find the LCM

① Find the LCM of 6 and 10.

METHOD 1 List the nonzero multiples.

List the multiples of 6 until you come to a number that is also a multiple of 10.

multiples of 6: 6, 12, 18, 24, **30**, …

multiples of 10: 10, 20, **30**, …

Notice that 30 is also a multiple of 10. The LCM of 6 and 10 is 30.

METHOD 2 Use prime factorization.

$6 = 2 \cdot 3$
$10 = 2 \cdot 5$

> The prime factors of 6 and 10 are 2, 3, and 5.

The LCM is the least product that contains the prime factors of each number. So, the LCM of 6 and 10 is $2 \cdot 3 \cdot 5$ or 30.

Lesson 4-8 Least Common Multiple **211**

Additional Answers

3. Both prisms have the same number of cubes when prism A has 3 rows and prism B has 2 rows.

4. Yes; Sample answer: Every third row in prism A will have the same number of cubes as every second row in prism B.

---

1 Focus

Vertical Alignment

Before Lesson 4-8
Determine the prime factors of all numbers through 50 and write the numbers as the product of their prime factors by using exponents to show multiples of a factor

Lesson 4-8
Determine the least common multiple of whole numbers

After Lesson 4-8
Add and subtract fractions by using factoring to find common denominators

2 Teach

▷ **MINI Lab**

Many students will recognize the patterns and thus be able to use multiplication to find the number of cubes in each prism.

Scaffolding Questions

Present the following scenario. Maria has a collection of quarters, dimes, and nickels. In order to count the coins, she wants to make several piles of each coin that are equal in value.

Ask:
• How many dimes equal 2 quarters? 5

• How many dimes equal 6 quarters? 15

• How many nickels equal 1 dime? 2

• How many nickels equal 4 dimes? 8

The **least common multiple** (LCM) of a set of numbers is the least product that contains the prime factors of each number.

One way to find the LCM of a set of numbers is to list their **nonzero multiples**.

Another way to find the LCM of a set of numbers is to write each number's **prime factorization**, and then multiply the greatest power of each prime factor.

Formative Assessment

Use the Check Your Progress exercises after each Example to determine students' understanding of concepts.

ADDITIONAL EXAMPLES

1 Find the LCM of 4 and 6. **12**

2 Find the LCM of 4 and 15. **60**

3 **WORK** On an assembly line, machine A must be oiled every 18 minutes, machine B every 24 minutes, and machine C every 48 minutes. If all three machines are turned on at the same time, in how many minutes will all three machines need to be oiled at the same time? **144 minutes**

Additional Examples are also in:

• Noteables™ Interactive Study Notebook with Foldables™

• Interactive Classroom PowerPoint® Presentations

Tips for New Teachers **Zero**

Make sure students realize that 0 is a multiple of every number but, by definition, is not considered the LCM of any set of numbers.

---

2 **Find the LCM of 45 and 75.**

Use Method 2. Find the prime factorization of each number.

$45 = 3 \cdot 3 \cdot 5$ or $3^2 \cdot 5$
$75 = 3 \cdot 5 \cdot 5$ or $3 \cdot 5^2$

> The prime factors of 45 and 75 are 3 and 5. Write the prime factorization using exponents.

The LCM is the product of the prime factors 3 and 5, with each one raised to the *highest* power it occurs in *either* prime factorization. The LCM of 45 and 75 is $3^2 \cdot 5^2$, which is 225.

✓CHOOSE Your Method

Find the LCM of each set of numbers.

a. 3, 12 **12**   b. 10, 12 **60**   c. 25, 30 **150**

**Real-World EXAMPLE**

3 **PARTY** Ling needs to buy paper plates, napkins, and cups for a party. Plates come in packages of 12, napkins come in packages of 16, and cups come in packages of 8. What is the least number of packages she will have to buy if she wants to have the same number of plates, napkins, and cups?

Real-World Link . . . .
Each day, about 700,000 people in the U.S. celebrate their birthday.

First find the LCM of 8, 12, and 16.

$8 = 2 \cdot 2 \cdot 2$ or 2^3
$12 = 2 \cdot 2 \cdot 3$ or $2^2 \cdot 3$
$16 = 2 \cdot 2 \cdot 2 \cdot 2$ or 2^4

> The prime factors of 8, 12, and 16 are 2 and 3. Write the prime factorization using exponents.

The LCM of 8, 12, and 16 is $2^4 \cdot 3$, which is 48.

To find the number of packages of each Ling needs to buy, divide 48 by the amount in each package.

cups: $48 \div 8$ or 6 packages

plates: $48 \div 12$ or 4 packages

napkins: $48 \div 16$ or 3 packages

So, Ling will need to buy 6 packages of cups, 4 packages of plates, and 3 packages of napkins.

✓CHECK Your Progress

d. **VEHICLES** Mr. Hernandez changes his car's oil every 3 months, rotates the tires every 6 months, and replaces the air filter once a year. If he completed all three tasks in April, what will be the next month he again completes all three tasks? **April**

212 **Chapter 4** Fractions, Decimals, and Percents

 **CHECK** Your Understanding

Examples 1–3
(pp. 211–212)

Find the LCM of each set of numbers.

1. 4, 14 **28**   2. 6, 7 **42**   3. 12, 15 **60**

4. 21, 35 **105**   5. 3, 5, 12 **60**   6. 6, 14, 21 **42**

Example 3
(p. 212)

7. **GOVERNMENT** The number of years per term for a U.S. President, senator, and representative is shown. Suppose a senator was elected in the presidential election year 2008. In what year will he or she campaign again during a presidential election year? **2020**

Elected Office	Term (yr)
President	4
Senator	6
Representative	2

Practice and Problem Solving

Find the LCM for each set of numbers.

HOMEWORK HELP

For Exercises	See Examples
8–13, 20	1, 2
14–19, 21	3

8. 6, 8 **24**   9. 8, 18 **72**   10. 12, 16 **48**

11. 24, 36 **72**   12. 11, 12 **132**   13. 45, 63 **315**

14. 2, 3, 5 **30**   15. 6, 8, 9 **72**   16. 8, 12, 16 **48**

17. 12, 15, 28 **420** 18. 22, 33, 44 **132**   19. 12, 16, 36 **144**

Exercise Levels
A: 8–21
B: 22–30
C: 31–34

20. **CHORES** Hernando walks his dog every two days. He gives his dog a bath once a week. Today, Hernando walked his dog and then gave her a bath. How many days will pass before he does both chores on the same day? **14 days**

21. **TEXT MESSAGING** Three friends use text messaging to notify their parents of their whereabouts. If all three contact their parents at 3:00 P.M., at what time will all three contact their parents again at the same time? **6:00 P.M.**

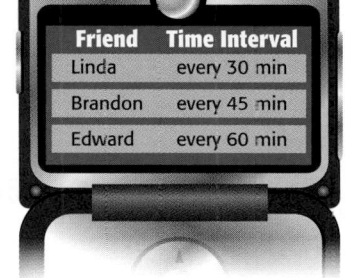

Friend	Time Interval
Linda	every 30 min
Brandon	every 45 min
Edward	every 60 min

Find the LCM of each set.

22. $3.00, $14.00 **$42**   23. 10¢, 25¢, 5¢ **50¢**   24. 9 inches, 2 feet **72 in. or 6 ft**

Write two numbers whose LCM is the given number.

25–28. Sample answers are given.

25. 35 **5, 7**   26. 56 **7, 8**   27. 70 **10, 35**   28. 30 **6, 15**

29. **SNACKS** Alvin's mom needs to buy snacks for soccer practice. Juice boxes come in packages of 10. Oatmeal snack bars come in packages of 8. She wants to have the same number of juice boxes and snack bars, what is the least number of packages of each snack that she will have to buy? **4 packages of juice boxes and 5 packages of oatmeal snack bars**

 **EXTRA PRACTICE**
See pages 678, 707.

30. **REASONING** The LCM of two consecutive positive numbers is greater than 200 and is a multiple of 7. What are the least possible numbers? **14 and 15**

Lesson 4-8 Least Common Multiple   **213**

3 Practice

✓ **Formative Assessment**

Use Exercises 1–7 to check for understanding.

Then use the chart at the bottom of this page to customize your assignments for students.

Intervention You may wish to use the Study Guide and Intervention Master on page 52 of the *Chapter 4 Resource Masters* for additional reinforcement.

Odd/Even Assignments

Exercises 8–21 are structured so that students practice the same concepts whether they are assigned odd or even problems.

DIFFERENTIATED HOMEWORK OPTIONS

Level	Assignment	Two-Day Option	
BL Basic	8–21, 32–46	9–21 odd, 35, 36	8–20 even, 32–34, 37–46
OL Core	9–19 odd, 20, 21–29 odd, 30, 32–46	8–21, 35, 36	22–30, 32–34, 37–46
AL Advanced/Pre-AP	22–43, (optional: 44–46)		

Crystal Ball Tell students that tomorrow's lesson is about comparing fractions, decimals, and percents. Ask them to write how they think what they learned today will connect with tomorrow's material.

H.O.T. Problems

31. CHALLENGE Two numbers have a GCF of $3 \cdot 5$. Their LCM is $2^2 \cdot 3 \cdot 5$. If one of the numbers is $3 \cdot 5$, what is the other number? **$2^2 \cdot 3 \cdot 5$, or 60**

32. Number sense; Sample answer: The LCM of 14, 16, and 8 is 112. So, 112 minutes later, or at 1:27 P.M.

32. SELECT A TECHNIQUE The schedule for each of three trains is shown. Suppose a train from each line leaves Clark Street at 11:35 A.M. Which of the following technique(s) might you use to determine the next time all three trains will be leaving at the same time? Justify your selection(s). Then use the technique to solve the problem.

Clark Street Train Station	
Train	**Leaves Station**
Red-line	every 14 minutes
Blue-line	every 16 minutes
Brown-line	every 8 minutes

mental math	number sense	estimation

33. OPEN ENDED Write three numbers that have an LCM of 30.
Sample answer: **3, 10, 15**

34.  **MATH** Describe the relationship between 4, 20, and 5 using the words *factor* and *multiple*. **4 and 5 are factors of 20; 20 is a multiple (and LCM) of 4 and 5.**

TEST PRACTICE

35. Which rule describes the common multiples of 12 and 18, where n represents the counting numbers? **C**

  A $12n$

  B $18n$

  C $36n$

  D $216n$

36. SHORT RESPONSE Wil swims every third day, runs every fourth day, and lifts weights every fifth day. If Wil does all three activities today, how many days will pass before he does all three activities on the same day again? **60**

Spiral Review

Write each percent as a decimal. (Lesson 4-7)

37. 55% **0.55**   **38.** 26.4% **0.264**   **39.** $\frac{1}{4}$% **0.0025**   **40.** 2% **0.02**

41. DIAMONDS Sixty-eight percent of engagement rings have a diamond that is round in shape. Write this percent as a fraction in simplest form. (Lesson 4-6) $\frac{17}{25}$

42. ALGEBRA Solve $3x = 18$. (Lesson 3-3) **6**

43. ALGEBRA Rose swam 7 laps more than twice the number of laps her sister swam. Write an algebraic expression to represent this situation. (Lesson 3-1) **$2s + 7$**

GET READY for the Next Lesson

PREREQUISITE SKILL Replace each ● with <, > or = to make a true sentence. (Page 670)

44. 6.85 ● 5.68 **>**   **45.** 2.34 ● 2.43 **<**   **46.** 6.9 ● 5.99 **>**

214 Chapter 4 Fractions, Decimals, and Percents

Pre-AP Activity   **Use after Exercise 33**

Tell students that the product of two numbers is 324 and that their GCF is 6. Have them find the numbers and their LCM. You may need to provide a hint, suggesting that students first find the prime factorization of 324. 54 and 6; 54

Comparing and Ordering Rational Numbers

PACING: **Regular:** 1 period,   **Block:** 0.5 period

Options for Differentiated Instruction

ELL = English Language Learner   **AL** = Above or Beyond Grade Level   **SS** = Struggling Students   **SN** = Special Needs

Vocabulary Development   **ELL**   **SS**   **SN**

Use after presenting the Examples.

Create a word wall with examples of GCF, LCM, and LCD. For sight impaired students, use large type or Braille coding.

Explain what each term is, how it is used, and whether the terms are related in any way. Be sure to give examples of all three.

Working in Pairs   **ELL**   **SS**

Use with the in-class Exercises.

Have students work through a number of problems in pairs. Have one student solve the problem using a calculator and the other using paper and pencil. Partners should switch methods with every problem. Have students compare answers, aiding one another in finding any mistakes in calculations.

Kinesthetic Learners   **ELL**   **AL**   **SS**   **SN**

Use after students complete Lesson 4-9.

Place students in groups of four. Give each group 12 cards, each of which shows a fraction, decimal, or percent. An example of a set of cards is shown below.

$\frac{1}{3}$	0.16	0.9	25%	$\frac{5}{6}$	0.09
0.72	28%	$\frac{3}{10}$	80%	0.46	$\frac{7}{15}$

Each member of the group draws one card. Then have students order the cards from least to greatest. Repeat the activity several times.

Leveled Lesson Resources

Chapter 4 Resource Masters

BL = Below or Approaching Grade Level **OL** = On Grade Level **AL** = Above or Beyond Grade Level **ELL** = English Language Learner

---

Lesson Reading Guide
p. 58 **BL** **OL** **ELL**

NAME _____ DATE _____ PERIOD _____

4-9 Lesson Reading Guide
Comparing and Ordering Rational Numbers

Get Ready for the Lesson
Complete the Mini Lab at the top of page 215 in your textbook. Write your answers below.

1. $-\frac{7}{8}, \frac{3}{8}$ $-\frac{7}{8} < \frac{3}{8}$
2. $-\frac{5}{8}, -1\frac{3}{8}$ $-\frac{5}{8} < -1\frac{3}{8}$
3. $-\frac{13}{8}, \frac{3}{8}$ $-\frac{13}{8} < \frac{3}{8}$
4. $-1\frac{7}{8}, -1\frac{5}{8}$ $-1\frac{7}{8} < -1\frac{5}{8}$
5. $-\frac{1}{2}, \frac{3}{4}$ $-\frac{3}{4} < -\frac{1}{4}$
6. $1\frac{1}{4}, -1\frac{1}{4}$ $-1\frac{1}{4} < 1\frac{1}{4}$

7. **MAKE A CONJECTURE** Which number is less: $-\frac{6}{7}$ or $-\frac{4}{7}$? $-\frac{6}{7} < -\frac{4}{7}$; Sample answer: Use a number line to explain your reasoning.
When both numbers are graphed on the number line using increments of sevenths, it is easy to see that $-\frac{6}{7} < -\frac{4}{7}$.

Read the Lesson
8. What are two ways in which you can compare fractions? 1) Rename the fractions using the LCD. 2) Write each fraction as a decimal and then compare the decimals. 3) Estimate, using a number line if necessary.
9. Complete the table of common fraction-decimal-percent equivalents.

Fraction	Decimal	Percent
$\frac{1}{5}$	0.2	20%
$\frac{3}{5}$	0.6	60%
$\frac{7}{10}$	0.7	70%
$\frac{1}{4}$	0.25	25%

10. How are the following sets of numbers related: whole numbers, rational numbers, integers? **Sample answer: The set of rational numbers includes all of the integers and whole numbers. The set of integers includes all whole numbers.**

Remember What You Learned
11. In this lesson you learned about the LCD. What do each of the following abbreviations stand for: LCD, LCM, and GCF? **Sample answer: How are the LCD and LCM related? LCD: least common denominator; LCM: least common multiple; GCF: greatest common factor. The LCD of a set of fractions is the LCM of the denominators of the fractions.**

Chapter 4   58   Course 2

Study Guide and Intervention*
p. 59 **BL** **OL** **ELL**

NAME _____ DATE _____ PERIOD _____

4-9 Study Guide and Intervention
Comparing and Ordering Rational Numbers

To compare fractions, rewrite them so they have the same denominator. The **least common denominator (LCD)** of two fractions is the LCM of their denominators. Another way to compare fractions is to express them as decimals. Then compare the decimals.

Example 1 Which fraction is greater, $\frac{3}{4}$ or $\frac{4}{5}$?

Method 1 Rename using the LCD.
$\frac{3}{4} = \frac{3 \times 5}{4 \times 5} = \frac{15}{20}$
$\frac{4}{5} = \frac{4 \times 4}{5 \times 4} = \frac{16}{20}$ The LCD is 20.
Because the denominators are the same, compare numerators.
Since $\frac{16}{20} > \frac{15}{20}$, then $\frac{4}{5} > \frac{3}{4}$.

Method 2 Write each fraction as a decimal. Then compare decimals.
$\frac{3}{4} = 0.75$
$\frac{4}{5} = 0.8$
Since 0.8 > 0.75, then $\frac{4}{5} > \frac{3}{4}$.

Exercises

Find the LCD of each pair of fractions.
1. $\frac{1}{2}, \frac{1}{8}$ 8
2. $\frac{1}{3}, \frac{1}{4}$ 12
3. $\frac{3}{4}, \frac{7}{10}$ 20

Replace each ● with <, >, or = to make a true sentence.
4. $\frac{1}{2} ● \frac{4}{9}$ >
5. $\frac{4}{5} ● \frac{8}{10}$ =
6. $\frac{3}{8} ● \frac{7}{8}$ <
7. $\frac{1}{2} ● \frac{5}{9}$ <
8. $\frac{9}{14} ● \frac{10}{17}$ >
9. $\frac{5}{7} ● \frac{6}{11}$ >
10. $\frac{8}{17} ● \frac{1}{2}$ <
11. $\frac{9}{10} ● \frac{17}{19}$ >

Chapter 4   59   Course 2

Skills Practice*
p. 60 **BL** **OL**

NAME _____ DATE _____ PERIOD _____

4-9 Skills Practice
Comparing and Ordering Rational Numbers

Find the LCD of each pair of fractions.
1. $\frac{4}{7}, \frac{3}{5}$ 35
2. $\frac{5}{12}, \frac{7}{24}$ 24
3. $\frac{6}{28}, \frac{3}{7}$ 28
4. $\frac{7}{15}, \frac{1}{4}$ 60
5. $\frac{5}{11}, \frac{3}{5}$ 55
6. $\frac{5}{17}, \frac{7}{8}$ 136
7. $\frac{5}{12}, \frac{7}{10}$ 60
8. $\frac{15}{16}, \frac{1}{4}$ 16
9. $\frac{5}{8}, \frac{3}{5}$ 40

Replace each ● with <, >, or = to make a true sentence.
10. $\frac{3}{10} ● \frac{2}{9}$ >
11. $\frac{3}{7} ● \frac{5}{11}$ <
12. $\frac{9}{12} ● \frac{3}{4}$ =
13. $\frac{12}{13} ● \frac{14}{15}$ <
14. $\frac{4}{5} ● \frac{5}{4}$ <
15. $\frac{17}{30} ● \frac{13}{20}$ <
16. $\frac{35}{60} ● \frac{49}{84}$ =
17. $3\frac{4}{11} ● 3\frac{7}{20}$ <
18. $1\frac{2}{8} ● 1\frac{6}{7}$ <

Order each set of ratios from least to greatest.
19. 0.48, 0.46, $\frac{9}{20}$ $\frac{9}{20}$, 0.46, 0.48
20. 0.99, 0.89, $\frac{7}{8}$ $\frac{7}{8}$, 0.89, 0.99
21. $\frac{1}{4}$, 0.2, 0.4   0.2, $\frac{1}{4}$, 0.4

Determine whether each number is rational. Write yes or no.
22. 2.323323332...   no
23. $\frac{7}{19}$ yes
24. $4.\overline{3}$ yes

Chapter 4   60   Course 2

Practice*
p. 61 **OL** **AL**

NAME _____ DATE _____ PERIOD _____

4-9 Practice
Comparing and Ordering Rational Numbers

Replace each ● with >, <, or = to make a true sentence.
1. $\frac{5}{6} ● \frac{1}{3}$ >
2. $\frac{4}{5} ● \frac{9}{10}$ <
3. $\frac{6}{9} ● \frac{4}{6}$ =
4. $\frac{2}{7} ● \frac{1}{8}$ >
5. $\frac{5}{21} ● \frac{12}{18}$ >
6. $\frac{24}{32} ● \frac{36}{48}$ =
7. $\frac{5}{11} ● \frac{10}{13}$ <
8. $\frac{14}{15} ● \frac{19}{20}$ <
9. $4\frac{1}{5} ● 4\frac{2}{10}$ =
10. $7\frac{3}{5} ● 7\frac{2}{3}$ <
11. $1\frac{17}{20} ● 1\frac{8}{10}$ >
12. $2\frac{3}{6} ● 2\frac{5}{3}$ <
13. 50% ● 8 out of 10   =
14. 0.65 ● 65 out of 100   =
15. 4 out of 5 ● 75%   >
16. 1 out of 3 ● 1.3   <
17. $\frac{2}{3}$ mile ● $\frac{5}{6}$ mile   >
18. $\frac{7}{10}$ gram ● 0.72 gram   <

Determine whether each number is rational. Write yes or no. Explain your reasoning.
19. $\frac{8}{21}$ Yes; it is a fraction.
20. 0.50550555 . . .   No; it cannot be written as a fraction.
21. 1.142857   Yes; the decimal repeats.

Order each set of numbers from least to greatest.
22. 63%, $\frac{2}{3}$, 0.65   63%, 0.65, $\frac{2}{3}$
23. $\frac{7}{8}$, 0.98, 98.5% $\frac{7}{8}$, 0.98, 98.5%
24. 0.2, 2%, $\frac{1}{12}$ 2%, $\frac{1}{12}$, 0.2

25. **BASEBALL** The pitchers for the home team had 12 strikeouts for 32 batters, while the pitchers for the visiting team had 15 strikeouts for 35 batters. Which pitching team had a greater fraction of strikeouts? **the visiting team**

26. **TRANSPORTATION** To get to school, 38% of the students ride in the family vehicle, 5 out of 12 students ride on the school bus, and 0.12 of the students ride a bike. Order the types of transportation students use to get to school from least to greatest. **0.12 (riding a bike), 38% (riding in the family vehicle), 5 out of 12 (riding the school bus)**

Chapter 4   61   Course 2

Word Problem Practice*
p. 62 **OL** **AL**

NAME _____ DATE _____ PERIOD _____

4-9 Word Problem Practice
Comparing and Ordering Rational Numbers

1. **RAIN** The amount of rainfall was measured after a recent storm. The north side of town received $\frac{7}{8}$ inch of rain, and the south side received $\frac{13}{15}$ inch of rain. Which side of town received more rain from the storm? **north**

2. **MOVIES** Because he sees movies at his local theater so often, Delmar is being offered a discount. He can have either $\frac{1}{3}$ off his next ticket or 30% off his next ticket. Which discount should Delmar choose? Explain. **$\frac{1}{3}$ off; $\frac{1}{3} > 30\%$**

3. **TRACK** Willie runs the 110-meter hurdles in $17\frac{3}{5}$ seconds, and Anier runs it in $17\frac{6}{8}$ seconds. Which runner is faster? **Anier**

4. **FARMING** Cassie successfully harvested $\frac{7}{12}$ of her crop, and Robert successfully harvested 58% of his crop. Which person successfully harvested the larger portion of his or her crop? **Cassie**

5. **TRANSPORTATION** My-Lien has enough room in her truck to move 3.385 tons of gravel. Her father has asked her to move $3\frac{5}{12}$ tons. Will My-Lien be able to move all of the gravel in only one trip? Explain. **Yes; $3\frac{5}{16} < 3.385$.**

6. **WOOD WORKING** Kishi has a bolt that is $\frac{5}{8}$ inch wide, and she drilled a hole 0.6 inch wide. Is the hole large enough to fit the bolt? Explain. **No; $\frac{5}{8} > 0.6$**

7. **PIZZA** In a recent pizza-eating contest, Alfonso ate $1\frac{5}{8}$ pizzas, Della ate $1\frac{7}{10}$ pizzas, and Delsin ate $1\frac{4}{5}$ pizzas. Which person won the contest? **Delsin**

8. **STUDYING** For a recent algebra exam, Pat studied $1\frac{7}{8}$ hours, Toni studied $1\frac{11}{12}$ hours, and Morgan studied $1\frac{15}{16}$ hours. List the students in order by who studied the most. **Morgan, Toni, Pat**

Chapter 4   62   Course 2

Enrichment
p. 63 **OL** **AL**

NAME _____ DATE _____ PERIOD _____

4-9 Enrichment

Intersection and Union of Sets
The darker shaded areas in the Venn diagrams show the *union* and *intersection* of sets A and B.

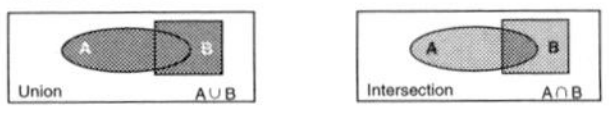

Union A ∪ B   Intersection A ∩ B

For example, if A = {1, 2, 3, 4} and B = {3, 4, 5, 6}, then their union and intersection are written as:
Union: A ∪ B = {1, 2, 3, 4, 5, 6}   Intersection: A ∩ B = {3, 4}

Draw a Venn diagram for sets A and B. Then write the numbers included in A ∪ B and A ∩ B. In Exercises 2 and 4, record the numbers as decimals.

1. A = {integers between 0 and 7}
B = {factors of 12}
A ∪ B = {1, 2, 3, 4, 5, 6, 12}
A ∩ B = {1, 2, 3, 4, 6}

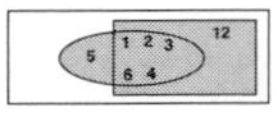

2. A = {one-place decimals between 0 and 0.5}
B = {fractions with 1, 2, 3, or 4 as numerator and 5 as a denominator}
A ∪ B = {0.1, 0.2, 0.3, 0.4, 0.6, 0.8}
A ∩ B = {0.2, 0.4}

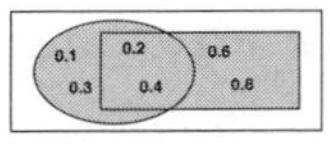

3. A = {perfect squares between 0 and 30}
B = {odd whole numbers less than 10}
A ∪ B = {1, 3, 4, 5, 7, 9, 16, 25}
A ∩ B = {1, 9}

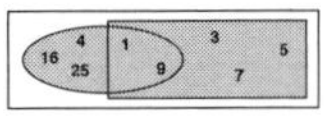

4. A = {$\frac{1}{3}$, $\frac{1}{2}$, $\frac{1}{4}$, $\frac{3}{5}$}
B = {0.1, 0.2, 0.3, 0.4, 0.5, 0.6, 0.7, 0.8, 0.9}
A ∪ B = {0.1, 0.2, 0.25, 0.3, 0.4, 0.5, $0.\overline{6}$, $0.\overline{7}$, 0.8, 0.9}
A ∩ B = {$0.\overline{3}$}

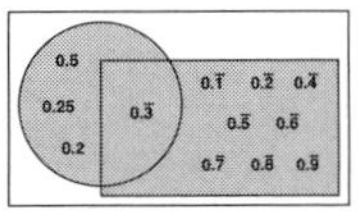

Chapter 4   63   Course 2

---

* Also available in Spanish **ELL**

Additional Lesson Resources

Transparencies
• *5-Minute Check Transparency*, Lesson 4-9

Other Print Products
• *Noteables™ Interactive Study Notebook with Foldables™*

Teacher Tech Tools
• *Interactive Classroom CD-ROM*, Lesson 4-9
• *AssignmentWorks*, Lesson 4-9

Student Tech Tools
glencoe.com
• Extra Examples, Chapter 4, Lesson 9
• Self-Check Quiz, Chapter 4, Lesson 9

Comparing and Ordering Rational Numbers

▷ MINI Lab

In Chapter 2, you used a number line to compare integers. You can also use a number line to compare positive and negative fractions. The number line shows that $-\frac{1}{8} < \frac{3}{8}$.

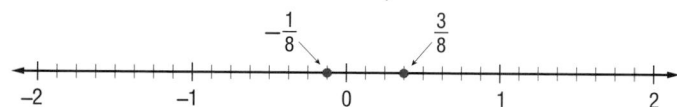

1–6. See Ch. 4 Answer Appendix for number lines.
Graph each pair of numbers on a number line. Then determine which number is less. 4. $-1\frac{7}{8} < -1\frac{5}{8}$

1. $-\frac{7}{8}, -\frac{3}{8}$ $-\frac{7}{8} < -\frac{3}{8}$ 2. $-\frac{5}{8}, -1\frac{1}{8}$ $-1\frac{1}{8} < -\frac{5}{8}$ 3. $-\frac{13}{8}, -\frac{3}{8}$ $-\frac{13}{8} < -\frac{3}{8}$

4. $-1\frac{7}{8}, -1\frac{5}{8}$ 5. $-\frac{1}{2}, -\frac{3}{4}$ $-\frac{3}{4} < -\frac{1}{2}$ 6. $1\frac{1}{4}, -1\frac{1}{4}$ $-1\frac{1}{4} < 1\frac{1}{4}$

The different types of numbers you have been using are all examples of rational numbers. A **rational number** is a number that can be expressed as a fraction. Fractions, terminating and repeating decimals, percents, and integers are all rational numbers. The points corresponding to rational numbers begin to "fill in" the number line.

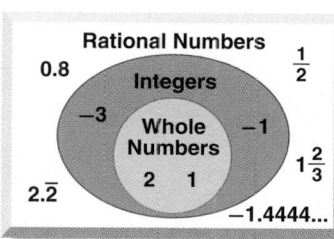

EXAMPLE   Compare Rational Numbers

1 Replace the ● with <, >, or = to make $-1\frac{5}{6}$ ● $-1\frac{1}{6}$ a true sentence.

Graph each rational number on a number line. Mark off equal size increments of $\frac{1}{6}$ between -2 and -1.

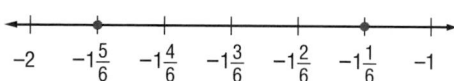

The number line shows that $-1\frac{5}{6} < -1\frac{1}{6}$.

✓ CHECK Your Progress

a. Replace the ● with <, >, or = to make $-5\frac{5}{9}$ ● $-5\frac{1}{9}$ a true sentence. **<**

Lesson 4-9 Comparing and Ordering Rational Numbers   **215**

Focus on Mathematical Content

Rational numbers can be written as the ratio of two integers (the second integer cannot be 0).

Decimals that neither terminate nor repeat are **not rational**.

✓ **Formative Assessment**

Use the Check Your Progress exercises after each Example to determine students' understanding of concepts.

ADDITIONAL EXAMPLES

Replace each ● with <, >, or = to make a true sentence.

1 $-3\frac{3}{8}$ ● $-3\frac{7}{8}$ >

2 $\frac{5}{12}$ ● $\frac{7}{16}$ <

3 DOGS According to the Pet Food Manufacturer's Association, 11 out of 25 people own large dogs and 13 out of 50 own medium dogs. Do more people own large or medium dogs? large

Additional Examples are also in:
• Noteables™ Interactive Study Notebook with Foldables™
• Interactive Classroom PowerPoint® Presentations

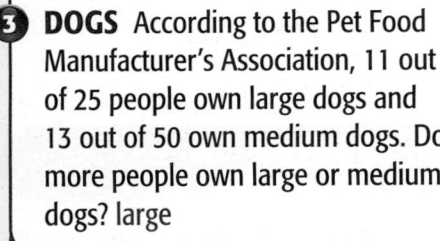

Tips for New Teachers

Rational Numbers

Help students remember the definition of *rational* numbers by pointing out that they can be written as a *ratio* of integers (provided the second integer isn't 0). You may also wish to remind students that in Lesson 4-5 they learned that terminating and repeating decimals can be written as fractions, or ratios.

A **common denominator** is a common multiple of the denominators of two or more fractions. The **least common denominator** or **LCD** is the LCM of the denominators. You can use the LCD to compare fractions.

EXAMPLE Compare Rational Numbers

2 Replace the ● with <, >, or = to make $\frac{7}{12}$ ● $\frac{8}{18}$ a true sentence.

$12 = 2^2 \cdot 3$ and $18 = 2 \cdot 3^2$. So, the LCM is $2^2 \cdot 3^2$ or 36. The LCD of the denominators 12 and 18 is 36.

$$\frac{7}{12} = \frac{7 \times 3}{12 \times 3} \qquad\qquad \frac{8}{18} = \frac{8 \times 2}{18 \times 2}$$

$$= \frac{21}{36} \qquad\qquad\qquad = \frac{16}{36}$$

Since $\frac{21}{36} > \frac{16}{36}$, then $\frac{7}{12} > \frac{8}{18}$.

✓ **CHECK Your Progress**

Replace each ● with <, >, or = to make a true sentence.

b. $\frac{5}{6}$ ● $\frac{7}{9}$ > c. $\frac{1}{5}$ ● $\frac{7}{50}$ > d. $-\frac{9}{16}$ ● $-\frac{7}{10}$ >

You can also compare fractions by writing each fraction as a decimal and then comparing the decimals.

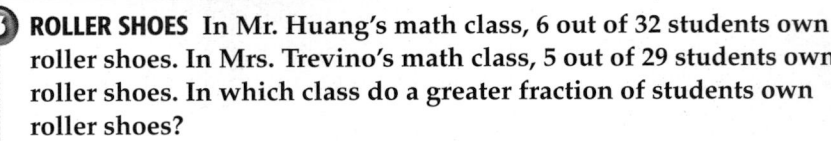 **Real-World EXAMPLE**

3 ROLLER SHOES In Mr. Huang's math class, 6 out of 32 students own roller shoes. In Mrs. Trevino's math class, 5 out of 29 students own roller shoes. In which class do a greater fraction of students own roller shoes?

Since the denominators are large, write $\frac{6}{32}$ and $\frac{5}{29}$ as decimals and then compare.

$6 \div 32 = 0.1875$ $\qquad$ $5 \div 29 \approx 0.1724$ $\qquad$ Divide.

Since $0.1875 > 0.1724$, then $\frac{6}{32} > \frac{5}{29}$.

So, a greater fraction of students in Mr. Huang's class own roller shoes.

Real-World Link . . . .
The first roller shoe was introduced in 2001.
Source: Associated Content, Inc.

✓ **CHECK Your Progress**

fifth period class

e. BOWLING Twelve out of 32 students in second period class like to bowl. In fifth period class, 12 out of 29 students like to bowl. In which class do a greater fraction of the students like to bowl?

These fraction-decimal-percent equivalents are used frequently.

Fractions-Decimals-Percents

$\frac{1}{4} = 0.25 = 25\%$	$\frac{1}{5} = 0.2 = 20\%$	$\frac{1}{8} = 0.125 = 12.5\%$	$\frac{1}{10} = 0.1 = 10\%$
$\frac{1}{2} = 0.5 = 50\%$	$\frac{2}{5} = 0.4 = 40\%$	$\frac{3}{8} = 0.375 = 37.5\%$	$\frac{3}{10} = 0.3 = 30\%$
$\frac{3}{4} = 0.75 = 75\%$	$\frac{3}{5} = 0.6 = 60\%$	$\frac{1}{3} = 0.\overline{3} = 33.\overline{3}\%$	$\frac{7}{10} = 0.7 = 70\%$
$1 = 1.00 = 100\%$	$\frac{4}{5} = 0.8 = 80\%$	$\frac{2}{3} = 0.\overline{6} = 66.\overline{6}\%$	$\frac{9}{10} = 0.9 = 90\%$

The Greek letter π (pi) represents the nonterminating and nonrepeating number whose first few digits are 3.1415926.... This number is not rational. You will learn more about *irrational numbers* in Chapter 12.

ADDITIONAL EXAMPLE

4 **TEST EXAMPLE** Four frozen dinners had the following amounts of vegetables: $\frac{7}{10}$, 0.6, 72%, and $\frac{16}{25}$. Which list shows the numbers in order from least to greatest? C

A $0.6, \frac{7}{10}, \frac{16}{25}, 72\%$

B $\frac{16}{25}, 0.6, 72\%, \frac{7}{10}$

C $0.6, \frac{16}{25}, \frac{7}{10}, 72\%$

D $72\%, \frac{7}{10}, 0.6, \frac{16}{25}$

TEST EXAMPLE

4 Which list shows the numbers 3.44, π, 3.14, and $3.\overline{4}$ in order from least to greatest?

A $\pi, 3.14, 3.44, 3.\overline{4}$ C $3.14, \pi, 3.\overline{4}, 3.44$

B $\pi, 3.14, 3.\overline{4}, 3.44$ D $3.14, \pi, 3.44, 3.\overline{4}$

Read the Item
Compare the digits using place value.

Solve the Item
Line up the decimal points and compare using place value.

3.140	Annex a zero.	3.440	Annex a zero.
3.1415926...	$\pi \approx 3.1415926...$	3.444...	$3.\overline{4} = 3.444...$
Since $0 < 1$, $3.14 < \pi$.		Since $0 < 4$, $3.44 < 3.\overline{4}$.	

So, the order of the numbers from least to greatest is 3.14, π, 3.44, and $3.\overline{4}$. The answer is D.

✓ CHECK Your Progress

f. The amount of rain received on four consecutive days was 0.3 inch, $\frac{3}{5}$ inch, 0.75 inch, and $\frac{2}{3}$ inch. Which list shows the amounts from least to greatest? **G**

F 0.3 in., $\frac{2}{3}$ in., $\frac{3}{5}$ in., 0.75 in.   H 0.75 in., $\frac{2}{3}$ in., $\frac{3}{5}$ in., 0.3 in.

G 0.3 in., $\frac{3}{5}$ in., $\frac{2}{3}$ in., 0.75 in.   J $\frac{3}{5}$ in., $\frac{2}{3}$ in., 0.3 in., 0.75 in.

3 Practice

 Formative Assessment

Use Exercises 1–7 to check for understanding.

Then use the chart at the bottom of this page to customize your assignments for students.

Intervention You may wish to use the Study Guide and Intervention Master on page 59 of the *Chapter 4 Resource Masters* for additional reinforcement.

Odd/Even Assignments

Exercises 8–31 are structured so that students practice the same concepts whether they are assigned odd or even problems.

Additional Answer

5. Elliot; 3 out of 4 has an average of 0.75; 7 out of 11 has an average of 0.64.

CHECK Your Understanding

Examples 1–2
(pp. 215–216)

Replace each ● with <, >, or = to make a true sentence. Use a number line if necessary.

1. $-\frac{4}{9}$ ● $-\frac{7}{9}$ >   2. $-1\frac{3}{4}$ ● $-1\frac{6}{8}$ =   3. $\frac{3}{8}$ ● $\frac{6}{15}$ <   4. $2\frac{4}{5}$ ● $2\frac{7}{8}$ <

Example 3
(p. 216)

5. **SOCCER** The table shows the average saves for two soccer goalies. Who has the better average, Elliot or Shanna? Explain. **See margin.**

Name	Average
Elliot	3 saves out of 4
Shanna	7 saves out of 11

6. **SCHOOL** On her first quiz in social studies, Majorie answered 23 out of 25 questions correctly. On her second quiz, she answered 27 out of 30 questions correctly. On which quiz did Majorie have the greater score? **her first quiz**

Example 4
(p. 217)

7. **MULTIPLE CHOICE** The lengths of four insects are 0.02 inch, $\frac{1}{8}$ inch, 0.1 inch, and $\frac{2}{3}$ inch. Which list shows the lengths in inches from least to greatest? **C**

A $0.1, 0.02, \frac{1}{8}, \frac{2}{3}$ C $0.02, 0.1, \frac{1}{8}, \frac{2}{3}$

B $\frac{1}{8}, 0.02, 0.1, \frac{2}{3}$ D $\frac{2}{3}, 0.02, 0.1, \frac{1}{8}$

Practice and Problem Solving

HOMEWORK HELP	
For Exercises	**See Examples**
8–19	1, 2
20–25, 49	3
26–31, 48	4

Exercise Levels:
A: 8–31
B: 32–44
C: 45–47

Replace each ● with <, >, or = to make a true sentence. Use a number line if necessary.

8. $-\frac{3}{5}$ ● $-\frac{4}{5}$ >   9. $-\frac{5}{7}$ ● $-\frac{2}{7}$ <   10. $-7\frac{5}{8}$ ● $-7\frac{1}{8}$ < 11. $-3\frac{2}{3}$ ● $-3\frac{4}{6}$ =

12. $\frac{7}{10}$ ● $\frac{2}{3}$ >   13. $\frac{4}{7}$ ● $\frac{5}{8}$ <   14. $\frac{2}{3}$ ● $\frac{10}{15}$ =   15. $-\frac{17}{24}$ ● $-\frac{11}{12}$ >

16. $2\frac{3}{4}$ ● $2\frac{2}{3}$ >   17. $6\frac{2}{3}$ ● $6\frac{1}{2}$ >   18. $5\frac{5}{7}$ ● $5\frac{11}{14}$ <   19. $3\frac{11}{16}$ ● $3\frac{7}{8}$ <

20. 40% ● 112 out of 250 <   21. 3 out of 5 ● 59% >

22. 0.82 ● 5 out of 6 <   23. 9 out of 20 ● 0.45 =

24. **MONEY** The table shows how much copper is in each type of coin. Which coin contains the greatest amount of copper? **quarter**

Coin	Amount of Copper
Dime	$\frac{12}{16}$
Nickel	$\frac{3}{4}$
Penny	$\frac{1}{400}$
Quarter	$\frac{23}{25}$

25. **BASKETBALL** Gracia and Jim were shooting free throws. Gracia made 4 out of 15 free throws. Jim *missed* the free throw 6 out of 16 times. Who made the free throw a greater fraction of the time? Jim; $\frac{10}{16} > \frac{4}{15}$

DIFFERENTIATED HOMEWORK OPTIONS

Level	Assignment	Two-Day Option	
BL Basic	8–31, 45, 47–62	9–31 odd, 48–50	8–30 even, 45, 47, 51–62
OL Core	9–23 odd, 24, 25–39 odd, 40–45, 47–62	8–31, 48–50	32–45, 47, 51–62
AL Advanced/Pre-AP	32–62		

26. 19%, $\frac{1}{5}$, 0.23

27. $\frac{8}{10}$, 0.805, 81%

28. $-\frac{5}{8}$, -0.62, -0.615

29. -1.4, -1.25, $-1\frac{1}{25}$

30. 7.49, 7.5, $7\frac{49}{50}$

31. 3.47, $3\frac{4}{7}$, $3\frac{3}{5}$

Real-World Link.....
The Olympic gold medals are actually made out of 92.5% silver, with the gold medal covered in 6 grams of pure gold.

42. Kitti's Hog-Nosed Bat, European Mole, Eastern Chipmunk, Spiny Pocket Mouse, Masked Shrew

EXTRA PRACTICE
See pages 679, 707.

Order each set of numbers from least to greatest.

26. 0.23, 19%, $\frac{1}{5}$

27. $\frac{8}{10}$, 81%, 0.805

28. -0.615, $-\frac{5}{8}$, -0.62

29. -1.4, $-1\frac{1}{25}$, -1.25

30. 7.49, $7\frac{49}{50}$, 7.5

31. $3\frac{4}{7}$, $3\frac{3}{5}$, 3.47

MEASUREMENT Replace each ● with <, >, or = to make a true sentence.

32. $\frac{5}{8}$ yard ● $\frac{1}{16}$ yard   >

33. 0.25 pound ● $\frac{2}{9}$ pound   >

34. $2\frac{5}{6}$ hours ● 2.8 hours   >

35. $1\frac{7}{12}$ gallons ● $1\frac{5}{8}$ gallons   <

MEASUREMENT Order each of the following from least to greatest. 36–39.
See margin.

36. 4.4 miles, $4\frac{3}{8}$ miles, $4\frac{5}{12}$ miles

37. 6.5 cups, $6\frac{1}{3}$ cups, 6 cups

38. 1.2 laps, 2 laps, $\frac{1}{2}$ lap

39. $\frac{1}{5}$ gram, 5 grams, 1.5 grams

ANIMALS For Exercises 40–42, use the table that shows the lengths of the smallest mammals.

Animal	Length (ft)
Eastern Chipmunk	$\frac{1}{3}$
Kitti's Hog-Nosed Bat	$0.8\overline{3}$
European Mole	$\frac{5}{12}$
Masked Shrew	$\frac{1}{6}$
Spiny Pocket Mouse	0.25

Source: *Scholastic Book of World Records*

40. Which animal is the smallest mammal? **Masked Shrew**
★

41. Which animal is smaller than the European mole but larger than the spiny pocket mouse? **Eastern Chipmunk**
★

42. Order the animals from greatest to least size.
★

SOFTBALL For Exercises 43 and 44, use the following table which shows the at-bats, hits, and home run statistics for four players on the 2004 Olympics U.S. Women's softball team.

Player	At-Bats	Hits	Home Runs
Crystal Bustos	26	9	5
Kelly Krestschman	21	7	1
Stacey Nuveman	16	5	2
Natasha Watley	30	12	0

Source: Olympic Movement

★ **43.** Write the ratio of hits to at-bats as a decimal to the nearest thousandth for each player. Who had the greatest batting average during the Olympic games? **Bustos: 0.346; Krestschman: 0.333; Nuveman: 0.313; Watley: 0.400; Watley**

44. Write the ratio of home runs to at-bats as a decimal for each player. Who had the greatest home run average during the Olympic games? **See margin.**
★

Lesson 4-9 Comparing and Ordering Rational Numbers   **219**

Additional Answers

36. $4\frac{3}{8}$ mi, 4.4 mi, $4\frac{5}{12}$ mi

37. 6 c, $6\frac{1}{3}$ c, 6.5 c

38. $\frac{1}{2}$ lap, 1.2 laps, 2 laps

39. $\frac{1}{5}$ g, 1.5 g, 5 g

44. Bustos: 0.192; Kretschman: 0.048; Nuveman: 0.125; Watley: 0.0; Bustos

---

Differentiated Instruction

Bodily/Kinesthetic Learners Before class, write a fraction, decimal, or percent on each of a package of index cards. Separate students into groups of four. Give each group 10 or 12 of the index cards, which should be placed in a pile, face down. Each student picks a card. Have the members of each group work together to order their cards from least to greatest. Have them repeat the activity several times.

4 **Assess**

Name the Math Write the following two pairs of fractions on, the chalkboard: $\frac{3}{8}$ and $\frac{5}{12}$; and $\frac{3}{18}$ and $\frac{5}{22}$. Have students tell what mathematical procedures they would use to compare the fractions in each pair. Have them explain their reasoning.

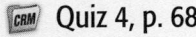 **Formative Assessment**

Check for student understanding of concepts in Lessons 4-8 and 4-9.

CRM Quiz 4, p. 68

 **Foldables™ Follow-Up**

Remind students to write—under the tab for this lesson of their Foldables—the answer to the question they wrote about the lesson.

Additional Answer

45. 0.08; 0.08 equals 8% and the other ratios equal 80%.

H.O.T. Problems

45. Which One Doesn't Belong? Identify the ratio that does not have the same value as the other three. Explain your reasoning. **See margin.**

| 12 out of 15 | 0.08 | 80% | $\frac{4}{5}$ |

46. CHALLENGE Explain how you know which number, $1\frac{15}{16}$, $\frac{17}{8}$, or $\frac{63}{32}$, is nearest to 2.
Sample answer: $\frac{63}{32}$ is closest to 2 because the difference of $\frac{63}{32}$ and 2 is the least.

47. 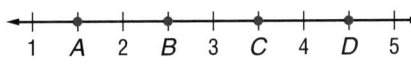 **MATH** Write a word problem about a real-world situation in which you would compare rational numbers. Then solve the problem.
Sample answer: Gwen needs $\frac{2}{5}$ yard of fabric and $\frac{3}{8}$ yard of ribbon to make a pillow. Which item does she need more, fabric or ribbon? Answer: fabric

TEST PRACTICE

48. Which point shows the location of $\frac{7}{2}$ on the number line? **C**

```
1   A   2   B   3   C   4   D   5
```

A point A
B point B
C point C
D point D

49. Which list of numbers is ordered from least to greatest? **H**

F $\frac{1}{4}$, $4\frac{1}{4}$, 0.4, 0.04

G 0.04, 0.4, $4\frac{1}{4}$, $\frac{1}{4}$

H 0.04, $\frac{1}{4}$, 0.4, $4\frac{1}{4}$

J 0.4, $\frac{1}{4}$, 0.04, $4\frac{1}{4}$

50. Which of the following fractions is closest to 0? **C**

A $-\frac{3}{4}$ C $\frac{7}{12}$

B $-\frac{2}{3}$ D $\frac{5}{8}$

Spiral Review

Find the LCM of each set of numbers. (Lesson 4-8)

51. 14, 21 **42**   **52.** 3, 13 **39**   **53.** 12, 16 **48**

SALES TAX The table shows the sales tax rate for the states shown. Write each sales tax rate as a decimal. (Lesson 4-7)

54. Kentucky **0.06**

55. Illinois **0.0625**

56. North Carolina **0.0425**

State	Sales Tax
Illinois	6.25%
Kentucky	6%
North Carolina	4.25%
South Carolina	5%

Source: Federation of Tax Administrators

Find the GCF of each set of numbers. (Lesson 4-2)

57. 18, 72 **18**   **58.** 40, 12 **4**   **59.** 72, 20 **4**

ALGEBRA Solve each equation. (Lesson 3-5)

60. $4x + 3 = 15$ **3**   **61.** $2n - 5 = 19$ **12**   **62.** $-8 = -3d + 1$ **3**

CHAPTER 4

Study Guide and Review

Study Organizer

GET READY to Study

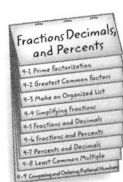

Be sure the following Big Ideas are noted in your Foldable.

BIG Ideas

Greatest Common Factor (Lesson 4-2)
• The greatest common factor or GCF is the greatest of the common factors of two or more numbers.

Fractions, Decimals, and Percents
(Lessons 4-4 to 4-7)
• A fraction is in simplest form when the GCF of the numerator and denominator is 1.

• A terminating decimal is a decimal whose digits end. Repeating decimals have a pattern in their digits that repeats forever.

• A percent is a part to whole ratio that compares a number to 100.

• To write a percent as a decimal, divide the percent by 100 and remove the percent symbol.

• To write a decimal as a percent, multiply the percent by 100 and add the percent symbol.

Least Common Multiple (Lesson 4-8)
• The least common multiple or LCM of two or more numbers is the least of their common multiples.

Rational Numbers (Lesson 4-9)
• A rational number is one that can be expressed as a fraction.

Key Vocabulary

bar notation (p. 197)
common denominator (p. 216)
composite number (p. 181)
equivalent fractions (p. 192)
factor tree (p. 182)
greatest common factor (GCF) (p. 186)
least common denominator (p. 216)
least common multiple (LCM) (p. 211)
multiple (p. 211)
percent (p. 202)
prime factorization (p. 182)
prime number (p. 181)
ratio (p. 202)
rational number (p. 215)
repeating decimal (p. 197)
simplest form (p. 192)
terminating decimal (p. 197)
Venn diagram (p. 186)

Vocabulary Check

State whether each sentence is *true* or *false*. If *false*, replace the underlined word or number to make a true sentence.

1. A ratio is a comparison of two numbers by <u>multiplication</u>. **false; division**

2. A <u>rational number</u> is a whole number greater than 1 that has exactly two factors, 1 and itself. **false; prime number**

3. 1.875 is an example of a <u>terminating decimal</u>. **true**

4. A common denominator for the fractions $\frac{2}{3}$ and $\frac{1}{4}$ is <u>12</u>. **true**

5. The <u>greatest common factor</u> of 3 and 5 is 15. **false; least common multiple**

6. A ratio that compares a number to <u>100</u> is a percent. **true**

7. The fractions $\frac{9}{21}$ and $\frac{3}{7}$ are <u>equivalent fractions</u>. **true**

Chapter 4 Study Guide and Review **221**

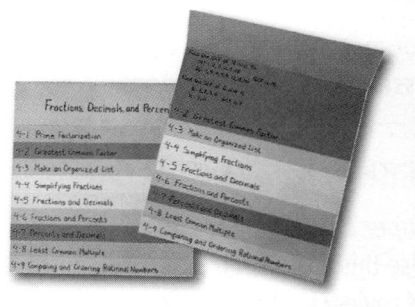
Study Organizer

Dinah Zike's Foldables

Have students look through the chapter to make sure they have answered the questions they wrote in their Foldables about each lesson.

Encourage students to refer to their Foldables while completing the Study Guide and Review and while preparing for the Chapter Test.

 Formative Assessment

Key Vocabulary The page references after each word in the Key Vocabulary denote where that term was first introduced. If students have difficulty answering Exercises 1–7, remind them that they can use these page references to refresh their memories about the vocabulary terms.

Math Online > glencoe.com

Vocabulary PuzzleMaker improves students' mathematics vocabulary using four puzzle formats–crossword, scramble, word search using a word list, and word search using clues. Students can work online or from a printed worksheet.

 Summative Assessment

 CRM Vocabulary Test, p. 70

Lesson-by-Lesson Review

Intervention If the given examples are not sufficient to review the topics covered by the questions, remind students that the page references tell them where to review that topic in their textbooks.

Two-Day Option Have students complete the Lesson-by-Lesson Review on pages 222–224. Then you can use ExamView® Assessment Suite to customize another review worksheet that practices all the objectives of this chapter or only the objectives on which your students need more help.

For more information on ExamView® Assessment Suite, see page 178C.

Differentiated Instruction

Super DVD: MindJogger Plus
Use this DVD as an alternative format of review for the test. For more information on this game show format, see page 178D.

Lesson-by-Lesson Review

4-1 **Prime Factorization** (pp. 181–184)

Find the prime factorization of each number.

8. 54   9. 128   10. 68   11. 95
2×3^3 2^7 $2^2 \times 17$ 5×19

12. **ALGEBRA** Factor $36x^2yz^3$.
$2 \cdot 2 \cdot 3 \cdot 3 \cdot x \cdot x \cdot y \cdot z \cdot z \cdot z$

13. **PLANTS** The palm tree *raffia* has leaves up to 65 feet long. Write this length as a product of primes. **65 = 5 • 13**

Example 1 Find the prime factorization of 18.

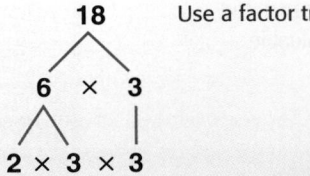

18   Use a factor tree

6 × 3

2 × 3 × 3

The prime factorization of 18 is 2×3^2.

4-2 **Greatest Common Factor** (p. 186–189)

Find the GCF of each set of numbers.

14. 18, 27 **9**   15. 30, 72 **6**

16. 28, 70, 98 **14**   17. 42, 63, 105 **21**

18. **ALGEBRA** Find the GCF of $18w$ and $54w^2y$. **18w**

19. **CLOTHING** Maria spent a total of $24 on earrings, $36 on shirts, and $48 on shorts. If each item cost the same amount, what is the greatest possible price per item? **$12**

Example 2 Find the GCF of 24 and 56.

First, make a list of all the factors of 24 and 56.

factors of 24: **1, 2**, 3, **4**, 6, **8**, 12, 24

factors of 56: **1, 2, 4**, 7, **8**, 14, 28, 56

common factors: 1, 2, 4, 8

The GCF of 24 and 56 is 8.

4-3 **PSI: Make an Organized List** (pp. 190–191)

Solve by making an organized list.

20. **SEATING** In how many ways can four friends sit in a row at the movies? **24 ways**

21. **TELEPHONES** A phone company offers 5 different types of long-distance plans and 3 different caller features (call waiting, caller ID, and call forward). How many different kinds of plans can be set up that include a long-distance service and a caller feature?

15 different plans

Example 3 In how many ways can the letters A, B, and C be arranged?

The possible outcomes are written below.

ABC   ACB
BAC   BCA
CAB   CBA

There are 6 different ways to arrange the letters.

222   **Chapter 4** Fractions, Decimals, and Percents

Mixed Problem Solving
For mixed problem-solving practice,
see page 707.

CHAPTER
4 Study Guide
and Review

4-4 Simplifying Fractions (pp. 192–195)

Write each fraction in simplest form.

22. $\frac{12}{15}$ **$\frac{4}{5}$** 23. $\frac{35}{60}$ **$\frac{7}{12}$** 24. $\frac{11}{121}$ **$\frac{1}{11}$**

25. $\frac{14}{63}$ **$\frac{2}{9}$** 26. $\frac{37}{45}$ **$\frac{37}{45}$** 27. $\frac{55}{110}$ **$\frac{1}{2}$**

28. **CATS** The average household cat sleeps 18 hours a day. Write a fraction in simplest form comparing the number of hours a household cat sleeps to the number of hours in a day. $\frac{3}{4}$

Example 4 Write $\frac{24}{32}$ in simplest form.

Find the GCF of the numerator and denominator.

$24 = 1, 2, 3, 4, 6, 8, 12, 24$

$32 = 1, 2, 4, 8, 16, 32$

$\frac{24}{32} = \frac{24 \div 8}{32 \div 8} = \frac{3}{4}$ Divide the numerator and denominator by the GCF.

4-5 Fractions and Decimals (pp. 196–200)

Write each fraction or mixed number as a decimal. Use bar notation if the decimal is a repeating decimal.

29. $\frac{3}{4}$ **0.75** 30. $\frac{7}{8}$ **0.875** 31. $\frac{5}{9}$ **$0.\overline{5}$**

32. $4\frac{1}{3}$ **$4.\overline{3}$** 33. $6\frac{2}{5}$ **6.4** 34. $1\frac{6}{7}$ **$1.\overline{857142}$**

Write each decimal as a fraction in simplest form.

35. 0.7 **$\frac{7}{10}$** 36. 0.44 **$\frac{11}{25}$** 37. 0.05 **$\frac{1}{20}$**

38. 0.18 **$\frac{9}{50}$** 39. 0.54 **$\frac{27}{50}$** 40. 0.08 **$\frac{2}{25}$**

41. **RUNNING** Jeremy ran a mile in 5 minutes and 8 seconds. Write this time in minutes as a decimal. **$5.1\overline{3}$ min**

Example 5 Write $\frac{3}{8}$ as a decimal.

$$
\begin{array}{r}
0.375 \\
8)\overline{3.000} \\
-\,24 \\
\hline
60 \\
-\,56 \\
\hline
40 \\
-\,40 \\
\hline
0
\end{array}
$$

So, $\frac{3}{8} = 0.375$.

Example 6 Write 0.64 as a fraction.

$0.64 = \frac{64}{100}$ Write as a fraction with a denominator of 100.

$= \frac{16}{25}$ Simplify.

4-6 Fractions and Percents (pp. 202–205)

Write each fraction as a percent.

42. $\frac{32}{100}$ 43. $\frac{11}{25}$ 44. $\frac{47}{50}$ 45. $\frac{8}{20}$
32%   **44%**   **94%**   **40%**

Write each percent as a fraction in simplest form.

46. 68% **$\frac{17}{25}$** 47. 95% **$\frac{19}{20}$** 48. 42% **$\frac{21}{50}$** 49. 16% **$\frac{4}{25}$**

50. **LUNCH** In Mrs. Soulise's class, 56% of the students buy their lunch. Write this percent as a fraction in simplest form. $\frac{14}{25}$

Example 7 Write $\frac{27}{50}$ as a percent.

$\frac{27}{50} = \frac{54}{100}$ Write an equivalent fraction with a denominator of 100.

$= 54\%$ Definition of percent

Example 8 Write 96% as a fraction.

$96\% = \frac{96}{100}$ Definition of percent

$= \frac{24}{25}$ Simplify.

CHAPTER **4** Study Guide and Review

Problem Solving Review

For additional practice in problem solving for Chapter 4, see the Mixed Problem Solving Appendix, page 707 in the Student Handbook section.

Anticipation Guide

Have students complete the Chapter 4 Anticipation Guide and discuss how their responses have changed now that they have completed Chapter 4.

CRM Anticipation Guide, p. 7

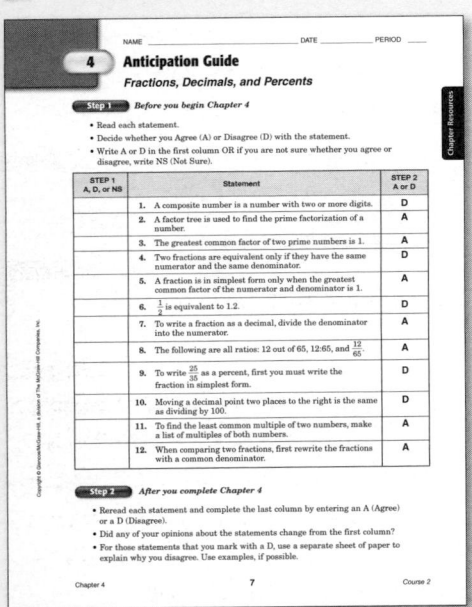

Additional Answer

66. 2 dozen muffins and 3 packages of orange juice containers

---

4-7 **Percents and Decimals** (pp. 206–210)

Write each percent as a decimal.

51. 48% **0.48**   52. 7% **0.07**

53. 12.5% **0.125**   54. $75\frac{1}{4}$% **0.7525**

Write each decimal as a percent.

55. 0.61   56. 0.055   57. 0.19   58. 0.999
61%   **5.5%**   **19%**   **99.9%**

59. **FOOD** A serving of oatmeal contains 3 grams of fiber. This is 12% of the recommended daily allowance. Write this percent as a decimal. **0.12**

Example 9 Write 35% as a decimal.

$35\% = \dfrac{35}{100}$ Write the percent as a fraction.

$\quad\ = 0.35$ Write the fraction as a decimal.

Example 10 Write 0.625 as a percent.

$0.625 = 0.625$ Multiply by 100.

$\quad\ = 62.5\%$ Add the % symbol.

4-8 **Least Common Multiple** (pp. 211–214)

Find the LCM of each set of numbers.

60. 9, 15 **45**   61. 4, 8 **8**

62. 16, 24 **48**   63. 3, 8, 12 **24**

64. 4, 9, 12 **36**   65. 15, 24, 30 **120**

66. **BREAKFAST** At a bakery, muffins come in dozens and individual serving containers of orange juice come in packs of 8. If Avery needs to have the same amount of muffins as orange juice containers, what is the least possible number of sets of each he needs to buy? **See margin.**

Example 11 Find the LCM of 8 and 36.

Write each prime factorization.

$8 = 2 \times 2 \times 2 = 2^3$

$36 = 2 \times 2 \times 3 \times 3 = 2^2 \times 3^2$

LCM: $2^3 \times 3^2 = 72$

The LCM of 8 and 36 is 72.

4-9 **Comparing and Ordering Rational Numbers** (pp. 215–220)

Replace each ● with <, >, or = to make a true sentence.

67. $\dfrac{3}{8}$ ● $\dfrac{2}{3}$ **<**   68. -0.45 ● $-\dfrac{9}{20}$ **=**

69. $\dfrac{8}{9}$ ● 85% **>**   70. $-3\dfrac{3}{4}$ ● $-3\dfrac{5}{8}$ **<**

71. **SCHOOL** Michael received a $\dfrac{26}{30}$ on his English quiz and received 81% on his biology test. In which class did he receive the higher score? **English**

Example 12 Replace ● with <, >, or = to make $\dfrac{3}{5}$ ● $\dfrac{5}{8}$ a true sentence.

Find equivalent fractions. The LCD is 40.

$\dfrac{3}{5} = \dfrac{3 \times 8}{5 \times 8} = \dfrac{24}{40}$ $\dfrac{5}{8} = \dfrac{5 \times 5}{8 \times 5} = \dfrac{25}{40}$

Since $\dfrac{24}{40} < \dfrac{25}{40}$, then $\dfrac{3}{5} < \dfrac{5}{8}$.

---

224 **Chapter 4** Fractions, Decimals, and Percents

1. Find the prime factorization of 72. **$2^3 \times 3^2$**

2. Find the GCF of 24 and 40. **8**

3. **SCHEDULES** Farijah registered for French, Pre-Algebra, Life Science, English, and Social Studies. French is only offered first period, Pre-Algebra is only offered fifth period, and she must have lunch fourth period. How many different schedules can she create out of a six period day? Use the *make an organized list* strategy. **6**

Write each fraction in simplest form.

4. $\frac{24}{60}$ **$\frac{2}{5}$**

5. $\frac{64}{72}$ **$\frac{8}{9}$**

Write each fraction, mixed number, or percent as a decimal. Use bar notation if the decimal is a repeating decimal.

6. $\frac{7}{9}$ **$0.\overline{7}$**

7. $4\frac{5}{8}$ **4.625**

8. 91% **0.91**

9. **COINS** The United States Mint released a new quarter every ten weeks from 1999 to 2008 commemorating the 50 states. By the end of 2006, 40 state coins had been released. What percent of the coins is this? **80%**

Write each decimal or percent as a fraction in simplest form.

10. 0.84 **$\frac{21}{25}$**

11. 0.006 **$\frac{3}{500}$**

12. 42% **$\frac{21}{50}$**

13. **MULTIPLE CHOICE** Which of the following is equivalent to the decimal 0.087? **B**

A 0.87%
B 8.7%
C 87%
D 870%

Write each fraction or decimal as a percent.

14. $\frac{15}{25}$ **60%**

15. 0.26 **26%**

16. 0.135 **13.5%**

17. **FLOORING** Mr. Daniels is putting new floor tiles in his bathroom. He has already tiled 34 square feet of the floor measuring 5 feet by 10 feet. What percent of the floor has he tiled? **68%**

18. **MULTIPLE CHOICE** What percent of the figure below is unshaded? **H**

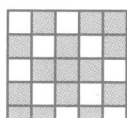

F 15%
G 30%
H 40%
J 60%

Find the LCM of each set of numbers.

19. 18, 42 **126**

20. 4, 5, 12 **60**

21. **PRACTICE** Rico has track practice every 3 days. He has saxophone practice every 4 days. If Rico has both track and saxophone practice today, after how many days will Rico have both track and saxophone practice again? **12 days**

Replace each ● with <, >, or = to make a true sentence.

22. $-\frac{3}{5}$ ● $-\frac{5}{9}$ **<**

23. $4\frac{7}{12}$ ● $4\frac{6}{8}$ **<**

24. $\frac{13}{20}$ ● 65% **=**

25. **BASKETBALL** To make it past the first round of tryouts for the basketball team, Paul must make at least 35% of his free-throw attempts. During the first round of tryouts he makes 17 out of 40 attempts. Did Paul make it to the next round of tryouts? Explain your reasoning. **See margin.**

✔ **Summative Assessment**

CRM **Chapter 4 Resource Masters**

Leveled Chapter 4 Tests			
Form	**Type**	**Level**	**Pages**
1	MC	**BL**	71–72
2A	MC	**OL**	73–74
2B	MC	**OL**	75–76
2C	FR	**OL**	77–78
2D	FR	**OL**	79–80
3	FR	**AL**	81–82

MC = multiple-choice questions
FR = free-response questions
BL = below or approaching grade level
OL = on grade level
AL = above or beyond grade level

• Vocabulary Test, p. 70
• Extended-Response Test, p. 83

 Customize and create multiple versions of your chapter test and their answer keys. All of the questions from the leveled chapter tests in the *Chapter 4 Resource Masters* are also available on ExamView® Assessment Suite.

Additional Answer

25. Yes; $\frac{17}{40} = 0.425$ and $0.425 > 35\%$ or 0.35.

Data-Driven Decision Making	**Exercises**	**Lesson**	**State/Local Standards**	**Resources for Review**
Diagnostic Teaching Based on the results of the Chapter 4 Practice Test, use the following to review concepts that students continue to find challenging.	1–3	4-1, 4-2, 4-3		CRM Study Guide and Intervention pp. 10, 17, 22, 27, 33, 40, 46, 52, and 59 Math Online > glencoe.com
	4–18	4-4, 4-5, 4-6, 4-7		• Extra Examples • Personal Tutor
	19–25	4-8, 4-9		• Concepts in Motion

TEST-TAKING TIP

Exercise 6 Ask students what word (or words) might indicate the operation in the equation (addition). Students should realize that *sum* indicates addition, which should lead them to examine answer choice H.

 Formative Assessment

You can use these three pages to benchmark student progress.

 Chapter 4 Resource Masters

• Standardized Test Practice, pp. 84–86

 Create practice worksheets or tests that align to your state's standards, as well as TIMSS and NAEP tests.

PART 1   Multiple Choice

Read each question. Then fill in the correct answer on the answer sheet provided by your teacher or on a sheet of paper.

1. A large school system estimates that 0.706 of its students will take the bus to school throughout the school year. Which number is greater than 0.706? **C**

   A $\frac{706}{1,000}$

   B $-1\frac{6}{7}$

   C $\frac{76}{100}$

   D -7.06

2. Debra is working on three different art projects. She has completed $\frac{1}{4}$, $\frac{3}{8}$, and $\frac{1}{2}$ of these projects, respectively. Which list shows the percent of work completed on these projects from least to greatest? **H**

   F 37.5%, 50%, 25%

   G 50%, 37.5%, 25%

   H 25%, 37.5%, 50%

   J 25%, 50%, 87.5%

3. Which of the following is the prime factored form of the lowest common denominator of $\frac{1}{6}$ and $\frac{3}{8}$? **D**

   A $2^2 \times 3 \times 5$ C 2×6

   B $2^3 \times 5$ D $2^3 \times 3$

TEST-TAKING TIP

Question 3 Eliminate any answer choices that you know are incorrect. Since the LCD, 24, does not have a factor of 5, you can eliminate answer choices A and B.

---

4. Solve the equation $x + 7 = -3$. What is the value of x? **J**

   F 4   H −4

   G 3   J −10

5. At a wedding reception, the number of seats s is equal to 8 times the number of tables t. Which equation matches this situation? **C**

   A $s = 8 + t$

   B $t = 8 \cdot s$

   C $s = 8 \cdot t$

   D $t = 8 - t$

6. Which problem situation matches the equation below? **H**

   $$x + 12 = 35$$

   F The difference between two numbers is 35. One of the numbers is 12. What is x, the other number?

   G Laura is 12 years younger than her brother. If Laura is 35 years old, find her brother's age x.

   H The sum of a number, x, and 12 is 35. What is the value of x?

   J Karen had $35. If she received $12, what is x, the total amount she now has?

7. Which of the following is true when evaluating the expression $3 \cdot 4^2 - 12 \div 6$? **B**

   A Multiply 3 by 4 first since multiplication comes before subtraction.

   B Evaluate 4^2 first since it is a power.

   C Divide 12 by 6 first since division comes before multiplication.

   D Multiply 3 by 4 first since all operations occur in order from left to right.

226   Chapter 4 Fractions, Decimals, and Percents

8. Which sequence follows the rule $2n + 5$, where n represents the position of a term in the sequence? **H**

   F 3, 5, 7, 9, 11, ...   H 7, 9, 11, 13, 15, ...

   G 6, 8, 10, 12, 14, ...   J 8, 12, 16, 20, 24, ...

9. Nicholas used the Distributive Property to evaluate the expression $5(12 + 7)$ mentally. Which of the following is a correct use of the Distributive Property to evaluate this expression? **A**

   A $5(12 + 7) = 5(12) + 5(7) = 60 + 35$ or 95

   B $5(12 + 7) = 5(12) + 7 = 60 + 7$ or 67

   C $5(12 + 7) = 12 + 5(7) = 12 + 35$ or 47

   D $5(12 + 7) = 5 + 60 + 5 + 7 = 65 + 12$ or 77

10. Which of the following relationships is represented by the data in the table? **F**

x	y
1	5,280
2	10,560
3	15,840
4	21,120
5	26,400

    F conversion of miles to feet

    G conversion of inches to yards

    H conversion of feet to miles

    J conversion of yards to inches

11. If $g = 4$, $m = 3$, and $n = 6$, then $\dfrac{mn + 2}{g} + 1$ is equivalent to which of the following? **A**

    A 6   C 3

    B 5   D 2

NEED EXTRA HELP?													
If You Missed Question...	1	2	3	4	5	6	7	8	9	10	11	12	13	14
Go to Lesson...	4-9	4-9	4-2	3-2	3-1	3-1	1-4	1-9	1-8	2-6	1-4	4-7	4-6	4-9

PART 2 Short Response/Grid In

Record your answers on the answer sheet provided by your teacher or on a sheet of paper.

12. Write 7.2% as a decimal. **0.072**

13. Jeremy expects 8 out of the 10 friends he invited to come to his party. What percent of his friends does he expect to come? **80%**

PART 3 Extended Response

Record your answers on the answer sheet provided by your teacher or on a sheet of paper. Show your work.

14. The prime factorization of 24 is $2 \times 2 \times 2 \times 3$. The table lists each unique prime factor and the products of all possible unique combinations of two, three, and four prime factors.

Unique Prime Factors	2, 3
Products of Two Factors	$2 \times 2, 2 \times 3$
Products of Three Factors	$2 \times 2 \times 2, 2 \times 2 \times 3$
Product of Four Factors	$2 \times 2 \times 2 \times 3$

    a. Find each product. **4, 6, 8, 12, 24**

    b. What do the products have in common? **The products are factors of 24.**

    c. What other numbers are factors of 24? **the unique factors and 1**

    d. Explain how you can use the prime factors of a number to find all of its factors. Test your conjecture by finding the factors of 60. **See margin.**

Answer Sheet Practice

Have students simulate taking a standardized test by recording their answers on a practice recording sheet.

CRM Student Recording Sheet, p. 65

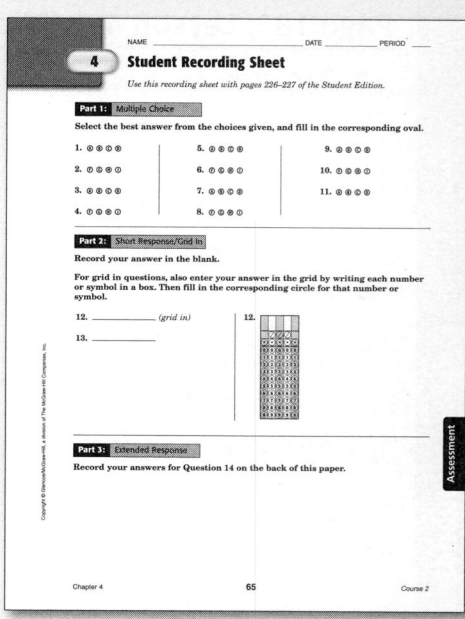

Additional Answer

14d. Sample answer: Make a list that includes 1, all of the unique prime factors, plus the products of all possible combinations of two, three, four, ... prime factors; $60 = 2 \times 2 \times 3 \times 5$. The factors are 1, 2, 3, 5, 2×2, 2×3, 2×5, $2 \times 2 \times 3$, $2 \times 2 \times 5$, $2 \times 3 \times 5$, and $2 \times 2 \times 3 \times 5$.

Homework Option

Get Ready for Chapter 5 Assign students the exercises on page 229 as homework to assess whether they possess the prerequisite skills needed for the next chapter.

Page 180, Explore 4-1

1. 1, 4, 9, 16, 25; Sample answer: They are equal to a number multiplied by itself. They have an odd number of factors.

2. Sample answer: Each of these numbers has an odd number of factors, so these lockers were touched by an odd number of students. This means the state of the locker was changed an odd number of times. Since a locker starts out closed, changing its state an odd number of times results in an open locker.

Page 181, Lesson 4-1 (Mini Lab)

1. 3 squares

4 squares

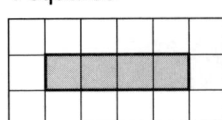

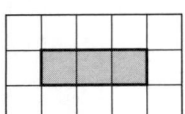

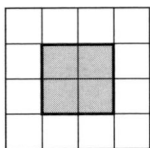

5 squares

6 squares

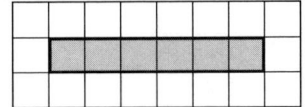

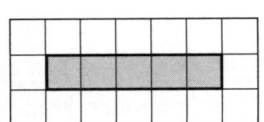

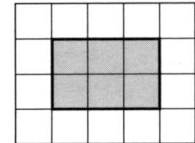

7 squares

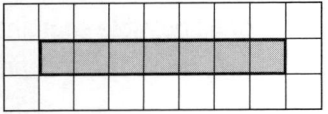

8 squares

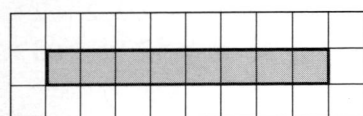

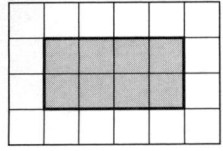

9 squares

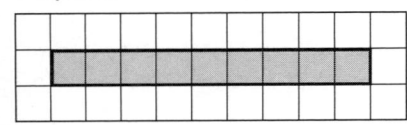

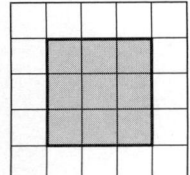

10 squares

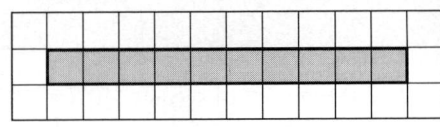

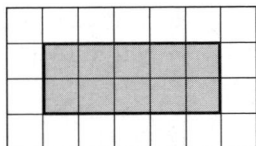

Page 184, Lesson 4-1

44.

1	2	3	4̸	5	6̸	7	8̸	9̸	1̸0̸
11	1̸2̸	13	1̸4̸	1̸5̸	1̸6̸	17	1̸8̸	19	2̸0̸
2̸1̸	2̸2̸	23	2̸4̸	2̸5̸	2̸6̸	2̸7̸	2̸8̸	29	3̸0̸
31	3̸2̸	3̸3̸	3̸4̸	3̸5̸	3̸6̸	37	3̸8̸	3̸9̸	4̸0̸
41	4̸2̸	43	4̸4̸	4̸5̸	4̸6̸	47	4̸8̸	4̸9̸	5̸0̸
5̸1̸	5̸2̸	53	5̸4̸	5̸5̸	5̸6̸	5̸7̸	5̸8̸	59	6̸0̸
61	6̸2̸	6̸3̸	6̸4̸	6̸5̸	6̸6̸	67	6̸8̸	6̸9̸	7̸0̸
71	7̸2̸	73	7̸4̸	7̸5̸	7̸6̸	7̸7̸	7̸8̸	79	8̸0̸
8̸1̸	8̸2̸	83	8̸4̸	8̸5̸	8̸6̸	8̸7̸	8̸8̸	89	9̸0̸
9̸1̸	9̸2̸	9̸3̸	9̸4̸	9̸5̸	9̸6̸	97	9̸8̸	9̸9̸	1̸0̸0̸;

The prime numbers up to 100 are 2, 3, 5, 7, 11, 13, 17, 19, 23, 29, 31, 37, 41, 43, 47, 53, 59, 61, 67, 71, 73, 79, 83, 89, and 97.

Page 215, Lesson 4-9 (Mini Lab)

1.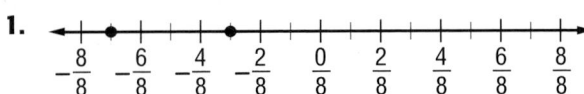

2.

3.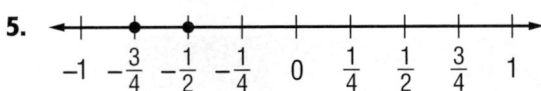

4.

5.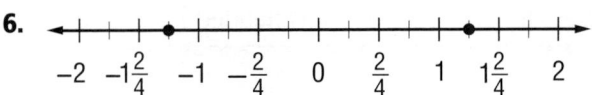

6.

NOTES

Lesson Plan		Pacing Your Lessons	
LESSONS AND OBJECTIVES	State/Local Standards	40–50 Minute Periods	90-Minute Periods
5-1 Estimating with Fractions (pp. 230–235) • Estimate sums, differences, products, and quotients of fractions and mixed numbers.		1	0.5
5-2 Adding and Subtracting Fractions (pp. 236–241) • Add and subtract fractions.		1	0.5
5-3 Adding and Subtracting Mixed Numbers (pp. 242–246) • Add and subtract mixed numbers.		1	0.5
5-4 Problem-Solving Investigation: Eliminate Possibilities (pp. 248–249) • Solve problems by eliminating possibilities.		1.5	0.5
Explore 5-5 Math Lab: Multiplying Fractions (p. 250–251) Use area models to multiply fractions and mixed numbers. **5-5 Multiplying Fractions and Mixed Numbers** (pp. 252–257) • Multiply fractions and mixed numbers.		1.5	0.5
5-6 Algebra: Solving Equations (pp. 258–263) • Solve equations with rational number solutions.		1	0.5
5-7 Dividing Fractions and Mixed Numbers (pp. 265–270) • Divide fractions and mixed numbers.		1	0.5
REVIEW		1	1
ASSESSMENT		1	0.5*
TOTAL		10	5

*The complete **Assessment Planner** for Chapter 5 is provided on page 229.*

* Begin Chapter 6 in the second half of the period.

Focal Points
G7-FP3 Number and Operations, and Algebra
For the complete wording of the Focal Points for Grade 7, please see page iv.

Professional Development

Vertical Alignment

Before Chapter 5

Related Topics from Grade 6

- identify and represent on a number line fractions and mixed numbers

- solve simple problems, including ones arising in concrete situations, involving the addition and subtraction of fractions and mixed numbers and express answers in the simplest form

- compute and perform simple multiplication and division of fractions and apply these procedures to solving problems

- use a letter to represent an unknown number; write and evaluate simple algebraic expressions in one variable by substitution

Chapter 5

Topics from Grade 7

- solve problems involving addition, subtraction, multiplication, and division of positive fractions

- explain the meaning of multiplication and division of positive fractions and perform the calculations

- determine the least common multiple of whole numbers; use them to solve problems with fractions

- write and solve one-step linear equations in one variable form

After Chapter 5

Preparation for Grade 8

- add, subtract, multiply, and divide rational numbers (integers, fractions, and terminating decimals) and take positive rational numbers to whole-number powers

- add and subtract fractions by using factoring to find common denominators

- multiply, divide, and simplify rational numbers by using the exponent rules

Backmapping and Vertical Alignment

McGraw-Hill's *Math Connnects* program was conceived and developed with the final results in mind: student success in Algebra 1 and beyond. The authors, using the **NCTM Focal Points and Focal Connections** as their guide, developed this brand-new series by backmapping from Algebra 1 concepts and vertically aligning the topics so that they build upon prior skills and concepts and serve as a foundation for future topics.

What the Research Says...

According to Marzano, Pickering, and Pollock in *Classroom Instruction that Works: Research Based Strategies for Increasing Student Achievement,* feedback has significant effects on student achievement.

- In each lesson in Chapter 5, Guided Practice exercises present practice problems similar to those in the homework exercises. Students are able to correct any misconceptions about solving problems involving fractions.

 **Professional Development**

Targeted professional development has been articulated throughout **McGraw-Hill's *Math Connects* program**. The **McGraw-Hill Professional Development Video Library** provides short videos that support the NCTM Focal Points and Focal Connections. For more information, visit **glencoe.com**.

| Model Lessons | Instructional Strategies |

TeacherWorks™ All-in-One Planner and Resource Center

All of the print materials from the Classroom Resource Masters are available on your TeacherWorks™ CD-ROM.

BL = Below or Approaching Grade Level   **OL** = On Grade Level   **AL** = Above or Beyond Grade Level   **ELL** = English Language Learner

Chapter Resource Masters				5-1	5-2	5-3	5-4	5-5	5-6	5-7
BL **OL** **ELL**	Lesson Reading Guide	9	15	21		31	38	44
BL **OL** **ELL**	Study Guide and Intervention*	10	16	22	27	32	39	45
BL **OL**	Skills Practice*	11	17	23	28	33	40	46
OL **AL**	Practice*	12	18	24	29	34	41	47
OL **AL**	Word Problem Practice*	13	19	25	30	35	42	48
OL **AL**	Enrichment	14	20	26		36	43	49
OL **AL**	Calculator and Spreadsheet Activities					37		
OL **AL**	Chapter Assessments*	53–54, 55, 56, 57–68						
BL **OL** **AL**	5-Minute Check Transparencies	✓	✓	✓	✓	✓	✓	✓
BL **OL**	Teaching Mathematics with Manipulatives					✓		
BL **OL** **AL**	Real-World Investigations for Differentiated Instruction	19–20, 57						

*Also available in Spanish

Graphing Calculator Easy Files

- Timesaving Tech Tools for the TI-Navigator
- Quick Checks to diagnose student progress
- Deliver Differentiated Instruction with Ready Files
- Vocabulary Review

AssignmentWorks

Differentiated Assignments, Answers, and Solutions

- Print a customized assignment worksheet using the Student Edition exercises along with an answer key or worked-out solutions.
- Use default lesson assignments as outlined in the Differentiated Homework Options in the Teacher Edition.

Interactive Classroom

This CD-ROM is a customizable Microsoft® PowerPoint® presentation that includes:

- In-Class Examples
- Your Turn Exercises*
- 5-Minute Check Transparencies*
- Links to Online Study Tools
- Concepts in Motion

*compatible with response pad technology

Your Turn

SWIMMING POOL A new children's swimming pool is being built at the local recreation center. The pool is circular in shape with a diameter of 18 feet. Find the circumference of the pool. Round to the nearest tenth.

18 ft

Answer: 56.5 ft²

ExamView®Assessment Suite

ExamView®
Assessment Suite

- Create, edit, and customize tests and worksheets using QuickTest Wizard
- Create multiple versions of tests and modify them for a desired level of difficulty
- Translate from English to Spanish and vice versa
- Build tests aligned with your state standards
- Track students' progress using the Teacher Management System

Student Tools

StudentWorks™ Plus

Textbook, Audio, Workbooks, and more

This CD-ROM is a valuable resource for students to access content online and use online resources to continue learning Chapter 5 concepts. Includes:

- Complete Student Edition
- English and Spanish audio
- Links to Concepts in Motion, Interactive Personal Tutor, and other online resources
- Access to all student worksheets
- Daily Assignments and Grade Log

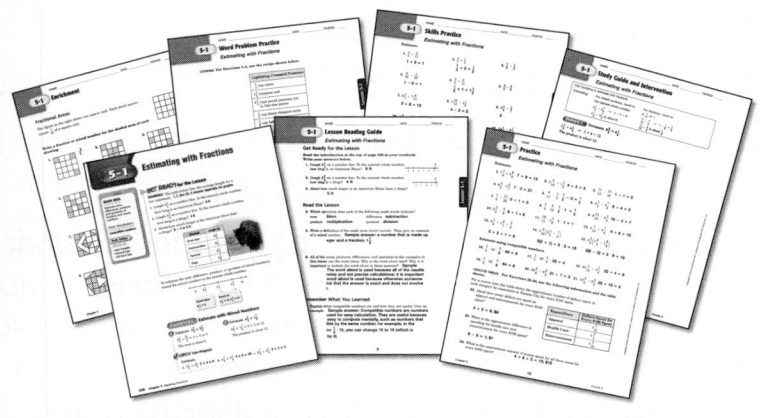

Super DVD

The Super DVD contains two Glencoe multimedia products.

MindJogger Plus An alternative review of concepts in which students work as teams in a game show format to gain points for correct answers.

What's Math Got to Do With It? Real-Life Math Videos
Engaging video that shows students how math is used in everyday situations.

Internet Resources

| Math Online | glencoe.com |

TEACHER	STUDENT	PARENT	
			Online Study Tools
	●	●	Online Student Edition
●	●	●	Multilingual Glossary
			Lesson Resources
	●	●	Extra Examples
	●	●	BrainPOPS
	●	●	Self-Check Quizzes
●	●	●	Concepts in Motion
	●	●	Other Calculator Keystrokes
	●	●	Real-World Careers
	●	●	Reading in the Content Area
●			Group Activity Cards
			Chapter Resources
	●	●	Family Letters and Activities
	●		Chapter Readiness Quiz
	●	●	Vocabulary Review
	●		Chapter Test
	●	●	Standardized Test Practice
			Unit Resources
●	●		WebQuest Project
			Other Resources
	●		Personal Tutor
●			NAEP Correlations
●			Key Concepts
●	●	●	Meet the Authors
●	●		Game Zone
●	●	●	Math Skills Maintenance
●			National Resources (Professional Organizations)
●			State Resources
●			Vocabulary PuzzleMakers

Noteables™ Interactive Study Notebook with Foldables™

This workbook is a study organizer that provides helpful steps for students to follow to organize their notes for Chapter 5.

- Students use Noteables to record notes and to complete their Foldables as you present the material for each lesson.

- Noteables correspond to the Examples in the *Teacher Edition* and *Interactive Classroom CD-ROM*.

Real-World Problem Solving Graphic Novels

Mathematical problem solving is presented in a motivating, graphic novel format. The novels contain real-world problems for each of the following mathematical strands: Number Sense, Algebraic Thinking, Geometry, Measurement, Statistics and Probability, and Mathematical Reasoning.

READING in the Content Area

This online worksheet provides strategies for reading and analyzing Lesson 5-2, Adding and Subtracting Fractions. Students are guided through questions about the main idea, subject matter, supporting details, conclusion, clarifying details, and vocabulary of the lesson.

glencoe.com

Recommended Outside Reading for Students

Mathematics and Star Wars

- *Dune* by Frank Herbert © 1965 [fiction]

This book is credited with providing ideas for the stories contained in the Star Wars movies. It has a young prince who grows from boy to warrior to ruler. The mathematics is the gift of the Mentats who are versions of human computers. The story includes computations with numbers like those found in Chapter 5.

Project CRISS℠

STUDY SKILL

Taking good notes will help students become actively involved in the learning process. For each lesson, have students read and then write notes about the topic. You may wish to show them the sample notes for Lesson 5-1 at the right to use as a guide. Afterward, allow class time for students to discuss their notes. Encourage students to talk about the procedures used in the lesson for solving the problems and how they addressed those procedures in their notes.

Lesson 5-1
Estimate with mixed numbers
• round to the nearest whole number
• Example: $7\frac{1}{5} + 5\frac{7}{10} \approx 7 + 6$, or 13
Estimate with fractions
• round to 0, $\frac{1}{2}$, or 1
• Example: $\frac{2}{3} + \frac{1}{5} \approx 1 + 0$, or 1

CReating **I**ndependence through **S**tudent-owned **S**trategies

Differentiated Instruction

Investigative Approach

MathScape™

This project was supported, in part, by the
National Science Foundation

MathScape is a mathematics curriculum for grades 6–8 developed by the Seeing and Thinking Mathematically Project at the Education Development Center.

Operating with Factors, Multiples, and Fractions

From Wholes to Parts

How to Use *MathScape* with Chapter 5

The unit *From Wholes to Parts* can be used to enhance Lessons 5-5 and 5-7.

- **Introduce** ➔ Before you begin **Lesson 5-5**, introduce multiplying fractions by using pages 130–131.

- **Enrich** ➔ After you complete **Lesson 5-7**, challenge students with fraction division by using pages 138–139.

RTI (Response to Intervention)

TIER 1 **On-Level Instruction** Use the *Math Connects* program as instruction for your on-level students.

TIER 2 **Strategic Intervention** For options to instruct struggling students, refer to the Diagnostic Assessment table on page 229.

TIER 3 **Intensive Intervention** *Math Triumphs* can provide intensive intervention for students who are at risk of not meeting the objectives addressed in Chapter 8.

Diagnose student readiness with the Quick Check and Quick Review on page 229. Then use *Math Triumphs* to accelerate their achievment.

Applying Fractions

Prerequisite Skill	*Math Triumphs*
Fractions	Ch. 1
Operations	Ch. 9

Practice and Review

Quick Review Math Handbook* is Glencoe's mathematical handbook for students and parents.

Hot Words includes a glossary of terms.

Hot Topics consists of two parts:

- explanations of key mathematical concepts
- exercises to check students' understanding.

Lesson	Hot Topics Section	Lesson	Hot Topics Section
5-2	2•3	5-6	2•4, 6•4
5-3	2•3	5-7	2•4
5-5	2•4		

*Also available in Spanish

FOLDABLES™
Study Organizer

Dinah Zike's Foldables

Focus This Foldable is designed to help students organize their notes about fractions and mixed numbers.

Teach Explain to students that they should record what they learn about fractions and mixed numbers on index cards and sort them into the appropriate pockets of their Foldables.

When to Use It

Pocket	Use with Lesson(s)
Fractions	5-1, 5-2, 5-4, 5-5, 5-6, 5-7
Mixed Numbers	5-1, 5-3, 5-4, 5-5, 5-6, 5-7

A version of a completed Foldable is shown on p. 271.

Differentiated Instruction

Student-Built Glossary, p. 1

Students complete the chart by providing the definition of each term and an example as they progress through Chapter 5.

This study tool can be used to review for the chapter test.

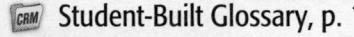

Materials Needed for Chapter 5

- rulers (Lesson 5-2)
- grid paper (Lesson 5-2, Explore 5-5 and Lesson 5-6)
- geoboards (Explore 5-5)
- geobands (Explore 5-5)
- colored pencils (Explore 5-5 and Lesson 5-6)
- paper plates (Lesson 5-7)
- scissors (Lesson 5-7)

CHAPTER 5

Applying Fractions

BIG Idea

- Add, subtract, multiply, and divide to solve fraction problems.

Key Vocabulary

compatible numbers (p. 232)
like fractions (p. 236)
reciprocal (p. 258)
unlike fractions (p. 237)

🌐 Real-World Link

Baking The measurements found on measuring cups and spoons are written as fractions. You will use fractions to find how much of each ingredient is needed when you make part of a whole recipe.

FOLDABLES®
Study Organizer

Applying Fractions Make this Foldable to help you organize your notes. Begin with a plain sheet of 11" by 17" paper, four index cards, and glue.

1 **Fold** the paper in half widthwise.

2 **Open** and fold along the length about $2\frac{1}{2}$" from the bottom.

3 **Glue** the edge on each side to form two pockets.

4 **Label** the pockets *Fractions* and *Mixed Numbers*, respectively. Place two index cards in each pocket.

GET READY for Chapter 5

Diagnose Readiness You have two options for checking Prerequisite Skills.

Option 1

Option 2

Math Online Take the Online Readiness Quiz at glencoe.com.

Take the Quick Quiz below. Refer to the Quick Review for help.

QUICK Quiz

(Used in Lessons 5-2 and 5-3)
Find the LCD of each pair of fractions. (Lesson 4-8)

1. $\frac{5}{7}, \frac{3}{5}$ **35**
2. $\frac{1}{2}, \frac{4}{9}$ **18**
3. $\frac{8}{15}, \frac{1}{6}$ **30**
4. $\frac{3}{4}, \frac{7}{10}$ **20**

(Used in Lessons 5-5 and 5-7)
Multiply or divide. (Prior Grade)

5. 1.8×12 **21.6**
6. $99 \div 12$ **8.25**
7. $83 \div 100$ **0.83**
8. 4.6×0.3 **1.38**

9. **MEASUREMENT** How many 1.6-meter sections of rope can be cut from a length of rope 6.4 meters? (Prior Grade) **4**

10. **COINS** Manuel owes each of 8 friends $0.35. How much does he owe in all? (Prior Grade) **$2.80**

(Used in Lessons 5-3 and 5-7)
Complete to show equivalent mixed numbers. (Prior Grade)

11. $3\frac{1}{5} = 2\frac{\blacksquare}{5}$ **$2\frac{6}{5}$**
12. $9\frac{2}{3} = \blacksquare\frac{5}{3}$ **$8\frac{5}{3}$**
13. $6\frac{1}{4} = 5\frac{\blacksquare}{4}$ **$5\frac{5}{4}$**
14. $8\frac{6}{7} = 7\frac{\blacksquare}{7}$ **$7\frac{13}{7}$**

15. **RECIPES** A recipe calls for $4\frac{2}{3}$ cups of flour. This is equivalent to 3 cups of flour plus an additional how many cups of flour? (Prior Grade) $\frac{5}{3}$ or $1\frac{2}{3}$ c

QUICK Review

Example 1
Find the LCD of $\frac{5}{6}$ and $\frac{3}{10}$.
The LCD is the LCM of the denominators, 6 and 10, or 30.

Example 2
Find $7.8 \div 0.25$.

$$0.25\overline{)7.80\,0}$$

Move the decimal point 2 places to the right and divide as with whole numbers.

$$\begin{array}{r} 31.2 \\ 0.25\overline{)7.80\,0} \\ -7\,5 \\ \hline 30 \\ -25 \\ \hline 50 \\ -50 \\ \hline 0 \end{array}$$

Example 3
Complete $4\frac{2}{9} = \blacksquare\frac{11}{9}$ to show equivalent mixed numbers.

$$4\frac{2}{9} = 3 + 1\frac{2}{9}$$
$$= 3 + \frac{9}{9} + \frac{2}{9}$$
$$= 3 + \frac{11}{9}$$
$$= 3\frac{11}{9}$$

Chapter 5 Get Ready for Chapter 5   **229**

Diagnostic Assessment

Exercises	State/Local Standards	Intervention
1–4		SE Review Lesson 4–9, pp. 215–220
5–10		SE Concepts and Skills Bank, pp. 736 and 738
11–15		*Math Skills Maintenance Masters*, pp. 63–65

✓ Formative Assessment

CRM Anticipation Guide, pp. 7–8
Spotting Preconceived Ideas
Students complete this survey to determine prior knowledge about ideas from Chapter 5. Revisit this worksheet after completing the chapter. Also see page 274.

TE Lesson Activities

- Ticket Out the Door, pp. 249, 257, 270
- Crystal Ball, pp. 235, 241
- Name the Math, p. 246
- Yesterday's News, p. 263

Chapter Checkpoints

SE Mid-Chapter Quiz, p. 247
SE Study Guide and Review, pp. 271–274
SE Test Practice, pp. 276–277
CRM Quizzes, pp. 53 and 54
CRM Standardized Test Practice, pp. 70–72

Math Online glencoe.com
- Self-Check Quizzes
- Practice Test
- Standardized Test Practice

✓ Summative Assessment

SE Chapter Practice Test, p. 275
CRM Mid-Chapter Test, p. 55
CRM Vocabulary Test, p. 56
CRM Extended-Response Test, p. 69
CRM Leveled Chapter Tests, pp. 57–68
● ExamView® Assessment Suite

KEY

CRM *Chapter 5 Resource Masters*
SE Student Edition
TE Teacher Edition
● CD-ROM

Estimating with Fractions

PACING: **Regular:** 1 period, **Block:** 0.5 period

Options for Differentiated Instruction

 = English Language Learner   = Above or Beyond Grade Level   = Struggling Students   **SN** = Special Needs

Extending the Lesson Opener   SS

Use after presenting Get Ready for the Lesson.

After completing Get Ready for the Lesson, present the following problem to students.

Estimate how many Opossums would be needed to stand as tall as an American Bison. Explain how you determined your answer.

3: Since an Opossum is approximately 3 feet tall and an American Bison is approximately 9 feet tall it would require three 3 foot tall possums to equal one 9 foot tall American Bison.

Visual Clues

Use before presenting Examples 1–8.

Have students create an index card with several number lines with benchmark fractions that they can refer to, such as those shown at the right.

This will help them to judge whether to round fractions up or down.

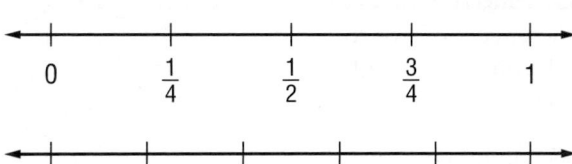

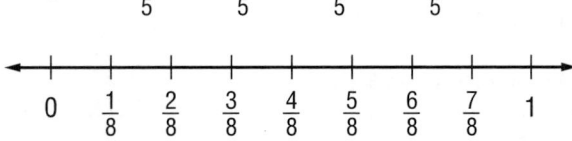

Logical Reasoning

Use after presenting Examples 1–8.

Have students create and label a table like the one shown below.

Estimation	
Makes Sense	**Does Not Make Sense**

Have them list situations in which estimating mixed numbers makes sense and situations in which it does not make sense to estimate. For example, when making a loaf of bread, estimating how much flour to buy makes sense; estimating how much flour to use for the dough does not.

Leveled Lesson Resources

Also on TeacherWorks™ Lesson 5-1

Chapter 5 Resource Masters

BL = Below or Approaching Grade Level **OL** = On Grade Level **AL** = Above or Beyond Grade Level **ELL** = English Language Learner

Lesson Reading Guide
p. 9 **BL OL ELL**

5-1 Lesson Reading Guide
Estimating with Fractions

Get Ready for the Lesson
Read the introduction at the top of page 230 in your textbook.
Write your answers below.
1. Graph $9\frac{1}{4}$ on a number line. To the nearest whole number, how long is an American Bison? **9 ft**
2. Graph $3\frac{3}{8}$ on a number line. To the nearest whole number, how long is a dingo? **4 ft**
3. About how much longer is an American Bison than a dingo? **9 − 4 or 5 ft**

Read the Lesson
4. Which operation does each of the following math words indicate?
sum **addition** difference **subtraction**
product **multiplication** quotient **division**
5. Write a definition of the math term *mixed number*. Then give an example of a mixed number. **Sample answer: a number that is made up of an integer and a fraction; $1\frac{1}{2}$**

6. All of the sums, products, differences, and quotients in the examples in this lesson use the word *about*. Why is the word *about* used? Why is it important to include the word *about* in these answers? **Sample answer: The word *about* is used because all of the results are estimates and not precise calculations; it is important that the word *about* is used because otherwise someone might think that the answer is exact and does not involve rounding.**

Remember What You Learned
7. Explain what compatible numbers are and how they are useful. Give an example. **Sample answer: Compatible numbers are numbers that are used for easy calculation. They are useful because they are easy to compute mentally, such as numbers that are divisible by the same number; for example, in the expression $\frac{1}{3} \cdot 15$, you can change 15 to 16 (which is divisible by 4).**

Chapter 5 9 Course 2

Study Guide and Intervention*
p. 10 **BL OL ELL**

5-1 Study Guide and Intervention
Estimating with Fractions

Use rounding to estimate with fractions.
Estimating: For mixed numbers, round to the nearest whole number. For fractions, round to 0, $\frac{1}{2}$, or 1.

Example 1 Estimate $2\frac{2}{3} \times 4\frac{1}{4}$.
$2\frac{2}{3} \times 4\frac{1}{4} \rightarrow 3 \times 4 = 12$
The product is about 12.

Example 2 Estimate $\frac{6}{7} - \frac{3}{8}$.
$\frac{6}{7}$ is about 1.
$\frac{3}{8}$ is about $\frac{1}{2}$.
$\frac{6}{7} - \frac{3}{8} \rightarrow 1 - \frac{1}{2} = \frac{1}{2}$ The difference is about $\frac{1}{2}$.

Exercises
Estimate.
1. $4\frac{1}{8} + 3\frac{4}{5}$ 4 + 4 = 8
2. $2\frac{1}{6} \times 3\frac{2}{3}$ 2 × 4 = 8
3. $\frac{7}{12} - \frac{1}{10}$ $\frac{1}{2} - 0 = \frac{1}{2}$
4. $5\frac{1}{8} - 1\frac{1}{2}$ 5 − 2 = 3
5. $4\frac{4}{5} + 1\frac{1}{5}$ 5 + 1 = 6
6. $\frac{5}{9} \times \frac{13}{14}$ $\frac{1}{2} \times 1 = \frac{1}{2}$
7. $\frac{1}{6} + \frac{8}{9}$ 0 + 1 = 0
8. $\frac{6}{7} \div \frac{9}{10}$ 1 ÷ 1 = 1
9. $13\frac{1}{8} + 1\frac{7}{8}$ 14 ÷ 2 = 7
10. $12\frac{1}{4} \div 5\frac{7}{8}$ 12 ÷ 6 = 2

Chapter 5 10 Course 2

Skills Practice*
p. 11 **BL OL**

5-1 Skills Practice
Estimating with Fractions

Estimate.
1. $\frac{4}{5} + \frac{7}{11}$ 1 + 0 = 1
2. $\frac{4}{7} + \frac{1}{5}$ $\frac{1}{2} + 0 = \frac{1}{2}$
3. $\frac{7}{9} - \frac{1}{5}$ 1 − 0 = 1
4. $\frac{9}{10} - \frac{1}{23}$ 1 − 0 = 1
5. $\frac{1}{2} + \frac{9}{11}$ $\frac{1}{2} + 1 = 1\frac{1}{2}$
6. $\frac{4}{5} - \frac{4}{9}$ 1 − $\frac{1}{2}$ = $\frac{1}{2}$
7. $5\frac{1}{7} + 7\frac{9}{11}$ 5 + 8 = 13
8. $3\frac{10}{11} - 2\frac{1}{12}$ 4 − 2 = 2
9. $5\frac{1}{8} - \frac{1}{7}$ 5 − 0 = 5
10. $8\frac{3}{7} - 2\frac{1}{8}$ 8 − 3 = 5
11. $2\frac{1}{8} + 6\frac{9}{10}$ 2 + 7 = 9
12. $10\frac{1}{8} - 3\frac{1}{11}$ 10 − 3 = 7
13. $\frac{4}{9} \times \frac{8}{9}$ 1 × 1 = 1
14. $\frac{6}{7} + \frac{10}{11}$ 1 ÷ 1 = 1
15. $3\frac{8}{9} \times 2\frac{1}{10}$ 4 × 2 = 8
16. $16\frac{1}{3} \div 3\frac{8}{9}$ 16 ÷ 4 = 4
17. $31\frac{3}{4} \div 2\frac{1}{9}$ 32 ÷ 2 = 16
18. $3\frac{4}{9} \cdot 1\frac{1}{4}$ 4 · 1 = 4
19. $12 \div 2\frac{6}{7}$ 12 ÷ 3 = 4
20. $44\frac{1}{5} \div 3\frac{7}{8}$ 44 ÷ 4 = 11
21. $10\frac{1}{2} \cdot 4\frac{1}{9}$ 10 · 4 = 40
22. $5\frac{1}{8} \cdot 6\frac{9}{11}$ 5 · 7 = 35
23. $\frac{3}{12} \div 4\frac{4}{5}$ 0 ÷ 5 = 0
24. $2\frac{1}{2} + 3\frac{1}{3}$ 3 + 3 = 1
25. Estimate $36\frac{1}{4}$ divided by 6. 36 ÷ 6 = 6
26. Estimate the sum of $7\frac{9}{10}$, $2\frac{1}{8}$, and $3\frac{2}{3}$. 8 + 2 + 4 = 14

Chapter 5 11 Course 2

Practice*
p. 12 **OL AL**

5-1 Practice
Estimating with Fractions

Estimate.
1. $7\frac{1}{6} + 5\frac{8}{9}$ 7 + 6 = 13
2. $4\frac{2}{10} + 1\frac{1}{2}$ 4 + 2 = 6
3. $\frac{11}{13} - \frac{15}{16}$ 1 − 1 = 0
4. $6\frac{4}{5} \cdot 3\frac{2}{7}$ 7 · 3 = 21
5. $\frac{6}{11} - \frac{1}{5} - \frac{1}{2}$ 0 − 0 = $\frac{1}{2}$
6. $6\frac{1}{4} + 3\frac{7}{8}$ 8 + 4 = 2
7. $\frac{1}{7} + \frac{17}{20}$ 0 + 1 = 0
8. $\frac{5}{8} \div \frac{9}{10}$ $\frac{1}{2} \div 1 = \frac{1}{2}$
9. $9\frac{14}{15} - 2\frac{3}{4}$ 10 − 3 = 7
10. $5\frac{3}{8} \div 5$ 6 ÷ 1 = 6
11. $\frac{10}{11} \cdot 1\frac{1}{9}$ 1 · 1 = 1
12. $4\frac{1}{8} + 5\frac{7}{8}$ 4 + 6 = 10
13. $5\frac{1}{9} + 1\frac{6}{7} + \frac{5}{6}$ 5 + 2 + 1 = 8
14. $4\frac{9}{10}(2\frac{1}{8} + \frac{7}{8})$ 5(2 + 1) = 5 · 3 = 15
15. $3\frac{1}{4}(7\frac{2}{3} - 1\frac{8}{9})$ 3(8 − 2) = 3 · 6 = 18

Estimate using compatible numbers.
16. $\frac{1}{5} \cdot 44$ $\frac{1}{5} \cdot 45 = 9$
17. $\frac{1}{7} \cdot 29$ $\frac{1}{7} \cdot 28 = 4$
18. $33\frac{1}{10} \div 4\frac{1}{3}$ 32 ÷ 4 = 8
19. $\frac{1}{8} \cdot 62$ $\frac{1}{8} \cdot 64 = 8$
20. $20\frac{5}{6} \div 6\frac{5}{12}$ 21 ÷ 7 = 3
21. $19\frac{4}{5} \div 8\frac{3}{2}$ 20 ÷ 10 = 2

ANALYZE TABLES For Exercises 22–24, use the following information and the table shown.
For a recent year, the table shows the approximate number of dollars spent in each category by consumers in Kansas City for every $100 spent.

Expenditure	Dollars Spent for Every $100 Spent
Apparel	$3\frac{7}{10}$
Health Care	$5\frac{3}{5}$
Entertainment	$5\frac{3}{10}$

22. About how many dollars are spent on apparel and entertainment for every $100 spent? 4 + 5 = 9; $9
23. What is the approximate difference in spending for health care and entertainment for every $100 spent? 6 − 5 = 1; $1
24. What is the approximate amount of money spent for all three areas for every $100 spent? 4 + 6 + 5 = 15; $15

Chapter 5 12 Course 2

Word Problem Practice*
p. 13 **OL AL**

5-1 Word Problem Practice
Estimating with Fractions

COOKING For Exercises 1–4, use the recipe shown below.

Lightning Creamed Potatoes
$\frac{1}{3}$ cup water
$1\frac{1}{2}$ teaspoon salt
$3\frac{2}{3}$ cups pared potatoes, cut in bite-size pieces
$\frac{1}{3}$ cup finely chopped onion
$\frac{1}{2}$ cup light cream
serves 6

1. Daniel wants to serve twelve people the Lightning Creamed Potatoes. Estimate how much salt he will need if he doubles the recipe. **2 × 2 or 4 tsp**
2. Rosita wants to triple the recipe above. Estimate how many cups of pared potatoes she will need. **3 × 4 or 12 c**
3. Alvin is going to serve six people. He only has $1\frac{1}{4}$ cups of pared potatoes. About how many cups of potatoes will he have to borrow? **4 − 1 or 3 c**
4. Katrina wants to make half of the recipe. About how many cups of potatoes will she need? **$\frac{1}{2} \times 4$ or 2 c**
5. **CARPENTRY** A board is $17\frac{3}{4}$ inches long. Carmen wants to shorten the length by about $1\frac{7}{8}$ inches. Estimate the length of the board after the board has been shortened. **18 − 2 or 16 in.**
6. **TRACK** Akira ran two miles. He ran the first mile in $7\frac{3}{4}$ minutes and the second mile in $8\frac{2}{9}$ minutes. Estimate how long it took Akira to run two miles. **8 + 9 or 17 min**

Chapter 5 13 Course 2

Enrichment
p. 14 **OL AL**

5-1 Enrichment

Fractional Areas
The figure at the right shows one square inch. Each small square equals $\frac{1}{16}$ of a square inch.

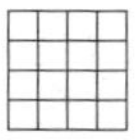

Write a fraction or mixed number for the shaded area of each drawing.
1. $\frac{3}{16}$ in² 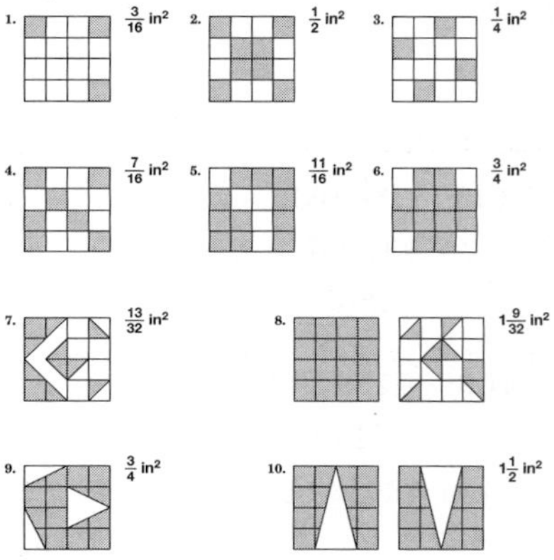
2. $\frac{1}{2}$ in²
3. $\frac{1}{4}$ in²
4. $\frac{7}{16}$ in²
5. $\frac{11}{16}$ in²
6. $\frac{3}{4}$ in²
7. $\frac{13}{32}$ in²
8. $\frac{9}{32}$ in²
9. $\frac{3}{4}$ in²
10. $1\frac{1}{2}$ in²

Chapter 5 14 Course 2

Additional Lesson Resources

* **Also available in Spanish** **ELL**

Transparencies
• *5-Minute Check Transparency*, Lesson 5-1

Other Print Products
• *Noteables™ Interactive Study Notebook with Foldables™*

Teacher Tech Tools
• *Interactive Classroom CD-ROM*, Lesson 5-1
• *AssignmentWorks*, Lesson 5-1

Student Tech Tools
glencoe.com
• Extra Examples, Chapter 5, Lesson 1
• Self-Check Quiz, Chapter 5, Lesson 1

1 Focus

Vertical Alignment

Before Lesson 5-1
Identify and represent on a number line fractions and mixed numbers

Lesson 5-1
Solve problems involving addition, subtraction, multiplication, and division of positive fractions

After Lesson 5-1
Add, subtract, multiply, and divide rational numbers (integers, fractions, and terminating decimals) and take positive rational numbers to whole-number powers

2 Teach

Scaffolding Questions

Tell students that a sixth-grade class went to a pizzeria.

Ask:

- If $\frac{1}{2}$ of a mushroom pizza and $\frac{1}{3}$ of a cheese pizza were left over, about how much pizza was left over? **about 1 whole pizza, or about $\frac{3}{4}$**

- If $1\frac{1}{4}$ pepperoni pizzas and $\frac{5}{6}$ of a sausage pizza were left over, about how much pizza was left over? **about 2 pizzas**

- If Nick, Lenny, and Miguel each ate $\frac{3}{8}$ of a pizza, about how much pizza did they eat altogether? **about 1 pizza**

MAIN IDEA

Estimate sums, differences, products, and quotients of fractions and mixed numbers.

New Vocabulary

compatible numbers

Math Online

glencoe.com

- Extra Examples
- Personal Tutor
- Self-Check Quiz

▶ **GET READY for the Lesson**

MAMMALS The table below lists the average length for a few mammals. **1, 2. See Ch. 5 Answer Appendix for graphs.**

1. Graph $9\frac{1}{4}$ on a number line. To the nearest whole number, how long is an American Bison? **9 ft**

2. Graph $3\frac{3}{4}$ on a number line. To the nearest whole number, how long is a dingo? **4 ft**

3. About how much longer is the American bison than a dingo? **9 − 4 or 5 ft**

Mammal	Length (ft)
Brown Bear	$6\frac{1}{2}$
American Bison	$9\frac{1}{4}$
Opossum	$2\frac{1}{2}$
Dingo	$3\frac{3}{4}$

To estimate the sum, difference, product, or quotient of mixed numbers, round the mixed numbers to the nearest whole number.

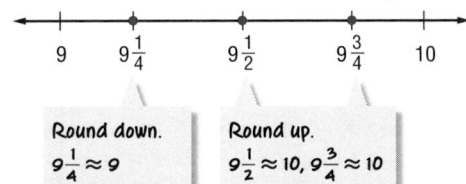

Round down. $9\frac{1}{4} \approx 9$

Round up. $9\frac{1}{2} \approx 10,\ 9\frac{3}{4} \approx 10$

EXAMPLES **Estimate with Mixed Numbers**

① Estimate $3\frac{2}{3} + 5\frac{1}{6}$.

$3\frac{2}{3} + \frac{31}{6} \approx 4 + 5$ or 9

The sum is *about* 9.

② Estimate $6\frac{2}{5} \times 1\frac{7}{8}$.

$6\frac{2}{5} \times 1\frac{7}{8} \approx 6 \times 2$ or 12

The product is *about* 12.

✓ **CHECK Your Progress**

Estimate.

a. $2\frac{1}{5} + 3\frac{1}{2}$ **2 + 4 = 6**   b. $4\frac{3}{8} \times 5\frac{1}{4}$ **4 × 5 = 20**   c. $8\frac{7}{9} \div 2\frac{3}{4}$ **9 ÷ 3 = 3**

230 Chapter 5 Applying Fractions

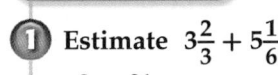

Estimating with Mixed Numbers

Tips for New Teachers

Using front-end estimation, students can add the integers and then estimate the sum of the fractions. For example, to estimate the sum of $3\frac{2}{3}$ and $5\frac{1}{6}$, find 3 + 5, or 8. Then estimate the sum of $\frac{2}{3}$ and $\frac{1}{6}$, which is about 1. An estimate of $3\frac{2}{3} + 5\frac{1}{6}$ is thus about 8 + 1, or 9.

To estimate the sum, difference, product, or quotient of fractions, round each fraction to 0, $\frac{1}{2}$, or 1, whichever is closest. Number lines and fraction models, like the ones shown below, can help you decide how to round.

Fractions Close to 0	Fractions Close to $\frac{1}{2}$	Fractions Close to 1
$0 \quad \frac{1}{6} \qquad 1$	$0 \qquad \frac{1}{2} \, \frac{5}{8} \quad 1$	$0 \qquad\qquad \frac{9}{10} \, 1$
$\frac{1}{7}$	$\frac{4}{9}$	$\frac{5}{6}$
The numerator is much smaller than the denominator.	The numerator is about half of the denominator.	The numerator is almost as large as the denominator.

EXAMPLES Estimate with Fractions

3 Estimate $\frac{1}{8} + \frac{2}{3}$.

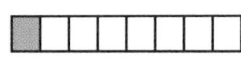
1 is much smaller than 8, so $\frac{1}{8} \approx 0$.

2 is close to half of 3, so $\frac{2}{3} \approx \frac{1}{2}$.

$\frac{1}{8} + \frac{2}{3} \approx 0 + \frac{1}{2} = \frac{1}{2}$ The sum is *about* $\frac{1}{2}$.

4 Estimate $\frac{6}{7} - \frac{7}{10}$.

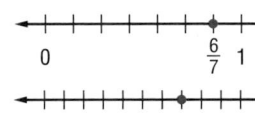
$0 \qquad\qquad \frac{6}{7} \, 1$
6 is almost as large as 7, so $\frac{6}{7} \approx 1$.

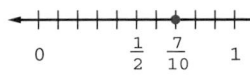
$0 \qquad \frac{1}{2} \, \frac{7}{10} \quad 1$
7 is about half of 10, so $\frac{7}{10} \approx \frac{1}{2}$.

$\frac{6}{7} - \frac{7}{10} \approx 1 - \frac{1}{2} = \frac{1}{2}$ The difference is *about* $\frac{1}{2}$.

5 Estimate $\frac{8}{9} \div \frac{5}{6}$.

$\frac{8}{9} \div \frac{5}{6} \approx 1 \div 1 = 1 \qquad \frac{8}{9} \approx 1$ and $\frac{5}{6} \approx 1$.

The quotient is *about* 1.

✓CHECK Your Progress

Estimate.

d. $\frac{1}{7} + \frac{3}{5}$ **$\frac{1}{2}$**   e. $\frac{7}{8} - \frac{5}{9}$ **$\frac{1}{2}$**   f. $\frac{3}{5} \times \frac{11}{12}$ g. $\frac{7}{8} \div \frac{2}{5}$

Study Tip

Estimating with Fractions If one of the fractions is a mixed number, such as $3\frac{5}{8} + \frac{2}{3}$, round the mixed number to the nearest whole number and the fraction to the nearest half. $3\frac{5}{8} + \frac{2}{3} \approx 4 + \frac{1}{2}$ or about $4\frac{1}{2}$.

f. $\frac{1}{2} \times 1 = \frac{1}{2}$

g. $1 \div \frac{1}{2} = 2$

Focus on Mathematical Content

A good way to estimate the product or quotient of mixed numbers is to adjust them to **compatible numbers**.

Compatible numbers (such as $\frac{1}{3} \cdot 6$, and $8 \div 2$) can be computed mentally.

✓ Formative Assessment

Use the Check Your Progress exercises after the Examples to determine students' understanding of concepts.

ADDITIONAL EXAMPLES

1 Estimate $5\frac{1}{4} + 3\frac{5}{8}$. $5 + 4$, or 9

2 Estimate $7\frac{3}{4} \times 1\frac{7}{8}$. 8×2, or 16

3 Estimate $\frac{1}{3} + \frac{4}{7}$. $\frac{1}{2} + \frac{1}{2}$, or 1

4 Estimate $\frac{5}{8} - \frac{1}{4}$. $\frac{1}{2} - 0$, or $\frac{1}{2}$

5 Estimate $\frac{5}{6} \div \frac{4}{5}$. $1 \div 1$, or 1

Additional Examples are also in:
- Noteables™ Interactive Study Notebook with Foldables™
- Interactive Classroom PowerPoint® Presentations

Tips for New Teachers

Estimating with Fractions

If students round fractions such that they get $\frac{1}{2} \div \frac{1}{2}$, they should recognize that the estimated answer will be 1 since any number divided by itself is 1. If students round fractions such that they get $1 \div 0$, have them round the divisor differently since $1 \div 0$ is undefined. If students round fractions such that they get $\frac{1}{2} \times \frac{1}{2}$, have them round both fractions to zero (0×0) and both to one (1×1). The estimated product is between 0 and 1.

Compatible numbers, or numbers that are easy to compute mentally, can also be used to estimate.

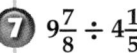

EXAMPLES **Use Compatible Numbers**

Estimate using compatible numbers.

6 $\frac{1}{3} \cdot 14$ **THINK** What is $\frac{1}{3}$ of 14?

$\frac{1}{3} \cdot 14 \approx \frac{1}{3} \cdot 15$ or 5   Round 14 to 15, since 15 is divisible by 3.

$\frac{1}{3}$ of 15 is $15 \div 3$ or 5.

7 $9\frac{7}{8} \div 4\frac{1}{5}$

$9\frac{7}{8} \div 4\frac{1}{5} \approx 10 \div 4\frac{1}{5}$ Round $9\frac{7}{8}$ to 10.

$\approx 10 \div 5$ or 2   Round $4\frac{1}{5}$ to 5, since 10 is divisible by 5.

Study Tip

Compatible Numbers
When dividing mixed numbers, round so that the dividend is a multiple of the divisor.

CHECK Your Progress

Estimate using compatible numbers.

h. $\frac{1}{4} \cdot 21$ $\frac{1}{4} \cdot 20 = 5$ i. $\frac{1}{3} \cdot 17$ $\frac{1}{3} \cdot 18 = 6$ j. $12 \div 6\frac{2}{3}$ $12 \div 6 = 2$

Real-World EXAMPLE

Real-World Link
The monster truck shown is $15\frac{1}{2}$ feet tall and weighs 28,000 pounds.
Source: Monster Trucks UK

8 **MONSTER TRUCKS** The height of the wheels on the monster truck at the left is about $\frac{2}{3}$ of the total height of the truck. Estimate the height of the wheels.

Words	Wheel height is $\frac{2}{3}$ of the truck height.
Variable	Let x represent the wheel height.
Equation	$x = \frac{2}{3} \cdot 15\frac{1}{2}$

$x \approx \frac{2}{3} \cdot 15$ Round $15\frac{1}{2}$ to 15, since 15 is divisible by 3.

$x \approx 10$ $\frac{1}{3}$ of 15 is 5, so $\frac{2}{3}$ of 15 is $2 \cdot 5$ or 10.

The wheels are about 10 feet high.

CHECK Your Progress

k. **MEASUREMENT** The area of a rectangle is $19\frac{3}{4}$ square feet. The width of the rectangle is $5\frac{1}{4}$ feet. What is the approximate length of the rectangle? **4 ft**

✔ CHECK Your Understanding
★ indicates multi-step problem

Examples 1–5
(p. 230–231)

Estimate.   1. $8 + 2 = 10$ 2. $3 - 1 = 2$ 3. $6 \times 3 = 18$ 4. $9 \div 3 = 3$

1. $8\frac{3}{8} + 1\frac{4}{5}$ 2. $2\frac{5}{6} - 1\frac{1}{8}$ 3. $5\frac{5}{7} \cdot 2\frac{7}{8}$ 4. $9\frac{2}{7} \div 2\frac{2}{3}$

5. $\frac{1}{6} + \frac{2}{5}$ $0 + \frac{1}{2} = \frac{1}{2}$ 6. $\frac{6}{7} - \frac{1}{5}$ $1 - 0 = 1$ 7. $\frac{5}{8} \cdot \frac{8}{9}$ $\frac{1}{2} \times 1 = \frac{1}{2}$ 8. $\frac{4}{5} \div \frac{6}{7}$ $1 \div 1 = 1$

1–10. Sample answers are given.

Examples 6, 7
(p. 232)

Estimate using compatible numbers.

9. $\frac{1}{4} \cdot 16 = 4$ 9. $\frac{1}{4} \cdot 15$ 10. $21\frac{5}{6} \div 9\frac{3}{4}$ $22 \div 11 = 2$

Example 8
(p. 232)

11. **BIRDS** A seagull's wingspan is about $\frac{2}{3}$ of a bald eagle's wingspan. The eagle's wingspan is shown at the right. Estimate the wingspan of a seagull.
$\frac{2}{3}$ of $6 \approx 4$ ft

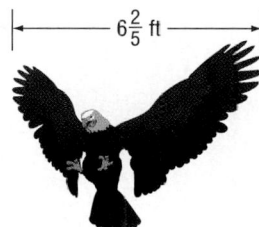

$\overleftrightarrow{6\frac{2}{5}\text{ ft}}$

▶ Practice and Problem Solving

HOMEWORK HELP	
For Exercises	**See Examples**
12–19	1, 2
20–29	3–5
30–35	6–8

Exercise Levels
A: 12–35
B: 36–43
C: 44–48

12. $4 + 5 = 9$
13. $1 + 6 = 7$
14. $5 - 3 = 2$
15. $4 - 2 = 2$
16. $3 \cdot 6 = 18$
17. $2 \cdot 3 = 6$
18. $6 \div 2 = 3$
19. $9 \div 3 = 3$
20. $1 + \frac{1}{2} = 1\frac{1}{2}$
21. $\frac{1}{2} + \frac{1}{2} = 1$
22. $\frac{1}{2} - 0 = \frac{1}{2}$
23. $1 - \frac{1}{2} = \frac{1}{2}$

Estimate.   12–27. Sample answers are given.

12. $3\frac{3}{4} + 4\frac{5}{6}$ 13. $1\frac{1}{8} + 5\frac{11}{12}$ 14. $5\frac{1}{3} - 3\frac{1}{6}$ 15. $4\frac{2}{5} - 1\frac{1}{2}$

16. $2\frac{2}{3} \cdot 6\frac{1}{3}$ 17. $1\frac{4}{5} \cdot 3\frac{1}{4}$ 18. $6\frac{1}{8} \div 1\frac{2}{3}$ 19. $8\frac{1}{2} \div 2\frac{5}{8}$

20. $\frac{3}{4} + \frac{3}{8}$ 21. $\frac{5}{8} + \frac{3}{7}$ 22. $\frac{5}{9} - \frac{1}{6}$ 23. $\frac{3}{4} - \frac{3}{5}$

24. $\frac{1}{8} \cdot \frac{3}{4}$ $0 \times 1 = 0$ 25. $\frac{4}{9} \cdot \frac{11}{12}$ $\frac{1}{2} \cdot 1 = \frac{1}{2}$ 26. $\frac{4}{5} \div \frac{7}{8}$ $1 \div 1 = 1$ 27. $\frac{1}{10} \div \frac{5}{6}$
$0 \div 1 = 0$

28. **COOKING** Joaquim wants to make the macaroni and cheese shown at the right, but he has only about $1\frac{3}{4}$ cups of macaroni. About how much more macaroni does he need?
$3 - 2$ or 1 c

Macaroni & Cheese
3 tbsp butter
$2\frac{1}{2}$ c uncooked macaroni
1 tbsp salt
$\frac{1}{4}$ tbsp pepper
1 qt milk
$\frac{1}{2}$ lb cheese

29. **MEASUREMENT** Isabella is sewing a trim that is $1\frac{1}{8}$ inches wide on the bottom of a skirt that is $15\frac{7}{8}$ inches long. Approximately how long will the skirt be? $16 + 1$ or 17 in.

Estimate using compatible numbers.   30–33. Sample answers are given.

30. $\frac{1}{4} \cdot 39$ 31. $\frac{1}{6} \cdot 37$ 32. $23\frac{2}{9} \div 3$ 33. $25\frac{3}{10} \div 5\frac{2}{3}$
$\frac{1}{4} \times 40 = 10$ $\frac{1}{6} \times 36 = 36$ $24 \div 3 = 8$ $25 \div 5 = 5$

34. **MONEY** Arleta has \$22. She uses $\frac{1}{3}$ of her money to buy a pair of earrings. About how much money did she spend on the earrings? $\frac{1}{3} \times \$21$ or \$7

35. **SNACKS** A cereal company has 24 pounds of granola to package in bags that contain $1\frac{3}{4}$ pounds of granola. About how many bags will they have?
$24 \div 2 = 12$

Lesson 5-1 Estimating with Fractions   **233**

3 Practice

✔ Formative Assessment

Use Exercises 1–11 to check for understanding.

Then use the chart at the bottom of this page to customize your assignments for students.

Intervention You may wish to use the Study Guide and Intervention Master on page 10 of the *Chapter 5 Resource Masters* for additional reinforcement.

Odd/Even Assignments

Exercises 12–35 are structured so that students practice the same concepts whether they are assigned odd or even problems.

DIFFERENTIATED HOMEWORK OPTIONS			
Level	**Assignment**	**Two-Day Option**	
BL Basic	12–35, 45–63	13–35 odd, 49, 50	12–34 even, 45–48, 51–63
OL Core	13–35 odd, 37, 39–43, 45–63	12–35, 49, 50	36–43, 45–48, 51–63
AL Advanced/Pre-AP	36–59 (optional: 60–63)		

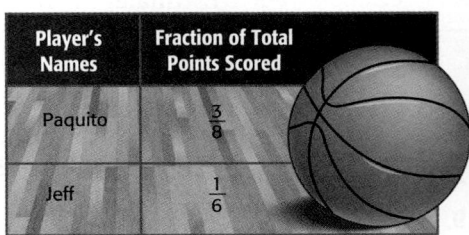
36. FIND THE DATA Refer to the Data File on pages 16–19. Choose some data and write a real-world problem in which you would estimate with fractions. **See students' work.**

★**37. SPORTS** Paquito and Jeff are on a basketball team. The table shows the approximate fraction of the team's points that each of them scored in a game. If the team scored a total of 72 points, about how many did Paquito and Jeff score together? **39**

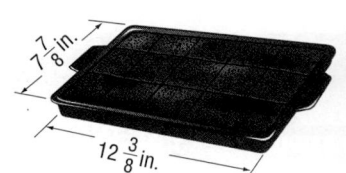

Player's Names	Fraction of Total Points Scored
Paquito	$\frac{3}{8}$
Jeff	$\frac{1}{6}$

38. RESEARCH Research the statistics of any basketball team. How can you use fractions to analyze the statistics? **See students' work.**

Real-World Link . . . . .
The femur or thigh bone is the longest in length, largest in volume, and strongest bone of the human body.

★**39. COOKING** Kathryn baked the sheet of brownies shown. She wants to cut it into brownies that are about 2 inches square. How many brownies will there be? **24**

$7\frac{7}{8}$ in.

$12\frac{3}{8}$ in.

ANALYZE TABLES For Exercises 40–43, use the following information and the table shown.

The adult human skeleton is made up of 206 bones. The table shows the approximate fraction of the bones that each body part(s) makes up.

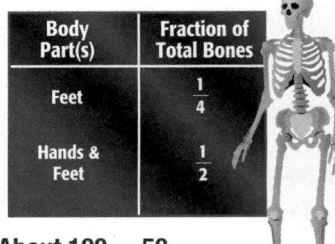

Body Part(s)	Fraction of Total Bones
Feet	$\frac{1}{4}$
Hands & Feet	$\frac{1}{2}$

40. $\frac{1}{4} \times 200$ or 50

40. About how many bones are in the feet?

★**41.** About how many bones are in both hands and feet? $\frac{1}{2} \times 200$ **or 100**

42. About 100 − 50 or 50; 50 ÷ 2 or 25

42. About how many bones are in one hand? **or 50; 50 ÷ 2 or 25**

★**43.** The length of your thighbone is equal to $\frac{1}{4}$ of your height. About how many inches long is your thighbone? **Sample answer:** $\frac{1}{4} \times 60$ **inches or 15 inches**

EXTRA PRACTICE
See pages 679, 708.

H.O.T. Problems

44. CHALLENGE In a division expression, the divisor is rounded up and the dividend is rounded down. How does the new quotient compare to the original quotient? Explain. **See margin.**

45. Sample answer:
$\frac{11}{12}$ and $\frac{7}{15}$; $\frac{11}{12} - \frac{7}{15} \approx 1 - \frac{1}{2}$ or $\frac{1}{2}$ and $\frac{11}{12} \cdot \frac{7}{15} \approx 1 \cdot \frac{1}{2}$ or $\frac{1}{2}$

45. OPEN ENDED Select two fractions whose estimated difference and product is $\frac{1}{2}$. Justify your selection.

46. NUMBER SENSE Decide which of the following have sums that are less than 1. Explain. **See margin.**

a. $\frac{1}{3} + \frac{2}{5}$

b. $\frac{7}{8} + \frac{1}{2}$

c. $\frac{5}{6} + \frac{2}{3}$

d. $\frac{1}{7} + \frac{3}{9}$

47. Estimation; Dion doesn't need an exact answer. Sample answer:
$3\frac{1}{4} + 1\frac{2}{3} + 1\frac{2}{3}$
is about halfway between 6 and 7 cups. Since this is more than 6 cups, Dion cannot use this bowl to mix the ingredients.

47. **SELECT A TECHNIQUE** To make the crust for a peach cobbler, Dion needs $3\frac{1}{4}$ cups of flour, $1\frac{2}{3}$ cups of sugar, and $1\frac{2}{3}$ cups of hot water. He needs to mix all of these in a large bowl. The largest bowl he can find holds 6 cups. Which of the following techniques might Dion use to determine whether he can use this bowl to mix the ingredients? Justify your selection(s). Then use the technique(s) to solve the problem.

| mental math | number sense | estimation |

48. **WRITING IN MATH** Explain when estimation would *not* be the best method for solving a problem. Then give an example. **See margin.**

TEST PRACTICE

49. **SHORT RESPONSE** A chef has $15\frac{2}{3}$ cups of penne pasta and $22\frac{1}{4}$ cups of rigatoni pasta. About how much pasta is there altogether? **38 cups**

50. On a full tank of gasoline, a certain car can travel 360 miles. The needle on its gasoline gauge is shown. Without refueling, which is the best estimate of how far the car can travel? **A**

- **A** 150 miles
- **B** 180 miles
- **C** 240 miles
- **D** 329 miles

Spiral Review

Replace each ● with <, >, or = to make a true sentence. (Lesson 4-9)

51. $2\frac{7}{8}$ ● 2.75 **>** 52. $\frac{-1}{3}$ ● $\frac{-7}{3}$ **>** 53. $\frac{5}{7}$ ● $\frac{4}{5}$ **<** 54. $3\frac{6}{11}$ ● $3\frac{9}{14}$ **<**

55. **SHOPPING** A store sells a 3-pack of beaded necklaces and a 5-pack of beaded bracelets. How many packages of each must you buy so that you have the same number of necklaces and bracelets? (Lesson 4-8) **5 pkg. of necklaces and 3 pkg. of bracelets.**

Write each decimal as a percent. (Lesson 4-7)

56. 0.56 **56%**   57. 0.375 **37.5%**   58. 0.07 **7%**   59. 0.019 **1.9%**

▷ **GET READY for the Next Lesson**

PREREQUISITE SKILL Find the LCD of each pair of fractions. (Lesson 4-9)

60. $\frac{3}{4}, \frac{5}{12}$ **12**   61. $\frac{1}{2}, \frac{7}{10}$ **10**   62. $\frac{1}{6}, \frac{1}{8}$ **24**   63. $\frac{4}{5}, \frac{2}{3}$ **15**

Crystal Ball Tell students that tomorrow's lesson will be about adding and subtracting fractions. Have them write how they think what they learned today will connect with tomorrow's material.

FOLDABLES Study Organizer **Foldables™ Follow-Up**

Remind students to record what they learn about estimating with fractions and mixed numbers on index cards, and then to store the cards in their Foldables.

Additional Answer

48. Sample answer: Sometimes you need to know an exact answer. When trying to figure out how much medicine to take, you need an exact answer. You would not want to round a dosage of $1\frac{1}{2}$ tsp of medicine to 2 tsp; you might take too much medicine.

Options for Differentiated Instruction

ELL = English Language Learner   **AL** = Above or Beyond Grade Level   **SS** = Struggling Students   **SN** = Special Needs

Review Vocabulary   **SS**   **SN**

Use before presenting Lesson 5-2.

To help students prepare for Lesson 5-2, provide a short review by presenting the following questions.

Ask:
- What is a least common denominator? How do you find it? the least common multiple of the denominators of two or more fractions; find the LCM of the denominators.
- What is one reason for renaming fractions with the LCD? to compare fractions with unlike denominators
  How do you write a fraction in simplest form? Divide the numerator and denominator by their GCF.
  For students who need additional practice, provide review sheets on these topics.

Using Manipulatives   **SS**   **SN**

Use before presenting Examples 1–6.

Have fractions strips available for students to model problems. Remind students that each strip represents one whole unit.

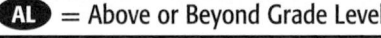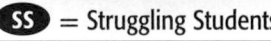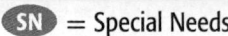

1

$\frac{1}{2}$	$\frac{1}{2}$

$\frac{1}{10}$	$\frac{1}{10}$	$\frac{1}{10}$	$\frac{1}{10}$	$\frac{1}{10}$	$\frac{1}{10}$	$\frac{1}{10}$	$\frac{1}{10}$	$\frac{1}{10}$	$\frac{1}{10}$

$\frac{1}{12}$	$\frac{1}{12}$	$\frac{1}{12}$	$\frac{1}{12}$	$\frac{1}{12}$	$\frac{1}{12}$	$\frac{1}{12}$	$\frac{1}{12}$	$\frac{1}{12}$	$\frac{1}{12}$	$\frac{1}{12}$	$\frac{1}{12}$

Kinesthetic Learning   **ELL**   **AL**   **SS**   **SN**

Use after presenting Examples 1–6.

Have pairs of students measure each other's vertical jumps in fractions of inches. Have them stand yardsticks on the ground vertically, and mark the highest point reached by each jumper's feet. Have students compare each other's vertical jumps by finding the differences in height. Students can jump multiple times and find their amount of improvement. Some students may not feel comfortable jumping, or may be unable to jump. Either assign these students the task of helping tabulate the class data, or ask for volunteers to help with this task.

Leveled Lesson Resources

Chapter 5 Resource Masters

BL = Below or Approaching Grade Level   **OL** = On Grade Level   **AL** = Above or Beyond Grade Level   **ELL** = English Language Learner

---

Lesson Reading Guide
p. 15 **BL** **OL** **ELL**

NAME _____ DATE _____ PERIOD _____

5-2 Lesson Reading Guide
Adding and Subtracting Fractions

Get Ready for the Lesson

Read the introduction at the top of page 236 in your textbook. Write your answers below.

1. What fraction uses LSR? BRB? $\frac{5}{10}, \frac{2}{10}$

2. What fraction uses either LSR or BRB? $\frac{7}{10}$

Read the Lesson

3. Describe the steps you take to add or subtract like fractions. **Sample answer: Add or subtract the numerators, and write the result over the denominator; simplify if necessary.**

4. How are like fractions different from unlike fractions? **Like fractions have the same denominators. Unlike fractions have different denominators.**

5. What does LCD stand for, and what does it mean? What is the LCD used for? **Sample answer: LCD stands for least common denominator, the least common multiple of the denominators of two or more fractions. You use the LCD when adding or subtracting unlike fractions. It is not needed for like fractions because like fractions have the same denominator.**

Remember What You Learned

6. Describe how the procedure for adding or subtracting unlike fractions is different from the procedure for adding or subtracting like fractions. **Sample answer: The procedure for adding or subtracting unlike fractions is the same as the procedure for adding or subtracting like fractions, except first you must find the LCD of the fractions and rename the fractions with the LCD.**

Chapter 5   15   Course 2

Study Guide and Intervention*
p. 16 **BL** **OL** **ELL**

NAME _____ DATE _____ PERIOD _____

5-2 Study Guide and Intervention
Adding and Subtracting Fractions

Like fractions are fractions that have the same denominator. To add or subtract like fractions, add or subtract the numerators and write the result over the denominator. Simplify if necessary.

To add or subtract *unlike* fractions, rename the fractions with a least common denominator. Then add or subtract as with like fractions.

Example 1 Subtract $\frac{3}{4} - \frac{1}{4}$. Write in simplest form.

$\frac{3}{4} - \frac{1}{4}$ Subtract the numerators.

$= \frac{3-1}{4}$ Write the difference over the denominator.

$= \frac{2}{4}$

$= \frac{1}{2}$ Simplify.

Example 2 Add $\frac{2}{3} + \frac{1}{12}$. Write in simplest form.

The least common denominator of 3 and 12 is 12.

$\frac{2}{3} = \frac{2 \times 4}{3 \times 4} = \frac{8}{12}$ Rename $\frac{2}{3}$ using the LCD.

$\frac{8}{12}$
$+ \frac{1}{12}$
$= \frac{9}{12}$ or $\frac{3}{4}$ Add the numerators and simplify.

Exercises

Add or subtract. Write in simplest form.

1. $\frac{5}{8} + \frac{1}{8}$ $\frac{3}{4}$ 2. $\frac{7}{9} - \frac{2}{9}$ $\frac{5}{9}$

3. $\frac{1}{3} + \frac{3}{4}$ $1\frac{1}{12}$ 4. $\frac{7}{8} - \frac{1}{2}$ $\frac{3}{8}$

5. $\frac{5}{6} + \frac{5}{9}$ $1\frac{7}{18}$ 6. $\frac{5}{6} - \frac{1}{12}$ $\frac{7}{24}$

7. $\frac{3}{10} + \frac{7}{6}$ $\frac{53}{60}$ 8. $\frac{5}{8} - \frac{1}{12}$ $\frac{7}{24}$

9. $\frac{7}{15} + \frac{5}{6}$ $1\frac{3}{10}$ 10. $\frac{7}{9} - \frac{1}{2}$ $\frac{5}{18}$

Chapter 5   16   Course 2

Skills Practice*
p. 17 **BL** **OL**

NAME _____ DATE _____ PERIOD _____

5-2 Skills Practice
Adding and Subtracting Fractions

Add or subtract. Write in simplest form.

1. $\frac{3}{8} + \frac{3}{8}$ $\frac{3}{4}$ 2. $\frac{7}{10} - \frac{5}{10}$ $\frac{1}{5}$ 3. $\frac{9}{10} + \frac{3}{10}$ $1\frac{1}{5}$

4. $\frac{4}{7} - \frac{2}{7}$ $\frac{2}{7}$ 5. $\frac{2}{3} + \frac{2}{3}$ $1\frac{1}{3}$ 6. $\frac{5}{9} - \frac{2}{9}$ $\frac{1}{3}$

7. $\frac{8}{15} - \frac{5}{15}$ $\frac{1}{5}$ 8. $\frac{5}{12} + \frac{5}{12}$ $1\frac{1}{4}$ 9. $\frac{3}{10} - \frac{3}{10}$ $\frac{3}{5}$

10. $\frac{7}{16} + \frac{3}{8}$ $\frac{13}{16}$ 11. $\frac{19}{20} - \frac{3}{10}$ $\frac{13}{20}$ 12. $\frac{5}{9} + \frac{7}{9}$ $1\frac{1}{3}$

13. $\frac{4}{9} - \frac{1}{12}$ $\frac{13}{36}$ 14. $\frac{2}{3} + \frac{3}{7}$ $1\frac{2}{21}$ 15. $\frac{3}{4} + \frac{1}{7}$ $\frac{25}{28}$

16. $\frac{7}{8} - \frac{2}{3}$ $\frac{5}{24}$ 17. $\frac{8}{9} - \frac{5}{6}$ $\frac{1}{18}$ 18. $\frac{5}{12} - \frac{3}{10}$ $\frac{7}{60}$

19. $\frac{7}{9} + \frac{2}{3}$ $1\frac{4}{9}$ 20. $\frac{3}{5} + \frac{4}{11}$ $\frac{53}{55}$ 21. $\frac{11}{12} - \frac{1}{4}$ $\frac{2}{3}$

ALGEBRA Evaluate each expression if $a = \frac{5}{6}$ and $b = \frac{3}{8}$.

22. $a + b$ $1\frac{5}{24}$ 23. $a - b$ $\frac{11}{24}$ 24. $\frac{9}{10} - a$ $\frac{1}{15}$

Chapter 5   17   Course 2

Practice*
p. 18 **OL** **AL**

NAME _____ DATE _____ PERIOD _____

5-2 Practice
Adding and Subtracting Fractions

Add or subtract. Write in simplest form.

1. $\frac{2}{5} + \frac{3}{5}$ 1   2. $\frac{2}{9} + \frac{4}{9}$ $\frac{2}{3}$ 3. $\frac{8}{11} - \frac{7}{11}$ $\frac{1}{11}$ 4. $\frac{4}{8} + \frac{5}{8}$ $1\frac{1}{8}$

5. $\frac{1}{18} + \frac{6}{9}$ $\frac{8}{9}$ 6. $\frac{7}{15} - \frac{1}{5}$ $\frac{4}{15}$ 7. $\frac{9}{16} - \frac{5}{12}$ $\frac{7}{48}$ 8. $\frac{5}{14} - \frac{2}{21}$ $\frac{11}{42}$

9. $\frac{7}{8} + \frac{1}{6}$ $\frac{17}{24}$ 10. $\frac{7}{10} - \frac{4}{15}$ $\frac{13}{30}$ 11. $\frac{5}{6} + \frac{3}{4}$ $1\frac{1}{12}$ 12. $\frac{2}{3} - \frac{1}{2}$ $\frac{1}{6}$

13. $1 + \frac{1}{6}$ $1\frac{1}{6}$ 14. $1 - \frac{3}{5}$ $\frac{2}{5}$ 15. $4 + \frac{8}{9}$ $4\frac{8}{9}$ 16. $5 - \frac{1}{4}$ $4\frac{3}{4}$

17. $\frac{2}{3} + \frac{4}{5} + \frac{1}{5}$ $1\frac{2}{15}$ 18. $\frac{7}{8} + \frac{1}{2} + \frac{3}{16}$ $1\frac{9}{16}$

19. $\left(\frac{3}{4} + \frac{1}{3}\right) - \frac{11}{12}$ $\frac{1}{6}$ 20. $\left(\frac{4}{5} - \frac{7}{10}\right) + \frac{1}{4}$ $\frac{7}{20}$

21. STATES Most of the state names in the United States end in a vowel. Of the 50 states, $\frac{1}{2}$ of the state names end in either an *a* or an *e* and $\frac{3}{50}$ end in either an *i* or an *o*. If none of the state names end in a *u*, what is the fraction of state names that end in a vowel? $\frac{31}{50}$

22. JIGSAW PUZZLES Over the weekend, Halverson had put together $\frac{3}{16}$ of a jigsaw puzzle, while Jaime put together $\frac{5}{8}$ of the puzzle. Who had completed a greater fraction of the jigsaw puzzle, and by how much? **Jaime completed $\frac{7}{16}$ more.**

ALGEBRA Evaluate each expression if $x = \frac{5}{8}$ and $y = \frac{5}{4}$.

23. $x - \frac{1}{2}$ $\frac{1}{8}$ 24. $y - x$ $\frac{5}{8}$ 25. $\frac{5}{16} + y$ $1\frac{9}{16}$ 26. $x + y$ $1\frac{7}{8}$

Chapter 5   18   Course 2

Word Problem Practice*
p. 19 **OL** **AL**

NAME _____ DATE _____ PERIOD _____

5-2 Word Problem Practice
Adding and Subtracting Fractions

RETAIL STORES For Exercises 1–4 use the table at the right. It shows what fraction of the stores at a mall fall into seven categories.

Type of Store	Fraction of Stores in Mall
jewelry	$\frac{1}{30}$
clothing	$\frac{8}{15}$
gifts	$\frac{3}{20}$
electronics	$\frac{1}{20}$
department	$\frac{1}{15}$
shoes	$\frac{1}{6}$
athletic	$\frac{1}{10}$

1. What fraction of the stores are jewelry or gift stores? $\frac{11}{60}$

2. What fraction of the stores are clothing or electronics stores? $\frac{7}{12}$

3. Which type of store has the greatest number of stores? **clothing stores**

4. How many more clothing stores are there than athletic stores? Write as a fraction. $\frac{13}{30}$

5. SEWING Jin wants to make a scarf and matching hat for his sister. The patterns call for $\frac{3}{4}$ yard of fabric for the scarf and $\frac{1}{2}$ yard of fabric for the hat. How much fabric should Jin buy? **Jin should buy $1\frac{1}{4}$ yards.**

6. RESTAURANT Ms. Malle owns a restaurant. Typically, $\frac{1}{6}$ of the customers order fish, while $\frac{2}{5}$ of the customers order poultry. What fraction of her customers order either fish or poultry? $\frac{17}{30}$

Chapter 5   19   Course 2

Enrichment
p. 20 **OL** **AL**

NAME _____ DATE _____ PERIOD _____

5-2 Enrichment

Fractions Maze

To solve this maze, start at the upper left corner. Then, draw a line to the next circle with the smallest sum or difference. The answers written in order will form a pattern. The same circle may not be used twice.

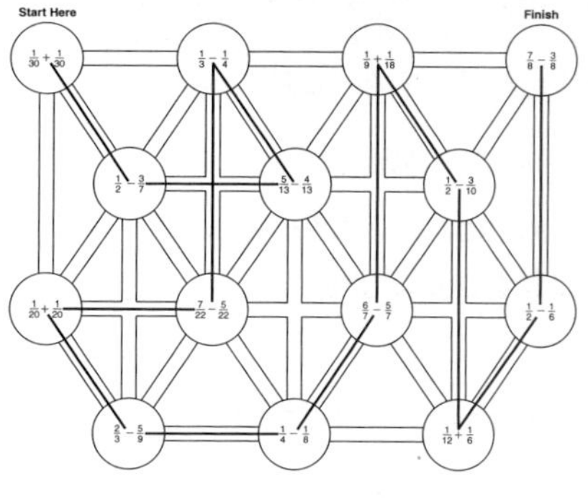

Describe the pattern in the fractions along the line you drew from start to finish. **Numerator is always 1; denominators decrease by one from 15 to 2.**

Chapter 5   20   Course 2

Additional Lesson Resources

Transparencies
• *5-Minute Check Transparency*, Lesson 5-2

Other Print Products
• *Noteables™ Interactive Study Notebook with Foldables™*

Teacher Tech Tools
• *Interactive Classroom CD-ROM*, Lesson 5-2
• *AssignmentWorks*, Lesson 5-2

Student Tech Tools
glencoe.com
• Extra Examples, Chapter 5, Lesson 2
• Self-Check Quiz, Chapter 5, Lesson 2

5-2 Adding and Subtracting Fractions

5-2 Lesson Notes

1 Focus

Vertical Alignment

Before Lesson 5-2
Solve simple problems, including ones arising in concrete situations, involving the addition and subtraction of fractions and mixed numbers and express answers in the simplest form

Lesson 5-2
Solve problems involving addition, subtraction, of positive fractions and explain why a particular operation was used for a given situation. Determine the least common multiple of whole numbers; use them to solve problems with fractions

After Lesson 5-2
Add and subtract fractions by using factoring to find common denominators

2 Teach

Scaffolding Questions

Tell students to look at a ruler to help them answer the questions.

Ask:

- What is the sum of $\frac{1}{8}$ inch and $\frac{4}{8}$ inch? $\frac{5}{8}$ in.

- What is the sum of $\frac{2}{4}$ inch and $\frac{1}{4}$ inch? $\frac{3}{4}$ in.

- What is the sum of $\frac{3}{16}$ inch and $\frac{5}{16}$ inch? $\frac{8}{16}$ in. or $\frac{1}{2}$ in.

MAIN IDEA

Add and subtract fractions.

New Vocabulary

like fractions
unlike fractions

Math Online

glencoe.com

- Extra Examples
- Personal Tutor
- Self-Check Quiz
- Reading in the Content Area

▷ GET READY for the Lesson

INSTANT MESSENGER Sean surveyed ten classmates to find which abbreviation they use most when they instant message.

1. What fraction uses L8R? BRB? $\frac{5}{10}$; $\frac{2}{10}$

2. What fraction uses either L8R or BRB? $\frac{7}{10}$

Abbreviation	Number
L8R	5
LOL	3
BRB	2

Fractions that have the same denominators are called **like fractions**.

Add and Subtract Like Fractions   Key Concept

Words	To add or subtract like fractions, add or subtract the numerators and write the result over the denominator.

Examples

Numbers	**Algebra**
$\frac{5}{10} + \frac{2}{10} = \frac{5+2}{10}$ or $\frac{7}{10}$	$\frac{a}{c} + \frac{b}{c} = \frac{a+b}{c}$, where $c \neq 0$
$\frac{11}{12} - \frac{4}{12} = \frac{11-4}{12}$ or $\frac{7}{12}$	$\frac{a}{c} - \frac{b}{c} = \frac{a-b}{c}$, where $c \neq 0$

EXAMPLES   Add and Subtract Like Fractions

1 Add $\frac{5}{9} + \frac{2}{9}$. Write in simplest form.

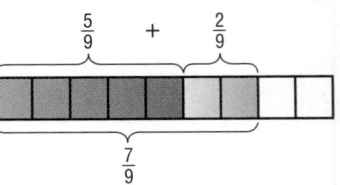

$\frac{5}{9} + \frac{2}{9} = \frac{5+2}{9}$ Add the numerators.

$= \frac{7}{9}$ Write the sum over the denominator.

2 Subtract $\frac{9}{10} - \frac{1}{10}$. Write in simplest form.

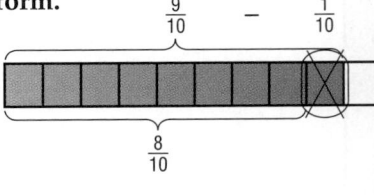

$\frac{9}{10} - \frac{1}{10} = \frac{9-1}{10}$ Subtract the numerators.

$= \frac{8}{10}$ Write the difference over the denominator.

$= \frac{4}{5}$ Simplify.

✓ CHECK Your Progress

a. $\frac{1}{6} + \frac{3}{6}$ $\frac{2}{3}$

b. $\frac{3}{7} - \frac{1}{7}$ $\frac{2}{7}$

Tips for New Teachers

Like Fractions

The denominator names the units of what is being added or subtracted. For example, $\frac{1}{5} + \frac{3}{5} = \frac{4}{5}$ can be thought of as 1 fifth + 3 fifths = 4 fifths.

To add or subtract **unlike fractions**, or fractions with different denominators, rename the fractions using the LCD. Then add or subtract as with like fractions.

EXAMPLES   Add and Subtract Unlike Fractions

3 Add $\frac{1}{2} + \frac{1}{6}$. Write in simplest form.   Estimate $\frac{1}{2} + 0 = \frac{1}{2}$

METHOD 1 **Use a model.**

$$\begin{array}{l} \frac{1}{2} \\ + \frac{1}{6} \\ \hline \frac{4}{6} \text{ or } \frac{2}{3} \end{array}$$

METHOD 2 **Use the LCD.**

The least common denominator (LCD) of $\frac{1}{2}$ and $\frac{1}{6}$ is 6.

Rename using the LCD, 6.   Add.

$$\frac{1}{2} \rightarrow \frac{1 \times 3}{2 \times 3} = \frac{3}{6} \rightarrow \frac{3}{6}$$

$$+\frac{1}{6} \rightarrow \frac{1 \times 1}{6 \times 1} = +\frac{1}{6} \rightarrow +\frac{1}{6}$$

$$\frac{4}{6} \text{ or } \frac{2}{3}$$

So, $\frac{1}{2} + \frac{1}{6} = \frac{2}{3}$.   **Check for Reasonableness** $\frac{2}{3} \approx \frac{1}{2}$ ✔

4 Subtract $\frac{11}{12} - \frac{3}{8}$. Write in simplest form.   **Estimate** $1 - \frac{1}{2} = \frac{1}{2}$

Since $12 = 2^2 \cdot 3$ and $8 = 2^3$, the LCM of 12 and 8 is $2^3 \cdot 3$ or 24. Rename each fraction using a denominator of 24. Then subtract.

Think: $12 \times 2 = 24$, so $\frac{11 \times 2}{12 \times 2}$ or $\frac{22}{24}$.

Think: $8 \times 3 = 24$, so $\frac{3}{8} = \frac{3 \times 3}{8 \times 3}$ or $\frac{9}{24}$.

$\frac{11}{12} - \frac{3}{8} = \frac{11 \times 2}{12 \times 2} - \frac{3 \times 3}{8 \times 3}$.   The LCD of $\frac{11}{12}$ and $\frac{3}{8}$ is 24.

$= \frac{22}{24} - \frac{9}{24}$ Rename the fractions using LCD, 24.

$= \frac{13}{24}$ Subtract the fractions.

Check for Reasonableness $\frac{13}{24} \approx \frac{1}{2}$ ✔

CHOOSE Your Method

c. $\frac{8}{9} - \frac{2}{3}$ **$\frac{2}{9}$**   d. $\frac{5}{6} - \frac{3}{8}$ **$\frac{11}{24}$**   e. $\frac{7}{8} + \frac{3}{4}$ **$1\frac{5}{8}$**

---

3 Practice

✓ Formative Assessment

Use Exercises 1–10 to check for understanding.

Then use the chart at the bottom of the next page to customize your assignments for students.

Intervention You may wish to use the Study Guide and Intervention Master on page 16 of the *Chapter 5 Resource Masters* for additional reinforcement.

Additional Answers

9. addition; Sample answer: To find how much smaller the total height of the photo is now, add $\frac{5}{16}$ and $\frac{3}{8}$.

10. subtraction; Sample answer: To find the part of the water that was used, subtract $\frac{1}{4}$ from $\frac{7}{8}$.

 Real-World EXAMPLES

SURVEYS In a recent survey, students were asked what they would choose for a healthy lunch. The results are shown in the graph.

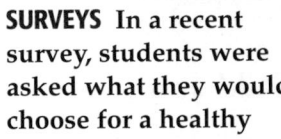 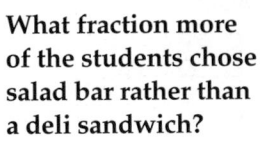

Healthy Lunch

None of these $\frac{3}{20}$ — Burger & Fries $\frac{1}{10}$ — Deli sandwich $\frac{3}{25}$ — Salad Bar $\frac{9}{20}$ — Chicken nuggets $\frac{1}{10}$ — Pizza $\frac{3}{20}$

Study Tip

Key Words The phrase *what fraction more* suggests subtraction.

5 What fraction more of the students chose salad bar rather than a deli sandwich?

$\frac{9}{20} - \frac{3}{25} = \frac{9 \times 5}{20 \times 5} - \frac{3 \times 4}{25 \times 4}$ The LCD of $\frac{9}{20}$ and $\frac{3}{25}$ is 100.

$= \frac{45}{100} - \frac{12}{100}$ Rename the fractions using the LCD.

$= \frac{33}{100}$ Subtract the numerators.

So, $\frac{33}{100}$ more students chose salad bar rather than a deli sandwich.

6 What fraction of students chose pizza or chicken nuggets?

$\frac{3}{20} + \frac{1}{10} = \frac{3}{20} + \frac{2}{20}$ Rename.

$= \frac{5}{20}$ Add.

$= \frac{1}{4}$ Simplify.

So, $\frac{1}{4}$ of the students chose pizza or chicken nuggets combined.

✓ CHECK Your Progress

f. **SURVEYS** What fraction more of the students chose a deli sandwich rather than a burger and fries? $\frac{1}{50}$

★ indicates multi-step problem

✓ CHECK Your Understanding

Examples 1–4
(pp. 236–237)

Add or subtract. Write in simplest form.

1. $\frac{4}{9} + \frac{2}{9}$ $\frac{2}{3}$ 2. $\frac{5}{6} + \frac{4}{9}$ $1\frac{5}{18}$ 3. $\frac{3}{8} - \frac{1}{8}$ $\frac{1}{4}$ 4. $\frac{4}{5} - \frac{2}{5}$ $\frac{2}{5}$

5. $\frac{1}{6} + \frac{3}{8}$ $\frac{13}{24}$ 6. $\frac{2}{3} + \frac{5}{6}$ $1\frac{1}{2}$ 7. $\frac{5}{6} - \frac{7}{12}$ $\frac{1}{4}$ 8. $\frac{3}{4} - \frac{1}{3}$ $\frac{5}{12}$

Examples 5, 6
(p. 238)

For Exercises 9 and 10, choose an operation to solve each problem. Explain your reasoning. Then solve the problem. **9, 10.** See margin for explanations.

9. **MEASUREMENT** Cassandra cuts $\frac{5}{16}$ inch off the top of a photo and $\frac{3}{8}$ inch off the bottom. How much smaller is the total height of the photo now? $\frac{11}{16}$ in.

10. **CHORES** A bucket was $\frac{7}{8}$ full with soapy water. After washing the car, the bucket was only $\frac{1}{4}$ full. What part of the water was used? $\frac{5}{8}$

Practice and Problem Solving

HOMEWORK HELP

For Exercises	See Examples
11–14	1, 2
15–22	3, 4
23–26	5, 6

Exercise Levels
A: 11–26
B: 27–44
C: 45–48

Add or subtract. Write in simplest form.

11. $\frac{3}{7} + \frac{1}{7}$ $\frac{4}{7}$
12. $\frac{5}{8} + \frac{7}{8}$ $1\frac{1}{2}$
13. $\frac{5}{6} - \frac{1}{6}$ $\frac{2}{3}$
14. $\frac{7}{10} - \frac{3}{10}$ $\frac{2}{5}$

15. $\frac{1}{15} + \frac{3}{5}$ $\frac{2}{3}$
16. $\frac{7}{12} + \frac{7}{10}$ $1\frac{17}{60}$
17. $\frac{5}{8} + \frac{11}{12}$ $1\frac{13}{24}$
18. $\frac{7}{9} + \frac{5}{6}$ $1\frac{11}{18}$

19. $\frac{7}{9} - \frac{1}{3}$ $\frac{4}{9}$
20. $\frac{4}{5} - \frac{1}{6}$ $\frac{19}{30}$
21. $\frac{4}{9} - \frac{2}{15}$ $\frac{14}{45}$
22. $\frac{3}{10} - \frac{1}{4}$ $\frac{1}{20}$

For Exercises 23–26, choose an operation to solve each problem. Explain your reasoning. Then solve the problem. 23–26. See margin for explanations.

23. **MEASUREMENT** Ebony is building a shelf to hold the two boxes shown. What is the smallest width she should make the shelf? $1\frac{11}{20}$ ft

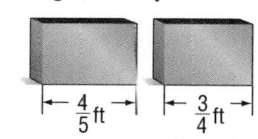

24. **WEATHER** Using the information under the photo, find the difference of the average precipitation for Boise in February and November. $\frac{3}{10}$ in.

25. **MEASUREMENT** Makayla bought $\frac{1}{4}$ pound of ham and $\frac{5}{8}$ pound of turkey. How much more turkey did she buy? $\frac{3}{8}$

26. **ANIMALS** The three-toed sloth can travel $\frac{3}{20}$ miles per hour while a giant tortoise can travel $\frac{17}{100}$ miles per hour. How much faster, in miles per hour, is the giant tortoise? $\frac{1}{50}$ mi/h

Simplify.

27. $\frac{1}{7} + \frac{1}{2} + \frac{5}{28}$ $\frac{23}{28}$
28. $\frac{1}{4} + \frac{5}{6} + \frac{7}{12}$ $1\frac{2}{3}$
29. $\frac{1}{6} + \left(\frac{2}{3} - \frac{1}{4}\right)$ $\frac{7}{12}$
30. $\frac{5}{6} - \left(\frac{1}{2} + \frac{1}{3}\right)$ 0

31. $1 + \frac{1}{4}$ $1\frac{1}{4}$
32. $1 - \frac{5}{8}$ $\frac{3}{8}$
33. $2 + \frac{2}{3}$ $2\frac{2}{3}$
34. $3 - \frac{1}{6}$ $2\frac{5}{6}$

35. **MONEY** Chellise saves $\frac{1}{5}$ of her allowance and spends $\frac{2}{3}$ of her allowance at the mall. What fraction of her allowance remains? $\frac{2}{15}$

36. **ANALYZE TABLES** Pepita and Francisco each spend an equal amount of time on homework. The table shows the fraction of their time they spend on each subject. Determine the missing fraction for each student.
Pepita: $\frac{1}{6}$ math; Franciso: $\frac{1}{8}$ English

Homework	Fraction of Time	
	Pepita	Francisco
Math	▪	$\frac{1}{2}$
English	$\frac{2}{3}$	▪
Science	$\frac{1}{6}$	$\frac{3}{8}$

ALGEBRA Evaluate each expression if $a = \frac{3}{4}$ and $b = \frac{5}{6}$.

37. $\frac{1}{2} + a$ $1\frac{1}{4}$
38. $b - \frac{7}{10}$ $\frac{2}{15}$
39. $b - a$ $\frac{1}{12}$
40. $a + b$ $1\frac{7}{12}$

Lesson 5-2 Adding and Subtracting Fractions **239**

Odd/Even Assignments

Exercises 11–26 are structured so that students practice the same concepts whether they are assigned odd or even problems.

Additional Answers

23. addition; Sample answer: To find the smallest width to make the shelf, add $\frac{4}{5}$ and $\frac{3}{4}$.

24. subtraction; Sample answer: To find the difference of the average precipitation for February and November for Boise, subtract $\frac{4}{10}$ from $\frac{7}{10}$.

25. subtraction; Sample answer: To find how much more turkey Makayla bought, subtract $\frac{1}{4}$ from $\frac{5}{8}$.

26. subtraction; Sample answer: To find how much faster the giant tortoise travels, subtract $\frac{3}{20}$ from $\frac{17}{100}$.

Real-World Link
The average precipitation for February and November for Boise, Idaho, is $\frac{4}{10}$ and $\frac{7}{10}$ inches, respectively.
Source: The Weather Channel

DIFFERENTIATED HOMEWORK OPTIONS

Level	Assignment	Two-Day Option	
BL Basic	11–26, 46–64	11–25 odd, 49, 50	12–26 even, 46, 48, 51–64
OL Core	11–35 odd, 36, 37, 39, 41–44, 46–64	11–26, 49, 50	27–44, 46–48, 51–64
AL Advanced/Pre-AP	27–59 (optional: 60–64)		

41. $\frac{2}{3} - \left(\frac{1}{6} + \frac{1}{4}\right) = \frac{1}{4}$

EXTRA PRACTICE

See pages 679, 708.

★**41. BOOK REPORTS** Four students were scheduled to give book reports in a 1-hour class period. After the first report, $\frac{2}{3}$ hour remained. If the next two students' reports took $\frac{1}{6}$ hour and $\frac{1}{4}$ hour, respectively, what fraction of the hour remained after the final students' report? Justify your answer.

42. MEASUREMENT Mrs. Escalante was riding a bicycle on a bike path. After riding $\frac{2}{3}$ of a mile, she discovered that she still needed to travel $\frac{3}{4}$ of a mile to reach the end of the path. How long is the bike path? **$1\frac{5}{12}$ mi**

43. CELL PHONES One hundred sixty cell phone owners were surveyed. What fraction of owners prefers using their cell phone for text messaging or taking pictures? **$\frac{3}{4}$**

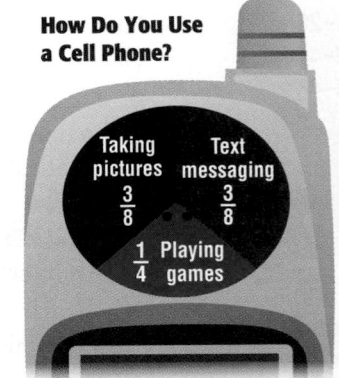

How Do You Use a Cell Phone?

Taking pictures $\frac{3}{8}$ Text messaging $\frac{3}{8}$

$\frac{1}{4}$ Playing games

★**44. MEASUREMENT** LaTasha and Eric are jogging on a track. LaTasha jogs $\frac{1}{4}$ of a mile and then stops. Eric jogs $\frac{5}{8}$ of a mile, stops and then turns around and jogs $\frac{1}{2}$ of a mile. Who is farther ahead on the track? How much farther?

H.O.T. Problems

45. CHALLENGE Fractions, such as $\frac{1}{2}$ or $\frac{1}{3}$, whose numerators are 1, are called *unit fractions*. Describe a method you can use to add two unit fractions mentally. Explain your reasoning and use your method to find $\frac{1}{99} + \frac{1}{100}$. **See margin.**

46. OPEN ENDED Provide a counterexample to the following statement. *The sum of three fractions with odd numerators is never $\frac{1}{2}$.* **Sample answer: $\frac{1}{4} + \frac{1}{6} + \frac{1}{12}$**

47. FIND THE ERROR Meagan and Lourdes are finding $\frac{1}{4} + \frac{3}{5}$. Who is correct? Explain.

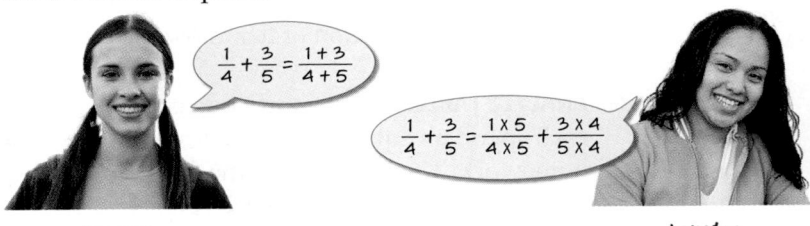

$\frac{1}{4} + \frac{3}{5} = \frac{1+3}{4+5}$

Meagan

$\frac{1}{4} + \frac{3}{5} = \frac{1 \times 5}{4 \times 5} + \frac{3 \times 4}{5 \times 4}$

Lourdes

48. **WRITING IN MATH** To make a cake, Felicia needs 1 cup of flour but she only has a $\frac{2}{3}$-measuring cup and a $\frac{3}{4}$-measuring cup. Which method will bring her closest to having the amount of flour she needs? Explain. **See margin.**

a. Fill the $\frac{2}{3}$-measuring cup twice.   b. Fill the $\frac{2}{3}$-measuring cup once.

c. Fill the $\frac{3}{4}$-measuring cup twice.   d. Fill the $\frac{3}{4}$-measuring cup once.

49. The table gives the number of hours Orlando spent at football practice for one week.

Day	Time (hours)
Monday	$1\frac{1}{2}$
Tuesday	2
Wednesday	$2\frac{1}{3}$
Thursday	$1\frac{5}{6}$
Friday	$2\frac{1}{2}$
Saturday	$1\frac{3}{4}$

How many more hours did he practice over the last three days than he did over the first three days? **A**

A $\frac{1}{4}$ h

B $\frac{1}{2}$ h

C $\frac{2}{3}$ h

D $\frac{3}{4}$ h

50. Which of the following is the prime factored form of the lowest common denominator of $\frac{7}{12} + \frac{11}{18}$? **H**

F 2×3

G 2×3^2

H $2^2 \times 3^2$

J $2^3 \times 3$

51. Find $\frac{5}{6} - \frac{1}{8}$. **D**

A $\frac{4}{7}$

B $\frac{3}{8}$

C $\frac{7}{12}$

D $\frac{17}{24}$

Spiral Review 52–55. Sample answers are given.

Estimate. (Lesson 5-1) **52.** $1 - \frac{1}{2} = \frac{1}{2}$ **53.** $4 + 4 = 8$ **54.** $16 \div 8 = 2$ **55.** $6 \cdot 3 = 18$

52. $\frac{6}{7} - \frac{5}{12}$ **53.** $4\frac{1}{9} + 3\frac{3}{4}$ **54.** $16\frac{2}{3} \div 8\frac{1}{5}$ **55.** $5\frac{4}{5} \cdot 3\frac{1}{3}$

56. WEATHER The table shows about how much rain falls in Albuquerque and Denver. Which city has the greater fraction of inches of rain per day? Explain. (Lesson 4-9) **Denver;** $\frac{15}{90} > \frac{9}{60}$

City	Amount of Rain (in.)	Number of Days
Albuquerque, NM	9	60
Denver, CO	15	90

Source: The Weather Channel

57. Write 0.248 as a percent. (Lesson 4-7) **24.8%**

ALGEBRA Find each sum if $a = -3$ and $b = 2$. (Lessons 2-4 and 2-5)

58. $a + b$ **−1** **59.** $a - b$ **−5** **60.** $b - a$ **5**

▷ GET READY for the Next Lesson

PREREQUISITE SKILL Complete.

61. $5\frac{2}{3} = 5 + \blacksquare$ **$\frac{2}{3}$** **62.** $1 = \frac{\blacksquare}{9}$ **9** **63.** $1 = \frac{\blacksquare}{5}$ **5** **64.** $\blacksquare = 4 + \frac{3}{8}$ **$4\frac{3}{8}$**

Pre-AP Activity — Use as an Extension.

Have students create a function table for $y = \frac{1}{2}x + \frac{2}{3}$ and then graph the function on grid paper.

---

4 Assess

Crystal Ball Tell students that tomorrow's lesson will be about adding and subtracting mixed numbers. Have them write how they think what they learned today will connect with tomorrow's material.

Formative Assessment

Check for student understanding of concepts in Lessons 5-1 and 5-2.

CRM Quiz 1, p. 53

FOLDABLES Study Organizer Foldables™ Follow-Up

Remind students to record what they learn about adding and subtracting like and unlike fractions on index cards, and then to store the cards in their Foldables.

Adding and Subtracting Mixed Numbers

PACING: **Regular:** 1 period,   **Block:** 0.5 period

Options for Differentiated Instruction

ELL = English Language Learner   **AL** = Above or Beyond Grade Level   **SS** = Struggling Students   **SN** = Special Needs

Conceptual Understanding   **SS**   **SN**

Use with Example 3.

Explain to students that when adding and subtracting mixed numbers, the way in which whole numbers are renamed depends on the problem. Present the following examples. Include pictures or diagrams like the ones shown below to help explain.

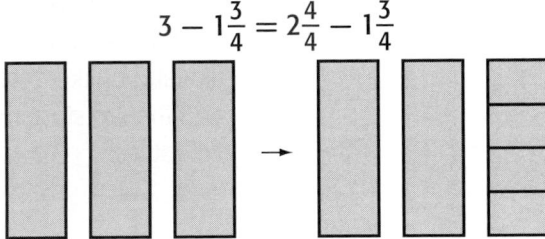

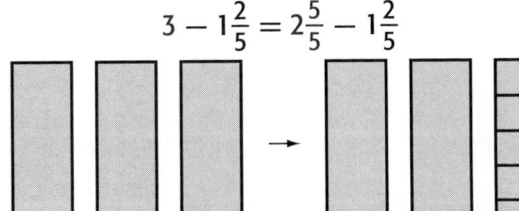

$$3 - 1\frac{3}{4} = 2\frac{4}{4} - 1\frac{3}{4}$$

3 is renamed as $2\frac{4}{4}$.

$$3 - 1\frac{2}{5} = 2\frac{5}{5} - 1\frac{2}{5}$$

3 is renamed as $2\frac{5}{5}$.

Additional Tips   **SS**

Use before presenting Example 3.

Explain why, when subtracting mixed numbers, it is important to look at the fraction parts first. Use pictures, diagrams, and examples to help explain your reasoning.

Kinesthetic Learning   **ELL**   **AL**

Use after presenting Examples 1–5.

Prepare a set of index cards, with each having a mixed number or fraction written on it. Examples are shown at the right.

$2\frac{1}{3}$ $1\frac{1}{3}$

Give each student one card, then call out a sum. Students should mingle, trying to find a student whose number, when added to theirs, equals the sum.

$5\frac{1}{2}$ $3\frac{5}{8}$

Suggestions:
- Plan well, to be sure that each student finds a match after three or four rounds.
- One possible resource is the Exercises provided in the Extra Practice on page 680.
- You may also wish to extend the activity to include subtraction.

Leveled Lesson Resources

Also on TeacherWorks™
Lesson 5-3

BL = Below or Approaching Grade Level **OL** = On Grade Level **AL** = Above or Beyond Grade Level **ELL** = English Language Learner

---

Lesson Reading Guide
p. 21 **BL** **OL** **ELL**

5-3 Lesson Reading Guide

Adding and Subtracting Mixed Numbers

Get Ready for the Lesson

Read the introduction at the top of page 242 in your textbook. Write your answers below.

1. Write an expression to find out how much more Nicolás weighs than Mia. $7\frac{15}{16} - 5\frac{7}{8}$

2. Rename the fractions using the LCD. $7\frac{15}{16} - 5\frac{14}{16}$

3. Find the difference of the fractional parts of the mixed numbers. $\frac{1}{16}$

4. Find the difference of the whole numbers. **2**

5. **MAKE A CONJECTURE** Explain how to find $7\frac{15}{16} - 5\frac{7}{8}$. Then use your conjecture to find the difference. **Write the fractions with a common denominator. Subtract the fractions and then the whole numbers.** $2\frac{1}{16}$

Read the Lesson

6. In the examples of adding and subtracting mixed numbers, the first step indicated is to estimate the result using whole numbers.

  a. Why do you think it's a good idea to use an estimate? **Sample answer: to have something to compare the actual answer to, so you can check your work**

  b. How do you find the whole numbers used in the estimates? **Sample answer: If the fraction part of the mixed number is $\frac{1}{2}$ or greater, round the whole number part of the mixed number up to the next whole number; if the fraction part is less than $\frac{1}{2}$, round down to the whole number part of the mixed number.**

7. What must you do if the fraction part of the mixed number is greater than the fraction part of the mixed number you are subtracting from? Give an example different from the one used in your textbook. **Sample answer: You must rename the mixed number from which you are subtracting. For example, to subtract $3\frac{3}{4}$ from $4\frac{1}{4}$, first you must rename $4\frac{1}{4}$ as $3\frac{5}{4}$.**

Remember What You Learned

8. Work with a partner. Take turns thinking of a mixed number and having our partner tell you how to rename the mixed number in the way described in this lesson. Repeat until each of you can rename mixed numbers easily. **See students' work.**

Study Guide and Intervention*
p. 22 **BL** **OL** **ELL**

5-3 Study Guide and Intervention

Adding and Subtracting Mixed Numbers

To add or subtract mixed numbers:
1. Add or subtract the fractions. Rename using the LCD if necessary.
2. Add or subtract the whole numbers.
3. Simplify if necessary.

Example 1 Find $14\frac{1}{2} + 18\frac{5}{6}$.

$$14\frac{1}{2} \rightarrow 14\frac{3}{6}$$ Rename the fractions.
$$+18\frac{5}{6} \rightarrow +18\frac{5}{6}$$ Add the whole numbers and add the fractions.
$$32\frac{8}{6} \text{ or } 33\frac{1}{3}$$ Simplify.

Example 2 Find $21 - 12\frac{5}{8}$.

$$21 \rightarrow 20\frac{8}{8}$$ Rename 21 as $20\frac{8}{8}$.
$$-12\frac{5}{8} \rightarrow -12\frac{5}{8}$$ First subtract the whole numbers and then the fractions.
$$8\frac{3}{8}$$

Exercises

Add or subtract. Write in simplest form.

1. $7\frac{3}{4} + 2\frac{3}{4}$ $10\frac{1}{2}$ 2. $14\frac{5}{9} - 6\frac{1}{9}$ $8\frac{4}{9}$ 3. $9\frac{1}{2} - 4\frac{3}{4}$ $4\frac{9}{20}$

4. $7\frac{1}{8} + 5\frac{3}{8}$ $12\frac{1}{2}$ 5. $7\frac{3}{4} + 2\frac{7}{12}$ $10\frac{5}{12}$ 6. $5\frac{1}{2} - 5\frac{1}{3}$ $\frac{1}{6}$

7. $5\frac{1}{2} - 3\frac{1}{4}$ $2\frac{1}{4}$ 8. $6\frac{1}{3} + 2\frac{1}{6}$ $8\frac{1}{2}$ 9. $9 - 3\frac{2}{5}$ $5\frac{3}{5}$

10. $2\frac{2}{3} + 7\frac{1}{2}$ $10\frac{1}{6}$ 11. $6\frac{1}{2} - 6\frac{1}{3}$ $\frac{1}{6}$ 12. $18\frac{1}{2} + 5\frac{5}{8}$ $24\frac{1}{8}$

Skills Practice*
p. 23 **BL** **OL**

5-3 Skills Practice

Adding and Subtracting Mixed Numbers

Add or subtract. Write in simplest form.

1. $3\frac{2}{7} + 2\frac{1}{7}$ $5\frac{3}{7}$ 2. $7\frac{1}{3} + 7\frac{1}{3}$ $14\frac{2}{3}$ 3. $9\frac{3}{5} - 2\frac{1}{5}$ $7\frac{2}{5}$

4. $7\frac{3}{4} - 5\frac{1}{4}$ $2\frac{1}{2}$ 5. $3\frac{1}{4} + 5\frac{1}{4}$ $8\frac{1}{2}$ 6. $6\frac{3}{4} - 5\frac{3}{4}$ 1

7. $12\frac{1}{8} + 9\frac{3}{8}$ $21\frac{1}{2}$ 8. $5\frac{2}{3} - 2\frac{1}{3}$ $3\frac{1}{3}$ 9. $14\frac{2}{3} - 9\frac{1}{3}$ $5\frac{1}{3}$

10. $5\frac{1}{2} + 3\frac{1}{4}$ $8\frac{3}{4}$ 11. $2\frac{1}{3} + 6\frac{1}{6}$ $8\frac{1}{2}$ 12. $6\frac{1}{2} - 6\frac{1}{4}$ $\frac{1}{12}$

13. $7\frac{5}{6} - 2\frac{2}{3}$ $5\frac{1}{6}$ 14. $6\frac{7}{10} + 5\frac{1}{4}$ $11\frac{19}{20}$ 15. $12\frac{1}{8} - 9\frac{1}{3}$ $3\frac{1}{24}$

16. $12\frac{13}{15} + 4\frac{1}{9}$ $16\frac{44}{45}$ 17. $15\frac{2}{3} - 7\frac{1}{5}$ $8\frac{7}{15}$ 18. $4\frac{7}{12} - 2\frac{3}{16}$ $2\frac{19}{48}$

19. $8\frac{3}{4} + 3\frac{1}{5}$ $12\frac{3}{20}$ 20. $12\frac{1}{3} - 8\frac{5}{9}$ $3\frac{7}{9}$ 21. $8 - 3\frac{2}{5}$ $4\frac{3}{5}$

22. $7\frac{7}{9} + 6\frac{1}{8}$ $14\frac{47}{72}$ 23. $7\frac{7}{9} - 6\frac{7}{8}$ $\frac{65}{72}$ 24. $10\frac{3}{8} + 7\frac{11}{12}$ $18\frac{7}{24}$

Practice*
p. 24 **OL** **AL**

5-3 Practice

Adding and Subtracting Mixed Numbers

Add or Subtract. Write in simplest form.

1. $3\frac{3}{8} + 5\frac{3}{8}$ $8\frac{3}{4}$ 2. $4\frac{1}{6} + 7\frac{1}{6}$ $11\frac{1}{3}$ 3. $9\frac{3}{4} - 6\frac{1}{4}$ $3\frac{1}{2}$ 4. $5\frac{5}{9} - 4\frac{2}{9}$ $1\frac{1}{3}$

5. $8\frac{2}{3} - 3\frac{1}{6}$ $5\frac{1}{2}$ 6. $10\frac{3}{5} - 5\frac{3}{8}$ $5\frac{9}{40}$ 7. $7\frac{3}{10} + 12\frac{2}{5}$ $19\frac{7}{10}$ 8. $1\frac{1}{6} + 1\frac{1}{8}$ $2\frac{7}{24}$

9. $6\frac{1}{3} - 3\frac{2}{3}$ $2\frac{2}{3}$ 10. $8\frac{5}{7} - 7\frac{5}{7}$ 1 11. $11\frac{1}{12} - 6\frac{5}{8}$ $4\frac{11}{24}$ 12. $3\frac{2}{5} - 1\frac{3}{4}$ $1\frac{13}{20}$

13. $5\frac{4}{6} + 6\frac{5}{6}$ $12\frac{19}{30}$ 14. $8\frac{2}{7} + 6\frac{1}{14}$ $14\frac{9}{14}$ 15. $9 - 7\frac{3}{8}$ $1\frac{5}{8}$ 16. $6\frac{4}{5} + 7\frac{1}{5}$ 14

17. $4\frac{3}{5} + 1\frac{11}{20} + 5\frac{7}{10}$ $11\frac{17}{20}$ 18. $10 - 9\frac{1}{3}$ $\frac{2}{3}$ 19. $2\frac{1}{4} + 5\frac{3}{8} + 4\frac{2}{3}$ 20. $7 - 6\frac{7}{8}$ $\frac{1}{8}$ $11\frac{1}{8}$

21. **LAND MEASUREMENT** Mr. Alfonso owns two adjacent pieces of land totaling $13\frac{3}{8}$ acres. One piece of land is $8\frac{7}{12}$ acres. Find the area of the other piece of land. $4\frac{19}{24}$ acres

GEOMETRY Find the perimeter of each figure.

22. $4\frac{1}{2}$ feet, $6\frac{5}{6}$ feet, $5\frac{2}{3}$ feet $16\frac{11}{12}$ feet

23. $1\frac{7}{8}$ inches, $1\frac{1}{2}$ inches, $1\frac{1}{2}$ inches, $1\frac{7}{8}$ inches $6\frac{4}{7}$ inches

---

Word Problem Practice*
p. 25 **OL** **AL**

5-3 Word Problem Practice

Adding and Subtracting Mixed Numbers

HEIGHT For Exercises 1–6, use the table below. It shows the heights of five students. Write all answers in simplest form.

Student	Height (ft)
Karen	$5\frac{1}{6}$
Arturo	6
Felisa	$4\frac{11}{12}$
Max	$5\frac{3}{4}$
Silvia	$5\frac{1}{4}$

1. How much taller is Max than Felisa? $\frac{5}{6}$ ft

2. How much shorter is Karen than Arturo? $\frac{5}{6}$ ft

3. If Silvia stood on a box that was $1\frac{5}{6}$ feet high, how far would the top of her head be from the floor? $7\frac{1}{12}$ ft

4. What is the sum of Felisa and Silvia's heights? $10\frac{1}{6}$ ft

5. The distance from the floor to Karen's knee is $1\frac{1}{4}$ feet. What is the distance from her knee to the top of her head? $3\frac{11}{12}$ ft

6. Max grew $\frac{5}{6}$ foot last year. How tall was he last year? $5\frac{5}{12}$ ft

---

Enrichment
p. 26 **OL** **AL**

5-3 Enrichment

Arithmetic Sequences of Fractions

Each term in an *arithmetic sequence* is created by adding or subtracting the same number to the term before. The number added or subtracted is called the *common difference*.

The sequence below is an increasing arithmetic sequence with a common difference of $\frac{1}{4}$.

$$\frac{1}{2}, \frac{3}{4}, 1, 1\frac{1}{4}, \ldots$$

Below is a decreasing arithmetic sequence with a common difference of $1\frac{1}{2}$.

$$7\frac{1}{2}, 6\frac{1}{2}, 5\frac{1}{2}, 4, 2\frac{1}{2}$$

Write the common difference for each arithmetic sequence.

1. $\frac{1}{2}, \frac{5}{8}, \frac{3}{4}, \frac{7}{8}, 1, 1\frac{1}{8}$ $\frac{1}{8}$ 2. $1\frac{1}{3}, 3\frac{5}{6}, 6\frac{1}{3}, 8\frac{5}{6}$ $2\frac{1}{2}$

3. $4\frac{1}{2}, 4\frac{3}{5}, 4\frac{3}{10}, 4\frac{1}{5}$ $\frac{1}{10}$ 4. $11, 9\frac{2}{3}, 8\frac{1}{3}, 7, 5\frac{2}{3}$ $1\frac{1}{3}$

Write the next term in each arithmetic sequence.

5. $\frac{3}{4}, \frac{5}{6}, \frac{11}{12}, 1$ $1\frac{1}{12}$ 6. $\frac{13}{20}, \frac{11}{20}, \frac{9}{20}, \frac{7}{20}$ $\frac{1}{4}$

7. $5\frac{1}{5}, 5\frac{7}{10}, 6\frac{1}{5}, 6\frac{7}{10}$ $7\frac{1}{5}$ 8. $4\frac{11}{12}, 3\frac{3}{4}, 2\frac{7}{12}, 1\frac{5}{12}$ $\frac{1}{4}$

Write the first five terms in each sequence.

9. This increasing sequence starts with $\frac{1}{6}$ and has a common difference of $1\frac{1}{5}$. $\frac{1}{6}, 1\frac{11}{30}, 2\frac{17}{30}, 3\frac{23}{30}, 4\frac{29}{30}$

10. This decreasing sequence starts with $6\frac{1}{4}$ and has a common difference of $\frac{3}{4}$. $6\frac{1}{4}, 5\frac{7}{12}, 4\frac{5}{6}, 4\frac{1}{12}, 3\frac{1}{3}$

Additional Lesson Resources

Also available in Spanish **ELL**

Transparencies
• *5-Minute Check Transparency*, Lesson 5-3

Other Print Products
• *Noteables™ Interactive Study Notebook with Foldables™*

Teacher Tech Tools
• *Interactive Classroom CD-ROM*, Lesson 5-3
• *AssignmentWorks*, Lesson 5-3

Student Tech Tools
glencoe.com
• Extra Examples, Chapter 5, Lesson 3
• Self-Check Quiz, Chapter 5, Lesson 3

5-3 Adding and Subtracting Mixed Numbers

Vertical Alignment

Before Lesson 5-3

Solve simple problems, including ones arising in concrete situations, involving the addition and subtraction of fractions and mixed numbers and express answers in the simplest form

Lesson 5-3

Solve problems involving addition, subtraction, of positive fractions and explain why a particular operation was used for a given situation. Determine the least common multiple of whole numbers; use them to solve problems with fractions

After Lesson 5-3

Add and subtract fractions by using factoring to find common denominators

2 Teach

Scaffolding Questions

Ask:
- What is $2\frac{1}{2}$ dollars plus $2\frac{1}{2}$ dollars? $5

- What is $1\frac{1}{4}$ dollars plus $1\frac{1}{2}$ dollars? $2.75, or $2\frac{3}{4}$ dollars

- What is 10 dollars minus $5\frac{1}{2}$ dollars? $4.50, or $4\frac{1}{2}$ dollars

- What is 4 dollars minus $1\frac{1}{4}$ dollars? $2.75, or $2\frac{3}{4}$ dollars

 Formative Assessment

Use the Check Your Progress exercises after each Example to determine students' understanding of concepts.

MAIN IDEA

Add and subtract mixed numbers.

Math Online

glencoe.com

- Extra Examples
- Personal Tutor
- Self-Check Quiz

▷ **GET READY** for the Lesson

BABIES The birth weights of several babies in the hospital nursery are shown.

Birth Weight (pounds)	
Jackson	$8\frac{1}{8}$
Nicolás	$7\frac{15}{16}$
Rebekah	$6\frac{13}{16}$
Mia	$5\frac{7}{8}$

1. Write an expression to find how much more Nicolás weighs than Mia. $7\frac{15}{16} - 5\frac{7}{8}$
2. Rename the fractions using the LCD. $7\frac{15}{16} - 5\frac{14}{16}$
3. Find the difference of the fractional parts of the mixed numbers. $\frac{1}{16}$
4. Find the difference of the whole numbers. **2**
5. **MAKE A CONJECTURE** Explain how to find $7\frac{15}{16} - 5\frac{7}{8}$. Then use your conjecture to find the difference.

To add or subtract mixed numbers, first add or subtract the fractions. If necessary, rename them using the LCD. Then add or subtract the whole numbers and simplify if necessary.

EXAMPLES Add and Subtract Mixed Numbers

① Find $7\frac{4}{9} + 10\frac{2}{9}$. Write in simplest form.

Estimate $7 + 10 = 17$

$$7\frac{4}{9}$$
$$+ 10\frac{2}{9}$$ Add the whole numbers and fractions separately.

$$17\frac{6}{9} \text{ or } 17\frac{2}{3}$$ Simplify.

Check for Reasonableness $17\frac{2}{3} \approx 17$ ✔

✓ **CHECK Your Progress**

a. $6\frac{1}{8} + 2\frac{5}{8}$ $8\frac{3}{4}$ b. $5\frac{1}{5} + 2\frac{3}{10}$ $7\frac{1}{2}$ c. $1\frac{5}{9} + 4\frac{1}{6}$ $5\frac{13}{18}$

5. Write the fractions with a common denominator. Subtract the fractions and then the whole numbers.
$2\frac{1}{16}$

ADDITIONAL EXAMPLE

① Find $3\frac{1}{12} + 14\frac{7}{12}$. Write in simplest form. $17\frac{2}{3}$

Additional Examples are also in:

- Noteables™ Interactive Study Notebook with Foldables™

- Interactive Classroom PowerPoint® Presentations

2 Find $8\frac{5}{6} - 2\frac{1}{3}$. Write in simplest form.

Estimate $9 - 2 = 7$

$$8\frac{5}{6} \quad \rightarrow \quad 8\frac{5}{6}$$

$$\underline{-2\frac{1}{3}} \quad \rightarrow \quad \underline{-2\frac{2}{6}}$$ Rename the fraction using the LCD. Then subtract.

$$6\frac{3}{6} \text{ or } 6\frac{1}{2}$$ Simplify.

Check for Reasonableness $6\frac{1}{2} \approx 7$ ✔

✓ CHECK Your Progress

Subtract. Write in simplest form.

d. $5\frac{4}{5} - 1\frac{3}{10}$ $4\frac{1}{2}$ e. $13\frac{7}{8} - 9\frac{3}{4}$ $4\frac{1}{8}$ f. $8\frac{2}{3} - 2\frac{1}{2}$ $6\frac{1}{6}$

g. $7\frac{3}{4} - 4\frac{1}{3}$ $3\frac{5}{12}$ h. $11\frac{5}{6} - 3\frac{1}{8}$ $8\frac{17}{24}$ i. $9\frac{4}{7} - 5\frac{1}{2}$ $4\frac{1}{14}$

Focus on Mathematical Content

If the fractional parts of mixed numbers are **unlike**, use the LCD to rename them before adding or subtracting.

ADDITIONAL EXAMPLES

2 Find $9\frac{7}{10} - 4\frac{3}{5}$. Write in simplest form. $5\frac{1}{10}$

3 Find $8\frac{1}{5} - 3\frac{3}{5}$. $4\frac{3}{5}$

Sometimes when you subtract mixed numbers, the fraction in the first mixed number is less than the fraction in the second mixed number. In this case, rename the first fraction as an improper fraction in order to subtract.

Study Tip

Improper Fractions An improper fraction has a numerator that is greater than or equal to the denominator. Examples of improper fractions are $\frac{5}{4}$ and $2\frac{6}{5}$.

EXAMPLES   Rename Mixed Numbers to Subtract

3 Find $2\frac{1}{3} - 1\frac{2}{3}$.

Estimate $2 - 1\frac{1}{2} = \frac{1}{2}$

Since $\frac{1}{3}$ is less than $\frac{2}{3}$, rename $2\frac{1}{3}$ before subtracting.

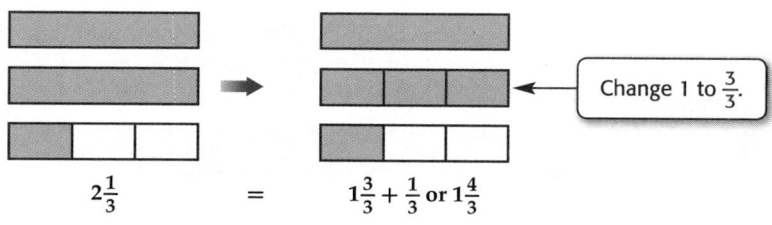

$2\frac{1}{3}$ = $1\frac{3}{3} + \frac{1}{3}$ or $1\frac{4}{3}$

Change 1 to $\frac{3}{3}$.

$$2\frac{1}{3} \quad \rightarrow \quad 1\frac{4}{3}$$ Rename $2\frac{1}{3}$ as $1\frac{4}{3}$.

$$\underline{-1\frac{2}{3}} \quad \rightarrow \quad \underline{-1\frac{2}{3}}$$

$$\frac{2}{3}$$ Subtract the whole numbers and then the fractions.

Check for Reasonableness $\frac{2}{3} \approx \frac{1}{2}$ ✔

3 Practice

Formative Assessment

Use Exercises 1–9 to check for understanding.

Then use the chart at the bottom of the next page to customize your assignments for students.

Daily Intervention You may wish to use the Study Guide and Intervention Master on page 22 of the *Chapter 5 Resource Masters* for additional reinforcement.

---

4 Find $8 - 3\frac{3}{4}$.   **Estimate** $8 - 4 = 4$

Using the denominator of the fraction in the subtrahend, $8 = 8\frac{0}{4}$.

Since $\frac{0}{4}$ is less than $\frac{3}{4}$, rename 8 before subtracting.

$$
\begin{array}{ccll}
8 & \rightarrow & 7\frac{4}{4} & \text{Rename 8 as } 7 + \frac{4}{4} \text{ or } 7\frac{4}{4}. \\
-3\frac{3}{4} & \rightarrow & -3\frac{3}{4} & \text{Subtract.} \\
\hline
& & 4\frac{1}{4} & \text{Check for Reasonableness } 4\frac{1}{4} \approx 4 ✔
\end{array}
$$

CHECK Your Progress

j. $11\frac{2}{5} - 2\frac{3}{5}$ $8\frac{4}{5}$ k. $5\frac{3}{8} - 4\frac{11}{12}$ $\frac{11}{24}$ l. $7 - 1\frac{1}{2}$ $5\frac{1}{2}$

Real-World EXAMPLE

Real-World Career . . . .
How Does an Urban Planner Use Math?
An urban planner uses math to measure and draw site plans for future development.

Math Online ▸
For more information, go to glencoe.com.

5 **MEASUREMENT** An urban planner is designing a skateboard park. What will be the length of the park and the parking lot combined?

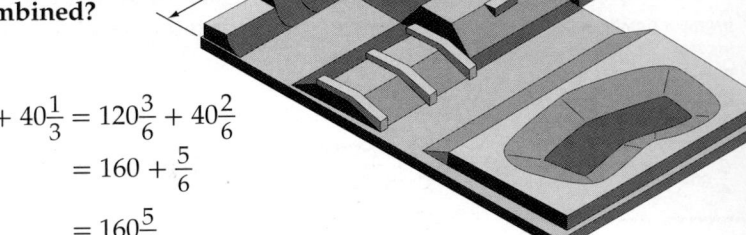

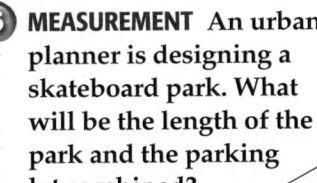

$$120\frac{1}{2} + 40\frac{1}{3} = 120\frac{3}{6} + 40\frac{2}{6}$$
$$= 160 + \frac{5}{6}$$
$$= 160\frac{5}{6}$$

The total length is $160\frac{5}{6}$ feet.

CHECK Your Progress

m. **MEASUREMENT** Jermaine walked $1\frac{5}{8}$ miles on Saturday and $2\frac{1}{2}$ miles on Sunday. How many more miles did he walk on Sunday? $\frac{7}{8}$ mi

★ indicates multi-step problem

CHECK Your Understanding

Examples 1–4
(pp. 242–244)

Add or subtract. Write in simplest form.

1. $1\frac{5}{7} + 8\frac{1}{7}$ $9\frac{6}{7}$ 2. $8\frac{1}{2} + 3\frac{4}{5}$ $12\frac{3}{10}$ 3. $7\frac{5}{6} - 3\frac{1}{6}$ $4\frac{2}{3}$ 4. $9\frac{4}{5} - 2\frac{3}{4}$ $7\frac{1}{20}$

5. $3\frac{1}{4} - 1\frac{3}{4}$ $1\frac{1}{2}$ 6. $5\frac{2}{3} - 2\frac{3}{5}$ $3\frac{1}{15}$ 7. $11 - 6\frac{3}{8}$ $4\frac{5}{8}$ 8. $16 - 5\frac{5}{6}$ $10\frac{1}{6}$

9. $3\frac{3}{20}$ gallons

Example 5
(p. 244)

9. **CARS** A hybrid car's gas tank can hold $11\frac{9}{10}$ gallons of gasoline. It contains $8\frac{3}{4}$ gallons of gasoline. How much more gasoline is needed to fill the tank?

Practice and Problem Solving

HOMEWORK HELP

For Exercises	See Examples
10–17	1, 2
18–23	3
24–25	4
26–29	5

Add or subtract. Write in simplest form.

10. $2\frac{1}{9} + 7\frac{4}{9}$ **$9\frac{5}{9}$**   11. $3\frac{2}{7} + 4\frac{3}{7}$ **$7\frac{5}{7}$**   12. $10\frac{4}{5} - 2\frac{1}{5}$ **$8\frac{3}{5}$**   13. $8\frac{6}{7} - 6\frac{5}{7}$ **$2\frac{1}{7}$**

14. $9\frac{4}{5} - 2\frac{3}{10}$ **$7\frac{1}{2}$**   15. $11\frac{3}{4} - 4\frac{1}{3}$ **$7\frac{5}{12}$**   16. $8\frac{5}{12} + 11\frac{1}{4}$ **$19\frac{2}{3}$**   17. $8\frac{3}{8} + 10\frac{1}{3}$ **$18\frac{17}{24}$**

18. $9\frac{1}{5} - 2\frac{3}{5}$ **$6\frac{3}{5}$**   19. $6\frac{1}{4} - 2\frac{3}{4}$ **$3\frac{1}{2}$**   20. $6\frac{3}{5} - 1\frac{2}{3}$ **$4\frac{14}{15}$**   21. $4\frac{3}{10} - 1\frac{3}{4}$ **$2\frac{11}{20}$**

22. $14\frac{1}{6} - 7\frac{1}{3}$ **$6\frac{5}{6}$**   23. $12\frac{1}{2} - 6\frac{5}{8}$ **$5\frac{7}{8}$**   24. $8 - 3\frac{2}{3}$ **$4\frac{1}{3}$**   25. $13 - 5\frac{5}{6}$ **$7\frac{1}{6}$**

Exercise Levels
A: 10–29
B: 30–36
C: 37–39

For Exercises 26–29, choose an operation to solve each problem. Explain your reasoning. Then solve the problem.

26. **HIKING** If Sara and Maggie hiked both of the trails listed in the table, how far did they hike altogether? **$6\frac{1}{2}$ mi**

    26–29. See margin for explanations.

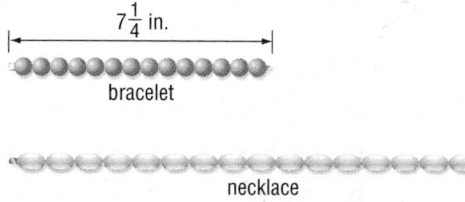

Trail	Length (mi)
Woodland Park	$3\frac{2}{3}$
Mill Creek Way	$2\frac{5}{6}$

27. **JEWELRY** Margarite made the jewelry shown at the right. If the necklace is $10\frac{5}{8}$ inches longer than the bracelet, how long is the necklace that Margarite made? **$17\frac{7}{8}$ in.**

    $7\frac{1}{4}$ in.
    bracelet

    necklace

28. **GARDENS** The length of Kasey's garden is $4\frac{5}{8}$ feet. Find the width of Kasey's garden if it is $2\frac{7}{8}$ feet shorter than the length. **$1\frac{3}{4}$ ft**

29. **HAIRSTYLES** Before Alameda got her haircut, the length of her hair was $9\frac{3}{4}$ inches. After her haircut, the length was $6\frac{1}{2}$ inches. How many inches did she have cut? **$3\frac{1}{4}$ in.**

Add or subtract. Write in simplest form.

30. $10 - 3\frac{5}{11}$ **$6\frac{6}{11}$**   31. $24 - 8\frac{3}{4}$ **$15\frac{1}{4}$**   32. $6\frac{1}{6} + 1\frac{2}{3} + 5\frac{5}{9}$ **$13\frac{7}{18}$** 33. $3\frac{1}{4} + 2\frac{5}{6} - 4\frac{1}{3}$ **$1\frac{3}{4}$**

★ 34. **TIME** Karen wakes up at 6:00 A.M. It takes her $1\frac{1}{4}$ hours to shower, get dressed, and comb her hair. It takes her $\frac{1}{2}$ hour to eat breakfast, brush her teeth, and make her bed. At what time will she be ready for school? **7:45 A.M.**

MEASUREMENT Find the perimeter of each figure.

35. 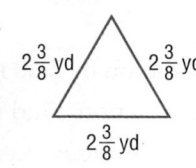 **$7\frac{1}{8}$ yd**

    $2\frac{3}{8}$ yd $2\frac{3}{8}$ yd

    $2\frac{3}{8}$ yd

36. 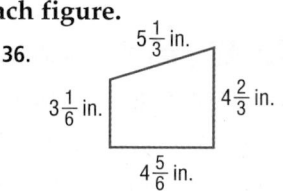 **18 in.**

    $5\frac{1}{3}$ in.

    $3\frac{1}{6}$ in. $4\frac{2}{3}$ in.

    $4\frac{5}{6}$ in.

EXTRA PRACTICE
See pages 680, 708.

Lesson 5-3 Adding and Subtracting Mixed Numbers **245**

DIFFERENTIATED HOMEWORK OPTIONS

Level	Assignment	Two-Day Option	
BL Basic	10–29, 37, 39–48	11–29 odd, 40, 41	10–28 even, 37, 39, 42–48
OL Core	11–33 odd, 34, 35, 37, 39–48	10–29, 40, 41	30–37, 39, 42–48
AL Advanced/Pre-AP	30–47 (optional: 48)		

Odd/Even Assignments

Exercises 10–29 are structured so that students practice the same concepts whether they are assigned odd or even problems.

Estimation

Tips for New Teachers

Encourage students to estimate each sum or difference before computing. The estimate will allow them to check the reasonableness of their solutions.

Additional Answers

26. addition; Sample answer: To find the distance in miles they hiked altogether, add $3\frac{2}{3}$ and $2\frac{5}{6}$.

27. addition; Sample answer: To find the length of the necklace, add $7\frac{1}{4}$ in. and $10\frac{5}{8}$ in.

28. subtraction; Sample answer: To find the width of Kasey's garden, subtract $2\frac{7}{8}$ from $4\frac{5}{8}$.

29. subtraction; Sample answer: To find how many inches Alameda had cut, subtract $6\frac{1}{2}$ from $9\frac{3}{4}$.

Name the Math Write a problem such as $9\frac{1}{3} - 6\frac{5}{8}$ on the board. Have students write the mathematical procedures they would use to solve the problem.

FOLDABLES Study Organizer **Foldables™ Follow-Up**

Remind students to record what they learn about adding and subtracting mixed numbers on index cards, and then store the cards in their Foldables.

Differentiated Instruction

Interpersonal Learners Have students work in groups of three or four. Have each group prepare a set of index cards, writing a mixed number between 1 and 21 on each one. Students should shuffle the cards and place them facedown in the middle. Students take turns picking cards and turning them over, two at a time. Everyone estimates the sum and writes his or her estimate on a piece of paper. Then everyone computes the actual sum. The student whose estimate was closest to the actual sum gets a point. In the next round, students find the difference; in the next round, the sum; and so on. The first student with 5 points wins.

Additional Answers

38. 20 ft; If the initial string is 20 feet and cut in half, the two halves would each be 10 feet. Cutting one fifth of one of these 10 foot halves would require splitting the 10 feet into five equal parts. Each part would be 2 feet. So, cutting one fifth of 10 feet would be the same as cutting 2 feet. The remaining portion would be 8 feet long.

39. Sample answer: Since the garden is a rectangle, the length of one side added to the length of the other side would equal half the

---

H.O.T. Problems

37. Estimation; You do not need an exact answer; Less than; $7 + 1 < 2 + 7$

37. NUMBER SENSE Which of the following techniques could be used to determine whether $6\frac{3}{4} + \frac{4}{5}$ is *greater than, less than,* or *equal to* $2\frac{1}{9} + 6\frac{7}{8}$? Justify your selection(s). Then use the technique(s) to solve the problem.

| number sense | mental math | estimation |

38. CHALLENGE A string is cut in half. One of the halves is thrown away. One fifth of the remaining half is cut away and the piece left is 8 feet long. How long was the string initially? Justify your answer. **See margin.**

39. ◖WRITING IN▶ MATH The fence of a rectangular garden is constructed from 12 feet of fencing wire. Suppose that one side of the garden is $2\frac{5}{12}$ feet long. Explain how to find the length of the other side. **See margin.**

TEST PRACTICE

40. The distance from home plate to the pitcher's mound is 60 feet 6 inches and from home plate to second base is 127 feet $3\frac{3}{8}$ inches. Find the distance from the pitcher's mound to second base. **D**

A 68 ft $3\frac{1}{4}$ in.

B 67 ft $8\frac{3}{4}$ in.

C 67 ft $2\frac{5}{8}$ in.

D 66 ft $9\frac{3}{8}$ in.

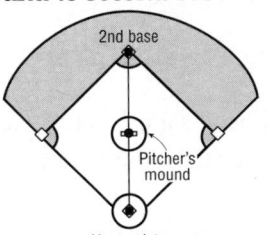

41. A recipe for party mix calls for $4\frac{3}{4}$ cups of cereal. The amount of peanuts needed is $1\frac{2}{3}$ cups less than the amount of cereal needed. How many cups of peanuts and cereal are needed? **H**

F $3\frac{1}{12}$ cups

G $6\frac{1}{2}$ cups

H $7\frac{5}{6}$ cups

J $8\frac{1}{2}$ cups

Spiral Review

42. **SCHOOL** Kai did $\frac{1}{5}$ of her homework in class and $\frac{1}{3}$ more of it on the bus. What fraction of homework does she still need to do? (Lesson 5-2) $\frac{7}{15}$

Estimate. (Lesson 5-1) **43–46. Sample answers are given.**

43. $\frac{8}{9} \div \frac{9}{10}$ $1 \div 1 = 1$ 44. $3\frac{1}{2} + 6\frac{2}{3}$ $4 + 7 = 11$ 45. $8\frac{4}{5} \times 7\frac{1}{9}$ $9 \times 7 = 63$ 46. $4\frac{2}{9} - 1\frac{1}{4}$ $4 - 1 = 3$

47. **MEASUREMENT** To carpet a living room with a length of 17 feet, 255 square feet of carpet is needed. Find the width of the living room. (Lesson 3-6) **15 ft**

▷ **GET READY** for the Next Lesson

48. **PREREQUISITE SKILL** Andre needs to be at the train station by 5:30 P.M. It takes him $\frac{1}{3}$ hour to pack and $1\frac{1}{4}$ hours to get to the station. Find the latest time he should begin packing. Use the *work backward* strategy. (Lesson 3-4) **3:55 P.M.**

length of the perimeter. If one side of the garden is $2\frac{5}{12}$ ft long, find 6 ft $- 2\frac{5}{12}$ ft, or $3\frac{7}{12}$ ft.

CHAPTER
5
Mid-Chapter Quiz

1. **MONEY** Latisha spends $\frac{3}{4}$ of her money on a birthday present for her brother. If she has $33, estimate the amount she spends on her brother's present. (Lesson 5-1) **$24**

Estimate. (Lesson 5-1) **2–7. Sample answers are given.**

2. $5\frac{1}{9} + 1\frac{7}{8}$ **5 + 2 = 7**   3. $13\frac{1}{2} \div 7\frac{2}{9}$ **14 ÷ 7 = 2**

4. $\frac{11}{20} - \frac{5}{8}$ **$\frac{1}{2} - \frac{1}{2} = 0$**   5. $4\frac{2}{3} \times 1\frac{3}{4}$ **5 × 2 = 10**

6. $7\frac{3}{4} \div 1\frac{4}{5}$ **8 ÷ 2 = 4**   7. $\frac{8}{9} + 2\frac{13}{15}$ **1 + 3 = 4**

8. **MULTIPLE CHOICE** Mrs. Ortega is making 5 batches of muffins for the school bake sale. Each batch uses $2\frac{1}{4}$ cups sugar and $1\frac{1}{2}$ cups milk. Which is the best estimate of the total amount of sugar and milk Mrs. Ortega uses for the muffins? (Lesson 5-1) **B**

   A less than 15 cups

   B between 15 and 20 cups

   C between 20 and 25 cups

   D more than 25 cups

Add or subtract. Write in simplest form.
(Lesson 5-2)

9. $\frac{11}{15} - \frac{1}{15}$ **$\frac{2}{3}$**   10. $\frac{4}{7} - \frac{3}{14}$ **$\frac{5}{14}$**

11. $\frac{1}{2} + \frac{2}{9}$ **$\frac{13}{18}$**   12. $\frac{5}{8} + \frac{3}{4}$ **$1\frac{3}{8}$**

13. **SCIENCE** $\frac{39}{50}$ of Earth's atmosphere is made up of nitrogen while only $\frac{21}{100}$ is made up of oxygen. What fraction of Earth's atmosphere is either nitrogen or oxygen? (Lesson 5-2) **$\frac{99}{100}$**

Add or subtract. Write in simplest form.
(Lesson 5-3)

14. $8\frac{3}{4} - 2\frac{5}{12}$ **$6\frac{1}{3}$**   15. $5\frac{1}{6} - 1\frac{1}{3}$ **$3\frac{5}{6}$**

16. $2\frac{5}{9} + 1\frac{2}{3}$ **$4\frac{2}{9}$**   17. $2\frac{3}{5} + 6\frac{13}{15}$ **$9\frac{7}{15}$**

18. **MULTIPLE CHOICE** The table shows the weight of a newborn infant for the first year. (Lesson 5-3)

Month	Weight (lb)
0	$7\frac{1}{4}$
3	$12\frac{1}{2}$
6	$16\frac{5}{8}$
9	$19\frac{4}{5}$
12	$23\frac{3}{20}$

During which three-month period was the infant's weight gain the greatest? **F**

   F 0–3 months   H 6–9 months

   G 3–6 months   J 9–12 months

19. **MEASUREMENT** How much does a $50\frac{1}{4}$-pound suitcase weigh after $3\frac{7}{8}$ pounds is removed? (Lesson 5-3) **$46\frac{3}{8}$ lb**

20. **MULTIPLE CHOICE** The table gives the average annual snowfall for several U.S. cities. (Lesson 5-3)

City	Average Snowfall (in.)
Anchorage, AK	$70\frac{4}{5}$
Mount Washington, NH	$259\frac{9}{10}$
Buffalo, NY	$93\frac{3}{5}$
Birmingham, AL	$1\frac{1}{2}$

Source: Fact Monster

On average, how many more inches of snow does Mount Washington, New Hampshire, receive than Anchorage, Alaska? **B**

   A $330\frac{7}{10}$ in.   C $166\frac{3}{10}$ in.

   B $189\frac{1}{10}$ in.   D $92\frac{1}{10}$ in.

 Mid-Chapter Quiz

 Formative Assessment

Use the Mid-Chapter Quiz to assess students' progress in the first half of the chapter.

Have students review the lesson indicated for the problems they answered incorrectly.

 Summative Assessment

CRM Mid-Chapter Test, p. 55

 Customize and create multiple versions of your Mid-Chapter Test and their answer keys.

 **Dinah Zike's Foldables**

Before students complete the Mid-Chapter Quiz, encourage them to review the notes they recorded about fractions and mixed numbers on the index cards stored in their Foldables.

Data-Driven Decision Making	Exercises	Lesson	State/Local Standards	Resources for Review
Diagnostic Teaching Based on the results of the Chapter 5 Mid-Chapter Quiz, use the following to review concepts that students continue to find challenging.	1–8	5–1		CRM Study Guide and Intervention pp. 10, 16, and 22
	9–13	5–2		**Math Online** glencoe.com • Extra Examples • Personal Tutor
	14–20	5–3		• Concepts in Motion

5-4

Problem-Solving Investigation
ELIMINATE POSSIBILITIES

PACING: **Regular:** 1.5 periods, **Block:** 0.5 period

Options for Differentiated Instruction

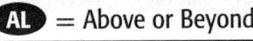 = English Language Learner    = Above or Beyond Grade Level   **SS** = Struggling Students   **SN** = Special Needs

Choosing the Strategy

Use before assigning the Exercises.

Prior to assigning Exercises 7–14, read each Exercise aloud and discuss with the class which strategy might be best to solve each problem. Possible discussion questions are listed below.

- What is the question asking?
- Have you seen problems like this before?
- What strategy might be helpful to solve the problem?
- How could you check your answer to make sure it is reasonable?

Working in Groups

Use before assigning the Exercises.

Organize students into groups of four or five. Provide each student with a worksheet of multiple-choice problems. An example of a problem is shown below.

Refer to the table at the right. If the trend continues, which is the best estimate for the average movie ticket price in 2008? C

   A $6.35   **C** $7.00

   B $6.59   **D** $7.89

Average U.S. Movie Ticket Price

Year	Ticket Price ($)
2002	5.80
2003	6.03
2004	6.21
2005	6.40
2006	6.57
2007	6.69

Tell students that they should discuss each problem, eliminate possibilities, and find the solution. Then they are to record the answer on their worksheets. Inform students that you will be collecting only one sheet from each group to determine the group members' scores.

Organizing Student Work and Thinking

Use after completing Lesson 5-4.

Have students add the eliminating possibilities strategy to their problem-solving booklets. They should include the following about the strategy:

- a description of the strategy
- an explanation of the best time to use the strategy
- examples of problems that are solved using the strategy
- advantages and disadvantages of using the strategy

Leveled Lesson Resources

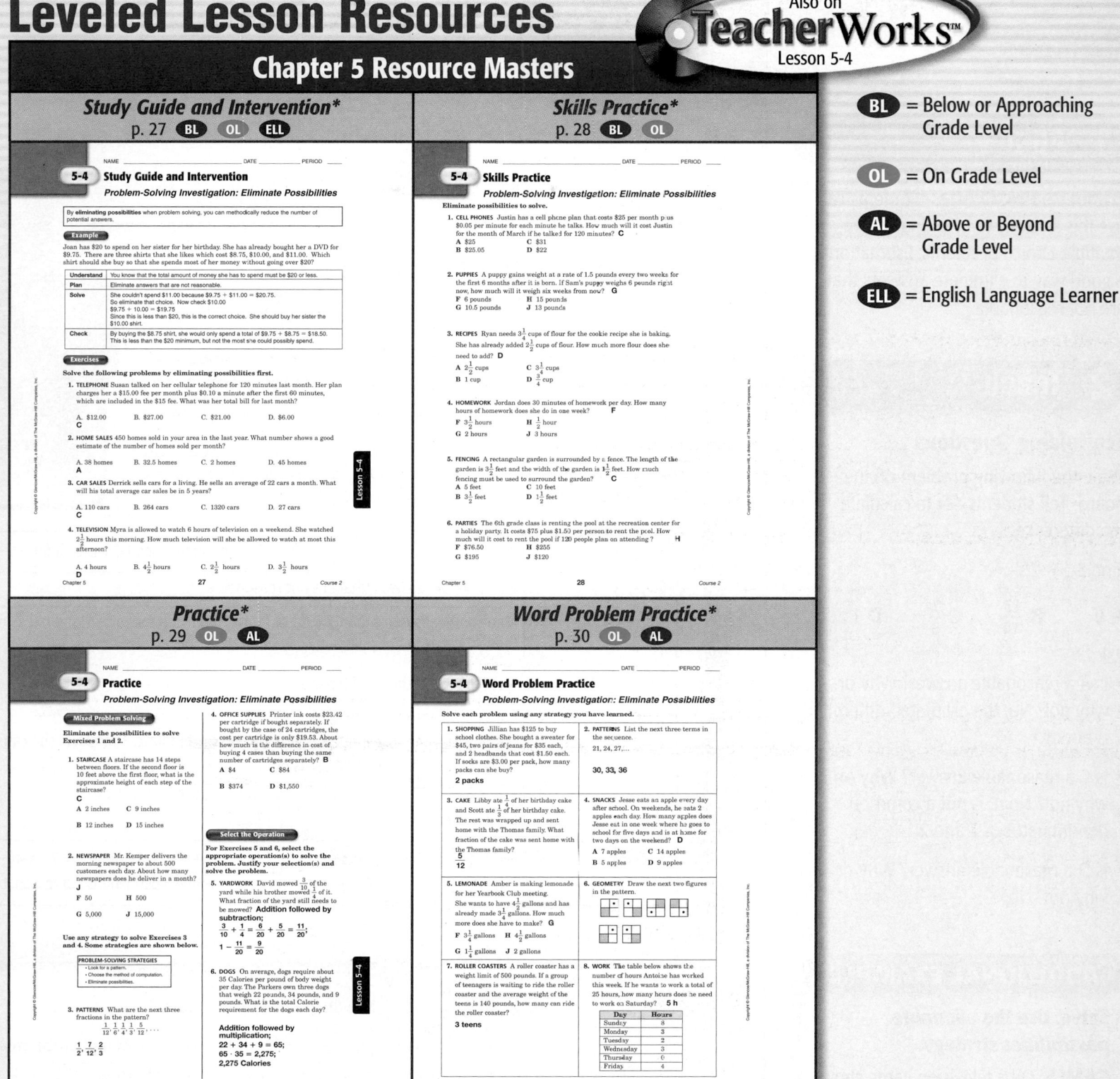

Also on
TeacherWorks™
Lesson 5-4

Chapter 5 Resource Masters

Study Guide and Intervention*
p. 27 **BL** **OL** **ELL**

NAME _____ DATE _____ PERIOD _____

5-4 Study Guide and Intervention
Problem-Solving Investigation: Eliminate Possibilities

By **eliminating possibilities** when problem solving, you can methodically reduce the number of potential answers.

Example

Joan has $20 to spend on her sister for her birthday. She has already bought her a DVD for $9.75. There are three shirts that she likes which cost $8.75, $10.00, and $11.00. Which shirt should she buy so that she spends most of her money without going over $20?

Understand	You know that the total amount of money she has to spend must be $20 or less.
Plan	Eliminate answers that are not reasonable.
Solve	She couldn't spend $11.00 because $9.75 + $11.00 = $20.75. So eliminate that choice. Now check $10.00 $9.75 + 10.00 = $19.75 Since this is less than $20, this is the correct choice. She should buy her sister the $10.00 shirt.
Check	By buying the $8.75 shirt, she would only spend a total of $9.75 + $8.75 = $18.50. This is less than the $20 minimum, but not the most she could possibly spend.

Exercises

Solve the following problems by eliminating possibilities first.

1. **TELEPHONE** Susan talked on her cellular telephone for 120 minutes last month. Her plan charges her a $15.00 fee per month plus $0.10 a minute after the first 60 minutes, which are included in the $15 fee. What was her total bill for last month? **C**

   A. $12.00   B. $27.00   C. $21.00   D. $6.00

2. **HOME SALES** 450 homes sold in your area in the last year. What number shows a good estimate of the number of homes sold per month? **A**

   A. 38 homes   B. 32.5 homes   C. 2 homes   D. 45 homes

3. **CAR SALES** Derrick sells cars for a living. He sells an average of 22 cars a month. What will his total average car sales be in 5 years? **C**

   A. 110 cars   B. 264 cars   C. 1320 cars   D. 27 cars

4. **TELEVISION** Myra is allowed to watch 6 hours of television on a weekend. She watched $2\frac{1}{2}$ hours this morning. How much television will she be allowed to watch at most this afternoon? **D**

   A. 4 hours   B. $4\frac{1}{2}$ hours   C. $2\frac{1}{2}$ hours   D. $3\frac{1}{2}$ hours

Chapter 5   27   Course 2

Skills Practice*
p. 28 **BL** **OL**

NAME _____ DATE _____ PERIOD _____

5-4 Skills Practice
Problem-Solving Investigation: Eliminate Possibilities

Eliminate possibilities to solve.

1. **CELL PHONES** Justin has a cell phone plan that costs $25 per month plus $0.05 per minute for each minute he talks. How much will it cost Justin for the month of March if he talked for 120 minutes? **C**

   A $25   C $31
   B $25.05   D $22

2. **PUPPIES** A puppy gains weight at a rate of 1.5 pounds every two weeks for the first 6 months after it is born. If Sam's puppy weighs 6 pounds right now, how much will it weigh six weeks from now? **G**

   F 6 pounds   H 15 pounds
   G 10.5 pounds   J 13 pounds

3. **RECIPES** Ryan needs $3\frac{1}{4}$ cups of flour for the cookie recipe she is baking. She has already added $2\frac{1}{2}$ cups of flour. How much more flour does she need to add? **D**

   A $2\frac{1}{2}$ cups   C $3\frac{1}{4}$ cups
   B 1 cup   D $3\frac{1}{4}$ cup

4. **HOMEWORK** Jordan does 30 minutes of homework per day. How many hours of homework does she do in one week? **F**

   F $3\frac{1}{2}$ hours   H 1 hour
   G 2 hours   J 3 hours

5. **FENCING** A rectangular garden is surrounded by a fence. The length of the garden is $3\frac{1}{2}$ feet and the width of the garden is $1\frac{1}{2}$ feet. How much fencing must be used to surround the garden? **C**

   A 5 feet   C 10 feet
   B $3\frac{1}{2}$ feet   D $1\frac{1}{2}$ feet

6. **PARTIES** The 6th grade class is renting the pool at the recreation center for a holiday party. It costs $75 plus $1.50 per person to rent the pool. How much will it cost to rent the pool if 120 people plan on attending? **H**

   F $76.50   H $255
   G $195   J $120

Chapter 5   28   Course 2

Practice*
p. 29 **OL** **AL**

NAME _____ DATE _____ PERIOD _____

5-4 Practice
Problem-Solving Investigation: Eliminate Possibilities

Mixed Problem Solving

Eliminate the possibilities to solve Exercises 1 and 2.

1. **STAIRCASE** A staircase has 14 steps between floors. If the second floor is 10 feet above the first floor, what is the approximate height of each step of the staircase? **C**

   A 2 inches   C 9 inches
   B 12 inches   D 15 inches

2. **NEWSPAPER** Mr. Kemper delivers the morning newspaper to about 500 customers each day. About how many newspapers does he deliver in a month? **J**

   F 50   H 500
   G 5,000   J 15,000

Use any strategy to solve Exercises 3 and 4. Some strategies are shown below.

PROBLEM-SOLVING STRATEGIES
• Look for a pattern.
• Choose the method of computation.
• Eliminate possibilities.

3. **PATTERNS** What are the next three fractions in the pattern?
   $\frac{1}{12}, \frac{1}{6}, \frac{1}{4}, \frac{1}{3}, \frac{5}{12} \ldots$
   $\frac{1}{2}, \frac{7}{12}, \frac{2}{3}$

4. **OFFICE SUPPLIES** Printer ink costs $23.42 per cartridge if bought separately. If bought by the case of 24 cartridges, the cost per cartridge is only $19.53. About how much is the difference in cost of buying 4 cases than buying the same number of cartridges separately? **B**

   A $4   C $84
   B $374   D $1,550

Select the Operation

For Exercises 5 and 6, select the appropriate operation(s) to solve the problem. Justify your selection(s) and solve the problem.

5. **YARDWORK** David mowed $\frac{3}{10}$ of the yard while his brother mowed $\frac{1}{4}$ of it. What fraction of the yard still needs to be mowed? **Addition followed by subtraction;**
   $\frac{3}{10} + \frac{1}{4} = \frac{6}{20} + \frac{5}{20} = \frac{11}{20}$;
   $1 - \frac{11}{20} = \frac{9}{20}$

6. **DOGS** On average, dogs require about 35 Calories per pound of body weight per day. The Parkers own three dogs that weigh 22 pounds, 34 pounds, and 9 pounds. What is the total Calorie requirement for the dogs each day?

   Addition followed by multiplication;
   22 + 34 + 9 = 65;
   65 · 35 = 2,275;
   2,275 Calories

Chapter 5   29   Course 2

Word Problem Practice*
p. 30 **OL** **AL**

NAME _____ DATE _____ PERIOD _____

5-4 Word Problem Practice
Problem-Solving Investigation: Eliminate Possibilities

Solve each problem using any strategy you have learned.

1. **SHOPPING** Jillian has $125 to buy school clothes. She bought a sweater for $45, two pairs of jeans for $35 each, and 2 headbands that cost $1.50 each. If socks are $3.00 per pack, how many packs can she buy? **2 packs**

2. **PATTERNS** List the next three terms in the sequence.
   21, 24, 27,…
   30, 33, 36

3. **CAKE** Libby ate $\frac{1}{4}$ of her birthday cake and Scott ate $\frac{1}{3}$ of her birthday cake. The rest was wrapped up and sent home with the Thomas family. What fraction of the cake was sent home with the Thomas family? **$\frac{5}{12}$**

4. **SNACKS** Jesse eats an apple every day after school. On weekends, he eats 2 apples each day. How many apples does Jesse eat in one week where he goes to school for five days and is at home for two days on the weekend? **D**

   A 7 apples   C 14 apples
   B 5 apples   D 9 apples

5. **LEMONADE** Amber is making lemonade for her Yearbook Club meeting. She wants to have $4\frac{2}{3}$ gallons and has already made $3\frac{1}{4}$ gallons. How much more does she have to make? **G**

   F $3\frac{1}{4}$ gallons   H $4\frac{2}{3}$ gallons
   G $1\frac{5}{12}$ gallons   J 2 gallons

6. **GEOMETRY** Draw the next two figures in the pattern.

7. **ROLLER COASTERS** A roller coaster has a weight limit of 500 pounds. If a group of teenagers is waiting to ride the roller coaster and the average weight of the teens is 140 pounds, how many can ride the roller coaster? **3 teens**

8. **WORK** The table below shows the number of hours Antoine has worked this week. If he wants to work a total of 25 hours, how many hours does he need to work on Saturday? **5 h**

Day	Hours
Sunday	8
Monday	3
Tuesday	2
Wednesday	3
Thursday	0
Friday	4

Chapter 5   30   Course 2

BL = Below or Approaching Grade Level

OL = On Grade Level

AL = Above or Beyond Grade Level

ELL = English Language Learner

Additional Lesson Resources

Transparencies
• *5-Minute Check Transparency*, Lesson 5-4

Other Print Products
• *Noteables™ Interactive Study Notebook with Foldables™*

Teacher Tech Tools
• *Interactive Classroom CD-ROM*, Lesson 5-4
• *AssignmentWorks*, Lesson 5-4

Student Tech Tools
glencoe.com
• Extra Examples, Chapter 5, Lesson 4
• Self-Check Quiz, Chapter 5, Lesson 4

MAIN IDEA: Solve problems by eliminating possibilities.

1 Focus

Eliminate Possibilities Students can use this strategy to help them solve multiple-choice problems. Estimation is a good way to eliminate answers that are *not* reasonable.

2 Teach

Scaffolding Questions

Write the following problem on the board. Tell students *not* to calculate the difference.

Find $3\frac{3}{7} - 2\frac{1}{2}$.

A 0   **B** $\frac{13}{14}$ **C** $\frac{7}{8}$ **D** 1

Ask:

- Is A a reasonable answer? Why or why not? No; the estimated difference is about 1.

- Is C a reasonable answer? Why or why not? No; 8 is not a common denominator of 7 and 2.

- Is D a reasonable answer? Why or why not? No; $\frac{3}{7} - \frac{1}{2} \neq 1$.

ADDITIONAL EXAMPLE

Solve. Use the *eliminate possibilities* strategy.

GAMES On a television game show, the winning contestant must answer three questions correctly to win the grand prize. Each question is worth twice as many points as the question before it. The third question is worth 1,000 points. How much is the first question worth—250, 500, or 2,000 points? 250 points

---

P.S.I. TERM +

e-Mail: ELIMINATE POSSIBILITIES

MADISON: I am making school pennants to decorate the cafeteria. I use $1\frac{1}{4}$ yards of fabric for each pennant.

YOUR MISSION: Eliminate possibilities to find the greatest number of pennants Madison can make with 12 yards of fabric. Is it 6, 9, or 12?

Understand	You know she has 12 yards of fabric. Each pennant uses $1\frac{1}{4}$ yards of fabric.
Plan	Eliminate the answers that are not reasonable.
Solve	Madison needs more than 1 yard of fabric for each pennant. So, she needs more than 12 yards for 12 pennants. Eliminate this choice. Now check the choice of 9 pennants. • $1\frac{1}{4} + 1\frac{1}{4} + 1\frac{1}{4} + 1\frac{1}{4} = 5$. So, Madison can make 4 pennants with 5 yards of fabric. Therefore, she can make 8 pennants out of 10 yards of fabric. • She can also make 1 more pennant with the remaining 2 yards. So, Madison can make 8 + 1 or 9 pennants.
Check	Making 6 pennants would take $1\frac{1}{4} + 1\frac{1}{4} + 1\frac{1}{4} + 1\frac{1}{4} + 1\frac{1}{4} + 1\frac{1}{4} = 7\frac{1}{2}$ yards. This is not the greatest number she can make. So, making 6 pennants is *not* reasonable.

Analyze The Strategy   1–3. See Ch. 5 Answer Appendix.

1. Describe different ways that you can eliminate possibilities when solving problems.

2. Explain how the strategy of eliminating possibilities is useful for taking multiple-choice tests.

3. **WRITING IN MATH** Write a problem that could be solved by eliminating possibilities.

Additional Examples are also in:

- Noteables™ Interactive Study Notebook with Foldables™

- Interactive Classroom PowerPoint® Presentations

Tips for New Teachers

Multiple-Choice Tests

Make sure students understand that the eliminate possibilities strategy can save them time. Often, students can use mental math or estimation to eliminate one or more answer choices in a multiple-choice problem. Then they can test the remaining answer choices by substituting them in the expression or equation.

EXTRA PRACTICE
See pages 679, 681.

Eliminate possibilities to solve Exercises 4–6.

4. **TRAINS** A train passes through an intersection at the rate of 3 cars per 30 seconds. Assume that it takes 5 minutes for the train to completely pass through the intersection. How many cars does the train have altogether? **C**

   A 6 cars   C 30 cars

   B 15 cars   D 45 cars

5. **PIZZA** A pizza shop used 100 pounds of pizza dough to make 125 pizzas. If a large pizza requires 1 pound of dough and a medium pizza requires $\frac{1}{2}$ pound, how many large- and medium-sized pizzas were made? **J**

   F 40 large, 85 medium

   G 65 large, 60 medium

   H 55 large, 70 medium

   J 75 large, 50 medium

6. **PILLOWS** Pat is making pillows out of fabric. He uses $\frac{3}{4}$ yard of fabric for each pillow. What is the greatest number of pillows Pat can make with 9 yards of fabric: 9, 12, or 15? **12 pillows**

Use any strategy to solve Exercises 7–14. Some strategies are shown below.

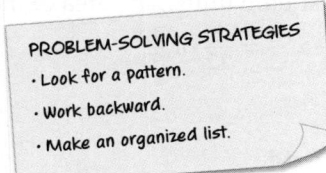

PROBLEM-SOLVING STRATEGIES
· Look for a pattern.
· Work backward.
· Make an organized list.

7. **MEASUREMENT** The diagram shows a shelf
★ that holds CDs. Each shelf is $\frac{1}{8}$ inch thick, and the distance between shelves is as shown. How much space is available on each layer of the shelf for a CD? $\frac{5}{8}$ **in.**

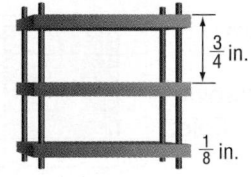

$\frac{3}{4}$ in.

$\frac{1}{8}$ in.

8. **BRIDGES** A covered bridge has a maximum capacity of 48,000 pounds. If an average school bus weighs 10,000 pounds, about how many school buses could a covered bridge hold? **4 buses**

9. **GEOMETRY** Draw the next two figures in the pattern. **See margin.**

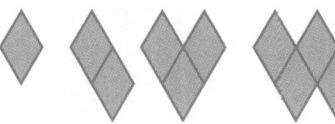

10. **SLEEP** A 9-month-old infant needs about
★ 14 hours of sleep each day while a teenager needs about 10 hours of sleep each day. How much more sleep does a 9-month-old need than a teenager? Write as a fraction of a day. $\frac{1}{6}$ **of a day**

11. **PRECIPITATION** In Olympia, Washington, the average annual precipitation is $50\frac{3}{5}$ inches. Is $\frac{1}{49}$ inch, 1 inch, or 14 inches the best estimate for the average precipitation per day? $\frac{1}{49}$ **inch**

12. **MONEY** Kristen has $15 to go to the movies.
★ Her ticket costs $7.25, drinks are $3.50, popcorn is $5.75, and pretzels are $4.25. Which two items can Kristen get from the concession stand? **a drink and a pretzel**

13. **PIZZA** Sebastian ate $\frac{2}{5}$ of a pizza while his
★ sister ate $\frac{1}{3}$ of the same pizza. The remainder was stored in the refrigerator. What fraction of the pizza was stored in the refrigerator? $\frac{4}{15}$

14. **GRADES** Jerome had an average of 88 on his first three science tests. His score on the second and third tests were 92 and 87. What was his score on the first test? **85**

Using the Exercises

Exercises 1–3 can be used to check students' understanding of the eliminate possibilities strategy.

Exercises 4–6 give students an opportunity to practice the eliminate possibilities strategy.

Exercises 7–14 give students the opportunity to practice many different problem-solving strategies. You may wish to review some of the strategies they have studied.

· use the four-step plan (p. 25)

· look for a pattern (p. 112)

· work backward (p. 148)

· make an organized list (p. 190)

4 Assess

Ticket Out the Door Write the following problem and answer choices on the board.

Find $1\frac{3}{8} + \frac{7}{12}$.

A $1\frac{1}{2}$ C $1\frac{15}{16}$

B $1\frac{23}{24}$ D $2\frac{23}{24}$

Have students pick one of the answer choices and write why it can be eliminated. Sample answer: D; $1\frac{3}{8} + \frac{7}{12}$ is about $1\frac{1}{2} + \frac{1}{2}$ or 2. Since $2\frac{23}{24}$ is about 3, choice D can be eliminated.

Formative Assessment

Check for student understanding of concepts in Lessons 5-3 and 5-4.

CRM Quiz 2, p. 53

Additional Answer

9.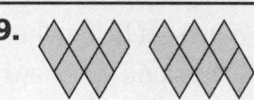

Math Lab
Multiplying Fractions

① Focus

Materials

- geoboards
- geobands
- grid paper
- blue and yellow pencils

Easy-to-Make Manipulatives

Teaching Mathematics with Manipulatives templates for:

- centimeter grid paper, p. 15

② Teach

Activity 1 Make sure students realize that the units of the geoboard model are shown by the number of spaces between the pegs on a side (and not by the number of pegs).

Activity 2 Tell students that the actual dimensions of the rectangles don't matter, provided the rectangles are the same size and are divided into fourths.

Differentiated Instruction

Bodily/Kinesthetic Learners
Students can also use geoboards in Activities 2 and 3. In Activity 2, ask students how they could model a whole number multiplied by a fraction, such as $2 \times \frac{1}{4}$ using a geoboard. Then in Activity 3, ask students how they could model a mixed number multiplied by a fraction, such as $1\frac{2}{3} \times \frac{1}{2}$ using a geoboard. Sample answer: For Activity 2, use two geoboards and on each one, use geobands to represent one-fourth of each geoboard. For Activity 3, use two geoboards. On the first geoboard use a geoband to represent half of the geoboard and on the second geoboard, use one geoband to represent $\frac{2}{3}$ and another geoband to represents $\frac{1}{2}$.

MAIN IDEA

Use area models to multiply fractions and mixed numbers.

Math Online

glencoe.com

- Concepts In Motion

Just as the product of 3 × 4 is the number of square units in a rectangle, the product of two fractions can be shown using area models.

ACTIVITY

① Find $\frac{3}{4} \times \frac{2}{3}$ using a geoboard.

The first factor is 3 *fourths* and the second factor is 2 *thirds*.

STEP 1 Use one geoband to show fourths and another to show thirds on the geoboard.

STEP 2 Use geobands to form a rectangle. Place one geoband on the peg to show 3 fourths and another on the peg to show 2 thirds.

STEP 3 Connect the geobands to show a small rectangle.

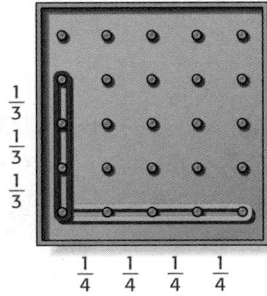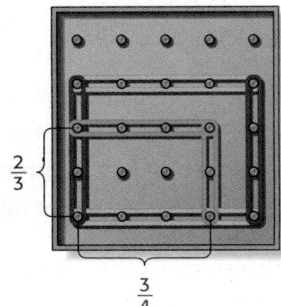

The area of the small square is 6 square units. The area of the large rectangle is 12 square units. So, $\frac{3}{4} \times \frac{2}{3} = \frac{6}{12}$ or $\frac{1}{2}$.

✓ CHECK Your Progress

Find each product using a geoboard.

a. $\frac{1}{4} \times \frac{1}{3}$ **$\frac{1}{12}$** b. $\frac{1}{2} \times \frac{1}{2}$ **$\frac{1}{4}$** c. $\frac{3}{4} \times \frac{1}{2}$ **$\frac{3}{8}$** d. $\frac{2}{3} \times \frac{1}{4}$ **$\frac{2}{12}$ or $\frac{1}{6}$**

a, b. See margin. **c, d. See Ch. 5 Answer Appendix.**

ACTIVITY

② Find $2 \times \frac{1}{4}$ using an area model.

STEP 1 To represent 2 or $\frac{2}{1}$, draw 2 large rectangles, side by side. Divide each rectangle horizontally into fourths. Color both large rectangles blue.

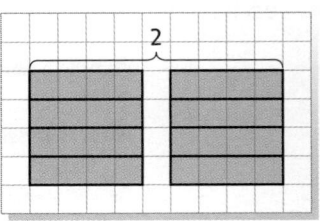

Additional Answers

a.
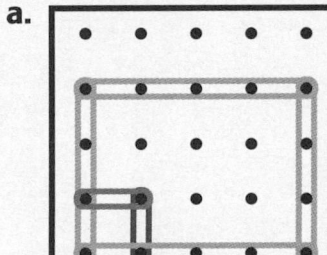

b.
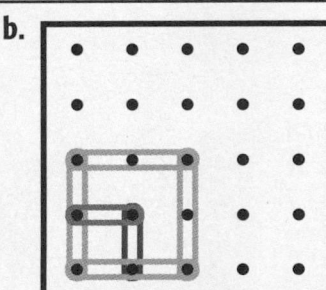

Study Tip

Shading
Yellow and blue make green. So, the green sections have been shaded twice and represent the product.

STEP 2 Color 1 fourth of each large rectangle yellow.

The fraction that compares the number of green sections, 2, to the number of sections in one rectangle, 4, is $\frac{2}{4}$ or $\frac{1}{2}$.

So, $2 \times \frac{1}{4} = \frac{1}{2}$.

✓**CHECK Your Progress**

Find each product using a model.

e. $3 \times \frac{2}{3}$ $\frac{6}{3}$ or 2   f. $2 \times \frac{2}{5}$ $\frac{4}{5}$ g. $4 \times \frac{1}{2}$ $\frac{4}{2}$ or 2   h. $3 \times \frac{3}{4}$ $\frac{9}{4}$ or $2\frac{1}{4}$

e, f. See margin for models.   g, h. See Ch. 5 Answer Appendix for models.

ACTIVITY

3 Find $1\frac{2}{3} \times \frac{1}{2}$ using a model.

STEP 1 Draw 2 rectangles divided vertically into thirds and horizontally into halves. Color $1\frac{2}{3}$ of the squares blue.

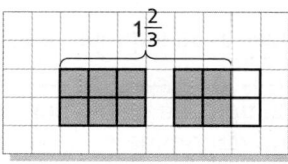

STEP 2 Color $\frac{1}{2}$ of the squares yellow. Then count the small squares that are green.

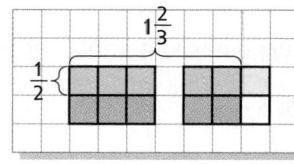

Since the green area is $\frac{3}{6}$ of the first rectangle and $\frac{2}{6}$ of the second rectangle, the total area shaded green is $\frac{3}{6} + \frac{2}{6}$ or $\frac{5}{6}$. So, $1\frac{2}{3} \times \frac{1}{2} = \frac{5}{6}$.

✓**CHECK Your Progress**

Find each product using a model.

i. $1\frac{1}{4} \times \frac{1}{5}$ $\frac{5}{20}$ or $\frac{1}{4}$ j. $2\frac{1}{2} \times \frac{3}{4}$ $\frac{15}{8}$ or $1\frac{7}{8}$ k. $1\frac{2}{3} \times \frac{1}{3}$ $\frac{5}{9}$

i–k. See Ch. 5 Answer Appendix for models.

ANALYZE THE RESULTS

1. The product of the numerators is equal to the numerator of the product. The product of the denominators is equal to the denominator of the product.

1. Analyze Exercises a–k. What is the relationship between the numerators of the factors and of the product? between the denominators of the factors and of the product?

2. **MAKE A CONJECTURE** Write a rule you can use to multiply two fractions. See Ch. 5 Answer Appendix.

Explore 5-5 Math Lab: Multiplying Fractions   **251**

Activity 3 Make sure students realize that each 3 × 2 rectangle represents 1, and that the rectangles have been separated into thirds and halves because the denominators of the factors are 3 and 2.

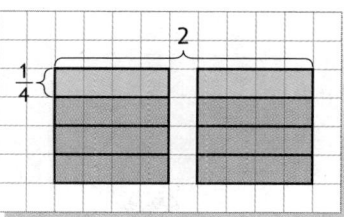

3 Assess

✓**Formative Assessment**

Use Exercise 1 to determine whether students understand how to multiply fractions.

From Concrete to Abstract Use Exercise 2 to bridge the gap between using models to multiply fractions and following the algorithm.

Extending the Concept If students can write the rule for multiplying fractions (Exercise 2), ask them how they might use the rule to multiply mixed numbers and fractions. by first rewriting the mixed number as an improper fraction

---

Additional Answers

e.
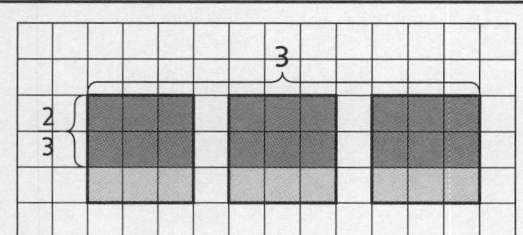

f.
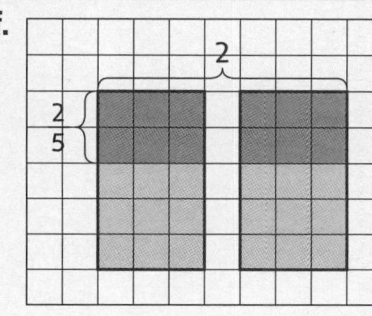

Multiplying Fractions and Mixed Numbers

PACING: **Regular:** 1.5 periods, **Block:** 0.5 period

Options for Differentiated Instruction

ELL = English Language Learner   **AL** = Above or Beyond Grade Level   **SS** = Struggling Students   **SN** = Special Needs

Reviewing Concepts   **SS**

Use before presenting Lesson 5-5.

Review with students how to write a mixed number as an improper fraction.

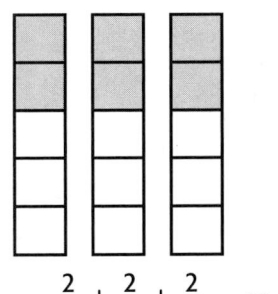

$6\frac{1}{2} \rightarrow 6 \times \frac{1}{2} + = \frac{(6 \times 2) + 1}{2} = \frac{13}{2}$

Multiply the whole number and denominator. Then add the numerator.

Have students use this method to write the following mixed numbers as improper fractions.

1. $2\frac{3}{4}$ $\frac{11}{4}$ **2.** $1\frac{7}{8}$ $\frac{15}{8}$ **3.** $3\frac{4}{7}$ $\frac{25}{7}$ **4.** $5\frac{1}{6}$ $\frac{31}{6}$

Using Models   **SS** **SN**

Use after presenting Example 2.

Remind students that multiplication is repeated addition. This is especially helpful for students to remember when they are multiplying a whole number by a fraction.

$3 \times \frac{2}{5}$ means 3 groups of $\frac{2}{5}$.

$$\frac{2}{5} + \frac{2}{5} + \frac{2}{5} \quad = \quad \frac{6}{5} \text{ or } 1\frac{1}{5}$$

Connections to Real-World Activities   **ELL** **AL** **SS** **SN**

Use before assigning the Exercises.

Have students use a cookbook to find a recipe that they would like to make. Ask them to rewrite the recipe, giving the amount of each ingredient that will be needed to serve the entire class.

Leveled Lesson Resources

Chapter 5 Resource Masters

BL = Below or Approaching Grade Level   **OL** = On Grade Level   **AL** = Above or Beyond Grade Level   **ELL** = English Language Learner

Lesson Reading Guide
p. 31 **BL** **OL** **ELL**

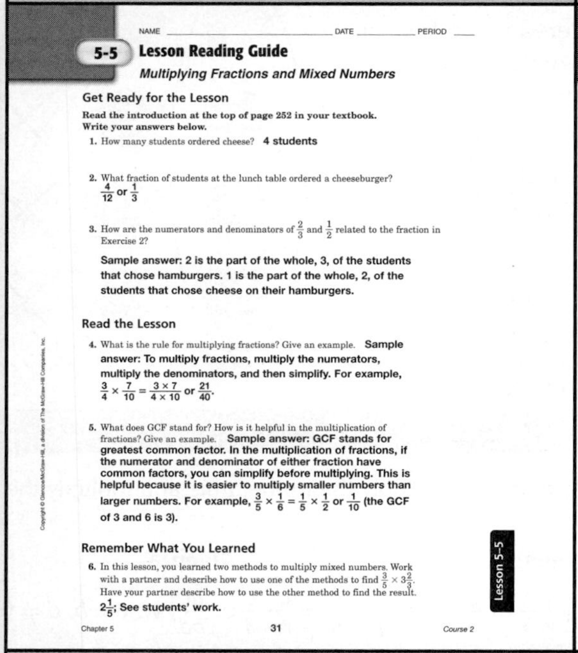

5-5 Lesson Reading Guide
Multiplying Fractions and Mixed Numbers

Get Ready for the Lesson
Read the introduction at the top of page 252 in your textbook. Write your answers below.

1. How many students ordered cheese? **4 students**

2. What fraction of students at the lunch table ordered a cheeseburger? $\frac{4}{12}$ or $\frac{1}{3}$

3. How are the numerators and denominators of $\frac{2}{3}$ and $\frac{1}{2}$ related to the fraction in Exercise 2?
Sample answer: 2 is the part of the whole, 3, of the students that chose hamburgers. 1 is the part of the whole, 2, of the students that chose cheese on their hamburgers.

Read the Lesson

4. What is the rule for multiplying fractions? Give an example. **Sample answer: To multiply fractions, multiply the numerators, multiply the denominators, and then simplify. For example, $\frac{3}{4} \times \frac{7}{10} = \frac{3 \times 7}{4 \times 10}$ or $\frac{21}{40}$.**

5. What does GCF stand for? How is it helpful in the multiplication of fractions? Give an example. **Sample answer: GCF stands for greatest common factor. In the multiplication of fractions, if the numerator and denominator of either fraction have common factors, you can simplify before multiplying. This is helpful because it is easier to multiply smaller numbers than larger numbers. For example, $\frac{3}{6} \times \frac{1}{5} = \frac{1}{5} \times \frac{1}{2}$ or $\frac{1}{10}$ (the GCF of 3 and 6 is 3).**

Remember What You Learned

6. In this lesson, you learned two methods to multiply mixed numbers. Work with a partner and describe how to use one of the methods to find $\frac{3}{4} \times 3\frac{1}{2}$. Have your partner describe how to use the other method to find the result. $2\frac{5}{8}$; **See students' work.**

Chapter 5   31   Course 2

Study Guide and Intervention*
p. 32 **BL** **OL** **ELL**

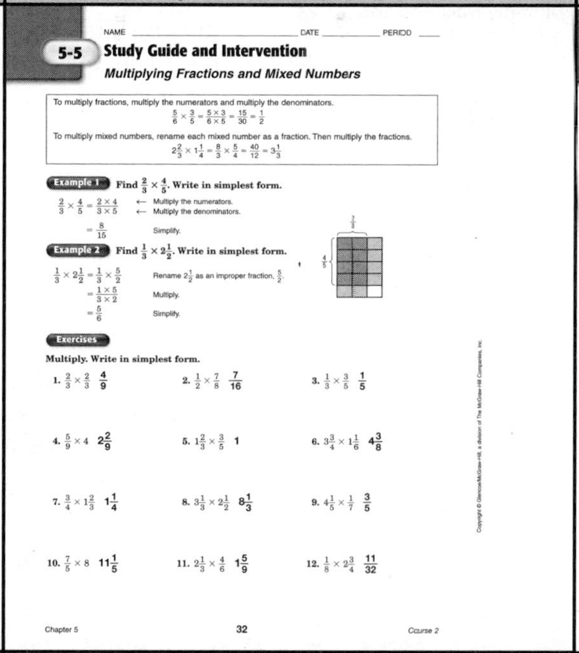

5-5 Study Guide and Intervention
Multiplying Fractions and Mixed Numbers

To multiply fractions, multiply the numerators and multiply the denominators.
$$\frac{5}{6} \times \frac{3}{5} = \frac{5 \times 3}{6 \times 5} = \frac{15}{30} = \frac{1}{2}$$

To multiply mixed numbers, rename each mixed number as a fraction. Then multiply the fractions.
$$2\frac{2}{3} \times 1\frac{1}{4} = \frac{8}{3} \times \frac{5}{4} = \frac{40}{12} = 3\frac{1}{3}$$

Example 1 Find $\frac{2}{3} \times \frac{4}{5}$. Write in simplest form.
$$\frac{2}{3} \times \frac{4}{5} = \frac{2 \times 4}{3 \times 5}$$
$$= \frac{8}{15}$$

Example 2 Find $\frac{1}{3} \times 2\frac{1}{2}$. Write in simplest form.
$$\frac{1}{3} \times 2\frac{1}{2} = \frac{1}{3} \times \frac{5}{2}$$
$$= \frac{1 \times 5}{3 \times 2}$$
$$= \frac{5}{6}$$

Exercises
Multiply. Write in simplest form.

1. $\frac{1}{5} \times \frac{4}{9}$ $\frac{4}{9}$
2. $\frac{1}{2} \times \frac{7}{8}$ $\frac{7}{16}$
3. $\frac{1}{3} \times \frac{3}{5}$ $\frac{1}{5}$
4. $\frac{5}{9} \times 4$ $2\frac{2}{9}$
5. $1\frac{2}{3} \times \frac{3}{5}$ 1
6. $3\frac{3}{4} \times 1\frac{1}{6}$ $4\frac{3}{8}$
7. $\frac{3}{4} \times 1\frac{2}{3}$ $1\frac{1}{4}$
8. $3\frac{1}{3} \times 2\frac{1}{2}$ $8\frac{1}{3}$
9. $4\frac{1}{5} \times \frac{1}{7}$ $\frac{3}{5}$
10. $\frac{7}{8} \times 8$ $11\frac{1}{5}$
11. $2\frac{1}{3} \times \frac{4}{6}$ $1\frac{5}{9}$
12. $\frac{1}{2} \times 2\frac{3}{8}$ $\frac{11}{32}$

Chapter 5   32   Course 2

Skills Practice*
p. 33 **BL** **OL**

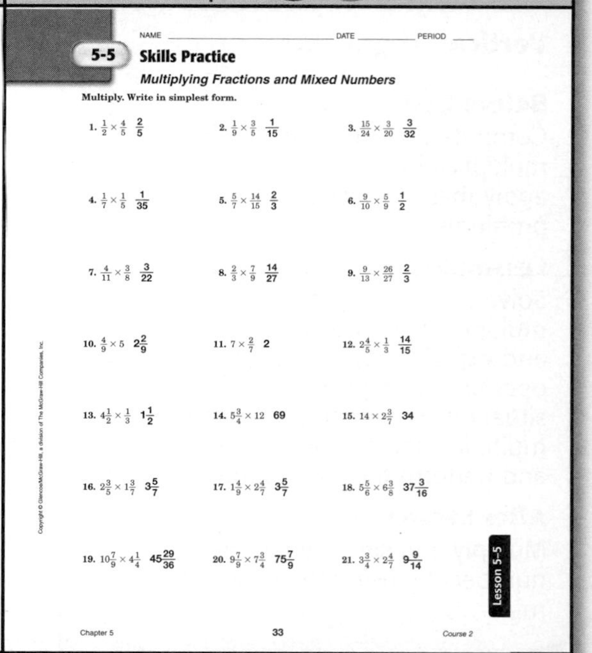

5-5 Skills Practice
Multiplying Fractions and Mixed Numbers

Multiply. Write in simplest form.

1. $\frac{1}{2} \times \frac{4}{5}$ $\frac{2}{5}$
2. $\frac{1}{9} \times \frac{3}{5}$ $\frac{1}{15}$
3. $\frac{15}{24} \times \frac{3}{20}$ $\frac{3}{32}$
4. $\frac{1}{7} \times \frac{5}{5}$ $\frac{1}{35}$
5. $\frac{5}{7} \times \frac{14}{15}$ $\frac{2}{3}$
6. $\frac{9}{10} \times \frac{5}{9}$ $\frac{1}{2}$
7. $\frac{4}{11} \times \frac{3}{8}$ $\frac{3}{22}$
8. $\frac{3}{9} \times \frac{7}{9}$ $\frac{14}{27}$
9. $\frac{9}{13} \times \frac{26}{27}$ $\frac{2}{3}$
10. $\frac{4}{9} \times 5$ $2\frac{2}{9}$
11. $7 \times \frac{2}{7}$ 2
12. $2\frac{4}{5} \times \frac{1}{3}$ $\frac{14}{15}$
13. $4\frac{1}{2} \times \frac{1}{3}$ $1\frac{1}{2}$
14. $5\frac{3}{4} \times 12$ 69
15. $14 \times 2\frac{3}{7}$ 34
16. $2\frac{3}{5} \times 1\frac{3}{7}$ $3\frac{5}{7}$
17. $1\frac{4}{5} \times 2\frac{1}{7}$ $3\frac{5}{7}$
18. $5\frac{1}{5} \times 6\frac{3}{8}$ $37\frac{3}{16}$
19. $10\frac{2}{9} \times 4\frac{1}{4}$ $45\frac{29}{36}$
20. $9\frac{1}{7} \times 7\frac{2}{8}$ $75\frac{7}{9}$
21. $3\frac{3}{4} \times 2\frac{4}{7}$ $9\frac{9}{14}$

Chapter 5   33   Course 2

Practice*
p. 34 **OL** **AL**

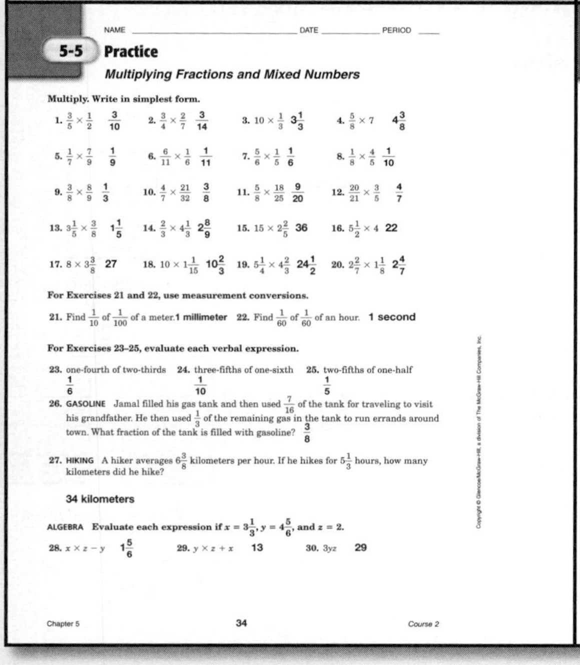

5-5 Practice
Multiplying Fractions and Mixed Numbers

Multiply. Write in simplest form.

1. $\frac{1}{5} \times \frac{1}{2}$ $\frac{1}{10}$
2. $\frac{3}{4} \times \frac{2}{7}$ $\frac{3}{14}$
3. $10 \times \frac{1}{3}$ $3\frac{1}{3}$
4. $\frac{5}{8} \times 7$ $4\frac{3}{8}$
5. $\frac{1}{7} \times \frac{7}{9}$ $\frac{1}{9}$
6. $\frac{6}{11} \times \frac{1}{6}$ $\frac{1}{11}$
7. $\frac{5}{12} \times \frac{1}{5}$ $\frac{1}{6}$
8. $\frac{1}{4} \times \frac{5}{5}$ $\frac{1}{10}$
9. $\frac{3}{5} \times \frac{1}{9}$ $\frac{1}{15}$
10. $\frac{4}{7} \times \frac{21}{24}$ $\frac{1}{2}$
11. $\frac{5}{6} \times \frac{18}{20}$ $\frac{9}{20}$
12. $20 \times \frac{3}{5}$ $\frac{4}{7}$
13. $\frac{3}{5} \times \frac{1}{8}$ $1\frac{1}{5}$
14. $\frac{3}{4} \times 4\frac{1}{3}$ $2\frac{8}{9}$
15. $15 \times 2\frac{2}{5}$ 36
16. $5\frac{1}{2} \times 4$ 22
17. $8 \times 3\frac{3}{8}$ 27
18. $10 \times 1\frac{1}{15}$ $10\frac{2}{3}$
19. $5\frac{1}{4} \times 4\frac{2}{3}$ $24\frac{1}{2}$
20. $2\frac{2}{5} \times 1\frac{1}{8}$ $2\frac{4}{7}$

For Exercises 21 and 22, use measurement conversions.

21. Find $\frac{1}{10}$ of $\frac{1}{100}$ of a meter. **1 millimeter**
22. Find $\frac{1}{60}$ of $\frac{1}{60}$ of an hour. **1 second**

For Exercises 23–25, evaluate each verbal expression.

23. one-fourth of two-thirds $\frac{1}{6}$
24. three-fifths of one-sixth $\frac{1}{10}$
25. two-fifths of one-half $\frac{1}{5}$

26. **GASOLINE** Jamal filled his gas tank and then used $\frac{7}{10}$ of the tank for traveling to visit his grandfather. He then used $\frac{1}{3}$ of the remaining gas in the tank to run errands around town. What fraction of the tank is filled with gasoline? $\frac{3}{8}$

27. **HIKING** A hiker averages $6\frac{3}{8}$ kilometers per hour. If he hikes for $5\frac{1}{3}$ hours, how many kilometers did he hike? **34 kilometers**

ALGEBRA Evaluate each expression if $x = 3\frac{1}{3}$, $y = 4\frac{5}{6}$, and $z = 2$.

28. $x \times z - y$ $1\frac{5}{6}$
29. $y \times z + x$ 13
30. $3yz$ 29

Chapter 5   34   Course 2

Word Problem Practice*
p. 35 **OL** **AL**

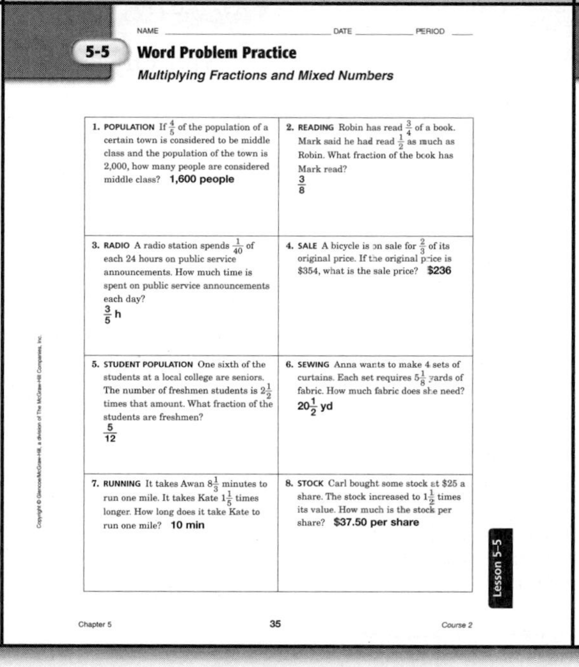

5-5 Word Problem Practice
Multiplying Fractions and Mixed Numbers

1. **POPULATION** If $\frac{4}{5}$ of the population of a certain town is considered to be middle class and the population of the town is 2,000, how many people are considered middle class? **1,600 people**

2. **READING** Robin has read $\frac{3}{4}$ of a book. Mark said he had read $1\frac{1}{2}$ as much as Robin. What fraction of the book has Mark read? $\frac{9}{8}$

3. **RADIO** A radio station spends $\frac{1}{40}$ of each 24 hours on public service announcements. How much time is spent on public service announcements each day? $\frac{3}{5}$ h

4. **SALE** A bicycle is on sale for $\frac{2}{3}$ of its original price. If the original price is $354, what is the sale price? **$236**

5. **STUDENT POPULATION** One sixth of the students at a local college are seniors. The number of freshmen students is $3\frac{1}{2}$ times that amount. What fraction of the students are freshmen? $\frac{5}{12}$

6. **SEWING** Anna wants to make 4 sets of curtains. Each set requires $5\frac{1}{8}$ yards of fabric. How much fabric does she need? $20\frac{1}{2}$ yd

7. **RUNNING** It takes Awan $8\frac{1}{3}$ minutes to run one mile. It takes Kate $1\frac{1}{5}$ times longer. How long does it take Kate to run one mile? **10 min**

8. **STOCK** Carl bought some stock at $25 a share. The stock increased to $1\frac{1}{2}$ times its value. How much is the stock per share? **$37.50 per share**

Chapter 5   35   Course 2

Enrichment
p. 36 **OL** **AL**

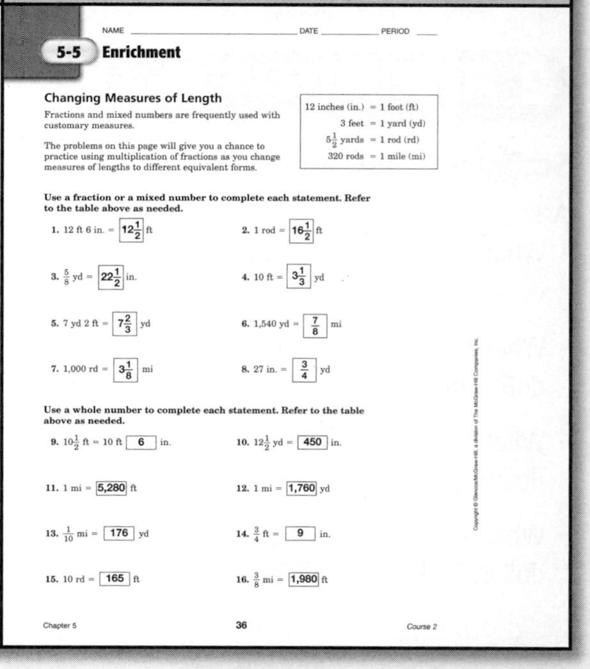

5-5 Enrichment

Changing Measures of Length

Fractions and mixed numbers are frequently used with customary measures.

The problems on this page will give you a chance to practice using multiplication of fractions as you change measures of lengths to different equivalent forms.

12 inches (in.)	= 1 foot (ft)
3 feet	= 1 yard (yd)
$5\frac{1}{2}$ yards	= 1 rod (rd)
320 rods	= 1 mile (mi)

Use a fraction or a mixed number to complete each statement. Refer to the table above as needed.

1. 12 ft 6 in. = $12\frac{1}{2}$ ft
2. 1 rod = $16\frac{1}{2}$ ft
3. $\frac{5}{6}$ yd = $22\frac{1}{2}$ in.
4. 10 ft = $3\frac{1}{3}$ yd
5. 7 yd 2 ft = $7\frac{2}{3}$ yd
6. 1,540 rd = $\frac{7}{8}$ mi
7. 1,000 rd = $3\frac{1}{8}$ mi
8. 27 in. = $\frac{3}{4}$ yd

Use a whole number to complete each statement. Refer to the table above as needed.

9. $10\frac{1}{2}$ ft = 10 ft   6 in.
10. $12\frac{1}{2}$ yd = 450 in.
11. 1 mi = 5,280 ft
12. 1 mi = 1,760 yd
13. $\frac{1}{10}$ mi = 176 yd
14. $\frac{3}{4}$ ft = 9 in.
15. 10 rd = 165 ft
16. $\frac{3}{8}$ mi = 1,980 ft

Chapter 5   36   Course 2

Additional Lesson Resources

Also available in Spanish **ELL**

Transparencies
- *5-Minute Check Transparency*, Lesson 5-5

Other Print Products
- *Teaching Mathematics with Manipulatives*
- *Noteables™ Interactive Study Notebook with Foldables™*

Teacher Tech Tools
- *Interactive Classroom CD-ROM*, Lesson 5-5
- *AssignmentWorks*, Lesson 5-5

Student Tech Tools
glencoe.com
- Extra Examples, Chapter 5, Lesson 5
- Self-Check Quiz, Chapter 5, Lesson 5

5-5

5-5 Multiplying Fractions and Mixed Numbers

1 Focus

Vertical Alignment

Before Lesson 5-5
Compute and perform simple multiplication of fractions and apply these procedures to solving problems

Lesson 5-5
Solve problems involving multiplication of positive fractions and explain why a particular operation was used for a given situation. Explain the meaning of multiplication of positive fractions and perform the calculations

After Lesson 5-5
Multiply and simplify rational numbers by using the exponent rules

2 Teach

Scaffolding Questions

Ask:
- What is half of $\frac{1}{2}$ of a dollar? $\frac{1}{4}$ dollar, or $0.25
- What is three times $\frac{1}{4}$ of a dollar? $\frac{3}{4}$ dollar, or $0.75
- What is one third of $1\frac{1}{2}$ dollars? $\frac{1}{2}$ dollar, or $0.50
- What is one quarter of $\frac{4}{5}$ of a dollar? $\frac{1}{5}$ dollar, or $0.20

Formative Assessment

Use the Check Your Progress exercises after the Examples to determine students' understanding of concepts.

MAIN IDEA

Multiply fractions and mixed numbers.

Math Online

glencoe.com
- Extra Examples
- Personal Tutor
- Self-Check Quiz

▶ **GET READY for the Lesson**

LUNCH Two thirds of the students at the lunch table ordered a hamburger for lunch. One half of those students ordered cheese on their hamburgers.

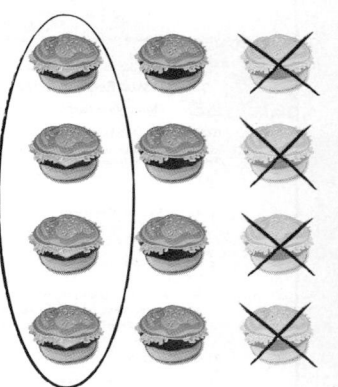

1. What fraction of the students at the lunch table ordered a cheeseburger? $\frac{4}{12}$ or $\frac{1}{3}$
2. How are the numerators and denominators of $\frac{2}{3}$ and $\frac{1}{2}$ related to the fraction in Exercise 1?

See Ch. 5 Answer Appendix.

Multiply Fractions
Key Concept

Words	To multiply fractions, multiply the numerators and multiply the denominators.

Examples	**Numbers**	**Algebra**
	$\frac{1}{2} \times \frac{2}{3} = \frac{1 \times 2}{2 \times 3}$ or $\frac{2}{6}$	$\frac{a}{b} \cdot \frac{c}{d} = \frac{a \cdot c}{b \cdot d}$ or $\frac{ac}{bd}$, where $b, d \neq 0$

EXAMPLES Multiply Fractions

Multiply. Write in simplest form.

① $\frac{1}{2} \times \frac{1}{3}$

$\frac{1}{2} \times \frac{1}{3} = \frac{1 \times 1}{2 \times 3}$ ← Multiply the numerators.
← Multiply the denominators.

$= \frac{1}{6}$ Simplify.

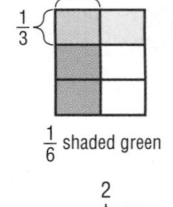

$\frac{1}{6}$ shaded green

② $2 \times \frac{3}{4}$

$2 \times \frac{3}{4} = \frac{2}{1} \times \frac{3}{4}$ Write 2 as $\frac{2}{1}$.

$= \frac{2 \times 3}{1 \times 4}$ ← Multiply the numerators.
← Multiply the denominators.

$= \frac{6}{4}$ or $1\frac{1}{2}$ Simplify.

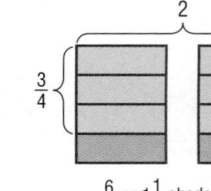

$\frac{6}{4}$ or $1\frac{1}{2}$ shaded green

Study Tip

Whole Numbers
When multiplying a fraction by a whole number, write the whole number as a fraction with a denominator of 1.

✓ **CHECK Your Progress**

a. $\frac{3}{5} \times \frac{1}{2}$ $\frac{3}{10}$

b. $\frac{1}{3} \times \frac{3}{4}$ $\frac{1}{4}$

c. $\frac{2}{3} \times 4$ $2\frac{2}{3}$

252 Chapter 5 Applying Fractions

Differentiated Instruction

Bodily/Kinesthetic Learners Students can use geoboards in the Get Ready for the Lesson. Ask students how they could model $\frac{1}{3} \times \frac{2}{5}$ using a geoboard. **Sample answer:** Use a geoband to represent $\frac{1}{3}$ of the geoboard and another geoband to represents $\frac{2}{5}$.

Tips for New Teachers

Models

For the Example in Get Ready for the Lesson, tell students that the hamburgers represent all students at the table. The top two rows are students who ordered hamburgers, or $\frac{2}{3}$. The circled hamburgers are $\frac{1}{2}$ of $\frac{2}{3}$ or $\frac{1}{3}$ of the students at the table who ordered cheese.

If the numerator and denominator of either fraction have common factors, you can simplify before multiplying.

Review Vocabulary

GCF the greatest of the common factors of two or more numbers; *Example:* the GCF of 8 and 12 is 4. (Lesson 4-2)

EXAMPLE Simplify Before Multiplying

③ Find $\frac{2}{7} \times \frac{3}{8}$. Write in simplest form.

$$\frac{2}{7} \times \frac{3}{8} = \frac{\overset{1}{\cancel{2}}}{7} \times \frac{3}{\underset{4}{\cancel{8}}} \qquad \text{Divide 2 and 8 by their GCF, 2.}$$

$$= \frac{1 \times 3}{7 \times 4} \text{ or } \frac{3}{28} \qquad \text{Multiply.}$$

✓ **CHECK Your Progress**

Multiply. Write in simplest form.

d. $\frac{1}{3} \times \frac{3}{7}$ **$\frac{1}{7}$**   e. $\frac{4}{9} \times \frac{1}{8}$ **$\frac{1}{18}$**   f. $\frac{5}{6} \times \frac{3}{5}$ **$\frac{1}{2}$**

EXAMPLE Multiply Mixed Numbers

④ Find $\frac{1}{2} \times 4\frac{2}{5}$. Write in simplest form. **Estimate** $\frac{1}{2} \times 4 = 2$

METHOD 1 Rename the mixed number.

$$\frac{1}{2} \times 4\frac{2}{5} = \frac{1}{\underset{1}{\cancel{2}}} \times \frac{\overset{11}{\cancel{22}}}{5} \qquad \begin{array}{l}\text{Rename } 4\frac{2}{5} \text{ as an improper fraction, } \frac{22}{5}.\\ \text{Divide 2 and 22 by their GCF, 2.}\end{array}$$

$$= \frac{1 \times 11}{1 \times 5} \qquad \text{Multiply.}$$

$$= \frac{11}{5} \text{ or } 2\frac{1}{5} \qquad \text{Simplify.}$$

Study Tip

Simplifying If you forget to simplify before multiplying, you can always simplify the final answer. However, it is usually easier to simplify before multiplying.

METHOD 2 Use mental math.

The mixed number $4\frac{2}{5}$ is equal to $4 + \frac{2}{5}$.

So, $\frac{1}{2} \times 4\frac{2}{5} = \frac{1}{2}\left(4 + \frac{2}{5}\right)$. Use the Distributive Property to multiply, then add mentally.

$$\frac{1}{2}\left(4 + \frac{2}{5}\right) = 2 + \frac{1}{5} \qquad \text{THINK Half of 4 is 2 and half of 2 fifths is 1 fifth.}$$

$$= 2\frac{1}{5} \qquad \text{Rewrite the sum as a mixed number.}$$

So, $\frac{1}{2} \times 4\frac{2}{5} = 2\frac{1}{5}$. **Check for Reasonableness** $2\frac{1}{5} \approx 2$ ✔

✓ **CHOOSE Your Method**

Multiply. Write in simplest form.

g. $\frac{1}{4} \times 8\frac{4}{9}$ **$2\frac{1}{9}$**   h. $5\frac{1}{3} \times 3$ **16**   i. $1\frac{7}{8} \times 2\frac{2}{5}$ **$4\frac{1}{2}$**

Focus on Mathematical Content

To multiply a fraction by a whole number or a mixed number, first **rename the whole number or mixed number** as an improper fraction.

Before multiplying fractions, check whether the numerator and denominator of either fraction have a common factor. If they do, **simplifying** them first will save time.

ADDITIONAL EXAMPLES

Multiply. Write in simplest form.

① $\frac{1}{8} \times \frac{1}{9}$ **$\frac{1}{72}$**

② $6 \times \frac{1}{3}$ **2**

③ $\frac{3}{12} \times \frac{4}{5}$ **$\frac{1}{5}$**

④ $\frac{1}{3} \times 6\frac{6}{7}$ **$2\frac{2}{7}$**

Additional Examples are also in:

- Noteables™ Interactive Study Notebook with Foldables™
- Interactive Classroom PowerPoint® Presentations

Lesson 5-5 Multiplying Fractions and Mixed Numbers **253**

Lesson 5-5 Multiplying Fractions and Mixed Numbers **253**

Tips for New Teachers

Unit Fractions

Explain to students that when unit fractions are used in multiplication, division can also be used. Point out that in Example 5, they can use the equation $d = 365\frac{1}{4} \div 3$ to solve the problem.

ADDITIONAL EXAMPLES

5 **BIKING** In a 48-hour bike race, Mel rode $289\frac{1}{3}$ miles. His father rode $\frac{3}{4}$ as far as Mel did. Find the number of miles his father rode. **217 mi**

6 **CANNING** Roberta canned 32 quarts of her prize-winning apricot jam. She sold $\frac{5}{8}$ of them at a street fair. Find the number of quarts she sold. **20 qt**

Study Tip

Meaning of Multiplication
Recall that one meaning of 3×4 is three groups with 4 in each group. In Example 5, there are $365\frac{1}{4}$ groups with $\frac{1}{3}$ in each group.

Real-World EXAMPLES

5 **SLEEP** Humans sleep about $\frac{1}{3}$ of each day. If each year is equal to $365\frac{1}{4}$ days, determine the number of days in a year the average human sleeps.

Words	Humans sleep about $\frac{1}{3}$ of $365\frac{1}{4}$ days.
Variable	Let d represent the number of days a human sleeps.
Equation	$d = \frac{1}{3} \cdot 365\frac{1}{4}$

$d = \frac{1}{3} \cdot 365\frac{1}{4}$ Write the equation.

$d = \frac{1}{3} \cdot \frac{1,461}{4}$ Rename the mixed number as an improper fraction.

$d = \frac{1}{\underset{1}{3}} \cdot \frac{\overset{487}{\cancel{1,461}}}{4}$ Divide 3 and 1,461 by their GCF, 3.

$d = \frac{487}{4}$ or $121\frac{3}{4}$ Multiply. Then rename as a mixed number.

The average human sleeps $121\frac{3}{4}$ days each year.

6 **ANIMALS** The house cat has an average lifespan that is $\frac{4}{5}$ of a lion's. If a lion's lifespan is 15 years, find the average lifespan of a house cat.

Real-World Link . . . .
The average group of lions, called a pride, consists of about 15 lions with about $\frac{2}{3}$ of the pride being female.
Source: African Wildlife Foundation

Words	The lifespan of a house cat is $\frac{4}{5}$ of that of the lion.
Variable	Let c represent the lifespan of a house cat.
Equation	$c = \frac{4}{5} \cdot 15$

$c = \frac{4}{5} \cdot 15$ Write the equation.

$c = \frac{4}{5} \cdot \frac{15}{1}$ Write the whole number 15 as an improper fraction.

$c = \frac{4}{\underset{1}{5}} \cdot \frac{\overset{3}{\cancel{15}}}{1}$ Divide 5 and 15 by their GCF, 5.

$c = \frac{12}{1}$ or 12   Multiply, then simplify.

The average lifespan of a house cat is 12 years.

CHECK Your Progress

j. **COOKING** Sofia wishes to make $\frac{1}{2}$ of a recipe. If the original recipe calls for $3\frac{3}{4}$ cups of flour, how many cups should she use? **$1\frac{7}{8}$ c**

CHECK Your Understanding

★ indicates multi-step problem

Examples 1–4
(pp. 252–253)

Multiply. Write in simplest form.

1. $\frac{2}{3} \times \frac{1}{3}$ **$\frac{2}{9}$**

2. $2 \times \frac{2}{5}$ **$\frac{4}{5}$**

3. $\frac{1}{6} \times 4$ **$\frac{2}{3}$**

4. $\frac{1}{4} \times \frac{8}{9}$ **$\frac{2}{9}$**

5. $2\frac{1}{4} \times \frac{2}{3}$ **$1\frac{1}{2}$**

6. $1\frac{5}{6} \times 3\frac{3}{5}$ **$6\frac{3}{5}$**

Examples 5, 6
(p. 254)

7. **WEIGHT** The weight of an object on Mars is about $\frac{2}{5}$ its weight on Earth. How much would an 80-pound dog weigh on Mars? **32 pounds**

Practice and Problem Solving

HOMEWORK HELP	
For Exercises	**See Examples**
8–11	1, 2
12–19	3, 4
20–23	5, 6

Exercise Levels
A: 8–23
B: 24–52
C: 53–55

21. $\frac{3}{16}$

33. $7\frac{1}{20}$ mi

Multiply. Write in simplest form.

8. $\frac{3}{4} \times \frac{1}{8}$ **$\frac{3}{32}$**

9. $\frac{2}{5} \times \frac{2}{3}$ **$\frac{4}{15}$**

10. $9 \times \frac{1}{2}$ **$4\frac{1}{2}$**

11. $\frac{4}{5} \times 6$ **$4\frac{4}{5}$**

12. $\frac{1}{5} \times \frac{5}{6}$ **$\frac{1}{6}$**

13. $\frac{4}{9} \times \frac{1}{4}$ **$\frac{1}{9}$**

14. $\frac{2}{3} \times \frac{1}{4}$ **$\frac{1}{6}$**

15. $\frac{1}{12} \times \frac{3}{5}$ **$\frac{1}{20}$**

16. $\frac{4}{7} \times \frac{7}{8}$ **$\frac{1}{2}$**

17. $\frac{2}{5} \times \frac{15}{16}$ **$\frac{3}{8}$**

18. $\frac{3}{8} \times \frac{10}{27}$ **$\frac{5}{36}$**

19. $\frac{9}{10} \times \frac{5}{6}$ **$\frac{3}{4}$**

20. **DVDs** Each DVD storage case is about $\frac{1}{5}$ inch thick. What will be the height of 12 cases sold together in plastic wrapping? **$2\frac{2}{5}$ in.**

21. **PIZZA** Mark left $\frac{3}{8}$ of a pizza in the refrigerator. On Friday, he ate $\frac{1}{2}$ of what was left of the pizza. What fraction of the entire pizza did he eat on Friday?

22. **MEASUREMENT** The width of a vegetable garden is $\frac{1}{3}$ times its length. If the length of the garden is $7\frac{3}{4}$ feet, what is the width? **$2\frac{7}{12}$ ft**

23. **RECIPES** A recipe to make one batch of blueberry muffins calls for $4\frac{2}{3}$ cups of flour. How many cups of flour are needed to make 3 batches of blueberry muffins? **14 c**

Multiply. Write in simplest form.

24. $4\frac{2}{3} \times \frac{4}{7}$ **$2\frac{2}{3}$**

25. $\frac{5}{8} \times 2\frac{1}{2}$ **$1\frac{9}{16}$**

26. $14 \times 1\frac{1}{7}$ **16**

27. $3\frac{3}{4} \times 8$ **30**

28. $9 \times 4\frac{2}{3}$ **42**

29. $4 \times 7\frac{5}{6}$ **$31\frac{1}{3}$**

30. $3\frac{1}{4} \times 2\frac{2}{3}$ **$8\frac{2}{3}$**

31. $5\frac{1}{3} \times 3\frac{3}{4}$ **20**

32. **MEASUREMENT** The width of the fish tank is $\frac{2}{5}$ of its length. What is the width of the fish tank? **12 in.**

33. **BICYCLING** Philip rode his bicycle at $9\frac{2}{5}$ miles per hour. If he rode for $\frac{3}{4}$ of an hour, how many miles did he cover?

30 in.

3 Practice

✔ **Formative Assessment**

Use Exercises 1–7 to check for understanding.

Then use the chart at the bottom of this page to customize your assignments for students.

Intervention You may wish to use the Study Guide and Intervention Master on page 32 of the *Chapter 5 Resource Masters* for additional reinforcement.

Odd/Even Assignments

Exercises 8–23 are structured so that students practice the same concepts whether they are assigned odd or even problems.

DIFFERENTIATED HOMEWORK OPTIONS			
Level	**Assignment**	**Two-Day Option**	
BL Basic	8–23, 54–66	9–23 odd, 56, 57	8–22 even, 54, 55, 58–66
OL Core	9–31 odd, 32, 33–39 odd, 40, 41–47 odd, 48, 49, 51, 54–66	8–23, 56, 57	24–52, 54, 55, 58–66
AL Advanced/Pre-AP	24–63 (optional: 64–66)		

Additional Answers

40. 1,167$\frac{1}{5}$ ft; sample answer: Find the perimeter of the pool and then multiply the distance by 4.

49. broccoli: 1$\frac{7}{8}$c, pasta: 5$\frac{5}{8}$c, salad dressing: 1c, cheese: 2c; Multiply each amount by 1$\frac{1}{2}$.

51. $\frac{2}{5} \times \frac{3}{5}$; $\frac{6}{25}$; Sample answer: The model shows that $\frac{3}{5}$ of the rectangle is 15 sections out of 25 sections. Since $\frac{2}{5}$ of 15 sections is six sections, $\frac{2}{5}$ of $\frac{3}{5}$ is $\frac{6}{25}$.

52. $\frac{3}{7} \times \frac{2}{3}$; $\frac{6}{21}$ or $\frac{2}{7}$; Sample answer: The model shows that $\frac{2}{3}$ of the rectangle is 14 sections out of 21 sections. Since $\frac{3}{7}$ of 14 sections is six sections, $\frac{3}{7}$ of $\frac{2}{3}$ is $\frac{6}{21}$, or $\frac{2}{7}$.

Evaluate each verbal expression.

34. one half of five eighths $\frac{5}{16}$

35. four sevenths of two thirds $\frac{8}{21}$

36. nine tenths of one fourth $\frac{9}{40}$

37. one third of eleven sixteenths $\frac{11}{48}$

MEASUREMENT Find the perimeter and area of each rectangle.

38. 17$\frac{1}{2}$ft; 18$\frac{3}{8}$ ft²

3$\frac{1}{2}$ ft

5$\frac{1}{4}$ ft

39. 16$\frac{1}{3}$ yd; 10$\frac{5}{6}$ yd²

1$\frac{2}{3}$ yd

6$\frac{1}{2}$ yd

Real-World Link . . . .
There are an estimated 5 million in-ground swimming pools in the U.S.
Source: *Pool & Spa Service Industry News*

40. POOLS A community swimming pool is 90$\frac{2}{5}$ feet long and 55$\frac{1}{2}$ feet wide. ★ If Natalie swims the perimeter of the pool four times, what is the total number of feet she will swim? Explain how you solved the problem. **See margin.**

MEASUREMENT For Exercises 41–44, use measurement conversions.

41. Find $\frac{1}{2}$ of $\frac{1}{4}$ of a gallon. **one pint**

42. What is $\frac{1}{60}$ of $\frac{1}{24}$ of a day? **one minute**

43. Find $\frac{1}{100}$ of $\frac{1}{1,000}$ of a kilometer. **one centimeter**

44. What is $\frac{1}{12}$ of $\frac{1}{3}$ of a yard? **one inch**

ALGEBRA Evaluate each expression if $a = 4$, $b = 2\frac{1}{2}$, and $c = 5\frac{3}{4}$.

45. $a \times b + c$ **15$\frac{3}{4}$**

46. $b \times c - a$ **10$\frac{3}{8}$**

47. $2bc$ **28$\frac{3}{4}$**

48. TELEVISION One evening, $\frac{2}{3}$ of the students in Rick's class watched ★ television, and $\frac{3}{8}$ of those students watched a reality show, of which $\frac{1}{4}$ taped the show. What fraction of the students in Rick's class watched and taped a reality TV show? $\frac{1}{16}$

49. FOOD Alano wants to make one and a ★ half recipes of the pasta salad recipe shown at the right. How much of each ingredient will Alano need? Explain how you solved the problem. **See margin.**

Pasta Salad Recipe	
Ingredient	**Amount**
broccoli	1$\frac{1}{4}$ c
cooked pasta	3$\frac{3}{4}$ c
salad dressing	$\frac{2}{3}$ c
cheese	1$\frac{1}{3}$ c

50. FIND THE DATA Refer to the Data File on pages 16–19. Choose some data and write a real-world problem in which you would multiply fractions. **See students' work.**

Write and evaluate a multiplication expression to represent each model. Explain how the models show the multiplication process. **51, 52. See margin.**

51.

52.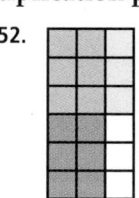

EXTRA PRACTICE
See pages 680, 708.

256 Chapter 5 Applying Fractions

53–55. See margin.

53. CHALLENGE Two improper fractions are multiplied. Is the product *sometimes*, *always*, or *never* less than 1? Explain your reasoning.

54. OPEN ENDED Write a word problem that involves finding the product of $\frac{3}{4}$ and $\frac{1}{8}$.

55. **WRITING IN MATH** Refer to Example 2. Explain how the model represents the meaning of the multiplication process.

TEST PRACTICE

56. Of the dolls in Marjorie's doll collection, $\frac{1}{5}$ have red hair. Of these, $\frac{3}{4}$ have green eyes. What fraction of Marjorie's doll collection has both red hair and green eyes? **B**

A $\frac{2}{9}$ **C** $\frac{4}{9}$

B $\frac{3}{20}$ **D** $\frac{19}{20}$

57. Which description gives the relationship between a term and n, its position in the sequence? **H**

Position	1	2	3	4	5	n
Value of Term	$\frac{1}{4}$	$\frac{1}{2}$	$\frac{3}{4}$	1	$1\frac{1}{4}$	

F Subtract 4 from n.

G Add $\frac{1}{4}$ to n.

H Multiply n by $\frac{1}{4}$.

J Divide n by $\frac{1}{4}$.

Spiral Review

58. MEASUREMENT Find which room dimensions would give an area of $125\frac{3}{8}$ square feet. Use the *eliminate possibilities* strategy. (Lesson 5-4) **D**

A $11\frac{1}{2}$ feet by $10\frac{3}{8}$ feet **C** $13\frac{5}{8}$ feet by 9 feet

B $10\frac{7}{8}$ feet by $12\frac{1}{4}$ feet **D** $14\frac{3}{4}$ feet by $8\frac{1}{2}$ feet

59. MEASUREMENT How much longer is a $2\frac{1}{2}$-inch-long piece of string than a $\frac{2}{5}$-inch-long piece of string? (Lesson 5-3) **$2\frac{1}{10}$ in.**

Replace each ● **with <, >, or = to make a true sentence.** (Lesson 4-9)

60. $\frac{5}{12}$ ● $\frac{2}{5}$ **>** **61.** $\frac{3}{16}$ ● $\frac{1}{8}$ **>** **62.** $3\frac{7}{6}$ ● $3\frac{6}{5}$ **<**

63. PHONES A long-distance telephone company charges a flat monthly fee of $4.95 and $0.06 per minute on all long-distance calls. Write and solve an equation to find the number of monthly minutes spent talking long-distance if the bill total was $22.95. (Lesson 3-5) **4.95 + .06x = 22.95; 300 min**

▷ **GET READY for the Next Lesson**

PREREQUISITE SKILL Solve each equation mentally. (Lesson 1-7)

64. $x + 2 = 8$ **6** **65.** $9 + m = 12$ **3** **66.** $7 - w = 2$ **5**

---

4 Assess

Ticket Out the Door Write a problem such as $\frac{5}{6} \cdot \frac{3}{10} \cdot \frac{4}{9}$ on the board. Have students write the answer to the problem on a small piece of paper.

FOLDABLES Study Organizer **Foldables™ Follow-Up**

Remind students to record what they learn about multiplying fractions and mixed numbers on index cards, and then to store the cards in their Foldables.

Additional Answers

53. Always; Sample answer: improper fractions are always greater than 1.

54. Sample answer: $\frac{3}{4}$ of the 200 students at Walnut Middle School were on the honor roll. Of that group, only $\frac{1}{8}$ of them were on the "All A" honor roll. How many students were on the "All A" honor roll?

55. Sample answer: The model shows that $\frac{3}{4}$ of one rectangle is 3 sections out of 4 sections shaded. Since 2 sets of rectangles with 3 sections out of 4 sections shaded is $\frac{6}{4}$, 2 of $\frac{3}{4}$ is $\frac{6}{4}$, or $1\frac{1}{2}$.

Pre-AP Activity   Use as an Extension.

Write two problems involving multiplication with negative fractions, such as $-\frac{2}{3} \cdot \frac{3}{4}$ and $-\frac{7}{10} \cdot \left(-\frac{5}{6}\right)$, on the board. Have students use what they know about multiplying fractions and multiplying integers to solve both problems, explaining the steps that they take.

 **Algebra: Solving Equations**

PACING: **Regular:** 1 period, **Block:** 0.5 period

Options for Differentiated Instruction

 = English Language Learner   = Above or Beyond Grade Level   = Struggling Students   = Special Needs

Reviewing Concepts

Use before beginning Lesson 5-6.

To help students prepare for Lesson 5-6, review the concepts involving inverse operations.

Ask:

- Which operations undo each other? addition and subtraction; multiplication and division
- What are the division facts related to the multiplication problem $3 \times 5 = 15$? $15 \div 3 = 5$ and $15 \div 5 = 3$
- What are the multiplication facts that are related to the division problem $\frac{24}{4} = 6$? $6 \times 4 = 24$ and $4 \times 6 = 24$
- How can you use what you know about inverse operations to solve equations like $3x = 15$ and $\frac{x}{4} = 6$? Sample answer: Use division to undo the multiplication of 3 and x in $3x = 15$; use multiplication to undo the division of x and 4 in $\frac{x}{4} = 6$.

Correcting Common Errors

Use after presenting Examples 1–6.

Write the following equation on the board.

$$-\frac{5}{6}q = 8$$

Ask students to write the first step they would use to solve the equation. Students may mistakenly write $(8) \cdot -5q = (6) \cdot 8$ or $(-6q) \cdot -\frac{5}{6}q = (6q) \cdot 8$, assuming that the q is in the denominator. Point out these errors, as well as the correct first step to solve.

$$\left(-\frac{6}{5}\right) \cdot \left(-\frac{5}{6}q\right) = \left(-\frac{6}{5}\right) \cdot 8$$

Leveled Lesson Resources

Chapter 5 Resource Masters

BL = Below or Approaching Grade Level   **OL** = On Grade Level   **AL** = Above or Beyond Grade Level   **ELL** = English Language Learner

---

Lesson Reading Guide
p. 38 **BL** **OL** **ELL**

NAME _____ DATE _____ PERIOD _____

5-6 Lesson Reading Guide
Algebra: Solving Equations

Get Ready for the Lesson

Read the introduction at the top of page 258 in your textbook. Write your answers below.

1. Write a multiplication expression to find how much time Shawnda spends doing homework. Then find the product.
$2 \times \frac{1}{2}$; 1

2. Complete the table below.

$\frac{3}{2} \times \frac{2}{3} =$ 1	$\frac{1}{5} \times ■ = \frac{5}{1}$	$\frac{5}{6} \times \frac{6}{5} = ■$ 1	$\frac{7}{8} \times \frac{8}{7} = ■$ 1
$■ \times \frac{5}{7} = 1$ $\frac{7}{5}$	$\frac{2}{6} \times \frac{6}{2} = ■$ 1	$\frac{1}{7} \times ■ = 1$ $\frac{7}{1}$	$■ \times 8 = 1$ $\frac{1}{8}$

3. What is true about the numerators and denominators in the fractions in Exercise 2? **They are switched.**

Read the Lesson

4. Write the Multiplication Property of Equality. **If you multiply each side of an equation by the same nonzero number, the two sides remain equal.**

5. When the coefficient of x in an equation is a fraction, explain how the reciprocal, or multiplicative inverse, of the coefficient is used to solve the equation. **Sample answer: Multiply both sides of the equation by the reciprocal.**

Remember What You Learned

6. The word *inverse* comes from a Latin verb that means "to turn upside down." How does this definition relate to the content of this lesson?
Sample answer: The inverse of a number like 2 is $\frac{2}{1}$ turned upside down, or $\frac{1}{2}$.

Chapter 5   38   Course 2

Study Guide and Intervention*
p. 39 **BL** **OL** **ELL**

NAME _____ DATE _____ PERIOD _____

5-6 Study Guide and Intervention
Algebra: Solving Equations

Multiplicative inverses, or **reciprocals**, are two numbers whose product is 1. To solve an equation in which the coefficient is a fraction, multiply each side of the equation by the reciprocal of the coefficient.

Example 1 Find the multiplicative inverse of $3\frac{1}{4}$.

$3\frac{1}{4} = \frac{13}{4}$ Rename the mixed number as an improper fraction.

$\frac{13}{4} \cdot \frac{4}{13} = 1$ Multiply $\frac{13}{4}$ by $\frac{4}{13}$ to get the product 1.

The multiplicative inverse of $3\frac{1}{4}$ is $\frac{4}{13}$.

Example 2 Solve $\frac{4}{5}x = 8$. Check your solution.

$\frac{4}{5}x = 8$ Write the equation.

$\left(\frac{5}{4}\right)\frac{4}{5}x = \left(\frac{5}{4}\right)8$ Multiply each side by the reciprocal of $\frac{4}{5}$, $\frac{5}{4}$.

$x = 10$ Simplify.

The solution is 10.

Exercises

Find the multiplicative inverse of each number.

1. $\frac{4}{9}$ $\frac{9}{4}$ or $2\frac{1}{4}$
2. $\frac{12}{13}$ $\frac{13}{12}$ or $1\frac{1}{12}$
3. $\frac{15}{■}$ $\frac{4}{15}$
4. $6\frac{1}{7}$ $\frac{7}{43}$

Solve each equation. Check your solution.

5. $\frac{3}{5}x = 12$ 20
6. $16 = \frac{10}{3}a$ $4\frac{4}{5}$
7. $\frac{c}{2} = 7$ 14
8. $\frac{15}{7}y = 3$ $1\frac{2}{5}$
9. $\frac{m}{6} = -4$ -24
10. $\frac{14}{3} = -\frac{7}{9}b$ -6

Chapter 5   39   Course 2

Skills Practice*
p. 40 **BL** **OL**

NAME _____ DATE _____ PERIOD _____

5-6 Skills Practice
Algebra: Solving Equations

Find the multiplicative inverse of each number.

1. $\frac{3}{7}$ $\frac{7}{3}$ or $2\frac{1}{3}$
2. $-\frac{4}{11}$ $-\frac{11}{4}$ or $-2\frac{3}{4}$
3. $\frac{7}{2}$ $\frac{2}{7}$
4. $\frac{5}{9}$ $\frac{9}{5}$
5. -5 $-\frac{1}{5}$
6. $6\frac{1}{3}$ $\frac{3}{19}$
7. $4\frac{1}{9}$ $\frac{9}{37}$
8. $17\frac{1}{2}$ $\frac{2}{35}$
9. $-15\frac{2}{3}$ $-\frac{3}{47}$

Solve each equation. Check your solution.

10. $\frac{x}{10} = 3$ 30
11. $7 = \frac{m}{4}$ 28
12. $\frac{a}{5} = -11$ -55
13. $-8 = \frac{t}{5}$ -40
14. $\frac{3}{4}c = 12$ 16
15. $-7 = -\frac{x}{6}$ 42
16. $\frac{2}{3}y = 6$ 10
17. $15 = \frac{3}{7}b$ 35
18. $\frac{6}{7}c = 18$ 21
19. $\frac{7}{9}x = \frac{2}{3}$ $\frac{2}{7}$
20. $\frac{11}{12} = \frac{3}{4}h$ $1\frac{2}{9}$
21. $\frac{9}{14}y = \frac{2}{3}$ $1\frac{1}{3}$
22. $\frac{m}{2.6} = -5$ -13
23. $0.6 = \frac{n}{5}$ 3
24. $\frac{r}{2.6} = -1.3$ -3.38

Chapter 5   40   Course 2

Practice*
p. 41 **OL** **AL**

NAME _____ DATE _____ PERIOD _____

5-6 Practice
Algebra: Solving Equations

Find the multiplicative inverse of each number.

1. $\frac{9}{7}$ $\frac{7}{9}$
2. $\frac{5}{2}$ $\frac{2}{5}$
3. $\frac{1}{9}$ 9
4. $\frac{1}{12}$ 12
5. 4 $\frac{1}{4}$
6. 15 $\frac{1}{15}$
7. $4\frac{1}{3}$ $\frac{3}{13}$
8. $5\frac{4}{5}$ $\frac{5}{29}$

Solve each equation. Check your solution.

9. $\frac{h}{8} = 5$ 40
10. $15 = \frac{y}{2}$ 30
11. $\frac{k}{3.1} = 7$ 21.7
12. $1 = \frac{v}{6.3}$ 6.3
13. $0.9 = \frac{m}{2.5}$ 2.25
14. $\frac{t}{5.4} = 9$ 48.6
15. $\frac{3}{7}g = 9$ 21
16. $28 = \frac{4}{5}d$ 35
17. $\frac{3}{8}n = \frac{1}{4}$ $\frac{2}{3}$
18. $\frac{2}{5} = \frac{4}{5}c$ $\frac{1}{2}$
19. $\frac{2}{3}z = 4\frac{1}{2}$ $6\frac{3}{4}$
20. $\frac{5}{6}b = 1\frac{7}{8}$ $2\frac{1}{4}$
21. $\frac{p}{-4} = 7$ -28
22. $-3 = \frac{w}{-5}$ 15
23. $27.3 = \frac{3}{4}y$ 36.4
24. $\frac{4}{7}x = -1.6$ -2.8

25. **DRAWING** An architect needs to make a scale drawing of a home. The width w of the home in the drawing, in inches, is given by the equation $\frac{w}{0.6} = 9.5$. What is the width of the home in the scale drawing? **5.7 inches**

26. **VOLUNTEERS** At a local shelter, 36 people volunteered to help prepare meals for disaster relief. If this represented $\frac{9}{16}$ of the volunteers at the shelter, write and solve an equation to determine how many volunteers helped at the local shelter.
$\frac{9}{16}v = 36$; $v = 64$; **64 volunteers**

Chapter 5   41   Course 2

Word Problem Practice*
p. 42 **OL** **AL**

NAME _____ DATE _____ PERIOD _____

5-6 Word Problem Practice
Algebra: Solving Equations

1. **BIKING** The speed s that Brandon can ride his bike if he rides $\frac{3}{5}$ of an hour and travels 4 miles is given by the equation $4 = \frac{3}{5}s$. What is Brandon's speed?
$6\frac{2}{3}$ mph

2. **BAND** The woodwind section of the middle school band makes up $\frac{1}{4}$ of the band. There are 9 members in the woodwind section. Use the equation $\frac{1}{4}m = 9$ to find the number of members m in the band. **36 members**

3. **SALE** A coat is selling for $\frac{3}{4}$ of the original price. The sale price is $180. The original price p can be found using the equation $\frac{3}{4}p = 180$. Find the original price. **$240**

4. **SALARIES** Aaron's annual salary is $\frac{2}{3}$ as much as Juanita's salary. Aaron makes $46,000. Find Juanita's salary x using the equation $46,000 = \frac{2}{3}x$. **$69,000**

5. **ENDANGERED SPECIES** In the U.S., there are $\frac{14}{25}$ as many endangered species of birds as of reptiles. The number of endangered species of birds b can be compared to the 14 endangered species of reptiles using $\frac{14}{25}b = 14$. Find the number of endangered species of birds. **29**

6. **SALES TAX** The sticker price p of a purchase with $\frac{1}{10}$ sales tax and a total price (including tax) of $5.28 can be found using the equation $\frac{11}{10}p = 5.28$. What is the sticker price? **$4.80**

7. **SEWING** Each costume uses $\frac{3}{4}$ yard of fabric. The number of costumes c that can be made using $11\frac{1}{4}$ yards of fabric can be found using the equation $\frac{3}{4}c = 11\frac{1}{4}$. Find the number of costumes that can be made. **15 costumes**

8. **SAVINGS** Jasmine saves $46 each month from her part-time job. She saves $\frac{2}{5}$ of her earnings. Her earnings a can be found by using the equation $\frac{2}{5}a = 46$. Find her earnings. **$115**

Chapter 5   42   Course 2

Enrichment
p. 43 **OL** **AL**

NAME _____ DATE _____ PERIOD _____

5-6 Enrichment

Trail Blazers

Each puzzle on this page is called a **trail blazer**. To solve it, you must find a trail that begins at any one of the small squares and ends at the goal square, following these rules.

1. The sum of all the fractions on the trail must equal the number in the goal square.
2. The trail can only go horizontally or vertically.
3. The trail cannot retrace or cross itself.

When you are solving a trail blazer, try to eliminate possibilities. For instance, in the puzzle at the right, you know that you cannot include $\frac{3}{4}$ using $\frac{3}{4} + \frac{1}{4} = 1$ because you can't reach the goal box. $\frac{3}{4} + \frac{1}{4} = 1$ will not work either as the goal for the entire trail is only 1. **Answers may vary.**

Chapter 5   43   Course 2

Additional Lesson Resources

Transparencies
- *5-Minute Check Transparency*, Lesson 5-6

Other Print Products
- *Noteables™ Interactive Study Notebook with Foldables™*

Teacher Tech Tools
- *Interactive Classroom CD-ROM*, Lesson 5-6
- *AssignmentWorks*, Lesson 5-6

Student Tech Tools
glencoe.com
- Extra Examples, Chapter 5, Lesson 6
- Self-Check Quiz, Chapter 5, Lesson 6

1 Focus

Vertical Alignment

Before Lesson 5-6
Use a letter to represent an unknown number; write and evaluate simple algebraic expressions in one variable by substitution

Lesson 5-6
Write and solve one-step linear equations in one variable

After Lesson 5-6
Solve two-step linear equations and inequalities in one variable over the rational numbers, interpret the solution or solutions in the context from which they arose, and verify the reasonableness of the results

2 Teach

▷ **GET READY**

Some students will recognize the pattern and follow it to complete the table. Other students may need to model each equation on grid paper. Make sure students realize that in order to find the products on grid paper they will have to mentally rearrange some of the shaded regions.

Scaffolding Questions

As you ask the following questions, write each equation on the board.

Ask:

• How can I solve $x + \frac{1}{2} = 5$? subtract $\frac{1}{2}$ from each side

• How can I solve $x - 8.4 = 21$? add 8.4 to each side

• How can I solve $6x = 54$? divide each side by 6

MAIN IDEA

Solve equations with rational number solutions.

New Vocabulary

multiplicative inverse
reciprocal

Math Online

glencoe.com

• Extra Examples
• Personal Tutor
• Self-Check Quiz

▷ **GET READY for the Lesson**

HOMEWORK Shawnda spends $\frac{1}{2}$ hour doing homework after school. Then she spends another $\frac{1}{2}$ hour doing homework before bed.

1. Write a multiplication expression to find how much time Shawnda spends doing homework. Then find the product. $2 \cdot \frac{1}{2}$; 1

2. Copy and complete the table below.

$\frac{3}{2} \times \frac{2}{3} = \blacksquare$ 1	$\frac{1}{5} \times \blacksquare = 1 \frac{5}{1}$	$\frac{5}{6} \times \frac{6}{5} = \blacksquare$ 1	$\frac{7}{8} \times \frac{8}{7} = \blacksquare$ 1
$\blacksquare \times \frac{5}{7} = 1 \frac{7}{5}$	$\frac{2}{6} \times \frac{6}{2} = \blacksquare$ 1	$\frac{7}{1} \times \blacksquare = 1 \frac{1}{7}$	$\blacksquare \times 8 = 1 \frac{1}{8}$

3. What is true about the numerators and denominators in the fractions in Exercise 2? **They are switched.**

Two numbers with a product of 1 are called **multiplicative inverses**, or **reciprocals**.

Inverse Property of Multiplication   Key Concept

Words   The product of a number and its multiplicative inverse is 1.

Examples   **Numbers**   **Algebra**

$\frac{3}{4} \times \frac{4}{3} = 1$ $\frac{a}{b} \cdot \frac{b}{a} = 1$, for $a, b \neq 0$

EXAMPLES Find Multiplicative Inverses

1 Find the multiplicative inverse of $\frac{2}{5}$.

$\frac{2}{5} \cdot \frac{5}{2} = 1$ Multiply $\frac{2}{5}$ by $\frac{5}{2}$ to get the product 1.

The multiplicative inverse of $\frac{2}{5}$ is $\frac{5}{2}$, or $2\frac{1}{2}$.

2 Find the multiplicative inverse of $2\frac{1}{3}$.

$2\frac{1}{3} = \frac{7}{3}$ Rename the mixed number as an improper fraction.

$\frac{7}{3} \cdot \frac{3}{7} = 1$ Multiply $\frac{7}{3}$ by $\frac{3}{7}$ to get the product 1.

The multiplicative inverse of $2\frac{1}{3}$ is $\frac{3}{7}$.

✓ **CHECK Your Progress**

a. $\frac{5}{6}$ $\frac{6}{5}$ or $1\frac{1}{5}$ b. $1\frac{1}{2}$ $\frac{2}{3}$ c. 8 $\frac{1}{8}$ d. $\frac{4}{3}$ $\frac{3}{4}$

258 Chapter 5 Applying Fractions

In Chapter 3, you learned to solve equations using the Addition, Subtraction, and Division Properties of Equality. You can also solve equations by multiplying each side by the same number. This is called the **Multiplication Property of Equality**.

Multiplication Property of Equality   Key Concept

Words	If you multiply each side of an equation by the same nonzero number, the two sides remain equal.

Examples	Numbers	Algebra

$$5 = 5$$

$$\frac{x}{2} = -3 \qquad \frac{2}{3}x = 4$$

$$5 \cdot 2 = 5 \cdot 2 \qquad \frac{x}{2}(2) = -3(2) \qquad \frac{3}{2} \cdot \frac{2}{3}x = \frac{3}{2} \cdot 4$$

$$10 = 10 \qquad x = -6 \qquad x = 6$$

Study Tip

Fractions
The fraction bar indicates division. So, $\frac{x}{2}$ means x divided by 2.

EXAMPLES   **Solve a Division Equation**

3   Solve $7 = \frac{n}{4}$. Check your solution.

$$7 = \frac{n}{4} \qquad \text{Write the equation.}$$

$$7 \cdot 4 = \frac{n}{4} \cdot 4 \qquad \text{Multiply each side of the equation by 4.}$$

$$28 = n \qquad \text{Simplify.}$$

Check $7 = \frac{n}{4}$ Write the original equation.

$$7 \stackrel{?}{=} \frac{28}{4} \qquad \text{Replace } n \text{ with 28.}$$

$$7 = 7 \checkmark \qquad \text{Is this sentence true?}$$

4   Solve $\frac{d}{3.5} = 4.2$.

$$\frac{d}{3.5} = 4.2 \qquad \text{Write the equation.}$$

$$\frac{d}{3.5} \cdot 3.5 = 4.2 \cdot 3.5 \qquad \text{Multiply each side by 3.5.}$$

$$d = 14.7 \qquad \text{Simplify.}$$

The solution is 14.7.

Check $\frac{d}{3.5} = 4.2$ Write the original equation.

$$\frac{14.7}{3.5} \stackrel{?}{=} 4.2 \qquad \text{Replace } d \text{ with 14.7.}$$

$$4.2 = 4.2 \checkmark \qquad \text{Is this sentence true?}$$

CHECK Your Progress

Solve each equation. Check your solution.

e. $6 = \frac{m}{8}$ **48**   f. $\frac{p}{2.8} = 1.5$ **4.2**   g. $\frac{k}{4.7} = 2.3$ **10.81**

Lesson 5-6 Algebra: Solving Equations   **259**

Focus on Mathematical Content

The multiplicative inverse of a fraction is a fraction in which the numerator and denominator have **switched positions**.

Multiplying each side of an equation by the same nonzero number maintains the equation.

A fraction such as $\frac{y}{4}$ can be read as **y divided by 4**.

Formative Assessment

Use the Check Your Progress exercises after the Examples to determine students' understanding of concepts.

ADDITIONAL EXAMPLES

Find the multiplicative inverse of each number.

1 $\frac{4}{7}$ $\frac{7}{4}$, or $1\frac{3}{4}$

2 $6\frac{1}{4}$ $\frac{4}{25}$

3   Solve $11 = \frac{p}{6}$. Check your solution. 66

4   Solve $\frac{y}{6.4} = 2.7$. Check your solution. 17.28

Additional Examples are also in:

- Noteables™ Interactive Study Notebook with Foldables™
- Interactive Classroom PowerPoint® Presentations

ADDITIONAL EXAMPLES

5. Solve $\frac{2}{5}x = \frac{6}{15}$. Check your solution. 1

6. **TEST EXAMPLE** Samantha answered $\frac{4}{5}$ of the questions on the science quiz correctly. If she answered 8 questions correctly, how many questions were on the quiz? C

A 2
B 6
C 10
D 14

EXAMPLE Solve a Multiplication Equation

5 **Solve $\frac{3}{4}x = \frac{12}{20}$.**

$\frac{3}{4}x = \frac{12}{20}$ Write the equation.

$\left(\frac{4}{3}\right) \cdot \frac{3}{4}x = \left(\frac{4}{3}\right) \cdot \frac{12}{20}$ Multiply each side by the reciprocal of $\frac{3}{4}$, $\frac{4}{3}$.

$\frac{\overset{1}{\cancel{4}}}{\underset{1}{\cancel{3}}} \cdot \frac{\overset{1}{\cancel{3}}}{\underset{1}{\cancel{4}}}x = \frac{\overset{1}{\cancel{4}}}{\underset{1}{\cancel{3}}} \cdot \frac{\overset{4}{\cancel{12}}}{\underset{5}{\cancel{20}}}$ Divide by common factors.

$x = \frac{4}{5}$ Simplify.

Study Tip

Fractions as Coefficients The expression $\frac{3}{4}x$ can be read as $\frac{3}{4}$ of x, $\frac{3}{4}$ multiplied by x, $3x$ divided by 4, or $\frac{x}{4}$ multiplied by 3.

CHECK Your Progress

Solve each equation. Check your solution.

h. $\frac{1}{2}x = 8$ **16** i. $\frac{3}{4}x = 9$ **12** j. $\frac{7}{8}x = \frac{21}{64}$ $\mathbf{\frac{3}{8}}$

TEST EXAMPLE

6 **Valerie needs $\frac{2}{3}$ yard of fabric to make each hat for the school play. How many hats can she make with 6 yards of fabric?**

A 12 C 8
B 9 D 4

Read the Item

Each hat needs $\frac{2}{3}$ yard of fabric. Given the number of hats, you would multiply by $\frac{2}{3}$ to find the number of yards of fabric needed.

Solve the Item

Write and solve a multiplication equation.

$\frac{2}{3}n = 6$ Write the equation.

$\left(\frac{3}{2}\right) \cdot \frac{2}{3}n = \left(\frac{3}{2}\right) \cdot 6$ Multiply each side by $\frac{3}{2}$.

$n = 9$ Simplify.

So, the answer is B.

Test-Taking Tip

Verify Your Answer It is a good idea to verify your answer by checking the other answer choices. By doing so, you can greatly reduce your chances of making an error.

CHECK Your Progress

k. Wilson has 9 pounds of trail mix. How many $\frac{3}{4}$-pound bags of trail mix can he make? **J**

F 3 H 9
G 6 J 12

260 Chapter 5 Applying Fractions

CHECK Your Understanding

★ indicates multi-step problem

Examples 1, 2
(p. 258)

Find the multiplicative inverse of each number.

1. $\frac{8}{5}$ **$\frac{5}{8}$**

2. $\frac{2}{9}$ **$\frac{9}{2}$ or $4\frac{1}{2}$**

3. $5\frac{4}{5}$ **$\frac{5}{29}$**

4. 9 **$\frac{1}{9}$**

Examples 3–5
(p. 259–260)

Solve each equation. Check your solution.

5. $\frac{k}{16} = 2$ **32**

6. $4 = \frac{y}{3}$ **12**

7. $\frac{b}{8.2} = 2.5$ **20.5**

8. $0.5 = \frac{h}{3.6}$ **1.8**

9. $\frac{3}{8}a = \frac{12}{40}$ **$\frac{4}{5}$**

10. $6 = \frac{4}{7}x$ **$10\frac{1}{2}$**

Example 5
(p. 260)

11. **FRUIT** Three fourths of the fruit in a refrigerator are apples. There are 24 apples in the refrigerator. The number of pieces of fruit is given by the equation $\frac{3}{4}f = 24$. How many pieces of fruit are in the refrigerator? **32**

Example 6
(p. 260)

12. **MULTIPLE CHOICE** Dillon deposited $\frac{3}{4}$ of his paycheck into the bank. The deposit slip shows how much he deposited. What was the amount of his paycheck? **C**

Great Savings Bank
Dillon Gates
Name
Amount Deposited: $45

A $15

C $60

B $33.75

D $75

Practice and Problem Solving

HOMEWORK HELP

For Exercises	See Examples
13–20	1, 2
21–26 33–34	3, 4
27–32	5
51–52	6

Exercise Levels
A: 13–34
B: 35–46
C: 47–50

Find the multiplicative inverse of each number.

13. $\frac{5}{6}$ **$\frac{6}{5}$ or $1\frac{1}{5}$**

14. $\frac{11}{2}$ **$\frac{2}{11}$**

15. $\frac{1}{6}$ **$\frac{6}{1}$ or 6**

16. $\frac{1}{10}$ **$\frac{10}{1}$ or 10**

17. 3 **$\frac{1}{3}$**

18. 14 **$\frac{1}{14}$**

19. $5\frac{1}{8}$ **$\frac{8}{41}$**

20. $6\frac{2}{3}$ **$\frac{3}{20}$**

Solve each equation. Check your solution.

21. $\frac{x}{12} = 3$ **36**

22. $28 = \frac{d}{4}$ **112**

23. $\frac{b}{2.4} = 6$ **14.4**

24. $5 = \frac{w}{4.9}$ **24.5**

25. $0.8 = \frac{h}{3.6}$ **2.88**

26. $\frac{m}{4.6} = 2.8$ **12.88**

27. $\frac{2}{5}t = \frac{12}{25}$ **$\frac{6}{5}$**

28. $\frac{24}{16} = \frac{3}{4}a$ **$\frac{8}{4}$ or 2**

29. $\frac{7}{8}k = \frac{5}{6}$ **$\frac{20}{21}$**

30. $\frac{2}{3} = \frac{8}{3}b$ **$\frac{1}{4}$**

31. $\frac{1}{2}g = 3\frac{1}{3}$ **$6\frac{2}{3}$**

32. $\frac{3}{5}c = 6\frac{1}{4}$ **$10\frac{5}{12}$**

33. **DISTANCE** The distance d Toya travels in her car while driving 60 miles per hour for 3.25 hours is given by the equation $\frac{d}{3.25} = 60$. How far did she travel? **195 mi**

34. **ANIMALS** An adult Fitch ferret weighs about 1.8 kilograms. To find its weight in pounds p, you can use the equation $\frac{p}{1.8} = 2.2$. How many pounds does an adult Fitch ferret weigh? **3.96 lb**

Lesson 5-6 Algebra: Solving Equations **261**

3 Practice

Formative Assessment

Use Exercises 1–12 to check for understanding.

Then use the chart at the bottom of this page to customize your assignments for students.

Intervention You may wish to use the Study Guide and Intervention Master on page 39 of the *Chapter 5 Resource Masters* for additional reinforcement.

Odd/Even Assignments

Exercises 13–34 are structured so that students practice the same concepts whether they are assigned odd or even problems.

DIFFERENTIATED HOMEWORK OPTIONS			
Level	**Assignment**	**Two-Day Option**	
BL Basic	13–32, 47, 48, 50–70	13–33 odd, 51, 52	14–34 even, 47, 48, 50, 53–70
OL Core	13–39 odd, 41–48, 50–70	13–34, 51, 52	35–48, 50, 53–70
AL Advanced/Pre-AP	35–66 (optional: 67–70)		

Whole Numbers

Make sure students know how to find the multiplicative inverse of a whole number such as 5. Ask, How can I rename 5 as an improper fraction? $\frac{5}{1}$

Additional Answer

49. Sample answer: Multiply each side by 2. Then divide each side by $(b_1 + b_2)$. So, $\frac{2A}{b_1 + b_2} = h$.

Solve each equation. Check your solution.

35. $\frac{a}{-5} = 15$ **—75**

36. $-8 = \frac{r}{-2}$ **16**

37. $34.5 = \frac{5}{6}m$ **41.4**

38. $\frac{5}{7}x = -1.5$ **—2.1**

39. $\frac{1}{4}t = \frac{3}{8}$ **1$\frac{1}{2}$**

40. $\frac{3}{8}m = 1\frac{1}{2}$ **4**

For Exercises 41–46, define a variable and write an equation. Then solve.

41. CAVES The self-guided Mammoth Cave Discovery Tour includes an elevation change of 140 feet. This is $\frac{7}{15}$ of the elevation change on the Wild Cave Tour. What is the elevation change on the Wild Cave Tour?
$x =$ elevation change on the Wild Cave Tour; $140 = \frac{7}{15}x$; **300 ft**

42. MUSEUMS Twenty-four students brought their permission slips to attend the class field trip to the local art museum. If this represented $\frac{4}{5}$ of the class, how many students are in the class?
$x =$ number of students; $\frac{4}{5}x = 24$; **30 students**

43. MEASUREMENT If one serving of cooked rice is $\frac{3}{4}$ cup, how many servings will $16\frac{1}{2}$ cups of rice yield? $x =$ number of servings; $\frac{3}{4}x = 16\frac{1}{2}$; **22 servings**

44. HIKING After Alana hiked $2\frac{5}{8}$ miles along a hiking trail, she realized that she was only $\frac{3}{4}$ of the way to the end of the trail. How long is the trail?
$x =$ length of the trail; $2\frac{5}{8} = \frac{3}{4}x$; $3\frac{1}{2}$ **miles**

45. SLEEP The average person spends $\frac{1}{3}$ of his life asleep. According to this, if a person has spent 26 years asleep, how old is he?
$x =$ the person's age; $\frac{1}{3}x = 26$; **78 years old**

★ **46. ANALYZE TABLES** Tierra recorded the distance she ran each day last week. If she ran $\frac{5}{6}$ of her weekly running goal, what was her running goal?
$x =$ her goal; $\frac{5}{6}x = 7\frac{1}{2}$; **9 mi**

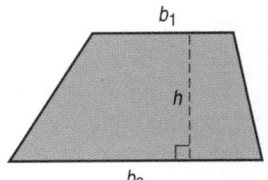

Real-World Link · · · ·

Kentucky's Mammoth Cave is the longest recorded cave system in the world, with more than 360 miles explored and mapped. The Wild Cave Tour requires visitors to crawl through an opening only 9 inches high.
Source: National Park Service

EXTRA PRACTICE
See pages 681, 708.

H.O.T. Problems

47. 20; Sample answer: By solving $8 = \frac{m}{4}$, you find that $m = 32$. So, replace m with 32 to find $32 - 12 = 20$.

48. $\frac{3}{5}$, 5; The other pairs of numbers are reciprocals.

50. Sample answer: If you multiply each side of an equation by the same nonzero number, two sides remain equal; $\frac{2}{5}x = 7$

47. REASONING Complete the statement: If $8 = \frac{m}{4}$, then $m - 12 = $ ■. Explain your reasoning.

48. Which One Doesn't Belong? Identify the pair of numbers that does not belong with the other three. Explain.

| $\frac{9}{6}, \frac{6}{9}$ | 4, $\frac{1}{4}$ | $\frac{3}{5}$, 5 | $\frac{2}{7}, \frac{7}{2}$ |

49. CHALLENGE The formula for the area of a trapezoid is $A = \frac{1}{2}h(b_1 + b_2)$, where b_1 and b_2 are both bases and h is the height. Find the value of h in terms of A, b_1, and b_2. Justify your answer. **See margin.**

50. **WRITING IN MATH** Explain the Multiplication Property of Equality. Then give an example of an equation in which you would use this property to solve the equation.

Distance Ran in One Week	
Day	**Distance (mi)**
Monday	$1\frac{3}{4}$
Wednesday	2
Friday	$1\frac{1}{2}$
Saturday	$2\frac{1}{4}$

Pre-AP Activity **Use after Exercise 46**

Write an equation such as $12x = 72$ on the board. Remind students that they know how to solve the equation by using the Division Property of Equality. Ask them whether they can also solve it by using the Multiplication Property of Equality. Have them explain their reasoning. Yes; by multiplying each side of the equation by the multiplicative inverse of 12, or $\frac{1}{12}$.

51. Audrey drove 200 miles in 3.5 hours. Which equation can you use to find the rate r at which Audrey was traveling? **A**

A $200 = 3.5r$

B $200 \cdot 3.5 = r$

C $\frac{r}{3.5} = 200$

D $200r = 3.5$

52. The table shows the results of a survey.

Music Preference	
Type	**Fraction of Students**
pop	$\frac{5}{8}$
jazz	$\frac{1}{8}$
rap	$\frac{1}{4}$

If there are 420 students surveyed, which equation can be used to find the number of students s who prefer rap? **G**

F $\frac{1}{4}s = 420$ H $s + \frac{1}{4} = 420$

G $s = \frac{1}{4} \cdot 420$ J $420 + s = \frac{1}{4}$

Spiral Review

Multiply. Write in simplest form. (Lesson 5-5)

53. $\frac{3}{8} \times \frac{4}{9}$ **$\frac{1}{6}$**

54. $1\frac{1}{2} \times 6$ **9**

55. $2\frac{2}{5} \times \frac{1}{6}$ **$\frac{2}{5}$**

56. $1\frac{1}{2} \times 1\frac{7}{9}$ **$2\frac{2}{3}$**

57. COOKING Lawana had $4\frac{2}{3}$ cups of chopped walnuts. She used $1\frac{1}{4}$ cups in a recipe. How many cups of chopped walnuts are left? (Lesson 5-3) **$3\frac{5}{12}$ c**

Write each percent as a decimal. (Lesson 4-7)

58. 25% **0.25**

59. 8% **0.08**

60. 25.6% **0.256**

61. 123% **1.23**

62. MEASUREMENT A farmer has a rectangular pumpkin field with a perimeter of 3,800 feet. If the width of the pumpkin field is 800 feet, what is the length of the field? (Lesson 3-6) **1,100 ft**

ALGEBRA Solve each equation. Check your solution. (Lesson 3-2)

63. $7 = x + 8$ **−1**

64. $k - 3 = -14$ **−11**

65. $-2 = m + 6$ **−8**

66. ALGEBRA The table shows the time needed to complete 4 art projects. If the pattern continues, how much time is needed to complete the fifth art project? (Lesson 2-7) **76 min**

Project	1	2	3	4	5
Time (min)	8	25	42	59	■

▷ **GET READY for the Next Lesson**

PREREQUISITE SKILL Estimate. (Lesson 5-1) **67–70. Sample answers are given.**

67. $18\frac{1}{6} \div 3$

68. $24\frac{3}{8} \div 11\frac{7}{9}$

69. $\frac{2}{11} \div \frac{11}{12}$

70. $\frac{9}{10} \div \frac{6}{7}$

67. $18 \div 3 = 6$
68. $24 \div 12 = 2$
69. $0 \div 1 = 0$
70. $1 \div 1 = 1$

Yesterday's News Remind students that yesterday's lesson was about multiplying fractions and mixed numbers. Have them write how yesterday's lesson helped them with today's material.

✓ **Formative Assessment**

Check for student understanding of concepts in Lessons 5-5 and 5-6.

 Quiz 3, p. 54

 **Foldables™ Follow-Up**

Remind students to record on index cards what they learn about finding multiplicative inverses and about using the Multiplication Property of Equality to solve equations. Students should then store the cards in their Foldables.

1 Focus

Students may sometimes be confused by division situations in word problems. Several kinds of situations call for division, though the mathematical operation remains the same. In this Activity, students learn to recognize three different situations that require division.

2 Teach

Make sure students understand that *taking away equal amounts* can also be described as *repeated subtraction*.

Before beginning the exercises, have volunteers pose the kind of questions they should ask themselves to determine which meaning of division is shown by a problem. Is a quantity being shared equally? Could the solution be found by repeated subtraction? Are two quantities being compared?

3 Assess

Tell students that tomorrow's lesson is about dividing fractions and mixed numbers. Have them write how they think what they learned today will connect with tomorrow's material.

Meaning of Division

You know that one meaning of division is to *put objects into equal groups*. But there are other meanings too. Look for these meanings when you're solving a word problem.

- ● **To share**

    Zach and his friend are going to share 3 apples equally. How many apples will each boy have?

- ● **To take away equal amounts**

    Isabel is making bookmarks from a piece of ribbon. Each bookmark is 6.5 centimeters long. How many bookmarks can she make from a piece of ribbon that is 27 centimeters long?

26 cm

6.5 cm | 6.5 cm | 6.5 cm | 6.5 cm

- ● **To find how many times greater**

    The Nile River, the longest river on Earth, is 4,160 miles long. The Rio Grande River is 1,900 miles long. About how many times longer is the Nile than the Rio Grande?

Nile River 4,160 mi

Rio Grande 1,900 mi | Rio Grande 1,900 mi

PRACTICE

1. Solve each problem above. **1.5 apples; 4 bookmarks; 2.2 times**

Identify the meaning of division shown in each problem. Then solve the problem.

2. A landscape architect wants to make a border along one side of a garden using bricks that are 0.25 meter long. If the garden is 11.25 meters long, how many bricks does she need? **repeated subtraction; 45 bricks**

3. The Jackson family wants to buy a flat-screen television that costs $1,200. They plan to pay in six equal payments. What will be the amount of each payment? **sharing; $200**

4. A full-grown blue whale can weigh 150 tons. An adult African elephant weighs about 5 tons. How many times greater does a blue whale weigh than an African elephant? **how many times greater; 30 times**

5. Each story in an office building is about 4 meters tall. The Eiffel Tower in Paris, France, is 300 meters tall. How many stories tall is the Eiffel Tower? **repeated subtraction; 75 stories**

264 Chapter 5 Applying Fractions

5-7 Dividing Fractions and Mixed Numbers

PACING: **Regular:** 1 period, **Block:** 0.5 period

Options for Differentiated Instruction

ELL = English Language Learner   **AL** = Above or Beyond Grade Level   **SS** = Struggling Students   **SN** = Special Needs

Using Patterns **ELL** **AL** **SS** **SN**

Use after presenting the Mini Lab.

Have students complete the following table and look for a pattern.

Ask:

What do you notice about the answers in each column? They are the same.
Use the pattern above to fill in the following blanks.

Multiply	Divide
$8 \times \frac{1}{2} = 4$	$8 \div 2 = 4$
$24 \times \frac{1}{4} = 6$	$24 \div 4 = 6$
$21 \times \frac{1}{3} = 7$	$21 \div 3 = 7$
$15 \times \frac{1}{5} = 3$	$15 \div 5 = 3$

$\frac{3}{4} \times \frac{1}{3} = \frac{3}{4} \div \underline{?}\ 3$ $\frac{3}{4} \times \frac{3}{1} = \frac{3}{4} \div \underline{?}\ \frac{1}{3}$

$\frac{2}{3} \times \frac{1}{3} = \frac{2}{3} \div \underline{?}\ 3$ $\qquad$ $\frac{2}{3} \times \frac{3}{1} = \frac{2}{3} \div \underline{?}\ \frac{1}{3}$

Write a rule for dividing fractions. Dividing by a fraction is the same as multiplying by its inverse.

Enhancing Memory **ELL** **AL** **SS**

Use after presenting Examples 1–3.

Mnemonics utilizes the five principles of learning and memory:

- meaningfulness
- organization
- association
- attention
- visualization

Mnemonics is therefore an effective tool for helping students learn and remember procedures and rules in mathematics. Some methods of doing this include using sentences, phrases, songs, and rhymes. Have students write a simple poem or rhyme that incorporates at least one method or rule for the division of fractions. Rules and methods for other operations on fractions can be included as well. You may wish to have students work in groups and create larger works of poetry or verse.

Leveled Lesson Resources

Chapter 5 Resource Masters

BL = Below or Approaching Grade Level   **OL** = On Grade Level   **AL** = Above or Beyond Grade Level   **ELL** = English Language Learner

---

Lesson Reading Guide
p. 44 **BL** **OL** **ELL**

NAME _____ DATE _____ PERIOD _____

5-7 Lesson Reading Guide
Dividing Fractions and Mixed Numbers

Get Ready for the Lesson

Complete the Mini Lab at the top of page 265 in your textbook.
Write your answers below.

1. How many $\frac{1}{4}$'s are in 2 plates? **8**

2. How would you model $3 \div \frac{1}{2}$?
   Cut 3 plates into 2 equal pieces each.

3. What is true about $3 \div \frac{1}{2}$ and 3×2? **They are equal.**

Read the Lesson

4. How does dividing a number by a fraction involve multiplication?
   Sample answer: To divide a number by a fraction, multiply the number by the multiplicative inverse of the fraction.

5. Rewrite each of the following division expressions as multiplication expressions.

   a. $\frac{7}{8} \div \frac{2}{3}$ **$\frac{7}{8} \cdot \frac{3}{2}$**

   b. $14 \div 3\frac{3}{5}$ **$14 \cdot \frac{5}{17}$**

   c. $\frac{5}{6} \div 2\frac{1}{4}$ **$\frac{5}{6} \cdot \frac{4}{9}$**

   d. $2\frac{1}{3} \div 1\frac{1}{6}$ **$\frac{7}{3} \cdot \frac{6}{7}$**

Remember What You Learned

6. To divide a mixed number by another mixed number can take up to 5 steps. List the steps in order. **Sample answer:**
   1. Rename the mixed numbers as improper fractions.
   2. Multiply by the reciprocal of the divisor.
   3. Divide out common factors.
   4. Multiply.
   5. Simplify.

Chapter 5   44   Course 2

Study Guide and Intervention*
p. 45 **BL** **OL** **ELL**

NAME _____ DATE _____ PERIOD _____

5-7 Study Guide and Intervention
Dividing Fractions and Mixed Numbers

To divide by a fraction, multiply by its multiplicative inverse or reciprocal. To divide by a mixed number, rename the mixed number as an improper fraction.

Example 1 Find $3\frac{1}{3} \div \frac{2}{9}$. Write in simplest form.

$3\frac{1}{3} \div \frac{2}{9} = \frac{10}{3} \div \frac{2}{9}$ Rename $3\frac{1}{3}$ as an improper fraction.
$= \frac{10}{3} \cdot \frac{9}{2}$ Multiply by the reciprocal of $\frac{2}{9}$, which is $\frac{9}{2}$.
$= \frac{5 \cdot 3}{1 \cdot 1}$ Divide out common factors.
$= 15$ Multiply.

Exercises

Divide. Write in simplest form.

1. $\frac{2}{3} \div \frac{3}{4}$ **$\frac{8}{9}$**
2. $\frac{2}{5} \div \frac{6}{5}$ **$\frac{1}{3}$**
3. $\frac{1}{5} \div \frac{2}{5}$ **$\frac{1}{2}$**

4. $5 \div \frac{1}{2}$ **10**
5. $\frac{5}{8} \div 10$ **$\frac{1}{16}$**
6. $7\frac{1}{3} \div 2$ **$3\frac{2}{3}$**

7. $\frac{5}{6} \div 3\frac{1}{2}$ **$\frac{5}{21}$**
8. $36 \div 1\frac{1}{2}$ **24**
9. $2\frac{1}{2} \div 10$ **$\frac{1}{4}$**

10. $5\frac{5}{8} \div 1\frac{7}{8}$ **3**
11. $6\frac{2}{9} \div 3\frac{1}{9}$ **$2\frac{1}{7}$**
12. $4\frac{1}{4} \div \frac{3}{8}$ **$11\frac{1}{3}$**

13. $4\frac{6}{7} \div 2\frac{3}{7}$ **2**
14. $12 \div 2\frac{1}{2}$ **$4\frac{4}{5}$**
15. $4\frac{1}{6} \div 3\frac{1}{6}$ **$1\frac{6}{19}$**

Chapter 5   45   Course 2

Skills Practice*
p. 46 **BL** **OL**

NAME _____ DATE _____ PERIOD _____

5-7 Skills Practice
Dividing Fractions and Mixed Numbers

Divide. Write in simplest form.

1. $\frac{1}{6} \div \frac{1}{5}$ **$\frac{5}{6}$**
2. $5 \div \frac{3}{5}$ **$8\frac{1}{3}$**
3. $\frac{6}{7} \div \frac{1}{7}$ **6**

4. $\frac{3}{4} \div \frac{1}{2}$ **$1\frac{1}{2}$**
5. $8 \div \frac{1}{3}$ **24**
6. $\frac{1}{5} \div \frac{1}{4}$ **$\frac{4}{5}$**

7. $7 \div \frac{3}{7}$ **$16\frac{1}{3}$**
8. $\frac{4}{7} \div \frac{8}{9}$ **$\frac{9}{14}$**
9. $8\frac{1}{3} \div 5$ **$1\frac{2}{3}$**

10. $\frac{9}{7} \div \frac{3}{14}$ **6**
11. $\frac{12}{5} \div \frac{3}{10}$ **8**
12. $5 \div 3\frac{3}{4}$ **$1\frac{1}{3}$**

13. $6\frac{4}{5} \div 17$ **$\frac{2}{5}$**
14. $7\frac{1}{3} \div 4$ **$1\frac{5}{6}$**
15. $\frac{3}{4} \div 5\frac{1}{2}$ **$\frac{3}{22}$**

16. $\frac{2}{7} \div 1\frac{13}{14}$ **$\frac{4}{27}$**
17. $\frac{3}{8} \div 6\frac{1}{4}$ **$\frac{3}{50}$**
18. $7\frac{1}{2} \div 2\frac{6}{9}$ **$2\frac{11}{17}$**

19. $3\frac{4}{9} \div 2\frac{1}{3}$ **$1\frac{10}{21}$**
20. $2\frac{5}{9} \div 1\frac{1}{6}$ **$2\frac{2}{7}$**
21. $4\frac{3}{4} \div 2\frac{1}{2}$ **$1\frac{9}{10}$**

Chapter 5   46   Course 2

Practice*
p. 47 **OL** **AL**

NAME _____ DATE _____ PERIOD _____

5-7 Practice
Dividing Fractions and Mixed Numbers

Divide. Write in simplest form.

1. $\frac{3}{5} \div \frac{3}{4}$ **$\frac{4}{5}$**
2. $\frac{4}{7} \div \frac{5}{9}$ **$\frac{9}{14}$**
3. $\frac{6}{7} \div \frac{5}{6}$ **$1\frac{1}{35}$**
4. $\frac{1}{4} \div \frac{1}{2}$ **$\frac{1}{2}$**

5. $7 \div \frac{1}{3}$ **21**
6. $\frac{6}{11} \div \frac{3}{2}$ **$\frac{4}{11}$**
7. $4\frac{1}{5} \div 7$ **$\frac{3}{5}$**
8. $8 \div 4\frac{2}{3}$ **$1\frac{5}{7}$**

9. $\frac{3}{7} \div 1\frac{1}{6}$ **$\frac{9}{14}$**
10. $\frac{7}{9} \div \frac{5}{27}$ **$\frac{8}{27}$**
11. $3\frac{2}{5} \div 5\frac{1}{10}$ **$\frac{2}{3}$**
12. $4\frac{8}{9} \div 2\frac{2}{3}$ **$7\frac{1}{3}$**

13. $2\frac{3}{5} \div 1\frac{1}{4}$ **$2\frac{2}{25}$**
14. $7\frac{1}{2} \div 2\frac{1}{3}$ **3**
15. $5\frac{1}{4} \div \frac{7}{8}$ **6**
16. $8\frac{1}{4} \div \frac{5}{9}$ **15**

17. **COOKING** Mrs. Lau rolls out $2\frac{3}{4}$ feet of dough to make noodles. If the noodles are $\frac{3}{8}$ of an inch wide, how many noodles will she make? **88 noodles**

PIZZA For Exercises 18 and 19, use the table that shows the weights of three sizes of pizza.

18. How many times heavier is the extra-large pizza than the small pizza? **4 times**

19. How many times heavier is the medium pizza than the small pizza? **2 times**

Pizza Size	Weight (lbs)
Extra large	$6\frac{1}{2}$
Medium	$3\frac{1}{4}$
Small	$1\frac{5}{8}$

ALGEBRA Evaluate each expression if $a = \frac{2}{5}$, $b = \frac{3}{10}$, and $c = 2\frac{1}{2}$.

20. $b \div a$ **$\frac{3}{4}$**
21. $a \div c$ **$\frac{4}{25}$**
22. $3a \div b$ **4**
23. $\frac{1}{5} \div a$ **$1\frac{1}{4}$**

Chapter 5   47   Course 2

Word Problem Practice*
p. 48 **OL** **AL**

NAME _____ DATE _____ PERIOD _____

5-7 Word Problem Practice
Dividing Fractions and Mixed Numbers

1. **PUPPETS** If a puppet requires $\frac{3}{4}$ yards of material, how many puppets can be made from 9 yards of material? **12 puppets**

2. **COOKING** A batch of cookies requires $1\frac{1}{2}$ cups of sugar. How many batches can Ty make with $7\frac{1}{2}$ cups of sugar? **5 batches**

3. **FOOD** Julia has $3\frac{1}{2}$ pounds of dog food. She plans to split it equally among her 7 dogs. How much dog food will each dog receive? **$\frac{1}{2}$ lb**

4. **SNOW CONES** Roger has a 28-pound block of ice for his snow cone stand. If each snow cone requires $\frac{2}{3}$ pound of ice, how many snow cones can Roger make? **42 snow cones**

5. **APPLES** Juan took 6 apples and cut each into one-eighths. How many pieces of apple did he have? **48 pieces**

6. **VACATION** The Torres family drove 1,375 miles during their $6\frac{1}{4}$-day vacation. Find the average number of miles they traveled each day. **220 mi**

7. **RUNNING** Hugo just joined the cross-country team and can run at a rate of $\frac{1}{7}$ mile each minute. How long will it take him to run a 5-mile race? **35 min**

8. **LUMBER** Mrs. Shin has a piece of lumber that is $11\frac{5}{8}$ inches wide. She plans to split the width of lumber into 3 equal pieces. How wide will each piece be? **$3\frac{7}{8}$ in.**

Chapter 5   48   Course 2

Enrichment
p. 49 **OL** **AL**

NAME _____ DATE _____ PERIOD _____

5-7 Enrichment

Continued Fractions

The expression at the right is an example of a *continued fraction*. Although continued fractions may look complicated, they are just a combination of addition and division. Here is one way to simplify a continued fraction.

$1 + \cfrac{1}{1 + \cfrac{1}{1 + \frac{1}{9}}}$

$1 + \cfrac{1}{1 + \cfrac{1}{1 + \frac{1}{9}}} = 1 + \left[1 + \left(1 + \left(1 + \frac{1}{9}\right)\right)\right]$

$= 1 + \left[1 + \left(1 + \left[1 + \frac{10}{9}\right]\right)\right]$

$= 1 + \left[1 + \left(1 + \frac{9}{10}\right)\right]$

$= 1 + \left[1 + \frac{10}{19}\right]$

$= 1 + \frac{19}{29}$

$= \frac{29}{19}$

Write each continued fraction as an improper fraction.

1. $1 + \cfrac{1}{3 + \frac{1}{3}}$ **$\frac{13}{10}$**
2. $2 + \cfrac{1}{2 + \frac{1}{5}}$ **$\frac{12}{5}$**
3. $1 + \cfrac{2}{3 + \frac{1}{2}}$ **$\frac{17}{11}$**

4. $1 + \cfrac{3}{3 + \frac{1}{4}}$ **$\frac{25}{13}$**
5. $5 + \cfrac{1}{1 + \frac{5}{6}}$ **$\frac{35}{6}$**
6. $2 + \cfrac{2}{2 + \frac{1}{2}}$ **$\frac{17}{5}$**

7. $1 + \cfrac{1}{1 + \cfrac{1}{1 + \frac{2}{5}}}$ **$\frac{8}{5}$**
8. $1 + \cfrac{1}{1 + \cfrac{1}{1 + \frac{4}{7}}}$ **$\frac{11}{7}$**
9. $1 + \cfrac{1}{1 + \cfrac{1}{1 + \frac{6}{5}}}$ **$\frac{17}{11}$**

10. $1 + \cfrac{1}{2 + \cfrac{1}{2 + \frac{5}{12}}}$ **$\frac{29}{12}$**
11. $3 + \cfrac{1}{3 + \cfrac{2}{1 + \frac{1}{2}}}$ **$\frac{29}{12}$**
12. $6 + \cfrac{1}{3 + \cfrac{1}{1 + \frac{2}{3}}}$ **$\frac{88}{13}$**

Chapter 5   49   Course 2

---

* Also available in Spanish **ELL**

Additional Lesson Resources

Transparencies
- *5-Minute Check Transparency*, Lesson 5-7

Other Print Products
- *Noteables™ Interactive Study Notebook with Foldables™*

Teacher Tech Tools
- *Interactive Classroom CD-ROM*, Lesson 5-7
- *AssignmentWorks*, Lesson 5-7

Student Tech Tools
glencoe.com
- Extra Examples, Chapter 5, Lesson 7
- Self-Check Quiz, Chapter 5, Lesson 7

5-7 Dividing Fractions and Mixed Numbers

MINI Lab

Cut two paper plates into four equal pieces each to show $2 \div \frac{1}{4}$.

1. How many $\frac{1}{4}$'s are in 2 plates? **8**

2. How would you model $3 \div \frac{1}{2}$?

3. What is true about $3 \div \frac{1}{2}$ and 3×2?
   They are equal.

2. Cut 3 plates into 2 equal pieces each.

Dividing 8 by 2 gives the same result as multiplying 8 by $\frac{1}{2}$, which is the reciprocal of 2. In the same way, dividing 4 by $\frac{1}{3}$ is the same as multiplying 4 by the reciprocal of $\frac{1}{3}$, or 3.

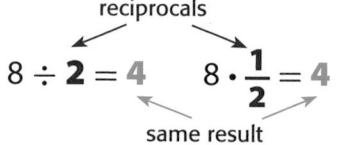

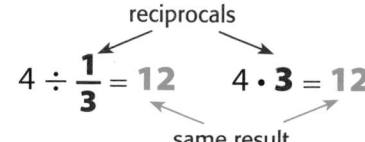

$$8 \div 2 = 4 \qquad 8 \cdot \frac{1}{2} = 4 \qquad 4 \div \frac{1}{3} = 12 \qquad 4 \cdot 3 = 12$$

same result   same result

Is this pattern true for any division expression?

Consider $\frac{7}{8} \div \frac{3}{4}$, which can be rewritten as $\dfrac{\frac{7}{8}}{\frac{3}{4}}$.

$$\frac{\frac{7}{8}}{\frac{3}{4}} = \frac{\frac{7}{8} \times \frac{4}{3}}{\frac{3}{4} \times \frac{4}{3}} \qquad \text{Multiply the numerator and denominator by the reciprocal of } \frac{3}{4}, \text{ which is } \frac{4}{3}.$$

$$= \frac{\frac{7}{8} \times \frac{4}{3}}{1} \qquad\qquad \frac{3}{4} \times \frac{4}{3} = 1$$

$$= \frac{7}{8} \times \frac{4}{3}$$

So, $\frac{7}{8} \div \frac{3}{4} = \frac{7}{8} \times \frac{4}{3}$. These examples suggest the following rule.

Divide by Fractions   Key Concept

Words	To divide by a fraction, multiply by its multiplicative inverse, or reciprocal.

Examples	**Numbers**	**Algebra**
	$\frac{7}{8} \div \frac{3}{4} = \frac{7}{8} \cdot \frac{4}{3}$	$\frac{a}{b} \div \frac{c}{d} = \frac{a}{b} \cdot \frac{d}{c}$, where $b, c, d \neq 0$

Lesson 5-7 Dividing Fractions and Mixed Numbers **265**

MAIN IDEA
Divide fractions and mixed numbers.

Math Online
glencoe.com
• Concepts In Motion
• Extra Examples
• Personal Tutor
• Self-Check Quiz

1 Focus

Vertical Alignment

Before Lesson 5-7
Compute and perform simple division of fractions and apply these procedures to solving problems

Lesson 5-7
Solve problems involving division of positive fractions and explain why a particular operation was used for a given situation. Explain the meaning of division of positive fractions and perform the calculations

After Lesson 5-7
Divide and simplify rational numbers by using the exponent rules

2 Teach

MINI Lab
In Exercise 2, you may need to help students model the expression. Return to the original problem, $2 \div \frac{1}{4}$, and compare it with $3 \div \frac{1}{2}$. Students should cut three paper plates into two equal pieces each to model $3 \div \frac{1}{2}$.

Scaffolding Questions
Ask:
• How many quarters are in $3? 12
• How many dimes are in $2? 20
• How many half-dollars are in $2.50? 5

Reinforcing the Concept

To reinforce the Mini Lab, have students cut two paper plates into three equal pieces each to show $2 \div \frac{2}{3}$. Ask students how many groups of $\frac{2}{3}$ there are in 2.

The shading shows that there are 3 groups of $\frac{2}{3}$, therefore $2 \div \frac{2}{3}$ is 3.

Have students make similar models to solve the following division problems: $1\frac{1}{2} \div \frac{1}{4}$, $\frac{3}{4} \div \frac{1}{2}$, $1\frac{1}{8} \div \frac{3}{4}$, $3\frac{1}{2} \div 2$ 6, $1\frac{1}{2}$, $1\frac{1}{2}$, $1\frac{3}{4}$

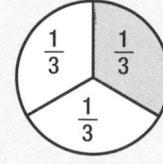

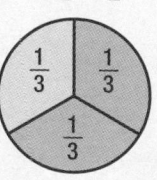

To divide by a mixed number, first **rename it as an improper fraction**.

Estimating a quotient is a good way to check a solution.

✔ Formative Assessment

Use the Check Your Progress exercises after each Example to determine students' understanding of concepts.

ADDITIONAL EXAMPLES

1 Find $\frac{2}{3} \div \frac{4}{9}$. Write in simplest form. $1\frac{1}{2}$

2 Find $\frac{5}{6} \div 2\frac{1}{2}$. Write in simplest form. $\frac{1}{3}$

Additional Examples are also in:
- Noteables™ Interactive Study Notebook with Foldables™
- Interactive Classroom PowerPoint® Presentations

Differentiated Instruction
Bodily/Kinesthetic Learners
Students can use construction paper or other concrete objects to model Example 2.

EXAMPLE · Divide by a Fraction

1 Find $\frac{3}{4} \div \frac{1}{2}$. Write in simplest form.

Estimate $1 \div \frac{1}{2} = $

Think: How many groups of $\frac{1}{2}$ are in 1? $1 \div \frac{1}{2} = 2$

$\frac{3}{4} \div \frac{1}{2} = \frac{3}{4} \cdot \frac{2}{1}$ Multiply by the reciprocal of $\frac{1}{2}$, which is $\frac{2}{1}$.

$= \frac{3}{\overset{2}{\cancel{4}}} \cdot \frac{\overset{1}{\cancel{2}}}{1}$ Divide 4 and 2 by their GCF, 2.

$= \frac{3}{2}$ or $1\frac{1}{2}$ Multiply.

Check for Reasonableness $1\frac{1}{2} \approx 2$ ✔

✔ CHECK Your Progress

Divide. Write in simplest form.

a. $\frac{3}{4} \div \frac{1}{4}$ **3** b. $\frac{4}{5} \div \frac{8}{9}$ **$\frac{9}{10}$** c. $\frac{5}{6} \div \frac{2}{3}$ **$1\frac{1}{4}$**

To divide by a mixed number, first rename the mixed number as an improper fraction. Then multiply the first fraction by the reciprocal, or multiplicative inverse, of the second fraction.

EXAMPLE · Divide by Mixed Numbers

2 Find $\frac{2}{3} \div 3\frac{1}{3}$. Write in simplest form.

Estimate $\frac{1}{2} \div 3 = \frac{1}{2} \times \frac{1}{3}$ or $\frac{1}{6}$

$\frac{2}{3} \div 3\frac{1}{3} = \frac{2}{3} \div \frac{10}{3}$ Rename $3\frac{1}{3}$ as an improper fraction.

$= \frac{2}{3} \cdot \frac{3}{10}$ Multiply by the reciprocal of $\frac{10}{3}$, which is $\frac{3}{10}$.

$= \frac{\overset{1}{\cancel{2}}}{\underset{1}{\cancel{3}}} \cdot \frac{\overset{1}{\cancel{3}}}{\underset{5}{\cancel{10}}}$ Divide out common factors.

$= \frac{1}{5}$ Multiply.

Check for Reasonableness $\frac{1}{5}$ is close to $\frac{1}{6}$. ✔

✔ CHECK Your Progress

Divide. Write in simplest form.

d. $5 \div 1\frac{1}{3}$ **$3\frac{3}{4}$** e. $-\frac{3}{4} \div 1\frac{1}{2}$ **$-\frac{1}{2}$** f. $2\frac{1}{3} \div 5$ **$\frac{7}{15}$**

g. **NUTS** In planning for a party, $5\frac{1}{4}$ pounds of cashews will be divided into $\frac{3}{4}$-pound bags. How many such bags can be made? **7 bags**

Study Tip
Dividing by a Whole Number
Remember that a whole number can be written as a fraction with a 1 in the denominator.

So, $2\frac{1}{3} \div 5$ can be rewritten as $2\frac{1}{3} \div \frac{5}{1}$.

$2|4$
$\times 6$
$\overline{66}$

1. $\frac{1}{8} \times \frac{3}{1} = \frac{3}{8}$

2. $\frac{3}{5} \times \frac{4}{1} = \frac{12}{5} = 2\frac{2}{5}$

32

3. $\frac{3}{1} \times \frac{7}{6} = \frac{21}{6} = 3\frac{3}{6} = 3\frac{1}{2}$

$\times 3 \quad 3\,r3$
$7\overline{)234}$
$\underline{21}\downarrow$
24
$\underline{-21}$
3

4. $\frac{3}{4} \times \frac{1}{6} = \frac{3}{24} = \frac{1}{8}$

$\frac{18}{2\overline{)36}}$

5. $\frac{1}{2} \times \frac{15}{2} = \frac{15}{4} = 3\frac{3}{4}$

$\frac{24}{16}$

6. $\frac{4}{7} \times \frac{9}{2} = \frac{36}{14} = \frac{18}{7} = 2\frac{4}{7}$

$\frac{216}{\times 3}$
54
80
34

7. $\frac{18}{5} \times \frac{14}{3} = \frac{86}{5} = 17\frac{1}{5}$

8. $\frac{13}{2} \times \frac{22}{7} = \frac{234}{7} = 33\frac{3}{7}$

9. $\frac{7}{1} \div \frac{1}{8} = \frac{7}{8}$ slices

10. $\frac{7}{2} \times \frac{2}{5} = \frac{14}{10} = \frac{7}{5} = 1\frac{2}{5}$

11.

Real-World EXAMPLE

3 WOODWORKING Students in a woodworking class are making butterfly houses. The side pieces of the house need to be $8\frac{1}{4}$ inches long. How many side pieces can be cut from a board measuring $49\frac{1}{2}$ inches long?

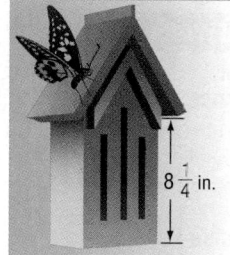

$8\frac{1}{4}$ in.

To find how many side pieces can be cut, divide $49\frac{1}{2}$ by $8\frac{1}{4}$.

Estimate Use compatible numbers. $48 \div 8 = 6$

$49\frac{1}{2} \div 8\frac{1}{4} = \frac{99}{2} \div \frac{33}{4}$ Rename the mixed numbers as improper fractions.

$= \frac{99}{2} \cdot \frac{4}{33}$ Multiply by the reciprocal of $\frac{33}{4}$, which is $\frac{4}{33}$.

$= \frac{\overset{3}{99}}{\underset{1}{\cancel{2}}} \cdot \frac{\overset{2}{\cancel{4}}}{\underset{1}{\cancel{33}}}$ Divide out common factors.

$= \frac{6}{1}$ or 6 Multiply.

So, 6 side pieces can be cut.

Check for Reasonableness The answer matches the estimate. ✔

 **CHECK Your Progress**

h. **FOOD** Suppose a small box of cereal contains $12\frac{2}{3}$ cups of cereal. How many $1\frac{1}{3}$-cup servings are in the box? **$9\frac{1}{2}$**

i. **MEASUREMENT** The area of a rectangular bedroom is $146\frac{7}{8}$ square feet. If the width of the bedroom is $11\frac{3}{4}$ feet, find the length. **$12\frac{1}{2}$ feet**

★ indicates multi-step problem

 **CHECK Your Understanding**

Examples 1–3
(pp. 266–267)

Divide. Write in simplest form.

1. $\frac{1}{8} \div \frac{1}{3}$ **$\frac{3}{8}$**
2. $\frac{3}{5} \div \frac{1}{4}$ **$2\frac{2}{5}$**
3. $3 \div \frac{6}{7}$ **$3\frac{1}{2}$**
4. $\frac{3}{4} \div 6$ **$\frac{1}{8}$**
5. $\frac{1}{2} \div 7\frac{1}{2}$ **$\frac{1}{15}$**
6. $\frac{4}{7} \div 1\frac{2}{7}$ **$\frac{4}{9}$**
7. $5\frac{3}{5} \div 4\frac{2}{3}$ **$1\frac{1}{5}$**
8. $6\frac{1}{2} \div 3\frac{5}{7}$ **$1\frac{3}{4}$**

Example 2
(p. 266)

9. **FOOD** Deandre has 7 apples, and each apple is divided evenly into eighths. How many apple slices does Deandre have? **56 slices**

Example 3
(p. 267)

10. **WALKING** On Saturday, Lindsay walked $3\frac{1}{2}$ miles in $1\frac{2}{5}$ hours. What was her walking pace, in miles per hour? **$2\frac{1}{2}$ mi/h**

Lesson 5-7 Dividing Fractions and Mixed Numbers **267**

Odd/Even Assignments

Exercises 11–32 are structured so that students practice the same concepts whether they are assigned odd or even problems.

Practice and Problem Solving

HOMEWORK HELP

For Exercises	See Examples
11–14	1
15–32	2, 3

Exercise Levels
A: 11–32
B: 33–47
C: 48–51

Divide. Write in simplest form.

11. $\frac{3}{8} \div \frac{6}{7}$ $\frac{7}{16}$

12. $\frac{5}{9} \div \frac{5}{6}$ $\frac{2}{3}$

13. $\frac{2}{3} \div \frac{1}{2}$ $1\frac{1}{3}$

14. $\frac{7}{8} \div \frac{3}{4}$ $1\frac{1}{6}$

15. $6 \div \frac{1}{2}$ 12

16. $\frac{4}{9} \div 2$ $\frac{2}{9}$

17. $2\frac{2}{3} \div 4$ $\frac{2}{3}$

18. $5 \div 1\frac{1}{3}$ $3\frac{3}{4}$

19. **FOOD** Mason has 8 cups of popcorn kernels to divide into $\frac{2}{3}$-cup portions. How many portions will there be? **12**

20. **MOVIES** Cheryl is organizing her movie collection. If each movie case is $\frac{3}{4}$ inch wide, how many movies can fit on a shelf 5 feet wide? **80 movies**

Divide. Write in simplest form.

21. $\frac{2}{3} \div 2\frac{1}{2}$ $\frac{4}{15}$

22. $\frac{8}{9} \div 5\frac{1}{3}$ $\frac{1}{6}$

23. $4\frac{1}{2} \div 6\frac{3}{4}$ $\frac{2}{3}$

24. $5\frac{2}{7} \div 2\frac{1}{7}$ $2\frac{7}{15}$

25. $3\frac{4}{5} \div 1\frac{1}{3}$ $2\frac{17}{20}$

26. $9\frac{1}{2} \div 2\frac{5}{6}$ $3\frac{6}{17}$

27. $5\frac{1}{5} \div \frac{2}{3}$ $7\frac{4}{5}$

28. $6\frac{7}{8} \div \frac{3}{4}$ $9\frac{1}{6}$

29. **ICE CREAM** Vinh bought $4\frac{1}{2}$ gallons of ice cream to serve at his birthday party. If a pint is $\frac{1}{8}$ of a gallon, how many pint-sized servings can be made? **36**

30. **BEVERAGES** William has $8\frac{1}{4}$ cups of fruit juice. If he divides the juice into $\frac{3}{4}$-cup servings, how many servings will he have? **11**

Real-World Link · · · ·
Red-tailed hawks are large, stocky birds with long, broad wings and short, broad tails. Females are larger than males and can weigh up to $3\frac{1}{2}$ pounds.
Source: Woodland Park Zoo

BIRDS For Exercises 31 and 32, use the table that gives information about several types of birds of prey found at the Woodland Park Zoo in Seattle, Washington.

31. How many times as heavy is the Golden Eagle as the Red-tailed Hawk? $3\frac{34}{35}$

32. How many times as heavy is the Golden Eagle as the Northern Bald Eagle? $1\frac{40}{99}$

Bird	Maximum Weight (lb)
Golden Eagle	$13\frac{9}{10}$
Northern Bald Eagle	$9\frac{9}{10}$
Red-Tailed Hawk	$3\frac{1}{2}$

Source: Woodland Park Zoo

Draw a model of each verbal expression and then evaluate the expression. Explain how the model shows the division process.

33. one half divided by two fifths $1\frac{1}{4}$

34. five eighths divided by one fourth $2\frac{1}{2}$

35. one and three eighths divided by one half $2\frac{3}{4}$

36. two and one sixth divided by two thirds $3\frac{1}{4}$

33–36. See Ch. 5 Answer Appendix for models and explanations.

★ 37. **PIZZA** A concession stand sells three types of pizza. The diagram shows how much pizza of each type is left after the concession stand was open for one hour. If the pizza is sold in slices that are $\frac{1}{8}$ of a whole pizza, how many more slices can be sold? **25**

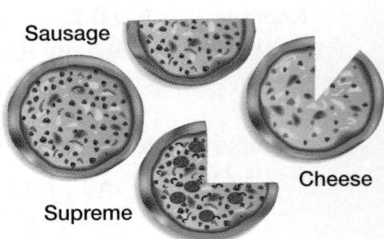

Sausage

Cheese

Supreme

	DIFFERENTIATED HOMEWORK OPTIONS		
Level	**Assignment**	**Two-Day Option**	
BL Basic	11–32, 49–60	11–31 odd, 52, 53	12–32 even, 49–51, 54–60
OL Core	11–41 odd, 42–47, 49–60	11–32, 52, 53	33–47, 49–51, 54–60
AL Advanced/Pre-AP	33–60		

ALGEBRA Evaluate each expression if $g = \frac{1}{6}$, $h = \frac{1}{2}$, and $j = 3\frac{2}{3}$.

38. $j \div h$ $7\frac{1}{3}$

39. $g \div j$ $\frac{1}{22}$

40. $3g \div h$ **1**

41. $h \div \left(\frac{1}{2}j\right)$ $\frac{3}{11}$

42. SHOPPING A supermarket sells pretzels in $\frac{3}{4}$-ounce snack-sized bags or $12\frac{1}{2}$-ounce regular-sized bags. How many times larger is the regular-sized bag than the snack-sized bag? **$16\frac{2}{3}$ times larger**

43. MEASUREMENT A recipe calls for $2\frac{2}{3}$ cups of brown sugar and $\frac{2}{3}$ cup of confectioner's sugar. How many times greater is the number of cups of brown sugar in the recipe than of confectioner's sugar? **4**

SCHOOL For Exercises 44 and 45, use the table that shows the number of hours students spend studying each week during the school year.

44. How many times greater was the number of students who spent over 10 hours each week studying than those who spent only 1–2 hours each week studying? **$2\frac{1}{2}$ times as many**

45. $7\frac{9}{10}$ **times as many**

★ **45.** How many times greater was the number of students who spent 3 or more hours each week studying than those who spent less than 3 hours each week studying?

Weekly Study Hours	
Hours	**Fraction of Students**
none	$\frac{1}{50}$
1–2	$\frac{2}{25}$
3–5	$\frac{11}{50}$
6–7	$\frac{17}{100}$
8–10	$\frac{1}{5}$
Over 10	$\frac{1}{5}$
Not sure	$\frac{3}{25}$

Source: *Time Magazine*

★ **46. SCHOOL SUPPLIES** Tara bought a dozen folders. She took $\frac{1}{3}$ of the dozen and then divided the remaining folders equally among her four friends. What fraction of the dozen did each of her four friends receive and how many folders was this per person? **$\frac{1}{6}$ of a dozen or 2 folders**

★ **47. WEATHER** A meteorologist has issued a thunderstorm warning. So far, the storm has traveled 35 miles in $\frac{1}{2}$ hour. If it is currently 5:00 P.M., and the storm is 105 miles away from you, at what time will the storm reach you? Explain how you solved the problem. **See margin.**

EXTRA PRACTICE
See pages 681, 708.

H.O.T. Problems

48. CHALLENGE If $\frac{5}{6}$ is divided by a certain fraction $\frac{a}{b}$, the result is $\frac{1}{4}$. What is the fraction $\frac{a}{b}$? $\frac{10}{3}$

49. Sample answer; You could use paper and pencil; $\frac{3}{4}$ of what number is $1\frac{1}{2}$? $1\frac{1}{2}$ feet $\div \frac{3}{4} = \frac{3}{2}$ feet $\cdot \frac{4}{3} = 2$ feet.

49. SELECT A TOOL Reynaldo cut a rope to make the running knot shown. The rope used to make the knot was $1\frac{1}{2}$ feet long and was $\frac{3}{4}$ of the original rope length. Which of the following tools could be used to determine the rope's original length? Justify your selection(s). Then use your tool(s) to find the length.

| paper and pencil | model | calculator | real object |

Lesson 5-7 Dividing Fractions and Mixed Numbers **269**

Differentiated Instruction

Visual/Spatial Learners Separate students into groups of three or four. Write the following expressions on the board: $2 \div \frac{1}{5}$, $3 \div \frac{1}{6}$, $3 \div \frac{3}{4}$, and $5 \div 1\frac{1}{4}$. Have the members of each group predict the quotients and then model the expressions and their solutions. Students might want to use paper plates, as in the Mini Lab draw figures on grid paper, or create their own models.

Additional Answer

47. 6:30 P.M.; Sample answer: $105 \div 35 = 3$, The storm will travel 105 miles in 3 sets of $\frac{1}{2}$ hour, or $1\frac{1}{2}$ hours. Adding $1\frac{1}{2}$ hours to 5:00 P.M. will make it 6:30 P.M.

Lesson 5-7 Dividing Fractions and Mixed Numbers **269**

50. José; Evan did not multiply by the reciprocal of $\frac{6}{7}$.

51. Yes; sample answer: If the first proper fraction is larger than the second proper fraction, then the resulting quotient will be a whole number or mixed number.

50. **FIND THE ERROR** Evan and José are finding $\frac{4}{5} \div \frac{6}{7}$. Who is correct? Explain your reasoning.

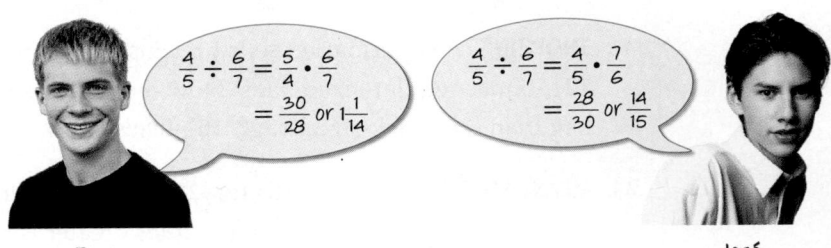

Evan

$$\frac{4}{5} \div \frac{6}{7} = \frac{5}{4} \cdot \frac{6}{7}$$
$$= \frac{30}{28} \text{ or } 1\frac{1}{14}$$

$$\frac{4}{5} \div \frac{6}{7} = \frac{4}{5} \cdot \frac{7}{6}$$
$$= \frac{28}{30} \text{ or } \frac{14}{15}$$

José

51. **WRITING IN MATH** If you divide a proper fraction by another proper fraction, is it possible to get a mixed number as an answer? Explain your reasoning.

TEST PRACTICE

52. The Corbett family owns 300 acres of land that they plan to rent to people for their horses. How many $7\frac{1}{2}$-acre lots can they make using the 300 acres?

A 21
B 40
C $40\frac{1}{2}$
D $292\frac{1}{2}$

B

53. How many $1\frac{1}{8}$-pound boxes of peanuts can be made using $6\frac{3}{4}$ pounds of peanuts? **H**

F 4
G 5
H 6
J 7

Spiral Review

Find the multiplicative inverse of each number. (Lesson 5-6)

54. $\frac{6}{7}$ $\frac{7}{6}$ or $1\frac{1}{6}$

55. $\frac{4}{13}$ $\frac{13}{4}$ or $3\frac{1}{4}$

56. 8 $\frac{1}{8}$

57. $5\frac{1}{4}$ $\frac{4}{21}$

58. Find $\frac{1}{10} \times \frac{5}{8}$. Write in simplest form. (Lesson 5-5) $\frac{1}{16}$

59. **MEASUREMENT** Find the length of a rectangular flower bed if the perimeter is 12 feet and the width is 1.5 feet. (Lesson 3-6) **4.5 ft**

60. **ANIMALS** An elephant herd can move 50 miles in a day. At this rate, about how many miles can an elephant herd move each hour? (Lesson 1-1) **2**

Problem Solving in Geography

Real-World Unit Project

A Traveling We Will Go It's time to complete your project. Use the data you have gathered about schedules and costs to prepare a travel brochure for your vacation destination. Be sure to include a paragraph describing why you chose your vacation spot.

Math Online ➤ Unit Project at glencoe.com

Math Online   glencoe.com
- STUDY *TO GO*
- Vocabulary Review

FOLDABLES
Study Organizer

▶ **GET READY** to Study

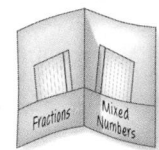

Be sure the following Big Ideas are noted in your Foldable.

BIG Ideas

Estimating with Fractions (Lesson 5-1)
- When the numerator is much smaller than the denominator, round the fraction to 0.
- When the numerator is about half of the denominator, round the fraction to $\frac{1}{2}$.
- When the numerator is almost as large as the denominator, round the fraction to 1.

Adding and Subtracting Fractions
(Lessons 5-2 and 5-3)
- To add or subtract like fractions, add or subtract the numerators and write the result over the denominator.
- To add or subtract unlike fractions, rename the fractions using the LCD. Then add or subtract as with like fractions.
- To add or subtract mixed numbers, first add or subtract the fractions. If necessary, rename them using the LCD. Then add or subtract the whole numbers and simplify if necessary.

Multiplying and Dividing Fractions
(Lessons 5-5 and 5-7)
- To multiply fractions, multiply the numerators and multiply the denominators.
- The product of a number and its multiplicative inverse is 1.
- To divide by a fraction, multiply by its multiplicative inverse, or reciprocal.

Solving Equations (Lesson 5-6)
If you multiply each side of an equation by the same nonzero number, the two sides remain equal.

Key Vocabulary

compatible numbers (p. 232)

like fractions (p. 236)

multiplicative inverse (p. 258)

reciprocal (p. 258)

unlike fractions (p. 237)

Vocabulary Check

Choose the correct term or number to complete each sentence.

1. To add like fractions, add the (numerators, denominators). **numerators**

2. The symbol ≈ means (*approximately*, *exactly*) *equal to*. **approximately**

3. When dividing by a fraction, multiply by its (value, reciprocal). **reciprocal**

4. When estimating, if the numerator of a fraction is much smaller than the denominator, round the fraction to $\left(0, \frac{1}{2}\right)$. **0**

5. Fractions with different denominators are called (like, unlike) fractions. **unlike**

6. The multiplicative inverse of $\frac{5}{6}$ is $\left(\frac{6}{5}, -\frac{5}{6}\right)$. **$\frac{6}{5}$**

7. The mixed number $2\frac{4}{7}$ can be renamed as $\left(2\frac{7}{7}, 1\frac{11}{7}\right)$. **$1\frac{11}{7}$**

8. When multiplying fractions, multiply the numerators and (multiply, keep) the denominators. **multiply**

9. The reciprocal of $\frac{1}{3}$ is (−3, 3). **3**

10. The fractions $\frac{4}{16}$ and $\frac{2}{4}$ are (like, unlike) fractions. **unlike**

11. Another word for multiplicative inverse is (reciprocal, denominator). **reciprocal**

12. The fraction $\frac{x}{2}$ can be read x *multiplied by* $\left(2, \frac{1}{2}\right)$. **$\frac{1}{2}$**

Summative Assessment

CRM   Vocabulary Test, p. 56

FOLDABLES™
Study Organizer

Dinah Zike's Foldables

Have students look through the chapter to make sure they have included study cards in their Foldables for the key concepts of each lesson.

Encourage students to refer to their Foldables while completing the Study Guide and Review and while preparing for the Chapter Test.

Formative Assessment

Key Vocabulary The page references after each word in the Key Vocabulary denote where that term was first introduced. If students have difficulty answering Exercises 1–12, remind them that they can use these page references to refresh their memories about the vocabulary terms.

Math Online ▶ glencoe.com

Vocabulary PuzzleMaker improves students' mathematics vocabulary using four puzzle formats—crossword, scramble, word search using a word list, and word search using clues. Students can work online or from a printed worksheet.

Lesson-by-Lesson Review

Intervention If the given examples are not sufficient to review the topics covered by the questions, remind students that the page references tell them where to review that topic in their textbooks.

Two-Day Option Have students complete the Lesson-by-Lesson on pages 272–274. Then you can use ExamView® Assessment Suite to customize another review worksheet that practices all the objectives of this chapter or only the objectives on which your students need more help.

For more information on ExamView® Assessment Suite, see page 228C.

Differentiated Instruction

Super DVD: MindJogger Plus
Use this DVD as an alternative format of review for the test. For more information on this game show format, see page 228D.

Lesson-by-Lesson Review

5-1 Estimating with Fractions (pp. 230–235)

Estimate. 13–20. Sample answers are given.

13. $2\frac{9}{10} \div 1\frac{1}{8}$ **$3 \div 1 = 3$** 14. $6\frac{2}{9} - 5\frac{1}{7}$ **$6 - 5 = 1$**

15. $\frac{13}{15} \times \frac{1}{5}$ **$1 \times 0 = 0$** 16. $\frac{1}{2} + \frac{3}{8}$ **$\frac{1}{2} + \frac{1}{2} = 1$**

17. $\frac{1}{2} \cdot 25\frac{1}{2}$ **$\times 26 = 13$** 18. $15\frac{6}{7} \div 7\frac{1}{3}$ **$16 \div 8 = 2$**

19. **MEASUREMENT** Gina wishes to carpet her living room. It has a length of $18\frac{5}{8}$ feet and the width of her living room is $9\frac{1}{2}$ feet. About how many square feet of carpet would be needed for her living room? **19×10 or about 190 ft²**

20. **FOOTBALL** Jamil practiced football for $1\frac{3}{4}$ hours on Saturday and $2\frac{2}{3}$ hours on Sunday. About how many more hours did he practice on Sunday than on Saturday? **3–2 or about 1 hour**

Example 1 Estimate $5\frac{1}{12} + 2\frac{5}{6}$.

1 is much smaller than 12, so $5\frac{1}{12} \approx 5$.

5 is almost as large as 6, so $2\frac{5}{6} \approx 3$.

$5\frac{1}{12} + 2\frac{5}{6} \approx 5 + 3$ or 8

The sum is *about* 8.

Example 2 Estimate $\frac{7}{8} - \frac{4}{7}$.

7 is almost as large as 8, so $\frac{7}{8} \approx 1$.

4 is about half of 7, so $\frac{4}{7} \approx \frac{1}{2}$.

$\frac{7}{8} - \frac{4}{7} \approx 1 - \frac{1}{2}$ or $\frac{1}{2}$

The difference is *about* $\frac{1}{2}$.

5-2 Adding and Subtracting Fractions (pp. 236–241)

Add or subtract. Write in simplest form.

21. $\frac{2}{6} - \frac{1}{6}$ **$\frac{1}{6}$** 22. $\frac{3}{7} + \frac{9}{14}$ **$1\frac{1}{14}$**

23. $\frac{1}{9} + \frac{5}{9}$ **$\frac{2}{3}$** 24. $\frac{9}{10} - \frac{3}{10}$ **$\frac{3}{5}$**

25. $\frac{5}{8} - \frac{5}{12}$ **$\frac{5}{24}$** 26. $\frac{3}{4} + \frac{7}{20}$ **$1\frac{1}{10}$**

27. **RAIN** At 8 A.M., Della's rain gauge read $\frac{1}{8}$ inch. By 4 P.M., the gauge read $\frac{3}{4}$ inch. How much rain fell between 8 A.M. and 4 P.M.? **$\frac{5}{8}$ in.**

28. **PIZZA** Owen ate $\frac{1}{8}$ of a pizza Tuesday night. The next day, he ate an additional $\frac{1}{2}$ of the pizza. What fraction of the pizza has he eaten? **$\frac{5}{8}$**

Example 3 Find $\frac{1}{6} + \frac{2}{3}$.

Use a model.

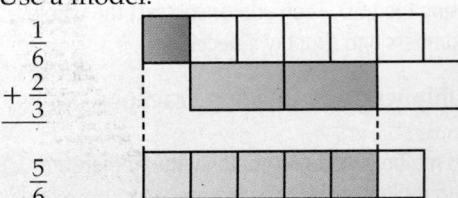

$\begin{array}{c} \frac{1}{6} \\ + \frac{2}{3} \\ \hline \frac{5}{6} \end{array}$

Example 4 Find $\frac{3}{10} - \frac{1}{4}$.

$\frac{3}{10} - \frac{1}{4} = \frac{6}{20} - \frac{5}{20}$ Rename the fractions using the LCD, 20.

$= \frac{1}{20}$ Subtract the numerators.

CHAPTER 5 Study Guide and Review

5-3 | **Adding and Subtracting Mixed Numbers** (pp. 242–246)

Add or subtract. Write in simplest form.

29. $3\frac{2}{15} + 6\frac{9}{15}$ $9\frac{11}{15}$ 　　30. $4\frac{1}{3} - 2\frac{2}{3}$ $1\frac{2}{3}$

31. $8\frac{2}{7} + 1\frac{6}{7}$ $10\frac{1}{7}$ 　　32. $7\frac{11}{12} - 4\frac{3}{12}$ $3\frac{2}{3}$

33. $7\frac{3}{5} - 5\frac{1}{3}$ $2\frac{4}{15}$ 　　34. $5\frac{3}{4} + 1\frac{1}{6}$ $6\frac{11}{12}$

35. $3\frac{5}{8} + 11\frac{1}{2}$ $15\frac{1}{8}$ 　　36. $4\frac{3}{10} - 2\frac{4}{5}$ $1\frac{1}{2}$

37. **BABYSITTING** Lucas watched his little sister for $2\frac{1}{2}$ hours on Friday, $3\frac{2}{3}$ hours on Saturday, and $1\frac{3}{4}$ hours on Sunday. How many hours did Lucas watch his little sister? $7\frac{11}{12}$ h

Example 5 Find $5\frac{2}{3} + 3\frac{1}{2}$.

$5\frac{2}{3} + 3\frac{1}{2} = 5\frac{4}{6} + 3\frac{3}{6}$ 　　Rename the fractions.

$= 8\frac{7}{6}$ 　　Add the whole numbers and add the fractions.

$= 9\frac{1}{6}$ 　　$8\frac{7}{6} = 8 + 1\frac{1}{6}$ or $9\frac{1}{6}$

Example 6 Find $4\frac{1}{5} - 2\frac{3}{5}$.

$4\frac{1}{5} - 2\frac{3}{5} = 3\frac{6}{5} - 2\frac{3}{5}$ 　　Rename $4\frac{1}{5}$ as $3\frac{6}{5}$.

$= 1\frac{3}{5}$ 　　Subtract the whole numbers and subtract the fractions.

5-4 | **PSI: Eliminate Possibilities** (pp. 248–249)

Solve by eliminating possibilities.

38. **SCHOOL** It takes Beth 15 minutes to walk to school, $\frac{1}{2}$ mile away. What is her walking pace? **A**

　A 2 miles per hour

　B 1 mile per hour

　C 7.5 miles per hour

　D 30 miles per hour

39. **COOKING** Which of the following would yield a larger batch of bagels? **G**

　F Multiply a recipe by $\frac{1}{2}$.

　G Divide a recipe by $\frac{1}{2}$.

　H Multiply a recipe by $\frac{3}{4}$.

　J Divide a recipe by 3.

Example 7 A group of friends went to a theme park. Six of the friends rode the Ferris wheel. If this was $\frac{2}{3}$ of the group, how many friends were in the group?

　A 3

　B 6

　C 9

　D 12

Since 6 friends rode the Ferris wheel and this was $\frac{2}{3}$ of the total number of friends in the group, the number of friends in the group must be greater than 6. So, eliminate choices A and B.

If there were 12 friends in the group, the 6 that rode the Ferris wheel would represent $\frac{1}{2}$ of the group. So, eliminate choice D.

Choice C is the only remaining possibility. Since 6 out of 9 is $\frac{6}{9}$ or $\frac{2}{3}$, C is correct.

Problem Solving Review

For additional practice in problem solving for Chapter 5, see the Mixed Problem Solving Appendix, page 708 in the Student Handbook section.

Anticipation Guide

Have students complete the Chapter 5 Anticipation Guide and discuss how their responses have changed now that they have completed Chapter 5.

CRM Anticipation Guide, p. 7

Differentiated Instruction

Bodily/Kinesthetic Learners

If students are having difficulty dividing fractions, remind them that they can use geoboards, construction paper, or other concrete objects to model Exercises 55–61.

5-5 **Multiplying Fractions and Mixed Numbers** (pp. 252–257)

Multiply. Write in simplest form.

40. $\frac{3}{5} \times \frac{2}{7}$ **$\frac{6}{35}$**

41. $\frac{5}{12} \times \frac{4}{9}$ **$\frac{5}{27}$**

42. $\frac{3}{5} \times \frac{10}{21}$ **$\frac{2}{7}$**

43. $4 \times \frac{13}{20}$ **$2\frac{3}{5}$**

44. $2\frac{1}{3} \times \frac{3}{4}$ **$1\frac{3}{4}$**

45. $4\frac{1}{2} \times 2\frac{1}{12}$ **$9\frac{3}{8}$**

46. **FOOD** An average slice of American cheese is about $\frac{1}{8}$ inch thick. What is the height of a package containing 20 slices? **$2\frac{1}{2}$ in.**

Example 8 Find $\frac{5}{9} \times \frac{2}{3}$.

$\frac{5}{9} \times \frac{2}{3} = \frac{5 \times 2}{9 \times 3}$ Multiply the numerators and multiply the denominators.

$= \frac{10}{27}$ Simplify.

Example 9 Find $3\frac{1}{2} \times 2\frac{3}{4}$.

$3\frac{1}{2} \times 2\frac{3}{4} = \frac{7}{2} \times \frac{11}{4}$ Rename $3\frac{1}{2}$ and $2\frac{3}{4}$.

$= \frac{7 \times 11}{2 \times 4}$ Multiply the numerators and multiply the denominators.

$= \frac{77}{8}$ or $9\frac{5}{8}$ Simplify.

5-6 **Algebra: Solving Equations** (pp. 258–263)   47. $\frac{12}{7}$ or $1\frac{5}{7}$

Find the multiplicative inverse of each number.

47. $\frac{7}{12}$

48. $5\frac{1}{5}$

49. $3\frac{1}{3}$ **$\frac{3}{10}$**

Solve each equation. Check your solution.

50. $8 = \frac{w}{2}$ **16**

51. $\frac{4}{5}b = 12$ **15**

52. $-7.6 = \frac{n}{3}$ **−22.8**

53. $\frac{x}{0.3} = 2.5$ **0.75**

54. **BOOKS** Of the books on a shelf, $\frac{2}{3}$ are mysteries. If there are 10 mystery books, how many books are on the shelf? **15**

Example 10 Find the multiplicative inverse of $\frac{9}{5}$.

$\frac{9}{5} \cdot \frac{5}{9} = 1$ The product of $\frac{9}{5}$ and $\frac{5}{9}$ is 1.

The multiplicative inverse of $\frac{9}{5}$ is $\frac{5}{9}$.

Example 11 Solve $\frac{3}{4}g = 2$.

$\frac{3}{4}g = 2$ Write the equation.

$\frac{4}{3} \cdot \frac{3}{4}g = \frac{4}{3} \cdot 2$ Multiply each side by the reciprocal of $\frac{3}{4}$.

$g = \frac{8}{3}$ or $2\frac{2}{3}$ Simplify.

5-7 **Dividing Fractions and Mixed Numbers** (pp. 265–270)

Divide. Write in simplest form.

55. $\frac{3}{5} \div \frac{6}{7}$ **$\frac{7}{10}$**

56. $4 \div \frac{2}{3}$ **6**

57. $2\frac{3}{4} \div \frac{5}{6}$ **$3\frac{3}{10}$**

58. $-\frac{2}{5} \div 3$ **$-\frac{2}{15}$**

59. $4\frac{3}{10} \div 2\frac{1}{5}$ **$1\frac{21}{22}$**

60. $-\frac{2}{7} \div \frac{8}{21}$ **$-\frac{3}{4}$**

61. **MEASUREMENT** How many $\frac{1}{8}$-inch lengths are in $6\frac{3}{4}$ inches? **54**

Example 12 Find $2\frac{4}{5} \div \frac{7}{10}$.

$2\frac{4}{5} \div \frac{7}{10} = \frac{14}{5} \div \frac{7}{10}$ Rename $2\frac{4}{5}$.

$= \frac{14}{5} \cdot \frac{10}{7}$ Multiply by the reciprocal of $\frac{7}{10}$.

$= \frac{4}{1}$ or 4   Simplify.

274 Chapter 5 Applying Fractions

Estimate. Sample answers given.

1. $5\frac{7}{9} - 1\frac{2}{13}$ **6 − 1 = 5**   2. $3\frac{1}{12} + 6\frac{5}{7}$ **3 + 7 = 10**

3. $\frac{3}{7} \times \frac{13}{15}$ **$\frac{1}{2} \times 1 = \frac{1}{2}$**   4. $5\frac{2}{3} \div 1\frac{4}{5}$ **6 ÷ 2 = 3**

5. **BAKING** A restaurant uses $2\frac{3}{4}$ pounds of flour to make a batch of dinner rolls. About how many pounds of flour are needed if 3 batches of dinner rolls are to be made?
Sample answer: about 3 × 3 or 9 lb

Add, subtract, multiply, or divide. Write in simplest form.

6. $\frac{4}{15} + \frac{8}{15}$ **$\frac{4}{5}$**   7. $\frac{7}{10} - \frac{1}{6}$ **$\frac{8}{15}$**

8. $\frac{5}{8} \times \frac{2}{5}$ **$\frac{1}{4}$**   9. $6 \times \frac{8}{21}$ **$2\frac{2}{7}$**

10. $4\frac{5}{12} - 2\frac{1}{12}$ **$2\frac{1}{3}$**   11. $6\frac{7}{9} + 3\frac{5}{12}$ **$10\frac{7}{36}$**

12. $8\frac{4}{7} - 1\frac{5}{14}$ **$7\frac{3}{14}$**   13. $4\frac{5}{6} \times 1\frac{2}{3}$ **$8\frac{1}{18}$**

14. $\frac{8}{9} \div 5\frac{1}{3}$ **$\frac{1}{6}$**   15. $\frac{1}{6} \div 5$ **$\frac{1}{30}$**

16. **MULTIPLE CHOICE** Seth drove $5\frac{3}{4}$ miles to the bank, $6\frac{1}{3}$ miles to the post office, and $4\frac{5}{6}$ miles to the park. What is the total distance Seth drove? **D**

A $15\frac{9}{13}$ miles

B $\frac{7}{12}$ miles

C $\frac{11}{12}$ miles

D $16\frac{11}{12}$ miles

17. **SPORTS** Tyler's football practice lasted $2\frac{1}{2}$ hours. If $\frac{1}{4}$ of the time was spent catching passes, how many hours were spent catching passes? **$\frac{5}{8}$ h**

18. **MEASUREMENT** The floor of a moving van is $11\frac{1}{3}$ feet long and $7\frac{5}{12}$ feet wide. Find the area of the moving van floor. **$84\frac{1}{18}$ ft²**

19. **MULTIPLE CHOICE** For his birthday, Keith received a check from his grandmother. Of this amount, the table shows how he spent or saved the money.

Fraction of Check	How Spent or Saved
$\frac{2}{5}$	spent on baseball cards
$\frac{1}{4}$	spent on a CD
$\frac{7}{20}$	deposited into savings account

Two weeks later, he withdrew $\frac{2}{3}$ of the amount he had deposited into his savings account. What fraction of the original check did he withdraw from his savings account? **H**

F $\frac{2}{3}$ H $\frac{7}{30}$

G $\frac{9}{23}$ J $\frac{7}{40}$

20. **MEASUREMENT** An ounce is $\frac{1}{16}$ of a pound. How many ounces are in $8\frac{3}{4}$ pounds? **140 oz**

ALGEBRA Solve each equation. Check your solution.

21. $\frac{y}{3.7} = 8.1$ **29.97**   22. $6 = \frac{2}{5}m$ **15**

23. $\frac{3}{4} = \frac{5}{8}x$ **$1\frac{1}{5}$**   24. $3\frac{1}{6} = \frac{2}{3}p$ **$4\frac{3}{4}$**

25. **MULTIPLE CHOICE** Maria is making a mural that is $9\frac{2}{3}$ feet long. She wants to divide the mural into sections that are each $\frac{5}{8}$ foot. Which equation can be used to find n, the number of sections in Maria's mural? **A**

A $\frac{5}{8}n = 9\frac{2}{3}$ C $\frac{5}{8} + n = 9\frac{2}{3}$

B $9\frac{2}{3}n = \frac{5}{8}$ D $n - \frac{5}{8} = 9\frac{2}{3}$

Chapter 5 Practice Test **275**

CHAPTER
5 **Practice Test**

✔ **Summative Assessment**

CRM **Chapter 5 Resource Masters**

Leveled Chapter 5 Tests			
Form	**Type**	**Level**	**Pages**
1	MC	BL	57–58
2A	MC	OL	59–60
2B	MC	OL	61–62
2C	FR	OL	63–64
2D	FR	OL	65–66
3	FR	AL	67–68

MC = multiple-choice questions
FR = free-response questions
BL = below or approaching grade level
OL = on grade level
AL = above or beyond grade level

• Vocabulary Test, p. 56
• Extended-Response Test, p. 69
• Unit 2 Test, pp. 73–74

ExamView®
Assessment Suite

Customize and create multiple versions of your chapter test and their answer keys. All of the questions from the leveled chapter tests in the *Chapter 5 Resource Masters* are also available on ExamView Assessment Suite.

Data-Driven Decision Making	Exercises	Lesson	State/Local Standards	Resources for Review
Diagnostic Teaching Based on the results of the Chapter 5 Practice Test, use the following to review concepts that students continue to find challenging.	1–7	5-1, 5-2		CRM Study Guide and Intervention pp. 10, 16, 22, 27, 32, 39, and 45
	10–12, 16, 19	5-3, 5-4		
	8, 9, 13, 17–20	5-5		Math Online ▷ glencoe.com • Extra Examples • Personal Tutor • Concepts in Motion
	14, 15, 21–25	5-6, 5-7		

TEST-TAKING TIP

Exercise 1 Ask students to look for a word or term in the problem that indicates which operation will be used in the equation. Students should realize that *less than* indicates subtraction, which should lead them to examine answer choice A.

 Formative Assessment

You can use these two pages to benchmark student progress.

 Chapter 5 Resource Masters

• Test Practice, pp. 70–72

 Create practice worksheets or tests that align to your state's standards, as well as TIMSS and NAEP tests.

PART 1 Multiple Choice

Read each question. Then fill in the correct answer on the answer sheet provided by your teacher or on a sheet of paper.

1. Mrs. Brown needs to make two different desserts for a dinner party. The first recipe requires $2\frac{1}{4}$ cups of flour, and the second recipe requires $\frac{3}{4}$ cup less than the first. Which equation can be used to find n, the number of cups of flour needed for the second recipe? **A**

   A $n = 2\frac{1}{4} - \frac{3}{4}$ C $n = 2\frac{1}{4} + \frac{3}{4}$

   B $n = 2\frac{1}{4} \cdot \frac{3}{4}$ D $n = 2\frac{1}{4} \div \frac{3}{4}$

2. Which of the following is true concerning the least common multiple of 6 and 9? **G**

   F It is greater than the least common multiple of 8 and 12.

   G It is greater than the least common multiple of 5 and 15.

   H It is less than the least common multiple of 4 and 6.

   J It is less than the least common multiple of 3 and 4.

3. Kyle's hockey team has 6 sixth graders, 9 seventh graders, and 5 eighth graders. Which statement below is true? **C**

   A One fourth of the team members are sixth graders.

   B More than half of the team members are seventh graders.

   C 25% of the team members are eighth graders.

   D 30% of the team members are seventh graders.

4. The fraction $\frac{5}{6}$ is found between which pair of fractions on a number line? **J**

   F $\frac{1}{4}$ and $\frac{5}{8}$

   G $\frac{1}{3}$ and $\frac{4}{9}$

   H $\frac{11}{12}$ and $\frac{31}{36}$

   J $\frac{7}{12}$ and $\frac{17}{18}$

5. The table shows the distance Kelly swam over a four-day period. What was the total distance, in miles, Kelly swam? **C**

Kelly's Swimming	
Day	Distance (miles)
Monday	1.5
Tuesday	$2\frac{3}{4}$
Wednesday	2.3
Thursday	$3\frac{1}{2}$

   A 10.5 miles   C $10\frac{1}{20}$ miles

   B $10\frac{1}{4}$ miles   D 9 miles

6. Which of the following gives the correct meaning of the expression $\frac{5}{8} \div \frac{1}{3}$? **G**

   F $\frac{5}{8} \div \frac{1}{3} = \frac{8}{5} \times \frac{3}{1}$

   G $\frac{5}{8} \div \frac{1}{3} = \frac{5}{8} \times \frac{3}{1}$

   H $\frac{5}{8} \div \frac{1}{3} = \frac{5+1}{8+3}$

   J $\frac{5}{8} \div \frac{1}{3} = \frac{5}{8} \times \frac{1}{3}$

276 Chapter 5 Applying Fractions

Preparing for Standardized Tests
For test-taking strategies and practice, see pages 716–733.

CHAPTER
5 Test Practice

7. What is the value of the expression $(3 + 4)^2 \div 7 - 2 \times 6$? **B**

   A −9   C 30

   B −5   D 1

8. Which line contains the ordered pair $(-1, 2)$? **F**

   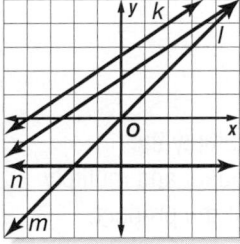

   F Line k

   G Line l

   H Line m

   J Line n

9. A pizza shop tried 45 new types of pizza during the past year and 20% of them became popular. Which best represents the fraction of pizzas that did *not* become popular? **D**

   A $\frac{1}{5}$ C $\frac{3}{5}$

   B $\frac{4}{9}$ D $\frac{4}{5}$

TEST-TAKING TIP

Question 9 Be sure to pay attention to emphasized words, or words that are italicized. In Question 9, you are asked to find which answer is *not* correct.

PART 2 **Short Response/Grid In**

Record your answers on the answer sheet provided by your teacher or on a sheet of paper.

10. Write an equation using two variables to show the relationship between the position x and the value of a term y. $4x + 1 = y$

Position (x)	1	2	3	4	5	n
Value of Term (y)	5	9	13	17	21	

11. Evan runs $2\frac{3}{8}$ miles each week. He runs $\frac{3}{4}$ mile on Mondays and $\frac{3}{4}$ mile on Tuesdays. How far does he run, in miles, if the only other day he runs each week is Thursday? $\frac{7}{8}$

12. Find $15 \div (-5)$. **−3**

PART 3 **Extended Response**

Record your answers on the answer sheet provided by your teacher or on a sheet of paper. Show your work.

13. A box of laundry detergent contains 35 cups. It takes $1\frac{1}{4}$ cups per load of laundry.

   a. Write an equation to represent how many loads ℓ you can wash with one box. $\ell = 35 \div 1\frac{1}{4}$

   b. How many loads can you wash with one box? **28 loads**

   c. How many loads can you wash with 3 boxes? **84 loads**

NEED EXTRA HELP?													
If You Missed Question...	1	2	3	4	5	6	7	8	9	10	11	12	13
Go to Lesson...	5-2	4-8	4-6	4-9	4-5	5-7	1-4	3-7	4-6	1-10	5-2	2-8	5-7

Answer Sheet Practice

Have students simulate taking a standardized test by recording their answers on a practice recording sheet.

CRM Student Recording Sheet, p. 51

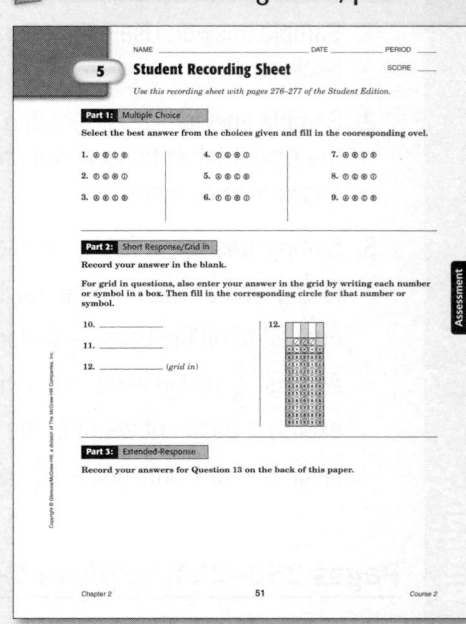

Homework Option

Get Ready for Chapter 6 Assign students the exercises on page 281 as homework to assess whether they possess the prerequisite skills needed for the next chapter.

Page 230, Lesson 5-1

1.
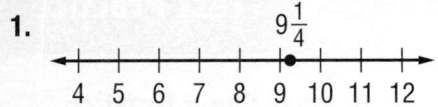

2.
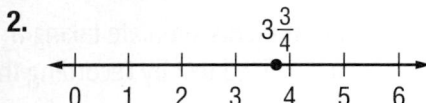

Page 248, Lesson 5-4

1. Sample answer: Use estimation, look for a pattern, work backward.

2. Sample answer: By eliminating possibilities, you can reduce the time it takes to solve the problem since there are fewer answers to consider.

3. Sample answer: A fishbowl holds $1\frac{1}{2}$ gallons of water. If there is $\frac{1}{3}$ gallon of water in the bowl, how many more gallons are needed to fill the bowl; $\frac{2}{3}$ gallons, $1\frac{1}{6}$ gallons, or $2\frac{1}{6}$ gallons. Answer: $\frac{2}{3}$ gallon is not enough because that would make exactly 1 gallon of water in the tank. $2\frac{1}{6}$ gallons is too much, since the tank only holds $1\frac{1}{2}$ gallons. The answer is $1\frac{1}{6}$ gallons.

Pages 250–251, Explore 5-5

c.
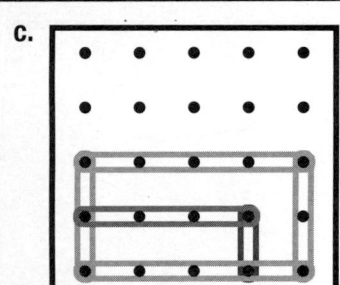

d.
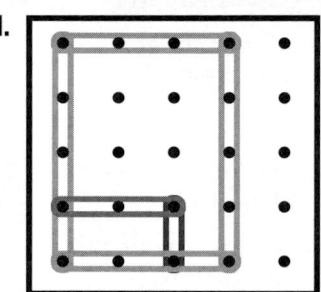

g.
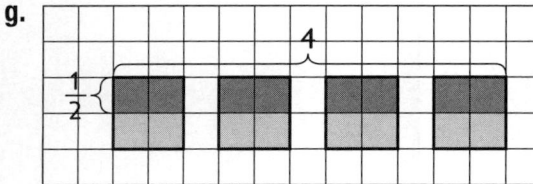

h.
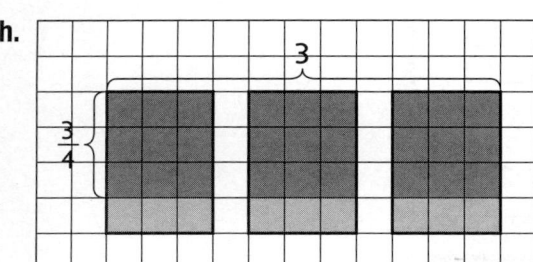

i.
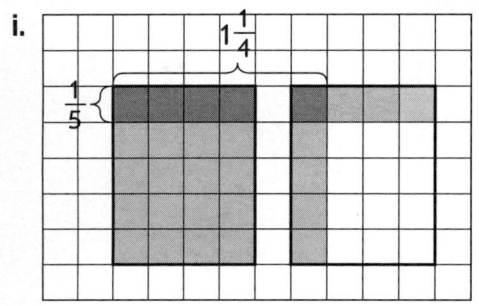

j.
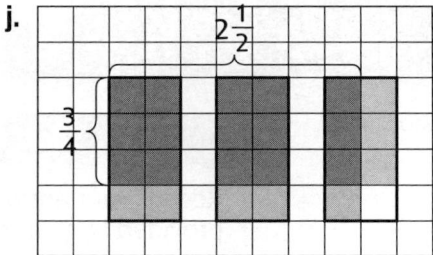

k.
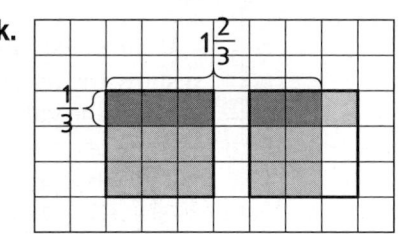

2. Sample answer: To multiply to fractions, multiply the numerators to get the numerator of the product and multiply the denominators to get the denominator of the product.

Page 252, Lesson 5-5 (Get Ready for the Lesson)

2. Sample answer: 2 is the part of the whole, 3, of the students that chose hamburgers. 1 is the part of the whole, 2, of the students that chose cheese on hamburgers.

Page 268, Lesson 5-7

33.
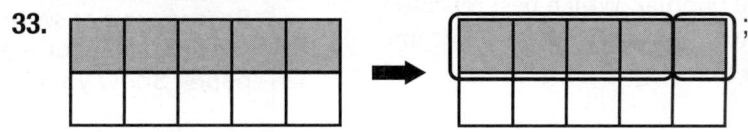

Sample answer: The model on the left shows that one half of a rectangle with ten sections is five sections. Two fifths of ten sections is four sections. The model on the right shows those five sections divided into $1\frac{1}{4}$ groups of four sections.

34.
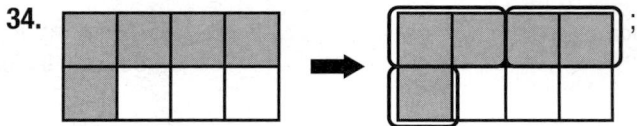

Sample answer: The model on the left shows that five eighths of a rectangle with eight sections is five sections. One fourth of eight sections is two sections. The model on the right shows those five sections divided into $2\frac{1}{2}$ groups of two sections.

35.
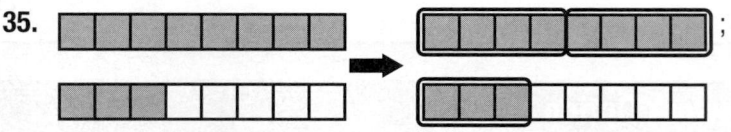

Sample answer: The model on the left shows that one and three eighths of a rectangle with eight sections is eleven sections. One half of eight sections is four sections. The model on the right shows those eleven sections divided into $2\frac{3}{4}$ groups of four sections.

36.

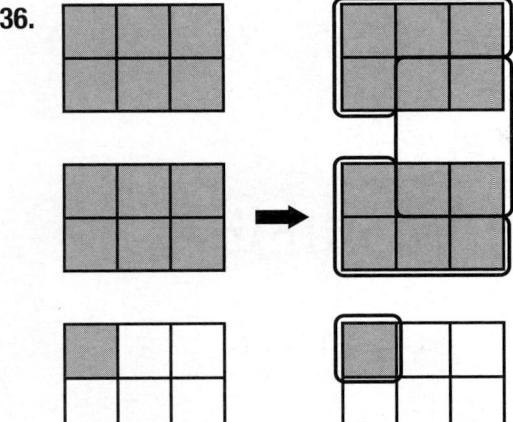

Sample answer: The model on the left shows that two and one sixth of a rectangle with six sections is thirteen sections. Two thirds of six sections is four sections. The model on the right shows those thirteen sections divided into $3\frac{1}{4}$ groups of four sections.

Unit 3 Notes

Introduction

In this unit, students will examine ratios and rates and solve proportions. They will make and interpret scale drawings and convert among fractions, decimals, and percents. In addition, they will use a percent proportion to calculate percent of change, sales tax, discounts, and simple interest, estimate percents, and use statistics to make predictions.

Assessment Options

Unit 3 Test Pages 81–82 of the *Chapter 7 Resource Masters* may be used as a test or a review for Unit 3. This assessment contains both multiple-choice and short-response items.

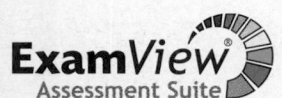

ExamView® Assessment Suite

Create additional customized Unit Tests and review worksheets for differentiated instruction.

Unit 3

Algebra and Number Sense: Proportions and Percents

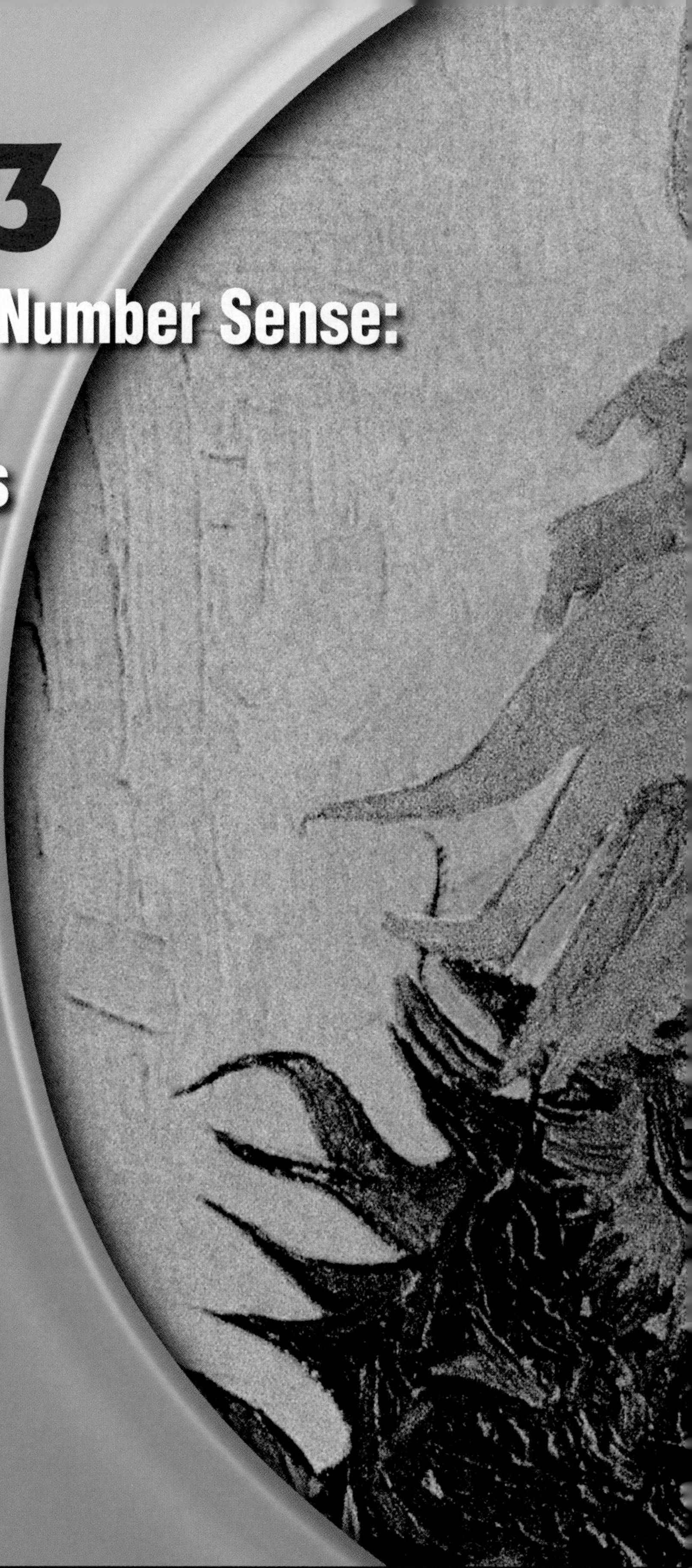

Focus

Develop an understanding of and apply proportionality.

CHAPTER 6
Ratios and Proportions

BIG Idea Use ratio and proportionality to solve problems, including those with tables and graphs.

CHAPTER 7
Applying Percents

BIG Idea Solve percent problems using ratios and proportions.

278

What's MATH Got To Do With It? DVD

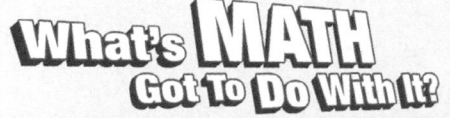

Real-Life Math Videos engage students, showing them how math is used in everyday situations. Use Video 3 with this unit to discuss how percents and proportions are used in wildlife management and shopping (also available on one Super DVD combined with MindJogger Videoquizzes).

It's Golden!

This cross-curricular project is an interactive project in which students do research on the Internet or in the library, gather data, and make presentations using word processing, graphing, pagemaking, or presentation software. In each chapter, students advance to the next step in the project. At the end of Chapter 7, the project culminates with a presentation of their findings.

Math Online

glencoe.com Log on for teaching suggestions and sample answers for this project.

Team Teaching You can use this project with your students' art teacher to make the connection from mathematics to ideas of the Golden Ratio in art the students are investigating.

Problem Solving in Art

Real-World Unit Project

It's Golden! On this adventure, you'll learn about the Golden Ratio in art and nature. Along the way, you'll research how artists use the Golden Ratio to create masterpieces. Also, you'll learn how the Golden Ratio occurs in nature as well. Our adventure will begin soon, so pack your art supplies and math tool kit. This is one golden adventure!

Math Online ⟩ **Log on to** glencoe.com **to begin.**

More Cross-Curricular Connections

You may wish to share these suggestions with your students' other teachers.

Math and Science
Research the Golden Ratio and where it is found in nature. What effect does the Golden Ratio have on objects in nature?

Math and Art
Create an art project that uses the Golden Ratio. Include an explanation as to where you used it and how it enhanced your artwork.

CHAPTER 6

Chapter Overview

Ratios and Proportions

Lesson Plan		Pacing Your Lessons		
LESSONS AND OBJECTIVES	State/Local Standards	45–50 Minute Periods	90-Minute Periods
6-1 Ratios (pp. 282–286) • Write ratios as fractions in simplest form, and determine whether two ratios are equivalent.		1	0.5
6-2 Rates (pp. 287–292) • Determine unit rates.		1.5	1
6-3 Rate of Change and Slope (pp. 293–297) • Identify rate of change and slope using tables and graphs.		2	1
6-4 Measurement: Changing Customary Units (pp. 298–303) • Change units in the customary system.		1	0.5
6-5 Measurement: Changing Metric Units (pp. 304–309) • Change units of length, capacity, and mass.		1	0.5
6-6 Algebra: Solving Proportions (pp. 310–315) • Solve proportions. **Extend 6-6 Math Lab: Inverse Proportionality** (p. 316) • Graph inverse variations.		2	1
6-7 Problem-Solving Investigation: Draw a Diagram (pp. 318–319) • Solve problems by drawing a diagram.		1	0.5
6-8 Scale Drawings (pp. 320–326) • Solve problems involving scale drawings. **Extend 6-8 Spreadsheet Lab: Scale Drawings** (p. 327) • Use a spreadsheet to calculate measurements for scale drawings.		1.5	1
6-9 Fractions, Decimals, and Percents (pp. 328–332) • Write percents as fractions and decimals, and vice versa.		1	0.5
REVIEW		1	0.5
ASSESSMENT		1	0.5*
TOTAL		14	7.5

*The complete **Assessment Planner** for Chapter 6 is provided on page 281.*

* Begin Chapter 7 in the second half of the period.

Focal Points

G7-FP1 Number and Operations
For the complete wording of the Focal Points for Grade 7, please see page iv.

Professional Development

Vertical Alignment

Before Chapter 6

Related Topics from Grade 6

- compute and perform simple multiplication and division of fractions and apply these procedures to solving problems

- differentiate between and use appropriate units of measures for two- and three-dimensional objects

- interpret percents as a part of a hundred; find decimal and percent equivalents for common fractions and explain why they represent the same value; compute a given percent of a whole number

Chapter 6

Topics from Grade 7

- interpret and use ratios in different contexts to show the relative sizes of two quantities, using appropriate notations

- use proportions to solve problems. Use cross-multiplication as a method for solving such problems, understanding it as the multiplication of both sides of an equation by a multiplicative inverse

- convert one unit of measurement to another

- demonstrate an understanding that rate is a measure of one quantity per unit value of another quantity

- solve problems involving rates

After Chapter 6

Preparation for Grade 8

- solve multistep problems involving rate, average speed, distance, and time or a direct variation

- construct and read drawings and models made to scale

Backmapping and Vertical Alignment

McGraw-Hill's *Math Connects* program was conceived and developed with the final results in mind: student success in Algebra I and beyond. The authors, using the **NCTM Focal Points and Focal Connections** as their guide, developed this brand-new series by backmapping from Algebra 1 concepts and vertically aligning the topics so that they build upon prior skills and concepts and serve as a foundation for future topics.

What the Research Says...

According to Lamon in "Ratio and Proportion: Connecting Content and Children's Thinking," which appeared in *Journal for Research in Mathematics Education*, the concept of *unit rate* is useful to students in solving problems involving proportions.

- Lesson 6-2 introduces unit rate. This concept helps students solve problems involving proportions in Lesson 6-6.

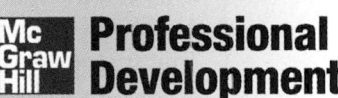 **Professional Development**

Targeted professional development has been articulated throughout **McGraw-Hill's *Math Connects*** program. The **McGraw-Hill Professional Development Video Library** provides short videos that support the NCTM Focal Points and Focal Connections. For more information, visit glencoe.com.

| Model Lessons | Instructional Strategies |

Technology Solutions

Teacher Resources

TeacherWorks™   All-in-One Planner and Resource Center

All of the print materials from the Classroom Resource Masters are available on your TeacherWorks™ CD-ROM.

BL = Below or Approaching Grade Level   **OL** = On Grade Level   **AL** = Above or Beyond Grade Level   **ELL** = English Language Learner

			Chapter Resource Masters	6-1	6-2	6-3	6-4	6-5	6-6	6-7	6-8	6-9
BL	OL		ELL Lesson Reading Guide	9	15	21	27	33	39		50	57
BL	OL		ELL Study Guide and Intervention*	10	16	22	28	34	40	46	51	58
BL	OL		Skills Practice*	11	17	23	29	35	41	47	52	59
	OL	AL	Practice*	12	18	24	30	36	42	48	53	60
	OL	AL	Word Problem Practice*	13	19	25	31	37	43	49	54	61
	OL	AL	Enrichment	14	20	26	32	38	44		55	62
	OL	AL	Calculator and Spreadsheet Activities						45		56	63
	OL	AL	Chapter Assessments*	65–86								
BL	OL	AL	5-Minute Check Transparencies	✓	✓	✓	✓	✓	✓	✓	✓	✓
BL	OL		Teaching Mathematics with Manipulatives	✓	✓			✓		✓		
BL	OL	AL	Real-World Investigations for Differentiated Instruction	pp. 41–38, 49–52								

Also available in Spanish.

Graphing Calculator Easy Files

Timesaving Tech Tools for the TI-Navigator:

- **Quick Checks** to diagnose student progress
- Motivate students with **Concept Launchers**
- Deliver differentiated instruction with **Ready Files**
- **Vocabulary Review**

AssignmentWorks

Differentiated Assignments, Answers, and Solutions

- Print a customized assignment worksheet using the Student Edition exercises along with an answer key or worked-out solutions.
- Use default lesson assignments as outlined in the Differentiated Homework Options in the Teacher Edition.

Interactive Classroom

This CD-ROM is a customizable Microsoft® PowerPoint® presentation that includes:

- In-Class Examples
- Your Turn Exercises
- 5-Minute Check Transparencies
- Links to Online Study Tools
- Concepts in Motion
- Compatible with response pad technology

ExamView®Assessment Suite

- Create, edit, and customize tests and worksheets
- Create multiple versions
- Translate from English to Spanish and vice versa
- Build tests aligned with your state standards

Student Tools

StudentWorks™ Plus

Textbook, Audio, Workbooks, and more

This CD-ROM is a valuable resource for students to access content online and use online resources to continue learning Chapter 6 concepts. Includes:

- Complete Student Editions in both English and Spanish
- English audio integrated throughout the text
- Links to Concepts in Motion, Personal Tutor, and other online resources
- Access to all student worksheets
- Daily Assignments and Grade Log

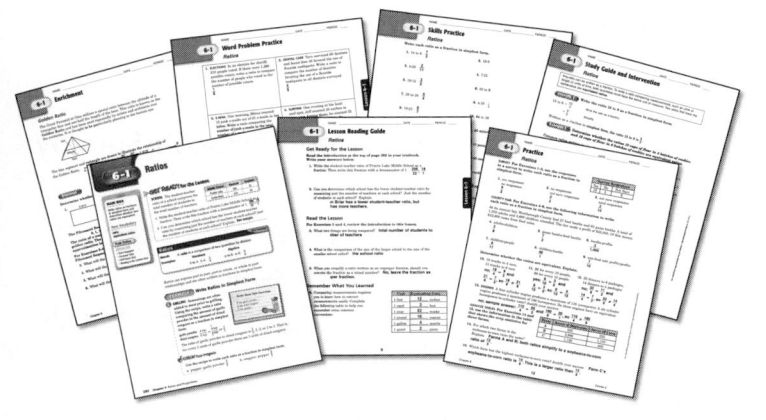

Super DVD

The Super DVD contains two Glencoe multimedia products.

MindJogger Plus An alternative review of concepts in which students work as teams in a game show format to gain points for correct answers.

What's Math Got to Do With It?
Real-Life Math Videos
Engaging video that shows students how math is used in everyday situations.

Internet Resources

TEACHER	STUDENT	PARENT	Online Study Tools
	●	●	Online Student Edition
●	●	●	Multilingual Glossary
			Lesson Resources
	●	●	Extra Examples
	●	●	BrainPOPS
	●	●	Self-Check Quizzes
●	●	●	Concepts in Motion
	●	●	Other Calculator Keystrokes
	●	●	Real-World Careers
	●	●	Reading in the Content Area
●			Group Activity Cards
			Chapter Resources
	●	●	Family Letters and Activities
	●		Chapter Readiness Quiz
	●	●	Vocabulary Review
	●	●	Chapter Test
	●	●	Standardized Test Practice
			Unit Resources
●	●		WebQuest Project
			Other Resources
	●		Personal Tutor
●			NAEP Correlations
●			Key Concepts
●	●	●	Meet the Authors
●	●		Game Zone
●	●	●	Math Skills Maintenance
●			National Resources (Professional Organizations)
●			State Resources
●			Vocabulary PuzzleMakers

Noteables™ Interactive Study Notebook with Foldables™

This workbook is a study organizer that provides helpful steps for students to follow to organize their notes for Chapter 6.

- Students use Noteables to record notes and to complete their Foldables as you present the material for each lesson.
- Noteables correspond to the Examples in the *Teacher Edition* and *Interactive Classroom CD-ROM*.

Real-World Problem Solving Graphic Novels

Mathematical problem solving is presented in a motivating, graphic novel format. The novels contain real-world problems for each of the following mathematical strands: Number Sense, Algebraic Thinking, Geometry, Measurement, Statistics and Probability, and Mathematical Reasoning.

READING in the Content Area

This online worksheet provides strategies for reading and analyzing Lesson 6-1, Ratios. Students are guided through questions about the main idea, subject matter, supporting details, conclusion, clarifying details, and vocabulary of the lesson.

glencoe.com

Recommended Outside Reading for Students

Mathematics and Humor

- *Cut Down to Size at High Noon* by Scott Sundby ©2000 [fiction]

This is a funny, Wild West adventure about two barbers who sculpture haircuts to scale in a showdown. This book gives a different look at scale drawings.

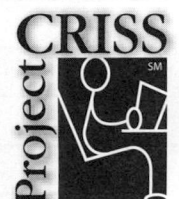

STUDY SKILL

A power map can help students organize and display their knowledge of a topic. Show students the sample power map at the right that deals with scale. Explain that the levels of detail in the map are represented by different geometric shapes. As students work through Chapter 6, ask them to think about some ways ratios can be used. Have them design a power map that illustrates what they learn.

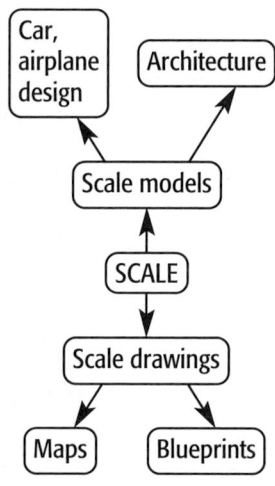

CReating **I**ndependence **t**hrough **S**tudent-owned **S**trategies

Differentiated Instruction

Investigative Approach

MathScape™

This project was supported, in part, by the
National Science Foundation

MathScape is a mathematics curriculum for grades 6–8 developed by the Seeing and
Thinking Mathematically Project at the Education Development Center.

> **Rates, Ratios, Percents,
> and Proportions**
>
> Buyer Beware

How to Use *MathScape* with Chapter 6
The unit *Buyer Beware* can be used to enhance
Lessons 6-2 and 6-6.

- **Reinforce** ⟶ Before you complete **Lesson 6-2**, you can use the activities on
  pages 6–13 to provide additional practice with unit rate and better buys.

- **Introduce** ⟶ Before you begin **Lesson 6-6**, you can introduce proportions by
  using the activities on page 18–19.

RTI (Response to Intervention)

① **On-Level Instruction** Use the *Math Connects*
program as instruction for your on-level students.

② **Strategic Intervention** For options to instruct
struggling students, refer to the Diagnostic
Assessment table on page 281.

③ **Intensive Intervention** *Math Triumphs* can
provide intensive intervention for students who
are two or more grade levels behind.

Diagnose student readiness with the Quick Check and
Quick Review on page 281. Then use *Math Triumphs* to
accelerate their achievement.

Ratios and Proportions

Prerequisite Skill	Math Triumphs
Ratios and Rates	Ch. 2
Customary and Metric Measurement Systems	Ch. 5

Practice and Review

Quick Review Math Handbook* is
Glencoe's mathematical handbook for
students and parents.

Hot Words includes a glossary of terms.

Hot Topics consists of two parts:

- explanations of key
  mathematical concepts

- exercises to check students'
  understanding.

Lesson	Hot Topics Section	Lesson	Hot Topics Section
6-1	6•5	6-5	8•1
6-2	6•5	6-6	6•5
6-3	6•8	6-8	6•5, 8•6
6-4	8•1	6-9	2•7, 2•9

*Also available in Spanish

FOLDABLES™ Study Organizer Dinah Zike's Foldables

Focus This Foldable is designed to help students organize their notes about ratios and proportions and to give them practice writing concise definitions.

Teach Have students make their Foldables and label the tabs. Explain to students that they should select one term or concept from each lesson and write its definition behind the appropriate tab. Encourage students to write the definitions in their own words. Finally, have students give an example or draw a diagram of the term or concept to the right of its definition.

When to Use It

Tab	Use with Lesson(s)
Ratios	6-1, 6-6, 6-7
Rates	6-2
Slope and Rate of Change	6-3
Customary/ Metric Units	6-4, 6-5
Proportions	6-6, 6-7
Scale	6-8, Extend 6-8
Fractions, Decimals, and Percents	6-9

Differentiated Instruction

CRM Student-Built Glossary, p. 1

Students complete the chart by providing a definition for each term and an example as they progress through Chapter 6.

This study tool can be used to review for the chapter test.

CHAPTER 6 Ratios and Proportions

BIG Idea

- Use ratio and proportionality to solve problems, including those with tables and graphs.

Key Vocabulary

rate (p. 287)
ratio (p. 282)
proportional (p. 310)

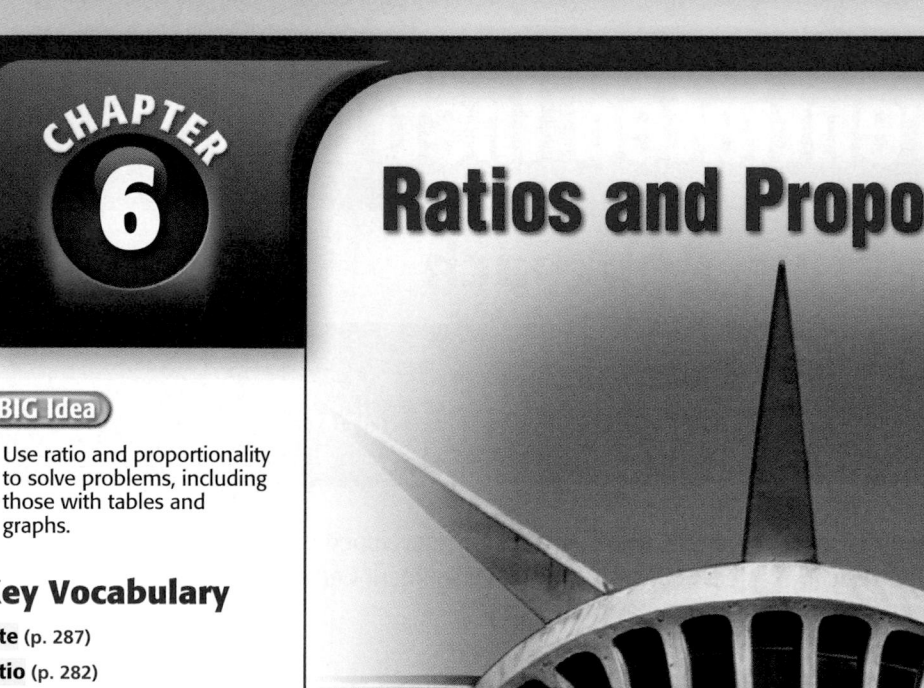

 Real-World Link

Statues A bronze replica of the Statue of Liberty can be found in Paris, France. The replica has the ratio 1 : 4 with the Statue of Liberty that stands in New York Harbor.

FOLDABLES® Study Organizer

Ratios and Proportions Make this Foldable to help you organize your notes. Begin with a sheet of notebook paper.

❶ **Fold** lengthwise to the holes.

❷ **Cut** along the top line and then make equal cuts to form 7 tabs.

❸ **Label** the major topics as shown.

 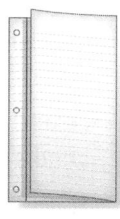 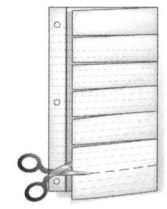 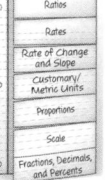

280 Chapter 6 Ratios and Proportions

Materials Needed for Chapter 6

- measuring tapes (Lesson 6-8)
- rulers (Lesson 6-8)
- $\frac{1}{4}$-inch grid paper (Lessons 6-4, 6-8, and 6-9)
- colored pencils (Lesson 6-9)
- computer spreadsheet program (Extend 6-8)

Diagnose Readiness You have two options for checking Prerequisite Skills.

Option 1

Take the Quick Quiz below. Refer to the Quick Review for help.

Option 2

Math Online Take the Online Readiness Quiz at glencoe.com.

QUICK Quiz

(Used in Lessons 6-2, 6-5, and 6-7)
Evaluate each expression. Round to the nearest tenth if necessary. (Lesson 1-4)

1. $100 \times 25 \div 52$ **48.1**   2. $10 \div 4 \times 31$ **77.5**

3. $\frac{63 \times 4}{34}$ **7.4**   4. $\frac{2 \times 100}{68}$ **2.9**

(Used in Lessons 6-1 through 6-4, 6-7, 6-8)
Write each fraction in simplest form.
(Lesson 4-4)

5. $\frac{9}{45}$ **$\frac{1}{5}$**   6. $\frac{16}{24}$ **$\frac{2}{3}$**   7. $\frac{38}{46}$ **$\frac{19}{23}$**

8. **AGES** Mikhail is 14 years old. His father is 49 years old. What fraction, in simplest form, of his father's age is Mikhail? (Lesson 4-4) **$\frac{2}{7}$**

(Used in Lesson 6-8)
Write each decimal as a fraction in simplest form. (Lesson 4-5)

9. 0.78 **$\frac{39}{50}$**   10. 0.320 **$\frac{8}{25}$**   11. 0.06 **$\frac{3}{50}$**

12. **SAVINGS** Belinda has saved 0.92 of the cost of a new bicycle. What fraction, in simplest form, represents her savings? (Lesson 4-5) **$\frac{23}{25}$**

(Used in Lesson 6-4)
Multiply. (Lesson 1-2)

13. 4.5×10^2 **450**   14. 1.78×10^3 **1,780**

15. 0.22×10^4 **2,200**   16. 0.03×10^5 **3,000**

QUICK Review

Example 1 Evaluate $15 \times 32 \div 40$.

$15 \times 32 \div 40 = 480 \div 40$ Multiply 15 by 32.
$= 12$ Divide.

Example 2 Write $\frac{16}{44}$ in simplest form.

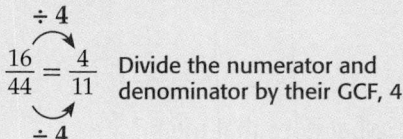

$\frac{16}{44} = \frac{4}{11}$ Divide the numerator and denominator by their GCF, 4.

Example 3 Write 0.62 as a fraction in simplest form.

$0.62 = \frac{62}{100}$ 0.62 is sixty-two hundredths.

$= \frac{31}{50}$ Divide the numerator and denominator by their GCF, 2.

Example 4 Find 3.9×10^3.

$3.9 \times 10^3 = 3,900$ Move the decimal point 3 places to the right. Annex two zeros.

$= 3,900$

Diagnostic Assessment

Exercises	State/Local Standards	Strategic Intervention
1–4		SE Review Lesson 1-4, pp. 38–41
5–8		SE Review Lesson 4-4, pp. 192–195
9–12		SE Review Lesson 4-5, pp. 196–200
13–16		*Math Skill Maintenance Masters*, p. 76

ASSESSMENT PLANNER

✓ Formative Assessment

CRM Anticipation Guide, p. 7–8
Spotting Preconceived Ideas
Students complete this survey to determine prior knowledge about ideas from Chapter 6. Revisit this worksheet after completing the chapter. Also see page 336.

TE Lesson Activities

- Ticket Out the Door, p. 303
- Crystal Ball, p. 319
- Name the Math, pp. 286, 309, 326
- Yesterday's News, pp. 292, 315

Chapter Checkpoints

SE Mid-Chapter Quiz, p. 317

SE Study Guide and Review, pp. 333–336

SE Test Practice, pp. 338–339

CRM Quizzes, pp. 67 and 68

CRM Standardized Test Practice, pp. 84–86

Math Online glencoe.com

- Self-Check Quizzes
- Practice Test
- Test Practice

✓ Summative Assessment

SE Chapter Practice Test, p. 337

CRM Mid-Chapter Test, p. 69

CRM Vocabulary Test, p. 70

CRM Extended-Response Test, p. 83

CRM Leveled Chapter Tests, pp. 71–82

💿 ExamView® Assessment Suite

KEY

CRM *Chapter 6 Resource Masters*

SE Student Edition

TE Teacher Edition

💿 CD-ROM

6-1 Ratios

PACING: **Regular:** 1 period,   **Block:** 0.5 period

Options for Differentiated Instruction

 = English Language Learner   **AL** = Above or Beyond Grade Level   **SS** = Struggling Students   **SN** = Special Needs

Collecting Data   **ELL**   **SS**   **SN**

Use after presenting the Lesson Opener.

Have students collect data to find the student-teacher ratios for their school. Suggest that they compile their data in a table like the one shown at the right.

	Number of Students	Number of Teachers
In the Classroom		
In the School		

Ask:

- What is the student-teacher ratio in the classroom?
- What is the student-teacher ratio in the school?
- Can the ratios be written as whole numbers? If not, what does that mean?

Real-World Applications   **ELL**   **AL**

Use before presenting Example 1.

Arrange students in small groups and have them make lists of how ratios are used in their daily lives. If students have trouble getting started, suggest the following applications:

- paper or photograph sizes
- playing fields
- room dimensions
- data given in news polls

Have them discuss the specific ratios involved, if they know them, as well as the importance of the ratios they mention.

Organizing Student Work and Thinking   **ELL**   **SN**

Use before assigning the Exercises.

Suggest to students that they use tables to organize the data for a given problem. A table for Exercise 38 is shown below.

Total Number of Students	24
Number of Boys	15
Number of Girls	

Using a table like this will help students to see that they need to find the number of girls before finding the ratio of girls to boys.

Leveled Lesson Resources

Also on
TeacherWorks™
Lesson 6-1

Chapter 6 Resource Masters

BL = Below or Approaching Grade Level   **OL** = On Grade Level   **AL** = Above or Beyond Grade Level   **ELL** = English Language Learner

---

Lesson Reading Guide
p. 9 **BL** **OL** **ELL**

NAME _____ DATE _____ PERIOD _____

6-1 Lesson Reading Guide
Ratios

Get Ready for the Lesson
Read the introduction at the top of page 282 in your textbook.
Write your answers below.

1. Write the student-teacher ratio of Prairie Lake Middle School as a fraction. Then write this fraction with a denominator of 1. $\frac{396}{22}$, $\frac{18}{1}$

2. Can you determine which school has the lower student-teacher ratio by examining just the number of teachers at each school? Just the number of students at each school? Explain.
No; Green Briar has a lower student-teacher ratio, but actually has more teachers.

Read the Lesson
For Exercises 3 and 4, review the introduction to this lesson.

3. What two things are being compared? total number of students to total number of teachers

4. What is the comparison of the size of the larger school to the size of the smaller school called? the school ratio

5. When you simplify a ratio written as an improper fraction, should you rewrite the fraction as a mixed number? No; leave the fraction as an improper fraction.

Remember What You Learned

6. Comparing measurements requires you to know how to convert measurements easily. Complete the following table to help you remember some common conversions.

Unit	Equivalent Unit
1 foot	12 inches
1 yard	3 feet
1 year	52 weeks
1 pound	16 ounces
1 gallon	4 quarts
1 quart	2 pints

Chapter 6   9   Course 2

Study Guide and Intervention*
p. 10 **BL** **OL** **ELL**

NAME _____ DATE _____ PERIOD _____

6-1 Study Guide and Intervention
Ratios

Any ratio can be written as a fraction. To write a ratio comparing measurements, such as units of length or units of time, both quantities must have the same unit of measure. Two ratios that have the same value are **equivalent ratios**.

Example 1 Write the ratio 15 to 9 as a fraction in simplest form.

$15 \text{ to } 9 = \frac{15}{9}$ Write the ratio as a fraction.
$= \frac{5}{3}$ Simplify.

Written as a fraction in simplest form, the ratio 15 to 9 is $\frac{5}{3}$.

Example 2 Determine whether the ratios 10 cups of flour in 4 batches of cookies and 15 cups of flour in 6 batches of cookies are equivalent ratios.

Compare ratios written in simplest form.

10 cups:4 batches $= \frac{10 \div 2}{4 \div 2} = \frac{5}{2}$ Divide the numerator and denominator by the GCF, 2

15 cups:6 batches $= \frac{15 \div 3}{6 \div 3} = \frac{5}{2}$ Divide the numerator and denominator by the GCF, 3

Since the ratios simplify to the same fraction, the ratios of cups to batches are equivalent.

Exercises
Write each ratio as a fraction in simplest form.

1. 30 to 12 $\frac{5}{2}$
2. 5:20 $\frac{1}{4}$
3. 49:42 $\frac{7}{6}$
4. 15 to 13 $\frac{15}{13}$
5. 28 feet:35 feet $\frac{4}{5}$
6. 24 minutes to 18 minutes $\frac{4}{3}$
7. 75 seconds:150 seconds $\frac{1}{2}$
8. 12 feet:60 feet $\frac{1}{5}$

Determine whether the ratios are equivalent. Explain.

9. $\frac{3}{4}$ and $\frac{12}{16}$ yes; $\frac{3}{4} = \frac{12}{16}$
10. 12:17 and 10:15 no; 12:17 $\neq$ 10:17, $\frac{12}{17} \neq \frac{2}{3}$
11. $\frac{25}{35}$ and $\frac{10}{14}$ yes; $\frac{25}{35} = \frac{5}{7}$ and $\frac{10}{14} = \frac{5}{7}$
12. 2 lb:36 oz and 3 lb:44 oz no; 2 lb:36 oz $= \frac{8}{9}$, 3 lb:44 oz $= \frac{12}{11}$, and $\frac{8}{9} \neq \frac{12}{11}$
13. 1 ft:4 in. and 3 ft:12 in. yes; 1 ft:4 in. $= \frac{3}{1}$ and 3 ft:12 in. $= \frac{3}{1}$

Chapter 6   10   Course 2

Skills Practice*
p. 11 **BL** **OL**

NAME _____ DATE _____ PERIOD _____

6-1 Skills Practice
Ratios

Write each ratio as a fraction in simplest form.

1. 14 to 6 $\frac{7}{3}$
2. 18:3 $\frac{6}{1}$
3. 4:22 $\frac{2}{11}$
4. 7:21 $\frac{1}{3}$
5. 18:12 $\frac{3}{2}$
6. 20 to 9 $\frac{20}{9}$
7. 25 to 20 $\frac{5}{4}$
8. 4:10 $\frac{2}{5}$
9. 18:21 $\frac{6}{7}$
10. 84 to 16 $\frac{21}{4}$
11. 33 ounces to 11 ounces $\frac{3}{1}$
12. 45 minutes:25 minutes $\frac{9}{5}$
13. 77 cups:49 cups $\frac{11}{7}$
14. 15 pounds to 39 pounds $\frac{5}{13}$
15. 40 seconds to 60 seconds $\frac{2}{3}$
16. 140 centimeters to 300 centimeters $\frac{7}{15}$
17. 9 weeks: 15 weeks $\frac{3}{5}$
18. 3 yards to 33 yards $\frac{1}{11}$

Determine whether the ratios are equivalent. Explain.

19. $\frac{3}{16}$ and $\frac{9}{48}$ yes; $\frac{3}{16} = \frac{9}{48}$
20. $\frac{7}{10}$ and $\frac{8}{11}$ no; $\frac{7}{10} \neq \frac{8}{11}$
21. 18 in.:3 ft and 12 in.:2 ft yes; 18 in.:3 ft $= \frac{1}{2}$ and 12 in.:2 ft $= \frac{1}{2}$
22. 6 mos:2 yr and 8 mos:3 yr no; 6 mos:2 yr $= \frac{1}{4}$, 8 mos:3 yr $= \frac{2}{9}$, and $\frac{1}{4} \neq \frac{2}{9}$

Chapter 6   11   Course 2

Practice*
p. 12 **OL** **AL**

NAME _____ DATE _____ PERIOD _____

6-1 Practice
Ratios

SURVEY For Exercises 1–3, use the responses to a survey to write each ratio as a fraction in simplest form.

Survey Responses		
Yes	No	Not Sure
18	4	6

1. *yes* responses: *no* responses $\frac{9}{2}$
2. *no* responses: *not sure* responses $\frac{2}{3}$
3. *not sure* responses: total responses $\frac{3}{14}$

COUNTY FAIR For Exercises 4–9, use the following information to write each ratio as a fraction in simplest form.
At its annual fair, Westborough County had 27 food booths and 63 game booths. A total of 1,350 adults and 3,600 children attended. The fair made a profit of $42,000. Of this money, $12,600 came from food sales.

4. adults:children $\frac{3}{8}$
5. game booths:food booths $\frac{7}{3}$
6. booths:profits $\frac{3}{1,400}$
7. children:people $\frac{8}{11}$
8. children:booths $\frac{40}{1}$
9. non-food sale profits:profits $\frac{7}{10}$

Determine whether the ratios are equivalent. Explain.

10. 18 trucks to 4 cars, 21 trucks to 6 cars no; $\frac{18}{4} = \frac{9}{2}$ and $\frac{21}{6} = \frac{7}{2}$, so $\frac{9}{2} \neq \frac{7}{2}$
11. $6 for every 10 people, $9 for every 15 people yes; $\frac{6}{10} = \frac{3}{5}$ and $\frac{9}{15} = \frac{3}{5}$, so $\frac{6}{10} = \frac{9}{15}$
12. 33 dinners to 6 packages, 14 dinners to 4 packages no; $\frac{33}{6} = \frac{11}{2}$ and $\frac{14}{4} = \frac{7}{2}$, so $\frac{33}{6} \neq \frac{14}{4}$

13. ENGINES A four cylinder engine produces a maximum of 110 horsepower. A six cylinder engine produces a maximum of 180 horsepower. Do these engines have an equivalent horsepower-to-cylinder ratio? Justify your answer.
no; sample answer: $\frac{110}{4} = \frac{55}{2}$ and $\frac{180}{6} = \frac{30}{1}$, so $\frac{110}{4} \neq \frac{180}{6}$

ANALYZE TABLES For Exercises 14 and 15, use the information in the table that shows the crop statistics for three farms.

Farm	Acres of Soybeans	Acres of Corn
A	585	225
B	2,990	1,150
C	1,120	400

14. For which two farms is the soybeans-to-corn ratio the same? Explain. Farms A and B; both ratios simplify to a soybeans-to-corn ratio of $\frac{13}{5}$.

15. Which farm has the highest soybeans-to-corn ratio? Justify your answer. Farm C's soybeans-to-corn ratio is $\frac{14}{5}$. This is a larger ratio than $\frac{13}{5}$.

Chapter 6   12   Course 2

Word Problem Practice*
p. 13 **OL** **AL**

NAME _____ DATE _____ PERIOD _____

6-1 Word Problem Practice
Ratios

1. ELECTIONS In an election for sheriff, 210 people voted. If there were 1,260 possible voters, write a ratio to compare the number of people who voted to the number of possible voters. $\frac{1}{6}$

2. DENTAL CARE Taru surveyed 60 dentists and found that 48 favored the use of fluoride toothpaste. Write a ratio to compare the number of dentists favoring the use of a fluoride toothpaste to all dentists surveyed. $\frac{4}{5}$

3. E-MAIL One morning, Mirna counted 15 junk e-mails out of 21 e-mails in her inbox. Write a ratio comparing the number of junk e-mails to the total number of e-mails. $\frac{5}{7}$

4. SURFING One evening at his local surf spot, Jeff counted 28 surfers in the water. Among those, he counted 21 that had hoods on their wetsuits. Write a ratio comparing the number of surfers with hoods to the total number of surfers. $\frac{3}{4}$

5. MUSIC A music company signed 12 new artists to its label in 2002. Out of the 12, 10 artists have hit songs. Write a ratio to compare the number of artists with hit songs to the total number of artists signed in 2002. $\frac{5}{6}$

6. BASEBALL Nate had 26 hits at 50 times at bat last season. Write a ratio to compare the number of hits to the number of times at bat. $\frac{13}{25}$

7. BASEBALL In baseball, David has 10 hits out of 14 at bats. Adam has 15 hits out of 21 at bats. For each player, write a ratio that represents his total number of hits out of times at bat. Are these ratios equivalent? 10:14 and 15:21; yes

8. DRIVING Sarah can drive 198 miles on 11 gallons of gasoline. On 6 gallons of gasoline, Rachel can travel 138 miles. Write a ratio that compares miles traveled per gallon of gasoline for each car. Do the cars get the same mileage? 198:11 and 138:6; no

Chapter 6   13   Course 2

Enrichment
p. 14 **OL** **AL**

NAME _____ DATE _____ PERIOD _____

6-1 Enrichment

Golden Ratio

The Great Pyramid at Giza utilizes a special ratio between the altitude of a triangular face and one-half the length of the base. This ratio is known as the **Golden Ratio** and has been used repeatedly by artists and architects over the centuries. It is thought to be particularly pleasing to the human eye.

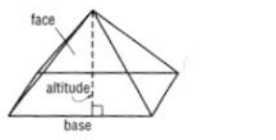

The line segment and rectangle are drawn to illustrate the relationship of the Golden Ratio. $\frac{BC}{AB} = \frac{AC}{BC} \approx 1.618$

Exercises
Determine whether each rectangle demonstrates the Golden Ratio.

1. yes (8.09 ft, 5 ft)
2. no (2.2 in., 5.76 in.)

The Fibonacci Sequence, shown below, is related to the Golden Ratio.
0, 1, 1, 2, 3, 5, 8, 13, 21, ...
The ratio of a number to the previous number approximates the golden ratio. The greater the numbers in the sequence, the closer the approximation is to the golden ratio.

For Exercises 3–6, use the Golden Ratio to determine numbers in the Fibonacci Sequence. Round each number to the nearest whole number.

3. What will the next five numbers be in the sequence? 34, 55, 89, 144, 233
4. What will the next number be after 610? 987
5. What will the next number be after 2,584? 4,181
6. What will the next number be after 6,765? 10,946

Chapter 6   14   Course 2

Additional Lesson Resources

* Also available in Spanish **ELL**

Transparencies
• *5-Minute Check Transparency,* Lesson 6-1

Other Print Products
• *Teaching Mathematics with Manipulatives*
• *Noteables™ Interactive Study Notebook with Foldables™*

Teacher Tech Tools
• *Interactive Classroom CD-ROM,* Lesson 6-1
• *AssignmentWorks,* Lesson 6-1

Student Tech Tools
glencoe.com
• Extra Examples, Chapter 6, Lesson 1
• Self-Check Quiz, Chapter 6, Lesson 1

1 Focus

Vertical Alignment

Before Lesson 6-1
Compute and perform simple multiplication and division of fractions and apply these procedures to solving problems

Lesson 6-1
Interpret and use ratios in different contexts to show the relative sizes of two quantities, using appropriate notations

After Lesson 6-1
Graph linear functions, noting that the vertical change per unit of horizontal change is always the same and know that the ratio is called the slope of the graph

2 Teach

Scaffolding Questions

As you ask the following questions, write each fraction or quantity on the board.

Ask:
- What is the fraction $\frac{15}{20}$ written in simplest form? $\frac{3}{4}$
- What is the fraction $\frac{8}{12}$ written in simplest form? $\frac{2}{3}$
- If I have 8 pennies and 12 nickels, what is my ratio of pennies to nickels? $\frac{8}{12}$, or $\frac{2}{3}$
- If my sister has 4 pennies and 6 nickels, what is her ratio of pennies to nickels? $\frac{4}{6}$, or $\frac{2}{3}$

MAIN IDEA

Write ratios as fractions in simplest form and determine whether two ratios are equivalent.

New Vocabulary

ratio
equivalent ratios

Math Online

glencoe.com
- Extra Examples
- Personal Tutor
- Self-Check Quiz
- Reading in the Content Area

▶ GET READY for the Lesson

SCHOOL The student-teacher ratio of a school compares the total number of students to the total number of teachers.

Middle School	Students	Teachers
Prairie Lake	396	22
Green Brier	510	30

1. Write the student-teacher ratio of Prairie Lake Middle School as a fraction. Then write this fraction with a denominator of 1. $\frac{396}{22}$; $\frac{18}{1}$
2. Can you determine which school has the lower student-teacher ratio by examining just the number of teachers at each school? just the number of students at each school? Explain. **See margin.**

Ratios Key Concept

Words	A **ratio** is a comparison of two quantities by division.

Examples	**Numbers**	**Algebra**
	3 to 4 3:4 $\frac{3}{4}$	a to b $a:b$ $\frac{a}{b}$

Ratios can express part to part, part to whole, or whole to part relationships and are often written as fractions in simplest form.

EXAMPLE Write Ratios in Simplest Form

1. **GRILLING** Seasonings are often added to meat prior to grilling. Using the recipe, write a ratio comparing the amount of garlic powder to the amount of dried oregano as a fraction in simplest form.

Recipe: Greek Style Seasonings

4 tsp. garlic powder
6 tsp. dried oregano
2 tsp. pepper

$$\frac{\text{garlic powder}}{\text{dried oregano}} \quad \frac{4 \text{ tsp}}{6 \text{ tsp}} = \frac{\overset{2}{\cancel{4 \text{ tsp}}}}{\underset{3}{\cancel{6 \text{ tsp}}}} \text{ or } \frac{2}{3}$$

The ratio of garlic powder to dried oregano is $\frac{2}{3}$, 2:3, or 2 to 3. That is, for every 2 units of garlic powder there are 3 units of dried oregano.

✓ CHECK Your Progress

Use the recipe to write each ratio as a fraction in simplest form.

a. pepper:garlic powder $\frac{1}{2}$ b. oregano:pepper $\frac{3}{1}$

Additional Answer

2. No; you need both the number of teachers and the number of students to determine the student-teacher ratio. Once the student-teacher ratio is determined for each school, the school with the lowest student-teacher ratio can be found. Green Brier Middle School has the lower student-teacher ratio with 17 students per teacher.

Ratios that express the same relationship between two quantities are called **equivalent ratios**. Equivalent ratios have the same value.

Focus on Mathematical Content

If two ratios (written as fractions) are equivalent, they can be **simplified to the same fraction**.

If two ratios (written as fractions) are equivalent, **multiplying the numerator and denominator of one ratio by the same number** will result in the second ratio.

EXAMPLE Identify Equivalent Ratios

2 Determine whether the ratios 250 miles in 4 hours and 500 miles in 8 hours are equivalent.

METHOD 1 Compare the ratios written in simplest form.

250 miles : 4 hours $= \dfrac{250 \div 2}{4 \div 2}$ or $\dfrac{125}{2}$ Divide the numerator and denominator by the GCF, 2

500 miles : 8 hours $= \dfrac{500 \div 4}{8 \div 4}$ or $\dfrac{125}{2}$ Divide the numerator and denominator by the GCF, 4

The ratios simplify to the same fraction.

METHOD 2 Look for a common multiplier relating the two ratios.

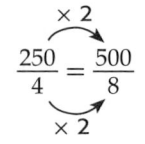

$\dfrac{250}{4} = \dfrac{500}{8}$ The numerator and denominator of the ratios are related by the same multiplier, 2.

The ratios are equivalent.

✔ CHOOSE Your Method

Determine whether the ratios are equivalent.

c. 20 nails for every 5 shingles, 12 nails for every 3 shingles

d. 2 cups flour to 8 cups sugar, 8 cups flour to 14 cups sugar

---

Real-World EXAMPLE

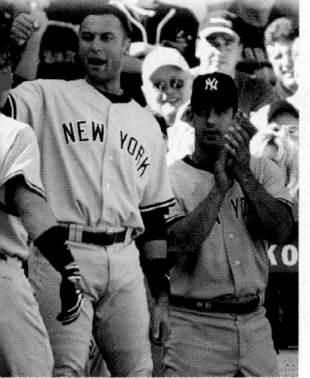

Real-World Link . . . .
In 2006, the New York Yankees had a 0.285 batting average as a team.
Source: Major League Baseball

3 **BASEBALL** Derek Jeter of the New York Yankees had 32 hits out of 93 times at bat. Jorge Posada had 11 hits out of 31 times at bat. Are these ratios equivalent? Justify your answer.

Derek Jeter
$32 : 93 = \dfrac{32}{93}$

Jorge Posada
$11 : 31 = \dfrac{11 \times 3}{31 \times 3}$ or $\dfrac{33}{93}$

Since $\dfrac{32}{93} \neq \dfrac{33}{93}$, the ratios are not equivalent.

✔ CHECK Your Progress

e. **SWIMMING** A community pool requires there to be at least 3 lifeguards for every 20 swimmers. There are 60 swimmers and 9 lifeguards at the pool. Is this the correct number of lifeguards based on the above requirement? Justify your answer.

Lesson 6-1 Ratios   **283**

Study Tip

Writing Ratios
Ratios greater than 1 are expressed as improper fractions and not as mixed numbers.

c. Yes; $\dfrac{20}{5} = \dfrac{4}{1}$ and $\dfrac{12}{3} = \dfrac{4}{1}$, so $\dfrac{20}{5} = \dfrac{12}{3}$.

d. No; $\dfrac{2}{8} \neq \dfrac{8}{14}$ since $2 \cdot 4 = 8$, but $8 \cdot 4 \neq 14$.

e. Yes; sample answer: $3 : 20 = \dfrac{3}{20}$ and $9 : 60 = \dfrac{9}{60}$ or $\dfrac{3}{20}$, so the recommended ratio is met.

✔ Formative Assessment

Use the Check Your Progress exercises after each Example to determine students' understanding of concepts.

ADDITIONAL EXAMPLES

1 **APPLES** Mr. Gale bought a basket of apples. Using the table below, write a ratio comparing the Red Delicious apples to the Granny Smith apples as a fraction in simplest form. $\dfrac{10}{3}$

Mr. Gale's Apples
12   Fuji
9   Granny Smith
30   Red Delicious

2 Determine whether the ratios 12 onions to 15 potatoes and 32 onions to 40 potatoes are equivalent. yes

3 **POOLS** It is recommended that no more than one person be allowed into the shallow end of an outdoor public pool for every 15 square feet of surface area. If a local pool's shallow end has a surface area of 1,800 square feet, are the lifeguards correct to allow 120 people into that part of the pool? yes

---

Additional Examples are also in:

- Noteables™ Interactive Study Notebook with Foldables™
- Interactive Classroom PowerPoint® Presentations

Choose Your Method

Tips for New Teachers

After students complete Example 2, have them discuss which method they found most effective or efficient in order to determine whether the ratios were equivalent. Some students may prefer one method over another. Ask students to explain their preferences. Are there any other methods they could have chosen to determine whether the ratios were equivalent? Have them choose a method in which to complete Choose Your Method c and d. Answers will vary.

Formative Assessment

Use Exercises 1–7 to check for understanding.

Then use the chart at the bottom of this page to customize your assignments for students.

Intervention You may wish to use the Study Guide and Intervention Master on page 10 of the *Chapter 6 Resource Masters* for additional reinforcement.

Odd/Even Assignments

Exercises 8–23 are structured so that students practice the same concepts whether they are assigned odd or even problems.

Additional Answers

5. yes; $\frac{12}{20} = \frac{3}{5}$ and $\frac{6}{10} = \frac{3}{5}$

6. no; $\frac{2}{7} \neq \frac{10}{15}$ or $\frac{2}{3}$

7. no;
Sample answer: $\frac{2 \text{ boxes}}{\$5} \neq \frac{6 \text{ boxes}}{\$20}$, since $2 \cdot 3 = 6$, but $5 \cdot 3 \neq 20$

21. no; $\frac{8}{6} = \frac{4}{3}$ and $\frac{12}{10} = \frac{6}{5}$, so $\frac{8}{6} \neq \frac{12}{10}$

22. yes; Sample answer: $\frac{1 \text{ h}}{2 \text{ lb}} = \frac{4.5 \text{ h}}{9 \text{ lb}}$, since $1 \cdot 4.5 = 4.5$ and $2 \cdot 4.5 = 9$

23. no; Sample answer: $\frac{12 \text{ in.}}{3 \text{ in.}} = \frac{4}{1}$ and $\frac{6 \text{ in.}}{1 \text{ in.}} = \frac{6}{1}$, so $\frac{12 \text{ in.}}{3 \text{ in.}} \neq \frac{6 \text{ in.}}{1 \text{ in.}}$

✓ CHECK Your Understanding

Example 1 (p. 282)

FIELD TRIPS Use the information in the table to write each ratio as a fraction in simplest form.

Field Trip Statistics	
Students	180
Adults	24
Buses	4

1. adults:students $\frac{2}{15}$
2. students:buses $\frac{45}{1}$
3. buses:people $\frac{1}{51}$
4. adults:people $\frac{2}{17}$

Example 2 (p. 283)

Determine whether the ratios are equivalent. Explain.

5. 12 out of 20 doctors agree
6 out of 10 doctors agree
See margin.

6. 2 DVDs to 7 CDs
10 DVDs to 15 CDs
See margin.

Example 3 (p. 283)

7. **SHOPPING** A grocery store has a brand-name cereal on sale at 2 boxes for $5. You buy 6 boxes and are charged $20. Based on the price ratio indicated, were you charged the correct amount? Justify your answer. **See margin.**

▶ Practice and Problem Solving

HOMEWORK HELP

For Exercises	See Examples
8–17	1
18–21	2
22–23	3

Exercise Levels
A: 8–23
B: 24–33
C: 34–36

18. No; $\frac{20}{8} = \frac{5}{2}$ and $\frac{34}{10} = \frac{17}{5}$, so $\frac{20}{8} \neq \frac{34}{10}$.

19. Yes; $\frac{4}{16} = \frac{1}{4}$ and $\frac{10}{40} = \frac{1}{4}$, so $\frac{4}{16} = \frac{10}{40}$.

20. Yes; $\frac{27}{6} = \frac{9}{2}$ and $\frac{18}{4} = \frac{9}{2}$, so $\frac{27}{6} = \frac{18}{4}$.

SOCCER Use the Madison Mavericks team statistics to write each ratio as a fraction in simplest form.

Madison Mavericks Team Statistics	
Wins	10
Losses	12
Ties	8

8. wins:losses $\frac{5}{6}$
9. losses:ties $\frac{3}{2}$
10. losses:games played $\frac{2}{5}$
11. wins:games played $\frac{1}{3}$

CARNIVALS Use the following information to write each ratio as a fraction in simplest form.

At its annual carnival, Brighton Middle School had 6 food booths and 15 games booths. A total of 66 adults and 165 children attended. The carnival raised a total of $1,600. Of this money, $550 came from ticket sales.

12. children:adults $\frac{5}{2}$
13. food booths:games booths $\frac{2}{5}$
14. children:games booths $\frac{11}{1}$
15. booths:money raised $\frac{21}{1,600}$
16. people:children $\frac{7}{5}$
17. non-ticket sale money:total money $\frac{21}{32}$

Determine whether the ratios are equivalent. Explain.

18. 20 female lions to 8 male lions, 34 female lions to 10 male lions
19. $4 for every 16 ounces, $10 for every 40 ounces
20. 27 students to 6 microscopes, 18 students to 4 microscopes
21. 8 roses to 6 babies breath, 12 roses to 10 babies breath **See margin.**

22. **BAKING** It is recommended that a ham be baked 1 hour for every 2 pounds of meat. Latrell baked a 9-pound ham for 4.5 hours. Did he follow the above recommendation? Justify your answer. **See margin.**

23. **FISHING** Kamala catches two similar looking fish. The larger fish is 12 inches long and 3 inches wide. The smaller fish is 6 inches long and 1 inch wide. Do these fish have an equivalent length to width ratio? Justify your answer. **See margin.**

DIFFERENTIATED HOMEWORK OPTIONS

Level	Assignment	Two-Day Option	
BL Basic	8–23, 34, 36–48	9–23 odd, 37, 38	8–22 even, 34, 36, 39–48
OL Core	9–21 odd, 22–34, 36–48	8–23, 37, 38	24–34, 36, 39–48
AL Advanced/Pre-AP	24–44 (optional: 45–48)		

MEASUREMENT The *aspect ratio* of a television is a ratio comparing the width and height. A wide screen television has an aspect ratio of 16:9. Televisions without the same aspect ratio crop the image to fit the screen. Determine which television sizes have a full 16:9 image. Justify your answers.

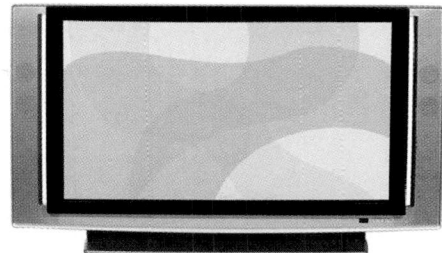

24. $32'' \times 18''$ **yes;** $\frac{32}{18} = \frac{16}{9}$ 25. $71'' \times 42''$ **no;** $\frac{71}{42} \neq \frac{16}{9}$ 26. $48'' \times 36''$ **no;** $\frac{48}{36} \neq \frac{16}{9}$

MAMMALS For Exercises 27 and 28, use the information below.

Mammal	Average Brain Weight (lb)	Average Body Weight (lb)
Adult Human	3	150
Adult Orca Whale	12	5,500

27. How much greater is the average weight of an adult orca whale's brain than the average weight of an adult human's brain? **9 lb**

28. Find the brain-to-body weight ratio for each mammal. Are these ratios equivalent? If not, which mammal has the greater brain-to-body weight ratio? Justify your answer and explain its meaning. **See margin.**

Real-World Link ....
An orca whale, also called a killer whale, is not really a whale, but a dolphin. Its average birth weight is 300 pounds.

29. **MUSIC** The pitch of a musical note is measured by the number of sound waves per second, or *hertz*. If the ratio of the frequencies of two notes can be simplified, the two notes are harmonious. Use the information at the right to find if notes E and G are harmonious. Explain. **yes;** $\frac{330}{396} = \frac{5}{6}$

E : 330 Hertz   G : 396 Hertz

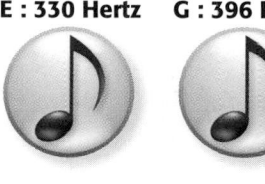

30. **FOOD** The ratio of the number of cups of chopped onion to the number of cups of chopped cilantro in a salsa recipe is 4:3. If the recipe calls for $\frac{2}{3}$ cup chopped onion, how many cups of chopped cilantro are needed? $\frac{1}{2}$ **c**

ANALYZE TABLES For Exercises 31–33, use the table below that shows the logging statistics for three areas of forest. **31–33. See margin.**

Area	Estimated Number of Trees Left to Grow	Estimated Number of Trees Removed for Timber
A	440	1,200
B	1,625	3,750
C	352	960

31. For which two areas was the growth-to-removal ratio the same? Explain.

32. Which area had the greatest growth-to-removal ratio? Justify your answer.

33. Find the additional number of trees that should be planted and left to grow in area A so that its growth-to-removal ratio is the same as area B's. Justify your answer.

EXTRA PRACTICE
See pages 681, 709.

Lesson 6-1 Ratios **285**

Differentiated Instruction

Visual Learners Separate students into groups of two or three. Have each group pick an occupational field such as cooking, business, sports, or science and research and explain how ratios are used in that field. You may wish to have students use a computer with Internet access, or they can consult newspapers or magazines. Have each group write a list of the ratios they find, explaining how they are used. You may wish to have a volunteer from each group present the group's ratios to the class.

 **Exercise Alert!**

Find the Error In Exercise 34, Cleveland added—rather than multiplied—the same number to the numerator and denominator of the first ratio. Remind students that two ratios are equivalent if their numerators and denominators are related by a common multiplier.

 **Assess**

Name the Math Write the following ratios on the board: 3 tablespoons : 2 gallons, and 27 tablespoons : 24 gallons. Have students determine whether the ratios are equivalent. Then have them write what mathematical procedures they used to solve the problem.

FOLDABLES Foldables™
Study Organizer **Follow-Up**

Remind students to select a term or concept about ratios and to define it in their Foldables. Encourage them to give an example of the term or concept.

H.O.T. Problems

34. FIND THE ERROR Cleveland and Luis are determining whether the ratios $\frac{6}{4}$ and $\frac{18}{16}$ are equivalent. Who is correct? Explain. **Luis; Sample answer: to determine equivalent ratios; use multiplication not addition.**

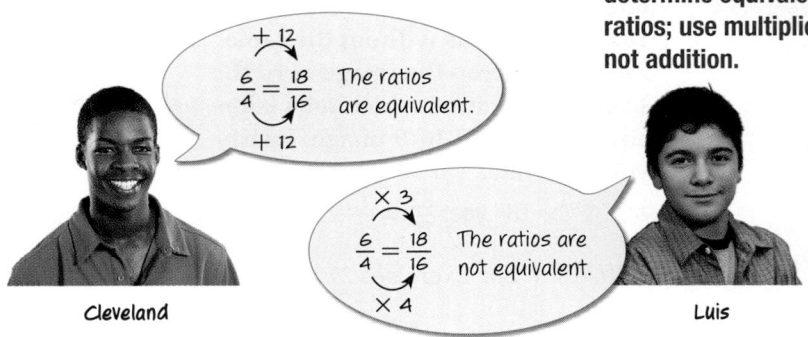

Cleveland   Luis

35. 2,400; The denominator of the ratios increases by 1;
$\frac{20}{40} = \frac{1}{2}, \frac{40}{120} = \frac{1}{3},$
$\frac{120}{480} = \frac{1}{4}$

35. CHALLENGE Find the missing number in the following pattern. Explain your reasoning. (*Hint*: Look at the ratios of successive numbers.)

20, 40, 120, 480, ▇

36. WRITING IN MATH Refer to the application in Exercises 31–33. What would a growth-to-removal ratio greater than 1 indicate? **Sample answer: It would mean that a greater portion of the trees in the area were being left to grow when compared to the number of trees that were removed.**

TEST PRACTICE

37. Which of the following ratios does *not* describe a relationship between the marbles in the jar? **B**

A 8 white : 5 black

B 2 white : 5 black

C 5 black : 13 total

D 8 white : 13 total

38. A class of 24 students has 15 boys. What ratio compares the number of girls to boys in the class? **F**

F 3:5   H 3:8

G 5:3   J 8:3

Spiral Review

39. Find $1\frac{4}{7} \div 1\frac{5}{6}$. Write in simplest form. (Lesson 5-7) $\frac{6}{7}$

ALGEBRA Solve each equation. Check your solution. (Lesson 5-6)

40. $\frac{y}{4} = 7$ **28**   **41.** $\frac{1}{3}x = \frac{5}{9}$ **1$\frac{2}{3}$**   **42.** $4 = \frac{p}{2.7}$ **10.8**   **43.** $2\frac{5}{6} = \frac{1}{2}a$ **5$\frac{2}{3}$**

44. MONEY Grant and his brother put together their money to buy a present for their mom. If they had a total of $18 and Grant contributed $10, how much did his brother contribute? (Lesson 3-2) **$8**

▷ **GET READY for the Next Lesson**

PREREQUISITE SKILL Divide. (p. 676)

45. $9.8 \div 2$ **4.9**   **46.** $\$4.30 \div 5$ **$0.86** **47.** $\$12.40 \div 40$ **$0.31** **48.** $27.36 \div 3.2$ **8.55**

6-2 Rates

PACING: **Regular:** 1.5 periods, **Block:** 1 period

Options for Differentiated Instruction

ELL = English Language Learner   **AL** = Above or Beyond Grade Level   **SS** = Struggling Students   **SN** = Special Needs

Using Modeling **ELL** **SS** **SN**

Use before presenting Example 1.

Have students model a unit rate using counters as the numerator and denominator and a pencil as the fraction bar. For example, show students the model at the right.

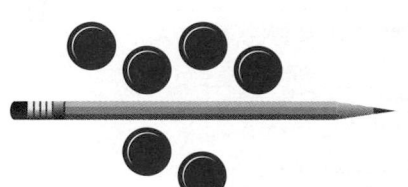

Instruct them to model the unit rate. 2 counters on top, 1 counter on the bottom

Real-Life Applications **ELL** **AL** **SS** **SN**

Use after presenting Example 3.

Have students collect data from two different grocery stores or advertisements. They should find a product that comes in several sizes, such as cereal, potatoes, or detergent. Have them record the size of the product (in ounces, pounds, liters, and so on) and the total cost of the item. Then have students calculate the unit price of the item for each store. Suggest that they organize their data in a table like the one shown below.

Store	Size of Product	Total Cost ($)	Unit Price ($)
1			
2			

Ask:
- Which store has the better price?
- What is the unit price for each store?

Writing **ELL** **AL**

Use after presenting Examples 1–4.

Have students write a problem that uses each type of ratio:
- average speed
- gas mileage
- unit price
- hourly wage

Have students exchange their problems with a classmate and solve each other's problems.

Leveled Lesson Resources

Chapter 6 Resource Masters

BL = Below or Approaching Grade Level   **OL** = On Grade Level   **AL** = Above or Beyond Grade Level   **ELL** = English Language Learner

---

Lesson Reading Guide
p. 15 **BL** **OL** **ELL**

NAME _____ DATE _____ PERIOD _____

6-2 Lesson Reading Guide
Rates

Get Ready for the Lesson
Do the Mini Lab at the top of page 287 in your textbook. Write your answers below.

1. Count the number of beats for each of you.
See students' work.

2. Write the ratio *beats to minutes* as a fraction. **See students' work.**

Read the Lesson

3. A rate is a special kind of ratio. What makes it special?
A rate is a ratio that compares two quantities with different kinds of units.

4. Describe what makes a rate different from a unit rate. Give an example of a rate and its equivalent unit rate. **Sample answer: A unit rate is a rate that has a denominator of 1 unit. For example,** $\frac{\$1.98}{6 \text{ cans of soda}} = \frac{\$0.33}{1 \text{ can of soda}}$

5. Write the ratios in words for each unit rate abbreviation.

Abbreviation	Ratio
m/s	number of meters / 1 second
ft/s	number of feet / 1 second
mi/h (mph)	number of miles / 1 hour
mi/gal (mpg)	number of miles / 1 gallon

Remember What You Learned

6. Go to a food store or find several different newspaper food advertisements. Compare prices for several different sizes of the same product, or compare prices for similar sizes of different brands of the same product. Which size or which brand costs the least per unit? Report your results to the class. **See students' work.**

Chapter 6   15   Course 2

Study Guide and Intervention*
p. 16 **BL** **OL** **ELL**

NAME _____ DATE _____ PERIOD _____

6-2 Study Guide and Intervention
Rates

A ratio that compares two quantities with different kinds of units is called a **rate**. When a rate is simplified so that it has a denominator of 1 unit, it is called a **unit rate**.

Example 1 DRIVING Alita drove her car 78 miles and used 3 gallons of gas. What is the car's gas mileage in miles per gallon?

Write the rate as a fraction. Then find an equivalent rate with a denominator of 1.

$\frac{78 \text{ mi}}{3 \text{ gal}}$ Write the rate as a fraction.

$= \frac{78 \text{ mi} \div 3}{3 \text{ gal} \div 3}$ Divide the numerator and the denominator by 3.

$= \frac{26 \text{ mi}}{1 \text{ gal}}$ Simplify.

The car's gas mileage, or unit rate, is 26 miles per gallon.

Example 2 SHOPPING Joe has two different sizes of boxes of cereal from which to choose. The 12-ounce box costs $2.54, and the 18-ounce box costs $3.50. Which box costs less per ounce?

Find the unit price, or the cost per ounce, of each box. Divide the price by the number of ounces.

12-ounce box $2.54 ÷ 12 ounces ≈ $0.21 per ounce
18-ounce box $3.50 ÷ 18 ounces ≈ $0.19 per ounce

The 18-ounce box costs less per ounce.

Exercises

Find each unit rate. Round to the nearest hundredth if necessary.

1. 18 people in 3 vans
6 people per van

2. $156 for 3 books
$52 per book

3. 115 miles in 2 hours
57.5 mi per h

4. 8 hits in 22 games
0.36 hits per game

5. 65 miles in 2.7 gallons
24.07 mi per gal

6. 2,500 Calories in 24 hours
104.17 C per h

Choose the better unit price.

7. $12.95 for 3 pounds of nuts or $21.45 for 5 pounds of nuts   **$21.45 for 5 lb**

8. A 32-ounce bottle of apple juice for $2.50 or a 48-ounce bottle for $3.84.
$2.50 for a 32-oz bottle

Chapter 6   16   Course 2

Skills Practice*
p. 17 **BL** **OL**

NAME _____ DATE _____ PERIOD _____

6-2 Skills Practice
Rates

Find each unit rate. Round to the nearest hundredth if necessary.

1. $112 in 8 hours
$14 per h

2. 150 miles in 6 gallons
25 mi per gal

3. 49 points in 7 games
7 points per game

4. 105 students in 3 classes
35 students per class

5. 120 problems in 5 hours
24 problems per h

6. 3 accidents in 12 months
0.25 accident per mo

7. 6 eggs in 7 days
0.86 egg per day

8. 8 batteries in 3 months
2.67 batteries per mo

9. 122 patients in 4 weeks
30.5 patients per wk

10. 51 gallons in 14 minutes
3.64 gal per min

11. $8.43 for 3 pounds
$2.81 per lb

12. 357 miles in 6.3 hours
56.67 mi per h

13. 25 letters in 4 days
6.25 letters per day

14. $99 for 12 CDs
$8.25 per CD

15. 5 breaks in 8 hours
0.63 break per h

16. 3 trips in 14 months
0.21 trip per mo

17. 2 pay raises in 3 years
0.67 raise per yr

18. 7 errors in 60 minutes
0.12 error per min

19. 15 pounds in 6 weeks
2.5 lb per wk

20. 8 commercials in 15 minutes
0.53 commercial per min

21. 8 glasses every 24 hours
0.33 glass per h

22. 13 feet in 5 steps
2.6 ft per step

Choose the better unit price.

23. $4.99 for 6 cans or $7.99 for 10 cans   **$7.99 for 10 cans**

24. $21.50 for 4 pounds of lunch meat or $15.10 for 3 pounds of lunch meat
$15.10 for 3 pounds

Chapter 6   17   Course 2

Practice*
p. 18 **OL** **AL**

NAME _____ DATE _____ PERIOD _____

6-2 Practice
Rates

Find each unit rate. Round to the nearest hundredth if necessary.

1. $11.49 for 3 packages
$3.83 per package

2. 2,550 gallons in 30 days
85 gallons per day

3. 88 students for 4 classes
22 students per class

4. 15.6 °F in 13 minutes
1.2 °F per minute

5. 175 Calories in 12 ounces
14.58 C per oz

6. 258.5 miles in 5.5 hours
47 mi per h

7. 549 vehicles on 9 acres
61 vehicles per acre

8. $920 for 40 hours
$23 per h

9. 13 apples for 2 pies
6.5 apples per pie

10. SPORTS The results of a track meet are shown. Who ran the fastest? Explain your reasoning. Round to the nearest ten thousandth.

Name	Event	Time (min)
Theo	3K Run	9.6
Esteban	5K Run	13.5
Tetsuo	10K Run	31.9

Sample answer: Esteban; Theo's rate ≈ 0.3125 km per min, Esteban's rate ≈ 0.3704 km per min, Tetsuo's rate ≈ 0.3135 km per min; 0.3704 km per min > 0.3135 km per min > 0.3125 km per min

11. MANUFACTURING A machinist can produce 114 parts in 6 minutes. At this rate, how many parts can the machinist produce in 15 minutes? **285 parts**

12. RECIPES A recipe that makes 8 jumbo blueberry muffins calls for $1\frac{1}{2}$ teaspoons of baking powder. How much baking powder is needed to make 3 dozen jumbo muffins? $6\frac{3}{4}$ **tsp**

Estimate the unit price for each item. Justify your answers.

13. $299 for 4 tires
$75 per tire;
$299 ÷ 4 ≈ $300 ÷ 4 or $75

14. 3 yards of fabric for $13.47
$4.50 per yard; $13.47 ÷ 3 ≈
$13.50 ÷ 3 or $4.50

UTILITIES For Exercises 15 and 16, use the table that shows the average monthly electricity and water usage.

Family Name	Family Size	Electricity (kilowatt-hours)	Water (gal)
Melendez	4	1,560	3,500
Barton	6	2,130	6,400
Stiles	2	1,490	2,500

15. Which family uses about twice the amount of electricity per person than the other two families? Explain your reasoning. **The Stiles family; The Melendez family uses 390 kwh per person, the Barton family uses 355 kwh per person, and the Stiles family uses 745 kwh per person.**

16. Which family uses the least amount of water per person? Explain your reasoning. **The Melendez family; The Melendez family uses 875 gal per person, the Barton family uses 1,067 gal per person, and the Stiles family uses 1,250 gal per person.**

Chapter 6   18   Course 2

Word Problem Practice*
p. 19 **OL** **AL**

NAME _____ DATE _____ PERIOD _____

6-2 Word Problem Practice
Rates

1. TRAVEL During Sonia's trip across the country, she traveled 2,884 miles. Her trip took 7 days. Find a unit rate to represent the average miles she traveled per day during the trip.
412 mi per day

2. BUDGET Steve was offered $5,025 per year for a weekend lifeguarding job at a local pool. He wants to know how much his monthly income will be at this salary level. What is his rate of pay in dollars per month?
$418.75 per mo

3. MUSIC Randall recorded 8 songs on his most recent CD. The total length of the CD is 49 minutes. Find a unit rate to represent the average length per song on the CD.
6.125 min per song

4. CARPETING Hana paid $1,200 for the carpet in her living room. The room has an area of 251.2 square feet. What was her unit cost of carpeting in dollars per square foot? Round to the nearest cent.
$4.78 per ft²

5. SHOPPING An 8-ounce can of tomatoes costs $1.14. A 12-ounce can costs $1.75. Which can of tomatoes has the better unit price? **8-oz can**

6. PETS Last month, Hao's dog ate 40 cans of dog food in 31 days. How many cans should Hao buy to feed his dog for the next 6 days? **8 cans**

Chapter 6   19   Course 2

Enrichment
p. 20 **OL** **AL**

NAME _____ DATE _____ PERIOD _____

6-2 Enrichment

An Educated Consumer

Choosing a checking account is something that most people do at some point in their lives. Because checking accounts vary from institution to institution, and from one type of account to another, you will need to consider the options associated with each account before choosing one of them.

Suppose a bank offers two kinds of checking accounts.

Account A: a $0.20 charge for writing each check and no service charge

Account B: a $0.10 charge for writing each check and a monthly service charge of $1.50

1. Which account would cost less if a person were to write 10 checks in a month? **Account A**

2. Which account would cost less if a person were to write 20 checks in a month? **Account B**

3. Using the guess-and-check strategy, find the number of checks that would have to be written for the cost of Account A to equal the cost of Account B. What is that cost? **It would take 15 checks; $3.00**

4. Which account would cost less if a person were to write 250 checks in a year? By how much? **Account B; $7.00**

5. Diana Durbin wrote 300 checks in one year. Her total charge for the use of the account that year was $72.00. The bank charges $0.15 for writing one check and charges a fixed amount each month for the use of the account. What is that monthly service charge? **$2.25**

Chapter 6   20   Course 2

Additional Lesson Resources

*** Also available in Spanish** **ELL**

Transparencies
- *5-Minute Check Transparency, Lesson 6-2*

Other Print Products
- *Teaching Mathematics with Manipulatives*
- *Noteables™ Interactive Study Notebook with Foldables™*

Teacher Tech Tools
- *Interactive Classroom CD-ROM, Lesson 6-2*
- *AssignmentWorks, Lesson 6-2*

Student Tech Tools
glencoe.com
- Extra Examples, Chapter 6, Lesson 2
- Self-Check Quiz, Chapter 6, Lesson 2

MAIN IDEA

Determine unit rates.

New Vocabulary

rate
unit rate

Math Online

glencoe.com
• Extra Examples
• Personal Tutor
• Self-Check Quiz

MINI Lab

Choose a partner and take turns taking each other's pulse for 2 minutes.

1. Count the number of beats for each of you. **See students' work.**

2. Write the ratio *beats* to *minutes* as a fraction. **See students' work.**

A ratio that compares two quantities with different kinds of units is called a **rate**.

$$\frac{160 \text{ beats}}{2 \text{ minutes}}$$

> The units *beats* and *minutes* are different.

When a rate is simplified so that it has a denominator of 1 unit, it is called a **unit rate**.

$$\frac{80 \text{ beats}}{1 \text{ minute}}$$

> The denominator is 1 unit.

The table below shows some common unit rates.

Rate	Unit Rate	Abbreviation	Name
$\frac{\text{number of miles}}{1 \text{ hour}}$	miles per hour	mi/h or mph	average speed
$\frac{\text{number of miles}}{1 \text{ gallon}}$	miles per gallon	mi/gal or mpg	gas mileage
$\frac{\text{number of dollars}}{1 \text{ pound}}$	price per pound	dollars/lb	unit price
$\frac{\text{number of dollars}}{1 \text{ hour}}$	dollars per hour	dollars/h	hourly wage

Real-World EXAMPLE   Find a Unit Rate

① WORKING Desiree earns $280 in 40 hours. What is her hourly pay rate?

$280 in 40 hours $= \dfrac{\$280}{40 \text{ h}}$ Write the rate as a fraction.

$= \dfrac{\$280 \div 40}{40 \text{ h} \div 40}$ Divide the numerator and the denominator by 40.

$= \dfrac{\$7}{1 \text{ h}}$ Simplify.

Desiree's hourly pay rate is $7.

✓ CHECK Your Progress

Find each unit rate. Round to the nearest hundredth if necessary.

a. $300 for 6 hours **$50 per hour**
b. 220 miles on 8 gallons **27.5 miles per gallon**

---

1 Focus

Vertical Alignment

Before Lesson 6-2
Compute and perform simple multiplication and division of fractions and apply these procedures to solving problems

Lesson 6-2
Interpret and use ratios in different contexts to show the relative sizes of two quantities, using appropriate notations; demonstrate an understanding that rate is a measure of one quantity per unit value of another quantity; solve problems involving rates

After Lesson 6-2
Solve multistep problems involving rate, average speed, distance, and time or a direct variation

2 Teach

MINI Lab

Have students work in pairs. One can take the pulse while the other tells when the 2-minute period begins and ends. Then they can reverse roles.

Scaffolding Questions

Ask:
• What is the speed limit on the highway? 60/65/70 miles per hour

• If you drive at that speed limit, how far will you travel in 1 hour? 60/65/70 miles

• If a student earned $12 in 2 hours, how much would she earn in 1 hour? $6

• If 3 pounds of tomatoes cost $6, how much would 1 pound cost? $2

Focus on Mathematical Content

Students use unit rates in their everyday lives to **measure** and **compare** rates such as speed, price, and wage.

Many real-world problems can be solved by **extending or projecting** a unit rate.

✓ Formative Assessment

Use the Check Your Progress exercises after each Example to determine students' understanding of concepts.

ADDITIONAL EXAMPLES

1 **READING** Julia read 52 pages in 2 hours. What is the average number of pages she read per hour? **26 pages per hour**

2 **SODA** Find the unit price per can if it costs $3 for 6 cans of soda. Round to the nearest hundredth if necessary. **$0.50 per can**

3 **TEST EXAMPLE** The costs of 4 different sizes of orange juice are shown in the table. Which container costs the least per ounce? **A**

Amount	Total Cost
16 oz	$1.28
32 oz	$1.92
64 oz	$2.56
96 oz	$3.36

A 96-oz container
B 64-oz container
C 32-oz container
D 16-oz container

Additional Examples are also in:
- Noteables™ Interactive Study Notebook with Foldables™
- Interactive Classroom PowerPoint® Presentations

Real-World EXAMPLE Find a Unit Rate

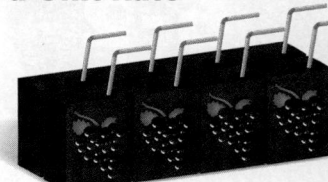

2 **JUICE** Find the unit price if it costs $2 for eight juice boxes. Round to the nearest cent if necessary.

$2 for eight boxes $= \dfrac{\$2}{8 \text{ boxes}}$ Write the rate as a fraction.

$= \dfrac{\$2 \div 8}{8 \text{ boxes} \div 8}$ Divide the numerator and the denominator by 8.

$= \dfrac{\$0.25}{1 \text{ box}}$ Simplify.

The unit price is $0.25 per juice box.

✓ CHECK Your Progress

c. ESTIMATION Find the unit price if a 4-pack of mixed fruit sells for $2.12. **$0.53**

Unit rates are useful when you want to make comparisons.

TEST EXAMPLE Compare Using Unit Rates

3 The prices of 3 different bags of dog food are given in the table. Which size bag has the lowest price per pound?

Dog Food Prices	
Bag Size (pounds)	Price
40	$49.00
20	$23.44
8	$9.88

A the 40-lb bag
B the 20-lb bag
C the 8-lb bag
D All three bag sizes have the same price per pound.

Test-Taking Tip

Alternative Method
One 40-lb bag is equivalent to two 20-lb bags or five 8-lb bags. The cost for one 40-lb bag is $49, the cost for two 20-lb bags is about 2 × $23 or $46, and the cost for five 8-lb bags is about 5 × $10 or $50. So the 20-lb bag has the lowest price per pound.

Read the Item

To determine the lowest price per pound, find and compare the unit price for each size bag.

Solve the Item

40-pound bag $49.00 ÷ 40 pounds = $1.225 per pound

20-pound bag $23.44 ÷ 20 pounds = $1.172 per pound

8-pound bag $9.88 ÷ 8 pounds = $1.235 per pound

At $1.172 per pound, the 20-pound bag sells for the lowest price per pound.

The answer is B.

Tips for New Teachers **Analyzing Cost**

You may wish to point out that the positions of the quantities being compared in a rate can be reversed. For instance, in Example 2, the unit rate per dollar is 4 juice boxes per dollar. Encourage students to analyze a problem to determine which rate is more helpful (e.g., the number of juice boxes per dollar or the cost per juice box). If a person wanted to know how many juice boxes she could buy for $7, the unit rate per dollar would be more helpful. But if a person wanted to compare the cost of juice boxes at different stores, the unit price per juice box would be more helpful.

d. Tito wants to buy some peanut butter to donate to the local food pantry. If Tito wants to save as much money as possible, which brand should he buy? **G**

Peanut Butter Sales	
Brand	**Sale Price**
Nutty	12 ounces for $2.19
Grandma's	18 ounces for $2.79
Bee's	28 ounces for $4.69
Save-A-Lot	40 ounces for $6.60

F Nutty, because the quality of the peanut butter is better

G Grandma's, because the price per ounce is about $0.16

H Bee's, because the price per ounce is about $0.14

J Save-A-Lot, because he wants to buy 40 ounces

Real-World Link . . . . .
Face paint can be made from 1 teaspoon cornstarch and $\frac{1}{2}$ teaspoon each of water and cold cream.

Real-World EXAMPLE   **Use a Unit Rate**

 FACE PAINTING Lexi painted 3 faces in 12 minutes at the Crafts Fair. At this rate, how many faces can she paint in 40 minutes?

Find the unit rate. Then multiply this unit rate by 40 to find the number of faces she can paint in 40 minutes.

$$3 \text{ faces in 12 minutes} = \frac{3 \text{ faces} \div 12}{12 \text{ min} \div 12} = \frac{0.25 \text{ faces}}{1 \text{ min}} \quad \text{Find the unit rate.}$$

$$\frac{0.25 \text{ faces}}{1 \text{ min}} \cdot 40 \text{ min} = 10 \text{ faces} \quad \text{Divide out the common units.}$$

Lexi can paint 10 faces in 40 minutes.

 CHECK Your Progress   e. $7.90

e. **SCHOOL SUPPLIES** Kimbel bought 4 notebooks for $6.32. At this same unit price, how much would he pay for 5 notebooks?

★ indicates multi-step problem

CHECK Your Understanding

Examples 1, 2
(pp. 287–288)

2. 420 kb per min
4. 9.5 feet per second

Find each unit rate. Round to the nearest hundredth if necessary.

1. 90 miles on 15 gallons **6 mi per gal**
2. 1,680 kilobytes in 4 minutes
3. 5 pounds for $2.49 **$0.50 per lb**
4. 152 feet in 16 seconds

Example 3
(pp. 288–289)

5. **MULTIPLE CHOICE** Four stores offer customers bulk CD rates. Which store offers the best buy? **C**

Bulk CD Offers	
Store	**Offer**
CD Express	4 CDs for $60
Music Place	6 CDs for $75
CD Rack	5 CDs for $70
Music Shop	3 CDs for $40

A CD Express   **C** Music Place

B CD Rack   **D** Music Shop

Example 4
(p. 289)

6. **TRAVEL** After 3.5 hours, Pasha had traveled 217 miles. At this same speed, how far will she have traveled after 4 hours? **248 mi**

ADDITIONAL EXAMPLE

 POTATOES An assistant cook peeled 18 potatoes in 6 minutes. At this rate, how many potatoes can he peel in 50 minutes? 150 potatoes

3 Practice

Formative Assessment

Use Exercises 1–6 to check for understanding.

Then use the chart at the bottom of the next page to customize your assignments for students.

Intervention You may wish to use the Study Guide and Intervention Master on page 16 of the *Chapter 6 Resource Masters* for additional reinforcement.

Odd/Even Assignments

Exercises 7–24 are structured so that students practice the same concepts whether they are assigned odd or even problems.

Exercise Levels
A: 7–24
B: 25–39
C: 40–44

8. 152 customers per day
9. 30.4 people per class
10. 203.75 Calories per serving
18. 9 bottles for $4.50; $0.50 < $0.57 < $0.63
19. Soft drinks A and B have about 3 grams of sodium per ounce and Soft drink C has about 6 grams per ounce.

Real-World Link . . . . .
North Carolina has approximately 8.9 million people living in 48,718 square miles.
Source: U.S. Census Bureau

▶ Practice and Problem Solving

HOMEWORK HELP

For Exercises	See Examples
7–16	1, 2
17–20	3
21–24	4

Find each unit rate. Round to the nearest hundredth if necessary.

7. 360 miles in 6 hours **60 mi/h**
8. 6,840 customers in 45 days
9. 152 people for 5 classes
10. 815 Calories in 4 servings
11. 45.5 meters in 13 seconds **3.5 m/s**
12. $7.40 for 5 pounds **$1.48/lb**
13. $1.12 for 8.2 ounces **$0.14/oz**
14. 144 miles in 4.5 gallons **32 mi/gal**

15. **ESTIMATION** Estimate the unit rate if 12 pairs of socks sell for $5.79. **about $0.50 per pair**

16. **ESTIMATION** Estimate the unit rate if a 26-mile marathon was completed in 5 hours. **about 5 mi/h**

17. **SPORTS** The results of a swim meet are shown. Who swam the fastest? Explain your reasoning. **Susana; 1.78 m/s > 1.66 m/s > 1.23 m/s**

Name	Event	Time (s)
Tawni	50-m Freestyle	40.8
Pepita	100-m Butterfly	60.2
Susana	200-m Medley	112.4

18. **MONEY** A grocery store sells three different packages of bottled water. Which package costs the least per bottle? Explain your reasoning.

6-pack for $3.79

9-pack for $4.50

12-pack for $6.89

NUTRITION For Exercises 19 and 20, use the table at the right.

19. Which soft drink has about twice the amount of sodium per ounce than the other two? Explain.

20. Which soft drink has the least amount of sugar per ounce? Explain. **Soft drink A; 1.83 < 1.88 < 4.29 g/oz**

Soft Drink Nutritional Information			
Soft Drink	Serving Size (oz)	Sodium (mg)	Sugar (g)
A	12	40	22
B	8	24	15
C	7	42	30

21. **WORD PROCESSING** Ben can type 153 words in 3 minutes. At this rate, how many words can he type in 10 minutes? **510 words**

22. **FABRIC** Marcus buys 3 yards of fabric for $7.47. Later he realizes that he needs 2 more yards. How much will he pay for the extra fabric? **$4.98**

23. **ESTIMATION** A player scores 87 points in 6 games. At this rate, about how many points would she score in the next 4 games? **Sample answer: about 60**

24. **JOBS** Dalila earns $94.20, for working 15 hours as a holiday helper wrapping gifts. If she works 18 hours the next week, how much money will she earn? **$113.04**

25. **POPULATION** Use the information at the left. What is the *population density* or number of people per square mile in North Carolina? **182.7**

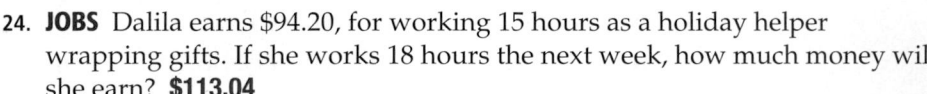

DIFFERENTIATED HOMEWORK OPTIONS

Level	Assignment	Two-Day Option	
BL Basic	7–24, 42–55	7–23, odd, 45, 46	8–24 even, 42–44, 47–55
OL Core	7–23 odd, 25–39, 42–55	7–24, 45, 46	25–39, 42–44, 47–55
AL Advanced/Pre-AP	25–51 (optional: 52–55)		

26. $1.25 per qt;
$2.49 ÷ 2 ≈ $2.50
÷ 2 or $1.25
27. 38¢ per lb;
$1.89 ÷ 5 ≈ $1.90
÷ 5 or $0.38
28. $0.06 per oz;
$1.13 ÷ 20 ≈ $1.20
÷ 20 or $0.06

ESTIMATION Estimate the unit price for each item. Justify your answers.

26.  $2.49

27. 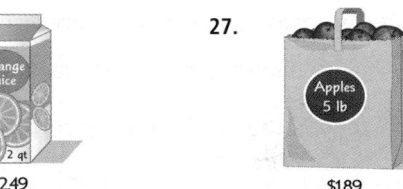 $1.89

28.  $1.13

29. RECIPES A recipe that makes 10 mini-loaves of banana bread calls for $1\frac{1}{4}$ cups flour. How much flour is needed to make 2 dozen mini-loaves using this recipe? **3 c**

Real-World Link....
The record for the Boston Marathon's wheelchair division is 1 hour, 18 minutes, and 27 seconds.
Source: Boston Athletic Association

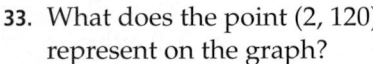

SPORTS For Exercises 30 and 31, use the information at the left.

30. The wheelchair division for the Boston Marathon is 26.2 miles long.
★ What was the average speed of the record winner of the wheelchair division? Round to the nearest hundredth. **20.04 mi/h**

31. At this rate, about how long would it take this competitor to complete
★ a 30 mile race? **about 1 h 29 min 49 s**

32. MONEY Suppose that 1 European euro is worth $1.25. In Europe, a book costs 19 euro. In Los Angeles, the same book costs $22.50. In which location is the book less expensive? **See margin.**

33. The bear's heart beats 120 times in 2 minutes when it is active.
34. The bear's heart beats 18 times in 1.5 minutes when it is hibernating.
35. the bear's heart rate in beats per minute
36. active: 60 beats per minute; hibernating: 12 beats per minute

ANIMALS For Exercises 33–37, use the graph that shows the average number of heartbeats for an active adult brown bear and a hibernating brown bear.

33. What does the point (2, 120) represent on the graph?

34. What does the point (1.5, 18) represent on the graph?

35. What does the ratio of the y-coordinate to the x-coordinate for each pair of points on the graph represent?

36. Use the graph to find the bear's average heart rate when it is active and when it is hibernating.

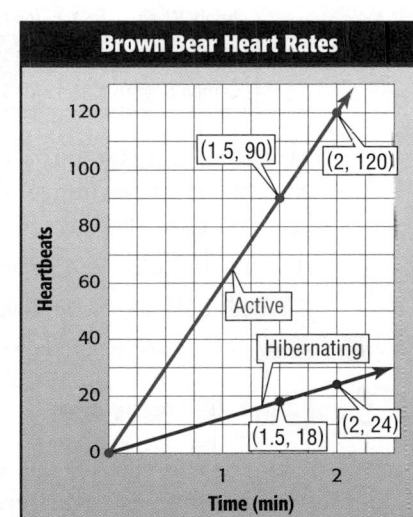

37. When is the bear's heart rate greater, when it is active or when it is hibernating? How can you tell this from the graph? **See margin.**

38. TIRES At Tire Depot, a pair of new tires sells for $216. The manager's special advertises the same tires selling at a rate of $380 for 4 tires. How much do you save per tire if you purchase the manager's special? **$13**

39. FIND THE DATA Refer to the Data File on pages 16–19. Choose some data and write a real-world problem in which you would compare unit rates or ratios. **See students' work.**

Yesterday's News Remind students that yesterday's lesson was about writing ratios in simplest form. Have them write how yesterday's concepts helped them with today's material.

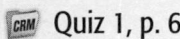 **Formative Assessment**

Check for student understanding of concepts in Lessons 6-1 and 6-2.

[CRM] Quiz 1, p. 67

 **Foldables™ Follow-Up**

Remind students to select a term or concept about unit rates and to define it in their Foldables. Encourage them to give an example of the term or concept.

Additional Answers

40. Sometimes; a ratio that compares two measurements with different units is a rate, such as $\frac{2 \text{ miles}}{10 \text{ minutes}}$. A ratio that compares two numbers or two measurements with like units is not a rate, such as $\frac{2 \text{ cups}}{3 \text{ cups}}$.

44. Sample answer: The rate 55 miles per hour is a measure of the number of miles traveled per unit hour.

H.O.T. Problems

41. Always; every rate is a ratio, because it is a comparison of two quantities by division.

42. Sample answer:
$\frac{30 \text{ mi}}{2 \text{ h}} = \frac{15 \text{ mi}}{1 \text{ h}}$

CHALLENGE Determine whether each statement is *sometimes, always,* or *never* true. Give an example or a counterexample.

40. A ratio is a rate. **See margin.**   **41.** A rate is a ratio.

42. OPEN ENDED Create a rate and then convert it to a unit rate.

43. NUMBER SENSE In which situation will the rate $\frac{x \text{ feet}}{y \text{ minutes}}$ increase? Give an example to explain your reasoning. **a;** $\frac{30 \text{ ft}}{2 \text{ min}} = 15 \text{ ft/min}, \frac{40 \text{ ft}}{2 \text{ min}} = 20 \text{ ft/min}$

  a. x increases, y is unchanged   b. x is unchanged, y increases

44. **WRITING IN MATH** Describe, using an example, how a *rate* is a measure of one quantity per unit of another quantity. **See margin.**

TEST PRACTICE

45. Mrs. Ross needs to buy dish soap. There are four different size containers at a store.

Dish Soap Prices	
Brand	**Price**
Lots of Suds	$0.98 for 8 ounces
Bright Wash	$1.29 for 12 ounces
Spotless Soap	$3.14 for 30 ounces
Lemon Bright	$3.45 for 32 ounces

Mrs. Ross wants to buy the one that costs the least per ounce. Which brand should she buy? **C**

A Lots of Suds   **C** Spotless Soap

B Bright Wash   **D** Lemon Bright

46. The table shows the total distance traveled by a car driving at a constant rate of speed.

Time (h)	Distance (mi)
2	130
3.5	227.5
4	260
7	455

Based on this information, how far will the car have traveled after 10 hours? **H**

F 520 miles   **H** 650 miles

G 585 miles   **J** 715 miles

Spiral Review

FLOWERS For Exercises 47–50, use the information in the table to write each ratio as a fraction in simplest form. (Lesson 6-1)

47. lilies : roses $\frac{2}{9}$ **48.** snapdragons : lilies $\frac{3}{2}$

49. roses : flowers $\frac{9}{14}$ **50.** flowers : snapdragons $\frac{14}{3}$

Flower Arrangement	
Lilies	4
Roses	18
Snapdragons	6

51. SANDWICHES Lawanda is making subs. She puts $1\frac{1}{2}$ slices of cheese on each sub. If she has 12 slices of cheese, how many subs can she make? (Lesson 5-6) **8 subs**

▷ **GET READY for the Next Lesson**

PREREQUISITE SKILL Write each fraction in simplest form. (Lesson 4-3)

52. $\frac{8}{12}$ $\frac{2}{3}$ **53.** $\frac{9}{18}$ $\frac{1}{2}$ **54.** $\frac{25}{35}$ $\frac{5}{7}$ **55.** $\frac{10}{40}$ $\frac{1}{4}$

292 Chapter 6 Ratios and Proportions

6-3 Rate of Change and Slope

PACING: **Regular:** 2 periods, **Block:** 1 period

Options for Differentiated Instruction

 = English Language Learner   = Above or Beyond Grade Level   **SS** = Struggling Students   **SN** = Special Needs

Mathematical Displays

Use after Example 3.

Have students create a poster that explains how to find the constant rate of change from a table and from a graph. The poster should include how to find the change in the y-value and the change in the x-value and how to use them to find the constant rate of change. It should also discuss how to determine whether the rate of change is linear or not.

Real-Life Applications **ELL** **AL** **SS** **SN**

Use after Example 3.

Have students write down the time traveled and the distance traveled when they go to visit a friend or relative. Have them write down the time and distance they travel each 5 minutes. Have them determine if the relationship between the distance and the time is linear. If it is, have them calculate the constant rate of change.

Writing **ELL** **AL**

Use after Example 3.

Have students create a table and a graph that have a constant rate of change. Have students exchange their problems with classmates and solve one another's problems.

Leveled Lesson Resources

Chapter 6 Resource Masters

BL = Below or Approaching Grade Level   **OL** = On Grade Level   **AL** = Above or Beyond Grade Level   **ELL** = English Language Learner

---

Lesson Reading Guide
p. 21 **BL** **OL** **ELL**

NAME _____ DATE _____ PERIOD _____

6-3 Lesson Reading Guide
Rate of Change and Slope

Get Ready for the Lesson

Read the introduction at the top of page 293 in your textbook. Write your answers below.

1. What is the change in Stephanie's height from ages 9 to 12? **6 inches**

2. Over what number of years did the change take place? **3 years**

3. Write a rate of change that compares the change in Stephanie's height to the change in age. Express your answer as a unit rate and explain its meaning. **2 inches per year; Stephanie's height increased by an average of 2 inches per year.**

Read the Lesson

4. Example 1 uses the unit rate to find the rate of change. Why is the rate of change usually written as a unit rate? **Sample answer: a unit rate makes it easier to compare rates of change.**

5. Example 2 uses ordered pairs to find the rate of change. What is an ordered pair? **An ordered pair describes the location of a point on a graph.**

6. The formula to find slope is given as $\frac{\text{change in } y}{\text{change in } x}$. Describe slope another way.

Sample answer: $\frac{\text{vertical change}}{\text{horizontal change}}$

Remember What You Learned

7. The table shows the amount of money Samantha earns for babysitting based on the number of hours she babysits. Find the rate of change for Samantha's earnings.

Hours	2	4	6	8	10
Amount earned (in dollars)	10	20	30	40	50

The rate of change is $5 per hour.

Chapter 6   21   Course 2

Study Guide and Intervention*
p. 22 **BL** **OL** **ELL**

NAME _____ DATE _____ PERIOD _____

6-3 Study Guide and Intervention
Rate of Change and Slope

- A rate of change is a rate that describes how one quantity changes in relation to another.
- Slope tells how steep the line is.
- Slope is given by the formula $\frac{\text{change in } y}{\text{change in } x}$ or $\frac{\text{vertical change}}{\text{horizontal change}}$.

Example 1 Find the rate of change for the table.

Students	Number of Textbooks
5	15
10	30
15	45
20	60

The change in the number of textbooks is 15 while the change in the number of students is 5.

$\frac{\text{change in number of textbooks}}{\text{change in number of students}} = \frac{15 \text{ textbooks}}{5 \text{ students}}$ The number of textbooks increased by 15 for every 5 students.

$= \frac{3 \text{ textbooks}}{1 \text{ student}}$ Write as a unit rate.

So, the number of textbooks increases by 3 textbooks per student.

Example 2 The band boosters are selling T-shirts at a linear rate. By 8 P.M., they had sold 25 T-shirts. By 10 P.M., they had sold 45 T-shirts. Find the slope of the line. Explain what the slope represents.

$\frac{\text{change in number of T-shirts}}{\text{change in time}} = \frac{45 - 25}{10 - 8}$ Definition of slope.

$= \frac{20}{2}$ Simplify.

$= 10$

The slope is 10 and it means that the shirts are selling at a rate of 10 shirts per hour.

Exercises

Find the rate of change for each table.

1.
Side Length	Perimeter
1	4
2	8
3	12
4	16

4

2.
Time (in hours)	Distance (in miles)
2	120
4	240
6	360
8	480

Sample answer: 60 miles per hour

3. The temperature at 10 A.M. was 72°F and at 2 P.M. was 88°F. Find the slope of the line. Explain what the slope represents. **4°F per hour; The temperature rose an average of 4°F per hour.**

Chapter 6   22   Course 2

Skills Practice*
p. 23 **BL** **OL**

NAME _____ DATE _____ PERIOD _____

6-3 Skills Practice
Rate of Change and Slope

Find the rate of change for each table.

1.
Time spent Mowing (in hours)	Money Earned (in dollars)
1	10
3	30
5	50
7	70

$10 per hour

2.
Time (in hours)	Temperature (in degrees)
9:00	60
10:00	62
11:00	64
12:00	66

2° per hour

3.
Number of Students	Number of Magazines Sold
10	100
15	150
20	200
25	250

10 magazines per student

4.
Number of Trees	Number of Apples
5	100
10	200
15	300
20	400

20 apples per tree

5.
Number of Volunteers	Number of Hours Logged
5	10
10	20
15	30
20	40

2 hours per volunteer

6.
Gas Left in Tank	Miles Driven
12	0
10	50
8	100
6	150

Decreasing 2 gallons per 50 miles; or 1 gallon per 25 miles

Find the rate of change for each graph.

7. Temperature Change

−2° F per hour

8. Meat

3 lbs per person

Chapter 6   23   Course 2

Practice*
p. 24 **OL** **AL**

NAME _____ DATE _____ PERIOD _____

6-3 Practice
Rate of Change and Slope

Find the rate of change for each table.

1.
Baby Age	Weight
0 months	0 pounds
3 months	12 pounds
6 months	24 pounds
9 months	36 pounds

4 pounds per month

2.
Number of Hours Worked	Money Earned ($)
4	80
6	120
8	160
10	200

$20 per hour

3.
Days	Plant Height (in.)
7	4
14	11
21	18
28	25

1 in. per day

4.
Months	Money Spent on Cable TV
2	82
4	164
6	246
8	328

$41 per month

Find the rate of change for each graph.

5. Students in Mr. Muni's Class

2 boys per girl

6. Jewelry Making

4 bracelets per girl

7. Graph the data. Then find the slope of the line. Explain what the slope represents.

Feet	1	2	3	4	5	6
Yards	3	6	9	12	15	18

Answer: slope = 3; There are 3 feet per yard. Graph:

Chapter 6   24   Course 2

Word Problem Practice*
p. 25 **OL** **AL**

NAME _____ DATE _____ PERIOD _____

6-3 Word Problem Practice
Rate of Change and Slope

1. **WATER** At 2 P.M., the level of the water in the pool was 10 feet. At 6 P.M., the level of water was 2 feet. Find the rate of change of the water. **decreasing 2 feet per hour**

2. **MONEY** JoAnne is depositing money into a bank account. After 3 months there is $150 in the account. After 6 months, there is $300 in the account. Find the rate of change of the account. **increasing by $50 per month**

3. **TEMPERATURE** The temperature at noon was 88°F. By 4 P.M., the temperature was 72°F. Find the rate of change of the temperature. **decreasing by 4°F per hour**

4. **GROWTH** Jaz was 43 inches tall. Eighteen months later, she was 52 inches tall. Find the rate of change for Jaz's height. **increasing by 0.5 inch per month**

5. **BIKING** The graph represents how far Kevin biked given the number of weeks he has been biking. Find the rate of change.

Biking

increasing by 11 miles per week

6. **HAIR** Graph the data. Find the slope of the line. Describe what the slope means.

Month	4	6	8	10
Length (in inches)	8	10	12	14

Slope is $\frac{2}{2}$. It means that her hair length is increasing by 2 inches per month.

Hair Length

Chapter 6   25   Course 2

Enrichment
p. 26 **OL** **AL**

NAME _____ DATE _____ PERIOD _____

6-3 Enrichment

Making Predictions

A scatter plot is a useful tool for making predictions. Information or data can be plotted on a coordinate grid. Then a line that is similar to the shape formed by the points is plotted. This line is known as a *line of best fit*. Using ordered pairs on the line of best fit, the approximate rate of change can be found. The rate of change can be used to predict future values.

1. Keep track of the growth of a plant over 6 months. Record the information in a table. **Sample answer:**

Month	1	2	3	4	5	6
Height (inches)	3	5	8	9	10	13

2. Plot the data you have collected. **Sample answer:**

Plant Growth

3. Draw a line that matches the shape of the points plotted. **Sample answer:**

Plant Growth

4. Find two ordered pairs on the line of best fit. **Sample answer: (2, 5) and (5, 10)**

5. Find the slope using the ordered pairs. **Sample answer: $\frac{5}{3}$**

6. If growth continues to follow the same pattern, how tall will the plant be in 12 months? **Sample answer: 20 inches**

Chapter 6   26   Course 2

*** Also available in Spanish** **ELL**

Additional Lesson Resources

Transparencies
- *5-Minute Check Transparency,* Lesson 6-3

Other Print Products
- *Teaching Mathematics with Manipulatives*
- *Noteables™ Interactive Study Notebook with Foldables™*

Teacher Tech Tools
- *Interactive Classroom CD-ROM,* Lesson 6-3
- *AssignmentWorks,* Lesson 6-3

Student Tech Tools
glencoe.com
- Extra Examples, Chapter 6, Lesson 3
- Self-Check Quiz, Chapter 6, Lesson 3

▷ **GET READY** for the Lesson

HEIGHTS The table shows Stephanie's height at ages 9 and 12.

Age (yr)	9	12
Height (in.)	53	59

1. What is the change in Stephanie's height from ages 9 to 12? **6 inches**

2. Over what number of years did this change take place? **3**

3. Write a rate that compares the change in Stephanie's height to the change in age. Express your answer as a unit rate and explain its meaning. **2 inches per year; Stephanie's height increased by an average of 2 inches per year.**

A **rate of change** is a rate that describes how one quantity changes in relation to another. A rate of change is usually expressed as a unit rate.

EXAMPLE · Find Rate of Change from a Table

① **FUNDRAISING** The table shows the amount of money a Booster Club made washing cars for a fundraiser. Use the information to find the rate of change in dollars per car.

Cars Washed

Number	Money ($)
5	40
10	80
15	120
20	160

+5 each step in Number; +40 each step in Money

Find the unit rate to determine the rate of change.

$$\frac{\text{change in money}}{\text{change in cars}} = \frac{40 \text{ dollars}}{5 \text{ cars}}$$ The money earned increases by $40 for every 5 cars.

$$= \frac{8 \text{ dollar}}{1 \text{ car}}$$ Write as a unit rate.

So, the number of dollars earned increases by $8 for every car washed.

✓ CHECK Your Progress

a. **PLANES** The table shows the number of miles a plane traveled while in flight. Use the information to find the approximate rate of change in miles per minute. **about 10 miles per minute**

Time (min)	30	60	90	120
Distance (mi)	290	580	870	1,160

---

2 Teach

Scaffolding Questions

Ask:

• What is the rate of change of a plant that grows 0.5 inch per day? $\frac{0.5 \text{ inch}}{1 \text{ day}}$

• What is the rate of change of a pool that is emptying by 25 gallons per minute? $\frac{25 \text{ gallons}}{1 \text{ minute}}$

• What is $\frac{75 \text{ feet}}{3 \text{ days}}$ in simplest form? $\frac{25 \text{ feet}}{1 \text{ day}}$

ADDITIONAL EXAMPLE

① The table shows the number of miles a car drove on a trip. Use the information to find the approximate rate of change. **65 miles per hour**

Distance (miles)	65	130	195	260
Time (hours)	1	2	3	4

Additional Examples also in:

• Noteables™ Interactive Study Notebook with Foldables™

• Interactive Classroom PowerPoint® Presentations

A rate of change describes how one quantity changes in relation to another.

Formative Assessment

Use the Check Your Progress exercises after each Example to determine students' understanding of concepts.

ADDITIONAL EXAMPLES

2 The graph represents the distance traveled flying in a plane. Use the graph to find the rate of change.

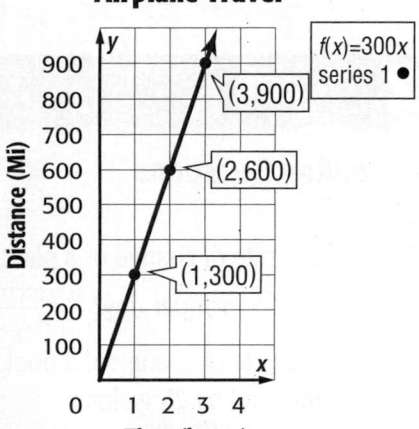

Airplane Travel

$f(x)=300x$ series 1 ●

(3,900)
(2,600)
(1,300)

Distance (Mi)
Time (hours)

300 miles per hour

3 **GRAPH THE DATA** Find the slope of the line. Explain what the slope represents.

Hours	Amount earned
3	45
6	90
9	135

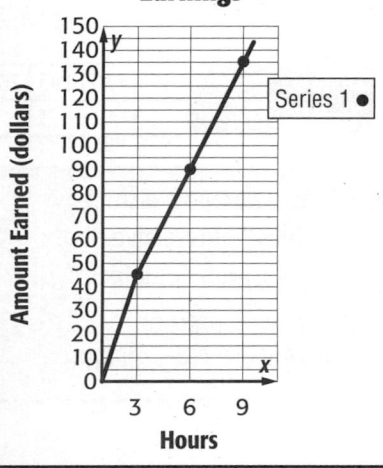

Earnings

Series 1 ●

Amount Earned (dollars)
Hours

The slope is $15 and represents the amount earned per hour.

Additional Examples are also in:

• Noteables™ Interactive Study Notebook with Foldables™

• Interactive Classroom PowerPoint® Presentations

EXAMPLE   Find Rate of Change from a Graph

2 **DRIVING** The graph represents the distance traveled while driving on a highway. Use the graph to find the rate of change in miles per hour.

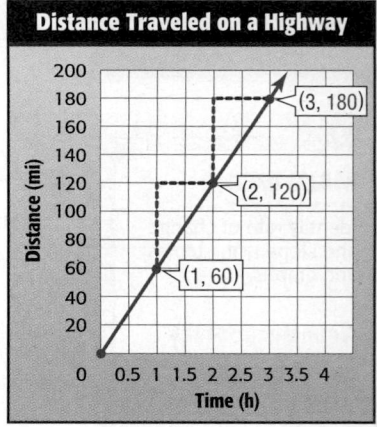

Distance Traveled on a Highway

(3, 180)
(2, 120)
(1, 60)

Distance (mi)
Time (h)

To find the rate of change, pick any two points on the line, such as (1, 60) and (2, 120).

$$\frac{\text{change in miles}}{\text{change in hours}} = \frac{(120 - 60)\text{ miles}}{(2 - 1)\text{ hours}}$$

$$= \frac{60\text{ miles}}{1\text{ hour}}$$

The distance increases by 60 miles in 1 hour. So, the rate of traveling on a highway is 60 miles per hour.

CHECK Your Progress

b. DRIVING Use the graph to find the rate of change in miles per hour while driving in the city. **30 miles per hour**

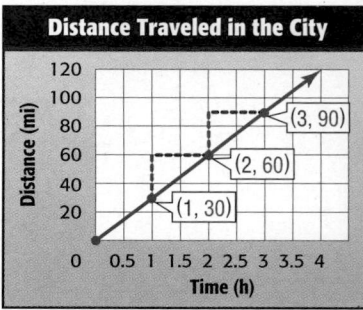

Distance Traveled in the City

(3, 90)
(2, 60)
(1, 30)

Distance (mi)
Time (h)

Notice that the graph in Example 2 about driving on a highway represents a rate of change of 60 mph. The graph in Check Your Progress about driving in the city is not as steep. It represents a rate of change of 30 mph.

The constant rate of change in y with respect to the constant change x is also called the slope of a line. Slope is a number that tells how steep the line is. The slope is the same for any two points on a straight line.

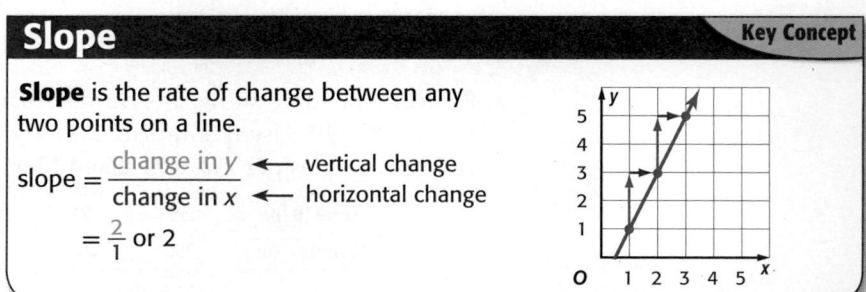

Slope   **Key Concept**

Slope is the rate of change between any two points on a line.

$$\text{slope} = \frac{\text{change in } y}{\text{change in } x} \leftarrow \text{vertical change} \atop \leftarrow \text{horizontal change}$$

$$= \frac{2}{1} \text{ or } 2$$

 **Real-World EXAMPLE**   **Find Slope**

3 **PHYSICAL SCIENCE** The table below shows the relationship between the number of seconds y it takes to hear the thunder after a lightning strike and the distance x you are from the lightning.

Distance (x)	0	1	2	3	4	5
Seconds (y)	0	5	10	15	20	25

Graph the data. Then find the slope of the line. Explain what the slope represents.

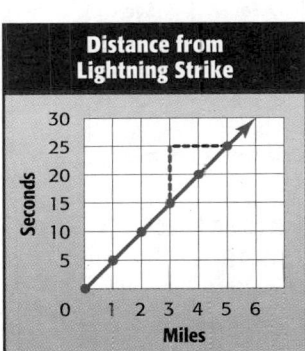

Distance from Lightning Strike

$$\text{slope} = \frac{\text{change in } y}{\text{change in } x} \quad \text{Definition of slope}$$

$$= \frac{25 - 10}{5 - 2} \quad \text{Use } (2, 10) \text{ and } (5, 25).$$

$$= \frac{15}{3} \xleftarrow{} \text{seconds} \xleftarrow{} \text{miles}$$

$$= \frac{5}{1} \quad \text{Simplify.}$$

So, for every 5 seconds between a lightning flash and the sound of the thunder, there is 1 mile between you and the lightning strike.

Real-World Link . . . .
Lightning strikes somewhere on the surface of Earth about 100 times every second.
Source: National Geographic

✓ **CHECK Your Progress**

c. **WATER** Graph the data. Then find the slope of the line. Explain what the slope represents. **See margin.**

Water Level Loss	
Week	**Water Loss (cm)**
1	1.5
2	3
3	4.5
4	6

★ indicates multi-step problem

✓ **CHECK Your Understanding**

Example 1
(p. 293)

1. Use the information in the table to find the rate of change in degrees per hour. **1.5°F per h**

Temperature (°F)	54	57	60	63
Time	6 A.M.	8 A.M.	10 A.M.	12 P.M.

Example 2
(p. 294)

★ **2.** **DISTANCE** The graph shows Benito's distance from the starting line. Use the graph to find the rate of change. **0.5 m per s**

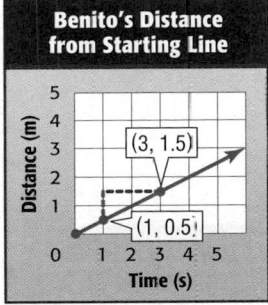

Benito's Distance from Starting Line

Lesson 6-3 Rate of Change and Slope   **295**

 Formative Assessment

Use Exercises 1–3 to check for understanding.

Then use the chart at the bottom of this page to customize your assignments for students.

Intervention You may wish to use the Study Guide and Intervention Master on page 22 of the *Chapter 6 Resource Masters* for additional reinforcement.

Odd/Even Assignments

Exercises 4–10 are structured so that students practice the same concepts whether they are assigned odd or even problems.

Additional Answer

c.

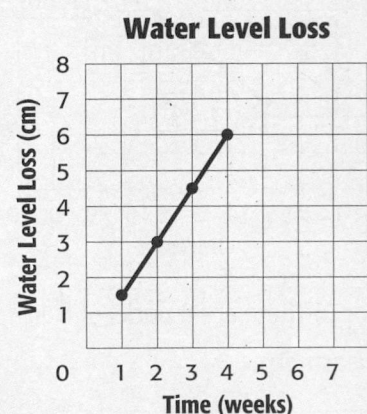

Water Level Loss

slope: $\frac{3}{2}$; Every two weeks, the water level falls 3 centimeters.

DIFFERENTIATED HOMEWORK OPTIONS			
Level	**Assignment**	**Two-Day Option**	
BL Basic	4–13, 15, 16, 17–24	5–13 odd, 15, 16	4–12 even, 14, 17–24
OL Core	4–8 even, 14–24	4–8, 15, 16	9–14, 17–24
AL Advanced/Pre-AP	9–24 (optional: 21–24)		

Ticket Out the Door Have students create a table of data that has a constant change. Have them find the rate of change for the table. Ask students to show their work as they leave.

FOLDABLES Study Organizer **Foldables™ Follow-Up**

Remind students to select a term or concept about rate of change and slope and to define it in their Foldables. Encourage them to give an example of the term or concept.

Additional Answers

3.

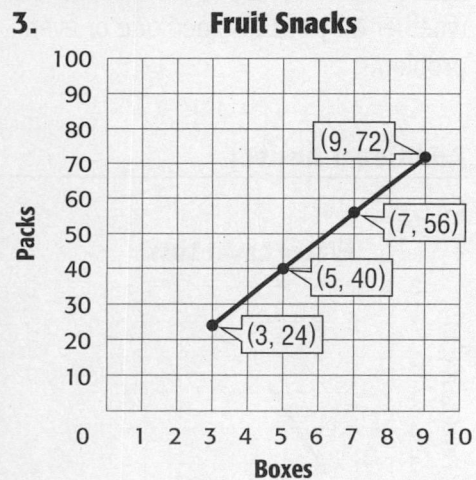

Fruit Snacks

slope: $\frac{8}{1}$ or 8; There are 8 packs of fruit snacks in each box.

9.

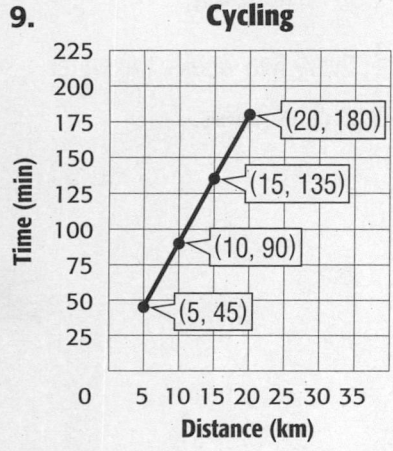

Cycling

slope: $\frac{9}{1}$ or 9: She ran 1 km every 9 minutes.

Example 3 (p. 295)

3. SNACKS The table below shows the number of small packs of fruit snacks y per box x. Graph the data. Then find the slope of the line. Explain what the slope represents. **See margin.**

Boxes (x)	3	5	7	9
Packs (y)	24	40	56	72

Practice and Problem Solving

HOMEWORK HELP

For Exercises	See Examples
4–6	1
7, 8	2
9, 10	3

Exercise Levels
A: 4–10
B: 11–12
C: 13–14

7. $9 per shirt
8. 12 in. of length for every 1 in. of height

EXTRA PRACTICE
See pages 682, 709.

For Exercises 4 and 5, find the rate of change for each table.

4.

Time (s)	Distance (m)
0	6
1	12
2	18
3	24

6 m per s

5.

Time (h)	Wage ($)
0	0
1	9
2	18
3	27

$9 per h

6. The number of minutes included in different cell phone plans and the costs are shown in the table. What is the approximate rate of change in cost per minute? **about $0.02 per minute**

Cost ($)	38	50	62	74	86
Minutes	1,000	1,500	2,000	2,500	3,000

For Exercises 7 and 8, find the rate of change for each graph.

7.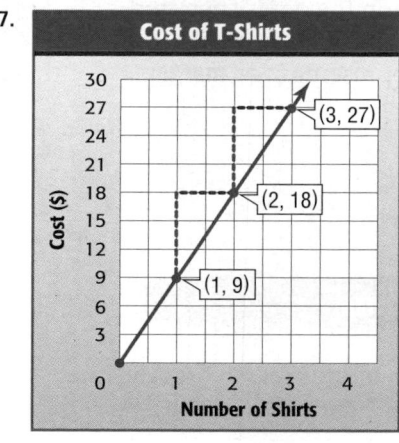

8.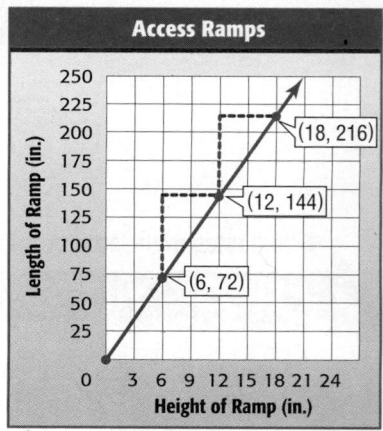

9. CYCLING The table shows the distance y Cheryl traveled in x minutes while competing in the cycling portion of a triathlon. Graph the data. Then find the slope of the line. Explain what the slope represents. **See margin.**

Time (min)	45	90	135	180
Distance (km)	5	10	15	20

296 Chapter 6 Ratios and Proportions

10. **MAPS** The table shows the key for a map. Graph the data. Then find the slope of the line. **See margin.**

Distance on Map (in.)	2	4	6	8
Actual Distance (mi)	40	80	120	160

11. **WATER** At 1:00, the water level in a pool is 13 inches. At 2:30, the water level is 28 inches. What is the rate of change? $\frac{1}{6}$ **inch per minute**

12. $25 per month for the first 3 months, then $50 per month after that

12. **MONEY** Dwayne opens a savings account with $75. He makes the same deposit every month and makes no withdrawals. After 3 months, he has $150. After 6 months, he has $300. After 9 months, he has $450 dollars. What is the rate of change?

H.O.T. Problems

13. **OPEN ENDED** Make a table where the rate of change is 6 inches for every foot. **See margin.**

14. **WRITING IN MATH** Write a problem to represent a rate of change of $15 per item. **Sample answer: At Sam's Shoes, 2 pairs of sandals cost $30 and 4 pairs cost $60. Find the rate of change.**

TEST PRACTICE

15. Use the information in the table to find the rate of change. **A**

Number of Apples	Number of Seeds
3	30
7	70
11	110

A $\frac{10}{1}$ C $\frac{40}{4}$

B $\frac{1}{10}$ D $\frac{4}{40}$

16. **SHORT RESPONSE** Find the slope of the line below that shows the distance Jairo traveled while jogging. $\frac{4}{1}$

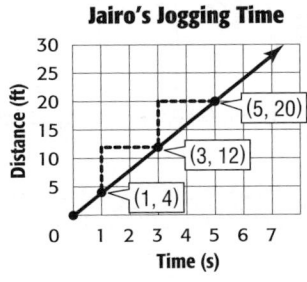

Jairo's Jogging Time

Spiral Review

17. **GROCERIES** Three pounds of pears cost $3.57. At this rate, how much would 10 pounds cost? (Lesson 6-2) **$11.90**

Write each ratio as a fraction in simplest form. (Lesson 6-1)

18. 9 feet in 21 minutes $\frac{3}{7}$ 19. 36 calls in 2 hours $\frac{18}{1}$ 20. 14 SUVs out of 56 vehicles $\frac{1}{4}$

GET READY for the Next Lesson

PREREQUISITE SKILL Solve. (Page 674)

21. 2.5×20 **50**   22. 3.5×4 **14**   23. $104 \div 16$ **6.5**   24. $4,200 \div 2,000$ **2.1**

Real-World Comparison

Draw a grid with tape on the floor. Have students stand in a line and have one student move vertically, then horizontally until they meet the next person in line. Explain that this number is the slope.

Additional Answers

10.   **Distances on a Map**

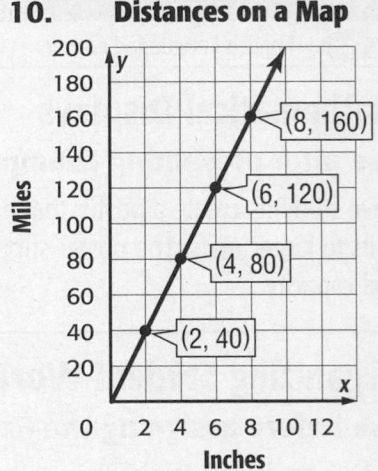

slope: $\frac{20}{1}$ or 20; Every inch on the map represents 20 miles.

13. Sample answer:

Length of Poster (ft)	Ribbon Needed (in.)
3	18
6	36
9	54
12	72

Measurement: Changing Customary Units

PACING: **Regular:** 1 period, **Block:** 0.5 period

Options for Differentiated Instruction

 **ELL** = English Language Learner   **AL** = Above or Beyond Grade Level   **SS** = Struggling Students   **SN** = Special Needs

Mathematical Displays **ELL** **SS**

Use after presenting Examples 1–5.

Have students create a poster that explains how to change from larger units to smaller units and from smaller units to larger units. The poster should include examples from the different types of measure: length, weight, and capacity.

Organizing Student Work and Thinking **SS** **SN**

Use before assigning the Exercises.

To help students organize their conversions between measures, have them use a template with the headings shown below. One sample entry is given.

Problem	What I Know	Calculations	Answer
20 ft = in.	1 foot = 12 inches	20 ft × 12 in./ft = 240 in.	20 ft = 240 in.

Research **AL**

Use after students complete Lesson 6–4.

Have students work in groups to research other customary units of measure that are less common. Examples are shown below.

- bales
- barrels
- bushels
- drams
- gills
- pecks

Students should present their findings accompanied by a conversion table similar to the one on page 298. Assign individual tasks based on students' strengths, such as who will do the research, who will write the report, who will make the table, and who will make a presentation to the class.

Leveled Lesson Resources

Chapter 6 Resource Masters

BL = Below or Approaching Grade Level   **OL** = On Grade Level   **AL** = Above or Beyond Grade Level   **ELL** = English Language Learner

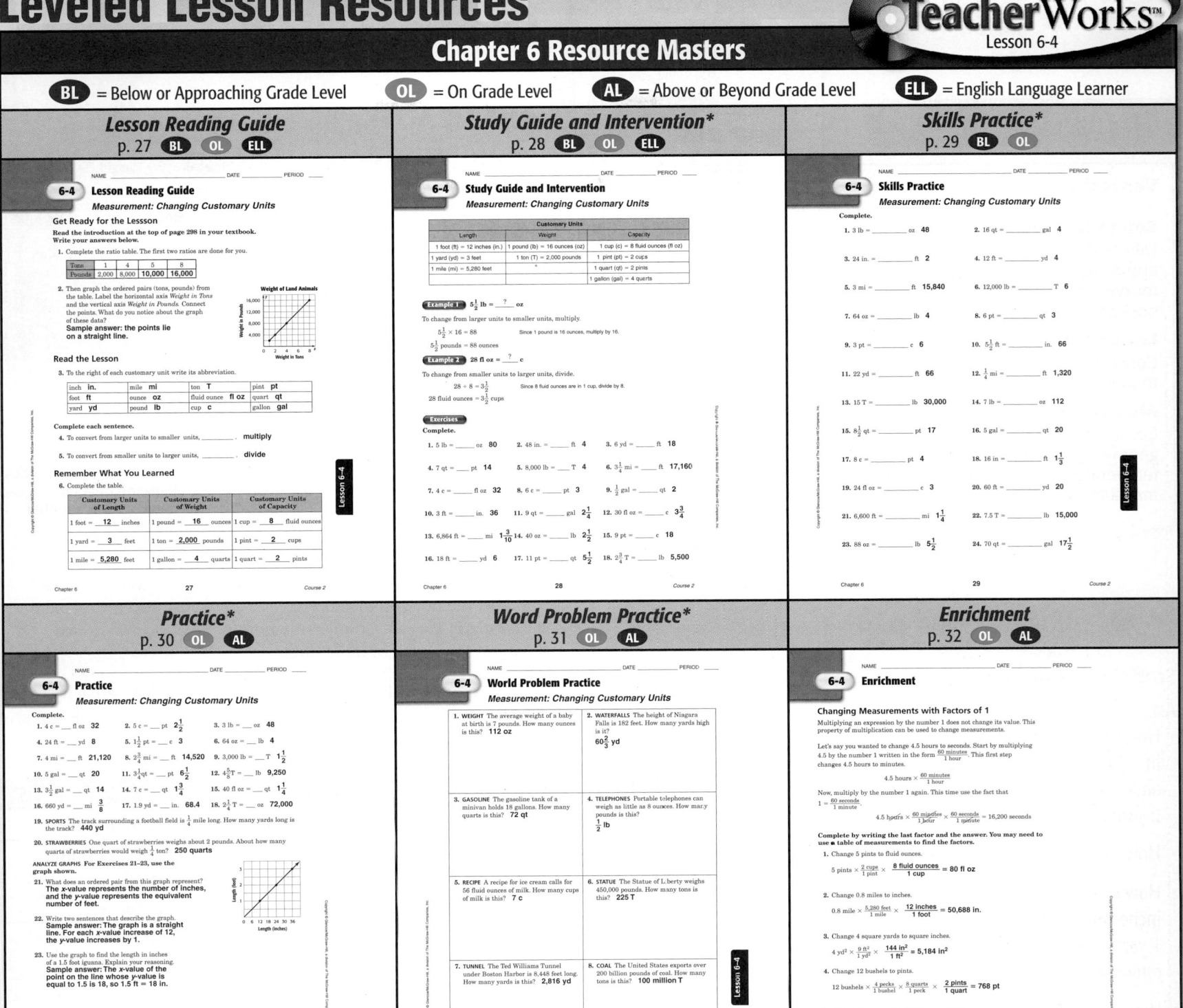

Lesson Reading Guide
p. 27 **BL** **OL** **ELL**

6-4 Lesson Reading Guide
Measurement: Changing Customary Units

Get Ready for the Lesson
Read the introduction at the top of page 298 in your textbook. Write your answers below.

1. Complete the ratio table. The first two ratios are done for you.

Tons	1	4	5	8
Pounds	2,000	8,000	10,000	16,000

2. Then graph the ordered pairs (tons, pounds) from the table. Label the horizontal axis *Weight in Tons* and the vertical axis *Weight in Pounds*. Connect the points. What do you notice about the graph of these data? **Sample answer: the points lie on a straight line.**

Read the Lesson

3. To the right of each customary unit write its abbreviation.

inch	**in.**	mile	**mi**	ton	**T**	pint	**pt**
foot	**ft**	ounce	**oz**	fluid ounce	**fl oz**	quart	**qt**
yard	**yd**	pound	**lb**	cup	**c**	gallon	**gal**

Complete each sentence.

4. To convert from larger units to smaller units, _____. **multiply**

5. To convert from smaller units to larger units, _____. **divide**

Remember What You Learned

6. Complete the table.

Customary Units of Length	Customary Units of Weight	Customary Units of Capacity
1 foot = **12** inches	1 pound = **16** ounces	1 cup = **8** fluid ounces
1 yard = **3** feet	1 ton = **2,000** pounds	1 pint = **2** cups
1 mile = **5,280** feet		1 gallon = **4** quarts	1 quart = **2** pints

Chapter 6   27   Course 2

Study Guide and Intervention*
p. 28 **BL** **OL** **ELL**

6-4 Study Guide and Intervention
Measurement: Changing Customary Units

Customary Units

Length	Weight	Capacity
1 foot (ft) = 12 inches (in.)	1 pound (lb) = 16 ounces (oz)	1 cup (c) = 8 fluid ounces (fl oz)
1 yard (yd) = 3 feet	1 ton (T) = 2,000 pounds	1 pint (pt) = 2 cups
1 mile (mi) = 5,280 feet		1 quart (qt) = 2 pints
		1 gallon (gal) = 4 quarts

Example 1 $5\frac{1}{2}$ lb = ___?___ oz

To change from larger units to smaller units, multiply.

$5\frac{1}{2} \times 16 = 88$ Since 1 pound is 16 ounces, multiply by 16.

$5\frac{1}{2}$ pounds = 88 ounces

Example 2 28 fl oz = ___?___ c

To change from smaller units to larger units, divide.

$28 \div 8 = 3\frac{1}{2}$ Since 8 fluid ounces are in 1 cup, divide by 8.

28 fluid ounces = $3\frac{1}{2}$ cups

Exercises
Complete.

1. 5 lb = ____ oz **80**   2. 48 in. = ____ ft **4**   3. 6 yd = ____ ft **18**

4. 7 qt = ____ pt **14**   5. 8,000 lb = ____ T **4**   6. $3\frac{1}{4}$ mi = ____ ft **17,160**

7. 4 c = ____ fl oz **32**   8. 6 c = ____ pt **3**   9. $\frac{1}{2}$ gal = ____ qt **2**

10. 3 ft = ____ in. **36**   11. 9 qt = ____ gal **$2\frac{1}{4}$**   12. 30 fl oz = ____ c **$3\frac{3}{4}$**

13. 6,864 ft = ____ mi **$1\frac{3}{10}$** 14. 40 oz = ____ lb **$2\frac{1}{2}$**   15. 9 pt = ____ c **18**

16. 18 ft = ____ yd **6**   17. 11 pt = ____ qt **$5\frac{1}{2}$**   18. $2\frac{3}{4}$ T = ____ lb **5,500**

Chapter 6   28   Course 2

Skills Practice*
p. 29 **BL** **OL**

6-4 Skills Practice
Measurement: Changing Customary Units

Complete.

1. 3 lb = ____ oz **48**   2. 16 qt = ____ gal **4**

3. 24 in. = ____ ft **2**   4. 12 ft = ____ yd **4**

5. 3 mi = ____ ft **15,840**   6. 12,000 lb = ____ T **6**

7. 64 oz = ____ lb **4**   8. 6 pt = ____ qt **3**

9. 3 pt = ____ c **6**   10. $5\frac{1}{2}$ ft = ____ in. **66**

11. 22 yd = ____ ft **66**   12. $\frac{1}{4}$ mi = ____ ft **1,320**

13. 15 T = ____ lb **30,000**   14. 7 lb = ____ oz **112**

15. $8\frac{1}{2}$ qt = ____ pt **17**   16. 5 gal = ____ qt **20**

17. 8 c = ____ pt **4**   18. 16 in. = ____ ft **$1\frac{1}{3}$**

19. 24 fl oz = ____ c **3**   20. 60 ft = ____ yd **20**

21. 6,600 ft = ____ mi **$1\frac{1}{4}$**   22. 7.5 T = ____ lb **15,000**

23. 88 oz = ____ lb **$5\frac{1}{2}$**   24. 70 qt = ____ gal **$17\frac{1}{2}$**

Chapter 6   29   Course 2

Practice*
p. 30 **OL** **AL**

6-4 Practice
Measurement: Changing Customary Units

Complete.

1. 4 c = ____ fl oz **32**   2. 5 c = ____ pt **$2\frac{1}{2}$**   3. 3 lb = ____ oz **48**

4. 24 ft = ____ yd **8**   5. $1\frac{1}{2}$ pt = ____ c **3**   6. 64 oz = ____ lb **4**

7. 4 mi = ____ ft **21,120**   8. $2\frac{3}{4}$ mi = ____ ft **14,520**   9. 3,000 lb = ____ T **$1\frac{1}{2}$**

10. 5 gal = ____ qt **20**   11. $3\frac{1}{4}$ qt = ____ pt **$6\frac{1}{2}$**   12. $4\frac{5}{8}$ T = ____ lb **9,250**

13. $3\frac{1}{2}$ gal = ____ qt **14**   14. 7 c = ____ qt **$1\frac{3}{4}$**   15. 40 fl oz = ____ qt **$1\frac{1}{4}$**

16. 660 yd = ____ mi **$\frac{3}{8}$**   17. ____ in. = 68.4 ft **$2\frac{1}{4}$** T = ____ oz **72,000**

19. **SPORTS** The track surrounding a football field is $\frac{1}{4}$ mile long. How many yards long is the track? **440 yd**

20. **STRAWBERRIES** One quart of strawberries weighs about 2 pounds. About how many quarts of strawberries would weigh $\frac{1}{4}$ ton? **250 quarts**

ANALYZE GRAPHS For Exercises 21–23, use the graph shown.

21. What does an ordered pair from this graph represent? **The x-value represents the number of inches, and the y-value represents the equivalent number of feet.**

22. Write two sentences that describe the graph. **Sample answer: The graph is a straight line. For each x-value increase of 12, the y-value increases by 1.**

23. Use the graph to find the length in inches of a 1.5 foot iguana. Explain your reasoning. **Sample answer: The x-value of the point on the line whose y-value is equal to 1.5 is 18, so 1.5 ft = 18 in.**

Chapter 6   30   Course 2

Word Problem Practice*
p. 31 **OL** **AL**

6-4 World Problem Practice
Measurement: Changing Customary Units

1. **WEIGHT** The average weight of a baby at birth is 7 pounds. How many ounces is this? **112 oz**

2. **WATERFALLS** The height of Niagara Falls is 182 feet. How many yards high is it? **$60\frac{2}{3}$ yd**

3. **GASOLINE** The gasoline tank of a minivan holds 18 gallons. How many quarts is this? **72 qt**

4. **TELEPHONES** Portable telephones can weigh as little as 8 ounces. How many pounds is this? **$\frac{1}{2}$ lb**

5. **RECIPE** A recipe for ice cream calls for 56 fluid ounces of milk. How many cups of milk is this? **7 c**

6. **STATUE** The Statue of Liberty weighs 450,000 pounds. How many tons is this? **225 T**

7. **TUNNEL** The Ted Williams Tunnel under Boston Harbor is 8,448 feet long. How many yards is this? **2,816 yd**

8. **COAL** The United States exports over 200 billion pounds of coal. How many tons is this? **100 million T**

Chapter 6   31   Course 2

Enrichment
p. 32 **OL** **AL**

6-4 Enrichment

Changing Measurements with Factors of 1

Multiplying an expression by the number 1 does not change its value. This property of multiplication can be used to change measurements.

Let's say you wanted to change 4.5 hours to seconds. Start by multiplying 4.5 by the number 1 written in the form $\frac{60\ minutes}{1\ hour}$. This first step changes 4.5 hours to minutes.

$$4.5\ hours \times \frac{60\ minutes}{1\ hour}$$

Now, multiply by the number 1 again. This time use the fact that $1 = \frac{60\ seconds}{1\ minute}$.

$$4.5\ hours \times \frac{60\ minutes}{1\ hour} \times \frac{60\ seconds}{1\ minute} = 16,200\ seconds$$

Complete by writing the last factor and the answer. You may need to use a table of measurements to find the factors.

1. Change 5 pints to fluid ounces.
$$5\ pints \times \frac{2\ cups}{1\ pint} \times \frac{8\ fluid\ ounces}{1\ cup} = 80\ fl\ oz$$

2. Change 0.8 miles to inches.
$$0.8\ mile \times \frac{5,280\ feet}{1\ mile} \times \frac{12\ inches}{1\ foot} = 50,688\ in.$$

3. Change 4 square yards to square inches.
$$4\ yd^2 \times \frac{9\ ft^2}{1\ yd^2} \times \frac{144\ in^2}{1\ ft^2} = 5,184\ in^2$$

4. Change 12 bushels to pints.
$$12\ bushels \times \frac{4\ pecks}{1\ bushel} \times \frac{8\ quarts}{1\ peck} \times \frac{2\ pints}{1\ quart} = 768\ pt$$

5. Change one-half of an acre to square inches.
$$\frac{1}{2}\ acre \times \frac{4,840\ yd^2}{1\ acre} \times \frac{9\ ft^2}{1\ yd^2} \times \frac{144\ in^2}{1\ ft^2} = 3,136,320\ in^2$$

Chapter 6   32   Course 2

Also available in Spanish **ELL**

Additional Lesson Resources

Transparencies
• *5-Minute Check Transparency*, Lesson 6-4

Other Print Products
• *Noteables™ Interactive Study Notebook with Foldables™*

Teacher Tech Tools
• *Interactive Classroom CD-ROM*, Lesson 6-4
• *AssignmentWorks*, Lesson 6-4

Student Tech Tools
glencoe.com
• Extra Examples, Chapter 6, Lesson 4
• Self-Check Quiz, Chapter 6, Lesson 4

1 Focus

Vertical Alignment

Before Lesson 6-4
Differentiate between and use appropriate units of measures for two- and three-dimensional objects

Lesson 6-4
Convert one unit of measurement to another

After Lesson 6-4
Compare weights, capacities, geometric measures, times, and temperatures within and between measurement systems

2 Teach

Scaffolding Questions

Ask:

• How can you find the number of feet in 2 yards? There are 3 feet in 1 yard, and 2 × 3 = 6, so there are 6 feet in 2 yards.

• How many feet are in $1\frac{2}{3}$ yards? 5 ft

• How can you find the number of inches in 1 yard? There are 3 feet in 1 yard and 12 inches in one foot, so multiply 3 × 12 = 36.

• How many inches are in $\frac{1}{2}$ yard? 18 in.

MAIN IDEA

Change units in the customary system.

New Vocabulary

unit ratio

Math Online

glencoe.com

• Extra Examples
• Personal Tutor
• Self-Check Quiz

▶ GET READY for the Lesson

ANIMALS The table shows the approximate weights in tons of several large land animals. One ton is equivalent to 2,000 pounds.

Animal	Weight (T)
Grizzly Bear	1
White Rhinoceros	4
Hippopotamus	5
African Elephant	8

You can use a *ratio table*, which have columns filled with ratios that have the same value, to convert each weight from tons to pounds.

1. Copy and complete the ratio table. The first two ratios are done for you. **See margin.**

×4

Tons	1	4	5	8
Pounds	2,000	8,000	■	■

×4

To produce equivalent ratios, multiply the quantities in each row by the same number.

2. Then graph the ordered pairs (tons, pounds) from the table. Label the horizontal axis *Weight in Tons* and the vertical axis *Weight in Pounds*. Connect the points. What do you notice about the graph of these data?

2. Sample answer: The points lie on a straight line. See margin for graph.

The relationships among the most commonly used customary units of length, weight, and capacity are shown in the table below.

Customary Units		Key Concept
Type of Measure	**Larger Unit** ⟶	**Smaller Unit**
Length	1 foot (ft) =	12 inches (in.)
	1 yard (yd) =	3 feet
	1 mile (mi) =	5,280 feet
Weight	1 pound (lb) =	16 ounces (oz)
	1 ton (T) =	2,000 pounds
Capacity	1 cup (c) =	8 fluid ounces (fl oz)
	1 pint (pt) =	2 cups
	1 quart (qt) =	2 pints
	1 gallon (gal) =	4 quarts

298 Chapter 6 Ratios and Proportions

Additional Answers

1.

Tons	5	8
Pounds	10,000	16,000

2.

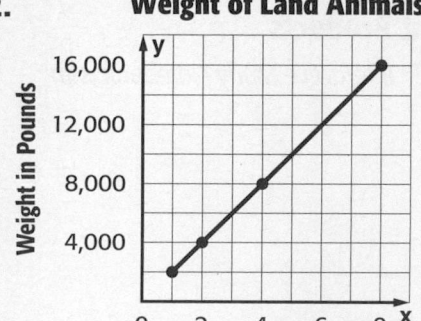

Weight of Land Animals

Each of the relationships above can be written as a unit ratio. Like a unit rate, a **unit ratio** is one in which the denominator is 1 unit.

$$\frac{3 \text{ ft}}{1 \text{ yd}} \qquad \frac{2{,}000 \text{ lb}}{1 \text{ T}} \qquad \frac{4 \text{ qt}}{1 \text{ gal}}$$

Notice that the numerator and denominator of each fraction above are equivalent, so the value of each ratio is 1. You can multiply by a unit ratio of this type to *convert* or change from larger units to smaller units.

EXAMPLES Convert Larger Units to Smaller Units

1 Convert 20 feet into inches.

Since 1 foot = 12 inches, the unit ratio is $\frac{12 \text{ in.}}{1 \text{ ft}}$.

$20 \text{ ft} = 20 \text{ ft} \cdot \dfrac{12 \text{ in.}}{1 \text{ ft}}$ Multiply by $\dfrac{12 \text{ in.}}{1 \text{ ft}}$.

$\phantom{20 \text{ ft}} = 20 \cancel{\text{ ft}} \cdot \dfrac{12 \text{ in.}}{1 \cancel{\text{ ft}}}$ Divide out common units, leaving the desired unit, inches.

$\phantom{20 \text{ ft}} = 20 \cdot 12 \text{ in. or } 240 \text{ in.}$ Multiply.

So, 20 feet = 240 inches.

2 **GARDENING** Clarence mixes $\frac{1}{4}$ cup of fertilizer with soil before planting each bulb. How many ounces of fertilizer does he use per bulb?

$\dfrac{1}{4} \text{ c} = \dfrac{1}{4} \cancel{\text{ c}} \cdot \dfrac{8 \text{ fl oz}}{1 \cancel{\text{ c}}}$ Since 1 cup = 8 fluid ounces, multiply by $\frac{8 \text{ fl oz}}{1 \text{ c}}$. Then, divide out common units.

$\phantom{\dfrac{1}{4} \text{ c}} = \dfrac{1}{4} \cdot 8 \text{ fl oz or } 2 \text{ fl oz}$ Multiply.

So, 2 fluid ounces of fertilizer are used per bulb.

CHECK Your Progress

Complete.

a. $36 \text{ yd} = \blacksquare \text{ ft}$ **108**   b. $\dfrac{3}{4} \text{ T} = \blacksquare \text{ lb}$ **1,500**   c. $1\dfrac{1}{2} \text{ qt} = \blacksquare \text{ pt}$ **3**

To convert from smaller units to larger units, multiply by the reciprocal of the appropriate unit ratio.

EXAMPLES Convert Smaller Units to Larger Units

3 Convert 15 quarts into gallons.

Since 1 gallon = 4 quarts, the unit ratio is $\frac{4 \text{ qt}}{1 \text{ gal}}$, and its reciprocal is $\frac{1 \text{ gal}}{4 \text{ qt}}$.

$15 \text{ qt} = 15 \text{ qt} \cdot \dfrac{1 \text{ gal}}{4 \text{ qt}}$ Multiply by $\frac{1 \text{ gal}}{4 \text{ qt}}$.

$\phantom{15 \text{ qt}} = 15 \cancel{\text{ qt}} \cdot \dfrac{1 \text{ gal}}{4 \cancel{\text{ qt}}}$ Divide out common units, leaving the desired unit, gallons.

$\phantom{15 \text{ qt}} = 15 \cdot \dfrac{1}{4} \text{ gal or } 3.75 \text{ gal}$ Multiplying 15 by $\frac{1}{4}$ is the same as dividing 15 by 4.

Lesson 6-4 Measurement: Changing Customary Units   **299**

4 **SOCCER** Tracy kicked a soccer ball 1,000 inches. How many feet did she kick the ball? $83\frac{1}{3}$ ft

5 **LEMONADE** Paul made 6 pints of lemonade and poured it into 10 glasses equally. How many cups of lemonade did each glass contain? $1\frac{1}{5}$ c

4 **COSTUMES** Umeka needs $4\frac{1}{2}$ feet of fabric to make a costume for a play. How many yards of fabric does she need?

$4\frac{1}{2}$ ft $= 4\frac{1}{2}$ ft $\cdot \dfrac{1 \text{ yd}}{3 \text{ ft}}$ Since 1 yard = 3 feet, multiply by $\dfrac{1 \text{ yd}}{3 \text{ ft}}$. Then, divide out common units.

$= \dfrac{\overset{3}{\cancel{9}}}{2} \cdot \dfrac{1}{\underset{1}{\cancel{3}}}$ yd   Write $4\frac{1}{2}$ as an improper fraction. Then divide out common factors.

$= \dfrac{3}{2}$ yd or $1\frac{1}{2}$ yd   Multiply.

So Umeka needs $1\frac{1}{2}$ yards of fabric.

✓ CHECK Your Progress

Complete.

d. 2,640 ft = ■ mi $\frac{1}{2}$

e. 5 pt = ■ qt $2\frac{1}{2}$

f. 100 oz = ■ lb $6\frac{1}{4}$

g. 76c = ■ gal $4\frac{3}{4}$

h. 3 c = ■ pt **6**

i. 18 in. = ■ ft $1\frac{1}{2}$

j. **FOOD** A 3-pound pork loin can be cut into 10 smaller pork chops of equal weight. How many ounces does each pork chop weigh? **4.8 oz**

You can also convert from one rate to another by multiplying by a unit rate or its reciprocal.

Real-World EXAMPLE   Convert Rates

5 **HELICOPTERS** A helicopter flies at a rate of 158 miles per hour. How many miles per second is this?

Since 1 hour = 3,600 seconds, multiply by $\dfrac{1 \text{ h}}{3,600 \text{ s}}$.

$\dfrac{158 \text{ mi}}{\text{h}} = \dfrac{158 \text{ mi}}{1 \text{ h}} \times \dfrac{1 \text{ h}}{3,600 \text{ s}}$ Multiply by $\dfrac{1 \text{ h}}{3,600 \text{ s}}$.

$= \dfrac{158 \text{ mi}}{1 \cancel{\text{h}}} \times \dfrac{1 \cancel{\text{h}}}{3,600 \text{ s}}$ Divide out common units.

$\approx \dfrac{0.04 \text{ mi}}{1 \text{ s}}$ Simplify.

So, a helicopter flies approximately 0.04 mile per second.

✓ CHECK Your Progress

Real-World Link . . . . .
A swordfish reaches a maximum size of 14 feet and almost 1,200 pounds.
Source: Sport Fishing Central

k. **FISH** A swordfish can swim at a rate of 60 miles per hour. How many feet per hour is this? **316,800 ft/h**

l. **WALKING** Ava walks at a speed of 7 feet per second. How many feet per hour is this? **25,200 ft/h**

CHECK Your Understanding

★ indicates multi-step problem

Examples 1, 2
(p. 299)

Complete.

1. 3 lb = ■ oz **48**

2. $5\frac{1}{3}$ yd = ■ ft **16**

3. 6.5 c = ■ fl oz **52**

4. **FISH** Grouper are members of the sea bass family. A large grouper can weigh $\frac{1}{3}$ ton. About how much does a large grouper weigh to the nearest pound? **667 lb**

Examples 3, 4
(pp. 299–300)

Complete.

5. 12 qt = ■ gal **3**

6. 28 in. = ■ ft $2\frac{1}{3}$

7. 15 pt = ■ qt $7\frac{1}{2}$

8. **VEHICLES** The world's narrowest electric vehicle is about 35 inches wide and is designed to move down narrow aisles in warehouses. About how wide is this vehicle to the nearest foot? **3 ft**

Example 5
(p. 300)

9. **RUNNING** The fastest a human has ever run is about 27 miles per hour. How many miles per minute is this? **0.45 mi/min**

Practice and Problem Solving

HOMEWORK HELP

For Exercises	See Examples
10–21	1–4
22–23	2
24–25	4
26–27	5

Complete.

10. 18 ft = ■ yd **6**

11. 72 oz = ■ lb $4\frac{1}{2}$

12. 2 lb = ■ oz **32**

13. 4 gal = ■ qt **16**

14. $4\frac{1}{2}$ pt = ■ c **9**

15. 3 c = ■ fl oz **24**

16. 2 mi = ■ ft **10,560**

17. $1\frac{1}{4}$ mi = ■ ft **6,600**

18. 5,000 lb = ■ T $2\frac{1}{2}$

19. 13 c = ■ pt $6\frac{1}{2}$

20. $2\frac{3}{4}$ qt = ■ pt $5\frac{1}{2}$

21. $3\frac{3}{8}$ T = ■ lb **6,750**

Exercise Levels
A: 10–27
B: 28–37
C: 38–43

22. **PUMPKINS** One of the largest pumpkins ever grown weighed about $\frac{1}{2}$ ton. How many pounds did the pumpkin weigh? **1,000 lb**

23. **SKIING** Speed skiing takes place on a course that is $\frac{2}{3}$ mile long. How many feet long is the course? **3,520 ft**

24. **BOATING** A 40-foot power boat is for sale by owner. About how long is this boat to the nearest yard? **13 yd**

25. **BLOOD** A total of 35 pints of blood were collected at a local blood drive. How many quarts of blood is this? $17\frac{1}{2}$ **qt**

26. **GO-KARTS** A go-kart's top speed is 607,200 feet per hour. How many miles per hour is this? **115 mi/h**

27. **BIRDS** A peregrine falcon can fly at over 200 miles per hour. How many feet per hour is this? **1,056,000 ft/h**

Lesson 6-4 Measurement: Changing Customary Units **301**

3 Practice

Formative Assessment

Use Exercises 1–9 to check for understanding.

Then use the chart at the bottom of this page to customize your assignments for students.

Intervention You may wish to use the Study Guide and Intervention Master on page 28 of the *Chapter 6 Resource Masters* for additional reinforcement.

Odd/Even Assignments

Exercises 10–27 are structured so that students practice the same concepts whether they are assigned odd or even problems.

DIFFERENTIATED HOMEWORK OPTIONS

Level	Assignment	Two-Day Option	
BL Basic	10–29, 38–41, 43–56	11–29 odd, 44, 45	10–28 even, 38–41, 43, 46–56
OL Core	11–33 odd, 34–41, 43–56	10–29, 44, 45	30–41, 43, 46–56
AL Advanced/Pre-AP	30–52 (optional: 53–56)		

34. The x-value represents the number of quarts and the y-value represents the equivalent number of gallons.

36. Sample answer: The point on the line whose y-value is equal to 2.5 is (10, 2.5), so 2.5 qt = 10 gal.

39. Sample answer: 16 in. is equivalent to 12 in. + 4 in. or 1 ft 4 in., $1\frac{1}{2}$ ft is equivalent to 1 ft 6 in., Since 1 ft 4 in. < 1 ft 6 in., 16 in. < $1\frac{1}{2}$ ft.

40. Sample answer: $8\frac{3}{4}$ gal is equivalent to 35 qt, Since 35 qt > 32 qt, $8\frac{3}{4}$ gal > 32 qt.

41. Sample answer: 2.7 T is equivalent to $2.7 \text{ T} \cdot \frac{2,000 \text{ lb}}{1 \text{ T}} \cdot \frac{16 \text{ oz}}{1 \text{ lb}}$ or 86,400 oz.

42. Yes; 2 quarts = 8 cups, so the ratio of cups of vinegar to water in the recommended mixture is $\frac{\frac{3}{4}\text{c}}{2\text{ qt}} = \frac{\frac{3}{4}\text{c}}{8\text{ c}} = \frac{3}{4} \div 8 = \frac{3}{4} \cdot \frac{1}{8}$ or $\frac{3}{32}$. The ratio of the new mixture is $\frac{1.5\text{ oz}}{16\text{ oz}} = \frac{1.5 \cdot 2}{16 \cdot 2}$ or $\frac{3}{32}$. The mixtures have the same ratio of vinegar to water.

43. 720 in^2; Square feet mean a unit of feet × feet. To divide out each unit, you must multiply by two conversion factors that have feet in the denominator and inches in the numerator.
$5 \text{ ft}^2 \cdot \frac{12 \text{ in.}}{1 \text{ ft}} \cdot \frac{12 \text{ in.}}{1 \text{ ft}} = 720 \text{ in}^2$

28. No; $2 + 2 + \frac{1}{4} + \frac{1}{3} + 4 = 8\frac{7}{12}$ c punch and a 2-qt pitcher holds 2 qt
$\cdot \frac{2 \text{ pt}}{1 \text{ qt}} \cdot \frac{2 \text{ c}}{1 \text{ pt}} = 2 \cdot 2$
• 2 c or 8 c. Since
$8 \text{ c} < 8\frac{7}{12}$ c, the pitcher will not hold all of the punch.

29. No; 15 in. + $4\frac{1}{2}$ in. + $6\frac{3}{4}$ in. = $26\frac{1}{4}$ in. and $26\frac{1}{4} \div 12 = 2\frac{3}{16}$. So, it snowed a total of $2\frac{3}{16}$ ft or about 2 ft, not $2\frac{1}{2}$ ft.

EXTRA PRACTICE
See pages 682, 709.

H.O.T. Problems

38. Sample answer: Annabelle is making brownies. The recipe calls for 2 cups of sour cream. She has 2 pints of sour cream. Does she have enough sour cream to make the brownies?

★ **28.** **PUNCH** Will a 2-quart pitcher hold the entire recipe of citrus punch given at the right? Explain your reasoning.

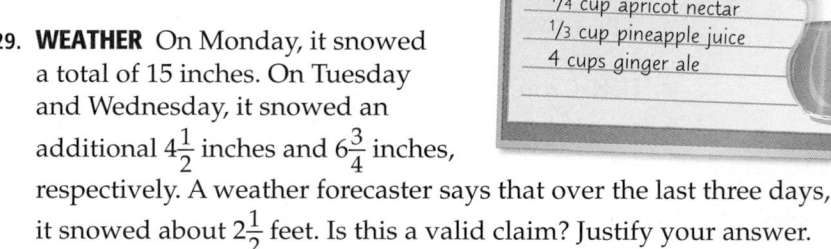

Recipe: Citrus Punch Drink
2 cups orange juice
2 cups grapefruit juice
1/4 cup apricot nectar
1/3 cup pineapple juice
4 cups ginger ale

★ **29.** **WEATHER** On Monday, it snowed a total of 15 inches. On Tuesday and Wednesday, it snowed an additional $4\frac{1}{2}$ inches and $6\frac{3}{4}$ inches, respectively. A weather forecaster says that over the last three days, it snowed about $2\frac{1}{2}$ feet. Is this a valid claim? Justify your answer.

MEASUREMENT Complete the following statements.

30. If 16 c = 1 gal, then $1\frac{1}{4}$ gal = ■ c **20**

31. If 1,760 yd = 1 mi, then 880 yd = ■ mi $\frac{1}{2}$

32. If 36 in. = 1 yd, then 2.3 yd = ■ in. **82.8**

★ **33.** **ESTIMATION** Cristos is a member of the swim team and trains by swimming an average of 3,000 yards a day. About how many miles would he swim by training at this rate for 5 days, to the nearest half-mile? **about $8\frac{1}{2}$ mi**

MEASUREMENT For Exercises 34–37, use the graph at the right.

34. What does an ordered pair from this graph represent? **See margin.**

35. Find the slope of the line. $\frac{1}{4}$

36. Use the graph to find the **See margin.** capacity in quarts of a 2.5-gallon container. Explain your reasoning.

37. Use the graph to predict the capacity in gallons of a 12-quart container. Explain your reasoning.
3 gal; Sample answer: the graph increases by 1 gallon for every 4 quarts.

(Graph: Capacity in Gallons (y-axis) vs. Capacity in Quarts (x-axis))

38. **OPEN ENDED** Write a problem about a real-world situation in which you would need to convert pints to cups.

REASONING Replace each ● with <, >, or = to make a true sentence. Justify your answers. **39–41. See margin for justification.**

39. 16 in. ● $1\frac{1}{2}$ ft **<**

40. $8\frac{3}{4}$ gal ● 32 qt **>**

41. 2.7 T ● 86,400 oz **=**

42. **CHALLENGE** To whiten fabrics, a certain Web site recommends that you soak them in a mixture of $\frac{3}{4}$ cup vinegar, 2 quarts water, and some salt. Does a mixture that contains 1.5 ounces vinegar and 16 ounces water have the same vinegar-to-water ratio as the recommended mixture? Explain. **See margin.**

43. **WRITING IN MATH** Use multiplication by unit ratios of equivalent measures to convert 5 square feet to square inches. Justify your answer. **See margin.**

302 Chapter 6 Ratios and Proportions

Pre-AP Activity Use after Exercise 37

Tell students that the average distance of Mars from the Sun is 227,940,000 kilometers. Tell students that astronomers use a unit of length called the astronomical unit (AU), which is equal to the average distance of Earth from the Sun. Have students research the astronomical unit on the Internet (or in an encyclopedia), find its relationship to kilometers, and convert the average distance of Mars from the Sun to astronomical units. 1 AU = 149,597,871 km; The average distance of Mars from the Sun is approximately 1.52 AU.

44. Which situation is represented by the graph? **D**

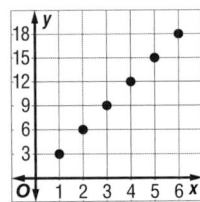

A conversion of inches to yards

B conversion of feet to inches

C conversion of miles to feet

D conversion of yards to feet

45. How many cups of milk are shown below? **G**

F $\frac{3}{4}$ c   H $2\frac{1}{2}$ c

G $1\frac{1}{4}$ c   J 10 c

46. How many ounces are in $7\frac{3}{4}$ pounds? **A**

A 124 oz   C 120 oz

B 122 oz   D 112 oz

4 Assess

Ticket Out the Door Tell students that the perimeter of a friend's backyard is 132 feet. Say the friend's dog runs around the backyard 16 times. What part of a mile has the dog run? 0.4 mi

FOLDABLES Foldables™
Study Organizer Follow-Up

Remind students to select a term or concept about units of measure and to define it in their Foldables. Encourage them to give an example of the term or concept.

Spiral Review

47. Use the information in the table to find the rate of change in dollars per hour. (Lesson 6-3) **$9 per h**

Wage ($)	0	9	18	27
Time (h)	0	1	2	3

48. GROCERIES Find the unit price if Anju spent $2 for six oranges. Round to the nearest cent if necessary. (Lesson 6-2) **$0.33 per orange**

49. MEASUREMENT By doubling just the length of the rectangular ice skating rink in Will's backyard from 16 to 32 feet, he increased its area from 128 square feet to 256 square feet. Find the width of both rinks. (Lesson 3-6) **8 ft**

ALGEBRA For Exercises 50–52, use the pay stub at the right. (Lesson 3-3)

50. Write and solve an equation to find the regular hourly wage. **$40r = 300$; $7.50/h**

51. Write and solve an equation to find the overtime hourly wage. **$2v = 22.50$; $11.25/h**

52. Write and solve an equation to find how many times greater Grace's overtime hourly wage is than her regular hourly wage. **$7.5t = 11.25$; 1.5**

Martin, Grace		Employee #: 4211
Description:	**Hours:**	**Earnings ($):**
Regular hours:	40	300.00
Overtime hours:	2	22.50

GET READY for the Next Lesson

PREREQUISITE SKILL Multiply. (p. 674)

53. 14.5×8.2 **118.9**   **54.** 7.03×4.6 **32.338**   **55.** 9.29×15.3 **142.137**   **56.** 1.84×16.7 **30.728**

Measurement: Changing Metric Units

6-5

PACING: **Regular:** 1 period,   **Block:** 0.5 period

Options for Differentiated Instruction

ELL = English Language Learner   **AL** = Above or Beyond Grade Level   **SS** = Struggling Students   **SN** = Special Needs

Visual Learners   **SS** **SN**

Use before presenting Examples 1–3.

Display the diagram showing metric prefixes on the board or overhead.

Point out the following to students:

- Each place value is 10 times the place value to its right.
- The value of each metric prefix is 10 times the value of the prefix to its right.

1,000	100	10	1	0.1	0.01	0.001
thousands	hundreds	tens	ones	tenths	hundredths	thousandths
kilo	hecto	deka	basic unit	deci	centi	milli

Making Resource Sheet   **ELL** **SS** **SN**

Use after presenting Examples 1–3.

Have students write step-by-step directions in their own words for how to convert between different metric units. Have them organize the information and include examples in a table like the one below.

Convert	Steps	Examples
centimeters to meters		
millimeters to meters		
grams to kilograms		
kilometers to centimeters		

Mathematical Displays   **ELL** **SS** **SN**

Use after students complete Lesson 6-5.

Have students work in pairs to create a poster about the metric system. Each poster should include the following:

- a drawing or picture of an object
- the metric units for length, mass, and/or capacity labeled on or near the object
- a comparison of that object's measures to the corresponding measures of similar objects

Leveled Lesson Resources

Also on
TeacherWorks™
Lesson 6-5

Chapter 6 Resource Masters

BL = Below or Approaching Grade Level **OL** = On Grade Level **AL** = Above or Beyond Grade Level **ELL** = English Language Learner

---

Lesson Reading Guide
p. 33 **BL** **OL** **ELL**

NAME _____ DATE _____ PERIOD _____

6-5 Lesson Reading Guide

Measurement: Changing Metric Units

Get Ready for the Lesson

Complete the Mini Lab at the top of page 304 in your textbook.
Write your answers below.

1. Select three other objects. Find and record the width of all five objects to the nearest millimeter and tenth of a centimeter. **See students' work.**

2. Compare the measurements of the objects, and write a rule that describes how to convert from millimeters to centimeters. **Divide by 10.**

3. Measure the length of your classroom in meters. Make a conjecture about how to convert this measure to centimeters. Explain. **Multiplication; there is a greater number of smaller units than larger units in a measure.**

Read the Lesson

Complete each sentence.

4. To convert from centimeters to kilometers, first divide by _____ to convert to meters, then divide by _____ to convert to kilometers. **100; 1,000**

5. To convert from kiloliters to milliliters, first multiply by _____ to convert to liters, then multiply by _____ to convert to milliliters. **1,000; 1,000**

6. To convert from _____ to centigrams, multiply by 100. **grams**

Remember What You Learned

7. Name an everyday object that you can associate with each base metric unit of measure to help you remember what each unit represents.

kilogram: **Sample answer: the mass of a one-liter bottle of water**

meter: **Sample answer: the distance from the floor to a doorknob**

liter: **Sample answer: the amount of soda in a standard bottle**

Chapter 6 • 33 • Course 2

Study Guide and Intervention*
p. 34 **BL** **OL** **ELL**

NAME _____ DATE _____ PERIOD _____

6-5 Study Guide and Intervention

Measurement: Changing Metric Units

The table below is a summary of how to convert measures in the metric system.

	Larger Units → Smaller Units	Smaller Units → Larger Units
Units of Length (meter)	km to m – multiply by 1,000 m to cm – multiply by 100 m to mm – multiply by 1,000 cm to mm – multiply by 10	mm to cm – divide by 10 mm to m – divide by 1,000 cm to m – divide by 100 m to km – divide by 1,000
Units of Mass (kilogram)	kg to g – multiply by 1,000 g to mg – multiply by 1,000	mg to g – divide by 1,000 g to kg – divide by 1,000
Units of Capacity (liter)	kL to L – multiply by 1,000 L to mL – multiply by 1,000	mL to L – divide by 1,000 L to kL – divide by 1,000

Examples 1 Complete. 62 cm = ___ m

To convert from centimeters to meters, divide by 100.
62 ÷ 100 = 0.62
62 cm = 0.62 m

Example 2 Complete. 2.6 kL = ___ L

To convert from kiloliters to liters, multiply by 1,000.
2.6 × 1,000 = 2,600
2.6 kL = 2,600 L

Exercises

Complete.

1. 650 cm = ___ m **6.5**
2. 57 kg = ___ g **57,000**
3. 751 mg = ___ g **0.751**
4. 8.2 L = ___ mL **8,200**
5. 52 L = ___ kL **0.052**
6. 892 mm = ___ m **0.892**
7. 121.4 kL = ___ L **121,400**
8. 0.72 cm = ___ mm **7.2**
9. 67.3 g = ___ kg **0.0673**
10. 5.2 g = ___ mg **5,200**
11. 0.05 m = ___ mm **50**
12. 2,500 mg = ___ g **2.5**
13. 32 mm = ___ cm **3.2**
14. 96 m = ___ cm **9,600**

Chapter 6 • 34 • Course 2

Skills Practice*
p. 35 **BL** **OL**

NAME _____ DATE _____ PERIOD _____

6-5 Skills Practice

Measurement: Changing Metric Units

Complete.

1. 660 m = ___ km **0.66**
2. 5.7 m = ___ cm **570**
3. 543 mL = ___ L **0.543**
4. 23.7 g = ___ mg **23,700**
5. 529 mg = ___ g **0.529**
6. 2,640 mL = ___ L **2.640**
7. 4.32 kL = ___ L **4,320**
8. 75.4 mg = ___ g **0.0754**
9. 8,300 mg = ___ g **8.3**
10. 7.3 m = ___ cm **730**
11. 250.3 kL = ___ L **250,300**
12. 799 g = ___ kg **0.799**
13. 8.5 cm = ___ mm **85**
14. 450 kg = ___ g **450,000**
15. 7.3 L = ___ mL **7,300**
16. 6,140 L = ___ kL **6.140**
17. 3,500 m = ___ km **3.5**
18. 89 km = ___ m **89,000**
19. 26.8 mm = ___ cm **2.68**
20. 750 m = ___ km **0.75**
21. 4.8 m = ___ cm **480**
22. 95 g = ___ mg **95,000**
23. 389 mm = ___ m **0.389**
24. 56 L = ___ kL **0.056**
25. 0.32 mm = ___ cm **0.032**
26. 39.1 g = ___ kg **0.0391**

Chapter 6 • 35 • Course 2

Practice*
p. 36 **OL** **AL**

NAME _____ DATE _____ PERIOD _____

6-5 Practice

Measurement: Changing Metric Units

Complete.

1. 570 cm = _?_ m **5.7**
2. 356 mm = _?_ m **0.356**
3. 4.7 m = _?_ cm **470**
4. 0.4 m = _?_ mm **400**
5. 0.63 cm = _?_ mm **6.3**
6. 0.18 mm = _?_ cm **0.018**
7. 0.42 km = _?_ m **420**
8. 0.09 km = _?_ mm **90,000**
9. 0.13 km = _?_ cm **13,000**
10. 27 kg = _?_ g **27,000**
11. 8.3 g = _?_ mg **8,300**
12. 257 mg = _?_ g **0.257**
13. 486 g = _?_ kg **0.486**
14. 55.5 g = _?_ kg **0.0555**
15. 68,700 mg = _?_ kg **0.0687**
16. 308 mL = _?_ L **0.308**
17. 1.7 L = _?_ mL **1,700**
18. 88 L = _?_ kL **0.088**
19. 0.059 kL = _?_ L **59**
20. 64,000 mL = _?_ L **64**
21. 30,000 mL = _?_ kL **0.03**

Order each set of measures from least to greatest.

22. 0.06 km, 47 m, 15,800 cm **47 m, 0.06 km, 15,800 cm**
23. 891 g, 7,800 mg, 0.5 kg **7,800 mg, 0.5 kg, 891 g**

24. **SPELUNKING** The survey length of an underground cave is 0.914 kilometers. How many meters in length is this cave? **914 m**

25. **FOOD** A 15-ounce box of granola contains 0.425 kilograms of cereal. How many grams of cereal are in the box of granola? **425 g**

Chapter 6 • 36 • Course 2

Word Problem Practice*
p. 37 **OL** **AL**

NAME _____ DATE _____ PERIOD _____

6-5 Word Problem Practice

Measurement: Changing Metric Units

1. **RUNNING** Each morning Carlos runs 1.5 kilometers. How many meters did he run? **1,500 m**

2. **AVIATION** A helicopter was flying 800 meters above the ground. How many kilometers above the ground was it flying? **0.8 km**

3. **SODA** A soda can contains 355 milliliters of liquid. How many liters of liquid does it contain? **0.355 L**

4. **CONSTRUCTION** The ceilings of most classrooms are about 2.5 meters above the floor. How many centimeters high is the ceiling? **250 cm**

5. **FENCING** Gerri's garden is 1,270 centimeters around the edges. How many meters of fencing material does she need to enclose her garden? **12.7 m**

6. **GARDENING** Mr. Chou's lawn sprinker sprays about 150 liters of water each hour. How many kiloliters of water does it spray? **0.15 kL**

7. **NUTRITION** For 11- to 14-year-olds, the Recommended Dietary Allowance (RDA) for protein is about 60 grams daily. How many milligrams do they need daily? **60,000 mg**

8. **MEASUREMENT** A measure of one pound is equivalent to about 454 grams. How many kilograms are in one pound? **0.454 kg; 454,000 mg**

Chapter 6 • 37 • Course 2

Enrichment
p. 38 **OL** **AL**

NAME _____ DATE _____ PERIOD _____

6-5 Enrichment

Using a Measurement Conversion Chart

You may sometimes need to convert customary measurements to metric measurements. For example, suppose you are reading about horses and want to know how long 5 furlongs are.

Start by finding a conversion table such as the one shown here. (Dictionaries often include such tables.)

1 mil = 0.001 inch	= 0.0254 millimeter	
1 inch = 1,000 mil	= 2.54 centimeters	
12 inches = 1 foot	= 0.3048 meter	
3 feet = 1 yard	= 0.9144 meter	
5½ yards, or 16½ feet = 1 rod	= 5.029 meters	
40 rods = 1 furlong	= 201.168 meters	
8 furlongs 5,280 feet 1,760 yards } = 1 (statute) mile	= 1.6093 kilometers	
3 miles = 1 (land) league	= 4.828 kilometers	

To change from a large unit to a small unit, multiply. To change from a small unit to a large one, divide.

Example 1 Change 5 furlongs to meters.

5 × 201.168 = 1,005.84
So, 5 furlongs is about 1,000 meters, or 1 kilometer.

Change each measurement to a metric measurement. Round each answer to the nearest tenth.

1. 10 yards **9.1 m**
2. 100 leagues **482.8 km**
3. 10 inches **25.4 cm**
4. 100 rods **502.9 m**
5. 1,000 mils **25.4 mm**
6. 10 feet **3.0 m**
7. 50 miles **80.5 km**
8. 50 furlongs **10,058.4 m, or 10.1 km**
9. 50 inches **127.0 cm**
10. 200 feet **61.0 m**
11. 200 miles **321.9 km**
12. 200 yards **182.9 m**

Chapter 6 • 38 • Course 2

*** Also available in Spanish** **ELL**

Additional Lesson Resources

Transparencies
- *5-Minute Check Transparency*, Lesson 6-5

Other Print Products
- *Noteables™ Interactive Study Notebook with Foldables™*

Teacher Tech Tools
- *Interactive Classroom CD-ROM*, Lesson 6-5
- *AssignmentWorks*, Lesson 6-5

Student Tech Tools
glencoe.com
- Extra Examples, Chapter 6, Lesson 5
- Self-Check Quiz, Chapter 6, Lesson 5

6-5 Measurement: Changing Metric Units

1 Focus

Vertical Alignment

Before Lesson 6-5
Differentiate between and use appropriate units of measures for two- and three-dimensional objects

Lesson 6-5
Convert one unit of measurement to another

After Lesson 6-5
Compare weights, capacities, geometric measures, times, and temperatures within and between measurement systems

2 Teach

▷ MINI Lab

For the first activity, suggest that students measure the width of small, rectangular objects (such as books, erasers, or notebook paper), since measuring to the nearest millimeter can be difficult.

Scaffolding Questions

Write a problem such as $9 \times \underline{\quad} = ?$ on the board. As you ask the following questions, fill in the missing factor and, when students answer, write the product.

Ask:
- What is 9 times <u>10</u>? 90
- What is 9 times <u>100</u>? 900
- What is 9 times <u>1,000</u>? 9,000
- What is 9 times <u>0.1</u>? 0.9
- What is 9 times <u>0.01</u>? 0.09
- What is 9 times <u>0.001</u>? 0.009

MAIN IDEA

Change metric units of length, capacity, and mass.

New Vocabulary

metric system
meter
liter
gram
kilogram

Math Online

glencoe.com
- Extra Examples
- Personal Tutor
- Self-Check Quiz

▷ MINI Lab

The lengths of two objects are shown below.

Object	Length (millimeters)	Length (centimeters)
paper clip	45	4.5
CD case	144	14.4

1. Select three other objects. Find and record the width of all five objects to the nearest millimeter and tenth of a centimeter.

2. Compare the measurements of the objects, and write a rule that describes how to convert from millimeters to centimeters.

3. Measure the length of your classroom in meters. Make a conjecture about how to convert this measure to centimeters. Explain. **1–3. See margin.**

The **metric system** is a decimal system of measures. The prefixes commonly used in this system are kilo-, centi-, and milli-.

Prefix	Meaning In Words	Meaning In Numbers
kilo-	thousands	1,000
centi-	hundredths	0.01
milli-	thousandths	0.001

In the metric system, the base unit of *length* is the **meter** (m). Using the prefixes, the names of other units of length are formed. Notice that the prefixes tell you how the units relate to the meter.

Unit	Symbol	Relationship to Meter	
kilometer	km	1 km = 1,000 m	1 m = 0.001 km
meter	m	1 m = 1 m	
centimeter	cm	1 cm = 0.01 m	1 m = 100 cm
millimeter	mm	1 mm = 0.001 m	1 m = 1,000 mm

The **liter** (L) is the base unit of *capacity*, the amount of dry or liquid material an object can hold. The **gram** (g) measures *mass*, the amount of matter in an object. The prefixes can also be applied to these units. Whereas the meter and liter are the base units of length and capacity, the base unit of mass is the **kilogram** (kg).

Real-World Comparison

Tips for New Teachers

A meter is about the distance from the floor to the doorknob on a door. A paper clip has a mass of about one gram. Some soft drinks are sold in two-liter bottles.

Additional Answers

1. See students' work.

2. Divide by 10.

3. Multiply by 100. There are 100 centimeters in 1 meter.

To change a metric measure of length, mass, or capacity from one unit to another, you can use the relationship between the two units and multiplication by a power of 10.

EXAMPLES Convert Units in the Metric System

Study Tip

Metric Conversions
When converting from a larger unit to a smaller unit, the power of ten being multiplied will be greater than 1.

When converting from a smaller unit to a larger unit, the power of ten will be less than 1.

1 **Convert 4.5 liters to milliliters.**

You need to convert liters to milliliters. Use the relationship
1 L = 1,000 mL.

$1 \text{ L} = 1{,}000 \text{ mL}$	Write the relationship.
$4.5 \times 1 \text{ L} = 4.5 \times 1{,}000 \text{ mL}$	Multiply each side by 4.5 since you have 4.5 L.
$4.5 \text{ L} = 4{,}500 \text{ mL}$	To multiply 4.5 by 1,000, move the decimal point 3 places to the right.

2 **Convert 500 millimeters to meters.**

You need to convert millimeters to meters. Use the relationship
1 mm = 0.001 m.

$1 \text{ mm} = 0.001 \text{ m}$	Write the relationship.
$500 \times 1 \text{ mm} = 500 \times 0.001 \text{ m}$	Multiply each side by 500 since you have 500 mm.
$500 \text{ mm} = 0.5 \text{ m}$	To multiply 500 by 0.001, move the decimal point 3 places to the left.

✓ CHECK Your Progress

Complete.

a. $25.4 \text{ g} = \blacksquare \text{ kg}$ **0.0254**

b. $158 \text{ mm} = \blacksquare \text{ m}$ **0.158**

Real-World EXAMPLE

3 **BEARS** The California Grizzly Bear was designated the official state animal in 1953. Use the information at the left to find the maximum weight of a grizzly bear in grams.

You are converting kilograms to grams. Since the maximum weight of a grizzly bear is 521.64 kilograms, use the relationship 1 kg = 1,000 g.

$1 \text{ kg} = 1{,}000 \text{ g}$	Write the relationship.
$521.64 \times 1 \text{ kg} = 521.64 \times 1{,}000 \text{ g}$	Multiply each side by 521.64 since you have 521.64 kg.
$521.64 \text{ kg} = 521{,}640 \text{ g}$	To multiply 521.64 by 1,000, move the decimal point 3 places to the right.

So, the maximum weight of a grizzly bear is 521,640 grams.

Real-World Link . . . .
The maximum weight of a grizzly bear is 521.64 kilograms.
Source: North American Bear Center

✓ CHECK Your Progress

c. **FOOD** A bottle contains 1.75 liters of juice. How many milliliters is this? **1,750 mL**

Lesson 6-5 Measurement: Changing Metric Units **305**

Focus on Mathematical Content

To convert **from a larger metric unit to a smaller metric unit**, multiply by a power of 10. Move the decimal point to the right the same number of places as the **number of zeros** in the power of 10.

To convert **from a smaller metric unit to a larger metric unit**, multiply by a power of 10 less than 1. Move the decimal point to the left the same number of places as the **number of decimal places** in the power of 10.

✓ **Formative Assessment**

Use the Check Your Progress exercises after each Example to determine students' understanding of concepts.

ADDITIONAL EXAMPLES

1 Complete $7.2 \text{ m} = \blacksquare \text{ mm}$. 7,200

2 Complete $40 \text{ cm} = \blacksquare \text{ m}$. 0.4

3 **FARMS** A bucket holds 12.8 liters of water. Find the capacity of the bucket in milliliters. 12,800 mL

Additional Examples are also in:

- Noteables™ Interactive Study Notebook with Foldables™
- Interactive Classroom PowerPoint® Presentations

Tips for New Teachers **Converting Units**

Make sure students understand that when converting from a larger unit to a smaller unit, there will be more of the smaller unit, so they should multiply by a power of 10 *greater than 1*. Similarly, when converting from a smaller unit to a larger unit, there will be fewer of the larger unit, so they should multiply by a power of 10 *less than 1*.

Focus on Mathematical Content

Metric System Students may think that the base unit of mass is the gram. However, in the metric system, the base unit of mass is the kilogram. This is because the mass of many everyday objects, like a textbook, is more easily measured in kilograms, not grams.

4 Convert 7.13 miles to kilometers. Round to the nearest hundredth if necessary. 11.48 km

5 Convert 925.48 grams to pounds. Round to the nearest hundredth if necessary. 2.04 lb

To convert measures between customary units and metric units, use the relationships below.

Customary and Metric Relationships   Key Concept

Type of Measure	Customary	→	Metric
Length	1 inch (in.)	≈	2.54 centimeters (cm)
	1 foot (ft)	≈	0.30 meter (m)
	1 yard (yd)	≈	0.91 meter (m)
	1 mile (mi)	≈	1.61 kilometers (km)
Weight/Mass	1 pound (lb)	≈	453.6 grams (g)
	1 pound (lb)	≈	0.4536 kilogram (kg)
	1 ton (T)	≈	907.2 kilograms (kg)
Capacity	1 cup (c)	≈	236.59 milliliters (mL)
	1 pint (pt)	≈	473.18 milliliters (mL)
	1 quart (qt)	≈	946.35 milliliters (mL)
	1 gallon (gal)	≈	3.79 liters (L)

EXAMPLES   Convert Between Measurement Systems

4 Convert 17.22 inches to centimeters. Round to the nearest hundredth if necessary.

Use the relationship 1 inch ≈ 2.54 centimeters.

1 inch ≈ 2.54 cm	Write the relationship.
17.22×1 in. $\approx 17.22 \times 2.54$ cm	Multiply each side by 17.22 since you have 17.22 in.
17.22 in. ≈ 43.7388 cm	Simplify.

So, 17.22 inches is approximately 43.74 centimeters.

5 Convert 828.5 milliliters to cups. Round to the nearest hundredth if necessary.

Since 1 cup ≈ 236.59 milliliters, multiply by $\frac{1\,c}{236.59\,mL}$.

$$828.5 \text{ mL} \approx 828.5 \text{ mL} \cdot \frac{1\,c}{236.59\,\text{mL}} \quad \text{Multiply by } \frac{1\,c}{236.59\,\text{mL}}.$$

$$\approx \frac{828.5\,c}{236.59} \text{ or } 3.5\,c \quad \text{Simplify.}$$

So, 828.5 milliliters is approximately 3.5 cups.

CHECK Your Progress

Complete. Round to the nearest hundredth if necessary.

d. 7.44 c ≈ ▮ mL   e. 22.09 lb ≈ ▮ kg   f. 35.85 L ≈ ▮ gal **9.46**

Study Tip

Alternative Method When converting 17.22 inches to centimeters, you can use the relationship 1 in. ≈ 2.54 cm or the unit ratio $\frac{2.54\,cm}{1\,in.}$.

Real-World EXAMPLE   Convert with Rates

6 **LIGHT** The speed of light is about 186,000 miles per second. Find the approximate speed of light in kilometers per second.

Since 1 mile ≈ 1.61 kilometers, multiply by $\frac{1.61 \text{ km}}{1 \text{ mi}}$.

$$\frac{186,000 \text{ mi}}{\text{s}} \approx \frac{186,000 \text{ mi}}{1 \text{ s}} \times \frac{1.61 \text{ km}}{1 \text{ mi}} \qquad \text{Multiply by } \frac{1.61 \text{ km}}{1 \text{ mi}}.$$

$$\approx \frac{299,460 \text{ km}}{1 \text{ s}} \qquad \text{Simplify.}$$

So, the speed of light is approximately 299,460 kilometers per second.

✓ CHECK Your Progress

g. **RUNNING** Chuck runs at a speed of 3 meters per second. About how many feet per second does Chuck run? **about 9.84 feet per second**

★ indicates multi-step problem

✓ CHECK Your Understanding

Examples 1, 2, 4, 5
(pp. 305–306)

Complete. Round to the nearest hundredth if necessary.

1. 3.7 m = ▆ cm **370**
2. 550 m = ▆ km **0.55**
3. 1,460 mg = ▆ g **1.46**
4. 2.34 kL = ▆ L **2,340**
5. 9.36 yd ≈ ▆ m **8.52**
6. 11.07 pt ≈ ▆ mL **5,238.10**
7. 58.14 kg ≈ ▆ lb **128.17**
8. 38.44 cm ≈ ▆ in. **15.13**

Examples 3, 6
(pp. 305, 307)

9. **SPORTS** About how many feet does a team of athletes run in a 1,600-meter relay race? **about 5,333.33 ft**

▶ Practice and Problem Solving

HOMEWORK HELP

For Exercises	See Examples
10–23	1, 2, 4, 5
24–27	3, 6

Exercise Levels
A: 10–27
B: 28–38
C: 39–43

Complete. Round to the nearest hundredth if necessary.

10. 720 cm = ▆ m **7.2**
11. 983 mm = ▆ m **0.98**
12. 3.2 m = ▆ cm **320**
13. 0.03 g = ▆ mg **30**
14. 997 g = ▆ kg **1.00**
15. 82.1 g = ▆ kg **0.08**
16. 9.1 L = ▆ mL **9,100**
17. 130.5 kL = ▆ L **130,500**
18. 3.75 c ≈ ▆ mL **887.21**
19. 41.8 in. ≈ ▆ cm **106.17**
20. 156.25 lb ≈ ▆ kg **70.88**
21. 9.5 gal ≈ ▆ L **36.01**
22. 680.4 g ≈ ▆ lb **1.5**
23. 4.725 m ≈ ▆ ft **15.75**

24. **WATERFALLS** At 979 meters tall, Angel Falls in Venezuela is the highest waterfall in the world. How many kilometers tall is the waterfall? **0.979 km**

25. **FOOD** An 18-ounce jar contains 510 grams of grape jelly. How many kilograms of grape jelly does the jar contain? **0.51 kg**

Lesson 6-5 Measurement: Changing Metric Units **307**

ADDITIONAL EXAMPLE

6 **FARMS** Pike's Peak near Colorado Springs, Colorado, rises to a height that is 14,110 feet above sea level. About how many meters high is Pike's Peak? 4,233 m

3 Practice

✓ Formative Assessment

Use Exercises 1–9 to check for understanding.

Then use the chart at the bottom of this page to customize your assignments for students.

Intervention You may wish to use the Study Guide and Intervention Master on page 34 of the *Chapter 6 Resource Masters* for additional reinforcement.

Odd/Even Assignments

Exercises 10–27 are structured so that students practice the same concepts whether they are assigned odd or even problems.

DIFFERENTIATED HOMEWORK OPTIONS

Level	Assignment	Two-Day Assignment	
BL Basic	10–27, 44, 45, 48–56	11–27 odd, 44, 45	10–26 even, 48–56
OL Core	11–23 odd, 24–27, 29–37 odd, 39, 43–56	10–23, 43–45	24–39, 46–56
AL Advanced/Pre-AP	28–52 (optional: 53–56)		

26. CYCLING Ramon rides his bike at a rate of 8 kilometers per hour. About how many miles per hour can Ramon ride his bike? **about 4.97 miles per hour**

★ **27. BIRDS** A gull can fly at a speed of 22 miles per hour. About how many meters per hour can a gull fly? **about 35,420 meters per hour**

Complete. Round to the nearest hundredth if necessary.

28. 8.18 qt ≈ ■ L **7.74**

29. 15.09 km ≈ ■ yd **16,582.42**

30. 72.26 cm ≈ ■ ft **2.37**

31. 0.445 T ≈ ■ g **403,704**

Order each set of measures from least to greatest.

32. 0.02 km, 3,000 cm, 50 m
33. 0.06 L, 660 mL, 6.6 kL

32. 0.02 km, 50 m, 3,000 cm

33. 660 mL, 0.06 L, 6.6 kL

34. 0.32 kg, 345 g, 35,100 mg
35,100 mg, 0.32 kg, 345 g

35. 2,650 mm, 130 cm, 5 m
130 cm, 2650 mm, 5 m

Real-World Link . . . . :
The Mackinac Bridge opened on November 1, 1957. It is the longest two-tower suspension bridge between bases in the Western Hemisphere.
Source: *Encyclopaedia Britannica*

★ **36. ANALYZE TABLES** The table shows the lengths of bridges in the United States. Which bridges are about 1 kilometer in length? Justify your answer. **See margin.**

Bridge	Length (m)
Mackinac, MI	1,158
George Washington, NY	1,067
Tacoma Narrows II, WA	853
Oakland Bay, CA	704
Pennybacker, TX	345
Sunshine Skyway, FL	8,712
Golden Gate, CA	2,780

★ **37. CARPENTRY** Jacinta needs a 2.5-meter pole for a birdfeeder that she is building. How many centimeters will she need to cut off a 3-meter pole in order to use it for the birdfeeder? **50 cm**

EXTRA PRACTICE
See pages 683, 709.

38. BAKING A bakery uses 900 grams of peaches per cobbler. How many
★ cobblers can be made using 10.5 pounds of peaches? **5 cobblers**

H.O.T. Problems ★ **39. FIND THE ERROR** Jake and Gerardo are converting 3.25 kilograms to grams. Who is correct? Explain your reasoning.

39. Jake; Gerardo divided 3.25 by 1,000. He should have multiplied.

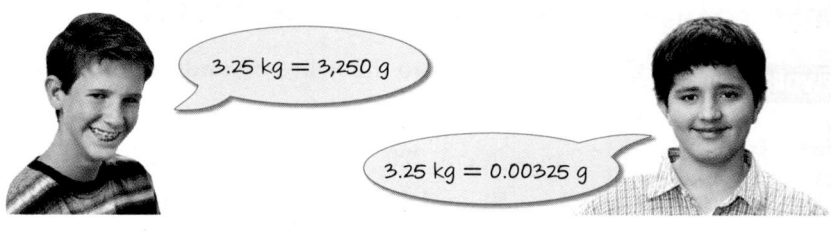

3.25 kg = 3,250 g

3.25 kg = 0.00325 g

Jake

Gerardo

CHALLENGE For Exercises 40–42, use the following information.
The metric prefix *giga* refers to something one billion times larger than the base unit.

40. How many meters are in one gigameter? **1,000,000,000 m**

41. About how many miles are in one gigameter? Round to the nearest hundredth. **about 621,118.01 mi**

42. about 149.73 gm

42. The distance from Earth to the Sun is approximately 93 million miles. About how many gigameters is this? Round to the nearest hundredth.

308 **Chapter 6** Ratios and Proportions

Differentiated Instruction

Verbal/Linguistic Learners Have students whose parents or grandparents immigrated from other countries record a recipe from the other country. What units of mass and capacity are used in the recipe? Have students rewrite the recipe, converting the units to smaller or larger units.

43. **WRITING IN MATH** Explain why it makes sense to multiply by a power of 10 that is greater than 1 when changing from a larger unit to a smaller unit. **There are a greater number of smaller units.**

TEST PRACTICE

44. The table shows the mass of four wireless telephones. Find the approximate total mass of the telephones in kilograms. **A**

Telephone Owner	Mass (g)
Elena	100.4
Kevin	70.8
Marissa	95.6
Corey	120.4

A 0.39 kilogram

B 3.9 kilograms

C 39.0 kilograms

D 390.0 kilograms

45. Which relationship between the given units of measure is correct? **H**

F One gram is $\frac{1}{100}$ of a centigram.

G One meter is $\frac{1}{100}$ of a centimeter.

H One gram is $\frac{1}{1,000}$ of a kilogram.

J One milliliter is $\frac{1}{100}$ of a liter.

Spiral Review

46. **MEASUREMENT** A certain car weighs 3,200 pounds. What is the weight of the car in tons? (Lesson 6-4) **1.6 T**

47. **MEASUREMENT** The table shows the number of inches per foot. Graph the data. Then find the slope of the line. Explain what slope represents.
(Lesson 6-3) **See margin for graph. Slope: $\frac{1}{12}$; there are 12 inches in every foot.**

Feet (x)	1	2	3	4
Inches (y)	12	24	36	48

Add or subtract. Write in simplest form. (Lesson 5-3)

48. $3\frac{4}{7} + 1\frac{1}{7}$ **$4\frac{5}{7}$** 49. $8\frac{3}{5} - 2\frac{2}{5}$ **$6\frac{1}{5}$** 50. $9\frac{1}{6} + 4\frac{3}{8}$ **$13\frac{13}{24}$** 51. $11\frac{7}{10} - 5\frac{3}{4}$ **$5\frac{19}{20}$**

52. **BASKETBALL** Jared made thirty-seven percent of his free-throw attempts during basketball practice. Write this percent as a decimal. (Lesson 4-7) **0.37**

GET READY for the Next Lesson

PREREQUISITE SKILL Solve each equation. (Lesson 3-3)

53. $5 \cdot 4 = x \cdot 2$ **10** 54. $9 \cdot 24 = 27 \cdot x$ **8** 55. $x \cdot 15 = 12 \cdot 4$ **3.2** 56. $8\frac{1}{2} \cdot x = 11 \cdot 17$ **22**

Lesson 6-5 Measurement: Changing Metric Units **309**

4 Assess

Name the Math Have students tell what mathematical procedures they used to solve one of the following exercises: 24, 25, 30, or 31.

Formative Assessment

Check for student understanding of concepts in Lessons 6-3, 6-4, and 6-5.

CRM Quiz 2, p. 67

FOLDABLES Study Organizer **Foldables™ Follow-Up**

Remind students to take notes about converting from one metric unit to another in their Foldables. Encourage them to include an example of converting from a smaller unit to a larger unit and an example of converting from a larger unit to smaller unit.

Additional Answer
47.

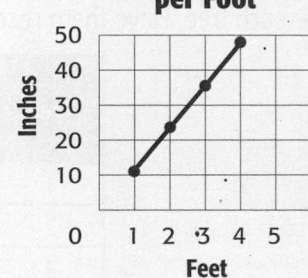

Number of Inches per Foot

Algebra: Solving Proportions

6-6

PACING: **Regular:** 2 periods, **Block:** 1 period

Options for Differentiated Instruction

ELL = English Language Learner   **AL** = Above or Beyond Grade Level   **SS** = Struggling Students   **SN** = Special Needs

Alternative Methods   **AL**

Use after presenting Example 2.

Remind students that they can solve some proportions without using cross products. Encourage them to try using techniques they already know, such as:

• simplifying fractions
• multiplying or dividing both the numerator and the denominator by the same number to find equivalent fractions

For example, in the proportion $\frac{21}{5} = \frac{c}{10}$, it is easy to see that $5 \times 2 = 10$.

Therefore, $21 \times 2 = 42$ is the value for c.

Naturalist Learning   **ELL**   **AL**   **SS**   **SN**

Use after presenting Examples 1–4.

Have students collect leaves from three kinds of trees, measure the length and width of each leaf, and find the ratio $\frac{l}{w}$ for each leaf. Have students measure the widths of the three trees, estimate the heights, and find the ratio $\frac{h}{w}$ for each tree. Have them record their data in a table like the one shown below.

Tree	Leaves			Trees		
	Length	Width	Ratio $\frac{l}{w}$	Height	Width	Ratio $\frac{h}{w}$
1						
2						
3						

Have students compare the ratio of each leaf's length and width to the ratio for the tree's height and width to see if they form a proportion.

Leveled Lesson Resources

Chapter 6 Resource Masters

BL = Below or Approaching Grade Level   **OL** = On Grade Level   **AL** = Above or Beyond Grade Level   **ELL** = English Language Learner

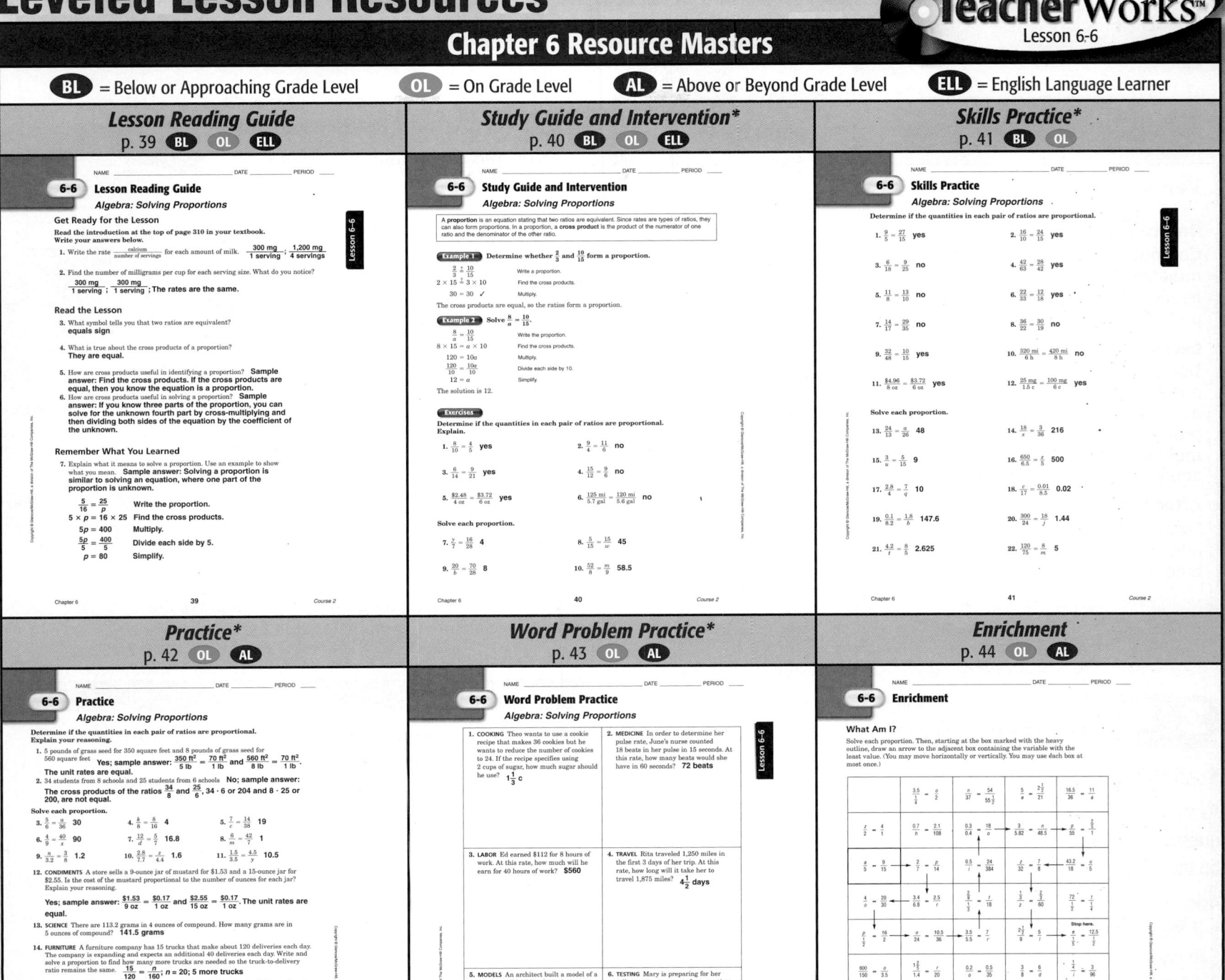

Lesson Reading Guide p. 39 BL OL ELL

*Study Guide and Intervention** p. 40 BL OL ELL

*Skills Practice** p. 41 BL OL

*Practice** p. 42 OL AL

*Word Problem Practice** p. 43 OL AL

Enrichment p. 44 OL AL

*** Also available in Spanish ELL**

Additional Lesson Resources

Transparencies
• *5-Minute Check Transparency,* Lesson 6-6

Other Print Products
• *Teaching Mathematics with Manipulatives*
• *Noteables™ Interactive Study Notebook with Foldables™*

Teacher Tech Tools
• *Interactive Classroom CD-ROM,* Lesson 6-6
• *AssignmentWorks,* Lesson 6-6

Student Tech Tools
glencoe.com
• Extra Examples, Chapter 6, Lesson 6
• Self-Check Quiz, Chapter 6, Lesson 6

6-6 Lesson Notes

Vertical Alignment

Before Lesson 6-6
Compute and perform simple multiplication and division of fractions and apply these procedures to solving problems

Lesson 6-6
Use proportions to solve problems; use cross-multiplication as a method for solving such problems, understanding it as the multiplication of both sides of an equation by a multiplicative inverse

After Lesson 6-6
Solve multi-step problems involving rate, average speed, distance, and time or a direct variation

2 Teach

Scaffolding Questions

As students answer the following questions, write each rate as a fraction on the board.

Ask:
- If Mark drove 50 miles on 2 gallons of gas, what was his mileage rate?
$$\frac{50 \text{ mi}}{2 \text{ gal}}$$

- If Alicia drove 75 miles on 3 gallons of gas, what was her mileage rate?
$$\frac{75 \text{ mi}}{3 \text{ gal}}$$

- If I drove 12.5 miles on half a gallon of gas, what was my mileage rate?
$$\frac{12.5 \text{ mi}}{0.5 \text{ gal}}$$

- What do you notice about these rates? Sample answers: They are equivalent; each rate can be written as the unit rate $\frac{25 \text{ mi}}{1 \text{ gal}}$.

MAIN IDEA

Solve proportions.

New Vocabulary

proportional
proportion
cross product

Math Online

glencoe.com

- Extra Examples
- Personal Tutor
- Self-Check Quiz

▷ **GET READY** for the Lesson

NUTRITION The amount of calcium in different servings of milk is shown. 1. $\frac{300 \text{ mg}}{1 \text{ serving}}, \frac{1{,}200 \text{ mg}}{4 \text{ servings}}$

1. Write the rate $\frac{\text{calcium}}{\text{number of servings}}$ for each amount of milk.

2. Find the number of milligrams per cup for each serving size. What do you notice? $\frac{300 \text{ mg}}{1 \text{ serving}}, \frac{300 \text{ mg}}{1 \text{ serving}}$; The rates are the same.

Calcium (mg)	Servings
300	1
1,200	4

Two quantities are **proportional** if they have a constant rate or ratio. In the example above, notice that the number of servings and amount of calcium change or *vary* in the same way.

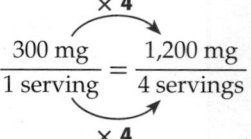

$$\frac{300 \text{ mg}}{1 \text{ serving}} = \frac{1{,}200 \text{ mg}}{4 \text{ servings}}$$

The unit rates for these different-sized servings are the same, a constant 300 milligrams per serving. So, the amount of calcium is proportional to the serving size.

Proportion		Key Concept
Words	A **proportion** is an equation stating that two ratios or rates are equivalent.	
Symbols	**Numbers** $\frac{1}{2} = \frac{3}{6}, \frac{8 \text{ ft}}{10 \text{ s}} = \frac{4 \text{ ft}}{5 \text{ s}}$	**Algebra** $\frac{a}{b} = \frac{c}{d}$, where $b, d \neq 0$

Consider the following proportion.

$$\frac{a}{b} = \frac{c}{d}$$

$$\frac{a}{\overset{1}{\cancel{b}}} \cdot \cancel{b}d = \frac{c}{\underset{1}{\cancel{d}}} \cdot b\cancel{d} \qquad \text{Multiply each side by } bd.$$

$$ad = bc \qquad \text{Simplify.}$$

The products ad and bc are called the **cross products** of this proportion. The cross products of any proportion are equal. You can compare unit rates or cross products to identify proportional relationships.

Reading Math

Nonproportional
When ratios do not form a proportion, they are called nonproportional.

EXAMPLE Identify Proportional Relationships

1 **RECREATION** A carousel makes 4 complete turns after 64 seconds and 5 complete turns after 76 seconds. Based on this information, is the number of turns made by this carousel proportional to the time in seconds? Explain.

METHOD 1 Compare unit rates.

$$\frac{\text{seconds}}{\text{complete turns}} \rightarrow \quad \frac{64\text{ s}}{4\text{ turns}} = \frac{16\text{ s}}{1\text{ turn}} \qquad \frac{76\text{ s}}{5\text{ turns}} = \frac{15.2\text{ s}}{1\text{ turn}}$$

Since the unit rates are not equal, the number of turns is not proportional to the time in seconds.

METHOD 2 Compare ratios by comparing cross products.

$$\frac{\text{seconds}}{\text{complete turns}} \rightarrow \quad \frac{64}{4} \overset{?}{=} \frac{76}{5} \quad \leftarrow \text{seconds} \\ \leftarrow \text{complete turns}$$

$$64 \cdot 5 \overset{?}{=} 4 \cdot 76 \qquad \text{Find the cross products.}$$

$$320 \neq 304 \qquad \text{Multiply.}$$

Since the cross products are not equal, the number of turns is not proportional to the time in seconds.

✓ **CHOOSE** Your Method

Determine if the quantities in each pair of ratios are proportional. Explain.

a. 60 voted out of 100 registered and 84 voted out of 140 registered

b. $12 for 16 yards of fabric and $9 for 24 yards fabric

You can also use cross products to find a missing value in a proportion. This is known as *solving the proportion*.

a. Yes; sample answer: The cross products of the ratios $\frac{60}{100}$ and $\frac{84}{140}$, 60 · 140 and 100 · 84, are both equal to 8,400.

b. No; sample answer: $\frac{\$12}{16\text{ yd}} = \frac{\$0.75}{1\text{ yd}}$ and $\frac{\$9}{24\text{ yd}} = \frac{\$0.375}{1\text{ yd}}$. The unit rates are not equal.

Study Tip

Mental Math
Some proportions can be solved using mental math.

$$\frac{2.5}{10} = \frac{x}{30}$$

×3

$$\frac{2.5}{10} = \frac{7.5}{30}$$

×3

EXAMPLES Solve a Proportion

2 Solve $\frac{21}{5} = \frac{c}{7}$.

$$\frac{21}{5} = \frac{c}{7} \qquad \text{Write the proportion.}$$

$$21 \cdot 7 = 5 \cdot c \qquad \text{Find the cross products.}$$

$$147 = 5c \qquad \text{Multiply.}$$

$$\frac{147}{5} = \frac{5c}{5} \qquad \text{Divide each side by 5.}$$

$$29.4 = c \qquad \text{Simplify.}$$

Check for Reasonableness Since $\frac{21}{5} \approx \frac{20}{5}$ or $\frac{4}{1}$ and $\frac{29.4}{7} \approx \frac{28}{7}$ or $\frac{4}{1}$, the answer is reasonable. ✔

Lesson 6-6 Algebra: Solving Proportions **311**

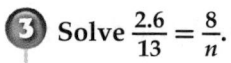

ADDITIONAL EXAMPLES

3 Solve $\frac{3.5}{14} = \frac{6}{n}$. $n = 24$

4 **FLAGS** According to specifications, the ratio of the length of the U.S. flag to its width must be 1.9 to 1. How long must a U.S. flag be if it is designed to have a width of 2.5 feet? **4.75 ft**

3 Solve $\frac{2.6}{13} = \frac{8}{n}$.

$\frac{2.6}{13} = \frac{8}{n}$ Write the proportion.

$2.6 \cdot n = 13 \cdot 8$ Find the cross products.

$2.6n = 104$ Multiply.

$\frac{2.6n}{2.6} = \frac{104}{2.6}$ Divide each side by 2.6.

$n = 40$ Simplify.

✓ **CHECK Your Progress**

c. $\frac{16}{k} = \frac{2}{3}$ **24**   d. $\frac{2}{6} = \frac{5}{h}$ **15**   e. $\frac{10}{k} = \frac{2.5}{4}$ **16**

Real-World EXAMPLE

4 **MEDICINE** For every 18 people who have a sore throat, there are 2 people who actually have strep throat. If 72 patients have sore throats, how many of these would you expect to have strep throat?

METHOD 1   Write and solve a proportion.

Let s represent strep throat.

$\frac{2 \text{ strep throats}}{18 \text{ sore throats}} = \frac{s}{72 \text{ sore throats}}$ Write a proportion.

$2 \cdot 72 = 18 \cdot s$ Find the cross products.

$144 = 18s$ Multiply.

$8 = s$ Divide each side by 18.

METHOD 2   Find and use a unit rate or ratio.

$\frac{2 \text{ strep throats} \div 2}{18 \text{ sore throats} \div 2} = \frac{1}{9}$ The ratio of strep throats to sore throats is 1 : 9.

Words	For every 9 sore throats, there is 1 strep throat.
Variable	Let s represent the number of strep throats.
Equation	$s = \frac{1}{9} \cdot 72$

$s = \frac{1}{9} \cdot 72$ or 8   Multiply.

So, you would expect 8 people to have strep throat.

✓ **CHOOSE Your Method**

f. **RUNNING** Salvador can run 120 meters in 24 seconds. At this rate, how many seconds will it take him to run a 300-meter race? **60 s**

Real-World Career . . . .
How Does a Physician's Assistant Use Math?
A physician's assistant uses math when calculating safe dosages of medications.

Math Online
For more information visit, glencoe.com.

Example 1
(p. 311)

1–4. See margin.

Determine if the quantities in each pair of ratios are proportional. Explain.

1. 2 adults for 10 children and 3 adults for 12 children

2. 12 inches by 8 inches and 18 inches by 12 inches

3. 8 feet in 21 seconds and 12 feet in 31.5 seconds

4. $5.60 for 5 pairs of socks and $7.12 for 8 pairs of socks

Examples 2, 3
(pp. 311–312)

Solve each proportion.

5. $\frac{5}{6} = \frac{t}{18}$ **15**

6. $\frac{6}{k} = \frac{24}{28}$ **7**

7. $\frac{21}{5} = \frac{c}{7}$ **29.4**

8. $\frac{15}{w} = \frac{2}{5}$ **37.5**

9. $\frac{3}{n} = \frac{2.7}{18}$ **20**

10. $\frac{0.2}{3} = \frac{3}{d}$ **45**

Example 4
(p. 312)

11. **GROCERIES** Orange juice is on sale at 3 half-gallons for $5. At this rate, find the cost of 5 half-gallons of orange juice to the nearest cent. **$8.33**

12. **TRAVEL** Franco drove 203 miles in 3.5 hours. At this rate, how long will it take him to drive another 29 miles to the next town? **0.5 h**

Practice and Problem Solving

HOMEWORK HELP	
For Exercises	See Examples
13–20	1
21–32	2, 3
33–36	4

Exercise Levels
A: 13–36
B: 37–44
C: 45–48

15–18. See Ch. 6 Answer Appendix.

19. No; $\frac{45 \text{ min}}{25 \text{ pages}}$
$= \frac{1.8 \text{ min}}{1 \text{ page}}$
and $\frac{60 \text{ min}}{30 \text{ pages}}$
$= \frac{2 \text{ min}}{1 \text{ page}}$. These rates are not equivalent.

Determine if the quantities in each pair of ratios are proportional. Explain.

13. 20 children from 6 families to 16 children from 5 families **13, 14. See margin.**

14. 5 pounds of dry ice melts in 30 hours and 4 pounds melts in 24 hours

15. 16 winners out of 200 entries and 28 winners out of 350 entries

16. 5 meters in 7 minutes and 25 meters in 49 minutes

17. 1.4 tons produced every 18 days and 10.5 tons every 60 days

18. 3 inches for every 4 miles and 7.5 inches for every 10 miles

19. **READING** Leslie reads 25 pages in 45 minutes. After 60 minutes, she has read a total of 30 pages. Is her time proportional to the number of pages she reads? Explain.

20. **PETS** A store sells 2 hamsters for $11 and 6 hamsters for $33. Is the cost proportional to the number of hamsters sold? Explain. **See Ch. 6 Answer Appendix.**

Solve each proportion.

21. $\frac{3}{8} = \frac{b}{40}$ **15**

22. $\frac{x}{12} = \frac{12}{4}$ **36**

23. $\frac{c}{7} = \frac{18}{42}$ **3**

24. $\frac{5}{k} = \frac{10}{22}$ **11**

25. $\frac{3}{8} = \frac{n}{4}$ **1.5**

26. $\frac{15}{4} = \frac{3}{8}$ **0.8**

27. $\frac{45}{5} = \frac{d}{7}$ **63**

28. $\frac{30}{a} = \frac{8}{20}$ **75**

29. $\frac{1.6}{m} = \frac{2}{3}$ **2.4**

30. $\frac{4.5}{5} = \frac{t}{7}$ **6.3**

31. $\frac{2.5}{4.5} = \frac{7.5}{x}$ **13.5**

32. $\frac{3.8}{5.2} = \frac{7.6}{z}$ **10.4**

33. **SCHOOL** If 4 notebooks weigh 2.8 pounds, how much do 6 of the same notebooks weigh? **4.2 lb**

34. **COOKING** There are 6 teaspoons in 2 tablespoons. How many teaspoons are in 1.5 tablespoons? **4.5 t**

Lesson 6-6 Algebra: Solving Proportions **313**

---

3 Practice

 Formative Assessment

Use Exercises 1–12 to check for understanding.

Then use the chart at the bottom of this page to customize your assignments for students.

Intervention You may wish to use the Study Guide and Intervention Master on page 40 of the *Chapter 6 Resource Masters* for additional reinforcement.

Odd/Even Assignments

Exercises 13–36 are structured so that students practice the same concepts whether they are assigned odd or even problems.

Additional Answers

1. No; sample answer:
$\frac{10 \text{ children}}{2 \text{ adults}} = \frac{5 \text{ children}}{1 \text{ adult}}$
and $\frac{12 \text{ children}}{3 \text{ adults}} = \frac{4 \text{ children}}{1 \text{ adult}}$.
The unit rates are not equal.

2. Yes; sample answer: The cross products of the ratios $\frac{12}{8}$ and $\frac{18}{12}$, 8 • 18 and 12 • 12, are both equal to 144.

3. Yes; sample answer: The cross products of the ratios $\frac{8}{21}$ and $\frac{12}{31.5}$, 8 • 31.5 and 21 • 12, are both equal to 252.

4. No; sample answer: $\frac{\$5.60}{5 \text{ pairs}} = \frac{\$1.12}{1 \text{ pair}}$ and $\frac{\$7.12}{8 \text{ pairs}} = \frac{\$0.89}{1 \text{ pair}}$. The unit rates are not equal.

13. No; sample answer: The cross products of the ratios $\frac{20}{6}$ and $\frac{16}{5}$, 20 • 5 or 100 and 6 • 16 or 96, are not equal.

14. Yes; sample answer: $\frac{30 \text{ h}}{5 \text{ lb}} = \frac{6 \text{ h}}{1 \text{ lb}}$ and $\frac{24 \text{ h}}{4 \text{ lb}} = \frac{6 \text{ h}}{1 \text{ lb}}$. The unit rates are equal.

DIFFERENTIATED HOMEWORK OPTIONS

Level	Assignment	Two-Day Option	
BL Basic	13–36, 45, 49–58	13–35 odd, 49, 50	14–36 even, 45, 51–58
OL Core	13–35 odd, 36–45, 47–58	13–36, 49, 50	35–45, 47, 48, 51–58
AL Advanced/Pre-AP	37–57 (optional: 58)		

Proportion Problems

Tips for New Teachers

Remind students that they can solve some proportion problems by simplifying the fractions or by multiplying (or dividing) the numerator and denominator of one fraction by the same number.

Additional Answers

37. (3, 15) represents 3 pizzas cost $15. (5, 25) represents 5 pizzas cost $25. Yes, as the number of pizzas increases by 1, the cost increases by $5.

38. (2, 13) represents 2 pizzas cost $13 with a delivery fee. (4, 23) represents 4 pizzas cost $23 with a delivery fee. No, the cost of the pizza does not increase by the same amount each time.

39. 5, with delivery fee; 5, no delivery fee; the slope represents the cost per pizza.

40. $3; the pizzas with the delivery fee always cost $3 more.

46. 30 c; Sample answer: The ratio of cups of bleach to cups of water is 1:5 which means that the ratio of cups of water to total cups of cleaning solution is 5:6. Set up and solve the proportion $\frac{5}{6} = \frac{x}{36}$, where x represents the number of cups of water.

---

35. SCIENCE The ratio of salt to water in a certain solution is 4 to 15. If the solution contains 6 ounces of water, how many ounces of salt does it contain? **1.6 oz**

36. CONCERTS Alethia purchased 7 advanced tickets for herself and her friends to a concert and paid $164.50. If the total cost of tickets to the concert is proportional to the number purchased, how many tickets to the same concert did Serefina purchase if she paid a total of $94? **4**

ANALYZE GRAPHS For Exercises 37–40, use the graph. It shows the cost of several pizzas, with and without a delivery fee.

Pizza Cost

37. What do the points (3, 15) and (5, 25) represent on the graph? Is this situation proportional? Explain. **See margin.**

38. What do the points (2, 13) and (4, 23) represent on the graph? Is this situation proportional? Explain. **See margin.**

Real-World Link · · · · ·
Film for an IMAX projection system passes through the projector at the rate of 330 feet per minute or 5.5 feet per second.
Source: IMAX Corporation

39. What is the slope of each line? What does the slope represent? **See margin.**

40. What is the delivery fee? Explain. **See margin.**

41. SAVINGS Pao spent $140 of his paycheck and put the remaining $20 in his savings account. If the number of dollars he spends is proportional to the number he saves, how much of a $156-paycheck will he put into savings? **$19.50**

42. MOVIES After 30 seconds, 720 frames of film have passed through a movie projector. At this rate, what is the approximate running time in minutes of a movie made up of 57,000 frames of film? **about 40 min**

43. SCHOOL There are 325 students and 13 teachers at a school. Next school year, the enrollment is expected to increase by 100 students. Write and solve a proportion to find the number of teachers that must be hired so the student-teacher ratio remains the same. $\frac{325}{13} = \frac{100}{x}$; **4**

EXTRA PRACTICE
See pages 683, 709.

44. FIND THE DATA Refer to the Data File on pages 16–19. Choose some data and write a real-world problem in which you would solve a proportion. **See students' work.**

H.O.T. Problems

45. \$5.70 for 6 lb;
Sample answer:
This ratio has a
unit rate of 0.95/lb,
while all of the
other ratios have a
unit rate of \$0.90/lb.

45. Which One Doesn't Belong? Identify the rate that is not proportional to the other three. Explain your reasoning.

| $4.50 for 5 lb | $2.88 for 3.2 lb | $5.70 for 6 lb | $4.86 for 5.4 lb |

46. CHALLENGE In a cleaning solution, the ratio of bleach to water is 1:5. If there are 36 cups of cleaning solution, how many cups of water are needed? Explain your reasoning. **See margin.**

RECIPE For Exercises 1–3, use the information in the table to write each ratio as a fraction in simplest form. (Lesson 6-1)

Cherry Punch Recipe	
Cherry Juice	4 cups
Apple Juice	2 cups
Ginger Ale	16 cups

1. cherry juice : apple juice $\frac{2}{1}$

2. apple juice : ginger ale $\frac{1}{8}$

3. cherry juice : ginger ale $\frac{1}{4}$

Determine whether the ratios are equivalent. Explain. (Lesson 6-1)

4. 6 out of 9 words spelled correctly
2 out of 3 words spelled correctly **yes; $\frac{6}{9} = \frac{2}{3}$**

5. 150 athletes to 15 coaches
3 athletes to 1 coach **no; 150:15 = 10:1**

6. 24 points in 4 games
72 points in 8 games
no; 24:4 = 6:1 and 72:8 = 9:1

7. **MULTIPLE CHOICE** Which amount of chocolate shown in the table has the best unit price? (Lesson 6-2) **B**

Weight (oz)	Cost ($)
12	2.50
18	3.69
24	4.95
30	6.25

A 12 oz   C 24 oz
B 18 oz   D 36 oz

8. Use the graph to find the rate of change in cost per magazine. (Lesson 6-3)

The cost increases by $4 for each magazine purchased.

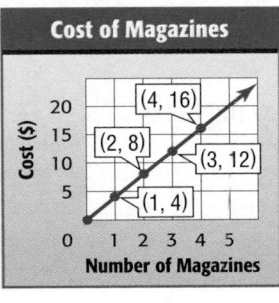
Cost of Magazines
(4, 16)
(2, 8)   (3, 12)
(1, 4)
Cost ($): 20, 15, 10, 5
Number of Magazines: 0 1 2 3 4 5

Complete. (Lesson 6-4)

9. 42 ft = ■ yd **14**
10. 9 pt = ■ qt **$4\frac{1}{2}$**
11. 7,600 lb = ■ T **3.8**
12. $7\frac{1}{2}$ gal = ■ qt **30**

13. **MULTIPLE CHOICE** Which situation is best represented by the graph? (Lesson 6-4) **G**

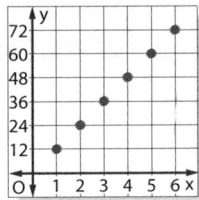

F conversion of inches to yards
G conversion of feet to inches
H conversion of inches to miles
J conversion of yards to feet

Complete. Round to the nearest hundredth if necessary. (Lesson 6-5)

14. 12.5 mi ≈ ■ km **20.13**
15. 4.75 gal ≈ ■ L **18.00**
16. 76 cm ≈ ■ in. **29.92**
17. 31.8 kg ≈ ■ lb **70.11**

Determine if the quantities in each pair of ratios are proportional. Explain. (Lesson 6-6)

18. 8 pages in 5 minutes and 40 pages in 25 minutes **See margin.**

19. 40 blank CDs for $9.60 and 24 blank CDs for $4.80 **See margin.**

Solve each proportion. (Lesson 6-6)

20. $\frac{3}{d} = \frac{12}{20}$ **5**
21. $\frac{7}{8} = \frac{m}{48}$ **42**
22. $\frac{w}{8} = \frac{1}{3}$ **$2\frac{2}{3}$**

23. **MEASUREMENT** It took 45 minutes to fill a circular pool of uniform depth to a level of 18 inches. At this rate, how long will it take to fill the pool to a level of 35 inches? (Lesson 6-6) **87.5 min**

Chapter 6 Mid-Chapter Quiz **317**

 Formative Assessment

Use the Mid-Chapter Quiz to assess students' progress in the first half of the chapter.

Have students review the lesson indicated for the problems they answered incorrectly.

 **Summative Assessment**

CRM Mid-Chapter Test, p. 69

ExamView Customize and create
Assessment Suite multiple versions
of your Mid-Chapter Quiz and their answer keys.

FOLDABLES **Dinah Zike's**
Study Organizer **Foldables**

Before students complete the Mid-Chapter Quiz, encourage them to review the definitions and examples they recorded about ratios, rates, units of measure, and proportions in their Foldables table.

Additional Answers

18. Yes; Sample answer: The cross products of the ratios $\frac{8}{5}$ and $\frac{40}{25}$, 40 • 5 and 25 • 8, are both equal to 200.

19. No; Sample answer: $\frac{\$4.80}{24\ CDs}$
$= \frac{\$0.20}{1\ CD}$ and $\frac{\$9.60}{40\ CDs} = \frac{\$0.24}{CD}$.
The unit rates are not equal.

Data-Driven Decision Making	Exercises	Lesson	State/Local Standards	Resources for Review
Diagnostic Teaching Based on the results of the Chapter 6 Mid-Chapter Quiz, use the following to review concepts that students continue to find challenging.	1–6	6–1		**CRM** Study Guide and Intervention pp. 10, 16, 22, 28, 34, and 40
	7, 8	6–2, 6–3		
	9–13	6–4		**Math Online** glencoe.com
	14–17	6–5		• Extra Examples • Personal Tutor
	18–23	6–6		• Concepts in Motion

6-7

Problem-Solving Investigation
DRAW A DIAGRAM

PACING: **Regular:** 1 period, **Block:** 0.5 period

Options for Differentiated Instruction

ELL = English Language Learner   **AL** = Above or Beyond Grade Level   **SS** = Struggling Students   **SN** = Special Needs

---

Additional Practice   **AL**

Use after students complete Exercises 1–2.

For students who complete the in-class assignment before the rest of the class is finished, present the following problem and have them draw a diagram to solve.

> Jack's house, the post office, the bank, and the library are on the same road. Jack lives 3.5 miles from the library, which is 2.25 miles farther from his house than the bank. The post office is between the bank and the library and 0.75 mile from the bank. How far is it from Jack's house to the post office?

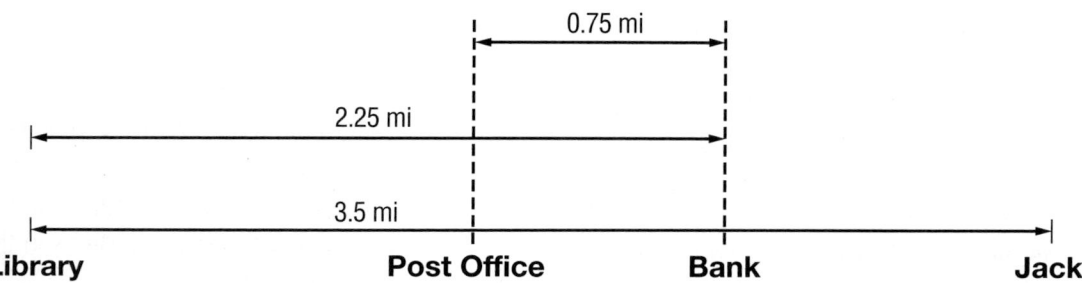

0.75 mi

2.25 mi

3.5 mi

Library   Post Office   Bank   Jack

Choosing the Strategy   **ELL**   **SS**   **SN**

Use before assigning the Exercises.

Prior to assigning Exercises 6–10, read each problem aloud and discuss with the group which strategy might be best to solve the problem. Possible discussion questions:

- What question do you need to answer?
- What information is given?
- Is this like any problems you have solved in the past?
- What strategy would be most effective to solve the problem?
- How could you check your answer to make sure it is reasonable?

Make sure that all students have chosen a strategy for each of the problems so they can complete the assignment independently.

Leveled Lesson Resources

Chapter 6 Resource Masters

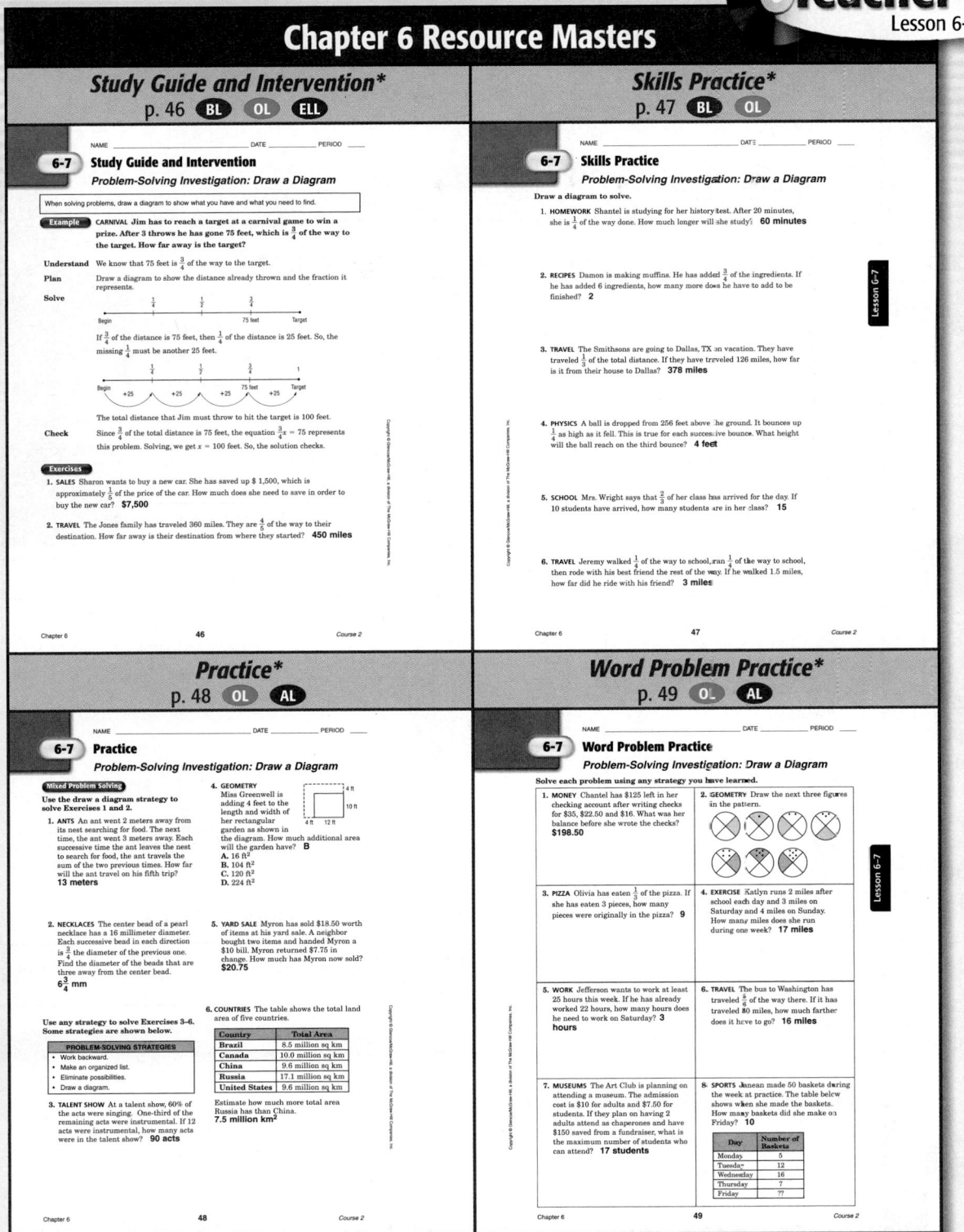

Study Guide and Intervention*
p. 46 BL OL ELL

Skills Practice*
p. 47 BL OL

BL = Below or Approaching Grade Level

OL = On Grade Level

AL = Above or Beyond Grade Level

ELL = English Language Learner

Practice*
p. 48 OL AL

Word Problem Practice*
p. 49 OL AL

* *Also available in Spanish* **ELL**

Additional Lesson Resources

Transparencies
- *5-Minute Check Transparency,* Lesson 6-7

Other Print Products
- *Noteables™ Interactive Study Notebook with Foldables™*

Teacher Tech Tools
- *Interactive Classroom CD-ROM,* Lesson 6-7
- *AssignmentWorks,* Lesson 6-7

Student Tech Tools
glencoe.com
- Extra Examples, Chapter 6, Lesson 7
- Self-Check Quiz, Chapter 6, Lesson 7

1 Focus

Draw a Diagram

Many real-world problems can be solved by drawing a diagram. Diagrams make clear what information is given, what information is needed, and how best to find the missing information. This strategy will be especially useful in Lesson 6-8, in which students solve problems about scale drawings.

2 Teach

Scaffolding Questions

Ask:

- What are some examples of diagrams that you use in everyday life? Sample answers: instructions for assembling a toy, map of a store's layout, instructions for using a DVD player

- What information do these diagrams include? Sample answers: labels of parts, measurements or distances, order or position of parts

- Why are diagrams useful? Sample answer: A diagram helps you visualize a situation.

ADDITIONAL EXAMPLE

Solve. Draw a diagram.

ROCK CLIMBING A rock climber stops to rest at a ledge 90 feet above the ground. If this represents 75% of the total climb, how high above the ground is the top of the rock? 120 ft

Additional Examples are also in:

- Noteables™ Interactive Study Notebook with Foldables™

- Interactive Classroom PowerPoint® Presentations

6-7 Problem-Solving Investigation

MAIN IDEA: Solve problems by drawing a diagram.

P.S.I. TEAM +

e-Mail: DRAW A DIAGRAM

CACEY: I dropped a ball from a height of 12 feet. It hits the ground and bounces up half as high as it fell. This is true for each successive bounce.

YOUR MISSION: Draw a diagram to find the height the ball reaches after the fourth bounce.

Understand	You know the ball is dropped from a height of 12 feet. It bounces up half as high as it falls.
Plan	Draw a diagram to show the height of the ball after each bounce.
Solve	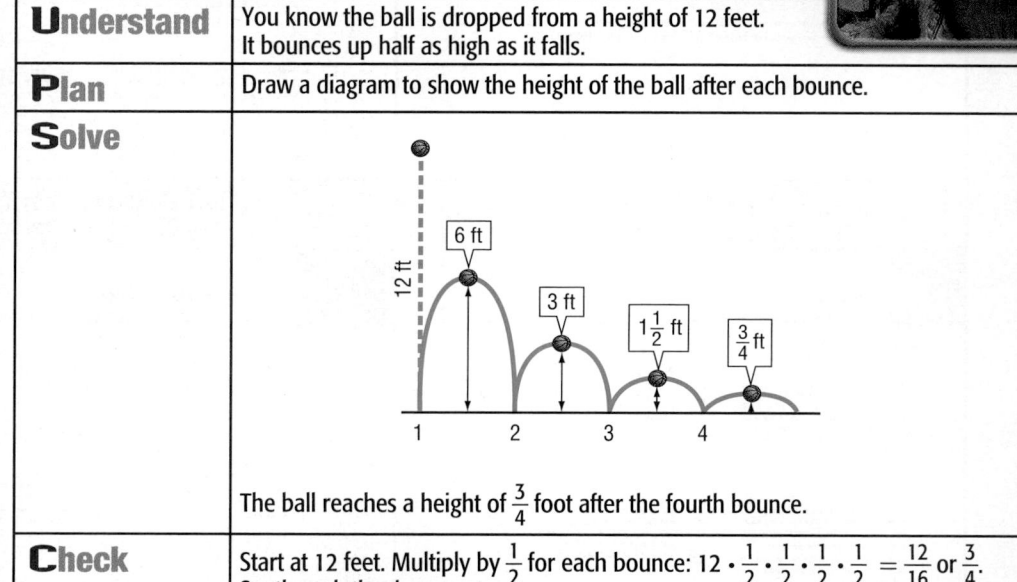 The ball reaches a height of $\frac{3}{4}$ foot after the fourth bounce.
Check	Start at 12 feet. Multiply by $\frac{1}{2}$ for each bounce: $12 \cdot \frac{1}{2} \cdot \frac{1}{2} \cdot \frac{1}{2} \cdot \frac{1}{2} = \frac{12}{16}$ or $\frac{3}{4}$. So, the solution is correct.

Analyze The Strategy

1. Determine what height a ball would reach after the fourth bounce if it is dropped from 12 feet and bounces up $\frac{2}{3}$ as high. Draw a new diagram for this situation. **See margin.**

2. **WRITING IN MATH** Write a problem that could be solved by drawing a diagram. Exchange your problem with a classmate and solve. **See margin.**

318 Chapter 6 Ratios and Proportions

Additional Answers

1. $\frac{3}{4}$ foot

2. There are 4 books in the front window of a book store. How many different ways can you arrange the books in the front window?; 24 ways

EXTRA PRACTICE
See pages 683, 709.

Solve Exercises 3–5. Use the *draw a diagram* strategy.

3. **TRAVEL** Mr. Garcia has driven 60 miles, which is $\frac{2}{3}$ of the way to his sister's house. How much farther does he have to drive to get to his sister's house? **30 miles**

4. **DISTANCE** Alejandro and Pedro are riding their bikes to school. After 1 mile, they are $\frac{4}{5}$ of the way there. How much farther do they have to go? $\frac{1}{4}$ **mi**

5. **VOLUME** A swimming pool is being filled with water. After 25 minutes, $\frac{1}{6}$ of the swimming pool is filled. How much longer will it take to completely fill the pool, assuming the water rate is constant? **125 minutes**

Use any strategy to solve Exercises 6–10. Some strategies are shown below.

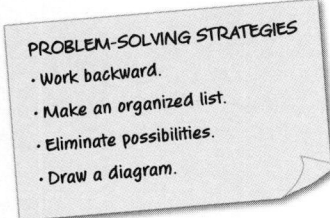

PROBLEM-SOLVING STRATEGIES
· Work backward.
· Make an organized list.
· Eliminate possibilities.
· Draw a diagram.

6. ★ **BASEBALL** Of Lee's baseball cards, $\frac{1}{5}$ show California players. Of these, $\frac{3}{8}$ show San Diego Padres players. Is the fraction of Lee's collection that show Padres players $\frac{23}{40}$, $\frac{4}{13}$, or $\frac{3}{40}$? $\frac{3}{40}$

7. **GAMES** Eight members of a chess club are having a tournament. In the first round, every player will play a chess game against every other player. How many games will be in the first round of the tournament? **28 games**

8. **MEASUREMENT** Kiaya is adding a 2-inch border to the length and width of a photograph as shown.

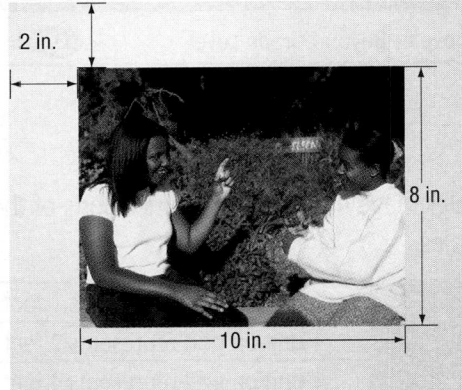

2 in.

8 in.

10 in.

Which expression represents the area of the border to be added to the original photograph? **B**

A $(8 + 4)(10 + 4)$

B $(8 + 4)(10 + 4) - (8)(10)$

C $(8 - 4)(10 - 4)$

D $(8 - 4)(10 - 4) - (8)(10)$

9. **RACES** Anna, Isabela, Mary, and Pilar ran a race. Anna is just ahead of Pilar. Pilar is two places behind Isabela. Isabela is a few seconds behind the leader, Mary. Use the table to place the girls in order from first to last. **Mary, Isabela, Anna, Pilar**

10. **FRACTIONS** Marta ate a quarter of a whole pie. Edwin ate $\frac{1}{4}$ of what was left. Cristina then ate $\frac{1}{3}$ of what was left. What fraction of the pie remains? $\frac{3}{8}$

Lesson 6-7 Problem-Solving Investigation: Draw a Diagram **319**

3 Practice

Using the Exercises

Exercises 1 and 2 can be used to check students' understanding of the draw a diagram strategy.

Exercises 3–5 give students an opportunity to practice the draw a diagram strategy.

Exercises 6–10 give students the opportunity to practice many different problem-solving strategies. You may wish to have students review some of the strategies students have studied.

- Work backward (p. 148)
- Make an organized list (p. 190)
- Eliminate possibilities (p. 248)
- Draw a diagram (p. 318)

4 Assess

Crystal Ball Tell students that tomorrow's lesson is about solving problems involving scale drawings. Have them write how they think what they learned today will connect with tomorrow's material.

Differentiated Instruction

Visual Learners Separate students into pairs and distribute number tiles to each pair. Tell them that a contractor is laying new tiles for a kitchen floor. The tiles are 2 feet by 2 feet, and the floor is 16 feet by 12 feet. Have each pair use their number tiles to find the number of floor tiles the contractor needs. 48

Then have each pair draw a diagram of the problem, based on the model they used. Make sure they label the parts and distances in their diagrams. See students' work.

6-8 Scale Drawings

PACING: **Regular:** 1.5 periods, **Block:** 1 period

Options for Differentiated Instruction

ELL = English Language Learner   **AL** = Above or Beyond Grade Level   **SS** = Struggling Students   **SN** = Special Needs

Making Drawings

Use before presenting Lesson 6-8.

To help students see the effect of using different scales, have them find the dimensions of the classroom and create scale drawings on grid paper using the following scales.

Scale 1	1 unit on grid represents 1 foot.
Scale 2	1 unit on grid represents 2 feet.
Scale 3	1 unit on grid represents 4 feet.

Ask:
- How do the drawings compare?
- What are the similarities and differences?
- Why is it important to label each drawing with the scale you used?
- Would it make sense to use the scale 1 unit represents 3 feet? Why or why not?
- What are the advantages of making a scale drawing?

Research

Use after students complete Lesson 6-8.

Have students use the Internet or call a local architecture firm and interview an architect to find answers to the following questions:
- Do architects use the same scale for every blueprint they create?
- What scales are used most often?
- What scales do they use when they create a 3-dimensional model?

Tell students to be prepared to share the information with the class.

Relevant Applications

Use after presenting the Examples.

Have students make a scale drawing of a room in their home. The drawing should be an overhead view, including furniture that is rectangular in shape. Each student should describe a scale factor that is reasonable for the task.

Leveled Lesson Resources

Chapter 6 Resource Masters

BL = Below or Approaching Grade Level   **OL** = On Grade Level   **AL** = Above or Beyond Grade Level   **ELL** = English Language Learner

---

Lesson Reading Guide
p. 50 **BL** **OL** **ELL**

NAME _____ DATE _____ PERIOD _____

6-8 Lesson Reading Guide
Scale Drawings

Get Ready for the Lesson

Do the Mini Lab at the top of page 320 in your textbook.
Write your answers below.

1. Let 1 unit on the grid paper represent 2 feet. So, 4 units = 8 feet. Convert all your measurements to units. **See students' work.**

2. On grid paper, make a drawing of your gymnasium like the one shown at the top of page 320. **See students' work.**

Read the Lesson

3. Look at the map in the middle of page 320. What is the scale? What does the scale mean? **The scale is 1 centimeter = 20 miles; that means that a distance of 1 centimeter on the map is equal to 20 miles in actual distance.**

4. In Example 1, could you find the actual distance if you did not know the scale? Explain your answer. **Sample answer: No; there can be only one unknown value to solve the proportion. To find the actual distance you need three of the four values of the two cross products.**

5. Give another example of a scale drawing or scale model that is different from the examples of scale drawings and scale models given in this lesson in your textbook. **Sample answer: a scale model of a human heart**

Remember What You Learned

6. How is a scale drawing similar to a scale model? How is it different? **Sample answer: Both a scale drawing and a scale model use a scale and show accurate proportional measures. However, a scale drawing is flat (two-dimensional) and can show measures for any two of three measures (length, width, or height). A scale model can be built to show all three measures because a model is three-dimensional.**

Chapter 6   50   Course 2

Study Guide and Intervention*
p. 51 **BL** **OL** **ELL**

NAME _____ DATE _____ PERIOD _____

6-8 Study Guide and Intervention
Scale Drawings

A **scale drawing** represents something that is too large or too small to be drawn or built at actual size. Similarly, a **scale model** can be used to represent something that is too large or built too small for an actual-size model. The **scale** gives the relationship between the drawing/model measure and the actual measure.

Example On this map, each grid unit represents 50 yards. Find the distance from Patrick's Point to Agate Beach.

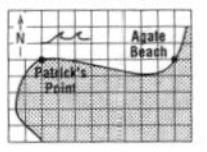

$$\text{scale} \quad \frac{1 \text{ unit}}{50 \text{ yards}} = \frac{8 \text{ units}}{x \text{ yards}} \quad \text{map} \atop \text{actual}$$

$1 \times x = 50 \times 8$ Cross products
$x = 400$ Simplify.

It is 400 yards from Patrick's Point to Agate Beach.

Exercises

Find the actual distance between each pair of cities. Round to the nearest tenth if necessary.

	Cities	Map Distance	Scale	Actual Distance
1.	Los Angeles and San Diego, California	6.35 cm	1 cm = 20 mi	127 mi
2.	Lexington and Louisville, Kentucky	15.6 cm	1 cm = 5 mi	78 mi
3.	Des Moines and Cedar Rapids, Iowa	16.27 cm	2 cm = 15 mi	122.0 mi
4.	Miami and Jacksonville, Florida	11.73 cm	$\frac{1}{2}$ cm = 20 mi	469.2 mi

Suppose you are making a scale drawing. Find the length of each object on the scale drawing with the given scale. Then find the scale factor.

5. an automobile 16 feet long; 1 inch:6 inches   32 in.; $\frac{1}{6}$

6. a lake 85 feet across; 1 inch = 4 feet $21\frac{1}{4}$ in.; $\frac{1}{48}$

7. a parking lot 200 meters wide; 1 centimeter:25 meters   8 cm; $\frac{1}{2,500}$

8. a flag 5 feet wide; 2 inches = 1 foot   10 in.; $\frac{1}{6}$

Chapter 6   51   Course 2

Skills Practice*
p. 52 **BL** **OL**

NAME _____ DATE _____ PERIOD _____

6-8 Skills Practice
Scale Drawings

ARCHITECTURE The scale on a set of architectural drawings for a house is $\frac{1}{2}$ inch = $1\frac{1}{2}$ feet. Find the length of each part of the house.

	Room	Drawing Length	Actual Length
1.	Living Room	5 inches	15 ft
2.	Dining Room	4 inches	12 ft
3.	Kitchen	$5\frac{1}{2}$ inches	$16\frac{1}{2}$ ft
4.	Laundry Room	$3\frac{1}{4}$ inches	$9\frac{3}{4}$ ft
5.	Basement	10 inches	30 ft
6.	Garage	$8\frac{1}{3}$ inches	25 ft

ARCHITECTURE As part of a city building refurbishment project, architects have constructed a scale model of several city buildings to present to the city commission for approval. The scale of the model is 1 inch = 9 feet.

7. The courthouse is the tallest building in the city. If it is $7\frac{1}{2}$ inches tall in the model, how tall is the actual building? $67\frac{1}{2}$ ft

8. The city commission would like to install new flagpoles that are each 45 feet tall. How tall are the flagpoles in the model?   5 in.

9. In the model, two of the flagpoles are 4 inches apart. How far apart will they be when they are installed?   36 ft

10. The model includes a new park in the center of the city. If the dimensions of the park in the model are 9 inches by 17 inches, what are the actual dimensions of the park?   81 ft by 153 ft

11. Find the scale factor. $\frac{1}{108}$

Chapter 6   52   Course 2

Practice*
p. 53 **OL** **AL**

NAME _____ DATE _____ PERIOD _____

6-8 Practice
Scale Drawings

For Exercises 1–3, use the diagram of a section of the art museum shown. Use a ruler to measure.

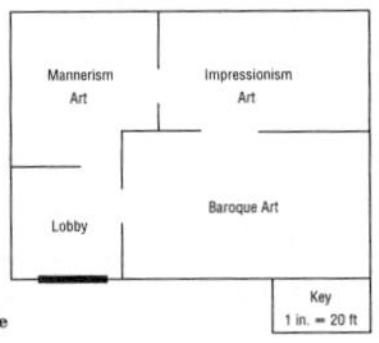

1. What is the actual length of the *Impressionism Art* room?   35 ft

2. Find the actual dimensions of the *Baroque Art* room. $41\frac{1}{4}$ ft by 25 ft

3. Find the scale factor for this blueprint. $\frac{1}{240}$

Find the length of each model on the scale drawing with the given scale.

4. 7.5 in.; $\frac{1}{96}$

5. 48 cm; $\frac{1}{400}$

6. 18 in.; $\frac{1}{9}$

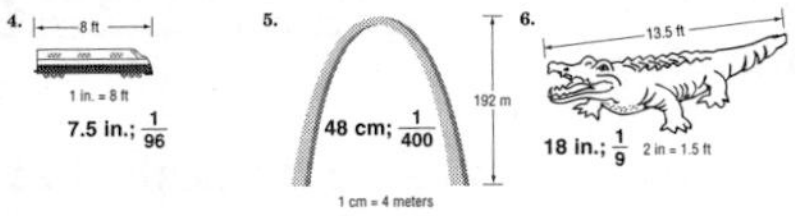

7. **SKYSCRAPER** A model of a skyscraper is made using a scale of 1 inch:75 feet. What is the height of the actual building if the height of the model is $19\frac{2}{5}$ inches?   1,455 ft

8. **GEOGRAPHY** Salem and Eugene, Oregon, are 64 miles apart. If the distance on the map is $3\frac{1}{4}$ inches, find the scale of the map.   1 in.:19.7 mi

9. **PYRAMIDS** The length of a side of the Great Pyramid of Khufu at Giza, Egypt, is 751 feet. If you were to make a model of the pyramid to display on your desk, which would be an appropriate scale: 1 in. = 10 ft or 1 ft = 500 ft? Explain your reasoning. **Sample answer: 1 ft = 500 ft; If using the 1 in. = 10 ft scale, the model would be about 75 inches in length. If using the 1 ft = 500 ft scale, the model would be about 1.5 feet, which would fit on the desk.**

Chapter 6   53   Course 2

Word Problem Practice*
p. 54 **OL** **AL**

NAME _____ DATE _____ PERIOD _____

6-8 Word Problem Practice
Scale Drawings

1. **CARS** A scale drawing of an automobile has a scale of 1 inch = $\frac{1}{2}$ foot. The actual width of the car is 8 feet. What is the width on the scale drawing?   16 in.

2. **MODELS** A model ship is built to a scale of 1 centimeter:5 meters. The length of the model is 30 centimeters. What is the length of the actual ship?   150 m

3. **BUILDING** Jose wants to build a model of a 180-meter tall building. He will be using a scale of 1.5 centimeters = 3.5 meters. How tall will the model be? Round your answer to the nearest tenth.   77.1 cm

4. **TRAVEL** Susan is driving to Mount Shasta. On her map, she is a distance of $7\frac{3}{4}$ inches away. The scale of the map is $\frac{1}{2}$ inch = 50 miles. How far must Susan travel to reach her destination?   775 mi

5. **MAPS** A map of Levi's property is being made with a scale of 2 centimeters:3 meters. What is the scale factor? $\frac{1}{150}$

6. **LANDSCAPING** A pond is being dug according to plans that have a scale of 1 inch = 6.5 feet. The maximum distance across the pond is 9.75 inches on the plans. What will be the actual maximum distance across the pond?   63.375 ft

Chapter 6   54   Course 2

Enrichment
p. 55 **OL** **AL**

NAME _____ DATE _____ PERIOD _____

6-8 Enrichment

Scale Drawings

Use the scale drawings of two different apartments to answer the questions.

Apartment A — Scale: 1 inch = 12 feet
Apartment B — Scale: 1 inch = 16 feet

1. Which apartment has the greater area?   **Apartment B**

2. What is the difference in square feet between Apartment A and Apartment B?   **48 ft²**

3. How much more closet space is offered by Apartment B than Apartment A?   **74 ft²**

4. How much more bathroom space is offered by Apartment A than Apartment B?   **12 ft²**

5. A one-year lease for Apartment A costs $450 per month. A one-year lease for Apartment B costs $525 per month. Which apartment offers the greatest value in terms of the cost per square foot?   **Apartment A**

Chapter 6   55   Course 2

Additional Lesson Resources

Also available in Spanish **ELL**

Transparencies
- *5-Minute Check Transparency,* Lesson 6-8

Other Print Products
- *Teaching Mathematics with Manipulatives*
- *Noteables™ Interactive Study Notebook with Foldables™*

Teacher Tech Tools
- *Interactive Classroom CD-ROM,* Lesson 6-8
- *AssignmentWorks,* Lesson 6-8

Student Tech Tools
glencoe.com
- Extra Examples, Chapter 6, Lesson 8
- Self-Check Quiz, Chapter 6, Lesson 8

6-8 **Scale Drawings**

1 Focus

Vertical Alignment

Before Lesson 6-8
Demonstrate proficiency with division, including division with positive decimals and long division with multidigit divisors

Lesson 6-8
Use proportions to solve problems; use cross-multiplication as a method for solving such problems, understanding it as the multiplication of both sides of an equation by a multiplicative inverse

After Lesson 6-8
Construct and read drawings and models made to scale

2 Teach

▶ MINI Lab

If you don't have enough measuring tapes for each pair of students, have pairs take turns using the tapes. To speed up the process, students can measure items in the gymnasium with yardsticks.

Scaffolding Questions

Tell students that you have a photo that shows a couch, a lamp, a dog, and Uncle Phil. You know that the couch is 8 feet long. In the photo, it is 8 inches long.

Ask:

• If the lamp is 3 feet tall, how tall will it appear in the photo? 3 in.

• If the dog is 2 inches long in the photo, how long is it in real life? 2 ft

• If Uncle Phil is $5\frac{1}{2}$ inches tall in the photo, how tall is he in real life? $5\frac{1}{2}$ ft

---

MAIN IDEA

Solve problems involving scale drawings.

New Vocabulary

scale drawing
scale model
scale
scale factor

Math Online ▶

glencoe.com

• Concepts In Motion
• Extra Examples
• Personal Tutor
• Self-Check Quiz

▶ MINI Lab

• Measure the length of each item in a room, such as a gymnasium.

• Record each length to the nearest $\frac{1}{2}$ foot.

1. Let 1 unit on the grid paper represent 2 feet. So, 4 units = 8 feet. Convert all your measurements to units. **See students' work.**

2. On grid paper, make a drawing of your gymnasium like the one shown at the right. **See students' work.**

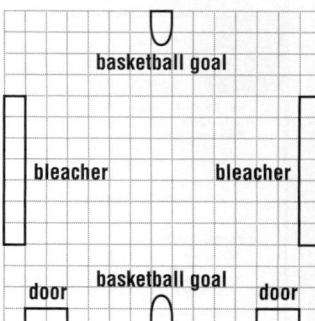

A map is an example of a scale drawing. **Scale drawings** and **scale models** are used to represent objects that are too large or too small to be drawn or built at actual size. The **scale** gives the ratio that compares the measurements of the drawing or model to the measurements of the real object. The measurements on a drawing or model are proportional to measurements of the actual object.

EXAMPLE Use a Map Scale

① **MAPS** What is the actual distance between Hagerstown and Annapolis?

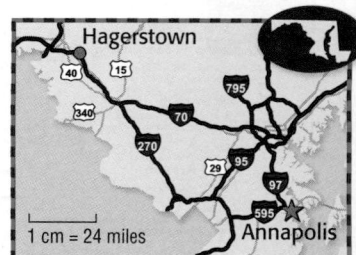

Step 1 Use a centimeter ruler to find the map distance between the two cities. The map distance is about 4 centimeters.

Step 2 Write and solve a proportion using the scale. Let d represent the actual distance between the cities.

$$
\begin{array}{c}
\quad \quad \text{Scale} \quad \quad \text{Length} \\
\text{map} \rightarrow \dfrac{1 \text{ centimeter}}{24 \text{ miles}} = \dfrac{4 \text{ centimeters}}{d \text{ miles}} \leftarrow \text{map} \\
\text{actual} \rightarrow \quad \quad \quad \quad \quad \quad \quad \quad \quad \leftarrow \text{actual}
\end{array}
$$

$1 \times d = 24 \times 4$ Cross products

$d = 96$ Simplify.

The distance between the cities is about 96 miles.

Tips for New Teachers

Scale Drawings

For the Mini Lab, you may wish to give students measurements of your gym yourself, or have them measure the classroom instead.

✓ **CHECK** Your Progress

a. **MAPS** On the map of Arkansas shown, find the actual distance between Clarksville and Little Rock. Use a ruler to measure. **80 mi**

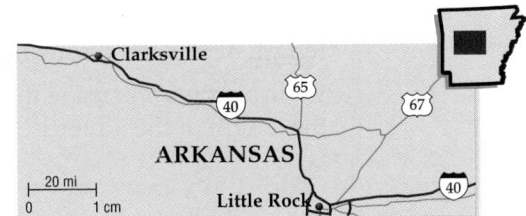

A blueprint is another example of a scale drawing.

EXAMPLE **Use a Blueprint Scale**

2 **DECKS** On the blueprint of the deck, each square has a side length of $\frac{1}{2}$ inch. What is the actual width of the deck?

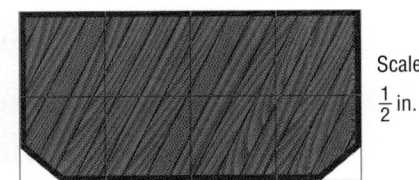

Scale
$\frac{1}{2}$ in. = 4 ft

The deck on the blueprint is 2 inches wide. Write and solve a proportion using the scale. Let w represent the actual width of the deck.

$$
\begin{array}{ccc}
& \text{Scale} & \text{Width} \\
\text{blueprint} \rightarrow & \dfrac{1}{2}\ \text{inch} & 2\ \text{inches} \\
\text{actual} \rightarrow & \dfrac{}{4\ \text{feet}} = & \dfrac{}{w\ \text{feet}} \\
\end{array}
\begin{array}{c}
\leftarrow \text{blueprint} \\
\leftarrow \text{actual}
\end{array}
$$

$\frac{1}{2} \times w = 4 \times 2$ Cross products

$\frac{1}{2}w = 8$ Multiply.

$w = 16$ Simplify. Multiply each side by 2.

The actual width of the deck is 16 feet.

✓ **CHECK** Your Progress

b. **INTERIOR DESIGN** On the blueprint of the living room, each square has a side length of $\frac{1}{4}$ inch. What are the actual dimensions of the living room? **12 ft by $10\frac{1}{2}$ ft**

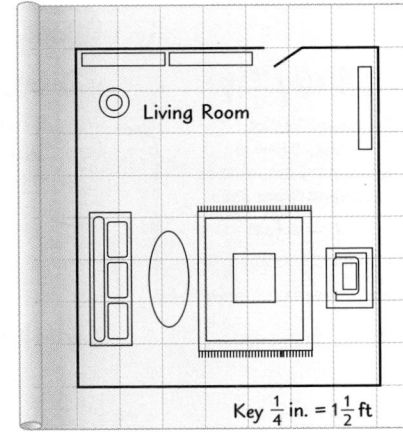

Key $\frac{1}{4}$ in. = $1\frac{1}{2}$ ft

Lesson 6-8 Scale Drawings **321**

ADDITIONAL EXAMPLES

1 **MAPS** What is the actual distance between Portland and Olympia? **about 103.7 mi**

$\frac{3}{8}$ inch = 23 mi

2 **ARCHITECTURE** On the blueprint of a new house, each square has a side length of $\frac{1}{4}$ inch. If the length of a bedroom on the blueprint is $1\frac{1}{2}$ inches, what is the actual length of the room? **15 ft**

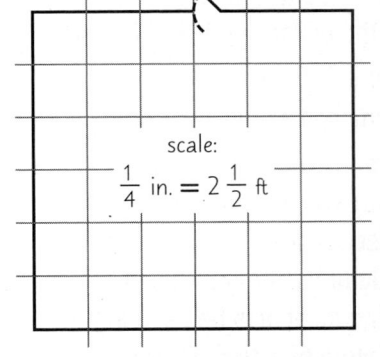

scale:
$\frac{1}{4}$ in. = $2\frac{1}{2}$ ft

Lesson 6-8 Scale Drawings **321**

3 **PHOTOGRAPHY** A model is being created from a picture frame which has a length of $4\frac{3}{4}$ inches. If the scale to be used is 8 inches = 1 inch, what is the length of the model? **38 in.**

4 Find the scale factor of a blueprint if the scale is $\frac{1}{2}$ inch = 3 feet. $\frac{1}{72}$

Focus on Mathematical Content

The distances shown in scale drawings or models are proportional to the actual distances. So students can calculate the actual distances by **writing and solving proportions.** One ratio of the proportion will be the scale itself.

Another way to calculate actual distance from a scale drawing or model is to **multiply by the reciprocal of the scale factor.**

Tips for New Teachers

Scale Factor

Point out that scale factors can be used to calculate actual distances from the distances shown in a scale drawing or map. If, for example, a drawing has a scale factor of $\frac{1}{96}$, then something that measures 1 inch in the drawing will actually measure 96 inches, or 8 feet. Since scale factors don't include units, the units used in the drawing must also be used in the calculation of actual distances.

Study Tip

Scale The scale is the ratio of the drawing/model measure to the actual measure. It is not always the ratio of a smaller measure to a larger measure.

EXAMPLE Use a Scale Model

3 **PHONES** A graphic artist is creating an advertisement for a new cell phone. If she uses a scale of 5 inches = 1 inch, what is the length of the cell phone on the advertisement?

Write a proportion using the scale. Let a represent the length of the advertisement cell phone.

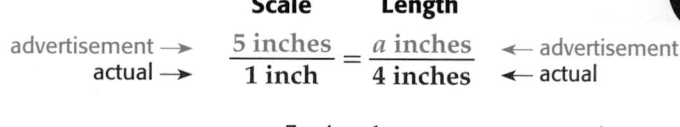

4 in.

	Scale	Length	
advertisement →	$\dfrac{5 \text{ inches}}{1 \text{ inch}}$	$= \dfrac{a \text{ inches}}{4 \text{ inches}}$	← advertisement
actual →			← actual

$5 \cdot 4 = 1 \cdot a$ Cross products

$20 = a$ Multiply.

The length of the cell phone on the advertisement is 20 inches long.

✓ CHECK Your Progress

c. **SCOOTERS** A scooter is $3\frac{1}{2}$ feet long. Find the length of a scale model of the scooter if the scale is 1 inch = $\frac{3}{4}$ feet. $4\frac{2}{3}$ **in.**

In Lesson 6-4, you used ratios to convert units. You can use a similar method to simplify a scale. A scale written as a ratio without units in simplest form is called the **scale factor.**

scale ➤ $\dfrac{\frac{1}{4} \text{ inch}}{2 \text{ feet}} = \dfrac{\frac{1}{4} \text{ inch}}{24 \text{ inches}}$ Convert 2 feet to inches.

$= \dfrac{4}{4} \cdot \dfrac{\frac{1}{4} \text{ inch}}{24 \text{ inches}}$ Multiply by $\frac{4}{4}$ to eliminate the fraction in the numerator. Divide out the common units.

$= \dfrac{1}{96}$ scale factor

Study Tip

Equivalent Scales
The scales below are equivalent because their scale factors are equal, $\frac{1}{72}$.
• 1 inch = 6 feet
• $\frac{1}{2}$ inch = 3 feet

EXAMPLE Find a Scale Factor

4 **SAILBOATS** Find the scale factor of a model sailboat if the scale is 1 inch = 6 feet.

$\dfrac{1 \text{ inch}}{6 \text{ feet}} = \dfrac{1 \text{ inch}}{72 \text{ inches}}$ Convert 6 feet to inches.

$= \dfrac{1}{72}$ Divide out the common units.

The scale factor is $\frac{1}{72}$.

✓ CHECK Your Progress

d. **CARS** What is the scale factor of a model car if the scale is 1 inch = 2 feet? $\dfrac{1}{24}$

CHECK Your Understanding

★ indicates multi-step problem

Example 1
(pp. 320–321)

GEOGRAPHY Find the actual distance between each pair of cities in New Mexico. Use a ruler to measure.

1. Carlsbad and Artesia **50 km**
2. Hobbs and Eunice **30 km**
3. Artesia and Eunice **130 km**
4. Lovington and Carlsbad **102.5 km**

Example 2
(p. 321)

BLUEPRINTS For Exercises 5 and 6, use the blueprint. Each square has a side length of $\frac{1}{4}$ inch.

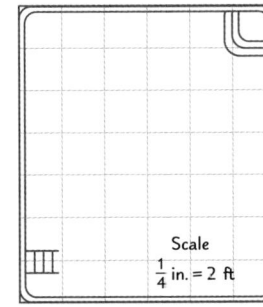

Scale
$\frac{1}{4}$ in. = 2 ft

5. What is the actual length of the pool? **14 feet**
6. What is the actual width of the pool? **12 feet**

Example 3
(p. 322)

BRIDGES For Exercises 7 and 8, use the following information.

An engineer makes a model of the bridge using a scale of 1 inch = 3 yards.

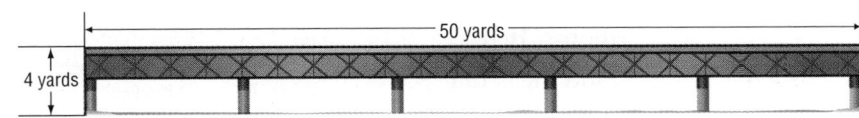
50 yards

4 yards

7. What is the length of the model? **$16\frac{2}{3}$ in.**
8. What is the height of the model? **$1\frac{1}{3}$ in.**

Example 4
(p. 322)

Find the scale factor of each scale drawing or model.

9.  $\frac{1}{48}$

1 inch = 4 feet

10. 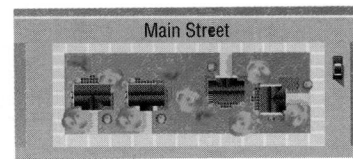 $\frac{2}{3}$

1 centimeter = 15 millimeters

11. $\frac{1}{63,360}$

11. **CITY PLANNING** In the aerial view of a city block at the right, the length of Main Street is 2 inches. If Main Street's actual length is 2 miles, find the scale factor of the drawing.

Main Street

✓ **Formative Assessment**

Use Exercises 1–11 to check for understanding.

Then use the chart at the bottom of the next page to customize your assignments for students.

Intervention You may wish to use the Study Guide and Intervention Master on page 51 of the *Chapter 6 Resource Masters* for additional reinforcement.

Odd/Even Assignments

Exercises 12–24 are structured so that students practice the same concepts whether they are assigned odd or even problems.

HOMEWORK HELP	
For Exercises	See Examples
12–15	1
16–17	2
18–24	3, 4

Exercise Levels
A: 12–24
B: 25–29
C: 30–33

GEOGRAPHY Find the actual distance between each pair of locations in South Carolina. Use a ruler to measure.

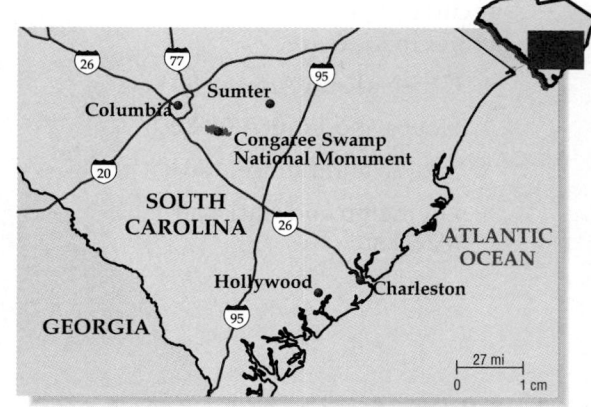

12. Columbia and Charleston **101 mi**   13. Hollywood and Sumter **81 mi**

14. Congaree Swamp and Charleston **81 mi**   15. Sumter and Columbia **40 mi**

For Exercises 16–18, use the blueprint of an apartment at the right. Each square has a side length of $\frac{1}{4}$ inch.

16. What is the actual length of the living room? **18 ft**

17. 12 ft by 9 ft

17. Find the actual dimensions of the master bedroom.

18. Find the scale factor for this blueprint. $\frac{1}{144}$

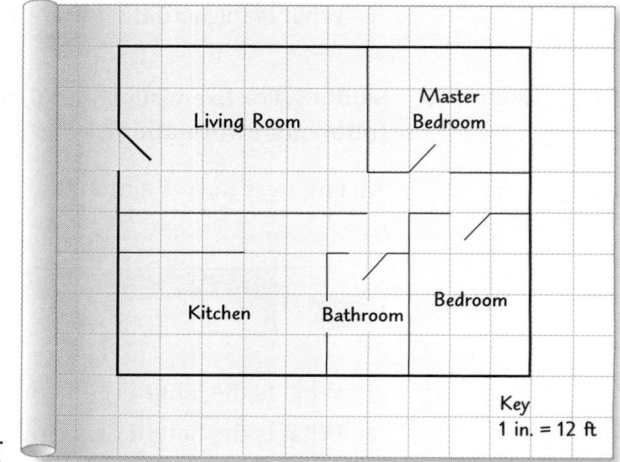

Find the length of each model. Then find the scale factor.

19. $11\frac{3}{5}$ in.; $\frac{1}{90}$

19.

21. 6 in.; $\frac{1}{720}$

21.

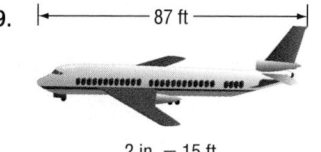

20. **12 cm; $\frac{1}{300}$**

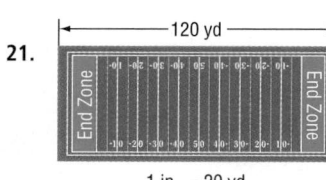

22. $11\frac{3}{4}$ in.; $\frac{2}{1}$

DIFFERENTIATED HOMEWORK OPTIONS			
Level	**Assignment**	**Two-Day Option**	
BL Basic	12–24, 30, 32–51	13–23 odd, 34–36	12–24 even, 30, 32, 33, 37–51
OL Core	13–23 odd, 24–30, 32–51	12–24, 34–36	25–30, 32, 33, 37–51
AL Advanced/Pre-AP	25–47 (optional: 48–51)		

Real-World Link . . . .

The statue of Thomas Jefferson inside the Jefferson Memorial in Washington, D.C., was made using a scale of 3 feet : 1 foot.

Source: National Register of Historic Places

23. **GEOGRAPHY** A map of Bakersfield, California, has a scale of 1 inch to 5 miles. If the city is $5\frac{1}{5}$ inches across on the map, what is the actual distance across the actual city? Use estimation to check your answer. **26 mi**

24. **TREES** A model of a tree is made using a scale of 1 inch : 25 feet. What is the height of the actual tree if the height of the model is $4\frac{3}{8}$ inches? **$109\frac{3}{8}$ ft**

25. **STATUES** Refer to the information at the left. Find the scale factor and the actual height of Thomas Jefferson if the height of the statue is 19 feet. **$\frac{1}{3}$, about 6.33 feet**

26. **GEOGRAPHY** Lexington and Elizabethtown, Kentucky, are 79 miles apart. If the distance on the map is $2\frac{1}{2}$ inches, find the scale of the map. **1 in : 31.6 mi**

27. **RESEARCH** Find the dimensions of any U.S. presidential monument. Give an appropriate scale that can be used to make a scale model of the monument. State the dimensions of the model using your scale. **See students' work.**

28. **BUILDINGS** If you are making a model of your bedroom, which would be an appropriate scale: 1 inch = 2 feet, or 1 inch = 12 feet? **See margin.**

★ 29. **LIFE SCIENCE** A scale drawing of a red blood cell is shown below. If the blood cell's actual diameter is 0.008 millimeter, use a ruler to find the scale factor of the drawing. **$\frac{5,000}{1}$**

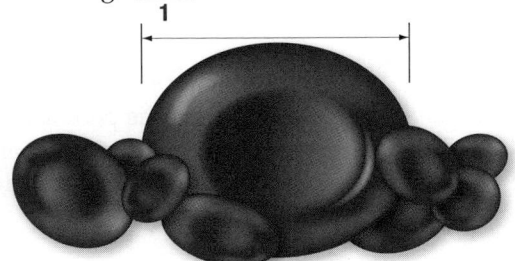

EXTRA PRACTICE
See pages 684, 709.

H.O.T. Problems

30. **OPEN ENDED** On grid paper, create a scale drawing of a room in your home. Include the scale that you used. **See students' work.**

31. **CHALLENGE** Montoya constructed three models, A, B, and C, of the same figure, with scales of 0.5 cm = 1 mm, 1.5 mm = 4 cm, and 0.25 cm = 2.5 mm, respectively. **a–c. See margin.**

    a. Which model is larger than the actual figure? Justify your answer.

    b. Which model is smaller than the actual figure? Justify your answer.

    c. Which model is the same size as the actual figure? Justify your answer.

32. **REASONING** Compare and contrast the terms *scale* and *scale factor*. Include an example in your comparison. **See margin.**

33. **WRITING IN MATH** Explain how you could use estimation to find the actual distance between San Diego, California, and Seattle, Washington, on a map. **See margin.**

Lesson 6-8 Scale Drawings **325**

⚠ Exercise Alert!

Use the Internet Exercise 27 requires students to research the dimensions of a presidential monument. You may wish to have students use the Internet or reference material such as an encyclopedia.

Additional Answers

28. 1 in. = 2 ft because it would make the model about 6 to 12 inches in length; the second scale is more appropriate for modeling a much larger object. It would make your room model only 1 or 2 inches in length.

31a. A; 0.5 cm is larger than 1 mm. If 0.5 cm on the model is equal to 1 mm on the actual figure, then model A must be larger than the actual figure.

31b. B; 1.5 mm is smaller than 4 cm. If 1.5 mm on the model is equal to 4 cm on the actual figure, then model B must be smaller than the actual figure.

31c. C; 0.25 cm is equal to 2.5 mm. If 0.25 cm on the model is equal to 2.5 mm on the actual figure, then model C must be the same size as the actual figure.

32. Sample answer: The scale is the ratio comparing the measurements, including the units, on the model to the measurements on the actual figure. Once the units have been converted to the same unit, the scale factor is this ratio written without units as a fraction in simplest form. For example, if the scale of the model to the actual figure is 1 in. = 4.5 ft, then the scale factor would be $\frac{1}{4.5 \times 12}$ or $\frac{1}{54}$.

33. Sample answer: Using the scale given on the map, look at the distance between the two cities on the map and then estimate the actual distance based on the distance given in the scale.

Pre-AP Activity **Use after Exercise 30**

Have students find a map of the United States in an atlas. What is the scale factor? Have them use the scale factor to calculate how many miles are represented by 1 inch on the map. Sample answer: 1:12,000,000; so, 1 inch on the map shows 12,000,000 actual inches, or 1,000,000 feet, or 189.4 mi.

Name the Math Tell students that a map has a scale of 1 inch = 125 miles. Have students write what mathematical procedures they would use to find the actual distance between two points shown on the map.

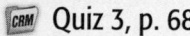 **Formative Assessment**

Check for student understanding of concepts in Lessons 6-6, 6-7, and 6-8.

CRM Quiz 3, p. 68

 **Foldables™ Follow-Up**

Remind students to select a term or concept about scale drawings and to define it in their Foldables. Encourage them to give an example of the term or concept.

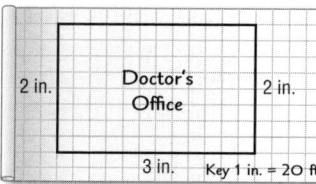 **TEST PRACTICE**

34. A scale drawing of a doctor's office is shown.

[diagram: Doctor's Office, 2 in. left, 2 in. right, 3 in. bottom, Key 1 in. = 20 ft]

What are the actual dimensions of the doctor's office? **C**

A 24 feet by 48 feet

B 30 feet by 52 feet

C 40 feet by 60 feet

D 37.5 feet by 65 feet

35. A certain map has a scale of $\frac{1}{4}$ inch = 30 miles. How many miles are represented by 4 inches on this map? **F**

F 480 miles

G 120 miles

H 30 miles

J 16 miles

36. Ernesto drew a map of his school. He used a scale of 1 inch : 50 feet. What distance on Ernesto's map should represent the 625 feet between the cafeteria and the science lab? **C**

A 8 in.

B 10.5 in.

C 12.5 in.

D 15 in.

Spiral Review

37. FAMILY At Nelia's family reunion, $\frac{4}{5}$ of the people are 18 years of age or older. Half of the remaining people are under 12 years old. If 20 children are under 12 years old, how many people are at the reunion? Use the *draw a diagram* strategy. (Lesson 6-7) **200 people**

Solve each proportion. (Lesson 6-6)

38. $\frac{5}{7} = \frac{a}{35}$ **25**

39. $\frac{12}{p} = \frac{36}{45}$ **15**

40. $\frac{3}{9} = \frac{21}{k}$ **63**

41. JOGGING The table shows the number of miles Tonya jogged each week for the past several weeks. Estimate the total number of miles she jogged. (Lesson 5-1)
Sample answer: 7 + 9 + 10 + 12 + 7 or 45 mi

Week	Miles
1	$7\frac{1}{6}$
2	$8\frac{3}{4}$
3	10
4	$12\frac{1}{4}$
5	$6\frac{2}{3}$

Find the LCM of each set of numbers. (Lesson 4-8)

42. 2, 4 **4**

43. 4, 8, 12 **24**

44. 3, 7, 5 **105**

45. 5, 10, 15 **30**

46. 2, 6, 9 **18**

47. 3, 15, 20 **60**

▷ **GET READY for the Next Lesson**

PREREQUISITE SKILL Divide. Write in simplest form. (Lesson 5-7)

48. $2\frac{3}{4} \div 10$ $\frac{11}{40}$

49. $4\frac{1}{3} \div 10$ $\frac{13}{30}$

50. $30\frac{2}{3} \div 100$ $\frac{23}{75}$

51. $87\frac{1}{2} \div 100$ $\frac{7}{8}$

Spreadsheet Lab
Scale Drawings

MAIN IDEA

Use a spreadsheet to calculate measurements for scale drawings.

A computer spreadsheet is a useful tool for calculating measures for scale drawings. You can change the scale factors and the dimensions, and the spreadsheet will automatically calculate the new values.

ACTIVITY

Suppose you want to make a scale drawing of your school. Set up a spreadsheet like the one shown below. In this spreadsheet, the actual measures are in feet, and the scale drawing measures are in inches.

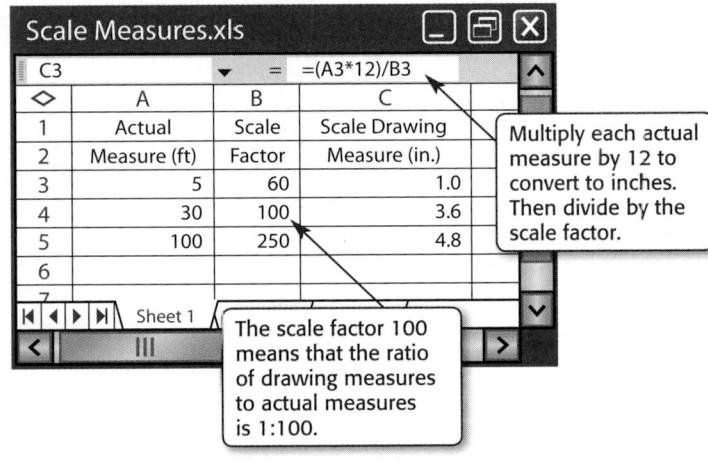

Multiply each actual measure by 12 to convert to inches. Then divide by the scale factor.

The scale factor 100 means that the ratio of drawing measures to actual measures is 1:100.

ANALYZE THE RESULTS

1. The length of one side of the school building is 100 feet. If you use a scale factor of 1:250, what is the length on your scale drawing? **4.8 in.**

2. The length of a classroom is 30 feet. What is the scale factor if the length of the classroom on a scale drawing is 3.6 inches? **1:100**

3. Calculate the length of a 30-foot classroom on a scale drawing if the scale factor is 1:10. **36 in. or 3 ft**

4. The width of a hallway is 20 feet. What is the scale factor if the width of the hallway on a scale drawing is 2.5 inches? **1:96**

5. Sample answer: Enter 50 in B3 and enter the formula (A3*100)/B3 in C3. Then enter the actual dimensions in A3.

5. Suppose the actual measures of your school are given in meters. Describe how you could use a spreadsheet to calculate the scale drawing measures in centimeters using a scale factor of 1:50.

6. Choose three rooms in your home and use a spreadsheet to make scale drawings. First, choose an appropriate scale and calculate the scale factor. Include a sketch of the furniture drawn to scale in each room. **See students' work.**

Extend 6-8 Spreadsheet Lab: Scale Drawings **327**

Extend 6-8 Spreadsheet Lab: Scale Drawings **327**

1 Focus

Materials

- computers
- spreadsheet software

Teaching Tip

Make sure students understand that the spreadsheet screen is a table divided into columns and rows. The columns are labeled with letters, and the rows are labeled with numbers, so the third cell in the first column is A3, the third cell in the second column is B3, and so on.

2 Teach

Activity You may need to remind students that scale factors don't include units, so the spreadsheet program first converts actual measurements (in feet) into inches. Encourage students to experiment with different scale factors for their scale drawings (Exercise 5). If they want to make their drawings on standard notepaper, what is an appropriate scale factor?

3 Assess

 Formative Assessment

Use Exercises 1–4 to determine whether students understand how to use a spreadsheet to calculate measurements for a scale drawing.

From Concrete to Abstract Use Exercise 5 to bridge the gap between using a spreadsheet to calculate customary measurements and conceptualizing how to use the spreadsheet to calculate metric measurements.

Extending the Concept Have students use the spreadsheet to calculate measurements for a scale drawing of an object too small to draw as its actual size.

Fractions, Decimals, and Percents

PACING: **Regular:** 1 period, **Block:** 0.5 period

Options for Differentiated Instruction

ELL = English Language Learner   **AL** = Above or Beyond Grade Level   **SS** = Struggling Students   **SN** = Special Needs

Reviewing Concepts **SS** **SN**

Use before beginning Lesson 6-9.

Before beginning this lesson, review with students the common fraction-decimal-percent equivalencies that they have already used, such as the ones shown in the table below.

Fraction	Decimal	Percent
$\frac{1}{4}$	0.25	25%
$\frac{1}{2}$	0.5	50%
$\frac{3}{4}$	0.75	75%
$\frac{1}{5}$	0.2	20%
$\frac{2}{5}$	0.4	40%
$\frac{3}{5}$	0.6	60%
$\frac{4}{5}$	0.8	80%

Kinesthetic Learning **ELL** **AL** **SS** **SN**

Use after presenting Examples 1–6.

Create a set of 10 cards, each containing one number, a fraction, a decimal, or percent. An example of a set of cards is shown below. For above grade level students, change the number of cards or the difficulty of the numbers.

35%	0.325	$\frac{1}{3}$	0.4	50%
$\frac{4}{9}$	$\frac{11}{20}$	45%	$\frac{7}{15}$	0.72%

Have students work in pairs and order the numbers from least to greatest. Once students have finished, have them write the strategies they used to determine the order. Have them explain their reasoning.

Leveled Lesson Resources

Chapter 6 Resource Masters

BL = Below or Approaching Grade Level   **OL** = On Grade Level   **AL** = Above or Beyond Grade Level   **ELL** = English Language Learner

---

Lesson Reading Guide
p. 57 **BL OL ELL**

6-9 Lesson Reading Guide
Fractions, Decimals, and Percents

Get Ready for the Lesson
Read the introduction at the top of page 328 in your textbook.
Write your answers below.

1. What percent of the teens chose comedy? **26%**
2. Write this percent as a ratio in simplest form. **13:50 or $\frac{13}{50}$**

Read the Lesson

3. Write $6\frac{1}{2}\%$ as a fraction in simplest form. **$\frac{13}{200}$**
4. CLOTHING A pair of jeans sells for 180% of its wholesale price. Write this percent as a fraction in simplest form. **$\frac{9}{5}$**
5. How do you write 100 as a fraction? **$\frac{100}{1}$**
6. If the denominator is not a factor of 100, you can write fractions as percents by using a proportion. In Examples 3 and 4, why is the ratio $\frac{n}{100}$ used as part of the proportions? **Sample answer: because you want to write the fraction as a percent, and to convert a fraction to a percent you want the denominator to be 100**

Remember What You Learned

7. Complete the following table of equivalent fractions. Look for patterns in each column. How do the percents increase? How do the fractions increase? Work with a partner. Figure out ways to remember the equivalents.

Common Fraction/Decimal/Percent Equivalents

Fraction	Decimal	Percent	Fraction	Decimal	Percent
$\frac{1}{3}$	$0.\overline{3}$	$33\frac{1}{3}\%$	$\frac{3}{8}$	0.375	$37\frac{1}{2}\%$
$\frac{2}{3}$	$0.\overline{6}$	$66\frac{2}{3}\%$	$\frac{5}{8}$	0.625	$62\frac{1}{2}\%$
$\frac{1}{8}$	0.125	$12\frac{1}{2}\%$	$\frac{7}{8}$	0.875	$87\frac{1}{2}\%$

Chapter 6   57   Course 2

Study Guide and Intervention*
p. 58 **BL OL ELL**

6-9 Study Guide and Intervention
Fractions, Decimals, and Percents

Example 1 Write $4\frac{3}{8}\%$ as a fraction in simplest form.

$4\frac{3}{8}\% = \frac{4\frac{3}{8}}{100}$ Write a fraction.
$= 4\frac{3}{8} \div 100$ Divide.
$= \frac{35}{8} \div 100$ Write $4\frac{3}{8}$ as an improper fraction.
$= \frac{35}{8} \times \frac{1}{100}$ Multiply by the reciprocal of 100, which is $\frac{1}{100}$.
$= \frac{35}{800}$ or $\frac{7}{160}$ Simplify.

Example 2 Write $\frac{5}{16}$ as a percent.

$\frac{5}{16} = \frac{n}{100}$ Write a proportion using $\frac{n}{100}$.
$500 = 16n$ Find the cross products.
$\frac{500}{16} = \frac{16n}{16}$ Divide each side by 16.
$31\frac{1}{4} = n$ Simplify.
So, $\frac{5}{16} = 31\frac{1}{4}\%$ or 31.25%.

Exercises

Write each percent as a fraction in simplest form.

1. 60% $\frac{3}{5}$
2. $68\frac{3}{4}\%$ $\frac{11}{16}$
3. $27\frac{1}{2}\%$ $\frac{11}{40}$
4. 37.5% $\frac{3}{8}$

Write each fraction as a percent. Round to the nearest hundredth if necessary.

5. $\frac{2}{5}$ 40%
6. $\frac{5}{8}$ 62.5%
7. $\frac{9}{16}$ 56.25%
8. $\frac{2}{3}$ 66.67%

Chapter 6   58   Course 2

Skills Practice*
p. 59 **BL OL**

6-9 Skills Practice
Fractions, Decimals, and Percents

Write each percent as a fraction in simplest form.

1. 18% $\frac{9}{50}$
2. 67.5% $\frac{27}{40}$
3. 21.25% $\frac{17}{80}$
4. 87.5% $\frac{7}{8}$
5. $31\frac{1}{4}\%$ $\frac{5}{16}$
6. 17.5% $\frac{7}{40}$
7. $18\frac{3}{4}\%$ $\frac{3}{16}$
8. $68\frac{3}{4}\%$ $\frac{11}{16}$
9. 7.5% $\frac{3}{40}$
10. 130% $\frac{13}{10}$
11. 0.5% $\frac{1}{200}$
12. 0.02% $\frac{1}{5000}$

Write each fraction as a percent. Round to the nearest hundredth if necessary.

13. $\frac{3}{5}$ 60%
14. $\frac{3}{8}$ 37.5%
15. $\frac{2}{18}$ 11.11%
16. $\frac{3}{16}$ 18.75%
17. $\frac{7}{9}$ 77.78%
18. $\frac{21}{50}$ 42%
19. $\frac{1}{3}$ 33.33%
20. $\frac{40}{42}$ 95.24%
21. $\frac{7}{16}$ 43.75%
22. $\frac{17}{10}$ 170%
23. $\frac{1}{500}$ 0.2%
24. $\frac{26}{25}$ 104%

Chapter 6   59   Course 2

Practice*
p. 60 **OL AL**

6-9 Practice
Fractions, Decimals, and Percents

Write each percent as a fraction in simplest form.

1. 37.5% $\frac{3}{8}$
2. 5.8% $\frac{29}{500}$
3. 43.75% $\frac{7}{16}$
4. 52.5% $\frac{21}{40}$
5. $83\frac{1}{3}\%$ $\frac{5}{6}$
6. $66\frac{2}{3}\%$ $\frac{2}{3}$
7. 135% $\frac{27}{20}$
8. 0.01% $\frac{1}{10,000}$

Write each fraction as a percent. Round to the nearest hundredth if necessary.

9. $\frac{13}{20}$ 65%
10. $\frac{9}{25}$ 36%
11. $\frac{7}{8}$ 87.5%
12. $\frac{39}{40}$ 97.5%
13. $\frac{5}{9}$ 55.56%
14. $\frac{6}{7}$ 85.71%
15. $\frac{2}{1}$ 200%
16. $\frac{1}{1000}$ 0.1%

Replace each ● with >, < or = to make a true statement.

17. $\frac{3}{16}$ ● 24% **<**
18. 0.775 ● $\frac{31}{40}$ **=**
19. 16% ● 0.016 **>**

Order each set of numbers from least to greatest.

20. 0.6, 23%, 0.07, $\frac{2}{3}$ **0.07, 23%, 0.6, $\frac{2}{3}$**
21. $\frac{4}{5}$%, 0.37, $\frac{1}{4}$, 0.4   **$\frac{4}{5}$%, $\frac{1}{4}$, 0.37, 0.4**

22. SAVINGS Kayla has 14.5% of her salary placed into an Individual Retirement Account. What fraction is this? **$\frac{29}{200}$**
23. INTERNET At home, 2 out of 5 people have access to broadband technology. What percent is this? **40%**
24. SPORTS A golfer made par on 13 of 18 holes. To the nearest tenth, on what percent of the holes did he make par? **72.2%**

ANALYZE TABLES For Exercises 25 and 26, use the table that shows the percent of households with the listed appliance.

Appliance	Percent of Households
Refrigerator	99.3%
Washing Machine	82.0%
Dryer	77.8%
Dishwasher	56.0%

25. What fraction of households have a clothes dryer? **$\frac{389}{500}$**
26. Approximately 34 out of 67 households have a coffeemaker. Is this greater or less than the percent of households with a dishwasher? Explain. **less than; $\frac{34}{67} \approx 50.7\%$**

Chapter 6   60   Course 2

Word Problem Practice*
p. 61 **OL AL**

6-9 Word Problem Practice
Fractions, Decimals, and Percents

INTERNET For Exercises 1–4, use the table. It shows the percents of online shopping purchases made by all Internet users and the percents made by Internet users over age 55.

Most Popular Online Purchases

	Internet Users Over 55	All Internet Users
computer software	43%	19%
books	43%	21%
computer hardware	24%	13%
music CDs	29%	22%
clothing	19%	8%

1. What fraction of Internet users over 55 bought clothing online? **$\frac{19}{100}$**
2. What fraction of all Internet users bought clothing online? **$\frac{2}{25}$**
3. What fraction of all Internet users bought music CDs online? **$\frac{11}{50}$**
4. Is the fraction of Internet users over 55 who bought books online greater or less than $\frac{22}{50}$? Explain. **Less than; $\frac{22}{50} = 44\%$, and 43% is less than 44%.**
5. FOOTBALL In 2005, Indianapolis quarterback Peyton Manning completed 305 out of 453 passes. What was his pass completion percentage to the nearest tenth? **67.3%**
6. COMPUTERS In Joan's math class, there are 20 computers and 32 students. What percent of students will be able to use a computer without sharing? **62.5%**
7. VEHICLES In the town of Orick, 5 out of 13 vehicles are trucks. What percent of the vehicles are trucks? Round to the nearest tenth. **38.5%**
8. DENTISTRY Dana has fillings in 4 of her 32 teeth. What percent of her teeth have fillings? **12.5%**

Chapter 6   61   Course 2

Enrichment
p. 62 **OL AL**

6-9 Enrichment

Shaded Regions

The fractions or percents listed below each represent one of the shaded regions.

Match each fraction or percent with the shaded region it represents.

1. $\frac{1}{2}$ d
2. $\frac{25}{64}$ i
3. $\frac{11}{16}$ h
4. 25% b
5. $\frac{3}{4}$ a
6. $62\frac{1}{2}\%$ g
7. $\frac{29}{64}$ f
8. 37.5% c
9. $\frac{7}{16}$ e

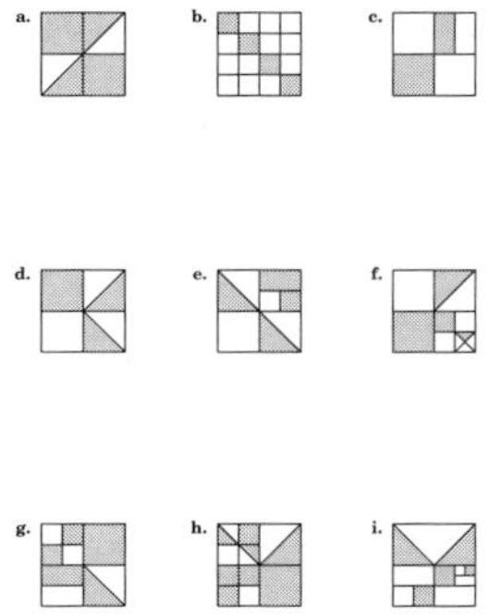

Chapter 6   62   Course 2

Additional Lesson Resources

Transparencies
- *5-Minute Check Transparency*, Lesson 6-9

Other Print Products
- *Noteables™ Interactive Study Notebook with Foldables™*

Teacher Tech Tools
- *Interactive Classroom CD-ROM*, Lesson 6-9
- *AssignmentWorks*, Lesson 6-9

Student Tech Tools
glencoe.com
- Extra Examples, Chapter 6, Lesson 9
- Self-Check Quiz, Chapter 6, Lesson 9

1 Focus

Vertical Alignment

Before Lesson 6-9
Demonstrate proficiency with division, including division with positive decimals and long division with multi-digit divisors

Lesson 6-9
Find decimal and percent equivalents for common fractions

After Lesson 6-9
Calculate given percentages of quantities and solve problems involving discounts at sales, interest earned, and tips

2 Teach

Scaffolding Questions

Ask:
- What fraction is equivalent to 10%? $\frac{10}{100}$, or $\frac{1}{10}$
- What fraction is equivalent to 25%? $\frac{25}{100}$, or $\frac{1}{4}$
- What decimal is equivalent to 96%? 0.96
- What decimal is equivalent to 96.5%? 0.965

Formative Assessment

Use the Check Your Progress exercises after each Example to determine students' understanding of concepts.

MAIN IDEA

Write percents as fractions, and decimals and vice versa.

Math Online

glencoe.com
- Extra Examples
- Personal Tutor
- Self-Check Quiz

▷ **GET READY for the Lesson**

SURVEYS The graph shows the results of a survey about favorite type of TV show.

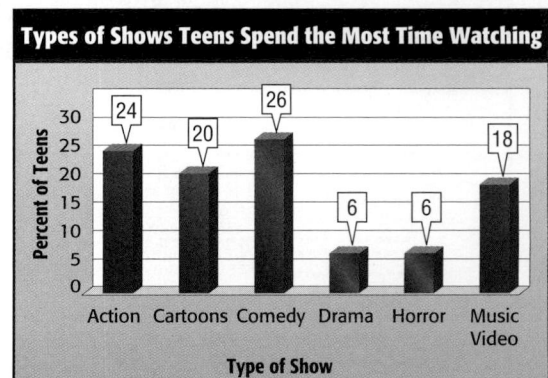

Types of Shows Teens Spend the Most Time Watching

Source: Kids USA Survey

1. What percent of the teens chose comedy? **26%**

2. Write this percent as a ratio in simplest form.
   13 : 50 or $\frac{13}{50}$

In Lesson 4-6, you wrote percents like 26% as fractions by writing fractions with denominators of 100 and then simplifying. You can use the same method to write percents like $8\frac{1}{3}\%$ and 190% as fractions.

EXAMPLES Percents as Fractions

① Write $8\frac{1}{3}\%$ as a fraction in simplest form.

$$8\frac{1}{3}\% = \frac{8\frac{1}{3}}{100} \qquad \text{Write a fraction.}$$

$$= 8\frac{1}{3} \div 100 \qquad \text{Divide.}$$

$$= \frac{25}{3} \div 100 \qquad \text{Write } 8\frac{1}{3} \text{ as an improper fraction.}$$

$$= \frac{25}{3} \cdot \frac{1}{100} \qquad \text{Multiply by the reciprocal of 100, which is } \frac{1}{100}.$$

$$= \frac{25}{300} \text{ or } \frac{1}{12} \qquad \text{Simplify.}$$

② **TOYS** A collectible action figure sold for 190% of its original price. Write this percent as a fraction in simplest form.

$$190\% = \frac{190}{100} \qquad \text{Definition of percent}$$

$$= \frac{19}{10} \text{ or } 1\frac{9}{10} \qquad \text{Simplify.}$$

> A percent greater than 100 is equal to a number greater than 1.

So, the toy sold for $1\frac{9}{10}$ of its original price.

328 Chapter 6 Ratios and Proportions

 **Tips for New Teachers**

Writing Percents as Fractions

Another way to write $8\frac{1}{3}\%$ as a fraction is to write and solve the proportion: $\frac{25}{3} = \frac{x}{100}$. Solve by finding the cross products.

CHECK Your Progress

Write each percent as a fraction in simplest form.

a. 150% $\frac{3}{2}$ b. $17\frac{1}{2}\%$ $\frac{7}{40}$ c. $33\frac{1}{3}\%$ $\frac{1}{3}$

To write a fraction like $\frac{8}{25}$ as a percent, multiply the numerator and the denominator by a number so that the denominator is 100. If the denominator is not a factor of 100, you can write fractions as percents by using a proportion.

EXAMPLES **Fractions as Percents**

3 Write $\frac{4}{15}$ as a percent. Round to the nearest hundredth.

Estimate $\frac{4}{15}$ is about $\frac{4}{16}$, which equals $\frac{1}{4}$ or 25%.

$\frac{4}{15} = \frac{n}{100}$ Write a proportion.

$400 = 15n$ Find the cross products.

$\frac{400}{15} = \frac{15n}{15}$ Divide each side by 15.

$26.67 \approx n$ Simplify.

So, $\frac{4}{15}$ is about 26.67%.

Check for Reasonableness $26.67\% \approx 25\%$ ✔

4 **BLOGGING** In Boston, $\frac{89}{100,000}$ residents blog. Write this fraction as a percent.

$\frac{89}{100,000} = \frac{n}{100}$ Write a proportion.

$8,900 = 100,000n$ Find the cross products.

$\frac{8,900}{100,000} = \frac{100,000n}{100,000}$ Divide each side by 100,000.

$0.089 = n$ Simplify.

A percent less than 1% is equal to a number less than 0.01 or $\frac{1}{100}$.

So, 0.089% of Boston's residents blog.

CHECK Your Progress

Write each fraction as a percent. Round to the nearest hundredth if necessary.

d. $\frac{2}{15}$ **13.33%**   e. $\frac{7}{1,600}$ **0.44%**   f. $\frac{17}{25}$ **68%**

Study Tip

Look Back You can review writing fractions as decimals in lesson 4-3.

In this lesson, you have written percents as fractions and fractions as percents. In Chapter 4, you wrote percents and fractions as decimals. You can also write a fraction as a percent by first writing the fraction as a decimal and then writing the decimal as a percent.

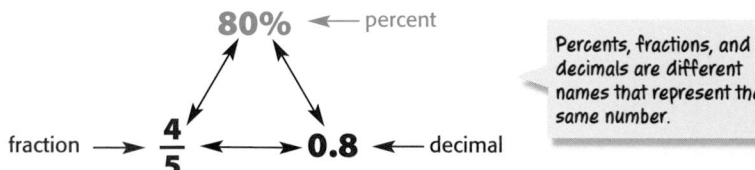

Percents, fractions, and decimals are different names that represent the same number.

EXAMPLES **Fractions as Percents**

5 Write $\frac{5}{6}$ as a percent. Round to the nearest hundredth.

$\frac{5}{6} = 0.833333333...$ Write $\frac{5}{6}$ as a decimal.

$\approx 83.33\%$ Multiply by 100 and add the %.

6 **BOOKS** Bryce has read $\frac{3}{5}$ of a book. What percent of the book has he read?

$\frac{3}{5} = 0.6$ Write the fraction as a decimal.

$= 60\%$ Multiply by 100 and add the %.

So, Bryce has read 60% of the book.

✓CHECK Your Progress

Write each fraction as a percent. Round to the nearest hundredth if necessary.

g. $\frac{5}{16}$ **31.25%**   h. $\frac{7}{12}$ **58.33%**   i. $\frac{2}{9}$ **22.22%**

j. **LAWNS** Mika is mowing lawns to earn extra money. She has mowed 6 out of 13 lawns. What percent of the lawns has she mowed?

46.15%

Some fractions with denominators that are not factors of 100 are used often in everyday situations. It is helpful to memorize these fractions and their equivalent decimals and percents. These common equivalents are shown below.

Common Equivalents					Key Concept
Fraction	Decimal	Percent	Fraction	Decimal	Percent
$\frac{1}{3}$	$0.\overline{3}$	$33\frac{1}{3}\%$	$\frac{3}{8}$	0.375	$37\frac{1}{2}\%$
$\frac{2}{3}$	$0.\overline{6}$	$66\frac{2}{3}\%$	$\frac{5}{8}$	0.625	$62\frac{1}{2}\%$
$\frac{1}{8}$	0.125	$12\frac{1}{2}\%$	$\frac{7}{8}$	0.875	$87\frac{1}{2}\%$

Differentiated Instruction

Logical Learners Have students study the use of percents and fractions in advertisements in magazines or newspapers. Have students clip or copy several ads and analyze how the percents or fractions are used. Does the advertiser want consumers to think the percent or fraction is a small number or a large number? What does the percent or fraction describe—price, content, consumer satisfaction? Would the ad be less effective if the equivalent fraction or percent were used?

 **Your Understanding**

Examples 1, 2
(pp. 328–329)

Write each percent as a fraction in simplest form.

1. 135% $\frac{27}{20}$ 2. 18.75% $\frac{3}{16}$ 3. $7\frac{1}{2}$% $\frac{3}{40}$ 4. $66\frac{2}{3}$% $\frac{2}{3}$

5. **FOOD** Steven and Rebecca ate 62.5% of a pizza. What fraction of the pizza did they eat? $\frac{5}{8}$

Examples 3–5
(pp. 329–330)

Write each fraction as a percent. Round to the nearest hundredth if necessary.

6. $\frac{3}{4}$ 75%   7. $\frac{4}{2,500}$ 0.16%   8. $\frac{4}{11}$ 36.36%   9. $\frac{1}{9}$ 11.11%

Example 6
(p. 330)

10. **SCHOOL** Moses has finished 11 out of 15 homework questions. To the nearest hundredth, what percent of the homework is complete? **73.33%**

Practice and Problem Solving

HOMEWORK HELP

For Exercises	See Examples
11–14, 19	1
15–18, 20	2
21–32	3–6
33–34	3

Exercise Levels
A: 11–34
B: 35–43
C: 44–45

Write each percent as a fraction in simplest form.

11. 62.5% $\frac{5}{8}$ 12. 6.2% $\frac{31}{500}$ 13. 28.75% $\frac{23}{80}$ 14. 56.25% $\frac{9}{16}$

15. $33\frac{1}{3}$% $\frac{1}{3}$ 16. $16\frac{2}{3}$% $\frac{1}{6}$ 17. $93\frac{3}{4}$% $\frac{15}{16}$ 18. $78\frac{3}{4}$% $\frac{63}{80}$

19. **ENVIRONMENT** Freshwater from lakes only accounts for 0.1% of the world's water supply. Write this percent as a fraction in simplest form. $\frac{1}{1,000}$

20. **ATTENDANCE** At last year's spring dance, $78\frac{1}{3}$% of the student body attended. What fraction of the student body is this? $\frac{47}{60}$

Write each fraction as a percent. Round to the nearest hundredth if necessary.

21. $\frac{111}{20}$ 555%   22. $\frac{180}{25}$ 720%   23. $\frac{30}{8}$ 375%   24. $\frac{210}{40}$ 525%

25. $\frac{29}{30}$ 96.67%   26. $\frac{8}{9}$ 88.89%   27. $\frac{5}{7}$ 71.43%   28. $\frac{1}{16}$ 6.25%

29. $\frac{1}{800}$ 0.13%   30. $\frac{57}{20,000}$ 0.29%   31. $\frac{5}{1,200}$ 0.42%   32. $\frac{7}{1,500}$ 0.47%

33. **FOOD** The size of a large milkshake is $\frac{7}{5}$ times the size of a medium milkshake. Write $\frac{7}{5}$ as a percent. **140%**

34. **PETS** In a class, 28 out of 32 students had a pet. What percent is this? **87.5%**

Replace each ● with >, <, or = to make a true statement.

35. 0.86 ● $\frac{7}{8}$ <   36. $\frac{9}{20}$ ● 45% =   37. 5% ● 0.004 >

Order each set of numbers from least to greatest.

Real-World Link · · · · ·
Out of the 50 states, 23 states border an ocean or the Gulf of Mexico.
Source: The US50

38. $\frac{1}{4}$, 22%, 0.3, 0.02 **0.02, 22%, $\frac{1}{4}$, 0.3**   39. 0.48, $\frac{1}{2}$%, 0.5, $\frac{2}{5}$ **$\frac{1}{2}$%, $\frac{2}{5}$, 0.48, 0.5**

40. **GEOGRAPHY** Use the information at the left. What percent of the states in the United States do *not* border an ocean or the Gulf of Mexico? **54%**

 Practice

Formative Assessment

Use Exercises 1–10 to check for understanding.

Then use the chart at the bottom of this page to customize your assignments for students.

Intervention You may wish to use the Study Guide and Intervention Master on page 58 of the *Chapter 6 Resource Masters* for additional reinforcement.

Odd/Even Assignments

Exercises 11–34 are structured so that students practice the same concepts whether they are assigned odd or even problems.

DIFFERENTIATED HOMEWORK OPTIONS

Level	Assignment	Two-Day Option	
BL Basic	11–34, 45–53	11–33 odd, 46, 47	12–34 even, 45, 48–53
OL Core	11–39 odd, 40–43, 45–53	11–34, 46, 47	35–43, 45, 48–53
AL Advanced/Pre-AP	35–49 (optional: 50–53)		

4 Assess

Formative Assessment

Check for student understanding of concepts in Lesson 6–9.

 Quiz 4 , p. 68

 **Foldables™ Follow-Up**

Remind students to select a term or concept about fractions, decimals, or percents and to define it in their Foldables. Encourage them to give an example of the term or concept.

Additional Answer

45. Sample answer: Since a percent is a ratio that compares a number to 100, 80% is the ratio $\frac{80}{100}$. The ratio $\frac{80}{100}$ can be read as *eighty-hundredths* or written as a decimal, 0.80 or 0.8. The ratio $\frac{80}{100}$ also simplifies to $\frac{4}{5}$ if you divide the numerator and denominator by the same number, 20.

---

41. FIND THE DATA Refer to the Data File on pages 16–19. Choose some data and write a real-world problem in which you would write a fraction as a percent. **See students' work.**

CARS For Exercises 42 and 43, use the table, which shows the percent of people in a recent survey who kept the listed items in their car.

Items in Car	Percent of People
Pen/Pencil	73.0%
Cassette Tapes/CDs	66.1%
First-Aid Kit	38.2%
Sports Equipment	28.9%

42. What fraction of people kept a first-aid kit in their car? $\frac{191}{500}$

43. Approximately 26 out of 125 people surveyed kept a hairbrush in their car. Is this greater or less than the percent who kept sports equipment? Explain. **Less than; $\frac{26}{125} = 20.8\%$.**

EXTRA PRACTICE See pages 684, 709.

44. CHALLENGE For what value of x does $\frac{1}{x} = x\%$? **10**

45. WRITING IN MATH Explain why 80%, 0.8, and $\frac{4}{5}$ all represent the same value. **See margin.**

TEST PRACTICE

46. Ms. Gallagher made 64 ounces of punch. The punch contained 17 ounces of apple juice. Which equation can be used to find x, the percent of apple juice in the punch? **D**

A $\frac{x}{100} = \frac{64}{17}$

B $\frac{x}{17} = \frac{64}{100}$

C $\frac{x}{64} = \frac{17}{100}$

D $\frac{x}{100} = \frac{17}{64}$

47. A group of 150 students were asked if they own a pet. The results are shown.

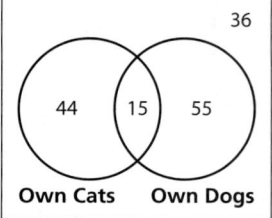

What percent of those surveyed own dogs? **G**

F 50%   H 36.7%

G 46.7%   J 30%

Spiral Review

48. COMPUTERS Designers are creating a larger model of the computer memory board. They use a scale of 20 inches = 1 inch. If the actual board is $5\frac{1}{4}$ inches long, what is the length of the model? (Lesson 6-8) **105 in.**

49. RECIPES Camila is making soup. She has added $\frac{2}{3}$ of the ingredients. If she has added 4 ingredients, how many more does she have to add to be finished? (Lesson 6-7) **2**

▷ GET READY for the Next Lesson

PREREQUISITE SKILL Write each fraction in simplest form. (Lesson 4-4)

50. $\frac{8}{10}$ $\frac{4}{5}$

51. $\frac{45}{100}$ $\frac{9}{20}$

52. $\frac{450}{100}$ $4\frac{1}{2}$

53. $\frac{175}{100}$ $1\frac{3}{4}$

 **Study Organizer**

GET READY to Study

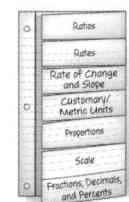

Be sure the following Big Ideas are noted in your Foldable.

BIG Ideas

Ratios and Rates (Lessons 6-1 and 6-2)
• A ratio is a comparison of two quantities by division.
• A rate is a ratio comparing two quantities with different kinds of units.

Slope and Rate of Change (Lesson 6-3)
• Slope is the rate of change between any two points on a line.

Changing Customary Units (Lesson 6-4)
• To convert from larger units to smaller units, multiply by the appropriate unit ratio.
• To convert from smaller units to larger units, multiply by the reciprocal of the appropriate unit ratio.

Changing Metric Units (Lesson 6-5)
• When converting metric units, multiply by the appropriate power of 10.
• When converting between customary and metric units, use the appropriate unit ratio or relationship.

Proportions (Lesson 6-6)
• Proportions are equations that state two ratios or rates are equivalent.

Scale Drawings (Lesson 6-8)
• Scale drawings represent something that is too large or too small to be drawn at actual size.

Key Vocabulary

cross products (p. 310)
equivalent ratios (p. 283)
inverse proportion (p. 316)
proportion (p. 310)
proportional (p. 310)
rate (p. 287)
rate of change (p. 293)
ratio (p. 282)
scale (p. 320)
scale drawing (p. 320)
scale factor (p. 322)
scale model (p. 320)
slope (p. 294)
unit rate (p. 287)
unit ratio (p. 299)

Vocabulary Check

Choose the term from the list above that best matches each phrase.

1. a comparison of two quantities by division **ratio**

2. two ratios that have the same value **equivalent ratios**

3. a ratio of two measurements with different units **rate**

4. an equation that shows that two ratios or rates are equivalent **proportion**

5. used to represent something that is too large or too small for an actual-size drawing **scale drawing**

6. the ratio of the distance on a map to the actual distance **scale**

7. a scale written as a ratio in simplest form without units of measurement **scale factor**

8. the constant rate of change in y with respect to the constant change in x **slope**

9. a rate that is simplified so that it has a denominator of 1 **unit rate**

10. two quantities that have a constant rate or ratio **proportional**

CHAPTER 6 Study Guide and Review

 **Study Organizer**

Dinah Zike's Foldables

Have students look through the chapter to make sure they have included definitions and examples about the key concepts of each lesson in their Foldables.

Encourage students to refer to their Foldables while completing the Study Guide and Review and while preparing for the Chapter Test.

 Formative Assessment

Key Vocabulary The page references after each word denote where that term was first introduced. If students have difficulty answering Exercises 1–10, remind them that they can use these page references to refresh their memories about the vocabulary terms.

Math Online > glencoe.com

Vocabulary PuzzleMaker improves students' mathematics vocabulary using four puzzle formats—crossword, scramble, word search using a word list, and word search using clues. Students can work online or from a printed worksheet.

 Summative Assessment

CRM Vocabulary Test, p. 70

Lesson-by-Lesson Review

Intervention If the given examples are not sufficient to review the topics covered by the questions, remind students that the page references tell them where to review that topic in their textbooks.

Two-Day Option Have students complete the Lesson-by-Lesson Review on pages 334–336. Then you can use ExamView® Assessment Suite to customize another review worksheet that practices all the objectives of this chapter or only the objectives on which your students need more help.

For more information on ExamView® Assessment Suite, see page 280C.

Differentiated Instruction

Super DVD: MindJogger Plus
Use this DVD as an alternative format of review for the test. For more information on this game show format, see page 280D.

Additional Answer

19.

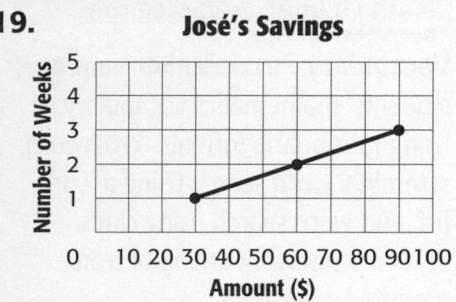

José's Savings

Lesson-by-Lesson Review

6-1 **Ratios** (pp. 282–286)

Write each ratio as a fraction in simplest form.

11. 16 dogs : 12 cats $\frac{4}{3}$ 12. 5 ft : 25 ft $\frac{1}{5}$
13. 50 boys : 75 girls $\frac{2}{3}$ 14. 36 ft : 6 ft. $\frac{6}{1}$

15. Determine whether the ratios 18 out of 24 and 5 out of 20 are equivalent.
no; $\frac{18}{24} = \frac{3}{4}$, $\frac{5}{20} = \frac{1}{4}$, and $\frac{3}{4} \neq \frac{1}{4}$

Example 1 Write the ratio 32 to 18 as a fraction in simplest form.

32 to 18 $= \frac{32}{18}$ Write the ratio as a fraction.
$= \frac{16}{9}$ Simplify.

Example 2 Determine whether 5:6 and 15:18 are equivalent.

$5:6 = \frac{5}{6}$ $15:18 = \frac{15}{18}$ or $\frac{5}{6}$
The ratios in simplest form both equal $\frac{5}{6}$. So, 5:6 and 15:18 are equivalent.

6-2 **Rates** (pp. 287–292)

Find each unit rate.

16. $23.75 for 5 pounds **$4.75 per lb**

17. 810 miles in 9 days **90 mi per day**

18. **SHAMPOO** Which bottle of shampoo shown at the right costs the least per ounce? **16 oz**

Bottle	Price
8 oz	$1.99
12 oz	$2.59
16 oz	$3.19

Example 3 Find the unit price of a 16-ounce box of pasta that is on sale for 96 cents.

16-ounce box for 96 cents $= \frac{96 \text{ cents} \div 16}{16 \text{ ounces} \div 16}$

$= \frac{6 \text{ cents}}{1 \text{ ounce}}$

The unit price is 6 cents per ounce.

6-3 **Rate of Change and Slope** (pp. 293–297)

Complete.

19. **MONEY** The table shows the amount of money José saved over a period of time. Graph the data. Then find the slope of the line. Explain what the slope represents.

Amount ($)	30	60	90
Weeks	1	2	3

See margin for graph. slope: $\frac{30}{1}$ or 30; José saved $30 every week.

Example 4 Find the rate of change in degrees per hour.

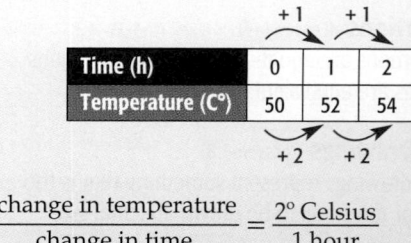

	+1	+1
Time (h)	0	1	2
Temperature (C°)	50	52	54
	+2	+2

$\frac{\text{change in temperature}}{\text{change in time}} = \frac{2° \text{ Celsius}}{1 \text{ hour}}$

So, the temperature increases by 2° Celsius each hour.

Mixed Problem Solving
For mixed problem-solving practice,
see page 709.

CHAPTER
6 Study Guide
and Review

6-4 **Measurement: Changing Customary Units** (pp. 298–303)

Complete.

20. 4 qt = ■ pt **8**   21. 6 gal = ■ qt **24**

22. 48 oz = ■ lb **3**   23. 9 c = ■ pt $4\frac{1}{2}$

24. **RUNNING** Kimi runs at a speed of 30 feet per second. About how many yards per second does Kimi run? **10 yd per s**

25. **ESTIMATION** One bushel of apples weighs about 40 pounds. About how many bushels of apples would weigh 1 ton? **50 bushels**

Example 5 Complete: 32 qt = ■ gal

Since 1 gallon = 4 quarts, multiply by $\frac{1\text{ gal}}{4\text{ qt}}$.

$32\text{ qt} = 32\text{ qt} \cdot \dfrac{1\text{ gal}}{4\text{ qt}}$ Multiply by $\frac{1\text{ gal}}{4\text{ qt}}$.

$= \overset{8}{\cancel{32}}\text{ qt} \cdot \dfrac{1\text{ gal}}{\underset{1}{\cancel{4\text{ qt}}}}$ Divide out common factors and units.

$= 8\text{ gal}$ Multiply.

6-5 **Measurement: Changing Metric Units** (pp. 304–309)

Complete. Round to the nearest hundredth if necessary. **27. 51,528.96**

26. 18.25 ft ≈ ■ m   27. 113.6 lb ≈ ■ g
    5.48

28. 24 L ≈ ■ gal   29. 46.8 cm ≈ ■ in.
    6.33   **18.43**

30. **RUNNING** Justine ran a 5-kilometer race. About how many miles did she run? **about 3.11 mi**

31 **BIRDS** The world's largest bird is the ostrich, whose mass can be as much as 156.5 kilograms. What is the approximate weight in pounds? **about 345 lb**

Example 6 Complete: 48.8 c ≈ ■ mL

Use the relationship 1 c ≈ 236.59 mL.

$1\text{ c} \approx 236.59\text{ mL}$

$48.8 \times 1\text{ c} \approx 48.8 \times 236.59\text{ mL}$

$48.8\text{ c} \approx 11{,}545.592\text{ mL}$

So, 48.8 cups is approximately 11,545.59 milliliters.

6-6 **Algebra: Solving Proportions** (pp. 310–315)

Solve each proportion.

32. $\dfrac{x}{10} = \dfrac{3}{5}$ **6**   33. $\dfrac{4}{9} = \dfrac{24}{m}$ **54**

34. $\dfrac{2}{t} = \dfrac{8}{50}$ **12.5**   35. $\dfrac{15}{w} = \dfrac{35}{21}$ **9**

36. $\dfrac{12}{8} = \dfrac{a}{6}$ **9**   37. $\dfrac{7}{18} = \dfrac{d}{6}$ $2\frac{1}{3}$

38. **WEIGHT** If 3 televisions weigh 240.6 pounds, how much do 9 of the same televisions weigh? **721.8 lb**

Example 7 Solve $\dfrac{6}{9} = \dfrac{n}{12}$.

$\dfrac{6}{9} = \dfrac{n}{12}$ Write the proportion.

$6 \cdot 12 = 9 \cdot n$ Find the cross products.

$72 = 9n$ Multiply.

$\dfrac{72}{9} = \dfrac{9n}{9}$ Divide each side by 9.

$8 = n$ Simplify.

Chapter 6 Study Guide and Review **335**

CHAPTER 6 Study Guide and Review

Problem Solving Review

For additional practice in problem solving for Chapter 6, see the Mixed Problem Solving Appendix, page 709 in the Student Handbook section.

Anticipation Guide

Have students complete the Chapter 6 Anticipation Guide and discuss how their responses have changed now that they have completed Chapter 6.

CRM Anticipation Guide, pp. 7–8

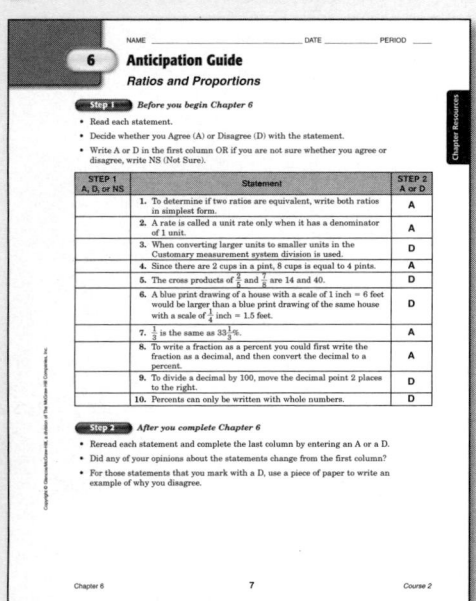

6-7 **PSI: Draw a Diagram** (pp. 318–319)

Solve each problem by drawing a diagram.

39. **PAINTING** Marian is painting a fence that is 72 feet long. She has already painted $\frac{5}{8}$ of the fence. How many feet of fence does she have left to paint? **27 feet**

40. **COOKIES** A cookie jar contains three types of cookies: oatmeal, chocolate chip, and sugar. 60 percent are chocolate chip. Half of the remaining cookies are oatmeal. If there are 9 oatmeal cookies, how many cookies are in the jar? **45**

Example 8 Ramiro has filled $\frac{1}{3}$ or 50 gallons of his fish tank. Find the total capacity of the fish tank.

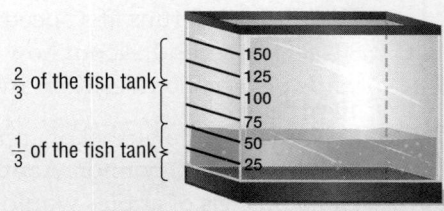

If $\frac{1}{3}$ of the fish tank is 50 gallons, then $\frac{2}{3}$ of the fish tank is 100 gallons. So, the missing two thirds must be 100 gallons. The total capacity of the fish tank is 50 + 100, or 150 gallons.

6-8 **Scale Drawings** (pp. 320–326)

41. **MAPS** Washington, D.C, and Baltimore, Maryland, are 2 inches apart on a map. If the scale is $\frac{1}{2}$ inch : 6 miles, what is the actual distance between the cities? **24 mi**

42. **MODELS** A Boeing 747 jet is 70.5 meters long and has a wingspan of 60 meters. A model of the 747 has a wingspan of 80 centimeters. What is the length of the model? **94 cm**

Example 9 On a map, the distance between two cities is 10.9 centimeters. If the scale is 1 centimeter = 250 kilometers, what is the actual distance?

$$\begin{array}{cc} & \textbf{Scale} \quad\quad \textbf{Distance} \\ \text{map} \rightarrow & \dfrac{1\ cm}{250\ km} = \dfrac{10.9\ cm}{n\ km} \leftarrow \text{map} \\ \text{actual} \rightarrow & \leftarrow \text{actual} \end{array}$$

$$1 \cdot n = 250 \cdot 10.9$$
$$n = 2{,}725$$

The actual distance is 2,725 kilometers.

6-9 **Fractions, Decimals, and Percents** (pp. 328–332)

Write each percent as a fraction in simplest form.

43. 27.5% $\frac{11}{40}$ 44. 5.40% $\frac{27}{500}$ 45. $45\frac{1}{4}$% $\frac{181}{400}$

46. **COINS** A quarter is made of $\frac{1}{12}$ nickel, and the rest is copper. Write the portion of a quarter that is copper as a percent. Round to the nearest hundredth if necessary. **91.67%**

Example 10 Write 82.5% as a fraction in simplest form.

$$82.5\% = \frac{82.5}{100} \quad \text{Write a fraction with a denominator of 100.}$$
$$= \frac{825}{1{,}000} \quad \text{Multiply 82.5 and 100 by 10 to eliminate the decimal.}$$
$$= \frac{33}{40} \quad \text{Simplify.}$$

LAWN CARE For Exercises 1 and 2, use the following information to write each ratio as a fraction in simplest form.

A bag of fertilizer nutrients contains 18 pounds of nitrogen, 6 pounds of phosphorus, and 12 pounds of potassium.

1. nitrogen : potassium $\frac{3}{2}$

2. phosphorus : nitrogen $\frac{1}{3}$

Find each unit rate. Round to the nearest hundredth if necessary.

3. 24 greeting cards for $4.80 **$0.20 per card**

4. 330 miles on 15 gallons of gasoline **22 mi per gal**

5. **MULTIPLE CHOICE** The population of bacteria in 4 different-sized lab dishes are given. Which dish has the lowest density of bacteria or bacteria per square inch? **B**

Dish	Bacteria	Dish Area
1	100	205 sq in.
2	50	125 sq in.
3	35	75 sq in.
4	180	300 sq in.

A Dish 1   C Dish 3
B Dish 2   D Dish 4

6. The graph shows the relationship between time and water level of a pool. Find the rate of change. **The water level increases by 1 foot for every 2 hours.**

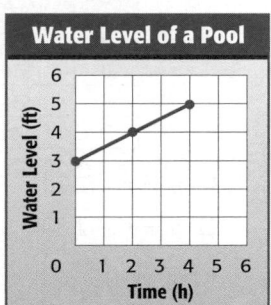
Water Level of a Pool

MEASUREMENT Complete. Round to the nearest tenth if necessary.

7. 7.62 yd ≈ ▧ m **6.93**
8. 50.8 lb ≈ ▧ kg **23.04**
9. 3,600 mL ≈ ▧ qt **3.80**
10. 19.25 m ≈ ▧ ft **64.17**

ALGEBRA Solve each proportion.

11. $\frac{2}{3} = \frac{x}{42}$ **28**

12. $\frac{t}{21} = \frac{15}{14}$ **22.5**

13. **NUTRITION** If an 8-ounce glass of orange juice has 72 milligrams of vitamin C, how much vitamin C is in a 7-ounce glass? **63 mg**

14. **MAPS** The table shows the key for a map. Graph the data. Then find the slope of the line. **See margin.**

Distance on Map (cm)	1	2	3	4
Actual Distance (km)	20	40	60	80

BLUEPRINTS For Exercises 15 and 16, use the following blueprint of a room.

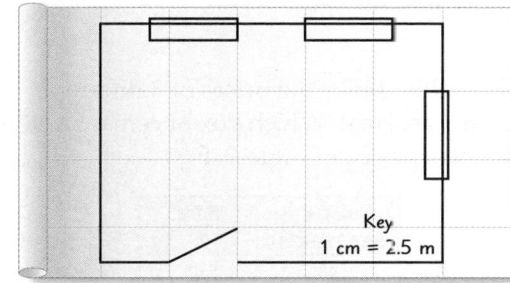

Key
1 cm = 2.5 m

15. Use a centimeter ruler to find the length of the wall with 2 windows. **12.5 m**

16. How wide would a 1.4-meter-wide dresser appear on this drawing? **0.56 cm**

Write each fraction as a percent. Round to the nearest hundredth if necessary.

17. $\frac{5}{8}$ **62.5%**

18. $\frac{7}{15}$ **46.67%**

19. **GUM** A company test-marketed 7 new flavors of gum last year. Only 2 of these received favorable ratings. Which represents the percent of flavors that did *not* receive favorable ratings? **71%**

20. **STOCKS** A company's stock increased 0.83% last month. Write 0.83% as a decimal. **0.0083**

CHAPTER **6** Practice Test

✓ **Summative Assessment**

CRM **Chapter 6 Resource Masters**

Leveled Chapter 6 Tests

Form	Type	Level	Pages
1	MC	BL	71–72
2A	MC	OL	73–74
2B	MC	OL	75–76
2C	FR	OL	77–78
2D	FR	OL	79–80
3	FR	AL	81–82

MC = multiple-choice questions
FR = free-response questions
BL = below or approaching grade level
OL = on grade level
AL = above or beyond grade level

• Vocabulary Test, p. 70
• Extended-Response Test, p. 83

ExamView Assessment Suite

Customize and create multiple versions of your chapter test and the answer keys. All of the questions from the leveled chapter tests in the *Chapter 6 Resource Masters* are also available on ExamView® Assessment Suite.

Data-Driven Decision Making	Exercises	Lesson	State/Local Standards	Resources for Review
Diagnostic Teaching Based on the results of the Chapter 6 Practice Test, use the following to review concepts that students continue to find challenging.	1–6, 14	6-1, 6-2, 6-3		CRM Study Guide and Intervention pp. 10, 16, 22, 28, 34, 40, 46, 51, and 58
	7–13	6-4, 6-5, 6-6		Math Online > glencoe.com
	15–20	6-7, 6-8, 6-9		• Extra Examples • Personal Tutor • Concepts in Motion

TEST-TAKING TIP

Exercise 4 Have students look for a word or term in the problem that indicates which operation will be used in the equation. Students should realize that *more than* indicates addition, which should lead them to examine answer choice G.

 Formative Assessment

You can use these two pages to benchmark student progress.

 *Chapter 6 Resource Masters*

• Standardized Test Practice, pp. 84–86

 Create practice worksheets or tests that align to your state's standards, as well as TIMSS and NAEP tests.

PART 1   Multiple Choice

Read each question. Then fill in the correct answer on the answer sheet provided by your teacher or on a sheet of paper.

1. Francesca typed 496 words in 8 minutes. Which of the following is a correct understanding of this rate? **C**

   A On average, it takes 62 minutes for Francesca to type one word.

   B On average, Francesca can type 62 words in 8 minutes.

   C On average, Francesca can type 62 words in one minute.

   D On average, Francesca can type 8 words in one minute.

2. The table shows the prices of 3 different boxes of cereal. Which box of cereal has the highest price per ounce? **F**

Cereal Box Size (ounces)	Price ($)
48	5.45
32	3.95
20	3.10

   F The 20-ounce box

   G The 32-ounce box

   H The 48-ounce box

   J All three boxes have the same price per ounce.

3. A bakery sells 6 bagels for a total of $2.99 and 4 muffins for a total of $3.29. If you bought 4 dozen bagels and 16 muffins, what is the total cost of the bagels and muffins, not including tax? **B**

   A $64.60   C $31.10

   B $37.08   D $26.50

---

4. Mrs. Black is making 2 pasta salads for a picnic. The first pasta salad requires $4\frac{2}{3}$ cups of pasta, and the second pasta salad requires $\frac{1}{3}$ cup more than the first. Which of the following equations can be used to find n, the number of cups of pasta needed for the second recipe? **G**

   F $n = 4\frac{2}{3} \div \frac{1}{3}$

   G $n = 4\frac{2}{3} + \frac{1}{3}$

   H $n = 4\frac{2}{3} - \frac{1}{3}$

   J $n = 4\frac{2}{3} \times \frac{1}{3}$

5. Simplify the expression below.
   $$8 + 3(15 - 5) - 3^2 \;\; \textbf{D}$$

   A 101   C 39

   B 44   D 29

6. A shoe store had to increase prices. The table shows the regular price r and the new price n of several shoes. Which of the following formulas can be used to calculate the new price? **G**

Shoe	Regular Price (r)	New Price (n)
A	$25.00	$27.80
B	$30.00	$32.80
C	$35.00	$37.80
D	$40.00	$42.80

   F $n = r - 2.80$ H $n = r \times 0.1$

   G $n = r + 2.80$ J $n = r \div 0.1$

7. Annika can run 2 miles in 15 minutes. At this rate, about how long will it take her to run $3\frac{1}{2}$ miles? **A**

   A 26 minutes   C 36 minutes

   B 32 minutes   D 45 minutes

338   Chapter 6 Ratios and Proportions

Preparing for Standardized Tests
For test-taking strategies and practice, see pages 716–733.

CHAPTER
6 Test Practice

8. A building is 55 meters tall. About how tall is the building in feet (ft) and inches (in.)? (1 meter ≈ 39 inches) **G**

F 179 ft 0 in.

G 178 ft 9 in.

H 178 ft 8 in.

J 178 ft 6 in.

9. You can drive your car 21.75 miles with one gallon of gasoline. How many miles can you drive with 13.2 gallons of gasoline? **D**

A 13.2

B 21.75

C 150.2

D 287.1

10. The table shows the number of yards of material Leah used each day last week. What was the total number of yards Leah used last week? **F**

Day	Material (yd)
Monday	2.3
Tuesday	$1\frac{3}{4}$
Wednesday	2.8
Thursday	3.1
Friday	$3\frac{1}{4}$
Saturday	1.7
Sunday	$4\frac{1}{2}$

F 19.4 yd

G 17 yd

H 16.5 yd

J 16 yd

PART 2 Short Response/Grid In

Record your answers on the answer sheet provided by your teacher or on a sheet of paper.

11. Some employees work 40 hours a week. If there are 168 hours in one week, about what part of the week do they work? **25%**

12. During a visit to his favorite bookstore, Kevin bought 3 hardback books priced at $14.99 each and 4 paperbacks priced at $7.99 each. Find the total of Kevin's purchase, in dollars, before tax is included. **76.93**

PART 3 Extended Response

Record your answers on the answer sheet provided by your teacher or on a sheet of paper. Show your work.

13 Pistachios cost $3.99 a pound at the local health food store.

a. Set up a proportion to find the cost of 3 pounds. $\dfrac{\$3.99}{1\,lb} = \dfrac{x}{3\,lb}$

b. Solve the proportion. How much do 3 pounds of pistachios cost? **$11.97**

c. If the pistachios are on sale for $3.09 a pound, how much money will you save if you buy 3 pounds of pistachios? **$2.70**

TEST-TAKING TIP

Question 13 When a question involves information from a previous part of a question, make sure to check that information before you move on.

NEED EXTRA HELP?

If You Missed Question...	1	2	3	4	5	6	7	8	9	10	11	12	13
Go to Lesson...	6-2	6-2	1-1	5-2	1-4	1-10	6-2	6-8	6-6	5-2	6-9	6-7	6-2

Answer Sheet Practice

Have students simulate taking a standardized test by recording their answers on a practice recording sheet.

CRM Student Recording Sheet, p. 65

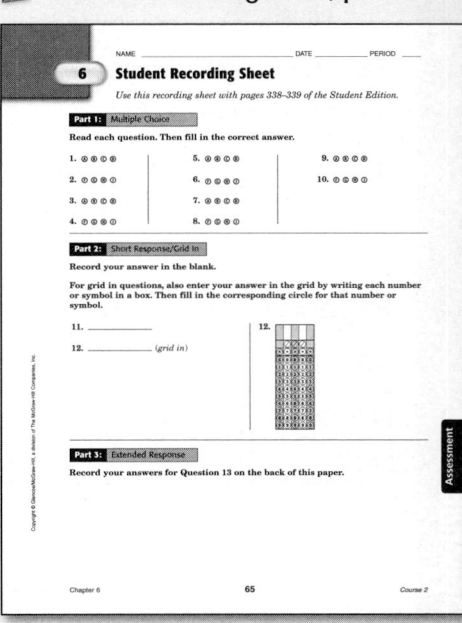

Homework Option

Get Ready for Chapter 7 Assign students the exercises on page 341 as homework to assess whether they possess the prerequisite skills needed for the next chapter.

Page 313, Lesson 6-6

15. Yes; sample answer: The cross products of the ratios $\frac{16}{200}$ and $\frac{28}{350}$, 16 • 350 and 200 • 28, are both equal to 5,600.

16. No; sample answer: The cross products of the ratios $\frac{5}{7}$ and $\frac{25}{49}$, 5 • 49 or 245 and 7 • 25 or 175, are not equal.

17. No; sample answer: The cross products of the ratios $\frac{1.4\text{ T}}{18\text{ days}}$ and $\frac{10.5\text{ T}}{60\text{ days}}$, 1.4 • 60 or 84 and 18 • 10.5 or 189, are not equal.

18. Yes; sample answer: $\frac{3\text{ in.}}{4\text{ mi}} = \frac{0.75\text{ in.}}{1\text{ mi}}$ and $\frac{7.5\text{ in.}}{10\text{ mi}} = \frac{0.75\text{ in.}}{1\text{ mi}}$; The unit rates are equal.

20. Yes; the cross products of the ratios $\frac{11}{2}$ and $\frac{33}{6}$, 11 • 6 and 2 • 33, are both equal to 66.

Page 316, Extend 6-6

3.

t (hours)	1	2	3	4
r ($)	240	120	80	60

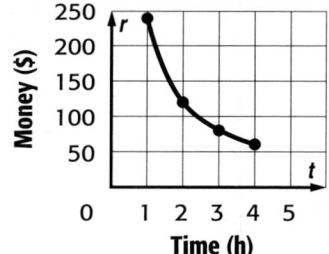

Mr. Anwar's Rate

t (hours)	1	2	3	4
r ($)	10	20	30	40

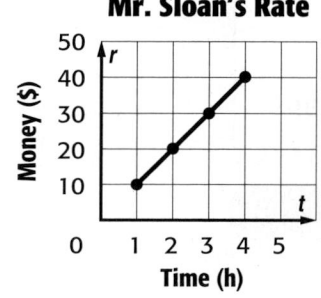

Mr. Sloan's Rate

Page 337, Practice Test

14. slope: $\frac{20}{1}$ or 20; Every centimeter on the map represents 20 kilometers.

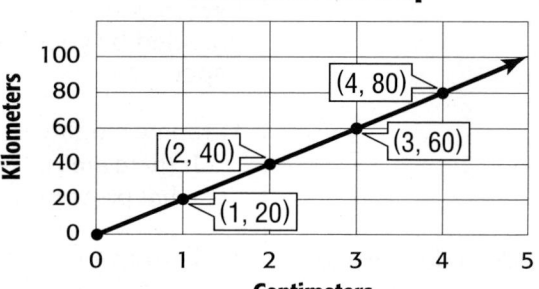

Distances on a Map

NOTES

Chapter 7

Chapter Overview

Applying Percents

Lesson Plan		Pacing Your Lessons	
LESSONS AND OBJECTIVES	State/Local Standards	45–50 Minute Periods	90-Minute Periods
Explore 7-1 Math Lab: Percent of a Number (pp. 342–343) • Use a model to find the percent of a number. **7-1 Percent of a Number** (pp. 344–348) • Find the percent of a number.		1.5	1
7-2 The Percent Proportion (pp. 350–354) • Solve problems using the percent proportion.		1	0.5
7-3 Percent and Estimation (pp. 355–360) • Estimate percents by using fractions and decimals.		1	0.5
7-4 Algebra: The Percent Equation (pp. 361–365) • Solve problems by using the percent equation.		1	0.5
7-5 Problem-Solving Investigation: Determine Reasonable Answers (pp. 366–367) • Solve problems by determining reasonable answers.		1	0.5
7-6 Percent of Change (pp. 369–374) • Find the percent of increase or decrease.		1	0.5
7-7 Sales Tax and Discount (pp. 375–378) • Solve problems involving sales tax and discount.		1	0.5
7-8 Simple Interest (pp. 379–382) • Solve problems involving simple interest. **Extend 7-8 Spreadsheet Lab: Simple Interest** (p. 383) • Use a spreadsheet to calculate simple interest.		1.5	1
REVIEW		1	0.5
ASSESSMENT		1	0.5*
TOTAL		11	6

*The complete **Assessment Planner** for Chapter 7 is provided on page 341.*

* Begin Chapter 8 in the second half of the period.

Focal Points

G7-FP1 Algebra
For the complete wording of the Focal Points for Grade 7, please see page iv.

Professional Development

Vertical Alignment

Before Chapter 7

Related Topics from Grade 6

- Interpret percents as a part of a hundred; find decimal and percent equivalents for common fractions and explain why they represent the same value; compute a given percent of a whole number

Chapter 7

Topics from Grade 7

- Interpret and use ratios in different contexts
- Use proportions to solve problems
- Calculate given percents of quantities and solve
- Write and solve one-step linear equations in one variable

After Chapter 7

Preparation for Grade 8

- Convert fractions to decimals and percents and use these representations in estimations, computations, and applications
- Solve problems that involve discounts, markups, commissions, and profit and compute simple and compound interest
- Calculate the percent of increases and decreases of a quantity

Backmapping and Vertical Alignment

McGraw-Hill's *Math Connects* was conceived and developed with the final results in mind: student success in Algebra 1 and beyond. The authors, using the **NCTM Focal Points and Focal Connections** as their guide, developed this brand-new series by backmapping from Algebra 1 concepts and vertically aligning the topics so that they build upon prior skills and concepts and serve as a foundation for future topics.

What the Research Says…

According to Sutherland and Rojano in "A Spreadsheet Approach to Solving Algebra Problems," which appeared in *Journal of Mathematical Behavior*, spreadsheets help students understand the meaning of variables and algebraic expressions.

- In the Spreadsheet Investigation on page 383, students use a spreadsheet to calculate simple interest I for different values of principal p, rate r, and time t.

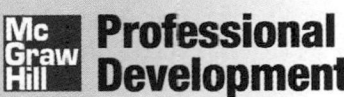 **Professional Development**

Targeted professional development has been articulated throughout **McGraw-Hill's *Math Connects*** program. The **McGraw-Hill Professional Development Video Library** provides short videos that support the NCTM Focal Points and Focal Connections. For more information, visit glencoe.com.

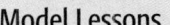

| Model Lessons | Instructional Strategies |

TeacherWorks™ All-in-One Planner and Resource Center

All of the print materials from the Classroom Resource Masters are available on your TeacherWorks™ CD-ROM.

BL = Below or Approaching Grade Level   **OL** = On Grade Level   **AL** = Above or Beyond Grade Level   **ELL** = English Language Learner

Chapter Resource Masters						7-1	7-2	7-3	7-4	7-5	7-6	7-7	7-8
BL	OL		ELL		Lesson Reading Guide	9	16	23	29		39	46	52
BL	OL		ELL		Study Guide and Intervention*	10	17	24	30	35	40	47	53
BL	OL				Skills Practice*	11	18	25	31	36	41	48	54
	OL	AL			Practice*	12	19	26	32	37	42	49	55
	OL	AL			Word Problem Practice*	13	20	27	33	38	43	50	56
	OL	AL			Enrichment	14	21	28	34		44	51	57
	OL	AL			Calculator and Spreadsheet Activities	15	22				45		
	OL	AL			Chapter Assessments*	59–80							
BL	OL	AL			5-Minute Check Transparencies	✓	✓	✓	✓	✓	✓	✓	✓
BL	OL				Teaching Mathematics with Manipulatives	✓		✓			✓		
BL	OL	AL			Real-World Investigations for Differentiated Instruction	53							

*Also available in Spanish.

Graphing Calculator Easy Files

- Timesaving Tech Tools for the TI-Navigator
- Quick Checks to diagnose student progress
- Deliver Differentiated Instruction with Ready Files
- Vocabulary Review

AssignmentWorks

Differentiated Assignments, Answers, and Solutions

- Print a customized assignment worksheet using the Student Edition exercises along with an answer key or worked-out solutions.
- Use a default lesson assignments as outlined in the Differentiated Homework Options in the Teacher Edition.

Interactive Classroom

This CD-ROM is a customizable Microsoft® PowerPoint® presentation that includes:

- In-Class Examples
- Your Turn Exercises*
- 5-Minute Check Transparencies*
- Links to Online Study Tools
- Concepts in Motion

*compatible with response pad technology

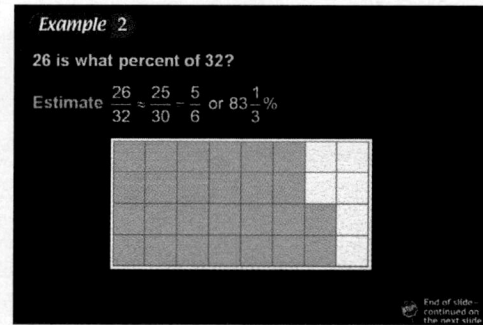

ExamView® Assessment Suite

- Create, edit, and customize tests and worksheets using QuickTest Wizard
- Create multiple versions of tests and modify them for a desired level of difficulty
- Translate from English to Spanish and vice versa
- Build tests aligned with your state standards
- Track students' progress using the Teacher Management System

Student Tools

StudentWorks™ Plus

Textbook, Audio, Workbooks, and more

This CD-ROM is a valuable resource for students to access content online and use online resources to continue learning Chapter 7 concepts. Includes:

- Complete Student Editions in both English and Spanish
- English audio integrated throughout the text
- Links to Concepts in Motion, Personal Tutor, and other online resources
- Access to all student worksheets
- Daily Assignments and Grade Log

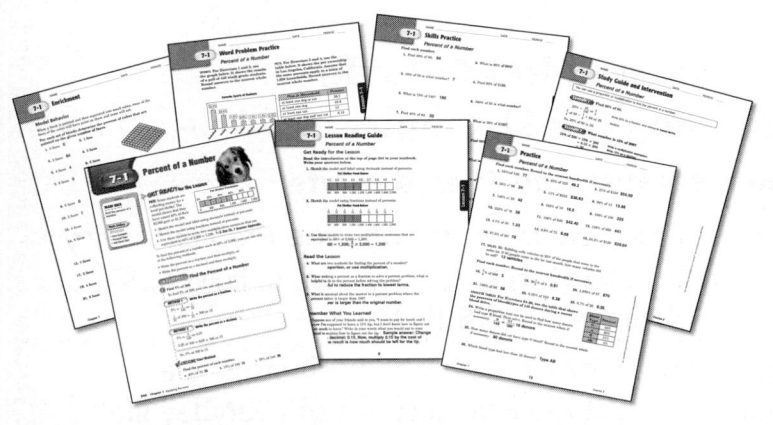

Super DVD

The Super DVD contains two Glencoe multimedia products.

MindJogger Plus An alternative review of concepts in which students work as teams in a game show format to gain points for correct answers.

What's Math Got to Do With It? Real-Life Math Videos Engaging video that shows students how math is used in everyday situations.

Internet Resources

Math Online glencoe.com

TEACHER	STUDENT	PARENT	Online Study Tools
	●	●	Online Student Edition
●	●	●	Multilingual Glossary
Lesson Resources			
	●	●	Extra Examples
	●	●	BrainPOPS®
	●	●	Self-Check Quizzes
●	●	●	Concepts in Motion
	●	●	Other Calculator Keystrokes
	●	●	Real-World Careers
	●	●	Reading in the Content Area
●			Group Activity Cards
Chapter Resources			
	●	●	Family Letters and Activities
	●		Chapter Readiness Quiz
	●	●	Vocabulary Review
	●		Chapter Test
	●	●	Standardized Test Practice
Unit Resources			
●	●		WebQuest Project
Other Resources			
	●		Personal Tutor
●			NAEP Correlations
●			Key Concepts
●	●	●	Meet the Authors
●	●		Game Zone
●	●	●	Math Skills Maintenance
●			National Resources (Professional Organizations)
●			State Resources
●			Vocabulary PuzzleMakers

Noteables™ Interactive Study Notebook with Foldables™

This workbook is a study organizer that provides helpful steps for students to follow to organize their notes for Chapter 7.

- Students use Noteables to record notes and to complete their Foldables as you present the material for each lesson.

- Noteables correspond to the Examples in the *Teacher Edition* and *Interactive Chalkboard CD-ROM*.

Real-World Problem Solving Graphic Novels

Mathematical problem solving is presented in a motivating, graphic novel format. The novels contain real-world problems for each of the following mathematical strands: Number Sense, Algebraic Thinking, Geometry, Measurement, Statistics and Probability, and Mathematical Reasoning.

READING in the Content Area

This online worksheet provides strategies for reading and analyzing Lesson 7-2, The Percent Proportion. Students are guided through questions about the main idea, subject matter, supporting details, conclusion, clarifying details, and vocabulary of the lesson.

glencoe.com

Recommended Outside Reading for Students

Mathematics and Everyday Life

- *57 Great Math Stories and the Problems They Present* by D. Haver, A. Kozoil, E. Haven, & D. Mulligan ©1998 [fiction]

Appropriate for Grades 5–8. Each story is a humorous yet realistic account of everyday life and the problems life presents. Many stories throughout the book utilize percents. Often the reader must make calculations using the percent equation or proportion to understand the outcome of the story.

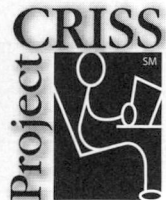

STUDY SKILL

Writing out the steps in a mathematical process using a point-by-point format can help students better understand that process. In order to explain a process, they must not only understand how to perform each step, but they must also understand the reasoning behind each step. Provide students with the description at the right as an example of using a point-by-point format to explain how to multiply a fraction and a whole number. After reading Lessons 7-7 and 7-8, have students write a description of how to solve sales tax and simple interest problems. Students may also find two-column notes to be a useful tool in this chapter.

Multiplying a Fraction and a Whole Number
1. Write the whole number as a fraction with a denominator of 1. For example, 8 would be written as $\frac{8}{1}$.
2. Multiply the fractions. The numerators should be multiplied and the denominators should be multiplied.
3. If the numerator is greater than the denominator, write the answer as a mixed number.
4. Be sure the answer is written in simplest form. If not, rename.

CReating **I**ndependence through **S**tudent-owned **S**trategies

Differentiated Instruction

Investigative Approach

MathScape™

This project was supported, in part, by the National Science Foundation

MathScape is a mathematics curriculum for grades 6–8 developed by the Seeing and Thinking Mathematically Project at the Education Development Center.

Rates, Ratios, Percents, and Proportions

Buyer Beware

How to Use *MathScape* with Chapter 7

The unit *Buyer Beware* can be used to enhance Lessons 7-2 and 7-3.

- **Introduce** ⟶ Before you start **Lesson 7-2**, you can introduce proportions by using the activities on pages 18–19.

- **Reinforce** ⟶ After you complete **Lesson 7-3**, you can use the activities on pages 26–33 to provide additional practice with percents.

RTI (Response to Intervention)

① On-Level Instruction Use the *Math Connects* program as instruction for your on-level students.

② Strategic Intervention For options to instruct struggling students, refer to the Diagnostic Assessment table on page 341.

③ Intensive Intervention *Math Triumphs* can provide intensive intervention for students who are two or more grade levels behind.

Diagnose student readiness with the Quick Check and Quick Review on page 341. Then use *Math Triumphs* to accelerate their achievment.

Applying Percents

Prerequisite Skill	*Math Triumphs*
Percentages	Ch. 3

Practice and Review

Quick Review Math Handbook* is Glencoe's mathematical handbook for students and parents.

Hot Words includes a glossary of terms.

Hot Topics consists of two parts:

- explanations of key mathematical concepts
- exercises to check students' understanding.

Lesson	Hot Topics Section	Lesson	Hot Topics Section
7-1	2•8, 2•9	7-6	2•8, 6•5
7-2	2•8, 6•5	7-7	2•8, 6•5
7-3	2•8	7-8	2•8, 9•4
7-4	2•8, 6•5		

*Also available in Spanish

FOLDABLES™
Study Organizer

Dinah Zike's Foldables

Focus This Foldable is designed to help students organize their notes about percents.

Teach Have students make the Foldable and label the sections. Tell them that they should record the main ideas and key terms of each lesson in the appropriate section. Encourage students also to include examples, explaining how their examples illustrate the lesson's main ideas.

When to Use It As students work through each lesson, remind them to take notes, define terms, and write examples in the corresponding sections of their Foldables.

A version of a completed Foldable is shown on p. 384.

Differentiated Instruction

CRM Student-Built Glossary, p. 1

Students complete the chart by providing the definition of each term and an example as they progress through Chapter 7.

This study tool can be used to review for the chapter test.

Materials Needed for Chapter 7

- grid paper (Explore 7-1)
- colored pencils (Explore 7-1)
- paper strips (Lesson 7-6)
- scissors (Lesson 7-6)
- tape (Lesson 7-6)
- computers with spreadsheet program (Extend 7-8)

CHAPTER
7

Applying Percents

BIG Idea

- Solve percent problems using ratios and proportionalities.

Key Vocabulary

percent equation (p. 361)
percent of change (p. 369)
percent proportion (p. 350)

🌐 **Real-World Link**

Boogie Boards You can buy a boogie board in Myrtle Beach, South Carolina, for $25. You will also pay a sales tax of 5%.

FOLDABLES®
Study Organizer

Applying Percents Make this Foldable to help you organize your notes. Begin with a piece of 11" by 17" paper.

❶ **Fold** the paper in half lengthwise.

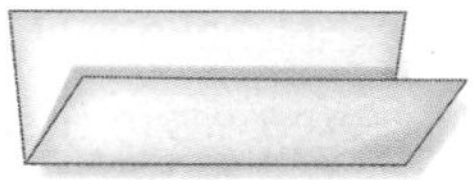

❷ **Open** and refold the paper into fourths along the opposite axis.

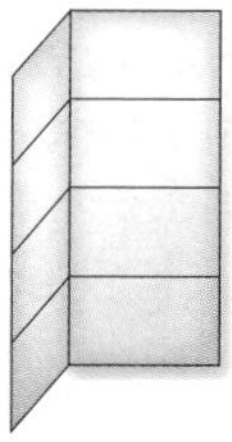

❸ **Trace** along the fold lines and label each section with a lesson title or number.

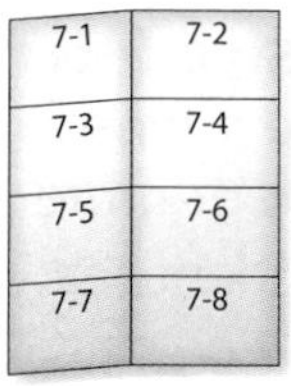

7-1	7-2
7-3	7-4
7-5	7-6
7-7	7-8

340 Chapter 7 Applying Percents

Diagnose Readiness You have two options for checking Prerequisite Skills.

Option 1

Option 2

Math Online > Take the Online Readiness Quiz at glencoe.com.

Take the Quick Quiz below. Refer to the Quick Review for help.

QUICK Quiz

(Used in Lesson 7-8)
Multiply. (Prior Grade)

1. $300 \times 0.02 \times 8$ **48**
2. $85 \times 0.25 \times 3$ **63.75**
3. $560 \times 0.6 \times 4.5$ **1,512**
4. $154 \times 0.12 \times 5$ **92.4**
5. **MONEY** If Nicole saves $0.05 every day, how much money will she have in 3 years? (Prior Grade) **$54.75**

(Used in Lessons 7-6 and 7-7)
Simplify. Write as a decimal. (Prior Grade)

6. $\frac{22-8}{8}$ **1.75**
7. $\frac{50-33}{50}$ **0.34**
8. $\frac{35-7}{35}$ **0.8**
9. **BASEBALL CARDS** Tim has 56 baseball cards. He gives 14 of them away. What decimal represents the portion he has left? (Prior Grade) **0.75**

(Used in Lessons 7-2 and 7-5)
ALGEBRA Solve. Round to the nearest tenth if necessary. (Lesson 3-3)

10. $0.4m = 52$ **130**
11. $21 = 0.28a$ **75**
12. $13 = 0.06s$ **216.7**
13. $0.95z = 37$ **38.9**

(Used in Lesson 7-5)
Write each percent as a decimal.
(Lesson 4-7)

14. 40% **0.4**
15. 17% **0.17**
16. 110% **1.1**
17. 157% **1.57**
18. 3.25% **0.0325**
19. 7.5% **0.075**
20. **FOOD** Approximately 92% of a watermelon is water. What decimal represents this amount? (Lesson 4-7) **0.92**

QUICK Review

Example 1

Evaluate $240 \times 0.03 \times 5$.

$240 \times 0.03 \times 5$
$= 7.2 \times 5$ Multiply 240 by 0.03.
$= 36$ Simplify.

Example 2

Simplify $\frac{17-8}{8}$. Write as a decimal.

$\frac{17-8}{8} = \frac{9}{8}$ Subtract 8 from 17.

$= 1.125$ Divide 9 by 8.

Example 3

Solve $0.6k = 7.8$

$0.6k = 7.8$ Write the equation.
$k = 13$ Divide each side by 0.6.

Example 4

Write 9.8% as a decimal.

$9.8\% = 0.098$ Move the decimal point two places to the left and remove the percent symbol.

✓ Diagnostic Assessment

Exercises	State/Local Standards	Strategic Intervention
1–5		SE Concepts and Skills Bank, p. 736
6–9		SE Review Lesson 4-5, pp. 196–200
10–13		SE Review Lesson 3-3, pp. 142–146
14–20		SE Review Lesson 4-7, pp. 206–210

ASSESSMENT PLANNER

✓ Formative Assessment

CRM Anticipation Guide, pp. 7–8
Spotting Preconceived Ideas
Students complete this survey to determine prior knowledge about ideas from Chapter 7. Revisit this worksheet after completing the chapter. Also see page 388.

TE Lesson Activities

- Ticket Out the Door, pp. 354, 360, 365, 382
- Crystal Ball, p. 374
- Name the Math, pp. 348, 378
- Yesterday's News, p. 367

Chapter Checkpoints

SE Mid-Chapter Quiz, p. 368

SE Study Guide and Review, pp. 384–388

SE Test Practice, pp. 390–391

CRM Quizzes, pp. 61 and 62

CRM Standardized Test Practice, pp. 78–80

Math Online > glencoe.com

- Self-Check Quizzes
- Practice Test
- Test Practice

✓ Summative Assessment

SE Chapter Practice Test, p. 389

CRM Mid-Chapter Test, p. 63

CRM Vocabulary Test, p. 64

CRM Extended-Response Test, p. 77

CRM Leveled Chapter Tests, pp. 65–76

💿 ExamView Pro® Assessment Suite

KEY

CRM *Chapter 7 Resource Masters*

SE Student Edition

TE Teacher Edition

💿 CD-ROM

1 Focus

Materials
- grid paper
- colored pencils

Easy-to-Use Manipulatives
Teaching Mathematics with Manipulatives, templates for:
- Quarter Inch Grid, p. 14

Teaching Tip
You may need to remind students that percent means *per 100*, so a percent is a ratio comparing a number to 100.

2 Teach

Activity 1 If students have difficulty finding the units for the left side of the scale (Step 2), ask:
- What is the original price of the backpack?
- How many intervals does the scale have?

Make sure students realize that they need to divide the original price by the number of intervals to get the units of the scale ($50 ÷ 10 = $5).

Tips for New Teachers

Percent Models
Teachers may be familiar with percent models that show 0% at the bottom and 100% at the top. We chose to render these models with 0% at the top and 100% at the bottom so that students can make connections with the set up of the proportions more easily.

Explore 7-1 | **Math Lab**
Percent of a Number

MAIN IDEA

Use a model to find the percent of a number.

Do you enjoy shopping? If so, you may have seen sales or other discounts represented as percents. For example, consider the following situation. A backpack is on sale for 30% off the original price. If the original price of the backpack is $50, how much will you save?

In this situation, you know the percent. You need to find what part of the original price you will save. In this lab, you will use a model to find the percent of a number or *part* of a whole.

ACTIVITY

1 Find 30% of $50 using a model.

STEP 1 Draw a 1-by-10 rectangle as shown on grid paper. Label the units on the right from 0% to 100% as shown.

Part	Percent
	0%
	10%
	20%
	30%
	40%
	50%
	60%
	70%
	80%
	90%
	100%

STEP 2 Since $50 represents the original price, mark equal units from $0 to $50 on the left side of the model as shown.

STEP 3 Draw a line from 30% on the right side to the left side of the model as shown and shade the portion of the rectangle above this line.

Part	Percent
$0	0%
$5	10%
$10	20%
$15	30%
$20	40%
$25	50%
$30	60%
$35	70%
$40	80%
$45	90%
$50	100%

The model shows that 30% of $50 is $15. So, you will save $15.

✓ CHECK Your Progress a–c. See Ch. 7 Answer Appendix for models.

Draw a model to find the percent of each number.
a. 20% of 120 **24**   b. 60% of 70 **42**   c. 90% of 400 **360**

Tips for New Teachers

Decimal Models
Point out to students that the decimal models used in Activities 1 and 2 use intervals of 10%. If students plan to use a decimal model to find a percent of a number that is not divisible by 10 or 5, they may need to modify the intervals on their decimal model or use their decimal model solely for estimation purposes.

Suppose a bicycle is on sale for 35% off the original price. How much will you save if the original price of the bicycle is $180?

ACTIVITY

2 Find 35% of $180 using a model.

STEP 1 Draw a 1-by-10 rectangle as shown on grid paper. Label the units on the right from 0% to 100% as shown.

Part	Percent
	0%
	10%
	20%
	30%
	40%
	50%
	60%
	70%
	80%
	90%
	100%

Study Tip

Equal Units
For the model at the right, use an interval of $18 since $180 ÷ 10 = $18.

STEP 2 The original price is $180. So, mark equal units from $0 to $180 on the left side of the model as shown.

Part	Percent
$0	0%
$18	10%
$36	20%
$54	30%
$72	40%
$90	50%
$108	60%
$126	70%
$144	80%
$162	90%
$180	100%

STEP 3 Draw a line from 35% on the right side to the left side of the model.

The model shows that 35% of $180 is halfway between $54 and $72, or $63.

So, you will save $63.

CHECK Your Progress   d–f. See Ch. 7 Answer Appendix for models.

Draw a model to find the percent of each number. If it is not possible to find an exact answer from the model, estimate.

d. 25% of 140 **35**   e. 7% of 50 **about 4**   f. 0.5% of 20 **less than 1**

ANALYZE THE RESULTS   1–3. See margin.

1. Tell how to determine the units that get labeled on the left side of a percent model.

2. Explain how to find 40% of 30 using a model.

3. **REASONING** How does knowing 10% of a number help you find the percent of the number when the percent is a multiple of 10%?

3 Assess

Formative Assessment

Use Exercise 2 to determine whether students understand how to use a model to find a percent of a number.

Extending the Concept Remind students that they can write a percent as a fraction or a decimal. Ask them how writing a percent as a fraction or a decimal might help them find the percent of a number. They would be able to multiply the number by the fraction or decimal.

Additional Answers

1. Sample answer: Take the original amount and divide by 10. The result gives the interval of the units that get labeled on the left side of the model.

2. Sample answer: Draw a line from 40% on the right side to the left side and estimate the amount on the left side of the model.

3. Sample answer: When you know 10% of a number and how many times 10% is a multiple of the number, you can multiply 10% of the number by how many times 10% is a multiple of the number to find the percent of the number.

7-1 Percent of a Number

PACING: **Regular:** 1.5 periods, **Block:** 1 period

Options for Differentiated Instruction

 = English Language Learner   = Above or Beyond Grade Level   = Struggling Students   = Special Needs

Using Models   **AL**

Use after presenting the Examples.

Have students explain how the model can be used to find 60% of 300.

Sample answer: Each square represents 3. Sixty squares are shaded. So, 60% of 300 is 60 × 3 or 180.

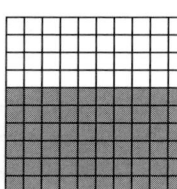

Working in Pairs   **ELL** **SS** **SN**

Use with Check Your Understanding.

Students with difficulty applying skills in an academic situation often are successful expressing what they know on an interpersonal level. Have students work in pairs to solve Exercises 1–7. Then have the pairs form groups of four and compare the steps and the strategies that they used to solve the problems.

Extensions and Challenges   **AL**

Use after students complete Lesson 7-1.

Have students think about the percent problems they solved in Lesson 7-1. Ask them to use what they learned to answer the following questions:

- 45 is what percent of 150? 30%
- 240 is what percent of 400? 60%

Be sure they explain how they determined their answers. Then let them know they will learn the steps for solving problems like these in Lesson 7-2.

Leveled Lesson Resources

Chapter 7 Resource Masters

BL = Below or Approaching Grade Level **OL** = On Grade Level **AL** = Above or Beyond Grade Level **ELL** = English Language Learner

Lesson Reading Guide
p. 9 **BL** **OL** **ELL**

NAME _____ DATE _____ PERIOD _____

7-1 Lesson Reading Guide
Percent of a Number

Get Ready for the Lesson

Read the introduction at the top of page 344 in your textbook.
Write your answers below.

1. Sketch the model and label using decimals instead of percents.

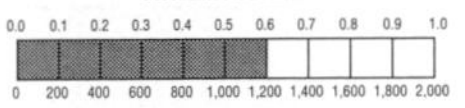

Pet Shelter Fund-Raiser

0.0 0.1 0.2 0.3 0.4 0.5 0.6 0.7 0.8 0.9 1.0

0 200 400 600 800 1,000 1,200 1,400 1,600 1,800 2,000

2. Sketch the model using fractions instead of percents.

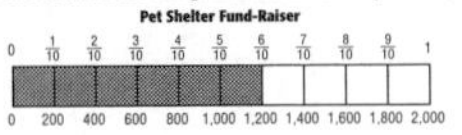

Pet Shelter Fund-Raiser

0 200 400 600 800 1,000 1,200 1,400 1,600 1,800 2,000

3. Use these models to write two multiplication sentences that are
equivalent to 60% of 2,000 = 1,200.
$0.6 \times 2,000 = 1,200$; $\frac{3}{5} \times 2,000 = 1,200$

Read the Lesson

4. What are two methods for finding the percent of a number?
Use a proportion, or use multiplication.

5. When writing a percent as a fraction to solve a percent problem, what is
helpful to do to the percent before solving the problem?
It is helpful to reduce the fraction to lowest terms.

6. What is unusual about the answer to a percent problem where the
percent taken is larger than 100?
The answer is larger than the original number.

Remember What You Learned

7. Suppose one of your friends said to you, "I want to pay for lunch and I
know I'm supposed to leave a 15% tip, but I don't know how to figure out
how much to leave." Write in your own words what you would say to your
friend to explain how to figure out the tip. **Sample answer: Change
15% to a decimal: 0.15. Now, multiply 0.15 by the cost of
lunch. The result is how much should be left for the tip.**

Chapter 7   9   Course 2

Study Guide and Intervention*
p. 10 **BL** **OL** **ELL**

NAME _____ DATE _____ PERIOD _____

7-1 Study Guide and Intervention
Percent of a Number

You can use a proportion or multiplication to find the percent of a number.

Example 1 Find 25% of 80.

$25\% = \frac{25}{100}$ or $\frac{1}{4}$ Write 25% as a fraction, and reduce to lowest terms.

$\frac{1}{4}$ of $80 = \frac{1}{4} \times 80$ or 20 Multiply.

So, 25% of 80 is 20.

Example 2 What number is 15% of 200?

15% of $200 = 15\% \times 200$ Write a multiplication expression.
$= 0.15 \times 200$ Write 15% as a decimal.
$= 30$ Multiply.

So, 15% of 200 is 30.

Exercises

Find each number.

1. Find 20% of 50. **10**
2. What is 55% of $400? **$220**
3. 5% of 1,500 is what number? **75**
4. Find 190% of 20. **38**
5. What is 24% of $500? **$120**
6. 8% of $300 is how much? **$24**
7. What is 12.5% of 60? **7.5**
8. Find 0.2% of 40. **0.08**
9. Find 3% of $800. **$24**
10. What is 0.5% of 180? **0.9**
11. 0.25% of 42 is what number? **0.105**
12. What is 0.02% of 280? **0.056**

Chapter 7   10   Course 2

Skills Practice*
p. 11 **BL** **OL**

NAME _____ DATE _____ PERIOD _____

7-1 Skills Practice
Percent of a Number

Find each number.

1. Find 80% of 80. **64**
2. What is 95% of 600? **570**
3. 35% of 20 is what number? **7**
4. Find 60% of $150. **$90**
5. What is 75% of 240? **180**
6. 380% of 30 is what number? **114**
7. Find 40% of 80. **32**
8. What is 30% of $320? **$96**
9. 12% of 150 is what number? **18**
10. Find 58% of 200. **116**
11. What is 18% of $450? **$81**
12. What is 70% of 1,760? **1,232**
13. Find 92% of 120. **110.4**
14. 45% of 156 is what number? **70.2**
15. What is 12% of 12? **1.44**
16. Find 60% of 264. **158.4**
17. 37.5% of 16 is what number? **6**
18. What is 82.5% of 400? **330**
19. What is 0.25% of 900? **2.25**
20. Find 1.5% of 220. **3.3**

Chapter 7   11   Course 2

Practice*
p. 12 **OL** **AL**

NAME _____ DATE _____ PERIOD _____

7-1 Practice
Percent of a Number

Find each number. Round to the nearest hundredth if necessary.

1. 55% of 140 **77**
2. 40% of 123 **49.2**
3. 37% of $150 **$55.50**
4. 25% of 96 **24**
5. 11% of $333 **$36.63**
6. 99% of 14 **13.86**
7. 140% of 30 **42**
8. 165% of 10 **16.5**
9. 150% of 150 **225**
10. 225% of 16 **36**
11. 106% of $40 **$42.40**
12. 126% of 350 **441**
13. 4.1% of 30 **1.23**
14. 8.9% of 75 **6.68**
15. 24.2% of $120 **$29.04**
16. 97.5% of 80 **78**

17. **SALES** Mr. Redding sells vehicles to 20% of the people that come to the
sales lot. If 65 people came to the lot last month, how many vehicles did
he sell? **13 vehicles**

Find each number. Round to the nearest hundredth if necessary.

18. $\frac{5}{6}$% of 600 **5**
19. $30\frac{1}{2}$% of 3 **0.91**
20. 1,000% of 87 **870**
21. 100% of 56 **56**
22. 0.25% of 150 **0.38**
23. 0.7% of 50 **0.35**

ANALYZE TABLES For Exercises 24–26, use the table that shows
the percents of blood types of 145 donors during a recent
blood drive.

Blood Type	Percent
O	45%
A	40%
B	11%
AB	4%

24. Write a proportion that can be used to find how many donors
had type B blood. Then solve. Round to the nearest whole if
necessary. $\frac{n}{145} = \frac{11}{100}$; **16 donors**

25. How many donors did *not* have type O blood? Round to the nearest whole
if necessary. **80 donors**

26. Which blood type had less than 10 donors? **Type AB**

Chapter 7   12   Course 2

Word Problem Practice*
p. 13 **OL** **AL**

NAME _____ DATE _____ PERIOD _____

7-1 Word Problem Practice
Percent of a Number

SPORTS For Exercises 1 and 2, use
the graph below. It shows the results
of a poll of 440 ninth grade students.
Round answers to the nearest whole
number.

Favorite Sports of Students

25.2% 23.4% 11.8% 8.9% 7.4% 7.4% 5.9%

Basketball Hockey Soccer Football Volleyball Baseball Other

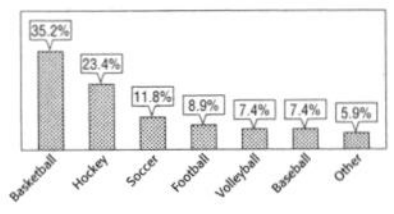

PETS For Exercises 3 and 4, use the
table below. It shows the pet ownership
in Los Angeles, California. Assume that
the same percents apply to a town of
1,650 households. Round answers to the
nearest whole number.

	Pets in Household	Percent
	at least one dog or cat	26.7
	at least one dog	19.9
	at least one cat	13
	at least one dog and one cat	6.1

1. Write the percent as a fraction to find
how many students surveyed chose
hockey as their favorite sport. Solve.
103 students

2. How many students surveyed chose
basketball as their favorite sport?
155 students

3. Write the percent as a decimal to find
how many households have at least
one dog. Solve.
328 households

4. How many households have at least
one dog or cat?
441 households

5. **VOTING** Going into a recent election,
only about 62% of people old enough to
vote were registered. In a community of
about 55,200 eligible voters, how many
people are registered?
34,224 people

6. **COLLEGE** A local college recently
reported that enrollment increased to
108% percent of last year. If enrollment
last year was at 17,113, about how
many students enrolled this year?
Round to the nearest whole number.
18,482 students

Chapter 7   13   Course 2

Enrichment
p. 14 **OL** **AL**

NAME _____ DATE _____ PERIOD _____

7-1 Enrichment

Model Behavior

When a block is painted and then separated into small cubes, some of the
faces of the cubes will have paint on them and some will not.

For each set of blocks determine the percent of cubes that are
painted on the given number of faces.

1. 0 faces **0**
2. 1 face **0**
3. 2 faces **64**
4. 3 faces **32**
5. 4 faces **4**
6. 5 faces **0**
7. 6 faces **0**

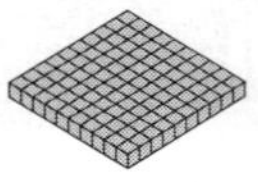

8. 0 faces **0**
9. 1 face **0**
10. 2 faces **0**
11. 3 faces **0**
12. 4 faces **90**
13. 5 faces **10**
14. 6 faces **0**

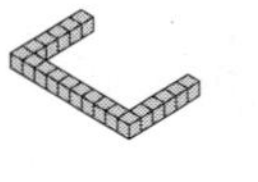

15. 0 faces **0**
16. 1 face **0**
17. 2 faces **0**
18. 3 faces **0**
19. 4 faces **100**
20. 5 faces **0**
21. 6 faces **0**

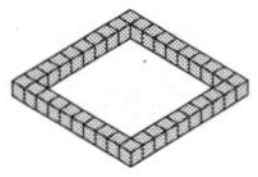

Chapter 7   14   Course 2

Additional Lesson Resources

* Also available in Spanish **ELL**

Transparencies
- *5-Minute Check Transparency*, Lesson 7-1

Other Print Products
- *Teaching Mathematics with Manipulatives*
- *Noteables™ Interactive Study Notebook with Foldables™*

Teacher Tech Tools
- *Interactive Classroom CD-ROM*, Lesson 7-1
- *AssignmentWorks*, Lesson 7-1

Student Tech Tools
glencoe.com
- Extra Examples, Chapter 7, Lesson 1
- Self-Check Quiz, Chapter 7, Lesson 1

1 Focus

Vertical Alignment

Before Lesson 7-1
Interpret percents as a part of a hundred; find decimal and percent equivalents for common fractions and explain why they represent the same value; compute a given percent of a whole number

Lesson 7-1
Calculate given percentages of quantities and solve problems

After Lesson 7-1
Convert fractions to decimals and percents and use these representations in estimations, computations, and applications; solve problems that involve discounts, markups, commissions, and profit and compute simple and compound interest

2 Teach

Scaffolding Questions

Ask:
- When would a percent be greater than one? When the percent is greater than 100%.

- If you multiplied a number by a percent less than 100%, would the result be less than or greater than the original number? less than

- What would you expect if the number you multiply by is greater than 100%? The result would be greater than the original number.

- What decimal is equivalent to 75%? 0.75

- What decimal is equivalent to 65%? 0.65

- What decimal is equivalent to 140%? 1.40

7-1 # Percent of a Number

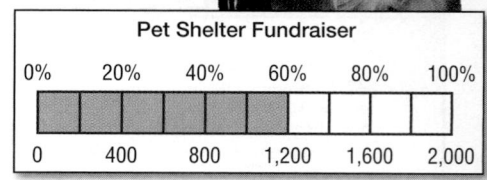

MAIN IDEA

Find the percent of a number.

Math Online

glencoe.com
- Extra Examples
- Personal Tutor
- Self-Check Quiz

▷ **GET READY for the Lesson**

PETS Some students are collecting money for a local pet shelter. The model shows that they have raised 60% of their $2,000 goal or $1,200.

Pet Shelter Fundraiser

0%	20%	40%	60%	80%	100%

| 0 | 400 | 800 | 1,200 | 1,600 | 2,000 |

1. Sketch the model and label using decimals instead of percents.
2. Sketch the model using fractions instead of percents.
3. Use these models to write two multiplication sentences that are equivalent to 60% of 2,000 = 1,200. **1–3. See Ch. 7 Answer Appendix.**

To find the percent of a number such as 60% of 2,000, you can use one of the following methods.

- Write the percent as a fraction and then multiply, or
- Write the percent as a decimal and then multiply.

EXAMPLE Find the Percent of a Number

① **Find 5% of 300.**

To find 5% of 300, you can use either method.

METHOD 1 Write the percent as a fraction.

$5\% = \frac{5}{100}$ or $\frac{1}{20}$

$\frac{1}{20}$ of 300 = $\frac{1}{20} \times 300$ or 15

METHOD 2 Write the percent as a decimal.

$5\% = \frac{5}{100}$ or 0.05

0.05 of 300 = 0.05 × 300 or 15

So, 5% of 300 is 15.

✔ **CHOOSE Your Method**

Find the percent of each number.
a. 40% of 70 **28**   b. 15% of 100 **15**   c. 55% of 160 **88**

 Formative Assessment

Use the Check Your Progress exercises after each Example to determine students' understanding of concepts.

EXAMPLE Use Percents Greater Than 100%

② Find 120% of 75.

METHOD 1   Write the percent as a fraction.

$$120\% = \frac{120}{100} \text{ or } \frac{6}{5}$$

$$\frac{6}{5} \text{ of } 75 = \frac{6}{5} \times 75$$

$$= \frac{6}{5} \times \frac{75}{1} \text{ or } 90$$

METHOD 2   Write the percent as a decimal.

$$120\% = \frac{120}{100} \text{ or } 1.2$$

$$1.2 \text{ of } 75 = 1.2 \times 75 \text{ or } 90$$

So, 120% of 75 is 90. Use a model to check the answer.

✓ **CHOOSE** Your Method

Find each number.

d. 150% of 20 **30**   e. 160% of 35 **56**

Real-World EXAMPLE

③ ANALYZE GRAPHS Refer to the graph. If 275 students took the survey, how many can be expected to have 3 televisions each in their houses?

To find 23% of 275, write the percent as a decimal. Then multiply.

$$23\% \text{ of } 275 = 23\% \times 275$$

$$= 0.23 \times 275$$

$$= 63.25$$

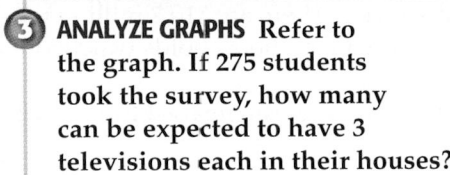

Survey Results of Number of Televisions in House

0	2%
1	9%
2	17%
3	23%
4	20%
More than 4	25%

 = 5%

So, about 63 students can be expected to have 3 televisions each in their houses.

✓ **CHECK** Your Progress

f. **ANALYZE GRAPHS** Refer to the graph above. Suppose 455 students took the survey. How many can be expected to have more than 4 televisions each in their houses? **about 114 students**

ADDITIONAL EXAMPLES

① Find 8% of 125. 10

② Find 125% of 64. 80

③ LANGUAGES The graph below shows that 30% of the people in a community speak Spanish as their first language. If a community has 800 people, how many people can be expected to speak Spanish as their first language? 240

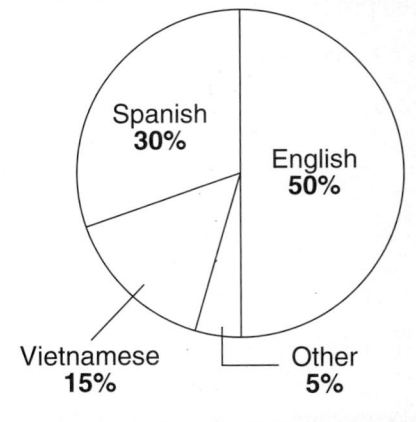

Spanish **30%**

English **50%**

Vietnamese **15%**

Other **5%**

Writing Percents

Tips for New Teachers

You may wish to remind students how to write a percent as a decimal (move the decimal point two places to the left and remove the percent sign).

 3 Practice

Formative Assessment

Use Exercises 1–7 to check for understanding.

Then use the chart at the bottom of this page to customize your assignments for students.

Intervention

You may wish to use the Study Guide and Intervention Master on page 10 of the *Chapter 7 Resource Masters* for additional reinforcement.

Odd/Even Assignments

Exercises 8–27 are structured so that students practice the same concepts whether they are assigned odd or even problems.

✓ CHECK Your Understanding   ★ indicates multi-step problem

Find each number. Round to the nearest tenth if necessary.

Examples 1–2
(pp. 344–345)

1. 8% of 50 **4**
2. 95% of 40 **38**
3. 42% of 263 **110.5**
4. 110% of 70 **77**
5. 115% of 20 **23**
6. 130% of 78 **101.4**

Example 3
(p. 345)

7. **TAXES** Mackenzie wants to buy a new backpack that costs $50. If the tax rate is 6.5%, how much tax will she pay when she buys the backpack? **$3.25**

▶ Practice and Problem Solving

HOMEWORK HELP

For Exercises	See Examples
8–13, 20–25	1
14–19	2
26–27	3

Exercise Levels
A: 8–27
B: 28–52
C: 53–56

Find each number. Round to the nearest tenth if necessary.

8. 65% of 186 **120.9**
9. 45% of $432 **$194.40**
10. 23% of $640 **$147.20**
11. 54% of 85 **45.9**
12. 12% of $230 **$27.60**
13. 98% of 15 **14.7**
14. 130% of 20 **26**
15. 175% of 10 **17.5**
16. 150% of 128 **192**
17. 250% of 25 **62.5**
18. 108% of $50 **$54**
19. 116% of $250 **$290**
20. 3.2% of 40 **1.3**
21. 5.4% of 65 **3.5**
22. 23.5% of 128 **30.1**
23. 75.2% of 130 **97.8**
24. 67.5% of 76 **51.3**
25. 18.5% of 500 **92.5**

26. **BASEBALL** Tomás got on base 60% of the times he was up to bat. If he was up to bat 5 times, how many times did he get on base? **3**

27. **TELEVISION** In a recent year, 17.7% of households watched the finals of a popular reality series. There are 110.2 million television households in the United States. How many households watched the finals? **about 19.5 million**

Find each number. Round to the nearest hundredth if necessary.

28. $\frac{4}{5}$% of 500 **4**
29. $5\frac{1}{2}$% of 60 **3.3**
30. $20\frac{1}{4}$% of 3 **0.61**
31. 1,000% of 99 **990**
32. 100% of 79 **79**
33. 520% of 100 **520**
34. 0.15% of 250 **0.38**
35. 0.3% of 80 **0.24**
36. 0.28% of 50 **0.14**

★ 37. **TIPPING** A customer wants to tip 15% of the restaurant bill. How much change should there be after the tip if the customer pays with a $50 bill? **$9.75**

Sal's Bistro	
Herbed Salmon	$16.25
Chicken Pasta	15.25
Iced Tea	1.75
Iced Tea	1.75
Total	$35.00

★ 38. **INTERNET** A family pays $19 each month for Internet access. Next month, the cost will increase 5%. After this increase, what will be the cost for the Internet access? **$19.95**

★ 39. **BUSINESS** A store sells a certain brand of a lawn mower for $275. Next year, the cost of the lawn mower will increase by 8%. What will be the cost of the lawn mower next year? **$297**

DIFFERENTIATED HOMEWORK OPTIONS

Level	Assignment	Two-Day Option	
BL Basic	8–27, 53, 54, 56–67	9–27 odd, 57, 58	8–26 even, 53, 54, 56, 59–67
OL Core	9–35 odd, 37–54, 56–67	8–27, 57, 58	28–54, 56, 59–67
AL Advanced/Pre-AP	28–63 (optional: 64–67)		

ANALYZE GRAPHS For Exercises 40–42, use the graph below that shows the results of a poll of 2,632 listeners. Round to the nearest whole number.

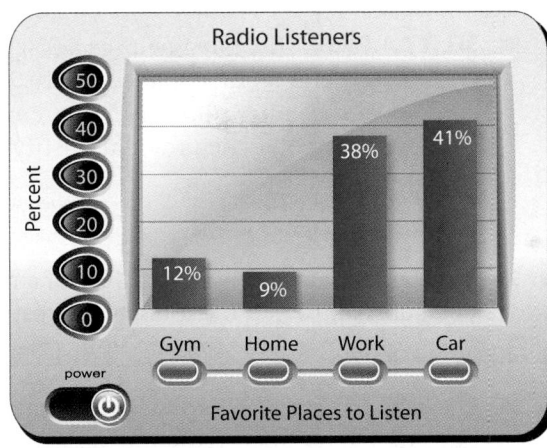

Radio Listeners

Favorite Places to Listen

40. How many people listen to the radio during work? **1,000**

41. How many people like to listen to the radio while they are at the gym? **316**

42. Determine how many more people listen to the radio in the car than at home. **842**

Use mental math to find each percent. Justify your answer. **43–45. See margin.**

43. 53% of 60   44. 24% of 48   45. 75% of 19

ANALYZE GRAPHS For Exercises 46–49, use the graph that shows the results of a favorite fruit survey.

46. How many people were surveyed? **250**

47. Of those surveyed, how many people prefer peaches? **80**

48. Which type of fruit did more than 100 people prefer? **berries**

49. Of those surveyed, how many people did *not* prefer cherries? Explain how you arrived at the answer. **See margin.**

250 people were asked which type of fruit they preferred.

44%   32%   24%

Berries   Peaches   Cherries

★ 50. **SHOPPING** The Leather Depot sells a certain leather coat for $179.99. If sales tax is 6.25%, what will be the approximate total cost of the coat?
Sample answer: about $191.24

★ 51. **SCHOOL** Suppose there are 20 questions on a multiple-choice test. If 25% of the answers are choice B, how many of the answers are *not* choice B? **15**

★ 52. **COMMISSION** In addition to her salary, Ms. Lopez earns a 3% *commission*, or fee paid based on a percent of her sales, on every vacation package that she sells. One day, she sold the three vacation packages shown. What was her total commission? **$241.50**

Package #1	Package #2	Package #3
$2,375	$3,950	$1,725

Lesson 7-1 Percent of a Number **347**

Additional Answers

43. Sample answer: 53% of 60 →
    50% × 60 or $\frac{1}{2}$ × 60 = 30

44. Sample answer: 24% of 48 →
    25% × 48 or $\frac{1}{4}$ × 48 = 12

45. Sample answer: 75% of 19 →
    75% × 20 or $\frac{3}{4}$ × 20 = 15

49. Sample answer: 24% × 250 or 60 people prefer cherries. So, 250 − 60 or 190 people did not prefer cherries.

Differentiated Instruction

Kinesthetic Learners Separate students into groups of three or four and give several index cards to each group. Have the members of each group write a percent on each index card. Students should then shuffle the cards, place them facedown in the middle, and turn the top card over. Each person uses a pencil and paper, calculator, or mental math to find the equivalent fraction or decimal. The first student to find an equivalent number gets a point. The first student with 10 points wins.

Name the Math Write a problem such as 1.4% of 25 on the board. Have students solve the problem and tell what mathematical procedures they used. Encourage them to use mental math.

Foldables™ Follow-Up

Remind students to record both methods for finding a percent of a number in their Foldables table. Encourage students to use an original problem and explain how and why they might change a percent to a decimal or a fraction.

Additional Answer

53. Sample answer: Determine the number of questions answered correctly on a test and find how much to tip a restaurant server.

H.O.T. Problems

54. Sample answer: Estimation; $25 + $20 = $45. A 7% sales tax would add $3.15. Since $45 + $3.15 = $48.15, the gift card will cover the entire purchase.
55. Less than the original number; you are subtracting 10% of a greater number.

53. **OPEN ENDED** Give two examples of real-world situations in your life in which you would find the percent of a number. **See margin.**

54. **SELECT A TECHNIQUE** Maggie uses a $50 gift card to buy a pair of shoes that costs $24.99 and a purse that costs $19.99. If the tax rate is 7%, will the gift card cover the entire purchase? Select and use one or more of the following techniques to solve the problem. Justify your selection(s).

| mental math | number sense | estimation |

55. **CHALLENGE** Suppose you add 10% of a number to the number, and then you subtract 10% of the total. Is the result *greater than*, *less than*, or *equal to* the original number? Explain your reasoning.

56. **WRITING IN MATH** Explain which method you prefer to use to find the percent of a number: write the percent as a fraction or write the percent as a decimal. Explain your reasoning. **See students' work.**

TEST PRACTICE

57. Reggie has memorized 60% of the 50 state capitals for a social studies test. How many more capitals does Reggie need to memorize before the test? **C**

   A 35   C 20

   B 30   D 18

58. **SHORT RESPONSE** Tanner has 200 baseball cards. Of those, 42% are in mint condition. How many of the cards are *not* in mint condition? **116**

Spiral Review

59. **PETS** In Rebecca's class, 17 out of 24 students have pets. What percent of the students have pets? Round to the nearest percent. (Lesson 6-9) **71%**

60. **MODELS** On a scale model of a building, 3 in. = 12 ft. If the model is 8 inches tall, how tall is the actual building? (Lesson 6-8) **32 ft**

Add or subtract. Write in simplest form. (Lesson 6-2)

61. $\frac{7}{10} - \frac{1}{10}$ **$\frac{3}{5}$**

62. $\frac{20}{21} - \frac{3}{7}$ **$\frac{11}{21}$**

63. $\frac{5}{6} - \frac{1}{8}$ **$\frac{17}{24}$**

64. **ALGEBRA** What are the next three numbers in the pattern 3, 10, 17, 24, …? (Lesson 1-9)

   31, 38, 45

GET READY for the Next Lesson

PREREQUISITE SKILL Solve each equation. (Lesson 3-3)

65. $12b = 144$ **12**

66. $9x = 630$ **70**

67. $8,100 = 100k$ **81**

Meaning of Percent

When you solve percent problems, look for three parts: the *part,* the *whole,* and the *percent.* Consider this example.

The table at the right shows the results of a survey about favorite flavor of sugarless gum.

Favorite Flavor of Sugarless Gum	
Flavor	**Number**
Cinnamon	10
Peppermint	18
Watermelon	12
Total	40

- **Part**

  Ten students chose cinnamon as their favorite.

- **Whole**

  Forty students were surveyed.

- **Percent**

  25% of the students who were surveyed (10 out of 40) chose cinnamon as their favorite.

Using all three parts, 25% of 40 is 10.

PRACTICE

Identify each statement as the *part,* the *whole,* or the *percent.* Then write a sentence using all three parts.

1. The table at the right shows the results of a survey about which "bugs" people dislike most.
   a. Fifty people were surveyed. **whole**
   b. 60% disliked spiders the most. **percent**
   c. Thirty people disliked spiders.
   part; 60% of 50 is 30.

Least Favorite "Bug"	
Kind	**Number**
Centipede	2
Cockroach	18
Spider	30
Total	50

2. Suppose you find a sale at the mall.

   a. Everything was 20% off. **percent**
   b. The original price of a jacket was $30. **whole**
   c. You saved $6. **part; 20% of 30 is 6.**

3. You and your family are eating at a restaurant.
   a. The meal cost $34. **whole**
   b. You want to leave a tip of 15%. **percent**
   c. The tip is $5.10. **part; 15% of 34 is 5.10.**

4. Your sister plays basketball.
   a. She usually makes 75% of her free throws. **percent**
   b. In the last game, she made 6 free throws. **part**
   c. She had 8 free throws. **whole; 75% of 8 is 6.**

For students to master percents, they need to understand that a percent is a ratio of one number (or quantity) to another. In this Activity, students learn to identify percents, the numbers that make up the percents' ratios, and their relationship.

Make sure everyone understands the relationship among a percent, a whole, and a part (a percent **of** a whole **is** a part). After students have completed one or two of the exercises, you might want to write sample sentences on the board to make sure everyone understands the relationship. For example:

- *A*% **of** whole *B* **is** part *C*
- Part *C* **is** *A*% **of** whole *B*

Remind students that yesterday's lesson was about finding the percent of a number. Have students write how yesterday's material helped them with this reading activity.

7-2 The Percent Proportion

PACING: **Regular:** 1 period, **Block:** 0.5 period

Options for Differentiated Instruction

ELL = English Language Learner   AL = Above or Beyond Grade Level   SS = Struggling Students   SN = Special Needs

Creating a Template ELL SS

Use with the Exercises.

Explain to students that they can use a percent proportion to find a missing part, whole, or percent. Have them create the following template. Provide clear sheet protectors so students can use the template to help them complete the exercises.

Find the percent: $\frac{\text{part} \rightarrow \square}{\text{whole} \rightarrow \square} = \left.\frac{n}{100}\right\}$ percent

Find the part: $\frac{\text{part} \rightarrow n}{\text{whole} \rightarrow \square} = \left.\frac{\square}{100}\right\}$ percent

Find the whole: $\frac{\text{part} \rightarrow \square}{\text{whole} \rightarrow n} = \left.\frac{\square}{100}\right\}$ percent

For students with fine motor skills difficulties, provide a typed version of the template, making sure that the boxes are large enough for students to write in.

Creating a Checklist ELL SS SN

Use before assigning the Exercises.

Have students create a checklist they can use for solving proportions. A sample checklist is shown below.

- Identify what I need to find: *Percent*, *Part*, or *Whole*.
- Fill in the proportion with the given information.
- Find the cross products.
- Solve.

Leveled Lesson Resources

Chapter 7 Resource Masters

BL = Below or Approaching Grade Level   **OL** = On Grade Level   **AL** = Above or Beyond Grade Level   **ELL** = English Language Learner

---

Lesson Reading Guide
p. 16 **BL** **OL** **ELL**

7-2 Lesson Reading Guide
The Percent Proportion

Get Ready for the Lesson

Read the introduction at the top of page 350 in your textbook. Write your answers below.

1. Write the ratio of tire weight to total weight as a fraction. $\frac{3,600}{11,000}$

2. Use a calculator to write the fraction as a decimal to the nearest hundredth. **0.33**

3. What percent of the monster truck's weight are the tires? **33%**

Read the Lesson

4. What is a percent proportion? **a proportion that compares part of a quantity to the whole quantity using a percent**

5. Describe how the percent proportion is set up. **The part of the quantity is compared to the whole quantity as one ratio and the second ratio is the equivalent percent written over 100.**

6. Select the information that can be found by solving each percent problem.

c What number is 30% of 15?   a. Find the whole.

a 18 is 65% of what number?   b. Find the percent.

b What percent of 40 is 17?   c. Find the part.

Remember What You Learned

7. Write an example of each type of percent problem in the table below. (Be sure the examples are different from the ones given in the lesson and on this page.) Write the example in words and set up the correct proportion for each example. **Sample answer:**

Type	Example	Proportion
Find the Percent	What percent of 12 is 6?	$\frac{6}{12} = \frac{p}{100}$
Find the Part	What number is 45% of 60?	$\frac{a}{60} = \frac{45}{100}$
Find the Whole	80 is 60% of what number?	$\frac{80}{b} = \frac{60}{100}$

Chapter 7   16   Course 2

Study Guide and Intervention*
p. 17 **BL** **OL** **ELL**

7-2 Study Guide and Intervention
The Percent Proportion

A percent proportion compares part of a quantity to a whole quantity for one ratio and lists the percent as a number over 100 for the other ratio. $\frac{part}{whole} = \frac{percent}{100}$

Example 1 What percent of 24 is 18?

$\frac{part}{whole} = \frac{percent}{100}$ Percent proportion

Let n% represent the percent.

$\frac{18}{24} = \frac{n}{100}$ Write the proportion.

$18 \times 100 = 24 \times n$ Find the cross products.

$1,800 = 24n$ Simplify.

$\frac{1,800}{24} = \frac{24n}{24}$ Divide each side by 24.

$75 = n$

So, 18 is 75% of 24.

Example 2 What number is 60% of 150?

$\frac{part}{whole} = \frac{percent}{100}$ Percent proportion

Let a represent the part.

$\frac{a}{150} = \frac{60}{100}$ Write the proportion.

$a \times 100 = 150 \times 60$ Find the cross products.

$100a = 9,000$ Simplify.

$\frac{100a}{100} = \frac{9,000}{100}$ Divide each side by 24.

$a = 90$

So, 90 is 60% of 150.

Exercises

Find each number. Round to the nearest tenth if necessary.

1. What number is 25% of 20? **5**
2. What percent of 50 is 20? **40%**
3. 30 is 75% of what number? **40**
4. 40% of what number is 36? **90**
5. What number is 20% of 625? **125**
6. 12 is what percent of 30? **40%**

Chapter 7   17   Course 2

Skills Practice*
p. 18 **BL** **OL**

7-2 Skills Practice
The Percent Proportion

Find each number. Round to the nearest tenth if necessary.

1. 50 is 20% of what number? **250**
2. What percent of 20 is 4? **20%**
3. What number is 70% of 250? **175**
4. 10 is 5% of what number? **200**
5. What number is 45% of 180? **81**
6. 40% of what number is 82? **205**
7. What percent of 90 is 36? **40%**
8. 60 is 25% of what number? **240**
9. What number is 32% of 1,000? **320**
10. What percent of 125 is 5? **4%**
11. 73 is 20% of what number? **365**
12. 57% of 109 is what number? **62.1**
13. What percent of 185 is 35? **18.9%**
14. 25 is what percent of 365? **6.8%**
15. 85% of 190 is what number? **161.5**
16. 12.5 is 25% of what number? **50**
17. What percent of 128 is 24? **18.8%**
18. 5.25% of 170 is what number? **8.9**
19. What is 82% of 230? **188.6**
20. What percent of 49 is 7? **14.3%**

Chapter 7   18   Course 2

Practice*
p. 19 **OL** **AL**

7-2 Practice
The Percent Proportion

Find each number. Round to the nearest tenth if necessary.

1. What percent of 65 is 13? **20%**
2. 84 is what percent of $50? **8%**
3. What number is 35% of 22? **7.7**
4. 14% of 81 is what number? **11.34 ≈ 11.3**
5. 13 is 26% of what number? **50**
6. 55 is 40% of what number? **137.5**
7. What percent of 45 is 72? **160%**
8. 1% of what number is 7? **700**
9. 33 is 50% of what number? **66**
10. What number is 3% of 100? **3**
11. What percent of 200 is 0.5? **0.25% ≈ 0.3%**
12. What number is 0.4% of 20? **0.08 ≈ 0.1**
13. What number is 6.1% of 60? **3.66 ≈ 3.7**
14. What percent of 34 is 34? **100%**
15. 10.4% of what number is 13? **125**

16. **ALLOWANCE** Monica has $3 in her wallet. If this is 10% of her monthly allowance, what is her monthly allowance? **$30**

17. **WEDDING** Of the 125 guests invited to a wedding, 104 attended the wedding. What percent of the invited guests attended the wedding? **83.2%**

18. **CAMERA** The memory card on a digital camera can hold about 430 pictures. Melcher used 18% of the memory card while taking pictures at a family reunion. About how many pictures did Melcher take at the family reunion? Round to the nearest whole number. **77 pictures**

OCEANS For Exercises 19 and 20, use the table shown.

Ocean	Area (square miles)
Pacific	64 million
Atlantic	32 million
Indian	25 million

Source: *World Atlas*

19. The area of the Indian Ocean is what percent of the area of the Pacific Ocean? Round to the nearest whole percent. **39%**

20. If the area of the Arctic Ocean is 16% of the area of the Atlantic Ocean, what is the area of the Arctic Ocean? Round to the nearest whole million. **5 million square miles**

Chapter 7   19   Course 2

Word Problem Practice*
p. 20 **OL** **AL**

7-2 Word Problem Practice
The Percent Proportion

1. **DRIVING** David installed a device on his car that guaranteed to increase his gas mileage by 15%. He currently gets 22 miles per gallon. How much will the gas mileage increase after installing the device? **3.3 mi per gal**

2. **POPULATION** The number of students at Marita's school decreased to 98% of last year's number. Currently, there are 1,170 students. How many students were there last year? Round to the nearest whole number. **1,194 students**

3. **VOTING** Yolanda's club has 35 members. Its rules require that 60% of them must be present for any vote. At least how many members must be present to have a vote? **21 members**

4. **GARBAGE** This month, Chun's office produced 690 pounds of garbage. Chun wants to reduce the weight of garbage produced to 85% of the weight produced this month. What is the target weight for the garbage produced next month? **586.5 lb**

5. **SALARIES** Alma just received a 6% raise in salary. Before the raise, she was making $52,000 per year. How much more will Alma earn next year? **$3,120**

6. **SPORTS** Sally's soccer team played 25 games and won 17 of them. What percent did the team win? **68%**

Chapter 7   20   Course 2

Enrichment
p. 21 **OL** **AL**

7-2 Enrichment

Made in the Shade

To shade 25% of the figure below, ask yourself how many of the eight squares need to be shaded. Then use the percent proportion to find the answer.

$\frac{x}{8} = \frac{25}{100}$

$100x = 8 \times 25$

$\frac{100x}{100} = \frac{200}{100}$

$x = 2$

If you shade two squares, you have shaded 25% of the figure.

Shade the indicated percent of each diagram.

1. Shade 40%.
2. Shade 37.5%.
3. Shade $16\frac{2}{3}$%.

Shade the indicated percent of each diagram. You will need to divide the squares in each diagram into smaller squares.

4. Shade 30%.
5. Shade 62.5%.
6. Shade 27.5%.
7. Shade 28.125%.

Chapter 7   21   Course 2

Additional Lesson Resources

* Also available in Spanish **ELL**

Transparencies
- *5-Minute Check Transparency*, Lesson 7-2

Other Print Products
- *Noteables™ Interactive Study Notebook with Foldables™*

Teacher Tech Tools
- *Interactive Classroom CD-ROM*, Lesson 7-2
- *AssignmentWorks*, Lesson 7-2

Student Tech Tools
glencoe.com
- Extra Examples, Chapter 7, Lesson 2
- Self-Check Quiz, Chapter 7, Lesson 2

1 Focus

Vertical Alignment

Before Lesson 7-2
Interpret percents as a part of a hundred; find decimal and percent equivalents for common fractions and explain why they represent the same value; compute a given percent of a whole number

Lesson 7-2
Use proportions to solve problems; calculate given percentages of quantities and solve problems

After Lesson 7-2
Convert fractions to decimals and percents and use these representations in estimations, computations, and applications; solve problems that involve discounts, markups, commissions, and profit and compute simple and compound interest

2 Teach

Scaffolding Questions

Ask:

• How can you write a percent that is greater than 100 as a fraction? write the percent in the numerator and write one hundred in the denominator

• Will the fraction be less than or greater than one? The fraction will be greater than 1.

 Formative Assessment

Use the Check Your Progress exercises after each Example to determine students' understanding of concepts.

MAIN IDEA
Solve problems using the percent proportion.

New Vocabulary
percent proportion

Math Online

glencoe.com

• Extra Examples
• Personal Tutor
• Self-Check Quiz
• Reading in the Content Area

▶ **GET READY for the Lesson**

MONSTER TRUCKS The tires on a monster truck weigh approximately 3,600 pounds. The entire truck weighs about 11,000 pounds.

1. Write the ratio of tire weight to total weight as a fraction. $\frac{3,600}{11,000}$

2. Use a calculator to write the fraction as a decimal to the nearest hundredth. **0.33**

3. What percent of the monster truck's weight is the tires? **33%**

In a **percent proportion**, one ratio or fraction compares part of a quantity to the whole quantity, also called the *base*. The other ratio is the equivalent percent written as a fraction with a denominator of 100.

4 out of **5** is **80%**.

$$\text{part} \rightarrow \frac{4}{5} = \frac{80}{100} \Big\} \text{ percent}$$
$$\text{whole} \rightarrow$$

When given two of these pieces of information—part, whole, or percent—you can use the proportion to find the missing information.

 EXAMPLE Find the Percent

① What percent of $15 is $9?

The number 15 comes after the word *of*, so the whole is 15. You are asked to find the percent, so the part is the remaining number, 9.

Words	What percent of $15 is $9?
▼	
Variable	Let $n\%$ represent the percent.
▼	
Proportion	$\text{part} \rightarrow \frac{9}{15} = \frac{n}{100} \Big\} \text{percent}$ $\text{whole} \rightarrow$

$\frac{9}{15} = \frac{n}{100}$ Write the proportion.

$9 \cdot 100 = 15 \cdot n$ Find the cross products.

$900 = 15n$ Simplify.

$\frac{900}{15} = \frac{15n}{15}$ Divide each side by 15.

$60 = n$

So, $9 is 60% of $15.

ADDITIONAL EXAMPLE

① What percent of 24 is 18? 75%

Additional Examples are also in:

• Noteables™ Interactive Study Notebook with Foldables™

• Interactive Classroom PowerPoint® Presentations

✔ CHECK Your Progress

Find each number. Round to the nearest tenth if necessary.

a. What percent of 25 is 20? **80%**   b. $12.75 is what percent of $50?
25.5%

EXAMPLE Find the Part

② What number is 40% of 120?

The percent is 40%. Since the number 120 comes after the word *of*, the whole is 120. You are asked to find the part.

Words	What number is 40% of 120?
Variable	Let *p* represent the part.
Proportion	$\frac{\text{part} \rightarrow}{\text{whole} \rightarrow} \frac{p}{120} = \frac{40}{100}$ } percent

$\dfrac{p}{120} = \dfrac{40}{100}$ Write the proportion.

$p \cdot 100 = 120 \cdot 40$ Find the cross products.

$100p = 4{,}800$ Simplify.

$\dfrac{100p}{100} = \dfrac{4{,}800}{100}$ Divide each side by 100.

$p = 48$

So, 48 is 40% of 120.

✔ CHECK Your Progress

Find each number. Round to the nearest tenth if necessary.

c. What number is 5% of 60? **3**   d. 12% of 85 is what number? **10.2**

> **Study Tip**
>
> **The Percent Proportion**
> The part usually comes before or after the word *is* and the whole usually comes before or after the word *of*.

EXAMPLE Find the Whole

③ 18 is 25% of what number?

The percent is 25%. The words *what number* come after the word *of*. So, you are asked to find the whole. Thus, 18 is the part.

Words	18 is 25% of what number?
Variable	Let *w* represent the whole.
Proportion	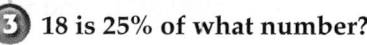 $\frac{\text{part} \rightarrow}{\text{whole} \rightarrow} \frac{18}{w} = \frac{25}{100}$ } percent

(continued on the next page)

Lesson 7-2 The Percent Proportion **351**

> **Focus on Mathematical Content**
>
> A **percent proportion** shows the equality of two ratios. One ratio compares part of a quantity to the whole quantity; the other ratio shows a percent written as a fraction.
>
> To solve a percent proportion, **find the cross products** and simplify.

ADDITIONAL EXAMPLES

② What number is 30% of 150? 45

③ 12 is 80% of what number? 15

Tips for New Teachers

Percent Proportion

To help students remember how the percent proportion is described in word problems, you may wish to write the following version on the board.

$$\frac{\text{is}}{\text{of}} = \frac{\%}{100}$$

4 **BREAKFAST** Sally read the nutrition facts on a box of her favorite cereal. Each cup of the cereal provides 7% of the recommended daily value of potassium. If a cup of the cereal contains 260 milligrams of potassium, what is the recommended daily value of potassium? **3,714 mg**

$$\frac{18}{w} = \frac{25}{100}$$ Write the proportion.

$18 \cdot 100 = w \cdot 25$ Find the cross products.

$1{,}800 = 25w$ Simplify.

$$\frac{1{,}800}{25} = \frac{25w}{25}$$ Divide each side by 25.

$72 = w$

So, 18 is 25% of 72.

✓ **CHECK Your Progress**

Find each number. Round to the nearest tenth if necessary.

e. 40% of what number is 26? **65**   f. 80 is 75% of what number? **106.7**

🌐 **Real-World EXAMPLE**

4 **ANIMALS** The average adult male Western Lowland gorilla eats about 33.5 pounds of fruit each day. How much food does the average adult male gorilla eat each day?

You know that 33.5 pounds of fruit is 67% of the total amount eaten daily. So, the problem asks 33.5 is 67% of what number. Thus, you need to find the whole.

Western Lowland Gorilla's Diet	
Food	**Percent**
Fruit	67%
Seeds, Leaves, Stems, and Pith	17%
Insects/ Insect Larvae	16%

$$\frac{33.5}{w} = \frac{67}{100}$$ Write the proportion.

$33.5 \cdot 100 = w \cdot 67$ Find the cross products.

$3{,}350 = 67w$ Simplify.

$$\frac{3{,}350}{67} = \frac{67w}{67}$$ Divide each side by 67.

$50 = w$

So, the average adult male gorilla eats 50 pounds of food each day.

🌐 **Real-World Link . . . .**
Male Western Lowland gorillas weigh about 350–400 pounds. Females weigh about 160–200 pounds.
Source: Columbus Zoo and Aquarium

✓ **CHECK Your Progress**

36%

g. **ZOO** If 200 of the 550 reptiles in a zoo are on display, what percent of the reptiles are on display? Round to the nearest whole number.

Types of Percent Problems		Key Concept
Type	**Example**	**Proportion**
Find the Percent	What percent of 6 is 3?	$\frac{3}{6} = \frac{n}{100}$
Find the Part	What number is 50% of 6?	$\frac{p}{6} = \frac{50}{100}$
Find the Whole	3 is 50% of what number?	$\frac{3}{w} = \frac{50}{100}$

★ indicates multi-step problem

✓ CHECK Your Understanding

Examples 1–3
(pp. 350–352)

Find each number. Round to the nearest tenth if necessary.

1. What percent of 50 is 18? **36%**
2. What percent of $90 is $9? **10%**
3. What number is 2% of 35? **0.7**
4. What number is 25% of 180? **45**
5. 9 is 12% of which number? **75**
6. 62 is 90.5% of what number? **68.5**

Example 4
(p. 352)

7. **MEASUREMENT** If a box of Brand A cereal contains 10 cups of cereal, how many more cups of cereal are in a box of Brand B cereal? **3 c**

Brand A

Brand B
30% More Cereal

▶ Practice and Problem Solving

HOMEWORK HELP	
For Exercises	**See Examples**
8–11	1, 2
12–17	3
18–21	4
22, 23	5

Exercise Levels
A: 8–17
B: 18–29
C: 30–32

Find each number. Round to the nearest tenth if necessary.

8. What percent of 60 is 15? **25%**
9. $3 is what percent of $40? **7.5%**
10. What number is 15% of 60? **9**
11. 12% of 72 is what number? **8.6**
12. 9 is 45% of what number? **20**
13. 75 is 20% of what number? **375**

14. **SCHOOL** Roman has 2 red pencils in his backpack. If this is 25% of the total number of pencils, how many pencils are in his backpack? **8**

15. **BASKETBALL** Lisa and Michelle scored 48% of their team's points. If their team had a total of 50 points, how many points did they score? **24**

16. **SHOES** A pair of sneakers are on sale as shown. This is 75% of the original price. What was the original price of the shoes? **$68**

Sale Price
$51

17. **BOOKS** Of the 60 books on a bookshelf, 24 are nonfiction. What percent of the books are nonfiction? **40%**

Find each number. Round to the nearest hundredth if necessary.

18. What percent of 25 is 30? **120%**
19. What number is 8.2% of 50? **4.1**
20. 40 is 50% of what number? **80**
21. 12.5% of what number is 24? **192**
22. What number is 0.5% of 8? **0.04**
23. What percent of 300 is 0.6? **0.2%**

★ 24. **BUSINESS** The first week of June, there were 404 customers at an ice cream parlor. Eight weeks later, the number of customers was 175% of this amount. How many customers were there eight weeks later? **707 customers**

★ 25. **MONEY** Ajamu saves 40% of his allowance each week. If he saves $16 in 5 weeks, how much allowance does Ajamu receive each week? **$8**

★ 26. **SCHOOL** A class picture includes 95% of the students. Seven students were absent. How many students are in the class? **140**

Lesson 7-2 The Percent Proportion **353**

---

3 Practice

✓ Formative Assessment

Use Exercises 1–7 to check for understanding.

Then use the chart at the bottom of this page to customize your assignments for students.

Intervention You may wish to use the Study Guide and Intervention Master on page 17 of the *Chapter 7 Resource Masters* for additional reinforcement.

Odd/Even Assignments

Exercises 8–17 are structured so that students practice the same concepts whether they are assigned odd or even problems.

Focus on Mathematical Content

Percent Greater than 100
Point out to students that when the percent is greater than 100, such as in Exercise 24, the part will be greater than the whole. This indicates an increase in the original quantity.

DIFFERENTIATED HOMEWORK OPTIONS

Level	Assignment	Two-Day Option	
BL Basic	8–17, 30, 32–43	9–17 odd, 33, 34	8–16 even, 30, 32, 35–43
OL Core	9–23 odd, 24–30, 32–43	8–17, 33, 34	18–30, 32, 35–43
AL Advanced/Pre-AP	18–40 (optional: 41–43)		

Ticket Out the Door Ask students who are wearing red to raise their hands. Have students use the percent proportion to find what percent of the class is wearing red.

 Formative Assessment

Check for student understanding of concepts in Lessons 7-1 and 7-2.

CRM Quiz 1, p. 61

 **Foldables™ Follow-Up**

Remind students to record how to use the percent proportion to find the missing part, whole, or percent in their Foldables tables, along with examples.

Additional Answer

31. 20% of 500, 20% of 100, 5% of 100; If the percent is the same but the base is greater, then the part is greater. If the base is the same but the percent is greater, then the part is greater.

ASTRONOMY For Exercises 27–29, use the table shown.

Planet	Radius (km)
Mercury	2,440
Mars	3,397
Jupiter	71,492

27. Mercury's radius is what percent of Jupiter's radius? **about 3.4%**

28. If the radius of Mars is about 13.7% of Neptune's radius, what is the radius of Neptune? **about 24,800 km**

EXTRA PRACTICE
See pages 685, 710.

29. Earth's radius is about 261.4% of Mercury's radius. What is the radius of Earth? **about 6,378 km**

H.O.T. Problems

30. **OPEN ENDED** Write a proportion that can be used to find the percent scored on a science quiz that has 10 questions. **Sample answer:** $\frac{8}{10} = \frac{x}{100}$

32. Sample answer: A runner won 15% of the races he ran. If he won 3 races, how many races did he run?

31. **CHALLENGE** Without calculating, arrange the following from greatest to least value. Justify your reasoning. **See margin.**

20% of 100, 20% of 500, 5% of 100

32. **WRITING IN MATH** Create a problem involving a percent that can be solved by using the proportion $\frac{3}{b} = \frac{15}{100}$.

TEST PRACTICE

33. Of the 273 students in a school, 95 volunteered to work the book sale. About what percent of the students did *not* volunteer? **B**

A 55%

B 65%

C 70%

D 75%

34. A customer at a restaurant leaves a tip of $2.70. This amount is 15% of the total bill. Which equation can be used to find x, the total amount of the food bill? **G**

F $\frac{2.70}{15} = \frac{15}{100}$ H $\frac{15}{2.70} = \frac{x}{100}$

G $\frac{2.70}{x} = \frac{15}{100}$ J $\frac{x}{2.70} = \frac{15}{100}$

Spiral Review

Find each number. Round to the nearest tenth if necessary. (Lesson 7-1)

35. What is 25% of 120? **30**

36. Find 45% of 70. **31.5**

37. **PLANTS** A plant was 275% taller than the month before. What decimal represents this percent? (Lesson 6-9) **2.75**

MEASUREMENT Complete. (Lesson 6-4)

38. 3,000 lb = ■ T **1.5**

39. 36 in. = ■ ft **3**

40. $4\frac{1}{2}$ lb = ■ oz **72**

▶ **GET READY for the Next Lesson**

PREREQUISITE SKILL Multiply. (Lesson 5-5)

41. $\frac{1}{2} \cdot 60$ **30**

42. $\frac{3}{4} \cdot 28$ **21**

43. $\frac{2}{5} \cdot 45$ **18**

7-3

Percent and Estimation

PACING: **Regular:** 1 period, **Block:** 0.5 period

Options for Differentiated Instruction

ELL = English Language Learner   **AL** = Above or Beyond Grade Level   **SS** = Struggling Students   **SN** = Special Needs

Using Writing **ELL** **SS** **SN**

Use after presenting the Examples.

Have students write a paragraph describing a situation in which estimating with percents would be appropriate. Their paragraphs should both describe the situation and include the numbers used as estimates. They may want to look through newspapers for ideas. Have them present their paragraphs to the class.

Visualizing the Concept **SS**

Use with the Examples.

Using number lines while presenting the examples may help students understand what it means to estimate percents. A possible use of number lines to represent Example 1 is shown below.

62% of 520 ~ 60% of 520

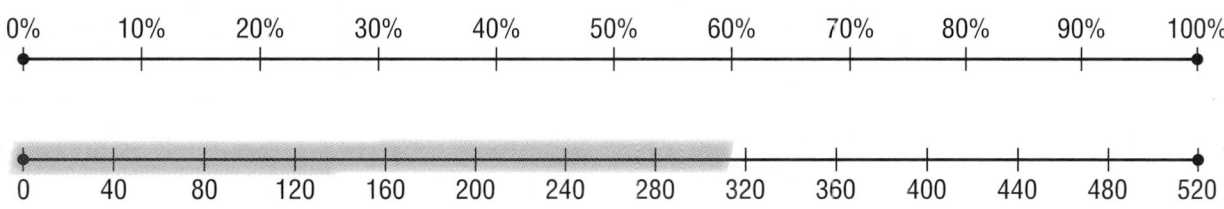

Additional Problems **AL**

Use after students complete Lesson 7-3.

Present the following problem to students.

> Catherine went shopping during a 20% off sale. She found a pair of jeans for $60.
> To figure out the sale price, she did the following multiplication: $8 \times 6 = 48$
> She concluded that the sale price was $48.

Have students explain why Catherine's method worked. 80% of $60 = $0.8 \times 60 = 8 \times 6$ Then have them use the same procedure to determine the sale price for each of the following:

- an item that is $80 and 30% off $8 \times 7 = $56
- an item that is $120 and 40% off $12 \times 6 = $72

Leveled Lesson Resources

Chapter 7 Resource Masters

BL = Below or Approaching Grade Level **OL** = On Grade Level **AL** = Above or Beyond Grade Level **ELL** = English Language Learner

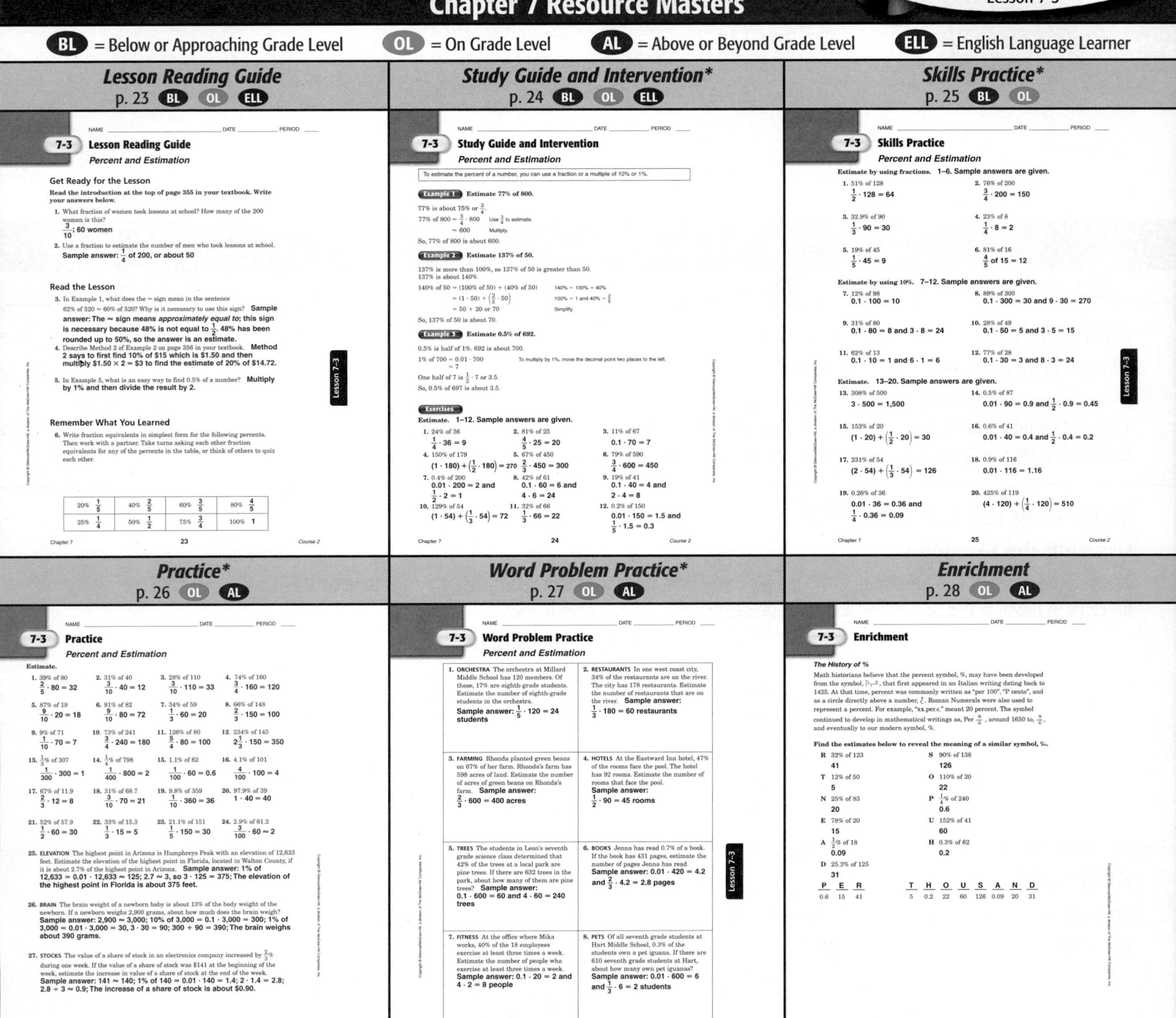

Lesson Reading Guide
p. 23 BL OL ELL

7-3 Lesson Reading Guide
Percent and Estimation

Get Ready for the Lesson
Read the introduction at the top of page 355 in your textbook. Write your answers below.

1. What fraction of women took lessons at school? How many of the 200 women is this? $\frac{3}{10}$; 60 women

2. Use a fraction to estimate the number of men who took lessons at school. Sample answer: $\frac{1}{4}$ of 200, or about 50

Read the Lesson

3. In Example 1, what does the ≈ sign mean in the sentence 62% of 520 ≈ 60% of 520? Why is it necessary to use this sign? **Sample answer:** The ≈ sign means *approximately equal to*; this sign is necessary because 48% is not equal to $\frac{1}{2}$. 48% has been rounded up to 50%, so the answer is an estimate.

4. Describe Method 2 of Example 2 on page 356 in your textbook. Method 2 says to first find 10% of $15 which is $1.50 and then multiply $1.50 × 2 = $3 to find the estimate of 20% of $14.72.

5. In Example 5, what is an easy way to find 0.5% of a number? Multiply by 1% and then divide the result by 2.

Remember What You Learned

6. Write fraction equivalents in simplest form for the following percents. Then work with a partner. Take turns asking each other fraction equivalents for any of the percents in the table, or think of others to quiz each other.

20% $\frac{1}{5}$	40% $\frac{2}{5}$	60% $\frac{3}{5}$	80% $\frac{4}{5}$
25% $\frac{1}{4}$	50% $\frac{1}{2}$	75% $\frac{3}{4}$	100% 1

Chapter 7   23   Course 2

Study Guide and Intervention*
p. 24 BL OL ELL

7-3 Study Guide and Intervention
Percent and Estimation

To estimate the percent of a number, you can use a fraction or a multiple of 10% or 1%.

Example 1 Estimate 77% of 800.
77% is about 75% or $\frac{3}{4}$.
77% of 800 ≈ $\frac{3}{4}$ · 800   Use $\frac{3}{4}$ to estimate.
≈ 600   Multiply.
So, 77% of 800 is about 600.

Example 2 Estimate 137% of 50.
137% is more than 100%, so 137% of 50 is greater than 50.
137% is about 140%.
140% of 50 = (100% of 50) + (40% of 50)   140% = 100% + 40%
= (1 · 50) + ($\frac{2}{5}$ · 50)   100% = 1 and 40% = $\frac{2}{5}$
= 50 + 20 or 70   Simplify.
So, 137% of 50 is about 70.

Example 3 Estimate 0.5% of 692.
0.5% is half of 1%. 692 is about 700.
1% of 700 = 0.01 · 700   To multiply by 1%, move the decimal point two places to the left.
= 7
One half of 7 is $\frac{1}{2}$ · 7 or 3.5.
So, 0.5% of 697 is about 3.5.

Exercises
Estimate. 1–12. Sample answers are given.

1. 24% of 36 $\frac{1}{4}$ · 36 = 9
2. 81% of 25 $\frac{4}{5}$ · 25 = 20
3. 11% of 67   0.1 · 70 = 7
4. 150% of 179   (1 · 180) + ($\frac{1}{2}$ · 180) = 270
5. 67% of 450 $\frac{2}{3}$ · 450 = 300
6. 79% of 590 $\frac{3}{4}$ · 600 = 450
7. 0.4% of 200   0.01 · 200 = 2 and $\frac{1}{2}$ · 2 = 1
8. 42% of 61   0.1 · 60 = 6 and 4 · 6 = 24
9. 19% of 41   0.1 · 40 = 4 and 2 · 4 = 8
10. 129% of 54   (1 · 54) + ($\frac{1}{3}$ · 54) = 72
11. 32% of 66 $\frac{1}{3}$ · 66 = 22
12. 0.2% of 150   0.01 · 150 = 1.5 and $\frac{1}{5}$ · 1.5 = 0.3

Chapter 7   24   Course 2

Skills Practice*
p. 25 BL OL

7-3 Skills Practice
Percent and Estimation

Estimate by using fractions. 1–6. Sample answers are given.

1. 51% of 128 $\frac{1}{2}$ · 128 = 64
2. 76% of 200 $\frac{3}{4}$ · 200 = 150
3. 32.9% of 90 $\frac{1}{3}$ · 90 = 30
4. 23% of 8 $\frac{1}{4}$ · 8 = 2
5. 19% of 45 $\frac{1}{5}$ · 45 = 9
6. 81% of 16 $\frac{4}{5}$ of 15 = 12

Estimate by using 10%. 7–12. Sample answers are given.

7. 12% of 98   0.1 · 100 = 10
8. 89% of 300   0.1 · 300 = 30 and 9 · 30 = 270
9. 31% of 80   0.1 · 80 = 8 and 3 · 8 = 24
10. 28% of 49   0.1 · 50 = 5 and 3 · 5 = 15
11. 62% of 13   0.1 · 10 = 1 and 6 · 1 = 6
12. 77% of 28   0.1 · 30 = 3 and 8 · 3 = 24

Estimate. 13–20. Sample answers are given.

13. 308% of 500   3 · 500 = 1,500
14. 0.5% of 87   0.01 · 90 = 0.9 and $\frac{1}{2}$ · 0.9 = 0.45
15. 153% of 20   (1 · 20) + ($\frac{1}{2}$ · 20) = 30
16. 0.6% of 41   0.01 · 40 = 0.4 and $\frac{1}{2}$ · 0.4 = 0.2
17. 231% of 54   (2 · 54) + ($\frac{1}{3}$ · 54) = 126
18. 0.9% of 116   0.01 · 116 = 1.16
19. 0.26% of 36   0.01 · 36 = 0.36 and $\frac{1}{4}$ · 0.36 = 0.09
20. 425% of 119   (4 · 120) + ($\frac{1}{4}$ · 120) = 510

Chapter 7   25   Course 2

Practice*
p. 26 OL AL

7-3 Practice
Percent and Estimation

Estimate.

1. 39% of 80 $\frac{2}{5}$ · 80 = 32
2. 31% of 40 $\frac{3}{10}$ · 40 = 12
3. 28% of 110 $\frac{1}{4}$ · 110 = 33
4. 74% of 160 $\frac{3}{4}$ · 160 = 120
5. 87% of 19 $\frac{9}{10}$ · 20 = 18
6. 91% of 82 $\frac{9}{10}$ · 80 = 72
7. 34% of 59 $\frac{1}{3}$ · 60 = 20
8. 66% of 148 $\frac{2}{3}$ · 150 = 100
9. 9% of 71 $\frac{1}{10}$ · 70 = 7
10. 73% of 241 $\frac{3}{4}$ · 240 = 180
11. 126% of 80 $\frac{5}{4}$ · 80 = 100
12. 234% of 145 $2\frac{1}{3}$ · 150 = 350
13. $\frac{1}{3}$% of 307 $\frac{1}{300}$ · 300 = 1
14. $\frac{1}{4}$% of 798 $\frac{1}{400}$ · 800 = 2
15. 1.1% of 62 $\frac{1}{100}$ · 60 = 0.6
16. 4.1% of 101 $\frac{4}{100}$ · 100 = 4
17. 67% of 11.9 $\frac{2}{3}$ · 12 = 8
18. 31% of 68.7 $\frac{3}{10}$ · 70 = 21
19. 9.8% of 359 $\frac{1}{10}$ · 360 = 36
20. 97.9% of 39   1 · 40 = 40
21. 52% of 57.9 $\frac{1}{2}$ · 60 = 30
22. 33% of 15.3 $\frac{1}{3}$ · 15 = 5
23. 21.1% of 151 $\frac{1}{5}$ · 150 = 30
24. 2.9% of 61.2 $\frac{3}{100}$ · 60 = 2

25. **ELEVATION** The highest point in Arizona is Humphreys Peak with an elevation of 12,633 feet. Estimate the elevation of the highest point in Florida, located in Walton County, if it is about 2.7% of the highest point in Arizona. **Sample answer:** 1% of 12,633 ≈ 0.01 · 12,633 = 125; 2.7 ≈ 3, so 3 · 125 = 375; The elevation of the highest point in Florida is about 375 feet.

26. **BRAIN** The brain weight of a newborn baby is about 13% of the body weight of the newborn. If a newborn weighs 2,900 grams, about how much does the brain weigh? **Sample answer:** 2,900 ≈ 3,000; 10% of 3,000 = 0.1 · 3,000 = 300; 1% of 3,000 = 0.01 · 3,000 = 30, 3 · 30 = 90; 300 + 90 = 390; The brain weighs about 390 grams.

27. **STOCKS** The value of a share of stock in an electronics company increased by $\frac{2}{3}$% during one week. If the value of a share of stock was $141 at the beginning of the week, estimate the increase in value of a share of stock at the end of the week. **Sample answer:** 141 ≈ 140; 1% of 140 = 0.01 · 140 = 1.4; 2 · 1.4 = 2.8; 2.8 ÷ 3 ≈ 0.9; The increase of a share of stock is about $0.90.

Chapter 7   26   Course 2

Word Problem Practice*
p. 27 OL AL

7-3 Word Problem Practice
Percent and Estimation

1. **ORCHESTRA** The orchestra at Millard Middle School has 120 members. Of these, 17% are eighth-grade students. Estimate the number of eighth-grade students in the orchestra. **Sample answer:** $\frac{1}{5}$ · 120 = 24 students

2. **RESTAURANTS** In one west coast city, 34% of the restaurants are on the river. The city has 178 restaurants. Estimate the number of restaurants that are on the river. **Sample answer:** $\frac{1}{3}$ · 180 = 60 restaurants

3. **FARMING** Rhonda planted green beans on 67% of her farm. Rhonda's farm has 598 acres of land. Estimate the number of acres of green beans on Rhonda's farm. **Sample answer:** $\frac{2}{3}$ · 600 = 400 acres

4. **HOTELS** At the Eastward Inn hotel, 47% of the rooms face the pool. The hotel has 92 rooms. Estimate the number of rooms that face the pool. **Sample answer:** $\frac{1}{2}$ · 90 = 45 rooms

5. **TREES** The students in Leon's seventh grade science class determined that 42% of the trees at a local park are pine trees. If there are 632 trees in the park, about how many of them are pine trees? **Sample answer:** 0.1 · 600 = 60 and 4 · 60 = 240 trees

6. **BOOKS** Jenna has read 0.7% of a book. If the book has 431 pages, estimate the number of pages Jenna has read. **Sample answer:** 0.01 · 420 = 4.2 and $\frac{2}{3}$ · 4.2 = 2.8 pages

7. **FITNESS** At the office where Mika works, 40% of the 18 employees exercise at least three times a week. Estimate the number of people who exercise at least three times a week. **Sample answer:** 0.1 · 20 = 2 and 4 · 2 = 8 people

8. **PETS** Of all seventh grade students at Hart Middle School, 0.3% of the students own a pet iguana. If there are 610 seventh grade students at Hart, about how many own pet iguanas? **Sample answer:** 0.01 · 600 = 6 and $\frac{1}{3}$ · 6 = 2 students

Chapter 7   27   Course 2

Enrichment
p. 28 OL AL

7-3 Enrichment

The History of %
Math historians believe that the percent symbol, %, may have been developed from the symbol, ℔, that first appeared in an Italian writing dating back to 1425. At that time, percent was commonly written as "per 100", "P cento", and as a circle directly above a number, ℔. Roman Numerals were also used to represent a percent. For example, "xx.per.c." meant 20 percent. The symbol continued to develop in mathematical writings as, Per $\frac{c}{o}$, around 1650 to, $\frac{c}{o}$, and eventually to our modern symbol, %.

Find the estimates below to reveal the meaning of a similar symbol, ‰.

R 32% of 123   41
S 90% of 138   126
T 12% of 50   5
O 110% of 20   22
N 25% of 83   20
P $\frac{1}{4}$% of 240   0.6
E 78% of 20   15
U 152% of 41   60
A $\frac{1}{2}$% of 18   0.09
H 0.3% of 62   0.2
D 25.3% of 125   31

P E R   T H O U S A N D
0.6 15 41   5 0.2 22 60 126 0.09 20 31

Chapter 7   28   Course 2

Additional Lesson Resources

*** Also available in Spanish ELL**

Transparencies
• *5-Minute Check Transparency,* Lesson 7-3

Other Print Products
• *Teaching Mathematics with Manipulatives*
• *Noteables™ Interactive Study Notebook with Foldables™*

Teacher Tech Tools
• *Interactive Classroom CD-ROM,* Lesson 7-3
• *AssignmentWorks,* Lesson 7-3

Student Tech Tools
glencoe.com
• Extra Examples, Chapter 7, Lesson 3
• Self-Check Quiz, Chapter 7, Lesson 3

▷GET READY for the Lesson

MUSIC Refer to the graph below.

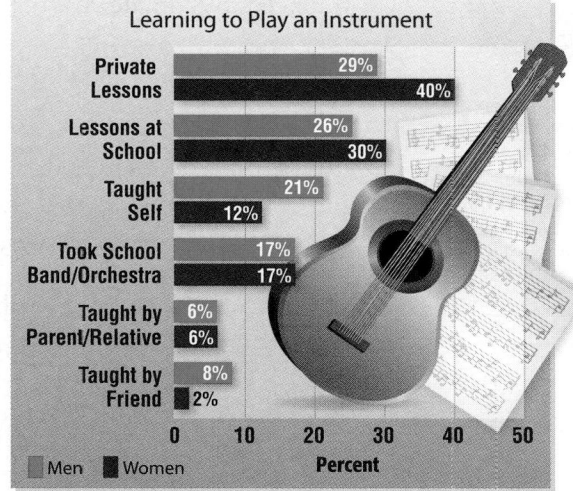

Learning to Play an Instrument

Category	Men	Women
Private Lessons	29%	40%
Lessons at School	26%	30%
Taught Self	21%	12%
Took School Band/Orchestra	17%	17%
Taught by Parent/Relative	6%	6%
Taught by Friend	8%	2%

1. What fraction of women took lessons at school? If 200 women were surveyed, how many of them took lessons at school? $\frac{3}{10}$; 60 women

2. Use a fraction to estimate the number of men who took lessons at school. Assume 200 men were surveyed. **2. Sample answer:** $\frac{1}{4}$ of 200 or about 50

Sometimes an exact answer is not needed when using percents. One way to estimate the percent of a number is to use a fraction.

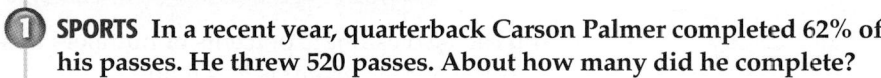

Real-World EXAMPLE

① SPORTS In a recent year, quarterback Carson Palmer completed 62% of his passes. He threw 520 passes. About how many did he complete?

62% of 520 ≈ 60% of 520   62% ≈ 60%

$\approx \frac{3}{5} \cdot 520$ $60\% = \frac{6}{10}$ or $\frac{3}{5}$

≈ 312 Multiply.

So, Carson Palmer completed about 312 out of 520 passes.

 **CHECK Your Progress** a. 48 years; $42\% \approx \frac{2}{5}$ and $\frac{2}{5} \cdot 120 = 48$

a. **REPTILES** Box turtles have been known to live for 120 years. American alligators have been known to live 42% as long as box turtles. About how long can an American alligator live?

Lesson 7-3 Percent and Estimation **355**

Lesson 7-3 Percent and Estimation **355**

1 Focus

Vertical Alignment

Before Lesson 7-3
Interpret percents as a part of a hundred; find decimal and percent equivalents for common fractions and explain why they represent the same value; compute a given percent of a whole number

Lesson 7-3
Calculate given percentages of quantities and solve problems involving tips

After Lesson 7-3
Convert fractions to decimals and percents and use these representations in estimations, computations, and applications; solve problems that involve discounts, markups, commissions, and profit and compute simple and compound interest

2 Teach

Scaffolding Questions

Ask:
• When might you need to round to the nearest 100%? Explain and give an example. if the percent is greater than 100%, such as 310%

 Formative Assessment

Use the Check Your Progress exercises after each Example to determine students' understanding of concepts.

ADDITIONAL EXAMPLE

① CONCERTS A town sold 407 tickets to a chamber music concert in the town square. Of the tickets sold, 61% were discounted for senior citizens. About how many senior citizens bought tickets for the concert? about 240

MAIN IDEA
Estimate percents by using fractions and decimals.

Math Online
glencoe.com
• Extra Examples
• Personal Tutor
• Self-Check Quiz

Real-World Link . . . .
In a recent year, the Internal Revenue Service estimated that Americans paid $15.37 billion in tips.

Another method for estimating the percent of a number is to first find 10% of the number and then multiply. For example, 70% = 7 · 10%. So, 70% of a number equals 7 times 10% of the number.

Real-World EXAMPLE

2 **MONEY** Marita decides to leave a 20% tip on a restaurant bill of $14.72. About how much money should she tip the restaurant server?

You need to estimate 20% of $14.72.

| METHOD 1 | Use a fraction to estimate. |

20% is $\frac{2}{10}$ or $\frac{1}{5}$.

20% of $14.72 ≈ $\frac{1}{5}$ · $15.00   20% = $\frac{1}{5}$ and round $14.72 to $15.00.

≈ $3.00   Multiply.

| METHOD 2 | Use 10% of a number to estimate. |

Step 1 Find 10% of the number.
$14.72 is about $15.00.
10% of $15.00 = 0.1 · $15.00   To multiply by 10%, move the
= $1.50   decimal point one place to the left.

Step 2 Multiply.
20% of $15.00 is 2 times 10% of $15.00.
2 · $1.50 = $3.00

So, Marita should tip the restaurant server about $3.00.

✓ CHOOSE Your Method

b. **MONEY** Dante plans to put 80% of his paycheck into a savings account. His paycheck this week was $295. About how much money will he put into his savings account? **about $240**

You can also estimate percents of numbers when the percent is greater than 100 or the percent is less than 1.

Study Tip

Check for Reasonableness
When estimating the percent of a number and the percent is greater than 100, the estimate will always be greater than the number.

EXAMPLES Percents Greater Than 100 or Less Than 1

3 Estimate 122% of 50.

122% is about 120%.

120% of 50 = (100% of 50) + (20% of 50)   120% = 100% + 20%

= (1 · 50) + ($\frac{1}{5}$ · 50)   100% = 1 and 20% = $\frac{1}{5}$

= 50 + 10 or 60   Simplify.

So, 122% of 50 is about 60.

4 **Estimate $\frac{1}{4}$% of 589.**

$\frac{1}{4}$% is one fourth of 1%. 589 is about 600.

1% of $600 = 0.01 \cdot 600$ — Write 1% as 0.01.

$= 6$ — To multiply by 1%, move the decimal point two places to the left.

One fourth of 6 is $\frac{1}{4} \cdot 6$ or 1.5. So, $\frac{1}{4}$% of 589 is about 1.5.

CHECK Your Progress

Estimate.

c. 174% of 200 d. 298% of 45 e. 0.25% of 789

c. 350; $1\frac{3}{4} \cdot 200 = 350$

d. 150; $3 \cdot 50 = 150$

e. 2; $\frac{1}{4} \cdot 0.01 \cdot 800 = 2$

Real-World EXAMPLE

5 **CELL PHONES In a recent year, there were about 200 million people in the U.S. with cell phones. Of those, about 0.5% used their phone as an MP3 player. Estimate the number of people who used their phone as an MP3 player.**

0.5% is half of 1%.

1% of 200 million $= 0.01 \cdot 200{,}000{,}000$

$= 2{,}000{,}000$

So, 0.5% of 200,000,000 is about $\frac{1}{2}$ of 2,000,000 or 1,000,000.

So, about 1,000,000 people used their phone as an MP3 player.

CHECK Your Progress

f. **ATTENDANCE** Last year, 639 students attended a summer camp. Of those who attended this year, 0.9% also attended last year. About how many people attended the camp two years in a row?

f. Sample answer: about $1\% \cdot 600$ or 6 people

★ indicates multi-step problem

CHECK Your Understanding

Examples 1–4 (pp. 355–357) **Estimate.** **1. 5; $\frac{1}{2} \cdot 10 = 5$; $0.1 \cdot 10 = 1$ and $5 \cdot 1 = 5$**

1. 52% of 10 2. 7% of 20 3. 38% of 62

3–6. See margin.

4. 79% of 489 5. 151% of 70 6. $\frac{1}{2}$% of 82

2. 2; $\frac{1}{10} \cdot 20 = 2$; $0.1 \cdot 20 = 2$ and $1 \cdot 2 = 2$

Example 1 (p. 355) 7. **BUSINESS** A bicycle store increases its prices by 23%. About how much more will a customer pay for a bicycle that originally costs $200?
about \$50; $\frac{1}{4} \cdot \$200 = \$50$; $0.1 \cdot 200 = 20$ and $2.5 \cdot 20 = \$50$

Example 2 (p. 356) 8. **BIRTHDAYS** Of the 78 teenagers at a youth camp, 63% have birthdays in the spring. About how many have birthdays in the spring?
about 48 teenagers; $\frac{3}{5} \cdot 80 = 48$; $0.1 \cdot 80 = 8$ and $6 \cdot 8 = 48$

Example 5 (p. 357) 9. **GEOGRAPHY** About 0.8% of the land in Maine is federally owned. If Maine is 19,847,680 acres, about how many acres are federally owned? **See margin.**

ADDITIONAL EXAMPLES

4 Estimate $\frac{1}{3}$% of 898. about 3

5 **GAME ATTENDANCE** Last weekend, 96,081 people attended a college football game. About 0.25% of them were reporters from newspapers and television and radio stations. About how many reporters were at the game? about 240 reporters

3 Practice

Formative Assessment

Use Exercises 1–9 to check for understanding.

Then use the chart on the next page to customize your assignments for students.

Intervention You may wish to use the Study Guide and Intervention Master on page 24 of the *Chapter 7 Resource Masters* for additional reinforcement.

Additional Answers

3. 24; $\frac{2}{5} \cdot 60 = 24$; $0.1 \cdot 60 = 6$ and $4 \cdot 6 = 24$

4. 400; $\frac{4}{5} \cdot 500 = 400$; $0.1 \cdot 500 = 50$ and $8 \cdot 50 = 400$

5. 105; $(1 \cdot 70) + \left(\frac{1}{2} \cdot 70\right) = 105$

6. 0.4; $0.01 \cdot 80 = 0.8$ and $\frac{1}{2} \cdot 0.8 = 0.4$

9. about 160,000 acres; $0.01 \cdot 20{,}000{,}000 = 200{,}000$ and $\frac{4}{5}$ of $200{,}000 = 160{,}000$

Exercises 10–31 are structured so that students practice the same concepts whether they are assigned odd or even problems.

Estimation

Tips for New Teachers

Explain to students that estimation isn't always done exactly the same way. Depending on the problem, students may find it easier to round the percent, to round the number, or to round both the percent and the number. Similarly, they may find it easier to approximate a percent with a fraction or with a decimal. Encourage students to analyze each problem, asking themselves which estimation method will work best with the given numbers.

Additional Answers

11. $18; \frac{1}{5} \cdot 90 = 18; 0.1 \cdot 90 = 9$ and $2 \cdot 9 = 18$

12. $48; \frac{2}{5} \cdot 120 = 48; 0.1 \cdot 120 = 12$ and $4 \cdot 12 = 48$

13. $135; \frac{3}{4} \cdot 180 = 135; 0.1 \cdot 180 = 18$ and $7.5 \cdot 18 = 135$

14. $18; \frac{3}{5} \cdot 30 = 18; 0.1 \cdot 30 = 3$ and $6 \cdot 3 = 18$

15. $90; \frac{9}{10} \cdot 100 = 90; 0.1 \cdot 100 = 10$ and $9 \cdot 10 = 90$

16. $12.5; \frac{1}{4} \cdot 50 = 12.5; 0.1 \cdot 50 = 5$ and $2.5 \cdot 5 = 12.5$

17. $36; \frac{3}{10} \cdot 120 = 36; 0.1 \cdot 120 = 12$ and $3 \cdot 12 = 36$

18. $180; \frac{9}{10} \cdot 200 = 180; 0.1 \cdot 200 = 20$ and $9 \cdot 20 = 180$

19. $90; \frac{3}{5} \cdot 150 = 90; 0.1 \cdot 150 = 15$ and $6 \cdot 15 = 90$

20. $100; \frac{2}{3} \cdot 150 = 100; 0.1 \cdot 150 = 15$ and $6.6 \cdot 15 \approx 100$

21. $168; \frac{7}{10} \cdot 240 = 168; 0.1 \cdot 240 = 24$ and $7 \cdot 24 = 168$

Practice and Problem Solving

HOMEWORK HELP	
For Exercises	See Examples
10–21	1, 3
22–23	2
24–25	3
26–27, 30	4
28–29, 31	5

Exercise Levels
A: 10–31
B: 32–45
C: 46–50

26. $0.01 \cdot 400 = 4$ and $\frac{1}{2} \cdot 4 = 2$

27. $0.01 \cdot 200 = 2$ and $\frac{3}{4} \cdot 2 = 1.5$

28. $0.01 \cdot 500 = 5$ and $\frac{2}{5} \cdot 5 = 2$

Estimate. **10.** $35; \frac{1}{2} \cdot 70 = 35; 0.1 \cdot 70 = 7$ and $5 \cdot 7 = 35$ **11–21. See margin.**

10. 47% of 70
11. 21% of 90
12. 39% of 120
13. 76% of 180
14. 57% of 29
15. 92% of 104
16. 24% of 48
17. 28% of 121
18. 88% of 207
19. 62% of 152
20. 65% of 152
21. 72% of 238

22. MONEY Jessica spent $42 at the hair salon. About how much money should she tip the hair stylist if she wants to leave a 15% tip? **about $6; $\frac{3}{20} \cdot \$40 = \$6$**

23. HEALTH You use 43 muscles to frown. When you smile, you use 32% of these same muscles. About how many muscles do you use when you smile? **about 12 muscles; $\frac{3}{10} \cdot 40 = 12$**

Estimate. **24.** $(1 \cdot 50) + \left(\frac{3}{10} \cdot 50\right) = 65$ **25.** $(2 \cdot 300) + \left(\frac{1}{4} \cdot 300\right) = 675$

24. 132% of 54
25. 224% of 320
26. $\frac{1}{2}$% of 412
27. $\frac{3}{4}$% of 168
28. 0.4% of 510
29. 0.9% of 74 $0.01 \cdot 70 = 0.7$

30. GEOGRAPHY The United States has 12,383 miles of coastline. If $\frac{4}{5}$% of the U.S. coastline is located in Georgia, about how many miles of coastline are in Georgia? **about 96 mi; $0.01 \cdot 12,000 = 120$ and $\frac{4}{5} \cdot 120 = 96$**

31. BIRDS During migration, 450,000 sandhill cranes stop to rest in Nebraska. About 0.6% of these cranes stop to rest in Oregon. About how many sandhill cranes stop in Oregon during migration? **about 2,700 birds; $0.01 \cdot 450,000 = 4,500$ and $\frac{3}{5} \cdot 4,500 = 2,700$**

Estimate.

32. 67% of 8.7
33. 54% of 76.8
34. 32% of 89.9
35. 10.5% of 238
36. 22.2% of 114
37. 98.5% of 45

ANALYZE GRAPHS For Exercises 38–40, use the graph shown.

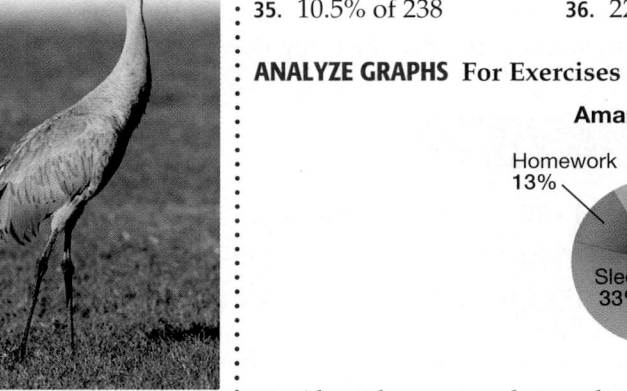

Amanda's Day
- Homework 13%
- School 27%
- Extracurricular Activities 8%
- Other 19%
- Sleep 33%

32. $\frac{2}{3} \cdot 9 = 6$
33. $\frac{1}{2} \cdot 80 = 40$
34. $\frac{1}{3} \cdot 90 = 30$
35. $\frac{1}{10} \cdot 240 = 24$
36. $\frac{1}{5} \cdot 100 = 20$
37. $1 \cdot 45 = 45$

38. About how many hours does Amanda spend doing her homework each day? **38–40. See Ch. 7 Answer Appendix.**

★ **39.** About how many more hours does Amanda spend sleeping than doing the activities in the "other" category? Justify your answer.

★ **40.** What is the approximate number of minutes Amanda spends each day on extracurricular activities?

358   Chapter 7 Applying Percents

DIFFERENTIATED HOMEWORK OPTIONS			
Level	Assignment	Two-Day Option	
BL Basic	10–31, 46, 48–70	11–31 odd, 51–53	10–30 even, 46, 48–50, 54–70
OL Core	11–37 odd, 38–46, 48–70	10–31, 51–53	32–46, 48–50, 54–70
AL Advanced/Pre-AP	32–66 (optional: 67–70)		

41. ANALYZE GRAPHS 2,075 tennis fans were asked to name the greatest all time female tennis player. The top five responses are shown. About how many more people chose Martina Navratilova than Steffi Graf? **1,200**

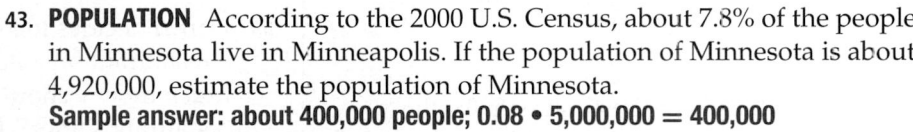
Greatest Female Tennis Players

★ **42. ANIMALS** The average white rhinoceros gives birth to a single calf that weighs about 3.8% as much as its mother. If the mother rhinoceros weighs 3.75 tons, about how many pounds does its calf weigh? **Sample answer: about 320 lb; 0.04 • 4 = 0.16; 0.16 • 2,000 = 320**

43. POPULATION According to the 2000 U.S. Census, about 7.8% of the people in Minnesota live in Minneapolis. If the population of Minnesota is about 4,920,000, estimate the population of Minnesota. **Sample answer: about 400,000 people; 0.08 • 5,000,000 = 400,000**

CLEANING For Exercises 44 and 45, use the following information.

A cleaning solution is made up of 0.9% chlorine bleach.

44. About how many ounces of bleach are in 189 ounces of cleaning solution? **1.8 ounces**

EXTRA PRACTICE
See pages 685, 710.

45. About how many ounces of bleach would be found in 412 ounces of cleaning solution? **3.6 ounces**

H.O.T. Problems

46. Sample answer: Of the students in a seventh grade class, 12% like to roller blade. If there are 50 students in the class, about how many like to roller blade?

47. Sample answer: Find 1% of $800, then multiply by $\frac{3}{8}$.

46. OPEN ENDED Write a real-world problem in which the answer can be found by estimating 12% of 50.

47. CHALLENGE Explain how you could find $\frac{3}{8}$% of $800.

48. FIND THE ERROR Tom and Elsa are estimating 1.5% of 210. Who is correct? Explain. **Tom; Elsa incorrectly changed 1.5% to 1.5, which is 150%.**

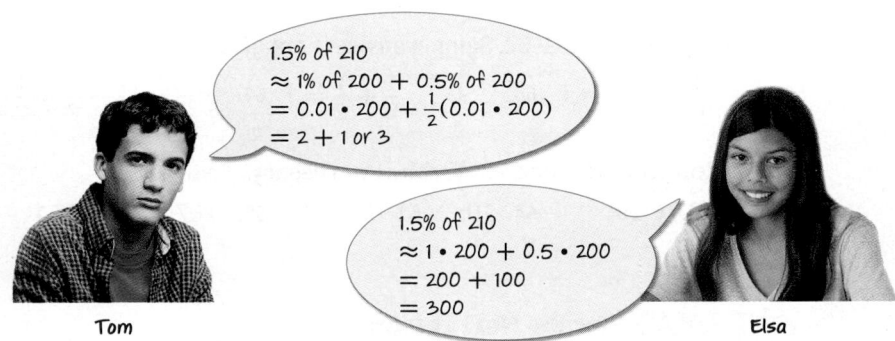

1.5% of 210
$\approx$ 1% of 200 + 0.5% of 200
= 0.01 • 200 + $\frac{1}{2}$(0.01 • 200)
= 2 + 1 or 3

Tom

1.5% of 210
$\approx$ 1 • 200 + 0.5 • 200
= 200 + 100
= 300

Elsa

49. NUMBER SENSE Is an estimate for the percent of a number *always*, *sometimes*, or *never* greater than the actual percent of the number? Give an example or a counterexample to support your answer. **See margin.**

Lesson 7-3 Percent and Estimation **359**

⚠ **Exercise Alert!**
Find the Error In Exercise 48, Elsa didn't follow the steps to write the percent as a decimal. Remind students that in order to write a percent as a decimal, they must move the decimal point two places to the left.

Additional Answer

49. Sometimes; sample answer: one estimate for 37% of 60 is $\frac{2}{5}$ • 60 = 24. This is greater than the actual answer because $\frac{2}{5}$ is greater than 37%. Another estimate is $\frac{1}{3}$ • 60 = 20. This is less than the actual answer because $\frac{1}{3}$ is less than 37%.

Ticket Out the Door Tell students that another class has about 120% of the number of students in your class. Have them estimate the number of students in the other class and write their estimates on a piece of paper.

FOLDABLES **Foldables™**
Study Organizer **Follow-Up**

Remind students to record what they learn about estimating percents of numbers in their Foldables tables, along with examples.

Additional Answer

50. Sample answer: One way to find 22% of 136 is to find $\frac{1}{5} \cdot 140 = 28$. Another way to find 22% of 136 is to first find $(0.1 \cdot 140)$ and then multiply by 2. The result is 28.

---

50. **WRITING IN MATH** Estimate 22% of 136 using two different methods. Justify the steps used in each method. **See margin.**

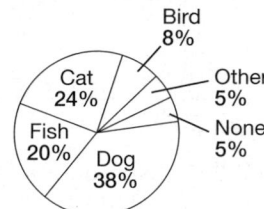 **TEST PRACTICE**

51. The graph shows the results of a survey of 510 students.

Pet Preferences

Bird 8%
Cat 24%
Other 5%
Fish 20%
None 5%
Dog 38%

Which is the best estimate for the number of students who prefer cats? **B**

A 75   C 225

B 125   D 450

52. Megan is buying an entertainment system for $1,789.43. The speakers are 39.7% of the total cost. Which is the best estimate for the cost of the speakers? **H**

F $540   H $720

G $630   J $810

53. Daniel decides to leave a 20% tip for a restaurant bill of $28.92. About how much money should he tip the restaurant server? **D**

A $2.00   C $4.00

B $3.00   D $6.00

Spiral Review

Find each number. Round to the nearest tenth if necessary. (Lesson 7-2)

54. 6 is what percent of 15? **40%**

55. Find 72% of 90. **64.8**

56. What number is 120% of 60? **72**

57. 35% of what number is 55? **157.1**

58. **HEALTH** Adults have 32 teeth. Children have 62.5% as many teeth as adults. How many teeth do children have? (Lesson 7-1) **20**

Estimate. (Lesson 5-1) **59–62. Sample answers are given.**

59. $\frac{8}{9} + \frac{1}{12}$ **1 + 0 = 1**   **60.** $\frac{4}{7} + \frac{7}{16}$ **$\frac{1}{2} + \frac{1}{2} = 1$**   **61.** $\frac{7}{8} - \frac{7}{16}$ **$1 - \frac{1}{2} = \frac{1}{2}$**   **62.** $\frac{4}{5} - \frac{9}{10}$ **1 − 1 = 0**

Solve. Round to the nearest tenth if necessary. (Lesson 3-3)

63. $40 = 0.8x$ **50**   **64.** $10r = 61$ **6.1**   **65.** $0.07t = 25$ **357.1**   **66.** $56 = 0.32n$ **175**

▶ **GET READY for the Next Lesson**

Solve each equation. Check your solution. (Lesson 3-3)

67. $14 = n \cdot 20$ **0.7**

68. $25 = n \cdot 40$ **0.625**

69. $28.5 = n \cdot 38$ **0.75**

70. $36 = n \cdot 80$ **0.45**

7-4

Algebra: The Percent Equation

PACING: **Regular:** 1 period, **Block:** 0.5 period

Options for Differentiated Instruction

ELL = English Language Learner   **AL** = Above or Beyond Grade Level   **SS** = Struggling Students   **SN** = Special Needs

Reviewing the Concept   **SN**

Use before beginning Lesson 7-4.

Remind students that to write a decimal as a percent, they need to multiply the decimal by 100, or move the decimal two spaces to the right.

Example:

0.35 as a percent is 0.35 × 100 ⟶ 35%

0.125 as a percent is 0.125 × 100 ⟶ 12.5%

Have students add this to their resource sheet if needed.

Using Models   **ELL** **AL** **SS** **SN**

Use before presenting the Examples.

Have students draw an 8 × 12 rectangle on grid paper. Then have them fold the rectangle into quarters and shade one of the quarters.

Ask:

- How many squares are shaded? 24 squares
- What is 25% of 96? 24

Repeat, using different percents or different rectangles.

Creating Problems   **AL**

Use after presenting the Examples.

Have students create problems that can be solved using the percent equation. Have them write two of each kind of problem:

- finding the part,
- finding the percent, and
- finding the whole.

Have students exchange their problems with a classmate.

Leveled Lesson Resources

Chapter 7 Resource Masters

BL = Below or Approaching Grade Level   **OL** = On Grade Level   **AL** = Above or Beyond Grade Level   **ELL** = English Language Learner

---

Lesson Reading Guide
p. 29 **BL** **OL** **ELL**

7-4 Lesson Reading Guide
Algebra: The Percent Equation

Get Ready for the Lesson
Read the introduction at the top of page 361 in your textbook. Write your answers below.

1. Use the percent proportion to find how many species are insects. **751,520**

2. Express the percent of insects as a decimal. Then multiply the decimal by 854,000. **0.88; 751,520; They are the same.**

Read the Lesson

3. The word *percent* is used in both the percent proportion and the percent equation. There is one major difference in the way percent is represented in each. What is the difference? **Sample answer: In the percent proportion, percent is written as the numerator of a fraction whose denominator is 100. In the percent equation, percent is written as a decimal.**

4. Write the following problems as percent proportions and as percent equations.

Problem	Percent Proportion	Percent Equation
9 is 60% of what number?	$\frac{9}{n} = \frac{60}{100}$	$9 = 0.6 \cdot n$
Find 50% of 6.	$\frac{n}{6} = \frac{50}{100}$	$n = 0.5 \cdot 6$
40% of what number is 48?	$\frac{48}{n} = \frac{40}{100}$	$48 = 0.4 \cdot n$
18 is what percent of 72?	$\frac{18}{72} = \frac{n}{100}$	$18 = n \cdot 72$

Remember What You Learned

5. Work with a partner. One person should ask a question like the questions given as examples in the concept summary box. The other person should name the type of percent problem and name the equation that should be used to solve the problem. Do not solve the equation. Then trade roles. Continue until each of you can name the problem type and the related equation easily. **See students' work.**

Study Guide and Intervention*
p. 30 **BL** **OL** **ELL**

7-4 Study Guide and Intervention
Algebra: The Percent Equation

To solve any type of percent problem, you can use the **percent equation**, part = percent · base, where the percent is written as a decimal.

Example 1 600 is what percent of 750?

600 is the part and 750 is the whole. Let n represent the percent.

part = percent · whole

$600 = n \cdot 750$ Write an equation.
$\frac{600}{750} = \frac{750n}{750}$ Divide each side by 750.
$0.8 = n$ Simplify.
$80\% = n$ Write 0.8 as a percent.

So, 600 is 80% of 750.

Example 2 45 is 90% of what number?

45 is the part and 90% or 0.9 is the percent. Let n represent the whole.

part = percent · whole

$45 = 0.9 \cdot n$ Write an equation.
$\frac{45}{0.9} = \frac{0.9n}{0.9}$ Divide each side by 0.9.
$50 = n$ The whole is 50.

So, 45 is 90% of 50.

Exercises

Write an equation for each problem. Then solve. Round to the nearest tenth if necessary.

1. What percent of 56 is 14?
$14 = n \cdot 56; 25\%$

2. 36 is what percent of 40?
$36 = n \cdot 40; 90\%$

3. 80 is 40% of what number?
$80 = 0.4 \cdot n; 200$

4. 65% of what number is 78?
$78 = 0.65 \cdot n; 120$

5. What percent of 2,000 is 8?
$8 = n \cdot 2,000; 0.4\%$

6. What is 110% of 80?
$n = 1.1 \cdot 80; 88$

7. 85 is what percent of 170?
$85 = n \cdot 170; 50\%$

8. Find 30% of 70.
$n = 0.3 \cdot 70; 21$

Skills Practice*
p. 31 **BL** **OL**

7-4 Skills Practice
Algebra: The Percent Equation

Write an equation for each problem. Then solve. Round to the nearest tenth if necessary.

1. 25% of 176 is what number?
$n = 0.25 \cdot 176; 44$

2. What is 90% of 20?
$n = 0.9 \cdot 20; 18$

3. 24 is what percent of 30?
$24 = n \cdot 30; 80\%$

4. 80% of what number is 94?
$94 = 0.8 \cdot n; 117.5$

5. What is 60% of 45?
$n = 0.6 \cdot 45; 27$

6. 9 is what percent of 30?
$9 = n \cdot 30; 30\%$

7. What percent of 125 is 25?
$25 = n \cdot 125; 20\%$

8. What is 120% of 20?
$n = 1.2 \cdot 20; 24$

9. 2% of what number is 5?
$5 = 0.02 \cdot n; 250$

10. 15% of 290 is what number?
$n = 0.15 \cdot 290; 43.5$

11. 16 is what percent of 4,000?
$16 = n \cdot 4,000; 0.4\%$

12. What is 140% of 60?
$n = 1.4 \cdot 60; 84$

13. 344.8 is what percent of 862?
$344.8 = n \cdot 862; 40\%$

14. 6% of what number is 21?
$21 = 0.06 \cdot n; 350$

15. What number is 60% of 605?
$n = 0.6 \cdot 605; 363$

16. 32% of 250 is what number?
$n = 0.32 \cdot 250; 80$

17. Find 30% of 70.
$n = 0.3 \cdot 70; 21$

18. What is 80% of 65?
$n = 0.8 \cdot 65; 52$

Practice*
p. 32 **OL** **AL**

7-4 Practice
Algebra: The Percent Equation

Write an equation for each problem. Then solve. Round to the nearest tenth if necessary.

1. What number is 27% of 52?
$n = 0.27 \cdot 52; n \approx 14.0$

2. Find 41% of 48.
$n = 0.41 \cdot 48; n \approx 19.7$

3. What percent of 88 is 33?
$n \cdot 88 = 33; n \approx 37.5\%$

4. 8 is what percent of 18?
$8 = n \cdot 18; n \approx 44.4\%$

5. What number is 33% of 360?
$n = 0.33 \cdot 360; n \approx 118.8$

6. What percent of 62 is 58?
$n \cdot 62 = 58; n \approx 93.5\%$

7. 55 is what percent of 100?
$55 = n \cdot 100; n = 55\%$

8. 22% of what number is 24.2?
$0.22 \cdot n = 24.2; n = 110$

9. 19 is 50% of what number?
$19 = 0.50 \cdot n; n = 38$

10. 25 is 32% of what number?
$25 = 0.32 \cdot n; n \approx 78.1$

11. 40% of what number is 28?
$0.40 \cdot n = 28; n = 70$

12. 30 is what percent of 60?
$30 = n \cdot 60; n = 50\%$

13. What percent of 5 is 2?
$n \cdot 5 = 2; n = 40\%$

14. 44% of 10 is what number?
$0.44 \cdot 10 = n; n = 4.4$

15. Find 110% of 88.
$1.10 \cdot 88 = n; n \approx 96.8$

16. What number is 60% of 21.8?
$n = 0.6 \cdot 21.8; n \approx 13.1$

17. What percent of 180 is 210?
$n \cdot 180 = 210; n \approx 116.7\%$

18. 220 is 95.3% of what number?
$220 = 0.953 \cdot n; n \approx 230.8$

19. **BASEBALL** A baseball player was at bat 473 times during the regular season. If he made a hit 31.5% of the times he was at bat, how many hits did he make during the regular season? Round to the nearest whole number if necessary. **149 hits**

ANALYZE GRAPHS For Exercises 20 and 21, use the graph shown. The total enrollment at Central High School is 798 students.

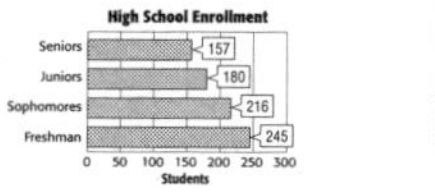

High School Enrollment
Seniors 157
Juniors 180
Sophomores 216
Freshman 245
0 50 100 150 200 250 300 Students

20. About what percent of the students at Central High are freshmen? Round to the nearest tenth if necessary. **30.7%**

21. About what percent of the students at Central High are seniors? Round to the nearest tenth if necessary. **19.7%**

Word Problem Practice*
p. 33 **OL** **AL**

7-4 Word Problem Practice
Algebra: The Percent Equation

1. **DINING** Jonas and Linda's restaurant bill comes to $23.40. They are planning to tip the waiter 15% of their bill. How much money should they leave for a tip? **$3.51**

2. **CHESS** The Briarwood Middle School chess club has 55 members. 22 of the members are in seventh grade. What percent of the members of the chess club are in seventh grade? **40%**

3. **TENNIS** In the city of Springfield, 75% of the parks have tennis courts. If 15 parks have tennis courts, how many parks does Springfield have altogether? **20 parks**

4. **COLLEGE** There are 225 students in eighth grade at Jefferson Middle School. A survey shows that 64% of them are planning to attend college. How many Jefferson eighth grade students are planning to attend college? **144 students**

5. **BASEBALL** In a recent season, the Chicago White Sox won 99 out of 162 games. What percent of games did the White Sox win? Round to the nearest tenth if necessary. **61.1%**

6. **HOUSING** In the Stoneridge apartment complex, 35% of the apartments have one bedroom. If there are 49 one-bedroom apartments, what is the total number of apartments at Stoneridge? **140 apartments**

7. **SPACE** On Mars, an object weighs 38% as much as on Earth. How much would a person who weighs 165 pounds on Earth weigh on Mars? **62.7 pounds**

8. **FOOTBALL** In a recent season, quarterback Jake Plummer of the Denver Broncos had 7 passes intercepted out of 456 attempts. What percent of Jake Plummer's passes were intercepted? Round to the nearest tenth if necessary. **1.5%**

Enrichment
p. 34 **OL** **AL**

7-4 Enrichment

Inherited Traits

Everyone inherits traits like eye color, hair color, and skin pigmentation from their parents and grandparents, but there are other interesting traits that are also inherited. Right or left handedness is an inherited trait, as are dimples in one's cheeks. The chart below shows some inherited traits and the percentage of the general population that shows the trait.

Trait	Percent of General Population
Right-handedness	87%
Left-handedness	13%
Dimples	75%
Earlobes attached	25%
Able to roll tongue	65%

1. Based on the information presented above, predict how many of your classmates will have each of these traits.

Trait	Number of Students
Right-handedness	See students' work
Left-handedness	See students' work
Dimples	See students' work
Earlobes attached	See students' work
Able to roll tongue	See students' work

2. Survey your classmates to find how many have these traits.

Trait	Number of Students	Percent of Students
Right-handedness	See students' work	See students' work
Left-handedness	See students' work	See students' work
Earlobes attached	See students' work	See students' work
Able to roll tongue	See students' work	See students' work
Dimples	See students' work	See students' work

3. Compare your predictions to your actual results. **See students' work. Sample answer: I predicted that 3 students in my class would be left-handed because that represents 13% of the students in the class. 5 students are left-handed, representing 21% of the students in the class.**

4. How do the class traits compare to the traits of the general population? **Sample answer: The percentage of students with dimples is higher than the percentage in the general population, but the percentage of students who can roll their tongues is lower than that of the general population.**

Additional Lesson Resources

* Also available in Spanish **ELL**

Transparencies
- *5-Minute Check Transparency*, Lesson 7-4

Other Print Products
- *Noteables™ Interactive Study Notebook with Foldables™*

Teacher Tech Tools
- *Interactive Classroom CD-ROM*, Lesson 7-4
- *AssignmentWorks*, Lesson 7-4

Student Tech Tools
glencoe.com
- Extra Examples, Chapter 7, Lesson 4
- Self-Check Quiz, Chapter 7, Lesson 4

MAIN IDEA

Solve problems by using the percent equation.

New Vocabulary

percent equation

Math Online

glencoe.com
• Extra Examples
• Personal Tutor
• Self-Check Quiz

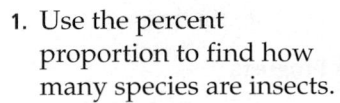**for the Lesson**

ARTHROPODS There are about 854,000 different species of spiders, insects, crustaceans, millipedes, and centipedes on Earth. The graph shows that 88% of the total numbers of species of arthropods are insects.

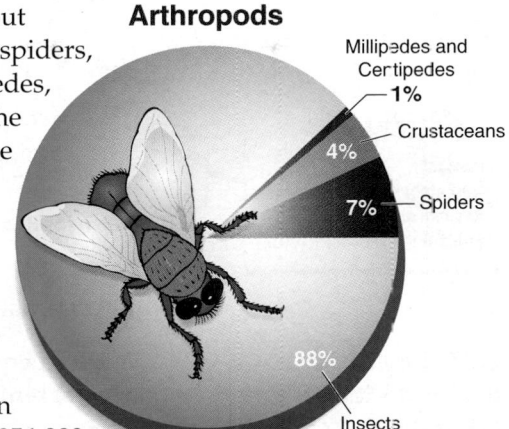

Arthropods

Millipedes and Centipedes — 1%
Crustaceans — 4%
Spiders — 7%
Insects — 88%

1. Use the percent proportion to find how many species are insects.

2. Express the percent of insects as a decimal. Then multiply the decimal by 854,000.

1. 751,520; 2. 0.88; 751,520; They are the same.

In Lesson 7-2, you used a percent proportion to find the missing part, percent, or whole. You can also use an equation. The percent equation is another form of the percent proportion.

$$\frac{\text{part}}{\text{whole}} = \text{percent}$$

The percent must be written as a decimal or fraction.

$$\frac{\text{part}}{\text{whole}} \cdot \text{whole} = \text{percent} \cdot \text{whole}$$

Multiply each side by the whole.

$$\text{part} = \text{percent} \cdot \text{whole}$$

This form is called the **percent equation**.

EXAMPLE **Find the Part**

① **What number is 12% of 150?** **Estimate** 12% of 150 ≈ 0.1 · 150 or 15

Write 12% as a decimal, 0.12. The whole is 150. You need to find the part. Let p represent the part.

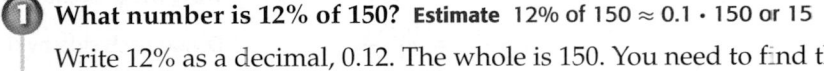

part = percent · whole

| p | $=$ | 0.12 | $\cdot$ | 150 | Write the percent equation. |
| p | $= 18$ | | | | Multiply. The part is 18. |

So, 18 is 12% of 150. **Check for Reasonableness** 18 is close to 15. ✔

Study Tip

Percent Equation
A percent must always be converted to a decimal or a fraction when it is used in an equation.

✓ **CHECK Your Progress**

a. $p = 0.06 \cdot 19$; 1.1
b. $p = 0.72 \cdot 90$; 64.8

Write an equation for each problem. Then solve. Round to the nearest tenth if necessary.

a. What is 6% of 19?   b. Find 72% of 90.

Lesson 7-4 Algebra: The Percent Equation **361**

Tips for New Teachers

Percent Equation

Remind students that the *whole* usually comes after the word *of* and the *part* usually comes before or after the word *is*. In Example 1, the *whole* is 150 and the *part* is the unknown.

1 **Focus**

Vertical Alignment

Before Lesson 7-4
Interpret percents as a part of a hundred; find decimal and percent equivalents for common fractions and explain why they represent the same value; compute a given percent of a whole number

Lesson 7-4
Calculate given percents of quantities and solve problems; write and solve one-step linear equations in one variable

After Lesson 7-4
Convert fractions to decimals and percents and use these representations in estimations, computations, and applications; solve problems that involve discounts, markups, commissions, and profit and compute simple and compound interest

2 **Teach**

Scaffolding Questions

Tell students that someone scored 90% on a math quiz.

Ask:
• If the quiz had 10 questions, how many questions did the student answer correctly? 9

• If the quiz had 20 questions, how many questions did the student answer correctly? 18

• If the quiz had 50 questions, how many questions did the student answer correctly? 45

• If the student answered 27 questions correctly, how many questions did the quiz have? 30.

Study Tip

Percent
Remember to write the decimal as a percent in your final answer.

c. $35 = n \cdot 70$; 50%
d. $75 = n \cdot 125$; 60%
e. $9 = n \cdot 40$; 22.5%
f. $27 = n \cdot 150$; 18%

g. $39 = 0.84 \cdot w$; 46.4
h. $0.26 \cdot w = 45$; 173.1
i. $0.14 \cdot w = 7$; 50
j. $24 = 0.32 \cdot w$; 75

EXAMPLE **Find the Percent**

2 **21 is what percent of 40?** **Estimate** $\frac{21}{40} \approx \frac{1}{2}$ or 50%

The part is 21. The whole is 40. You need to find the percent. Let n represent the percent.

$$\underbrace{part}_{} = \underbrace{percent}_{} \cdot \underbrace{whole}_{}$$

21	$=$	n	$\cdot$	40

Write the percent equation.

$$\frac{21}{40} = \frac{40n}{40}$$ Divide each side by 40.

$0.525 = n$ Since n represents the decimal form, the percent is 52.5%.

So, 21 is 52.5% of 40.

Check for Reasonableness 52.5% ≈ 50% ✔

✓ CHECK Your Progress

Write an equation for each problem. Then solve. Round to the nearest tenth if necessary.

c. 35 is what percent of 70?
d. What percent of 125 is 75?
e. What percent of 40 is 9?
f. 27 is what percent of 150?

EXAMPLE **Find the Whole**

3 **13 is 26% of what number?** **Estimate** $\frac{1}{4}$ of 48 = 12

The part is 13. The percent is 26, which when written as a decimal, is 0.26. You need to find the whole. Let w represent the whole.

$$\underbrace{part}_{} = \underbrace{percent}_{} \cdot \underbrace{whole}_{}$$

13	$=$	0.26	$\cdot$	w

Write the percent equation. 26% = 0.26

$$\frac{13}{0.26} = \frac{0.26w}{0.26}$$ Divide each side by 0.26.

$50 = w$ The number is 50.

So, 13 is 26% of 50.

Check for Reasonableness 50 is close to 48. ✔

✓ CHECK Your Progress

Write an equation for each problem. Then solve. Round to the nearest tenth if necessary.

g. 39 is 84% of what number?
h. 26% of what number is 45?
i. 14% of what number is 7?
j. 24 is 32% of what number?

Real-World Link . . . .
In the U.S., Anchorage, Alaska, has the highest percent of cell phone users.
Source: Polk's Research

 Real-World EXAMPLE

④ **CELL PHONES** A survey found that 25% of people age 18–24 gave up their home phone and only use a cell phone. If 3,264 people only use a cell phone, how many people were surveyed?

Words	3,264 people is 25% of what number of people?
Variable	Let n represent the number of people.
Equation	$3{,}264 \;=\; 0.25 \;\cdot\; n$

$3{,}264 = 0.25 \cdot n$ Write the percent equation. 25% = 0.25

$\dfrac{3{,}264}{0.25} = \dfrac{0.25n}{0.25}$ Divide each side by 0.25. Use a calculator.

$13{,}056 \approx n$ Simplify.

The number of people surveyed is about 13,056.

✔ **CHECK Your Progress**

k. **POPULATION** The Louisville-Jefferson County metropolitan area contains 17.2% of the population of Kentucky. If the population of Kentucky is about 4,040,000 people, what is the population of the Louisville-Jefferson County metropolitan area? **about 694,880 people**

Types of Percent Problems   Concept Summary

Type	Example	Equation
Find the Part	What number is 50% of 6?	$p = 0.5 \cdot 6$
Find the Percent	3 is what percent of 6?	$3 = n \cdot 6$
Find the Whole	3 is 50% of what number?	$3 = 0.5 \cdot w$

★ indicates multi-step problem

✔ **CHECK Your Understanding**

Examples 1–3
(pp. 361–362)

Write an equation for each problem. Then solve. Round to the nearest tenth if necessary.

1. What number is 88% of 300?
$p = 0.88 \cdot 300$; 264

2. What number is 12% of 250?
$p = 0.12 \cdot 250$; 30

3. 75 is what percent of 150?
$75 = n \cdot 150$; 50%

4. 24 is what percent of 120?
$24 = n \cdot 120$; 20%

5. 3 is 12% of what number?
$3 = 0.12 \cdot w$; 25

6. 84 is 60% of what number?
$84 = 0.6 \cdot w$; 140

Example 4
(p. 363)

7. **BUSINESS** A local bakery sold 60 loaves of bread in one day. If 65% of these were sold in the afternoon, how many loaves were sold in the afternoon?
39 loaves

Lesson 7-4 Algebra: The Percent Equation   **363**

ADDITIONAL EXAMPLE

 MOVIES Of the 1250 people surveyed, 36% preferred comedies over action movies. How many people preferred comedies?
450 people

③ Practice

✔ **Formative Assessment**

Use Exercises 1–7 to check for understanding.

Then use the chart on the next page to customize your assignments for students.

Intervention You may wish to use the Study Guide and Intervention Master on page 30 of the *Chapter 7 Resource Masters* for additional reinforcement.

Odd/Even Assignments

Exercises 8–23 are structured so that students practice the same concepts whether they are assigned odd or even problems.

Estimation

Tips for New Teachers

Remind students that a good way to check the reasonableness of their answers is by estimating. Encourage students to use mental math to estimate the unknown value in the percent equation.

13. $26 = n \cdot 96; 27.1\%$

14. $98 = n \cdot 392; 25\%$

15. $30 = n \cdot 64; 46.9\%$

16. $1.45 = 0.33 \cdot w;$ 4.4

17. $84 = 0.75 \cdot w; 112$

29. about 42%

▶ Practice and Problem Solving

HOMEWORK HELP

For Exercises	See Examples
8–11	1
12–15	2
16–19	3
20–23	4

Exercise Levels
A: 8–23
B: 24–32
C: 33–35

Write an equation for each problem. Then solve. Round to the nearest tenth if necessary. 8. $p = 0.65 \cdot 98; 63.7$ 11. $p = 0.53 \cdot 470; 249.1$ 12. $9 = n \cdot 45; 20\%$

8. What number is 65% of 98?

9. Find 39% of 65. $p = 0.39 \cdot 65; 25.4$

10. Find 24% of 25. $p = 0.24 \cdot 25; 6$

11. What number is 53% of 470?

12. 9 is what percent of 45?

13. What percent of 96 is 26?

14. What percent of 392 is 98?

15. 30 is what percent of 64?

16. 33% of what number is 1.45?

17. 84 is 75% of what number?

18. 17 is 40% of what number? $17 = 0.4 \cdot w; 42.5$

19. 80% of what number is 64? $64 = 0.8 \cdot w; 80$

20. **BOOKS** Emma bought 6 new books for her collection. This increased her collection by 12%. How many books did she have before her purchases?   **50 books**

21. **VIDEO GAMES** A store sold 550 video games during the month of December. If this made up 12.5% of their yearly video game sales, about how many video games did the store sell all year?   **4,400 games**

22. **MEASUREMENT** The length of Giselle's arm is 27 inches. The length of her lower arm is 17 inches. About what percent of Giselle's arm is her lower arm?   **63%**

23. **LOBSTERS** Approximately 0.02% of North Atlantic lobsters are born bright blue in color. Out of 5,000 North Atlantic lobsters, how many would you expect to be blue in color?   **1**

Write an equation for each problem. Then solve. Round to the nearest tenth if necessary. $p = 0.004 \cdot 82.1; 0.3$

24. Find 135% of 64. $p = 1.35 \cdot 64; 86.4$ 25. What number is 0.4% of 82.1?

26. 450 is 75.2% of what number? $450 = 0.752 \cdot w; 598.4$

27. What percent of 200 is 230? $230 = n \cdot 200; 115\%$

28. **SALARY** Suppose you earn $6 per hour at your part-time job. What will your new hourly rate be after a 2.5% raise?   **$6.15**

ANALYZE GRAPHS About 672 million metric tons of corn was produced worldwide in 2006. For Exercises 29–31, use the graph at the right.

29. About what percent of corn was produced in the United States?

30. About what percent of corn was produced in Mexico?   **about 3%**

31. What percent of the world's corn production do Brazil and China make together?   **about 27%**

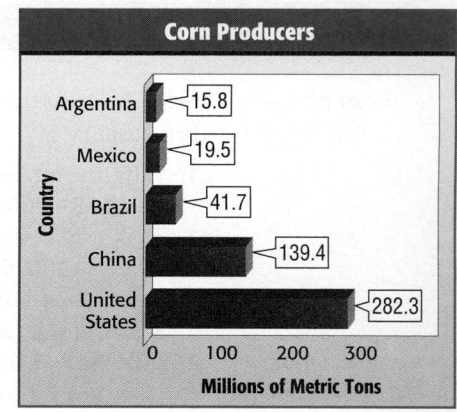

Corn Producers

Country	Millions of Metric Tons
Argentina	15.8
Mexico	19.5
Brazil	41.7
China	139.4
United States	282.3

DIFFERENTIATED HOMEWORK OPTIONS

Level	Assignment	Two-Day Option	
BL Basic	8–23, 33, 35–43	9–23 odd, 36–38	8–22 even, 33, 35, 39–43
OL Core	9–27 odd, 28–33, 35–43	8–23, 36–38	24–33, 35, 39–43
AL Advanced/Pre-AP	24–42 (optional: 43)		

EXTRA PRACTICE
See pages 685, 710.

32. MEASUREMENT A pool that holds 320 cubic feet of water is 84% filled to
★ capacity. Another pool that holds 400 cubic feet of water is 82.5% filled to
capacity. Which pool contains more water? How much more?
400-cubic foot pool; 61.2 cubic feet

H.O.T. Problems

33. OPEN ENDED Write a percent problem for which the percent is greater than
100% and the part is known. Use the percent equation to solve your
problem to find the base. **Sample answer: 30 is 125% of what number?; 24**

34. CHALLENGE If you need to find the percent of a number, explain how you
can predict whether the part will be less than, greater than, or equal to
the number. **See margin.**

35. WRITING IN MATH Compare the percent equation and the percent
proportion. Then explain when it might be easier to use the percent
equation rather than the percent proportion. **See margin.**

TEST PRACTICE

36. In a survey, 100 students were asked
to choose their favorite take-out food.
The table shows the results.

Favorite Take-Out Food	
Type of Food	**Percent**
Pizza	40
Sandwiches	32
Fried chicken	28

Based on this data, predict how many
out of 1,800 students would choose
sandwiches. **B**

A 504   C 680

B 576   D 720

37. If 60% of a number is 18, what is 90%
of the number? **H**

F 3   H 27

G 16   J 30

38. Taryn's grandmother took her out to
dinner. If the dinner was $34 and she
left a 20% tip, how much money did
Taryn's grandmother spend? **D**

A $6.80   C $39.50

B $27.20   D $40.80

Spiral Review

39. RESTAURANT Mitchell spent $13 on dinner. About how much money
should he tip the server if he wants to leave a 15% tip? (Lesson 7-3) **$1.95**

Find each number. Round to the nearest hundredth if necessary. (Lesson 7-2)

40. What percent of
15 is 20? **133.33%**

41. 20.5% of what
number is 35? **170.73**

42. What number is
0.5% of 10? **0.05**

▷ GET READY for the Next Lesson

43. PREREQUISITE SKILL To estimate the age of a dog in human years, count
the first year as 15 human years, the second year as 10 human years, and
all of the following years as 3 human years. How old in human years is a
6-year-old dog? (Lesson 1-1) **37 yr**

Lesson 7-4 Algebra: The Percent Equation **365**

4 Assess

Ticket Out the Door Have students
write a real-world problem involving
percent. Make sure they include two of
the three elements needed to solve the
problem (part, percent, whole).

 Formative Assessment

Check for student understanding of
concepts in Lessons 7-3 and 7-4.

 Quiz 2, p. 61

Additional Answers

34. Sample answer: If the percent is
less than 100%, then the part is
less than the base; if the percent
equals 100%, then the part equals
the base; if the percent is greater
than 100%, then the part is greater
than the base.

35. Sample answer: It may be easier
if the percent and the base are
known because after writing the
percent as a decimal or fraction,
the only step is to multiply. When
using the percent proportion, you
must first find the cross products
and then divide.

7-5

Problem-Solving Investigation
DETERMINE REASONABLE ANSWERS

PACING: **Regular:** 1 period, **Block:** 0.5 period

Options for Differentiated Instruction

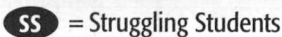 = English Language Learner   **AL** = Above or Beyond Grade Level   **SS** = Struggling Students   **SN** = Special Needs

Class Discussions   **SS** **SN**

Use before assigning the Exercises.

Before assigning problems for independent work, read aloud each problem and discuss which problem-solving strategy would be best to use for each problem. Have students write down which strategy to use so they have a place to start for each problem.

Ask:
- How do you decide which problem solving strategy to use?
- Are there particular words that would indicate to use one strategy over another? If so, what are they?
- What is the first step that you take when deciding which strategy to use?
- Are there problems that could be solved by using more than one strategy?

Visual Clues

Use with Exercise 10.

For students with organizational difficulties, provide a copy of the table below to help them solve Exercise 10.

First Roll	Second Roll	Total

Making Connections   **SN**

Use after students complete Lesson 7-5.

Have students develop a strategy for determining reasonable answers in another area of study. For example, if students are taking an Earth Science course, they may need to understand radiocarbon dating. This process is based on the half-life of carbon-14, or 5,730 years. Rounding the half-life of carbon-14 to 6,000 years might help students determine a reasonable, but not exact, answer to a radiocarbon dating problem.

Leveled Lesson Resources

Chapter 7 Resource Masters

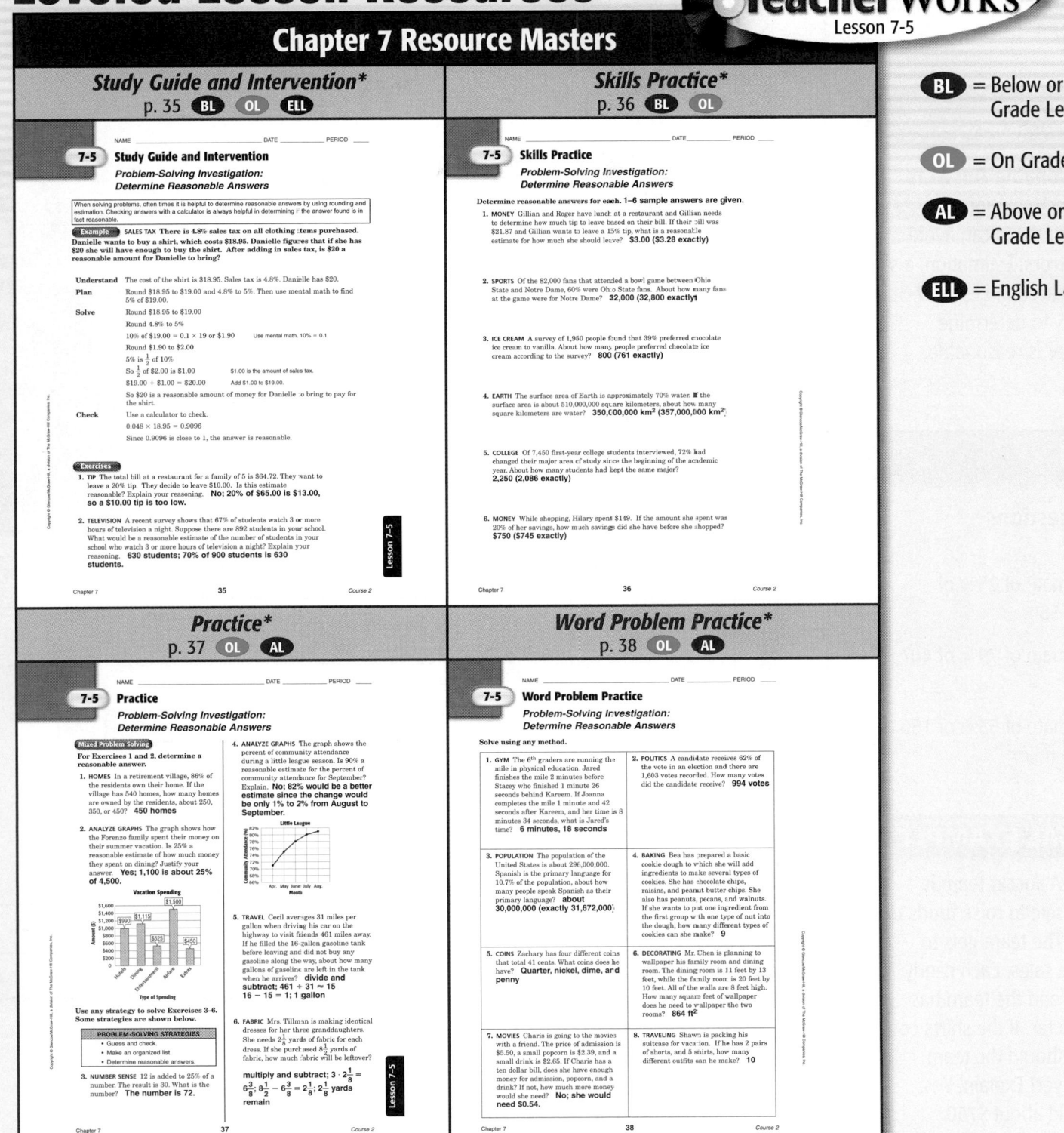

Study Guide and Intervention*
p. 35 BL OL ELL

NAME _____ DATE _____ PERIOD _____

7-5 Study Guide and Intervention
Problem-Solving Investigation:
Determine Reasonable Answers

When solving problems, often times it is helpful to determine reasonable answers by using rounding and estimation. Checking answers with a calculator is always helpful in determining if the answer found is in fact reasonable.

Example SALES TAX There is 4.8% sales tax on all clothing items purchased. Danielle wants to buy a shirt, which costs $18.95. Danielle figures that if she has $20 she will have enough to buy the shirt. After adding in sales tax, is $20 a reasonable amount for Danielle to bring?

Understand The cost of the shirt is $18.95. Sales tax is 4.8%. Danielle has $20.
Plan Round $18.95 to $19.00 and 4.8% to 5%. Then use mental math to find 5% of $19.00.
Solve Round $18.95 to $19.00.
Round 4.8% to 5%
10% of $19.00 = 0.1 × 19 or $1.90 Use mental math. 10% = 0.1
Round $1.90 to $2.00
5% is $\frac{1}{2}$ of 10%
So $\frac{1}{2}$ of $2.00 is $1.00 $1.00 is the amount of sales tax.
$19.00 + $1.00 = $20.00 Add $1.00 to $19.00.
So $20 is a reasonable amount of money for Danielle to bring to pay for the shirt.
Check Use a calculator to check.
0.048 × 18.95 = 0.9096
Since 0.9096 is close to 1, the answer is reasonable.

Exercises
1. TIP The total bill at a restaurant for a family of 5 is $64.72. They want to leave a 20% tip. They decide to leave $10.00. Is this estimate reasonable? Explain your reasoning. **No; 20% of $65.00 is $13.00, so a $10.00 tip is too low.**

2. TELEVISION A recent survey shows that 67% of students watch 3 or more hours of television a night. Suppose there are 892 students in your school. What would be a reasonable estimate of the number of students in your school who watch 3 or more hours of television a night? Explain your reasoning. **630 students; 70% of 900 students is 630 students.**

Chapter 7   35   Course 2

Skills Practice*
p. 36 BL OL

NAME _____ DATE _____ PERIOD _____

7-5 Skills Practice
Problem-Solving Investigation:
Determine Reasonable Answers

Determine reasonable answers for each. 1–6 sample answers are given.

1. MONEY Gillian and Roger have lunch at a restaurant and Gillian needs to determine how much tip to leave based on their bill. If their bill was $21.87 and Gillian wants to leave a 15% tip, what is a reasonable estimate for how much she should leave? **$3.00 ($3.28 exactly)**

2. SPORTS Of the 82,000 fans that attended a bowl game between Ohio State and Notre Dame, 60% were Ohio State fans. About how many fans at the game were for Notre Dame? **32,000 (32,800 exactly)**

3. ICE CREAM A survey of 1,950 people found that 39% preferred chocolate ice cream to vanilla. About how many people preferred chocolate ice cream according to the survey? **800 (761 exactly)**

4. EARTH The surface area of Earth is approximately 70% water. If the surface area is about 510,000,000 square kilometers, about how many square kilometers are water? **350,000,000 km² (357,000,000 km²)**

5. COLLEGE Of 7,450 first-year college students interviewed, 72% had changed their major area of study since the beginning of the academic year. About how many students had kept the same major? **2,250 (2,086 exactly)**

6. MONEY While shopping, Hilary spent $149. If the amount she spent was 20% of her savings, how much savings did she have before she shopped? **$750 ($745 exactly)**

Chapter 7   36   Course 2

Practice*
p. 37 OL AL

NAME _____ DATE _____ PERIOD _____

7-5 Practice
Problem-Solving Investigation:
Determine Reasonable Answers

Mixed Problem Solving

For Exercises 1 and 2, determine a reasonable answer.

1. HOMES In a retirement village, 86% of the residents own their home. If the village has 540 homes, how many homes are owned by the residents, about 250, 350, or 450? **450 homes**

2. ANALYZE GRAPHS The graph shows how the Forenza family spent their money on their summer vacation. Is 25% a reasonable estimate of how much money they spent on dining? Justify your answer. **Yes; 1,100 is about 25% of 4,500.**

Vacation Spending

4. ANALYZE GRAPHS The graph shows the percent of community attendance during a little league season. Is 90% a reasonable estimate for the percent of community attendance for September? Explain. **No; 82% would be a better estimate since the change would be only 1% to 2% from August to September.**

Little League

5. TRAVEL Cecil averages 31 miles per gallon when driving his car on the highway to visit friends 461 miles away. If he filled the 16-gallon gasoline tank before leaving and did not buy any gasoline along the way, about how many gallons of gasoline are left in the tank when he arrives? **divide and subtract; 461 ÷ 31 = 15 16 − 15 = 1; 1 gallon**

6. FABRIC Mrs. Tillman is making identical dresses for her three granddaughters. She needs $2\frac{1}{2}$ yards of fabric for each dress. If she purchased $8\frac{1}{2}$ yards of fabric, how much fabric is left over? **multiply and subtract; 3 · 2$\frac{1}{2}$ = 6$\frac{3}{2}$; 8$\frac{1}{2}$ − 6$\frac{3}{2}$ = 2$\frac{1}{8}$; 2$\frac{1}{8}$ yards remain**

Use any strategy to solve Exercises 3–6. Some strategies are shown below.

PROBLEM-SOLVING STRATEGIES
• Guess and check.
• Make an organized list.
• Determine reasonable answers.

3. NUMBER SENSE 12 is added to 25% of a number. The result is 30. What is the number? **The number is 72.**

Chapter 7   37   Course 2

Word Problem Practice*
p. 38 OL AL

NAME _____ DATE _____ PERIOD _____

7-5 Word Problem Practice
Problem-Solving Investigation:
Determine Reasonable Answers

Solve using any method.

1. GYM The 6th graders are running the mile in physical education. Jared finishes the mile 2 minutes before Stacey who finished 1 minute 26 seconds behind Kareem. If Joanna completes the mile 1 minute and 42 seconds after Kareem, and her time is 8 minutes 34 seconds, what is Jared's time? **6 minutes, 18 seconds**

2. POLITICS A candidate receives 62% of the vote in an election and there are 1,603 votes recorded. How many votes did the candidate receive? **994 votes**

3. POPULATION The population of the United States is about 296,000,000. Spanish is the primary language for 10.7% of the population, about how many people speak Spanish as their primary language? **about 30,000,000 (exactly 31,672,000)**

4. BAKING Bea has prepared a basic cookie dough to which she will add ingredients to make several types of cookies. She has chocolate chips, raisins, and peanut butter chips. She also has peanuts, pecans, and walnuts. If she wants to put one ingredient from the first group with one type of nut into the dough, how many different types of cookies can she make? **9**

5. COINS Zachary has four different coins that total 41 cents. What coins does he have? **Quarter, nickel, dime, and penny**

6. DECORATING Mr. Chen is planning to wallpaper his family room and dining room. The dining room is 11 feet by 13 feet, while the family room is 20 feet by 10 feet. All of the walls are 8 feet high. How many square feet of wallpaper does he need to wallpaper the two rooms? **864 ft²**

7. MOVIES Charis is going to the movies with a friend. The price of admission is $5.50, a small popcorn is $2.39, and a small drink is $2.65. If Charis has a ten dollar bill, does she have enough money for admission, popcorn, and a drink? If not, how much more money would she need? **No; she would need $0.54.**

8. TRAVELING Shawn is packing his suitcase for vacation. If he has 2 pairs of shorts, and 5 shirts, how many different outfits can he make? **10**

Chapter 7   38   Course 2

*** Also available in Spanish ELL**

BL = Below or Approaching Grade Level

OL = On Grade Level

AL = Above or Beyond Grade Level

ELL = English Language Learner

Additional Lesson Resources

Transparencies
• *5-Minute Check Transparency*, Lesson 7-5

Other Print Products
• *Noteables™ Interactive Study Notebook with Foldables™*

Teacher Tech Tools
• *Interactive Classroom CD-ROM*, Lesson 7-5
• *AssignmentWorks*, Lesson 7-5

Student Tech Tools
glencoe.com
• Extra Examples, Chapter 7, Lesson 5
• Self-Check Quiz, Chapter 7, Lesson 5

Lesson Notes

7-5

1 Focus

Determine Reasonable Answers
By learning to check solutions for reasonableness, students can avoid many common errors. Estimation, a skill that students practiced in Lesson 7-3, is often the best way to determine whether an answer is reasonable.

2 Teach

Scaffolding Questions

Ask:

• What is an estimate of 25% of $208.99? about $50

• What is an estimate of 79% of 40? about 32

• What is an estimate of 53% of 180 miles? about 90 miles

ADDITIONAL EXAMPLE

FUNDRAISER A soccer team is having a candy sale to raise funds to buy new shirts. The team gets to keep 25% of the sales. Each candy bar costs $1.50, and the team has sold 510 bars so far. If the shirts cost a total of $175, should the team order the shirts yet? Explain. **Yes; the team has sold about $750 (500 • 1.50), so they can keep about $187 ($\frac{1}{4}$ • 750), which is more than the cost of the shirts.**

Additional Examples are also in:
• Noteables™ Interactive Study Notebook with Foldables™
• Interactive Classroom PowerPoint® Presentations

7-5 Problem-Solving Investigation

MAIN IDEA: Solve problems by determining reasonable answers.

P.S.I. TEAM +

e-Mail: DETERMINE REASONABLE ANSWERS

Doug: My dad painted 25% of my bedroom in 28 minutes. I think the whole project will take about 3 hours.

YOUR MISSION: Determine whether it is reasonable for Doug's dad to paint the bedroom in 3 hours.

Understand	Twenty-five percent of the room has been painted in 28 minutes. Doug thinks it will take a total of 3 hours to paint the whole room.
Plan	Since 25% or $\frac{1}{4}$ of the room was painted in about 30 minutes, use a model of 25%.
Solve	Round 28 minutes to 30 minutes 30 minutes × 4 = 120 minutes 120 min = 2 h So, 2 hours would be a better estimate than 3 hours.
Check	Thirty minutes is $\frac{1}{2}$ hour. Since $\frac{1}{2}$ × 4 = 2, 2 hours is reasonable answer. ✔

Analyze The Strategy 1, 2. See margin.

1. Describe other problem-solving strategies that you could use to determine whether answers are reasonable.

2. **WRITING IN MATH** Write two word problems. One should have a reasonable answer and the other should not.

366 Chapter 7 Applying Percents

Differentiated Instruction

Verbal/Linguistic Have students create a word problem based on an interest rate of 2.761% and provide two estimated solutions: one being a reasonable answer and the other being an unreasonable answer. Have students exchange questions with a partner whose job is to determine which would be a reasonable answer and why.

Mixed Problem Solving ★ indicates multi-step problem

EXTRA PRACTICE
See pages 686, 710.

Determine reasonable answers for Exercises 3–6.

3. **SAVING** Aliayah saves $11 each month for her class trip. What is a reasonable estimate for the amount of money she will have saved after a year: about $100, $120, or $160? Explain.
Sample answer: $10 • 12 = $120

4. **SCHOOL** Of 423 students, 57.6% live within 5 miles of the school. What is a reasonable estimate for the number of students living within 5 miles of the school? Explain.
Sample answer: 0.6 • 400 or 240 students

5. **EXERCISE** A survey showed that 61% of middle school students do some kind of physical activity every day. If there are 828 middle school students in your school, would the number of students who exercise be about 300, 400, or 500? Explain.
500; 60% • 830 ≈ 500

6. **ANALYZE GRAPHS** A travel agency surveyed 140 families about their favorite vacation spots. Is 60, 70, or 80 families a reasonable estimate for the number of families that did *not* choose Hawaii? **70**

Favorite Vacation Spots

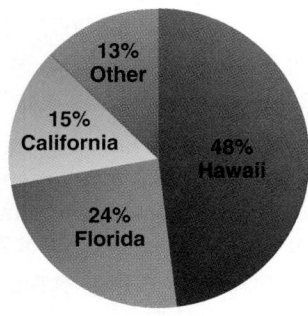

Use any strategy to solve Exercises 7–13. Some strategies are shown below.

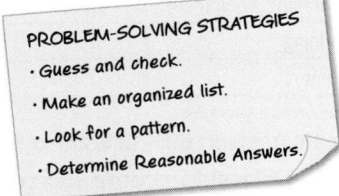

PROBLEM-SOLVING STRATEGIES
• Guess and check.
• Make an organized list.
• Look for a pattern.
• Determine Reasonable Answers.

7. **COINS** John has 10 coins that total $0.83. What are the coins? **2 quarters, 1 dime, 4 nickels, 3 pennies**

8. **ANALYZE GRAPHS** Refer to the graph. A pie is set out to cool. Is it reasonable to estimate that the pie will be 90°F after ten minutes of cooling?

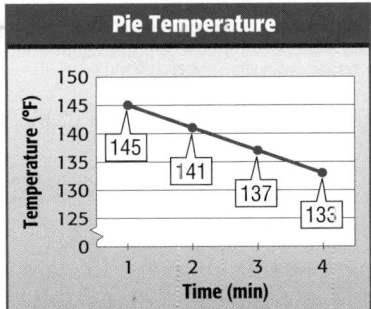

No, it is too low. 110°F would be a more reasonable estimate.

9. **SHOPPING** Deshawn wants to buy a shirt that has a regular price of $41, but is now on sale for 25% off. Is $25, $30, or $35 the best estimate for the cost of the shirt? **$30**

10. **BOWLING** In bowling, you get a spare when you knock down the ten pins in two throws. How many possible ways are there to get a spare? **9**

11. **TIPS** Shawnda decides to leave a 20% tip on a restaurant bill of $17.50. How much should she tip the restaurant server? **$3.50**

12. **FUNDRAISER** During a popcorn sale for
★ a fundraiser, the soccer team gets to keep 25% of the sales. One box of popcorn sells for $1.50, and the team has sold 510 boxes so far. Has the team raised a total of $175?
12, 13. See margin.

13. **MEASUREMENT** How many square yards of
★ carpet are needed to carpet the two rooms described below? Explain.

Room	Dimensions
living room	15 ft by 18 ft
TV room	18 ft by 20 ft

Lesson 7-5 Problem-Solving Investigation: Determine Reasonable Answers **367**

★ indicates multi-step problem

---

③ Practice

Using the Exercises

Exercises 1 and 2 can be used to check students' understanding of the determine reasonable answers strategy.

Exercises 3–6 give students an opportunity to practice the determine reasonable answers strategy.

Exercises 7–13 are structured so that students have the opportunity to practice many problem-solving strategies. You may wish to review some of the strategies students have studied.

• guess and check (p. 42)
• make an organized list (p. 190)

④ Assess

Yesterday's News Remind students that yesterday's lesson was about estimating percents of numbers. Have students write how yesterday's concepts helped them with today's material.

Additional Answers

1. Sample answer: Look for a rule or pattern in the data or number facts, estimation, guess and check, make an organized list, or work backward.

2. Sample answer: The cost of Traci's meal was $14.56. She wants to leave a 15% tip, so she left $1.50. (not reasonable) The cost of Traci's meal was $14.56. She wants to leave a 15% tip, so she left $2.20. (reasonable)

12. Yes; They have sold 510 • $1.50 or $765 worth of popcorn. So, they have earned 0.25 • $765 or $191.25, which is more than $175.

13. 15 • 18 + 18 • 20 = 630 ft². Then convert 630 ft² to square yards. 630 ÷ (3 • 3) = 70 yd².

Lesson 7-5 Problem-Solving Investigation: Determine Reasonable Answers **367**

CHAPTER 7 Mid-Chapter Quiz
Lessons 7-1 through 7-5

Find each number. Round to the nearest tenth if necessary. (Lesson 7-1)

1. Find 17% of 655. **111.4**

2. What is 235% of 82? **192.7**

3. Find 75% of 160. **120**

4. What number is 162.2% of 55? **89.2**

5. **MULTIPLE CHOICE** Ayana has 220 coins in her piggy bank. Of those, 45% are pennies. How many coins are not pennies? (Lesson 7-1) **A**

   A 121   C 109
   B 116   D 85

Find each number. Round to the nearest tenth if necessary. (Lesson 7-2)

6. What percent of 84 is 12? **14.3%**

7. 15 is 25% of what number? **60**

8. 85% of 252 is what number? **214.2**

ANALYZE GRAPHS For Exercises 9 and 10, refer to the graph that shows the results of a survey of 200 students' favorite DVDs.

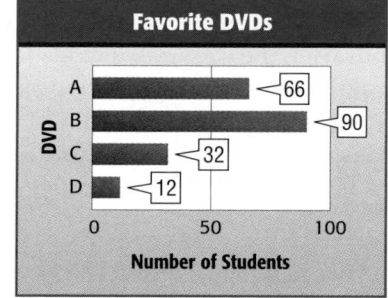

Favorite DVDs

9. What percent of students preferred DVD A? **33%**

10. Which DVD did about 15% of students prefer? **DVD C**

Estimate. (Lesson 7-3) **11–16. See margin for sample answers.**

11. 20% of 392   12. 78% of 112
13. 52% of 295   14. 30% of 42
15. 79% of 88   16. 41.5% of 212

17. **MULTIPLE CHOICE** A football player has made about 75% of the field goals he has attempted in his career. If he attempts 41 field goals in one season, about how many would he be expected to make? **B**

   A 35   C 25
   B 30   D 20

Write an equation for each problem. Then solve. Round to the nearest tenth if necessary. (Lesson 7-4)

18. What number is 35% of 72? $p = 0.35 \cdot 72$; **25.2**

19. 16.1 is what percent of 70? $16.1 = n \cdot 70$; **23%**

20. 27.2 is 68% of what number? $27.2 = 0.68 \cdot w$; **40**

21. 16% of 32 is what number? $p = 0.16 \cdot 32$; **5.1**

22. 55% of what number is 1.265? $1.265 = 0.55 \cdot w$; **2.3**

23. 17 is 40% of what number? $17 = 0.40 \cdot w$; **42.5**

24. **ANALYZE TABLES** The table shows the costs of owning a dog over an average 11-year lifespan. What percent of the total cost is veterinary bills? (Lesson 7-4) **about 26.9%**

Dog Ownership Costs	
Item	**Cost ($)**
Food	4,020
Veterinary Bills	3,930
Grooming, Equipment	2,960
Training	1,220
Other	2,470

Source: American Kennel Club

25. Sample answer: 60% of $850 = $510

25. **SHOPPING** A desktop computer costs $849.75 and the hard drive is 61.3% of the total cost. What is a reasonable estimate for the cost of the hard drive? (Lesson 7-5)

7-6 Percent of Change

PACING: **Regular:** 1 period, **Block:** 0.5 period

Options for Differentiated Instruction

ELL = English Language Learner   **AL** = Above or Beyond Grade Level   **SS** = Struggling Students   **SN** = Special Needs

Writing Problems **ELL** **AL** **SS**
Use after presenting Examples 1–3.

Have students write a percent of increase problem and a percent of decrease problem. To help them get started, ask the following questions.
- What information do you need to include for these types of problems?
- What are possible contexts for a percent of change problem?
- Where could you find realistic data for this type of problem?

Have students create an answer key for their problems and exchange them with a classmate to solve.

Preventing Mistakes **ELL** **SS** **SN**
Use with Check Your Understanding.

Some students may mistakenly want to divide the greater number into the lesser number. Encourage them to take the time to identify the amount of change and the original amount and write them as a ratio before calculating.

$$\frac{\text{amount of change} \longrightarrow}{\text{original amount} \longrightarrow}$$

Creating a Checklist **ELL** **SS** **SN**
Use before assigning the Exercises.

Have students create a checklist of steps for finding percent of change. A sample checklist is shown below.

> - Determine if the problem is a percent increase or percent decrease.
> - Subtract the two amounts.
> - Divide by the original amount.
> - Simplify.
> - Write as a percent.
> - Write the answer in sentence form.
>
> The percent of increase of _____ is _____.
> The percent of decrease of _____ is _____.

Have students exchange checklists and make suggestions for improving each other's checklist.

Leveled Lesson Resources

Chapter 7 Resource Masters

BL = Below or Approaching Grade Level   **OL** = On Grade Level   **AL** = Above or Beyond Grade Level   **ELL** = English Language Learner

---

Lesson Reading Guide
p. 39 BL OL ELL

7-6 Lesson Reading Guide
Percent of Change

Get Ready for the Lesson

Complete the Mini Lab at the top of page 369 in your textbook. Write your answers below.

Model each percent of change.

1. 25% increase   0% 100% 25%

2. 75% increase   0% 100% 75%

3. 30% increase   0% 100% 30%

4. Describe a model that represents a 100% increase, a 200% increase, and a 300% increase. **Sample answer: a straw that is twice as long, 3 times longer, and 4 times longer, respectively**

5. Describe how this process would represent a percent of decrease. **Subtract the percent of change from the original straw.**

Read the Lesson

6. In a percent of change, what are the two numbers that are being compared? **the number that represents the amount of change and the number that represents the original amount**

7. How can you tell if a percent of change is a percent of increase or a percent of decrease? **Sample answer: Compare the new amount to the original amount. If the original quantity is increased, then it is called a percent of increase. If the original quantity is decreased, then it is called a percent of decrease.**

8. Tell how to find the amount of increase and the amount of decrease. **The amount of increase is the new amount minus the original amount. The amount of decrease is the original amount minus the new amount.**

Remember What You Learned

9. Find an example of something in your life that has increased or decreased, such as your height in the past year. Calculate the percent of change and share your results with your class. **See students' work.**

Chapter 7   39   Course 2

Study Guide and Intervention*
p. 40 BL OL ELL

7-6 Study Guide and Intervention
Percent of Change

A **percent of change** is a ratio that compares the change in quantity to the original amount. If the original quantity is increased, it is a **percent of increase**. If the original quantity is decreased, it is a **percent of decrease**.

Example 1   Last year, 2,376 people attended the rodeo. This year, attendance was 2,950. What was the percent of change in attendance to the nearest whole percent?

Since this year's attendance is greater than last year's attendance, this is a percent of increase.

The amount of increase is 2,950 − 2,376 or 574.

percent of increase = amount of increase / original amount   ← new amount − original amount

= 574/2,376   Substitution

≈ 0.24 or 24%   Simplify.

Rodeo attendance increased by about 24%.

Example 2   John's grade on the first math exam was 94. His grade on the second math exam was 86. What was the percent of change in John's grade to the nearest whole percent?

Since the second grade is less than the first grade, this is a percent of decrease. The amount of decrease is 94 − 86 or 8.

percent of decrease = amount of decrease / original amount   ← original amount − new amount

= 8/94   Substitution

≈ 0.09 or 9%   Simplify.

John's math grade decreased by about 9%.

Exercises

Find each percent of change. Round to the nearest whole percent if necessary. State whether the percent of change is an *increase* or *decrease*.

1. original: 4 new: 5 **25% increase**
2. original: 1.0 new: 1.3 **30% increase**
3. original: 15 new: 12 **20% decrease**
4. original: $30 new: $18 **40% decrease**
5. original: 60 new: 63 **5% increase**
6. original: 160 new: 136 **15% decrease**
7. original: 7.7 new: 10.5 **36% increase**
8. original: 9.6 new: 5.9 **39% decrease**

Chapter 7   40   Course 2

Skills Practice*
p. 41 BL OL

7-6 Skills Practice
Percent of Change

Find each percent of change. Round to the nearest whole percent if necessary. State whether the percent of change is an *increase* or *decrease*.

1. original: 35 new: 70 **100%; inc.**
2. original: 8 new: 12 **50%; inc.**
3. original: 45 new: 30 **33%; dec.**
4. original: $350 new: $400 **14%; inc.**
5. original: $75 new: $60 **20%; dec.**
6. original: 250 new: 100 **60%; dec.**
7. original: $30 new: $110 **267%; inc.**
8. original: 35 new: 28 **20%; dec.**
9. original: $12.50 new: $15 **20%; inc.**
10. original: 80 new: 52 **35%; dec.**
11. original: 45 new: 63 **40%; inc.**
12. original: 120 new: 132 **10%; inc.**
13. original: $210 new: $105 **50%; dec.**
14. original: 84 new: 111 **32%; inc.**
15. original: $100 new: $84 **19%; dec.**
16. original: 6.8 new: 8.2 **21%; inc.**
17. original: 1.5 new: 2.5 **67%; inc.**
18. original: 91 new: 77 **15%; dec.**
19. original: $465.50 new: $350 **25%; dec.**
20. original: $87.05 new: $100 **15%; inc.**
21. original: 144 new: 108 **25%; dec.**
22. original: 20.8 new: 12.2 **41%; dec.**
23. original: $75 new: $15 **80%; dec.**
24. original: 8.6 new: 7 **19%; dec.**

Chapter 7   41   Course 2

Practice*
p. 42 OL AL

7-6 Practice
Percent of Change

Find each percent of change. Round to the nearest whole percent if necessary. State whether the percent of change is an *increase* or *decrease*.

1. 8 feet to 10 feet **25% increase**
2. 136 days to 85 days **38% decrease**
3. $0.32 to $0.37 **16% increase**
4. 62 trees to 31 trees **50% decrease**
5. 51 meters to 68 meters **33% increase**
6. 16.5 grams to 24.8 grams **50% increase**
7. 0.55 minutes to 0.1 minutes **82% decrease**
8. $180 to $210 **17% increase**
9. 2.9 months to 4.9 months **69% increase**
10. $\frac{1}{4}$ to $\frac{3}{8}$ **50% increase**
11. $\frac{1}{8}$ to $\frac{1}{4}$ **100% increase**
12. $\frac{4}{5}$ to $\frac{1}{5}$ **75% decrease**

13. **SURGERY** Recent developments in surgical procedures change the average healing time for some operations from 8 weeks to 3 weeks. **63% decrease**

14. **ROADS** The city added an extra lane in each direction to the 5-lane road. **40% increase**

GEOMETRY For Exercises 15 and 16, refer to the rectangle shown. Suppose the width is decreased by 3 inches.

15. Find the percent change in the perimeter. **30% decrease**

16. Find the percent change in the area. **50% decrease**

4 in.
6 in.

ANALYZE TABLES For Exercises 17 and 18, refer to the table that shows the average monthly rainfall during the first six months of the year for Singapore.

Month	Average Rainfall (inches/month)
January	9.4
February	6.5
March	6.8
April	6.6
May	6.7
June	6.4

17. Between which two consecutive months is the percent of decrease the greatest? What is the percent change? Round to the nearest whole percent. **January to February; 31%**

18. Between which two consecutive months is the percent of increase the least? What is the percent change? Round to the nearest whole percent. **April to May; 2%**

Chapter 7   42   Course 2

Word Problem Practice*
p. 43 OL AL

7-6 Word Problem Practice
Percent of Change

1. **SHOES** A popular brand of running shoes costs a local store $68 for each pair. If the store sells the shoes for $119, what is the percent of increase in the price? **75%**

2. **CLUBS** Last year the backgammon club had 30 members. This year the club has 24 members. Find the percent of decrease in the number of members. **20%**

3. **READING** In the seventh grade, Rachel read 15 books. In the eighth grade, she read 18 books. Find the percent of increase in the number of books Rachel read. **20%**

4. **VOTES** Last year 762 students voted in the student council election at San Bruno Middle School. This year 721 students voted. To the nearest tenth, what was the percent of change in the number of students that voted? **5.4% decrease**

5. **HEIGHT** When Hugo was 9 years old he was 56 inches tall. Hugo is now 12 years old and he is 62 inches tall. Find the percent of increase in Hugo's height to the nearest tenth. **10.7%**

6. **PLANTS** Alicia planted 45 tulip bulbs last year. This year she plans to plant 65 bulbs. Find the percent of increase in the number of tulip bulbs to the nearest tenth. **44.4%**

7. **PICTURES** The 2008 yearbook at Middleton Middle School had 236 candid pictures of students. The 2007 yearbook had 214 candid pictures of students. To the nearest tenth, what was the percent of change in the number of candid student pictures from 2007 to 2008? **10.3% increase**

8. **POPULATION** In 1990, there were 4,298,000 Mexican immigrants living in the United States. In 2000, this number had increased to 7,858,000. Find the percent of increase to the nearest tenth. **82.8%**

Chapter 7   43   Course 2

Enrichment
p. 44 OL AL

7-6 Enrichment

A Taxing Exercise

People who earn income are required by law to pay taxes. The amount of tax a person owes is computed by first subtracting the amount of all *exemptions* and *deductions* from the amount of income, then using a tax table like this.

Schedule X–Use if your filing status is **Single**

If the amount on Form 1040, line 37, is: Over—	But not over—	Enter on Form 1040, line 38	of the amount over—
$0	$20,350	----------------15%	$0
20,350	49,300	$3,052.50 + 28%	20,350
49,300	--------	11,158.50 + 31%	49,300

Compute each person's income. Subtract $5,550 for each person's exemption and deduction. Then use the tax rate schedule to compute the amount of federal tax owed.

1. A cashier works 40 hours each week, earns $7.50 per hour, and works 50 weeks each year. **$1,417.50**

2. A newspaper carrier works each day, delivers 154 papers daily, and earns $0.12 delivering each paper. **$179.28**

3. A baby-sitter earns $3.50 per hour per child. During a year, the baby-sitter works with two children every Saturday for 8 hours and with three children every other Sunday for 6 hours. **$0.00**

4. While home from college for the summer, a painter earns $17.00 per hour, working 45 hours each week for 15 weeks. **$888.75**

5. Working before and after school in the school bookstore, an employee works 2.5 hours each day for 170 days and earns $4.60 per hour. **$0.00**

6. After graduating from college, a computer programmer accepts a position earning $2,450 monthly. **$4,032.50**

Chapter 7   44   Course 2

Additional Lesson Resources

* Also available in Spanish ELL

Transparencies

- *5-Minute Check Transparency,* Lesson 7-6

Other Print Products

- *Teaching Mathematics with Manipulatives*
- *Noteables™ Interactive Study Notebook with Foldables™*

Teacher Tech Tools

- *Interactive Classroom CD-ROM,* Lesson 7-6
- *AssignmentWorks,* Lesson 7-6

Student Tech Tools

glencoe.com

- Extra Examples, Chapter 7, Lesson 6
- Self-Check Quiz, Chapter 7, Lesson 6

Percent of Change

MAIN IDEA

Find the percent of increase or decrease.

New Vocabulary

percent of change
percent of increase
percent of decrease

MAIN IDEA

Find the percent of increase or decrease.

New Vocabulary

percent of change
percent of increase
percent of decrease

Math Online

glencoe.com

• Concepts In Motion
• Extra Examples
• Personal Tutor
• Self-Check Quiz

MINI Lab

You can model a 50% increase using straws.

100%

50%

150%

• Begin with two straws. The first straw will represent 100%.
• Cut the second straw in half. One part represents 50%.
• Tape the two straws together. This new straw represents a 50% increase or 150% of the original straw.

Model each percent of change.

1. 25% increase   2. 75% increase   3. 30% increase
1–3. See margin.
4. Describe a model that represents a 100% increase, a 200% increase, and a 300% increase. **See Ch. 7 Answer Appendix.**

5. Describe how this process would change to show percent of decrease. **See Ch. 7 Answer Appendix.**

One way to describe a change in quantities is to use percent of change.

Percent of Change		*Key Concept*
Words	A **percent of change** is a ratio that compares the change in quantity to the original amount.	
Equation	$\text{percent of change} = \dfrac{\text{amount of change}}{\text{original amount}}$	

The percent of change is based on the original amount. If the original quantity is increased, then it is called a **percent of increase**. If the original quantity is decreased, then it is called a **percent of decrease**.

$$\text{percent of increase} = \frac{\text{amount of increase}}{\text{original amount}} \longleftarrow \text{new} - \text{original}$$

$$\text{percent of decrease} = \frac{\text{amount of decrease}}{\text{original amount}} \longleftarrow \text{original} - \text{new}$$

Lesson 7-6 Percent of Change   **369**

---

1 Focus

Vertical Alignment

Before Lesson 7-6
Interpret percents as a part of a hundred; find decimal and percent equivalents for common fractions and explain why they represent the same value; compute a given percent of a whole number

Lesson 7-6
Interpret and use ratios in different contexts

After Lesson 7-6
Calculate the percent of increases and decreases of a quantity; solve problems that involve discounts, markups, commissions, and profit and compute simple and compound interest

2 Teach

MINI Lab

Have students compare the lengths of the original straw and the taped straw. Make sure they understand that the taped straw is $1\frac{1}{2}$ times as long as the original straw.

Scaffolding Questions

Ask:

• If a baseball player hit 20 home runs last year and 25 home runs this year, how did his home run production change? **increased by 5 home runs**

• If a football player rushed 83 yards per game last year and 60 yards per game this year, how did his yardage change? **decreased by 23 yards**

• If a basketball player made 14 points per game last year and 21 points per game this year, how did her points production change? **increased by 7 points**

Additional Answers

1. 0%   100% 25%

2. 0%   100%   75%

3. 0%   100% 30%

Lesson 7-6 Percent of Change   **369**

✔ **Formative Assessment**

Use the Check Your Progress exercises after each Example to determine students' understanding of concepts.

ADDITIONAL EXAMPLES

1 SHOPPING Last year a sweater sold for $56. This year the same sweater sells for $60. Find the percent of change in the cost of the sweater. Round to the nearest percent if necessary. **7% increase**

2 ATTENDANCE On the first day of school this year, 435 students reported to Howard Middle School. Last year on the first day, 460 students attended. Find the percent of change for the first day's attendance. Round to the nearest whole percent if necessary. **5% decrease**

Additional Examples are also in:

• Noteables™ Interactive Study Notebook with Foldables™

• Interactive Classroom PowerPoint® Presentations

EXAMPLE   **Find Percent of Increase**

1 GASOLINE Find the percent of change in the cost of gasoline from 1981 to 2007. Round to the nearest whole percent if necessary.

1981

2007

Since the 2007 price is greater than the 1981 price, this is a percent of increase. The amount of increase is $2.85 − $1.30 or $1.55.

$$\text{percent of increase} = \frac{\text{amount of increase}}{\text{original amount}}$$

$$= \frac{\$1.55}{\$1.30} \qquad \text{Substitution}$$

$$\approx 1.19 \qquad \text{Simplify.}$$

$$\approx 119\% \qquad \text{Write 1.19 as a percent.}$$

The cost of gasoline increased 119% from 1981 to 2007.

✔ **CHECK Your Progress**

a. **MEASUREMENT** Find the percent of change from 10 yards to 13 yards. **30% increase**

EXAMPLE   **Find Percent of Decrease**

2 DVD RECORDER Yusuf bought a DVD recorder for $280. Now, it is on sale for $220. Find the percent of change in the price. Round to the nearest whole percent if necessary.

Since the new price is less than the original price, this is a percent of decrease. The amount of decrease is $280 - $220 or $60.

$$\text{percent of decrease} = \frac{\text{amount of decrease}}{\text{original amount}}$$

$$= \frac{\$60}{\$280} \qquad \text{Substitution}$$

$$\approx 0.21 \qquad \text{Simplify.}$$

$$\approx 21\% \qquad \text{Write 0.21 as a percent.}$$

The price of the DVD recorder decreased by about 21 percent.

✔ **CHECK Your Progress**

b. **MONEY** Find the percent of change from $20 to $15. **25% decrease**

Study Tip

Percents
In the percent of change formula, the decimal representing the percent of change must be written as a percent.

3 The table shows about how many people attended the home games of a high school football team for five consecutive years. Which statement is supported by the information in the table?

Attendance of Home Games	
Year	Total Attendance (thousands)
2003	16.6
2004	16.4
2005	15.9
2006	17.4
2007	17.6

A The attendance in 2006 was 15% greater than the attendance in 2005.

B The greatest decrease in attendance occurred from 2003 to 2004.

C The attendance in 2005 was 3% less than the attendance in 2004.

D The greatest increase in attendance occurred from 2006 to 2007.

Read the Item

You need to determine which statement is best supported by the information given in the table.

Solve the Item

- Check **A.** The percent of change from 2005 to 2006 was $\frac{17.4 - 15.9}{15.9}$ or about 10%, not 15%.

- Check **B.**
  From 2003 to 2004, the decrease was $16.6 - 16.4$ or 0.2.
  From 2004 to 2005, the decrease was $16.4 - 15.9$ or 0.5.
  This statement is not supported by the information.

- Check **C.** The percent of change from 2004 to 2005 was $\frac{16.4 - 15.9}{16.4}$ or about 3%. This statement is supported by the information.

- Check **D.**
  From 2005 to 2006, the increase was $17.4 - 15.9$ or 1.5.
  From 2006 to 2007, the increase was $17.6 - 17.4$ or 0.2.
  This statement is not supported by the information.

The solution is **C**.

Test-Taking Tip

Check the Results If you have time, check all of the choices given. By doing so, you will verify that your choice is correct.

✓CHECK Your Progress

c. Which of the following represents the greatest percent of change?

H

F A savings account that had $500 now has $470.

G An MP3 player that stored 15 GB now stores 30 GB.

H A plant grew from 3 inches to 8 inches in one month.

J An airplane ticket that was originally priced at $345 is now $247.

Lesson 7-6 Percent of Change **371**

---

3 **TEST EXAMPLE** The table shows the annual city budget of Layton for four years.

Annual Budget City of Layton	
Year	Budget (millions of $)
2007	23.1
2008	24.9
2009	26.2
2010	25.5

Which statement is supported by the table? D

A The budget decreased and then increased.

B The greatest budget increase occurred from 2008 to 2009.

C The budget increased 15% from 2007 to 2010.

D The budget decreased about 3% from 2009 to 2010.

 Tips for New Teachers

Calculating Change

You may wish to point out that the amount of change—whether an increase or decrease—is always a positive number.

##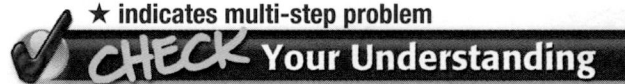

★ indicates multi-step problem

CHECK Your Understanding

Formative Assessment

Use Exercises 1–5 to check for understanding.

Then use the chart at the bottom of this page to customize your assignments for students.

Intervention You may wish to use the Study Guide and Intervention Master on page 40 of the *Chapter 7 Resource Masters* for additional reinforcement.

Odd/Even Assignments

Exercises 6–19 are structured so that students practice the same concepts whether they are assigned odd or even problems.

Find each percent of change. Round to the nearest whole percent if necessary. State whether the percent of change is an *increase* or a *decrease*.

Examples 1, 2
(p. 370)

1. 30 inches to 24 inches
   20% decrease
2. 20.5 meters to 35.5 meters
   73% increase
3. $126 to $150 **19% increase**
4. $75.80 to $94.75 **25% increase**

Example 3
(p. 371)

5. **MULTIPLE CHOICE** The table shows the number of youth 7 years and older who played soccer from 1998 to 2006. Which statement is supported by the information in the table? **C**

   A The greatest decrease in the number of players occurred from 1998 to 2000.

   B There were 7% fewer youth playing soccer in 2004 than in 2002.

   C The number of players in 2002 was 6% greater than the number of players in 2000.

   D There were 10% more youth playing soccer in 2000 than in 1998.

Playing Soccer	
Year	Number (millions)
1998	13.2
2000	12.9
2002	13.7
2004	13.3
2006	14.0

Source: National Sporting Goods Association

Practice and Problem Solving

HOMEWORK HELP	
For Exercises	See Examples
6–7, 14–15 18–19	1
8–13 16–17	2
39, 40	3

Exercise Levels
A: 6–19
B: 20–33
C: 34–38

9. 71% decrease
10. 30% decrease
20. 50% decrease
21. 75% decrease
22. 300% increase
23. 150% increase

For Exercises 6–19, find each percent of change. Round to the nearest whole percent if necessary. State whether the percent of change is an *increase* or a *decrease*.

6. 15 yards to 18 yards **20% increase**
7. 100 acres to 140 acres **40% increase**
8. $12 to $6 **50% decrease**
9. 48 notebooks to 14 notebooks
10. 125 centimeters to 87.5 centimeters
11. $15.60 to $11.70 **25% decrease**
12. 1.6 hours to 0.95 hour **41% decrease**
13. 132 days to 125.4 days **5% decrease**
14. $240 to $320 **33% increase**
15. 624 feet to 702 feet **13% increase**

16. **BOOKS** On Monday, Kenya spent 60 minutes reading her favorite book. Today, she spent 45 minutes reading this book. **25% decrease**

17. **EXERCISE** Three months ago, Ernesto could walk 2 miles in 40 minutes. Today he can walk 2 miles in 25 minutes. **38% decrease**

18. **SCHOOL** Last school year the enrollment of Gilboa Middle School was 465 students. This year the enrollment is 525. **13% increase**

19. **MONEY** Jake had $782 in his checking account. He now has $798.
    2% increase

Find each percent of change. Round to the nearest whole percent if necessary. State whether the percent of change is an *increase* or a *decrease*.

20. $\frac{1}{2}$ to $\frac{1}{4}$
21. $\frac{4}{6}$ to $\frac{1}{6}$
22. $\frac{1}{5}$ to $\frac{4}{5}$
23. $\frac{2}{3}$ to $\frac{5}{3}$

372 Chapter 7 Applying Percents

DIFFERENTIATED HOMEWORK OPTIONS			
Level	Assignment	Two-Day Option	
BL Basic	6–19, 34–36, 38–48	7–19 odd, 39, 40	6–18 even, 34–36, 38, 41–48
OL Core	7–23 odd, 24–36, 38–48	6–19, 39, 40	20–36, 38, 41–48
AL Advanced/Pre-AP	20–44 (optional: 45–48)		

MEASUREMENT For Exercises 24 and 25, refer to the rectangle at the right. Suppose the side lengths are doubled.

24. Find the percent of change in the perimeter. **100%**

25. Find the percent of change in the area. **400%**

8 cm

3 cm

26. **MUSIC PHONES** Between 2006 and 2007, music phone owners increased from 6.8 million to 33 million. Find the percent of increase. Round to the nearest whole percent. **385%**

27. **FIND THE DATA** Refer to the Data File on pages 16–19. Choose some data and write a real-world problem in which you would find the percent of change. **See students' work.**

28. **ANALYZE GRAPHS** Use the graphic shown to find the percent of change in CD sales from 2005 to 2006. **about 4.2%**

29. **SHOES** In 2009, shoe sales for a certain company were $25.9 billion. Sales are expected to increase by about 20% from 2009 to 2010. Find the projected amount of shoe sales in 2010. **about $31 billion**

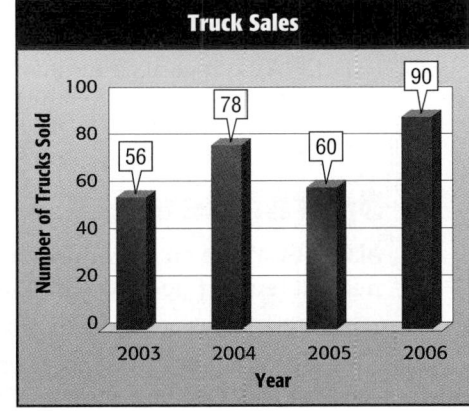

Drop in CD Sales

Year	
2005	283 million
2006	271 million

270   275   280   285   290
Sale of CDs (in millions)

Source: Fox News

★ 30. **BABYSITTING** The table shows how many hours Catalina spent babysitting during the months of April and May. If Catalina charges $6.50 per hour, what is the percent of change in the amount of money earned from April to May? **20% decrease**

Month	Hours Worked
April	40
May	32

ANALYZE GRAPHS For Exercises 31–33, refer to the graph.

34. Sample answer: The sale price of a T-shirt is $14. If the shirt originally cost $25, what is the percent discount? Answer: 44% decrease

31. Find the percent of decrease of truck sales from 2004 to 2005. Round to the nearest whole percent. **23%**

32. Find the percent of increase of truck sales from 2003 to 2004. Round to the nearest whole percent. **39%**

33. Between which two consecutive years is the percent of increase the greatest? What is the percent of increase? Round to the nearest whole percent. **2005 to 2006; 50%**

Truck Sales

Number of Trucks Sold

100
80
60
40
20
0

56   78   60   90

2003   2004   2005   2006
Year

EXTRA PRACTICE
See pages 686, 710.

H.O.T. Problems

34. **OPEN ENDED** Write a percent of change problem using the quantities 14 and 25, and state whether there is a percent of increase or decrease. Find the percent of change.

35. The $60 sound system since 10 is a greater part of 60 than of 90.

35. **NUMBER SENSE** The costs of two different sound systems were decreased by $10. The original costs of the systems were $90 and $60, respectively. Without calculating, which had greater percent of decrease? Explain.

Differentiated Instruction

Logical Learners Separate students into pairs. Tell them that a tree's height increased 10% from 2007 to 2008, and 5% from 2008 to 2009. Have students discuss whether the tree's height increased by 15% from 2007 to 2009. Then have them use the guess-and-check strategy to test their analyses. The tree's height did not increase by 15% from 2007 to 2009. Each percent of change is calculated separately; the 5% increase is compared to 2008's height, not to 2007's height.

36. Sade; Trish did not write a ratio comparing the change to the original amount.

36. **FIND THE ERROR** Sade and Trish are finding the percent of change from $52 to $125. Who is correct? Explain.

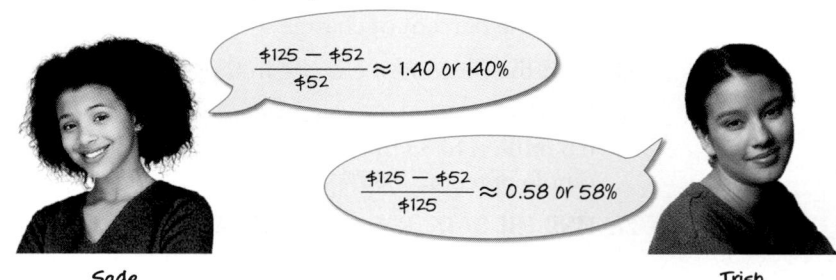

Sade

Trish

37. **CHALLENGE** If a quantity increases by 10% and then decreases by 10%, will the result be the original quantity? Explain. **See margin.**

38. **WRITING IN MATH** Explain how you know whether a percent of change is a percent of increase or a percent of decrease. **See margin.**

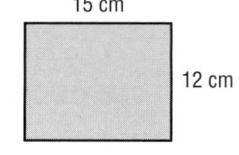 **TEST PRACTICE**

39. Which of the following represents the least percent of change? **D**

   A A coat that was originally priced at $90 is now $72.

   B A puppy who weighed 6 ounces at birth now weighs 96 ounces.

   C A child grew from 54 inches to 60 inches in 1 year.

   D A savings account increased from $500 to $550 in 6 months.

40. If each dimension of the rectangle is doubled, what is the percent of increase in the area? **H**

15 cm

12 cm

   F 100%   H 300%
   G 200%   J 400%

Spiral Review

ALGEBRA Write an equation for each problem. Then solve. Round to the nearest tenth if necessary. (Lesson 7-4)

41. **FOOD** Of 823 students 47.2% of the students chose pizza as their favorite food. What is a reasonable estimate for the number of students who chose pizza as their favorite food? Explain. (Lesson 7-5) **Sample answer: 0.5 • 800 or 400 students**

42. 30% of what number is 17?
   $0.3w = 17$; 56.7

43. What is 21% of 62?
   $n = 0.21 • 62$; 13.0

44. **SHOPPING** Four pounds of pecans cost $12.75. How much is this per pound? (Lesson 6-2) **about $3.19/lb**

▶ **GET READY for the Next Lesson**

PREREQUISITE SKILL Write each percent as a decimal. (Lesson 6-8)

45. 6.5% **0.065**   46. $5\frac{1}{2}\%$ **0.055**   47. $8\frac{1}{4}\%$ **0.0825**   48. $6\frac{3}{4}\%$ **0.0675**

7-7 Sales Tax and Discount

PACING: **Regular:** 1 period, **Block:** 0.5 period

Options for Differentiated Instruction

ELL = English Language Learner   **AL** = Above or Beyond Grade Level   **SS** = Struggling Students   **SN** = Special Needs

Reviewing Concepts **SS** **SN**

Use before presenting Lesson 7-7.

Review with students how to write percents as decimals. Make sure they understand how to work with single digit percents. They often forget to put a zero in the tenths place.

Vocabulary Development **ELL** **SS** **SN**

Use before assigning the Exercises.

Some students may confuse the discount with the discount price. Display the following on the board.

discount price = regular price − discount

Focus on the meaning of the terms by having students write simple descriptions of the terms on an index card.

Term	Description
rate of discount	a percent
discount	the amount of money the price is reduced
discount price	the cost after subtracting the discount

Use Real-World Data **ELL** **AL**

Use after students complete Lesson 7-7.

Bring in advertisements from a newspaper or flyer showing sale or discounted items. Then present the following problem.

> Your task is to spend as close to $100 as possible without going over. You have three coupons to use:
>
> | 20% off a single item | | 35% off a single item | | 40% off a single item |
>
> You may buy as many items as you need to get close to $100, but you need to use each coupon at least once.

Ask:
- Which coupons did you use with each item?
- How much did you save per item?
- What was your total amount of savings?
- What was the total amount of money you spent?

Have students include calculations to support their work.

Leveled Lesson Resources

Also on
TeacherWorks™
Lesson 7-7

Chapter 7 Resource Masters

BL = Below or Approaching Grade Level   **OL** = On Grade Level   **AL** = Above or Beyond Grade Level   **ELL** = English Language Learner

---

Lesson Reading Guide
p. 46 **BL** **OL** **ELL**

7-7 Lesson Reading Guide
Sales Tax and Discount

Get Ready for the Lesson

Read the introduction at the top of page 375 in your textbook. Write your answers below.

1. Calculate the sales tax by finding 4.25% of $1,849. Round to the nearest cent. **$78.58**

2. What will be the total cost including the sales tax? **$1,927.58**

3. Multiply 1.0425 and 1,849. How does the result compare to your answer in Exercise 2? **1,927.58; It is the same.**

Read the Lesson

4. In Example 1, the ≈ is used when the sales tax is found. Why is the value of 0.0575 times 140 rounded? **Sample answer: For dollar amounts, if the decimal has more than two places, the amount is rounded to the nearest cent.**

5. In Method 2 of Example 1, why is the sales tax added to 100%? **Sample answer: 100% represents the cost of the item; the cost of the item plus the sales tax equals 100% plus the percent that is sales tax.**

6. In Examples 2 and 3, the percent equation is used to find discount price and to find the original price. When using the percent equation, how do you represent the percent? **Sample answer: as a decimal**

Remember What You Learned

7. Use the Internet to find the state sales tax in your state, including tax on food, prescription drugs, and nonprescription drugs, if applicable. Then suppose you have a cold and you go to a local pharmacy. You purchase a box of crackers for $2.99 and a bottle of over-the-counter pain reliever for $8.49. Your doctor ordered a prescription for you for your cold and you pay $10 for this prescription. Using the sales tax for your state, what is your total cost at the pharmacy, including taxes? **See students' work.**

Chapter 7   46   Course 2

Study Guide and Intervention*
p. 47 **BL** **OL** **ELL**

7-7 Study Guide and Intervention
Sales Tax and Discount

Sales tax is a percent of the purchase price and is an amount paid in addition to the purchase price. **Discount** is the amount by which the regular price of an item is reduced.

Example 1 SOCCER Find the total price of a $17.75 soccer ball if the sales tax is 6%.

Method 1
First, find the sales tax.
6% of $17.75 = 0.06 · 17.75
≈ 1.07
The sales tax is $1.07.
Next, add the sales tax to the regular price.
1.07 + 17.75 = 18.82
The total cost of the soccer ball is $18.82.

Method 2
100% + 6 % = 106%   Add the percent of tax to 100%.
The total cost is 106% of the regular price.
106% of $17.75 = 1.06 · 17.75
≈ 18.82

Example 2 TENNIS Find the price of a $69.50 tennis racket that is on sale for 20% off.

First, find the amount of the discount d.
part = percent · whole
d = 0.2 · 69.50   Use the percent equation.
d = 13.90   The discount is $13.90.
So, the sale price of the tennis racket is $69.50 − $13.90 or $55.60.

Exercises

Find the total cost or sale price to the nearest cent.

1. $22.95 shirt; 7% sales tax **$24.56**
2. $39.00 jeans; 25% discount **$29.25**
3. $35 belt; 40% discount **$21**
4. $115.48 watch; 6% sales tax **$122.41**
5. $16.99 book; 5% off **$16.14**
6. $349 television; 6.5% sales tax **$371.69**

Chapter 7   47   Course 2

Skills Practice*
p. 48 **BL** **OL**

7-7 Skills Practice
Sales Tax and Discount

Find the total cost or sale price to the nearest cent.

1. $49.95 CD player; 5% discount **$47.45**
2. $69 shoes; 6% sales tax **$73.14**
3. $2.99 socks; 5.5% sales tax **$3.15**
4. $119 coat; 40% discount **$71.40**
5. $299 DVD player; 7% sales tax **$319.93**
6. $49 tie; 15% discount **$41.65**
7. $59 power tool; 5% sales tax **$61.95**
8. $17.99 CD; 10% discount **$16.19**
9. $79 cell phone; 20% discount **$63.20**
10. $65 concert ticket; 7.5% sales tax **$69.88**
11. $459 television; 30% discount **$321.30**
12. $19,995 car; 6.5% sales tax **$21,294.68**

Find the original price to the nearest cent.

13. boots: discount, 30% sale price, $62.50 **$89.29**
14. video game: discount, 15% sale price, $12.64 **$14.87**
15. drum set: discount, 10% sale price, $1,099 **$1,221.11**
16. gloves: discount, 30% sale price, $16.40 **$23.43**
17. sweater: discount, 30% sale price, $34 **$48.57**
18. sunglasses: discount, 20% sale price, $62.95 **$78.69**
19. dinner for two: discount, 5% sale price, $70 **$73.68**
20. bicycle: discount, 25% sale price, $147.85 **$197.13**

Chapter 7   48   Course 2

Practice*
p. 49 **OL** **AL**

7-7 Practice
Sales Tax and Discount

Find the total cost or sale price to the nearest cent.

1. $18 haircut; 10% discount **$16.20**
2. $299 lawn mower; 5% tax **$313.95**
3. $9.99 meal; 25% discount **$7.49**
4. $149 guitar; 20% discount **$119.20**
5. $15.75 music CD; 4% tax **$16.38**
6. $24 gym bag; 8% tax **$25.92**
7. $32.88 jacket; 50% discount **$16.44**
8. $3.45 coffee; 33% discount **$2.31**
9. $9.99 chair; 8½% tax **$10.84**

Find the original price to the nearest cent.

10. bracelet: discount, 40% sale price, $13.80 **$23.00**
11. bicycle: discount, 35% sale price, $79 **$121.54**

12. TICKETS State residents get discounts at various theme parks throughout the state. One theme park charges a state resident $51.70. If this price represents a 15% discount from the regular adult admission, find the cost of a regular adult admission to the nearest cent. **$60.82**

13. TRUCKS What is the sales tax on a $17,500 truck if the tax rate is 6%? **$1,050**

COMPUTERS For Exercises 14–16, use the following information.
Lionel is buying a computer that normally sells for $890. The state sales tax is 6%.

14. What is the total cost of the computer including tax? **$943.40**

15. If the computer is on sale with a 10% discount, what is the sale price of the computer before adding the sales tax? **$801.00**

16. What is the sales tax on the discounted price? **$48.06**

Chapter 7   49   Course 2

Word Problem Practice*
p. 50 **OL** **AL**

7-7 Word Problem Practice
Sales Tax and Discount

1. SKATEBOARDS Ines wants to buy a skateboard but she does not know if she has enough money. The price of the skateboard is $85 and the sales tax is 6%. What will be the total cost of the skateboard? **$90.10**

2. PRETZELS The Spanish club sold hot pretzels as a fund-raiser. The pretzels normally sold for $1.50, but near the end of the sale they wanted to sell as many as possible, so they reduced the price by 30%. What was the new price for a hot pretzel? **$1.05**

3. COMPUTERS Andrea ordered a computer on the Internet. The computer cost $1,499 plus 7½% sales tax. What was the total amount Andrea paid for her computer? **$1,611.43**

4. BOOKS Nate went shopping at a bookstore. The price of the book he selected was $14.95, but it had a sale sticker on it. When he paid for the book, he was charged $12.71 before sales tax was added. What was the percent of discount to the nearest percent? **15%**

5. CELL PHONES Justin is buying a cell phone that has a regular price of $149. The cell phone is on sale for 15% off the regular price. What will be the sale price? **$126.65**

6. MAGAZINES Ivan bought two magazines for $4.95 each. If the sales tax was 6.75%, what was the total amount that he paid for the magazines? **$10.57**

7. MOVIES A video store is having a sale in which DVDs are on sale for 20% off. During this sale, what is the cost of three DVDs that regularly cost $16.99? **$40.78**

8. MODELS The original price of a collectible model airplane is $115. The discounted price is $99. What is the percent of discount to the nearest percent? **14%**

Chapter 7   50   Course 2

Enrichment
p. 51 **OL** **AL**

7-7 Enrichment

Taxes

Texas is one of the few states that does not impose a state income tax on residents. However, the state does collect sales and use taxes. The Texas state sales tax rate is 6.25%. Local taxing authorities can require additional tax of up to 2%, raising the total possible tax rate to 8.25%.

Use the Sales and Use Tax Chart below to solve the following problems.

Texas City	Total Sales and Use Tax
Abilene	8.25%
Corral City	8%
Sadler	7.25%
Ackerly	7.75%
San Antonio	8.125%
Raccoon Bend	6.75%
Dallas	8.25%

1. Kendra purchases a sweater that costs $24.99 at the Corral City Mall. What is the total cost of the sweater? **$26.99**

2. Brandon agrees to buy a new car for $21,525. As an employee of the company that produces the car, he is entitled to an additional 15% discount. He must pay the Dallas City sales tax. What is the total amount Brandon will pay for his new car? **$19,805.69**

3. While at the Abilene Outlet Store, Barbara purchases an outfit that is regularly priced $113.49 on sale for $99.00. What is the percent of discount? **12.8%**

4. Sara pays a total of $32.43 for an item after a 25% discount and the Ackerly City tax were applied. What is the original amount of Sara's purchase? **$40.13**

5. Davis makes a list of the cost of each item he would like to buy with his $100.00 gift card. Determine if Davis has enough money to purchase everything on his list after the Sadler City tax is applied. If not, how much more money will he need? If so, what is the gift card balance?

Item	Cost of Item
CD	$14.99
DVD	$19.99
Headphones	$59.99

No, Davis will need an additional $1.86 to purchase all of the items on his list.

Chapter 7   51   Course 2

Additional Lesson Resources

* Also available in Spanish **ELL**

Transparencies
- *5-Minute Check Transparency*, Lesson 7-7

Other Print Products
- *Teaching Mathematics with Manipulatives*
- *Noteables™ Interactive Study Notebook with Foldables™*

Teacher Tech Tools
- *Interactive Classroom CD-ROM*, Lesson 7-7
- *AssignmentWorks*, Lesson 7-7

Student Tech Tools
glencoe.com
- Extra Examples, Chapter 7, Lesson 7
- Self-Check Quiz, Chapter 7, Lesson 7

Sales Tax and Discount

MAIN IDEA

Solve problems involving sales tax and discount.

New Vocabulary

sales tax
discount

Math Online

glencoe.com

• Extra Examples
• Personal Tutor
• Self-Check Quiz

▷ **GET READY for the Lesson**

KAYAKS Horatio plans to buy a new kayak that costs $1,849. He lives in North Carolina where there is a 4.25% sales tax.

1. Calculate the sales tax by finding 4.25% of $1,849. Round to the nearest cent. **$78.58**

2. What will be the total cost including the sales tax? **$1,927.58**

3. Multiply 1.0425 and 1,849. How does the result compare to your answer in Exercise 2? **1,927.58; It is the same.**

Sales tax is an additional amount of money charged on items that people buy. The total cost of an item is the regular price plus the sales tax.

EXAMPLE Find the Total Cost

① **ELECTRONICS** A DVD player costs $140, and the sales tax is 5.75%. What is the total cost of the DVD player?

METHOD 1 Add sales tax to the regular price.

First, find the sales tax.

5.75% of $140 = 0.0575 × 140   Write 5.75% as a decimal.
            = 8.05   The sales tax is $8.05.

Next, add the sales tax to the regular price.
$8.05 + $140 = $148.05

METHOD 2 Add the percent of tax to 100%.

100% + 5.75% = 105.75%   Add the percent of tax to 100%.

The total cost is 105.75% of the regular price.

105.75% of $140 = 1.0575 × $140   Write 105.75% as a decimal.
              = $148.05   Multiply.

So, the total cost of the DVD player is $148.05.

✓ **CHOOSE Your Method**

a. **CLOTHES** What is the total cost of a sweatshirt if the regular price is $42 and the sales tax is $5\frac{1}{2}$%? **$44.31**

Study Tip

Sales Tax and Discount
If both are represented as percents, sales tax is a percent of increase, and discount is a percent of decrease.

Discount is the amount by which the regular price of an item is reduced. The sale price is the regular price minus the discount.

1 Focus

Vertical Alignment

Before Lesson 7-7
Interpret percents as a part of a hundred; find decimal and percent equivalents for common fractions and explain why they represent the same value; compute a given percent of a whole number

Lesson 7-7
Calculate given percents of quantities and solve problems

After Lesson 7-7
Solve problems that involve discounts, markups, commissions, and profit and compute simple and compound interest

2 Teach

Scaffolding Questions

Ask:

• If I buy a radio for $100, and the tax is 5%, how much will I pay? $105

• If I buy a chair for $100, and the tax is 3%, how much will I pay? $103

• If a video game normally costs $100, but is on sale at a 10% discount, how much will it cost? $90

✓ **Formative Assessment**

Use the Check Your Progress exercises after each Example to determine students' understanding of concepts.

Tips for New Teachers

Sales Tax

It may be helpful to point out to students that sales tax varies by states and that some states, like Alaska and Montana, do not have sales tax.

Additional Examples are also in:

• Noteables™ Interactive Study Notebook with Foldables™

• Interactive Classroom PowerPoint® Presentations

ADDITIONAL EXAMPLE

① **GOLF** A set of golf balls sells for $20, and the sales tax is 5.75%. What is the total cost? $21.15

EXAMPLE Find the Sale Price

2 **BOOGIE BOARDS** A boogie board that has a regular price of $69 is on sale at a 35% discount. What is the sale price of the boogie board?

METHOD 1 Subtract the discount from the regular price.

First, find the amount of the discount.

35% of $69 = 0.35 · $69   Write 35% as a decimal.
           = $24.15   The discount is $24.15.

Next, subtract the discount from the regular price.
$69 − $24.15 = $44.85

METHOD 2 Subtract the percent of discount from 100%.

100% − 35% = 65%   Subtract the discount from 100%.

The sale price is 65% of the regular price.

65% of $69 = 0.65 · $69   Write 65% as a decimal.
           = 44.85   Multiply.

So, the sale price of the boogie board is $44.85.

✓ CHOOSE Your Method

b. **MUSIC** A CD that has a regular price of $15.50 is on sale at a 25% discount. What is the sale price of the CD? **$11.63**

Study Tip

Percent Equation
Remember that, in the percent equation, the percent must be written as a decimal. Since the sale price is 70% of the original price, use 0.7 to represent 70% in the percent equation.

EXAMPLE Find the Original Price

3 **CELL PHONES** A cell phone is on sale for 30% off. If the sale price is $239.89, what is the original price?

The sale price is 100% − 30% or 70% of the original price.

Words	$239.89 is 70% of what price?
Variable	Let p represent the original price.
Equation	$239.89 = 0.7 \times p$

$239.89 = 0.7p$ Write the equation.

$\dfrac{239.89}{0.7} = \dfrac{0.7p}{0.7}$ Divide each side by 0.7.

$342.70 = p$ Simplify.

The original price is $342.70.

✓ CHECK Your Progress **$293.57**

c. Find the original price if the sale price of the cell phone is $205.50.

★ indicates multi-step problem

✓ CHECK Your Understanding

Find the total cost or sale price to the nearest cent.

Example 1
(p. 375)

1. $2.95 notebook; 5% tax **$3.10**

2. $46 shoes; 2.9% tax **$47.33**

Example 2
(p. 376)

3. $1,575 computer; 15% discount
$1,338.75

4. $119.50 skateboard; 20% off **$95.60**

Example 3
(p. 376)

5. **IN-LINE SKATES** A pair of in-line skates is on sale for $90. If this price represents a 9% discount from the original price, what is the original price to the nearest cent? **$98.90**

▶ Practice and Problem Solving

HOMEWORK HELP	
For Exercises	**See Examples**
6–13	1–2
14–17	3

Exercise Levels
A: 6–17
B: 18–22
C: 23–26

Find the total cost or sale price to the nearest cent. 6. **$46.40**

6. $58 ski lift ticket; 20% discount

7. $1,500 computer; 7% tax **$1,605**

8. $99 CD player; 5% tax **$103.95**

9. $12.25 pen set; 60% discount **$4.90**

10. $4.30 makeup; 40% discount **$2.58**

11. $7.50 meal; 6.5% tax **$7.99**

12. $39.60 sweater; 33% discount
$26.53

13. $89.75 scooter; $7\frac{1}{4}$% tax **$96.26**

14. **COSMETICS** A bottle of hand lotion is on sale for $2.25. If this price represents a 50% discount from the original price, what is the original price to the nearest cent? **$4.50**

15. **TICKETS** At a movie theater, the cost of admission to a matinee is $5.25. If this price represents a 30% discount from the evening price, find the evening price to the nearest cent. **$7.50**

Find the original price to the nearest cent.

16. calendar: discount, 75%
sale price, $2.25 **$9.00**

17. telescope: discount, 30%
sale price, $126 **$180.00**

18. **VIDEO GAMES** What is the sales tax of a $178.90 video game system if the tax rate is 5.75%? **$10.29**

★ 19. **RESTAURANTS** A restaurant bill comes to $28.35. Find the total cost if the tax is 6.25% and a 20% tip is left on the amount before tax. **$35.79**

SKATEBOARDS For Exercises 20–22, use the information in the table at the right.

A skateboard costs $320, not including the sales tax.

State	2007 Sales Tax Rate
Washington	6.5%
Kansas	5.3%
North Carolina	4.25%

Source: Federation of Tax Administrators

20. What is the total cost of the skateboard, including tax in Washington? **$340.80**

21. What is the total cost of the skateboard, including tax, in North Carolina? **$333.60**

★ 22. A store in Kansas has the skateboard on sale for 20% off. If the sales tax is calculated after the discount, what is the cost of the skateboard? **$269.57**

EXTRA PRACTICE
See pages 686, 710.

Lesson 7-7 Sales Tax and Discount **377**

3 Practice

✓ Formative Assessment

Use Exercises 1–5 to check for understanding.

Then use the chart at the bottom of this page to customize your assignments for students.

Intervention You may wish to use the Study Guide and Intervention Master on page 47 of the *Chapter 7 Resource Masters* for additional reinforcement.

Odd/Even Assignments

Exercises 6–17 are structured so that students practice the same concepts whether they are assigned odd or even problems.

DIFFERENTIATED HOMEWORK OPTIONS

Level	Assignment	Two-Day Option	
BL Basic	6–17, 24–36	7–17 odd, 27–29	6–16 even, 24–26, 30–36
OL Core	7–17 odd, 18–22, 24–36	6–17, 27–29	18–22, 24–26, 30–36
AL Advanced/Pre-AP	18–33 (optional: 34–36)		

Name the Math Tell students that a music CD that normally costs $18 is on sale at a 25% discount. If the sales tax is 6.25%, have them write what mathematical procedures they would use to find the actual cost of the CD.

Additional Answer

26. One method is to find 30% of the regular price, then subtract the amount from the regular price. Another method is to find 70% of the regular price. Sample answer: The second method is more efficient because it can be done in one step rather than in two.

H.O.T. Problems

24. Sample answer: The regular price of a CD is $17.95. The total cost is $18.98.

25. $50, $25; The percent of discount is 50%. All of the other pairs have a discount of 25%.

23. **CHALLENGE** A gift store is having a sale in which all items are discounted 20%. Including tax, Colin paid $21 for a picture frame. If the sales tax rate is 5%, what was the original price of the picture frame? **$25**

24. **OPEN ENDED** Give an example of the regular price of an item and the total cost including sales tax if the tax rate is 5.75%.

25. **Which One Doesn't Belong?** In each pair, the first value is the regular price of an item and the second value is the sale price. Identify the pair that does not have the same percent of discount as the other three. Explain.

| $24, $18 | $50, $25 | $12, $9 | $80, $60 |

26. **WRITING IN MATH** Describe two methods for finding the sale price of an item that is discounted 30%. Which method do you prefer? Explain.
See margin.

TEST PRACTICE

27. A computer software store is having a sale. The table shows the regular price, r, and the sales price, s, of various items.

Item	Regular Price (r)	Sale Price (s)
A	$5.00	$4.00
B	$8.00	$6.40
C	$10.00	$8.00
D	$15.00	$12.00

Which formula can be used to calculate the sale price? **C**

A $s = r \times 0.2$ C $s = r \times 0.8$

B $s = r - 0.2$ D $s = r - 0.8$

28. A chair that costs $210 was reduced by 40% for a one day sale. After the sale, the sale price was increased by 40%. What is the price of the chair? **F**

F $176.40   H $205.50

G $185.30   J $210.00

29. Juanita paid $10.50 for a T-shirt at the mall. It was on sale for 30% off. What was the original price before the discount? **C**

A $3.15   C $15.00

B $7.35   D $35.00

Spiral Review

Find each percent of change. Round to the nearest whole percent if necessary. State whether the percent of change is an *increase* or *decrease*. (Lesson 7-6)

30. 4 hours to 6 hours
50% increase

31. $500 to $456
9% decrease

32. 20.5 meters to 35.5 meters
73% increase

33. **TRAVEL** Out of a 511-mile trip, Mya drove about 68% on Monday. Determine a reasonable estimate for the number of miles she drove on Monday. (Lesson 7-5)
about 500 × 0.7 or 350 mi

GET READY for the Next Lesson

PREREQUISITE SKILL Multiply. Write in simplest form. (Lesson 5-5)

34. $\frac{2}{7} \cdot \frac{4}{5}$ $\frac{8}{35}$

35. $\frac{1}{8} \cdot \frac{4}{9}$ $\frac{1}{18}$

36. $\frac{6}{11} \cdot \frac{9}{24}$ $\frac{9}{44}$

Simple Interest

PACING: **Regular:** 1.5 periods, **Block:** 1 period

Options for Differentiated Instruction

 = English Language Learner   = Above or Beyond Grade Level   **SS** = Struggling Students   **SN** = Special Needs

Creating Study Cards

Use before presenting the Examples.

Have students create a study card for simple interest. It should include the formula, a description of each variable, and a checklist of steps to use to find simple interest.

> $I = prt$
>
> I → interest
>
> p → principal, the amount of money deposited or invested
>
> r → rate, written as a decimal
>
> t → time, time invested or borrowed in years
>
> Checklist of steps:
> - Write the rate as a decimal.
> - Make sure the time is in years.
> - Multiply.

Real-World Connections

Use after presenting Lesson 7-8.

Have students go to several banks in their community or neighborhood and collect information about the interest offered for savings accounts.

Ask:
- Which bank has the best interest on their savings accounts?
- Are there any restrictions about how much money needs to be in the account?
- Are there other types of accounts that offer a higher interest?

Cooperative Learning **ELL** **AL** **SS** **SN**

Use after students complete Lesson 7-8.

Pair students with different math abilities. Then have partners take turns role-playing banking scenarios similar to those in the lesson. The banker must present options, such as better rates for longer time periods, and provide calculations for interest earned or paid. The customer must verify the calculations and choose an option. Each pair should write a summary of the transactions.

Leveled Lesson Resources

Also on TeacherWorks™ Lesson 7-8

Chapter 7 Resource Masters

BL = Below or Approaching Grade Level   **OL** = On Grade Level   **AL** = Above or Beyond Grade Level   **ELL** = English Language Learner

---

Lesson Reading Guide
p. 52 **BL** **OL** **ELL**

NAME _____ DATE _____ PERIOD _____

7-8 Lesson Reading Guide
Simple Interest

Get Ready for the Lesson

Read the introduction at the top of page 379 in your textbook. Write your answers below.

1. Calculate 2.50% of $200 to find the amount of money that Suni can earn in one year at Federal Credit Bank. **$5**

2. Calculate 2.75% of $200 to find the amount of money Suni can earn in one year at First Bank. **$5.50**

Read the Lesson

3. In Example 4, why is t replaced with $\frac{1}{12}$? **Sample answer: because the length of time is one month, one-twelfth of a year**

4. Complete the following table that gives the conversion of months to years.

Number of months	2	3	4	6	8	9	10
Ratio of number of months to 12 months	$\frac{2}{12}$	$\frac{3}{12}$	$\frac{4}{12}$	$\frac{6}{12}$	$\frac{8}{12}$	$\frac{9}{12}$	$\frac{10}{12}$
Simplified ratio	$\frac{1}{6}$	$\frac{1}{4}$	$\frac{1}{3}$	$\frac{1}{2}$	$\frac{2}{3}$	$\frac{3}{4}$	$\frac{5}{6}$

Remember What You Learned

5. Write the formula for simple interest and explain what each of the letters in the formula stands for. **$I = prt$; I represents the simple interest; p represents the principal, the amount of money originally deposited, invested, or borrowed; r represents the annual interest rate written as a decimal; t represents the amount of time in years that the principal is invested or borrowed.**

6. Look up the word *interest* in a dictionary. Write the meaning that matches the way the word is used in this lesson. **Sample answer: money paid for the use of money**

7. When do you earn interest? When do you have to pay interest? **You earn interest on money you deposit or invest. You pay interest on money you borrow.**

Chapter 7   52   Course 2

Study Guide and Intervention*
p. 53 **BL** **OL** **ELL**

NAME _____ DATE _____ PERIOD _____

7-8 Study Guide and Intervention
Simple Interest

Simple interest is the amount of money paid or earned for the use of money. To find simple interest I, use the formula $I = prt$. Principal p is the amount of money deposited or invested. Rate r is the annual interest rate written as a decimal. Time t is the amount of time the money is invested in years.

Example 1 Find the simple interest earned in a savings account where $136 is deposited for 2 years if the interest rate is 7.5% per year.

$I = prt$ Formula for simple interest
$I = 136 \cdot 0.075 \cdot 2$ Replace p with $136, r$ with 0.075, and t with 2.
$I = 20.40$ Simplify.
The simple interest earned is $20.40.

Example 2 Find the simple interest for $600 invested at 8.5% for 6 months.

6 months $= \frac{6}{12}$ or 0.5 year   Write the time as years.
$I = prt$ Formula for simple interest
$I = 600 \cdot 0.085 \cdot 0.5$ $p = $600, r = 0.085, t = 0.5$
$I = 25.50$ Simplify.
The simple interest is $25.50.

Exercises

Find the interest earned to the nearest cent for each principal, interest rate, and time.

1. $300, 5%, 2 years **$30**
2. $650, 8%, 3 years **$156**
3. $575, 4.5%, 4 years **$103.50**
4. $735, 7%, $2\frac{1}{2}$ years **$128.63**
5. $1,665, 6.75%, 3 years **$337.16**
6. $2,105, 11%, $1\frac{3}{4}$ years **$405.21**
7. $903, 8.75%, 18 months **$118.52**
8. $4,275, 19%, 3 months **$203.06**

Chapter 7   53   Course 2

Skills Practice*
p. 54 **BL** **OL**

NAME _____ DATE _____ PERIOD _____

7-8 Skills Practice
Simple Interest

Find the interest earned to the nearest cent for each principal, interest rate, and time.

1. $500, 4%, 2 years **$40**
2. $350, 6.2%, 3 years **$65.10**
3. $740, 3.25%, 2 years **$48.10**
4. $725, 4.3%, $2\frac{1}{2}$ years **$77.94**
5. $955, 6.75%, $3\frac{1}{4}$ years **$209.50**
6. $1,540, 8.25%, 2 years **$254.10**
7. $3,500, 4.2%, $1\frac{3}{4}$ years **$257.25**
8. $568, 16%, 8 months **$60.59**

Find the interest paid to the nearest cent for each loan balance, interest rate, and time.

9. $800, 9%, 4 years **$288**
10. $280, 5.5%, 4 years **$61.60**
11. $1,150, 7.6%, 5 years **$437**
12. $266, 5.2%, 3 years **$41.50**
13. $450, 22%, 1 year **$99**
14. $2,180, 7.7%, $2\frac{1}{2}$ years **$419.65**
15. $2,650, 3.65%, $4\frac{1}{2}$ years **$435.26**
16. $1,245, 5.4%, 6 months **$33.62**

Chapter 7   54   Course 2

Practice*
p. 55 **OL** **AL**

NAME _____ DATE _____ PERIOD _____

7-8 Practice
Simple Interest

Find the simple interest earned to the nearest cent for each principal, interest rate, and time.

1. $750, 7%, 3 years **$157.50**
2. $1,200, 3.5%, 2 years **$84.00**
3. $450, 5%, 4 months **$7.50**
4. $1,000, 2%, 9 months **$15.00**
5. $530, 6%, 1 year **$31.80**
6. $600, 8%, 1 month **$4.00**

Find the simple interest paid to the nearest cent for each loan, interest rate, and time.

7. $668, 5%, 2 years **$66.80**
8. $720, 4.25%, 3 months **$7.65**
9. $2,500, 6.9%, 6 months **$86.25**
10. $500, 12%, 18 months **$90.00**
11. $300, 9%, 3 years **$81.00**
12. $2,000, 20%, 1 year **$400.00**

13. **ELECTRONICS** Rita charged $126 for a DVD player at an interest rate of 15.9%. How much will Rita have to pay after 2 months if she makes no payments? **$129.34**

14. **VACATION** The average cost for a vacation is $1,050. If a family borrows money for the vacation at an interest rate of 11.9% for 6 months, what is the total cost of the vacation including the interest on the loan? **$1,112.48**

For Exercises 15–17, use the following information.
Robin has $2,500 to invest in a CD (certificate of deposit).

15. If Robin invests the $2,500 in the CD that yields 4% interest, what will the CD be worth after 2 years? **$2,700**

16. Robin would like to have $3,000 altogether. If the interest rate is 5%, in how many years will she have $3,000? **4 years**

17. Suppose Robin invests the $2,500 for 3 years and earns $255. What was the rate of interest? **3.4%**

Chapter 7   55   Course 2

Word Problem Practice*
p. 56 **OL** **AL**

NAME _____ DATE _____ PERIOD _____

7-8 Word Problem Practice
Simple Interest

1. **SAVINGS ACCOUNT** How much interest will Hannah earn in 4 years if she deposits $630 in a savings account at 6.5% simple interest? **$163.80**

2. **INVESTMENTS** Terry invested $2,200 in the stock market for 2 years. If the investment earned 12% simple interest, how much money did Terry earn in interest in 2 years? **$528**

3. **SAVINGS ACCOUNT** Malik deposited $1,050 in a savings account, and it earned $241.50 in simple interest after four years. Find the interest rate on Malik's savings account. **5.75%**

4. **INHERITANCE** Kelli Rae's inheritance from her great-grandmother was $220,000 after taxes. If Kelli Rae invests this money in a savings account that earns $18,260 in simple interest every year, what is the interest rate on her account? **8.3%**

5. **RETIREMENT** Mr. Pham has $410,000 in a retirement account that earns 3.85% simple interest each year. Find the amount earned each year by this investment. **$15,785**

6. **COLLEGE FUND** When Melissa was born, her parents put $8,000 into a college fund account that earned 9% simple interest. Find the total amount in the account after 18 years. **$20,960**

7. **LOTTERY** Raj won $900,000 in a regional lottery. After paying $350,000 in taxes, he invested the remaining money in a savings account at 4.25% simple interest. How much money is in the account if Raj makes no deposits or withdrawals for two years? **$596,750**

8. **SAVINGS** Mona opened a savings account with a $500 deposit and a simple interest rate of 5.6%. If there were no deposits or withdrawals, how much money is in the account after $8\frac{1}{2}$ years? **$738**

Chapter 7   56   Course 2

Enrichment
p. 57 **OL** **AL**

NAME _____ DATE _____ PERIOD _____

7-8 Enrichment

Taking an Interest

When interest is paid on both the amount of the deposit and any interest already earned, interest is said to be **compounded**. You can use the formula below to find out how much money is in an account for which interest is compounded.

$$A = P(1 + r)^n$$

In the formula, P represents the principal, or amount deposited, r represents the rate applied each time interest is paid, n represents the number of times interest is given, and A represents the amount in the account.

Example A customer deposited $1,500 in an account that earns 8% per year. If interest is compounded and earned semiannually, how much is in the account after 1 year?

Use the formula $A = P(1 + r)^n$.
Since interest is earned semiannually, $r = 8 \div 2$ or 4% and $n = 2$.
$A = 1,500(1 + 0.04)^2$ Use a calculator.
$= 1,622.40$
After 1 year, there is $1,622.40 in the account.

Exercises

Use the compound interest formula and a calculator to find the value of each of these investments. Round each answer to the nearest cent.

1. $2,500 invested for 1 year at 6% interest compounded semiannually **$2,652.25**
2. $3,600 invested for 2 years at 7% interest compounded semiannually **$4,131.08**
3. $1,000 invested for 5 years at 8% interest compounded annually **$1,469.33**
4. $2,000 invested for 6 years at 12% interest compounded quarterly **$4,065.59**
5. $4,800 invested for 10 years at 9% interest compounded annually **$11,363.35**
6. $10,000 invested for 15 years at 7.5% interest compounded semiannually **$30,174.71**

Chapter 7   57   Course 2

Additional Lesson Resources

* Also available in Spanish **ELL**

Transparencies
• *5-Minute Check Transparency*, Lesson 7-8

Other Print Products
• *Noteables™ Interactive Study Notebook with Foldables™*

Teacher Tech Tools
• *Interactive Classroom CD-ROM*, Lesson 7-8
• *AssignmentWorks*, Lesson 7-8

Student Tech Tools
glencoe.com
• Extra Examples, Chapter 7, Lesson 8
• Self-Check Quiz, Chapter 7, Lesson 8

7-8 Simple Interest

MAIN IDEA

Solve problems involving simple interest.

New Vocabulary

principal
simple interest

Math Online

glencoe.com

• Extra Examples
• Personal Tutor
• Self-Check Quiz

▷ GET READY for the Lesson

INVESTING Suni plans to save the $200 she received for her birthday. The graphs shows the average yearly rates at three different banks.

1. Calculate 2.50% of $200 to find the amount of money Suni can earn in one year at Federal Credit Bank. **$5**

2. Calculate 2.75% of $200 to find the amount of money Suni can earn in one year at First Bank. **$5.50**

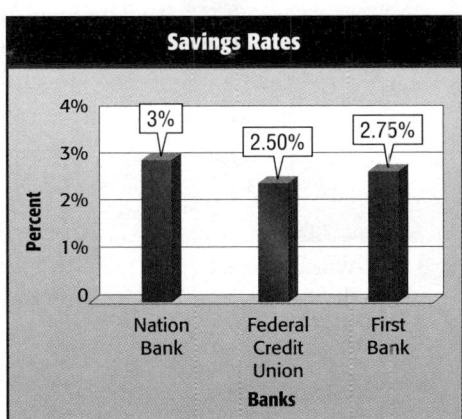

Savings Rates

Principal is the amount of money deposited or borrowed.

Simple interest is the amount paid or earned for the use of money. To find simple interest *I*, use the following formula.

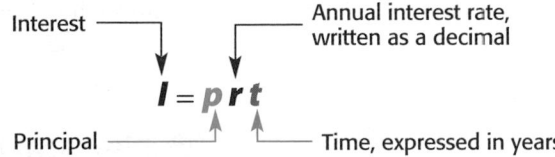

Interest ⎯⎯⎯⎯⎯⎯⎯ Annual interest rate, written as a decimal

$$I = prt$$

Principal ⎯⎯⎯⎯⎯ Time, expressed in years.

EXAMPLES Find Interest Earned

CHECKING Arnold has $580 in a savings account that pays 3% simple interest. How much interest will he earn in each amount of time?

1 **5 years**

$I = prt$	Formula for simple interest
$I = 580 \cdot 0.03 \cdot 5$	Replace *p* with $580, *r* with 0.03, and *t* with 5.
$I = 87$	Simplify.

Arnold will earn $87 in interest in 5 years.

2 **6 months**

6 months $= \frac{6}{12}$ or 0.5 year	Write the time as years.
$I = prt$	Formula for simple interest
$I = 580 \cdot 0.03 \cdot 0.5$	$p = \$580, r = 0.03, t = 0.5$
$I \approx 8.7$	Simplify.

Arnold will earn $8.70 in interest in 6 months.

Lesson 7-8 Simple Interest **379**

Tips for New Teachers — Fractions of Years

The amount of time, *t*, must be expressed in years in order to use the formula $I = prt$. Since 9 months $= \frac{9}{12}$ or 0.75 year, use either $\frac{9}{12}$ or 0.75 for *t*.

ADDITIONAL EXAMPLES

SAVINGS Brandon found a bank offering a certificate of deposit that pays 4% simple interest. He has $1,500 to invest. How much interest will he earn in each amount of time?

1 3 years $180

2 30 months $150

1 Focus

Vertical Alignment

Before Lesson 7-8
Interpret percents as a part of a hundred; find decimal and percent equivalents for common fractions and explain why they represent the same value; compute a given percent of a whole number

Lesson 7-8
Calculate given percents of quantities and solve problems

After Lesson 7-8
Solve problems that involve discounts, markups, commissions, and profit and compute simple and compound interest

2 Teach

Scaffolding Questions

Ask:

• How many of you have savings accounts in a bank?

• What are the advantages of keeping your money in a bank? Security; the bank pays interest.

• What is the rate of interest your bank pays on your account? Answers will vary.

 Formative Assessment

Use the Check Your Progress exercises after the Examples to determine students' understanding of concepts.

Real-World Career...
How does a Car Salesperson Use Math?
A car salesperson must be able to determine values of cars, calculate interest rates, and determine monthly payments.

Math Online ▸
For more information go to glencoe.com.

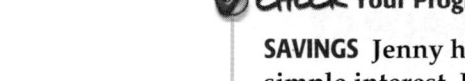

✓ **CHECK Your Progress**

SAVINGS Jenny has $1,560 in a savings account that pays 2.5% simple interest. How much interest will she earn in each amount of time?

a. 3 years **$117**   b. 6 months **$19.50**

The formula $I = prt$ can also be used to find the interest owed when you borrow money. In this case, p is the amount of money borrowed, and t is the amount of time the money is borrowed.

EXAMPLE Find Interest Paid on a Loan

③ LOANS Rondell's parents borrow $6,300 from the bank for a new car. The interest rate is 6% per year. How much simple interest will they pay if they take 2 years to repay the loan?

$I = prt$	Formula for simple interest
$I = 6,300 \cdot 0.06 \cdot 2$	Replace p with $6,300$, r with 0.06, and t with 2.
$I = 756$	Simplify.

Rondell's parents will pay $756 in interest in 2 years.

✓ **CHECK Your Progress**

c. **LOANS** Mrs. Hanover borrows $1,400 at a rate of 5.5% per year. How much simple interest will she pay if it takes 8 months to repay the loan? **$51.33**

EXAMPLE Find Total Paid on a Credit Card

④ CREDIT CARDS Derrick's dad bought new tires for $900 using a credit card. His card has an interest rate of 19%. If he has no other charges on his card and does not pay off his balance at the end of the month, how much money will he owe after one month?

$I = prt$	Formula for simple interest
$I = 900 \cdot 0.19 \cdot \frac{1}{12}$	Replace p with 900, r with 0.19, and t with $\frac{1}{12}$.
$I = 14.25$	Simplify.

The interest owed after one month is $14.25. So, the total amount owed would be $900 + $14.25 or $914.25.

Study Tip

Fractions of Years
Remember to express 1 month as $\frac{1}{12}$ year in the formula.

✓ **CHECK Your Progress**

d. **CREDIT CARDS** An office manager charged $425 worth of office supplies on a charge card with an interest rate of 9.9%. How much money will he owe if he makes no other charges on the card and does not pay off the balance at the end of the month? **$428.51**

 **Your Understanding**

Examples 1, 2
(pp. 379–380)
Find the simple interest earned to the nearest cent for each principal, interest rate, and time.

1. $640, 3%, 2 years **$38.40**

2. $1,500, 4.25%, 4 years **$255**

3. $580, 2%, 6 months **$5.80**

4. $1,200, 3.9%, 8 months **$31.20**

Example 3
(p. 380)
Find the simple interest paid to the nearest cent for each loan, interest rate, and time.

5. $4,500, 9%, 3.5 years **$1,417.50**

6. $290, 12.5%, 6 months **$18.13**

Example 4
(p. 380)
7. **FINANCES** The Masters family financed a computer that costs $1,200. If the interest rate is 19%, how much will the family owe after one month if no payments are made? **$1,219.00**

Practice and Problem Solving

HOMEWORK HELP	
For Exercises	See Examples
8–9	1
10–11	2
12–15	3
16–17	4

Exercise Levels
A: 8–17
B: 18–21
C: 22–24

Find the simple interest earned to the nearest cent for each principal, interest rate, and time.

8. $1,050, 4.6%, 2 years **$96.60**

9. $250, 2.85%, 3 years **$21.38**

10. $500, 3.75%, 4 months **$6.25**

11. $3,000, 5.5%, 9 months **$123.75**

Find the simple interest paid to the nearest cent for each loan, interest rate, and time.

12. $1,000, 7%, 2 years **$140**

13. $725, 6.25%, 1 year **$45.31**

14. $2,700, 8.2%, 3 months **$55.35**

15. $175.80, 12%, 8 months **$14.06**

16. **CREDIT CARDS** Leon charged $75 at an interest rate of 12.5%. How much will Leon have to pay after one month if he makes no payments? **$75.78**

17. **TRAVEL** A family charged $1,345 in travel expenses. If no payments are made, how much will they owe after one month if the interest rate is 7.25%? **$1,353.13**

BANKING For Exercises 18 and 19, use the table.

18. What is the simple interest earned on $900 for 9 months? **$19.58**

19. Find the simple interest earned on $2,500 for 18 months. **$116.25**

Home Savings and Loan	
Time	Rate
6 months	2.4%
9 months	2.9%
12 months	3.0%
18 months	3.1%

INVESTING For Exercises 20 and 21, use the following information.

Ramon has $4,200 to invest for college.

20. If Ramon invests $4,200 for 3 years and earns $630, what was the simple interest rate? **5%**

See pages 687, 711.

21. Ramon's goal is to have $5,000 after 4 years. Is this possible if he invests with a rate of return of 6%? Explain. **Yes, he would have $5,208.**

 Practice

 **Formative Assessment**

Use Exercises 1–7 to check for understanding.

Then use the chart at the bottom of this page to customize your assignments for students.

Intervention You may wish to use the Study Guide and Intervention Master on page 53 of the *Chapter 7 Resource Masters* for additional reinforcement.

Odd/Even Assignments

Exercises 8–17 are structured so that students practice the same concepts whether they are assigned odd or even problems.

Tips for New Teachers **Interest**
Some students may be aware that credit card companies normally do not charge interest on a new balance for the first month. Example 4 and Exercise 16 are meant to be illustrative, not necessarily realistic.

DIFFERENTIATED HOMEWORK OPTIONS			
Level	Assignment	Two-Day Option	
BL Basic	8–17, 22, 24–33	9–17 odd, 25, 26	8–16 even, 22, 24, 27–33
OL Core	9–17 odd, 18–22, 24–33	8–17, 25, 26	18–22, 24, 27–33
AL Advanced/Pre-AP	18–33		

Ticket Out the Door Have students write whether they would prefer to deposit $1,000 at a simple interest rate of 3% for 5 years, or $1,000 at a simple interest rate of 4% for 4 years. Make sure they explain their reasoning.

 Formative Assessment

Check for student understanding of concepts in Lessons 7-7 and 7-8.

CRM Quiz 4, p. 62

FOLDABLES Foldables™
Study Organizer Follow-Up

Remind students to record how to calculate simple interest in their Foldables tables, along with examples.

 **Compound Interest**

After students complete Exercise 23, point out that this way of calculating interest and principal is called compound interest. At the end of each time period, the interest is added, or compounded, to the principal. Most banks and financial institutions use this method of compound interest rather than simple interest.

Additional Answer

24. Sample answer: Write the interest rate as a decimal and write the months in years. Then multiply $500 \cdot 0.06 \cdot 1.5 = \$45$.

H.O.T. Problems

22. Sample answer: If the rate is increased by 1%, then the interest earned is $60 more. If the time is increased by 1 year, then the interest earned is $36 more.

22. **OPEN ENDED** Suppose you earn 3% on a $1,200 deposit for 5 years. Explain how the simple interest is affected if the rate is increased by 1%. What happens if the time is increased by 1 year?

23. **CHALLENGE** Mrs. Antil deposits $800 in a savings account that earns 3.2% interest annually. At the end of the year, the interest is added to the principal or original amount. She keeps her money in this account for three years without withdrawing any money. Find the total in her account after each year for three years. **$825.60, $852.02, $879.28**

24. **WRITING IN MATH** List the steps you would use to find the simple interest on a $500 loan at 6% interest rate for 18 months. Then find the simple interest. **See margin.**

TEST PRACTICE

25. Jada invests $590 in a money market account. Her account pays 7.2% simple interest. If she does not add or withdraw any money again, how much interest will Jada's account earn after 4 years of simple interest? **C**

  A $75.80
  B $158.67
  C $169.92
  D $220.67

26. Mr. Sprockett borrows $3,500 from his bank to buy a used car. The loan has a 7.4% annual simple interest rate. If it takes Mr. Sprockett two years to pay back the loan, what is the total amount he will be paying? **G**

  F $3,012
  G $4,018
  H $4,550
  J $3,598

Spiral Review

27. Find the total cost of a $19.99 DVD if the tax rate is 7%. (Lesson 7-7) **$21.39**

Find each percent of change. Round to the nearest whole percent if necessary. State whether the percent of change is an increase or decrease. (Lesson 7-6)

28. 35 birds to 45 birds
29% increase

29. 60 inches to 38 inches
37% decrease

30. $2.75 to $1.80
35% decrease

Divide. Write in simplest form. (Lesson 5-7)

31. $\frac{3}{5} \div \frac{1}{2}$ $1\frac{1}{5}$

32. $\frac{4}{7} \div \frac{5}{8}$ $\frac{32}{35}$

33. $2\frac{2}{3} \div 1\frac{1}{4}$ $2\frac{2}{15}$

Problem Solving in Art
Real-World Unit Project

It's Golden! It's time to complete your project. Use the information and data you have gathered about the Golden Ratio to prepare a Power Point presentation. Be sure to include your reports and calculations in your presentation.

Math Online Unit Project at glencoe.com

MAIN IDEA

Use a spreadsheet to calculate simple interest.

A computer spreadsheet is a useful tool for quickly calculating simple interest for different values of principal, rate, and time.

ACTIVITY

Max plans on opening a "Young Savers" account at his bank. The current rate on the account is 4%. He wants to see how different starting balances, rates, and times will affect his account balance. To find the balance at the end of 2 years for different principal amounts, he enters the values B2 = 4 and C2 = 2 into the spreadsheet below.

Simple Interest.xls

◇	A	B	C	D	E
1	Principal (*p*)	Rate (*r*)	Time (*t*)	Interest (*I*)	New Balance
2					
3	500	=B2/100	=C2	=A3*B3*C3	=A3+D3
4	1000	=B2/100	=C2	=A4*B4*C4	=A4+D4
5	1500	=B2/100	=C2	=A5*B5*C5	=A5+D5
6	2000	=B2/100	=C2	=A6*B6*C6	=A6−D6
7	2500	=B2/100	=C2	=A7*B7*C7	=A7−D7

Sheet 1 \ Sheet 2 \ Sheet 3 /

For each principal given in column A, simple interest is calculated for any values of rate and time entered in B2 and C2, respectively.

The spreadsheet adds simple interest to the principal.

ANALYZE THE RESULTS

1. Why is the rate in column B divided by 100? **to change the percent to a decimal**

2. What is the balance in Max's account after 2 years if the principal is $1,500 and the simple interest rate is 4%? **$1,620**

3. How much interest does Max earn in 2 years if his account has a principal of $2,000 and a simple interest rate of 4%? **$160**

4. Is the amount of principal proportional to the interest Max earns if his account earns 4% simple interest over 2 years? Explain.

5. Is the amount of principal proportional to the balance in Max's account if it earns 4% simple interest over 2 years? Explain.

6. What entries for cells B2 and C2 would you use to calculate the simple interest on a principal of $1,500 at a rate of 7% for a 9-month period? **B2: 7, C2: 0.75**

4, 5. See margin.

7. What is the balance of this account at the end of the 9 months? **$1,578.75**

Teaching notes

1 Focus

Materials

• computers with spreadsheet program

Teaching Tip

If your classroom has computers with a spreadsheet program, you might want to have students use the computers to complete the lab. If so, have students work in pairs or groups of three.

2 Teach

Activity Make sure students realize that the spreadsheet uses the same formula for simple interest that they learned in Lesson 7-8 (see column D).

3 Assess

 Formative Assessment

Use Exercise 2 to determine whether students understand how a spreadsheet calculates simple interest.

From Concrete to Abstract Use Exercise 6 to bridge the gap between using a spreadsheet to calculate simple interest and knowing what information the spreadsheet would need.

Additional Answers

4. Yes; Sample answer: As the amount of principle triples from $500 to $1,500, the amount of interest triples from $40 to $120. This indicates that the principle is proportional to the interest for an account earning 4% interest over 2 years.

5. Yes; Sample answer: As the amount of principal triples from $500 to $1,500, the balance in the account triples from $540 to $1,620. This indicates that the principle is proportional to the balance in an account earning 4% interest over 2 years.

CHAPTER 7
Study Guide
and Review

CHAPTER 7
Study Guide and Review

Math Online glencoe.com
• STUDY *TO GO*
• Vocabulary Review

FOLDABLES
Study Organizer
Dinah Zike's Foldables

Have students look through the chapter to make sure they have included key concepts and examples for each lesson in their Foldable tables.

Encourage students to refer to their Foldables while completing the Study Guide and Review and while preparing for the Chapter Test.

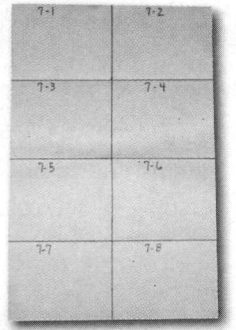

 Formative Assessment

Key Vocabulary The page references after each word denote where that term was first introduced. If students have difficulty answering Exercises 1–10, remind them that they can use these page references to refresh their memories about the vocabulary terms.

Math Online glencoe.com

Vocabulary PuzzleMaker improves students' mathematics vocabulary using four puzzle formats—crossword, scramble, word search using a word list, and word search using clues. Students can work online or from a printed worksheet.

 Summative Assessment

CRM Vocabulary Test, p. 64

384 Chapter 7 Applying Percents

FOLDABLES
Study Organizer
GET READY to Study

Be sure the following Big Ideas are noted in your Foldable.

7-1	7-2
7-3	7-4
7-5	7-6
7-7	7-8

BIG Ideas

Percent of a Number (Lesson 7-1)
• To find the percent of a number, first write the percent as either a fraction or decimal and then multiply.

Percent Proportion (Lesson 7-2)
$$\frac{part}{whole} = \frac{n}{100} \Big\} \ percent$$

Percent and Estimation (Lesson 7-3)
• One way to estimate the percent of a number is to use a fraction. The other way is to first find 10% of the number and then multiply.

Percent Equation (Lesson 7-4)
$$part = percent \cdot whole$$

Percent of Change (Lesson 7-6)
• A percent of change is a ratio that compares the change in quantity to the original amount.
$$percent \ of \ change = \frac{amount \ of \ change}{original \ amount}$$

Sales Tax and Discount (Lesson 7-7)
• Sales tax is an additional amount of money charged on items. The total cost of an item is the regular price plus the sales tax.

• Discount is the amount by which the regular price of an item is reduced. The sale price is the regular price minus the discount.

Simple Interest (Lesson 7-8)
• Simple interest is the amount paid or earned for the use of money.
$$I = prt$$
9. false; original

384 Chapter 7 Applying Percents

Key Vocabulary

discount (p. 375)	percent proportion (p. 350)
percent equation (p. 361)	principal (p. 379)
percent of change (p. 369)	sales tax (p. 375)
percent of decrease (p. 369)	simple interest (p. 379)
percent of increase (p. 369)	

Vocabulary Check

State whether each sentence is *true* or *false*. If *false*, replace the underlined word or number to make a true sentence.

1. The sale price of a discounted item is the regular price <u>minus</u> the discount. **true**

2. A ratio that compares the change in quantity to the original amount is called the <u>percent of change</u>. **true**

3. A <u>percent proportion</u> compares part of a quantity to the whole quantity using a percent. **true**

4. The formula for simple interest is <u>$I = prt$</u>. **true**

5. A method for estimating the percent of a number is to find <u>21%</u> of the number and then multiply. **false; 10%.**

6. The equation part = percent • whole is known as the <u>principal</u> equation. **false; percent**

7. The <u>principal</u> is the amount of money deposited or borrowed. **true**

8. A <u>tax</u> is the amount by which the regular price of an item is reduced. **false; discount**

9. To find a percent of increase, compare the amount of the increase to the <u>new</u> amount.

10. If the new amount is greater than the original amount, then the percent of change is percent of <u>decrease</u>. **false; increase**

Lesson-by-Lesson Review

7-1 **Percent of a Number** (pp. 344–348)

Find each number. Round to the nearest tenth if necessary.

11. Find 78% of 50. **39**

12. 45.5% of 75 is what number? **34.1**

13. What is 225% of 60? **135**

14. 0.75% of 80 is what number? **0.6**

Example 1 Find 24% of 200.

24% of 200

$= 24\% \times 200$ Write the expression.

$= 0.24 \times 200$ Write 24% as a decimal.

$= 48$ Multiply.

So, 24% of 200 is 48.

7-2 **The Percent Proportion** (pp. 350–354)

Find each number. Round to the nearest tenth if necessary.

15. **SOCCER** A soccer team lost 30% of their games. If they played 20 games, how many did they win? **14 games**

16. 6 is what percent of 120? **5%**

17. Find 0.8% of 35. **0.3**

18. What percent of 375 is 40? **10.7%**

19. **PHONE SERVICE** A family pays $21.99 each month for their long distance phone service. This is 80% of the original price of the phone service. What is the original price of the phone service? Round to the nearest cent if necessary.

Example 2 What percent of 90 is 18?

$\dfrac{18}{90} = \dfrac{n}{100}$ Write the proportion.

$18 \cdot 100 = 90 \cdot n$ Find the cross products.

$1{,}800 = 90n$ Simplify.

$\dfrac{1{,}800}{90} = \dfrac{90n}{90}$ Divide each side by 90.

$20 = n$ So, 18 is 20% of 90.

Example 3 52 is 65% of what number?

$\dfrac{52}{w} = \dfrac{65}{100}$ Write the proportion.

$52 \cdot 100 = w \cdot 65$ Find the cross products.

$5{,}200 = 65w$ Simplify.

$\dfrac{5{,}200}{65} = \dfrac{65w}{65}$ Divide each side by 65.

$80 = w$ So, 52 is 65% of 80.

19. $27.49

7-3 **Percent and Estimation** (pp. 355–360) 20–25. Sample answers are given. 21. 40; $\frac{1}{3} \cdot 120 = 40$

Estimate. 20. 20; $\frac{1}{4} \cdot 80 = 20$

20. 25% of 81   21. 33% of 122

22. 77% of 38   23. 19.5% of 96
   30; $\frac{3}{4} \cdot 40 = 30$ 20; $\frac{1}{5} \cdot 100 = 20$

Estimate by using 10%.

24. 12% of 77   25. 88% of 400

8; 0.1 · 80 = 8   360; 0.1 · 400 = 40; 9 · 40 = 360

26. **BOOKS** About 26% of the 208 books in Deja's collection are nonfiction. Estimate how many of Deja's books are nonfiction. **See margin.**

Example 4 Estimate 52% of 495.

$52\% \approx 50\%$ or $\frac{1}{2}$, and $495 \approx 500$.

52% of $495 \approx \frac{1}{2} \cdot 500$ or 250

So, 52% of 495 is about 250.

Example 5 Estimate 68% of 80.

10% of 80 = 0.1 · 80 or 8   Find 10% of 80.

68% is about 70%.

7 · 8 = 56   70% of 80 ≈ 7 · (10% of 80)

So, 68% of 80 is about 56.

Lesson-by-Lesson Review

Intervention If the given examples are not sufficient to review the topics covered by the questions, remind students that the page references tell them where to review that topic in their textbooks.

Two-Day Option Have students complete the Lesson-by-Lesson Review on pages 385–388. Then you can use ExamView® Assessment Suite to customize another review worksheet that practices all the objectives of this chapter or only the objectives on which your students need more help.

For more information on ExamView® Assessment Suite, see page 340C.

Differentiated Instruction

Super DVD: MindJogger Plus
Use this DVD as an alternative format of review for the test. For more information on this game show format, see page 340D.

Additional Answer

26. Sample answer: $\frac{1}{4} \cdot 200 = 50$ books

7-4 **Algebra: The Percent Equation** (pp. 361–365)

Write an equation for each problem. Then solve. Round to the nearest tenth if necessary. **28. $39 = 0.65 \cdot w$; 60**

27. 32 is what percent of 50? **$32 = p \cdot 50$; 64%**

28. 65% of what number is 39?

29. Find 42% of 300. **$n = 0.42 \cdot 300$; 126**

30. 7% of 92 is what number?
30. $n = 0.07 \cdot 92$; 6.4

31. 12% of what number is 108?
$108 = 0.12 \cdot w$; 900

32. **SALONS** A local hair salon increased their sales of hair products by about 12.5% this week. If they sold 48 hair products, how many hair products did they sell last week? **43**

Example 6 27 is what percent of 90?

27 is the part and 90 is the base.

Let n represent the percent.

$$\underset{\text{part}}{27} = \underset{\text{percent}}{n} \cdot \underset{\text{base}}{90}$$ Write an equation.

$\dfrac{27}{90} = \dfrac{90n}{90}$ Divide each side by 90.

$0.3 = n$ The percent is 30%.

So, 27 is 30% of 90.

7-5 **PSI: Determine Reasonable Answers** (pp. 366–367)

Determine a reasonable answer for each problem.

33. **CABLE TV** In a survey of 1,813 consumers, 18% said that they would be willing to pay more for cable if they got more channels. Is 3.3, 33, or 333 a reasonable estimate for the number of consumers willing to pay more for cable? **333**

34. **SCHOOL** There are 880 students at Medina Middle School. If 68% of the students are involved in sports, would the number of students involved in sports be about 510, 630, or 720? **630**

35. **VACATION** Suppose you are going on vacation for $689 and the airfare accounts for 43.5% of the total cost. What is a reasonable cost of the airfare?

Example 7 Mr. Swanson harvested 1,860 pounds of apples from one orchard, 1,149 pounds from another, and 905 pounds from a third. The apples will be placed in crates that hold 42 pounds of apples. Will Mr. Swanson need 100, 200, or 400 crates?

Since an exact answer is not needed, we can estimate the total of pounds.

1,860	→	1,900
1,149	→	1,100
+ 905	→	+ 900
		3,900

Since 3,900 ÷ 40 is about 100, it is reasonable that 100 crates need to be ordered.

35. Sample answer: $700 × 0.4 = $280

Mixed Problem Solving
For mixed problem-solving practice,
see page 710.

CHAPTER 7 Study Guide
and Review

7-6 Percent of Change (pp. 369–374)

Find each percent of change. Round to the nearest whole percent if necessary. State whether the percent of change is an *increase* or *decrease*.

36. original: 172
    new: 254

37. original: $200
    new: $386

38. original: 75
    new: 60
    20% decrease

39. original: $49.95
    new: $54.95
    10% increase

40. Tyree bought a collectible comic book for $49.62 last year. This year, he sold it for $52.10. Find the percent of change of the price of the comic book. Round to the nearest percent. **5% increase**

36. **48% increase**
37. **93% increase**

Example 8 A magazine that originally cost $2.75 is now $3.55. Find the percent of change. Round to the nearest whole percent.

The new price is greater than the original price, so this is a percent of increase.

amount of increase $= 3.55 - 2.75$ or 0.80

$$\text{percent of increase} = \frac{\text{amount of increase}}{\text{original amount}}$$

$$= \frac{0.80}{2.75} \quad \text{Substitution}$$

$$\approx 0.29 \quad \text{Simplify.}$$

The percent of increase is about 29%.

7-7 Sales Tax and Discount (pp. 375–378)

Find the total cost or sale price to the nearest cent.

41. $25 backpack; 7% tax **$26.75**

42. $210 bicycle; 15% discount **$178.50**

43. $8,000 car; $5\frac{1}{2}$% tax **$8,440**

44. $40 sweater; 33% discount **$26.80**

Find the percent of discount to the nearest percent.

45. shirt: regular price: $42
    sale price: $36 **14%**

46. boots: regular price: $78
    sale price: $70 **10%**

47. **MONEY** At the media store a certain DVD normally costs $21.99. This week the DVD is on sale for 25% off. Tara buys the DVD and pays using a $20 bill. Not including tax, how much change will she receive to the nearest cent? **$3.51**

Example 9 A new computer system is priced at $2,499. Find the total cost if the sales tax is 6.5%.

First, find the sales tax.

6.5% of $2,499 = $0.065 \cdot 2,499$

$$\approx 162.44$$

Next, add the sales tax. The total cost is $162.44 + 2,499$ or $2,661.44.

Example 10 A pass at a water park is $58. At the end of the season, the same pass costs $46.40. What is the percent of discount?

$58 - 46.40 = 11.60$ Find the amount of discount.

Next, find what percent of 58 is 11.60.

$11.60 = n \cdot 58$ Write an equation.

$0.2 = n$ Divide each side by 58.

The percent of discount is 20%.

Problem Solving Review

For additional practice in problem solving for Chapter 7, see the Mixed Problem Solving Appendix, page 710 in the Student Handbook section.

Anticipation Guide

Have students complete the Chapter 7 Anticipation Guide and discuss how their responses have changed now that they have completed Chapter 7.

CRM Anticipation Guide, p. 7

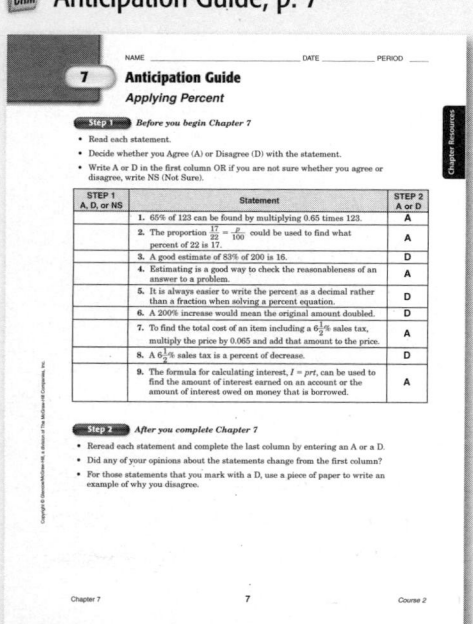

7-8 **Simple Interest** (pp. 379–382)

Find the interest earned to the nearest cent for each principal, interest rate, and time.

48. $475, 5%, 2 years **$47.50**

49. $5,000, 10%, 3 years **$1,500**

50. $2,500, 11%, $1\frac{1}{2}$ years **$412.50**

51. **SAVINGS** Tonya deposited $450 into a savings account earning 3.75% annual simple interest. How much interest will she earn in 6 years? **$101.25**

Find the interest paid to the nearest cent for each loan balance, interest rate, and time.

52. $3,200, 8%, 4 years **$1,024**

53. $1,980, 21%, 9 months **$311.85**

54. **CREDIT CARDS** David bought a computer for $600 using his credit card. The interest rate on his credit card is 19%. How much will he pay in all for the computer, if he pays off the balance at the end of 2 years? **$828**

Example 11 Find the interest earned on $400 at 9% for 3 years.

$I = prt$ Simple interest formula

$I = 400 \cdot 0.09 \cdot 3$ $p = \$400, r = 0.09, t = 3$

$I = 108$ Simplify.

The interest earned is $108.

Example 12 Elisa has a loan for $1,300. The interest rate is 7%. If she pays it off in 6 months, how much interest will she pay?

$I = prt$ Simple interest formula

$I = 1,300 \cdot 0.07 \cdot 0.5$ $p = \$1,300, r = 0.07, t = 0.5$

$I = 45.5$ Simplify.

The interest she will pay after 6 months is $45.50.

Find each number. Round to the nearest tenth if necessary.

1. Find 55% of 164. **90.2**

2. What is 355% of 15? **53.3**

3. Find 25% of 80. **20**

4. **MULTIPLE CHOICE** Of 365 students, 210 bought a hot lunch. About what percent of the students did *not* buy a hot lunch? **B**

   A 35%   C 56%
   B 42%   D 78%

Estimate. 5–8. See margin.

5. 18% of 246   6. 145% of 81

7. 71% of 324   8. 56% of 65.4

9. **COMMUNICATION** Theresa makes a long distance phone call and talks for 50 minutes. Of these minutes, 25% were spent talking to her brother. Would the time spent talking with her brother be about 8, 12, or 15 minutes? Explain your reasoning.
   12 min; 0.25 × 48 = 12

Write an equation for each problem. Then solve. Round to the nearest tenth if necessary.

10. Find 14% of 65. **p = 0.14 • 65; 9.1**

11. What number is 36% of 294?

12. 82% of what number is 73.8? **73.8 = 0.82 • w; 90**

13. 75 is what percent of 50? **75 = n • 50; 150%**
    11. p = 0.36 • 294; 105.8

Find each percent of change. Round to the nearest whole percent if necessary. State whether the percent of change is an *increase* or a *decrease*.

14. $60 to $75 **25% increase**

15. 145 meters to 216 meters **49% increase**

16. 48 minutes to 40 minutes **17% decrease**

FOOD For Exercises 17 and 18, use the table below. It shows the results of a survey in which 175 students were asked what type of food they wanted for their class party.

Type of Food	Percent
Subs	32%
Tex-Mex	56%
Italian	12%

17. How many of the 175 students chose Italian food for their class party? **21**

18. How many students chose Tex-Mex food for the party? **98**

Find the total cost or sale price to the nearest cent.

19. $2,200 computer, $6\frac{1}{2}$% sales tax **$2,343**

20. $16 hat, 55% discount **$7.20**

21. $35.49 jeans, 33% discount **$23.78**

Find the simple interest earned to the nearest cent for each principal, interest rate, and time.

22. $750, 3%, 4 years **$90**

23. $1,050, 4.6%, 2 years **$96.60**

24. $2,600, 4%, 3 months **$26**

25. **MULTIPLE CHOICE** Mr. Jackson borrows $3,500 to renovate his home. His loan has an annual simple interest rate of 15%. If he pays off the loan after 6 months, about how much will he pay in all? **F**

    F $3,763
    G $3,500
    H $3,720
    J $4,025

Chapter 7 Practice Test **389**

CHAPTER
7 Practice Test

Summative Assessment

CRM **Chapter 7 Resource Masters**

Leveled Chapter 7 Tests			
Form	**Type**	**Level**	**Pages**
1	MC	**BL**	65–66
2A	MC	**OL**	67–68
2B	MC	**OL**	69–70
2C	FR	**OL**	71–72
2D	FR	**OL**	73–74
3	FR	**AL**	75–76

MC = *multiple-choice questions*
FR = *free-response questions*
BL = *below or approaching grade level*
OL = *on grade level*
AL = *above or beyond grade level*

• Vocabulary Test, p. 64
• Extended-Response Test, p. 77
• Unit 3 Test, pp. 81–82

ExamView®
Assessment Suite

Customize and create multiple versions of your chapter tests and the answer keys. All of the questions from the leveled chapter test in the *Chapter 7 Resource Masters* are also available on ExamView® Assessment Suite.

Additional Answers

5. Sample answer: 50; $\frac{1}{5}$ • 250 = 50

6. Sample answer: 120; 0.1 • 80 = 8 and 8 • 15 = 120

7. Sample answer: 224; 0.1 • 320 = 32 and 7 • 32 = 224

8. Sample answer: 33; $\frac{1}{2}$ • 66 = 33

Data-Driven Decision Making	Exercises	Lesson	State/Local Standards	Resources for Review
Diagnostic Teaching Based on the results of the Chapter 7 Practice Test, use the following to review concepts that students continue to find challenging.	1–8	7-1, 7-2, 7-3		CRM Study Guide and Intervention pp. 10, 17, 24, 30, 35, 40, 47, and 53
	9–18	7-4, 7-5, 7-6		Math Online > glencoe.com
	19–25	7-7, 7-8		• Extra Examples • Personal Tutor • Concepts in Motion

TEST-TAKING TIP

Exercise 6 Have students use mental math to eliminate incorrect answer choices. Since $12 \times 3 = 36$, $12.5 \times 3 > 36$. So, answer choices H and J can be eliminated. Since the product 12.5×3 must end with the digit 5, answer choice F can also be eliminated.

 Formative Assessment

You can use these two pages to benchmark student progress.

 Chapter 7 Resource Masters
• Standardized Test Practice, pp. 78–80

ExamView
Assessment Suite
Create practice worksheets or tests that align to your state's standards, as well as TIMSS and NAEP tests.

PART 1 Multiple Choice

Read each question. Then fill in the correct answer on the answer document provided by your teacher or on a sheet of paper.

1. Sarah wants to buy pillows for her living room. Which store offers the best buy on pillows? **C**

Store	Sale Price
A	3 pillows for $40
B	4 pillows for $50
C	2 pillows for $19
D	1 pillow for $11

A Store A   C Store C
B Store B   D Store D

2. The graph below shows the attendance at a summer art festival from 2002 to 2007. If the trend in attendance continues, which is the best prediction of the attendance at the art festival in 2010? **G**

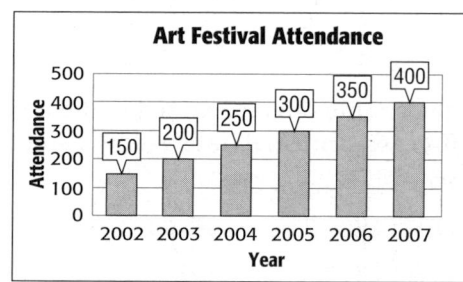

F Fewer than 200
G Between 500 and 600
H Between 700 and 800
J More than 800

3. At their annual car wash, the science club washes 30 cars in 45 minutes. At this rate, how many cars will they wash in 1 hour?

A 40   C 50   **A**
B 45   D 60

---

4. The cost of Ken's haircut was $23.95. If he wants to give his hair stylist a 15% tip, about how much of a tip should he leave? **G**

F $2.40
G $3.60
H $4.60
J $4.80

5. At a pet store, 38% of the animals are dogs. If there are a total of 88 animals at the pet store, which equation can be used to find x, the number of dogs at the pet store? **C**

A $\dfrac{x}{88} = \dfrac{100}{38}$

B $\dfrac{38}{88} = \dfrac{100}{x}$

C $\dfrac{x}{88} = \dfrac{38}{100}$

D $\dfrac{100}{88} = \dfrac{x}{38}$

6. An architect made a model of an office building using a scale of 1 inch equals 3 meters. If the height of the model is 12.5 inches, which of the following represents the actual height of the building? **G**

F 40.0 m
G 37.5 m
H 36.0 m
J 28.4 m

7. Mrs. Stewart painted the door to her deck. The door is a rectangle with length x feet and width y feet. In the middle of the door, there is a rectangular panel of glass that measures 5 feet by 2 feet. Which expression gives the painted area of the door in square feet? **C**

A $x + y - 10$
B $xy + 10$
C $xy - 10$
D $x + y + 10$

---

390 Chapter 7 Applying Percents

Preparing for Standardized Tests
For test-taking strategies and practice, see pages 716–733.

CHAPTER 7 Test Practice

8. At a grocery store, half-gallons of milk are on sale 5 for $4. Find the cost of 7 half-gallons of milk to the nearest cent. **J**

   F $2.86   H $5.40
   G $4.75   J $5.60

9. If point B is translated 3 units to the left and 2 units up, what will be point B's new coordinates? **D**

   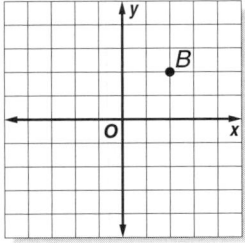

   A $(-3, 2)$ C $(4, -1)$
   B $(5, 0)$ D $(-1, 4)$

10. In Nadia's DVD collection, she has 8 action DVDs, 12 comedy DVDs, 7 romance DVDs, and 3 science fiction DVDs. What percent of Nadia's DVD collection are comedies? **J**

    F 25%   H 35%
    G 30%   J 40%

11. Cassandra bought 2 dozen juice boxes priced at 6 juice boxes for $2.29 and 24 snack packages priced at 8 snack packages for $6.32. What is the total amount, not including tax, she spent on juice boxes and snack packages? **C**

    A $34.44   C $28.12
    B $32.15   D $25.83

PART 2   Short Response/Grid In

Record your answers on the answer sheet provided by your teacher or on a sheet of paper.

12. The average cost of a 2-bedroom apartment in Grayson was $625 last year. This year, the average cost is $650. What is the percent of increase from last year to this year? **4%**

13. A necklace regularly sells for $18.00. The store advertises a 15% discount. What is the sale price of the necklace in dollars? **15.30**

PART 3   Extended Response

Record your answers on the answer sheet provided by your teacher or on a sheet of paper. Show your work.

TEST-TAKING TIP

Question 14 Remember to show all of your work. You may be able to get partial credit for your answers, even if they are not entirely correct.

14. Cable Company A increases their rates from $98 a month to $101.92 a month.

    a. What is the percent of increase? **4%**

    b. Cable Company B offers their cable for $110 dollars a month, but gives a 10% discount for new customers. Describe two ways to find the cost for new customers. **See margin.**

    c. If you currently use Cable Company A, would it make sense to change to Cable Company B? **See margin.**

Answer Sheet Practice

Have students simulate taking a standardized test by recording their answers on a practice recording sheet.

CRM Student Recording Sheet, p. 59

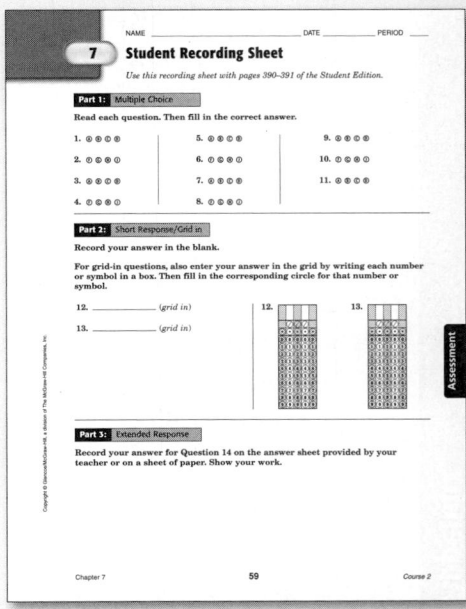

Additional Answer

14b. Sample answer: You can find 10% of $110 and subtract the amount from $110; $110 − $11 = $99. You can also subtract 10% from 100% and multiply the new percent by $110; 90% × $110 = $99.

14c. Yes, Company B is $2.92 cheaper a month.

NEED EXTRA HELP?													
If You Missed Question...	1	2	3	4	5	6	7	8	9	10	11	12	13	14
Go to Lesson...	6-2	2-6	6-2	7-1	7-2	6-8	3-6	6-6	2-3	7-5	6-1	7-6	7-7	7-6

Homework Option

Get Ready for Chapter 8   Assign students the exercises on page 395 as homework to assess whether they possess the prerequisite skills needed for the next chapter.

Pages 342–343, Explore 7-1

a.

0	0%
12	10%
24	20%
36	30%
48	40%
60	50%
72	60%
84	70%
96	80%
108	90%
120	100%

b.

0	0%
7	10%
14	20%
21	30%
28	40%
35	50%
42	60%
49	70%
56	80%
63	90%
70	100%

c.

0	0%
40	10%
80	20%
120	30%
160	40%
200	50%
240	60%
280	70%
320	80%
360	90%
400	100%

d.

0	0%
14	10%
28	20%
42	30%
56	40%
70	50%
84	60%
98	70%
112	80%
126	90%
140	100%

e.

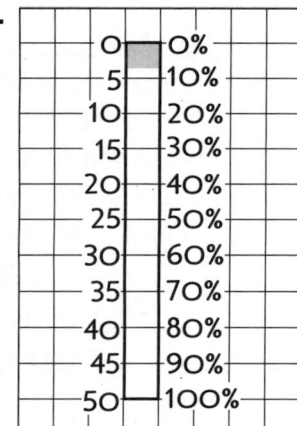

0	0%
5	10%
10	20%
15	30%
20	40%
25	50%
30	60%
35	70%
40	80%
45	90%
50	100%

f.

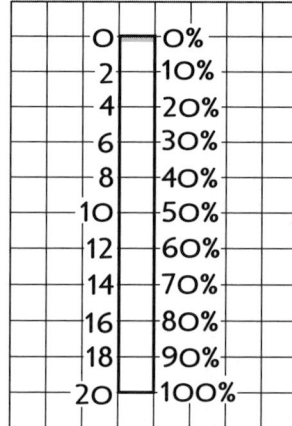

0	0%
2	10%
4	20%
6	30%
8	40%
10	50%
12	60%
14	70%
16	80%
18	90%
20	100%

Page 344, Lesson 7-1 (Get Ready for the Lesson)

1.

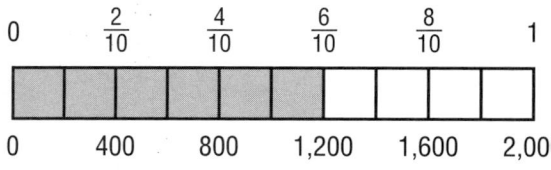

Pet Shelter Fundraiser

0.0　0.2　0.4　0.6　0.8　1.0

0　400　800　1,200　1,600　2,000

2.

Pet Shelter Fundraiser

0　$\frac{2}{10}$　$\frac{4}{10}$　$\frac{6}{10}$　$\frac{8}{10}$　1

0　400　800　1,200　1,600　2,000

3. $0.6 \times 2,000 = 1,200;\ \frac{3}{5} \times 2,000 = 1,200$

Page 358, Lesson 7-3

38. about 2.4 hours; $\frac{1}{10} \cdot 24 = 2.4$

39. about 3 hours; Method 1: $\frac{1}{3} \cdot 24 = 8$ and $\frac{1}{5} \cdot 24 \approx 5;\ 8 - 5 = 3$

40. There are $24 \cdot 60$ or 1,440 minutes in one day. So, Amanda spends about $\frac{1}{10}$ of 1,440 or 144 minutes each day on extracurricular activities.

Page 369, Lesson 7-6

4. Sample answer: a straw that is twice as long, 3 times longer, and 4 times longer, respectively.

5. Subtract the percent of change from the original straw.

NOTES

Student Handbook

Built-In Workbooks

Reference

Pages 392–665 can be found in Volume 2.

How to Use the Student Handbook

The Student Handbook is the additional skill and reference material found at the end of books. The Student Handbook can help answer these questions.

What If I Need More Practice?

You, or your teacher, may decide that working through some additional problems would be helpful. The **Extra Practice** section provides these problems for each lesson so you have ample opportunity to practice new skills.

What If I Have Trouble with Word Problems?

The **Mixed Problem Solving** portion of the book provides additional word problems that use the skills presented in each chapter. These problems give you real-world situations where the math can be applied.

What If I Need to Prepare for a Standardized Test?

The **Preparing for Standardized Tests** section provides worked-out examples and practice problems for multiple-choice, gridded response, short-response, and extended-response questions.

What If I Forget What I Learned Last Year?

Use the **Concepts and Skills** section to refresh your memory about topics you have learned in other math classes or to prepare for next year.

What If I Forget a Vocabulary Word?

The **English-Spanish Glossary** provides a list of important, or difficult, words used throughout the textbook. It provides a definition in English and Spanish as well as the page number(s) where the word can be found.

What If I Need to Check a Homework Answer?

The answers to the odd-numbered problems are included in **Selected Answers**. Check your answers to make sure you understand how to solve all of the assigned problems.

What If I Need to Find Something Quickly?

The **Index** alphabetically lists the subjects covered throughout the entire textbook and the pages on which each subject can be found.

What If I Forget a Formula?

Inside the back cover of your math book is a list of **Formulas and Symbols** that are used in the book.

Extra Practice

Lesson 1-1
Pages 25–29

Use the four-step plan to solve each problem.

1. The Reyes family rode their bicycles for 9 miles to the park. The ride back was along a different route for 14 miles. How many miles did they ride in all? **23 mi**

2. Four hundred sixty people are scheduled to attend a banquet. If each table seats 8 people, how many tables are needed? **58 tables**

3. A group of 251 people is eating dinner at a school fund-raiser. If each person pays $8.00 for their meal, how much money is raised? **$2,008**

4. Sherita's service charges a monthly fee of $20.00 plus $0.15 per minute. One monthly bill is $31.25. How many minutes did Sherita use during the month? **75 min**

5. ABC Car Rental charges $25 per day to rent a mid-sized car plus $0.20 per mile driven. Mr. Ruiz rents a mid-sized car for 3 days and drives a total of 72 miles. Find the amount of Mr. Ruiz's bill. **$89.40**

Lesson 1-2
Pages 30–33

Write each power as a product of the same factor.

1. 13^4 **$13 \cdot 13 \cdot 13 \cdot 13$**
2. 9^6 **$9 \cdot 9 \cdot 9 \cdot 9 \cdot 9 \cdot 9$**
3. 1^7 **$1 \cdot 1 \cdot 1 \cdot 1 \cdot 1 \cdot 1 \cdot 1$**
4. 12^2 **$12 \cdot 12$**
5. 5^8 **$5 \cdot 5 \cdot 5 \cdot 5 \cdot 5 \cdot 5 \cdot 5 \cdot 5$**
6. 15^4 **$15 \cdot 15 \cdot 15 \cdot 15$**

Evaluate each expression.

7. 5^6 **15,625**
8. 17^3 **4,913**
9. 2^{12} **4,096**
10. 3^5 **243**
11. 1^4 **1**
12. 5^3 **125**
13. 10^2 **100**
14. 2^8 **256**
15. 8^2 **64**
16. 7^4 **2,401**
17. 20^3 **8,000**
18. 42^3 **74,088**

Write each product in exponential form.

19. $2 \cdot 2 \cdot 2 \cdot 2 \cdot 2$ **2^5**
20. $3 \cdot 3 \cdot 3$ **3^3**
21. $1 \cdot 1 \cdot 1 \cdot 1 \cdot 1 \cdot 1$ **1^6**
22. $18 \cdot 18 \cdot 18 \cdot 18$ **18^4**
23. $9 \cdot 9 \cdot 9 \cdot 9 \cdot 9 \cdot 9 \cdot 9 \cdot 9$ **9^8**
24. $10 \cdot 10 \cdot 10 \cdot 10 \cdot 10 \cdot 10$ **10^6**

Lesson 1-3
Pages 34–37

Find the square of each number.

1. 4 **16**
2. 19 **361**
3. 13 **169**
4. 25 **625**
5. 9 **81**
6. 2 **4**
7. 14 **196**
8. 24 **576**
9. 40 **1,600**
10. 50 **2,500**
11. 100 **10,000**
12. 250 **62,500**

Find each square root.

13. $\sqrt{324}$ **18**
14. $\sqrt{900}$ **30**
15. $\sqrt{2,500}$ **50**
16. $\sqrt{576}$ **24**
17. $\sqrt{8,100}$ **90**
18. $\sqrt{676}$ **26**
19. $\sqrt{100}$ **10**
20. $\sqrt{784}$ **28**
21. $\sqrt{1,024}$ **32**
22. $\sqrt{841}$ **29**
23. $\sqrt{2,304}$ **48**
24. $\sqrt{3,025}$ **55**

Lesson 1-4
Pages 38–41

Evaluate each expression.

1. $14 - (5 + 7)$ **2**
2. $(32 + 10) - 5 \times 6$ **12**
3. $(50 - 6) + (12 + 4)$ **60**
4. $12 - 2 \cdot 3$ **6**
5. $16 + 4 \times 5$ **36**
6. $(5 + 3) \times 4 - 7$ **25**
7. $2 \times 3 + 9 \times 2$ **24**
8. $6 \cdot (8 + 4) \div 2$ **36**
9. $7 \times 6 - 14$ **28**
10. $8 + (12 \times 4) \div 8$ **14**
11. $13 - 6 \cdot 2 + 1$ **2**
12. $(80 \div 10) \times 8$ **64**
13. $14 - 2 \cdot 7 + 0$ **0**
14. $156 - 6 \times 0$ **156**
15. $30 - 14 \cdot 2 + 8$ **10**
16. $3 \times 4 - 3^2$ **3**
17. $10^2 - 5$ **95**
18. $3 + (10 - 5 + 1)^2$ **39**
19. $(4 + 3)^2 \div 7$ **7**
20. 8×10^3 **8,000**
21. $10^4 \times 6$ **60,000**
22. 4.5×10^3 **4,500**
23. 1.8×10^2 **180**
24. $3 + 5(1.7 + 2.3)$ **23**
25. $4(3.6 + 5.4) - 9$ **27**
26. $10 + 3(6.1 + 3.7)$ **39.4**
27. $6(7.5 + 2.1) - 2.3$ **55.3**

Lesson 1-5
Pages 42–43

Use the *guess and check* strategy to solve each problem.

1. **NUMBERS** A number is divided by 3. Then 8 is added to the quotient. The result is 15. What is the number? **21**

2. **NUMBERS** Benny is thinking of two numbers. Their product is 32 and their difference is 4. Find the numbers. **4 and 8**

3. **MONEY** A theater is charging $5 for children under 12 and $8 for everyone else. If the total for a group of people was $36, how many people under the age of 12 were in the group? **4**

4. **PLACE VALUE** Mindy wrote down a decimal number. The digit in the tenth's place is half the digit in the hundredth's place. If the product of the two digits is 18, what is the number? **0.36**

5. **MONEY** Penny has 14 coins totaling $1.55. She has one more nickel than she has dimes, and three less quarters than nickels. How many quarters, dimes, and nickels does she have if these are the only coin types she has? **3 quarters, 5 dimes, and 6 nickels**

6. **SOUVENIRS** A souvenir shop sells standard-sized postcards in packages of 5 and large-sized postcards in packages of 3. If Juan bought 16 postcards, how many packages of each did he buy? **Juan bought 2 standard size packages and 2 large size packages.**

Lesson 1-6
Pages 44–47

Evaluate each expression if $a = 3$, $b = 4$, $c = 12$, and $d = 1$.

1. $a + b$ **7**
2. $c - d$ **11**
3. $a + b + c$ **19**
4. $b - a$ **1**
5. $c - ab$ **0**
6. $a + 2d$ **5**
7. $b + 2c$ **28**
8. ab **12**
9. $a + 3b$ **15**
10. $6a + c$ **30**
11. $\frac{c}{d}$ **12**
12. abc **144**
13. $2(a + b)$ **14**
14. $\frac{2c}{b}$ **6**
15. $144 - abc$ **0**
16. $2ab$ **24**
17. $\frac{b}{2}$ **2**
18. a^2 **9**
19. $c^2 - 100$ **44**
20. $a^3 + 3$ **30**
21. $2b^2$ **32**
22. $b^3 + c$ **76**
23. $\frac{a^2}{d}$ **9**
24. $5a^2 + 2d^2$ **47**
25. $\frac{4d^2}{b}$ **1**
26. $\frac{15}{ab}$ **5**
27. $3a^2$ **27**
28. $10d^3$ **10**
29. $\frac{ab}{c}$ **1**
30. $\frac{(a+b)}{d}$ **7**
31. $2.5b + c$ **22**
32. $\frac{10}{d}$ **10**
33. $\frac{(2c+b)}{b}$ **7**
34. $\frac{(b^2+2d)}{a}$ **6**
35. $\frac{(2c+ab)}{c}$ **3**
36. $\frac{(3.5c+2)}{11}$ **4**

Lesson 1-7
Pages 49–52

Solve each equation mentally.

1. $b + 7 = 12$ **5**
2. $a + 3 = 15$ **12**
3. $s + 10 = 23$ **13**
4. $9 + n = 13$ **4**
5. $20 = 24 - n$ **4**
6. $4x = 36$ **9**
7. $2y = 10$ **5**
8. $15 = 5h$ **3**
9. $j \div 3 = 2$ **6**
10. $14 = w - 4$ **18**
11. $24 \div k = 6$ **4**
12. $b - 3 = 12$ **15**
13. $c \div 10 = 8$ **80**
14. $6 = t \div 5$ **30**
15. $14 + m = 24$ **10**
16. $3y = 39$ **13**
17. $\frac{f}{2} = 12$ **24**
18. $16 = 4v$ **4**
19. $81 = 80 + a$ **1**
20. $9 = \frac{72}{x}$ **8**
21. $66 = 22m$ **3**
22. $77 - 12 = a$ **65**
23. $9k = 81$ **9**
24. $95 + d = 100$ **5**
25. $b = \frac{72}{6}$ **12**
26. $z = 15 + 22$ **37**
27. $15b = 225$ **15**
28. $43 + s = 57$ **14**
29. $4w = 52$ **13**
30. $e - 10 = 0$ **10**
31. $62 - d = 12$ **50**
32. $14f = 14$ **1**
33. $48 \div n = 8$ **6**
34. $a - 82 = 95$ **177**
35. $\frac{x}{2} = 36$ **72**
36. $99 = c \div 2$ **198**

Lesson 1-8
Pages 53–56

13–24. See Student Handbook Answer Appendix for justification.

Use the Distributive Property to evaluate each expression.

1. $3(4 + 5)$ **27**
2. $(2 + 8)6$ **60**
3. $4(9 - 6)$ **12**
4. $8(6 - 3)$ **24**
5. $5(200 - 50)$ **750**
6. $20(3 + 6)$ **180**
7. $(20 - 5)8$ **120**
8. $50(8 + 2)$ **500**
9. $15(1{,}000 - 200)$ **12,000**
10. $3(2{,}000 + 400)$ **7,200**
11. $12(1{,}000 + 10)$ **12,120**
12. $7(1{,}000 - 50)$ **6,650**

Find each expression mentally. Justify each step.

13. $(5 + 17) + 25$ **47**
14. $13 + (22 + 17)$ **52**
15. $(8 + 18) + 92$ **118**
16. $(11 + 32) + 9$ **52**
17. $4 + (15 + 76)$ **95**
18. $(25 + 56) + 75$ **156**
19. $(4 \cdot 21) \cdot 25$ **2,100**
20. $5 \cdot (40 \cdot 8)$ **1,600**
21. $(2 \cdot 38) \cdot 50$ **3,800**
22. $(12 \cdot 7) \cdot 5$ **420**
23. $25 \cdot (12 \cdot 4)$ **1,200**
24. $(15 \cdot 9) \cdot 2$ **270**

Lesson 1-9
Pages 57–61

1–24. See Student Handbook Answer Appendix.

Describe the relationship between the terms in each arithmetic sequence. Then write the next three terms in each sequence.

1. 5, 9, 13, 17, …
2. 3, 5, 7, 9, …
3. 10, 15, 20, 25, …
4. 90, 93, 96, 99, …
5. 8, 14, 20, 26, …
6. 4.5, 5.4, 6.3, 7.2, …
7. 0.3, 0.4, 0.5, …
8. 2.3, 3.4, 4.5, 5.6, …
9. 8.9, 9.1, 9.3, 9.5, …
10. 3, 11, 19, 27, …
11. 350, 375, 400, 425, …
12. 620, 635, 650, 665, …
13. 2, 7, 12, 17, …
14. 10, 17, 24, 31, …
15. 0, 7, 14, 21, …
16. 1, 7, 13, 19, …
17. 95, 101, 107, 113, …
18. 9, 90, 171, 252, …
19. 2.6, 2.8, 3.0, 3.2, …
20. 4.1, 4.6, 5.1, 5.6, …
21. 6.6, 6.7, 6.8, 6.9, …
22. 19.5, 21, 22.5, 24, …
23. 14.5, 14.8, 15.1, 15.4, …
24. 0.1, 0.4, 0.7, 1.0, …

Lesson 1-10
Pages 63–67

Copy and complete each function table. Then identify the domain and range.

1.

x	2x	y
0	2(0)	0
1	2(1)	2
2	2(2)	4
3	2(3)	6

domain: {0, 1, 2, 3}
range: {0, 2, 4, 6}

2.

x	3x + 1	y
1	3(1) + 1	4
2	3(2) + 1	7
3	3(3) + 1	10
4	3(4) + 1	13

domain: {1, 2, 3, 4}
range: {4, 7, 10, 13}

3.

x	x − 2	y
3	3 − 2	1
4	4 − 2	2
5	5 − 2	3
6	6 − 2	4

domain: {3, 4, 5, 6}
range: {1, 2, 3, 4}

4.

x	x + 0.1	y
2	2 + 0.1	2.1
3	3 + 0.1	3.1
4	4 + 0.1	4.1
5	5 + 0.1	5.1

domain: {2, 3, 4, 5}
range: {2.1, 3.1, 4.1, 5.1}

Lesson 2-1
Pages 80–83

Write an integer for each situation.

1. seven degrees below zero **−7**
2. a loss of 3 pounds **−3**
3. a loss of 20 yards **−20**
4. a profit of $25 **25**
5. 112°F above 0 **112**
6. 2,830 feet above sea level **2,830**

Graph each set of integers on a number line.

7. {−2, 0, 2}
8. {1, 3, 5}
9. {−2, −5, 3}
10. {7, −1, 4}

7–10. See Student Handbook Answer Appendix.

Evaluate each expression.

11. $|1|$ **1**
12. $|-8|$ **8**
13. $|0|$ **0**
14. $|-82|$ **82**
15. $|64|$ **64**
16. $|-128|$ **128**
17. $|-22| + 5$ **27**
18. $|-40| - 8$ **32**
19. $|-18| + |10|$ **28**
20. $|-7| + |-1|$ **8**
21. $|98| - |-5|$ **93**
22. $|-49| - |-10|$ **39**

Lesson 2-2
Pages 84–87

Replace each ● with < or > to make a true sentence.

1. 7 ● −7 **>**
2. −8 ● 4 **<**
3. −4 ● −9 **>**
4. −3 ● 0 **<**
5. 8 ● 10 **<**
6. −5 ● −4 **<**
7. 6 ● −7 **>**
8. −12 ● −13 **>**
9. 3 ● 1 **>**
10. −2 ● 2 **<**
11. 7 ● −1 **>**
12. −15 ● −20 **>**
13. −40 ● 30 **<**
14. 0 ● −3 **>**
15. −5 ● 0 **<**
16. 85 ● −17 **>**

Order the integers from least to greatest.

17. −2, −8, 4, 10, −6, −12 **−12, −8, −6, −2, 4, 10**
18. −21, −19, −14, 18, 19, 32 **−21, −19, −14, 18, 19, 32**
19. 18, 23, 95, −95, −18, −23, 2 **−95, −23, −18, 2, 18, 23, 95**
20. 46, −48, −47, −52, −18, 12 **−52, −48, −47, −18, 12, 46**
21. 0, −10, −6, −8, 12 **−10, −8, −6, 0, 12**
22. −15, 18, −1, 0, 14, −20 **−20, −15, −1, 0, 14, 18**

Lesson 2-3

Pages 88–92

Write the ordered pair for each point graphed at the right. Then name the quadrant or axis on which each point is located.

1. A (3, −1), IV
2. B (−2, 2), II
3. C (0, −1), y-axis
4. D (3, 2), I
5. E (−2, −1), III
6. F (1, −2), IV
7. G (1, 1), I
8. H (−3, 1), II
9. I (−1, 0), x-axis
10. J (4, 3), I
11. K (3, 4), I
12. L (2, −3), IV

On graph paper, draw a coordinate plane. Then graph and label each point.

13. $N(-4, 3)$
14. $K(2, 5)$
15. $W(-6, -2)$
16. $X(5, 0)$
17. $Y(4, -4)$
18. $M(0, -3)$
19. $Z(-2, 0.5)$
20. $S(-1, -3)$
21. $A(0, 2)$
22. $C(-2, -2)$
23. $E(0, 1)$
24. $G(1, -1)$

13–24. See Student Handbook Answer Appendix.

Lesson 2-4

Pages 95–99

Add.

1. $-4 + 8$ **4**
2. $14 + 16$ **30**
3. $-7 + (-7)$ **−14**
4. $-9 + (-6)$ **−15**
5. $-18 + 11$ **−7**
6. $-36 + 40$ **4**
7. $42 + (-18)$ **24**
8. $-42 + 29$ **−13**
9. $18 + (-32)$ **−14**
10. $12 + (-9)$ **3**
11. $-24 + 9$ **−15**
12. $-7 + (-1)$ **−8**

Evaluate each expression if $a = 6$, $b = -2$, $c = -6$, and $d = 3$.

13. $-96 + a$ **−90**
14. $b + (-5)$ **−7**
15. $c + (-32)$ **−38**
16. $d + 98$ **101**
17. $-120 + b$ **−122**
18. $-120 + c$ **−126**
19. $5 + b$ **3**
20. $a + d$ **9**
21. $c + a$ **0**
22. $d + (-9)$ **−6**
23. $b + c$ **−8**
24. $d + c$ **−3**

Lesson 2-5

Pages 103–106

Subtract.

1. $3 - 7$ **−4**
2. $-5 - 4$ **−9**
3. $-6 - 2$ **−8**
4. $8 - 13$ **−5**
5. $6 - (-4)$ **10**
6. $12 - 9$ **3**
7. $-2 - 23$ **−25**
8. $63 - 78$ **−15**
9. $0 - (-14)$ **14**
10. $15 - 6$ **9**
11. $18 - 20$ **−2**
12. $-5 - 8$ **−13**
13. $21 - (-37)$ **58**
14. $-60 - 32$ **−92**
15. $57 - 63$ **−6**

Evaluate each expression if $k = -3$, $p = 6$, $n = 1$, and $d = -8$.

16. $55 - k$ **58**
17. $p - 7$ **−1**
18. $d - 15$ **−23**
19. $n - 12$ **−11**
20. $-51 - d$ **−43**
21. $k - 21$ **−24**
22. $n - k$ **4**
23. $-99 - k$ **−96**
24. $p - k$ **9**
25. $d - (-1)$ **−7**
26. $k - d$ **5**
27. $n - d$ **9**

Lesson 2-6

Pages 107–111

Multiply.

1. $5(-2)$ **−10**
2. $6(-4)$ **−24**
3. $4(21)$ **84**
4. $-11(-5)$ **55**
5. $-6(5)$ **−30**
6. $-50(0)$ **0**
7. $-5(-5)$ **25**
8. $-4(8)$ **−32**
9. $3(-13)$ **−39**
10. $12(-5)$ **−60**
11. $-9(-12)$ **108**
12. $15(-8)$ **−120**
13. $(-6)^2$ **36**
14. $(-2)^2$ **4**
15. $(-4)^3$ **−64**
16. $(-5)^3$ **−125**

Evaluate each expression if $a = -5$, $b = 2$, $c = -3$, and $d = 4$.

17. $-2d$ **−8**
18. $6a$ **−30**
19. $3ab$ **−30**
20. $-12d$ **−48**
21. $-4b^2$ **−16**
22. $-5cd$ **60**
23. a^2 **25**
24. $13ab$ **−130**

Lesson 2-7

Pages 112–113

Solve using the *look for a pattern* strategy.

1. **NUMBERS** Determine the next three numbers in the pattern below. **45, 51, 57**
15, 21, 27, 33, 39, …

2. **TIME** Determine the next two times in the pattern below. **3:50 A.M., 4:10 A.M.**
2:30 A.M., 2:50 A.M., 3:10 A.M., 3:30 A.M., …

3. **MONEY** The table shows Abigail's savings. If the pattern continues, what will be the total amount in week 6? **$2,400**

Week	Total ($)
1	$400
2	$800
3	$1,200
4	$1,600
5	$2,000
6	

4. **SCIENCE** A single rotation of Earth takes about 24 hours. Copy and complete the table to determine the number of hours in a week.

Number of Days	Number of Hours
1	24
2	48
3	72
4	96
5	120
6	144
7	168

Lesson 2-8

Pages 114–118

Divide.

1. $4 \div (-2)$ **−2**
2. $16 \div (-8)$ **−2**
3. $-14 \div (-2)$ **7**
4. $\frac{32}{8}$ **4**
5. $18 \div (-3)$ **−6**
6. $-18 \div 3$ **−6**
7. $8 \div (-8)$ **−1**
8. $0 \div (-1)$ **0**
9. $-25 \div 5$ **−5**
10. $\frac{-14}{-7}$ **2**
11. $-32 \div 8$ **−4**
12. $-56 \div (-8)$ **7**
13. $-81 \div 9$ **−9**
14. $-42 \div (-7)$ **6**
15. $121 \div (-11)$ **−11**
16. $-81 \div (-9)$ **9**
17. $18 \div (-2)$ **−9**
18. $\frac{-55}{11}$ **−5**
19. $\frac{25}{-5}$ **−5**
20. $-21 \div 3$ **−7**

Evaluate each expression if $a = -2$, $b = -7$, $x = 8$, and $y = -4$.

21. $-64 \div x$ **−8**
22. $\frac{16}{y}$ **−4**
23. $x \div 2$ **4**
24. $\frac{a}{2}$ **−1**
25. $ax \div y$ **4**
26. $\frac{bx}{y}$ **14**
27. $2y \div 1$ **−8**
28. $\frac{x}{ay}$ **1**
29. $-y \div a$ **−2**
30. $x^2 \div y$ **−16**
31. $\frac{ab}{1}$ **14**
32. $\frac{xy}{a}$ **16**

Lesson 3-1 1–20. See Student Handbook Answer Appendix.

Write each phrase as an algebraic expression.

1. six less than p
2. twenty more than c
3. the quotient of a and b
4. Juana's age plus 6
5. x increased by twelve
6. $1{,}000$ divided by z
7. 3 divided into y
8. the product of 7 and m
9. the difference of f and 9
10. twenty-six less q
11. 19 decreased by z
12. two less than x

Write each sentence as an algebraic equation.

13. Three times a number less four is 17.
14. The sum of a number and 6 is 5.
15. Twenty more than twice a number is −30.
16. The quotient of a number and −2 is −42.
17. Four plus three times a number is 18.
18. Five times a number minus 15 is 92.
19. Eight times a number plus twelve is 36.
20. The difference of a number and 24 is −30.

Lesson 3-2

Solve each equation. Check your solution.

1. $r - 3 = 14$ **17**
2. $t + 3 = 21$ **18**
3. $s + 10 = 23$ **13**
4. $7 + a = -10$ **−17**
5. $14 + m = 24$ **10**
6. $-9 + n = 13$ **22**
7. $s - 2 = -6$ **−4**
8. $6 + f = 71$ **65**
9. $x + 27 = 30$ **3**
10. $a - 7 = 23$ **30**
11. $-4 + b = -5$ **−1**
12. $w + 18 = -4$ **−22**
13. $k - 9 = -3$ **6**
14. $j + 12 = 11$ **−1**
15. $-42 + v = -42$ **0**
16. $s + 1.3 = 18$ **16.7**
17. $x + 7.4 = 23.5$ **16.1**
18. $p + 3.1 = 18$ **14.9**
19. $w - 3.7 = 4.63$ **8.33**
20. $m - 4.8 = 7.4$ **12.2**
21. $x - 1.3 = 12$ **13.3**
22. $y + 3.4 = 18$ **14.6**
23. $7.2 + g = 9.1$ **1.9**
24. $z - 12.1 = 14$ **26.1**
25. $v - 18 = 13.7$ **31.7**
26. $w - 0.1 = 0.32$ **0.42**
27. $r + 6.7 = 1.2$ **−5.5**

Lesson 3-3

Solve each equation. Check your solution.

1. $2m = 18$ **9**
2. $-42 = 6n$ **−7**
3. $72 = 8k$ **9**
4. $-20r = 20$ **−1**
5. $420 = 5s$ **84**
6. $325 = 25t$ **13**
7. $-14 = -2p$ **7**
8. $18q = 36$ **2**
9. $40 = 10a$ **4**
10. $100 = 20b$ **5**
11. $416 = 4c$ **104**
12. $45 = 9d$ **5**
13. $0.5m = 3.5$ **7**
14. $1.8 = 0.6x$ **3**
15. $0.4y = 2$ **5**
16. $1.86 = 6.2z$ **0.3**
17. $-8x = 24$ **−3**
18. $8.34 = 2r$ **4.17**
19. $1.67t = 10.02$ **6**
20. $243 = 27a$ **9**
21. $0.9x = 4.5$ **5**
22. $4.08 = 1.2y$ **3.4**
23. $8d = 112$ **14**
24. $5f = 180.5$ **36.1**
25. $59.66 = 3.14m$ **19**
26. $98.4 = 8p$ **12.3**
27. $208 = 26k$ **8**

Lesson 3-4

Use the *work backward* strategy to solve each problem.

1. **NUMBERS** A number is divided by 2. Then 4 is added to the quotient. Next, the sum of these numbers is multiplied by 3. The result is 21. Find the number. **6**

2. **MONEY** Holly spent $13.76 on a birthday present for her mom. She also spent $3.25 on a snack for herself. If she now has $7.74, how much money did she have initially? **$24.75**

3. ★ **DVDs** Jack rented 2 times as many DVDs as Paloma last month. Paloma rented 4 fewer than Greg, but 4 more than Grace. Greg rented 9 DVDs. How many DVDs did each person rent?

4. ★ **TIME** A portion of a shuttle bus schedule is shown. What is the earliest time after 9 A.M. when the bus departs? **9:43 A.M.**

Departs	Arrives
8:55 A.M.	9:20 A.M.
?	10:08 A.M.
10:31 A.M.	10:56 A.M.
11:19 A.M.	11:44 A.M.

5. **FOOD** After four days, 0.5 pound of lunch meat was left in the refrigerator. If half this amount was eaten on each of the previous four days, how much lunch meat was initially in the refrigerator? **1.5 lb**

Lesson 3-5 3. See Student Handbook Answer Appendix.

Solve each equation. Check your solution.

1. $3x + 6 = 6$ **0**
2. $2r - 7 = -1$ **3**
3. $-10 + 2d = 8$ **9**
4. $2b + 4 = -8$ **−6**
5. $5w - 12 = 3$ **3**
6. $5t - 4 = 6$ **2**
7. $2q - 6 = 4$ **5**
8. $2g - 3 = -9$ **−3**
9. $15 = 6y + 3$ **2**
10. $3s - 4 = 8$ **4**
11. $18 - 7f = 4$ **2**
12. $13 + 3p = 7$ **−2**
13. $7.5r + 2 = -28$ **−4**
14. $4.2 + 7z = 2.8$ **−0.2**
15. $-9m - 9 = 9$ **−2**
16. $32 + 0.2c = 1$ **−155**
17. $5t - 14 = -14$ **0**
18. $-0.25x + 0.5 = 4$ **−14**
19. $5w - 4 = 8$ **2.4**
20. $4d - 3 = 9$ **3**
21. $2g - 16 = -9$ **3.5**
22. $4k + 13 = 20$ **1.75**
23. $7 = 5 - 2x$ **−1**
24. $8z + 15 = -1$ **−2**
25. $92 - 16h = 12$ **5**
26. $14c + 14 - 28$ **1**
27. $1.1j + 2 = 7.5$ **5**

Lesson 3-6 6, 8. See Student Handbook Answer Appendix.

Find the perimeter and area of each rectangle.

1.

8 yd
3 yd

22 yd; 24 yd²

2.

12.2 cm
15.5 cm

55.4 cm; 189.1 cm²

3.

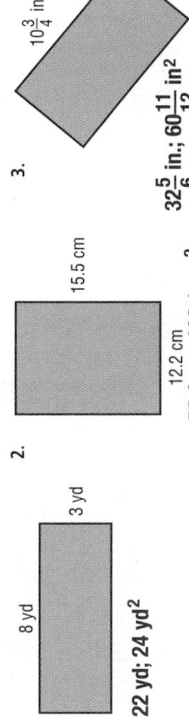

$10\frac{3}{4}$ in.
$5\frac{2}{3}$ in.

$32\frac{5}{6}$ in; $60\frac{11}{12}$ in²

4. $\ell = 80$ yd, $w = 20$ yd **200 yd; 1,600 yd²**
5. $\ell = 75$ cm, $w = 25$ cm **200 cm; 1,875 cm²**
6. $\ell = 5.25$ km, $w = 1.5$ km
7. $\ell = 8.6$ cm, $w = 2.5$ cm **22.2 cm; 21.5 cm²**
8. $\ell = 20.25$ m, $w = 4.75$ m
9. $\ell = 12$ ft, $w = 3$ ft **30 ft; 36 ft²**
10. $\ell = 5\frac{1}{4}$ mi, $w = 2\frac{1}{2}$ mi **$15\frac{1}{2}$ mi; $13\frac{1}{8}$ mi²**
11. $\ell = 10\frac{2}{3}$ ft, $w = 5\frac{5}{6}$ ft **33 ft; $62\frac{2}{9}$ ft²**

Lesson 3-7
Pages 163–167

1–11. See Student Handbook Answer Appendix.

Graph the function represented by the table.

1.

Total Cost of Tennis Balls	
Number of Tennis Balls	Total Cost ($)
3	6
4	8
5	10
6	12

2.

Convert Gallons to Quarts	
Gallon	Quarts
1	4
2	8
3	12
4	16

Graph each equation.

3. $y = 3x$
4. $y = 2x + 3$
5. $y = -x$
6. $y = 0.5x + 2$
7. $y = -x + 3$
8. $y = 0.25x + 6$
9. $y = -3x + 6$
10. $y = -x + 1$
11. $y = 5 - 0.5x$

Lesson 4-1
Pages 181–184

Determine whether each number is *prime* or *composite*.

1. 32 **composite**
2. 41 **prime**
3. 52 **composite**
4. 21 **composite**
5. 71 **prime**
6. 102 **composite**
7. 239 **prime**
8. 93 **composite**
9. 123 **composite**

Find the prime factorization of each number.

10. 81 3^4
11. 72 $2^3 \times 3^2$
12. 144 $2^4 \times 3^2$
13. 245 5×7^2
14. 423 $3^2 \times 47$
15. 525 $3 \times 5^2 \times 7$
16. 750 $2 \times 3 \times 5^3$
17. 914 2×457
18. 975 $3 \times 5^2 \times 13$

Factor each expression. 19–24. See Student Handbook Answer Appendix.

19. $35xy$
20. $14a^2$
21. $30n$
22. $27cd^2$
23. $4s^2t^2$
24. $60p^2qr$

Lesson 4-2
Pages 186–189

Find the GCF of each set of numbers.

1. 12, 16 **4**
2. 63, 81 **9**
3. 225, 500 **25**
4. 37, 100 **1**
5. 32, 240 **16**
6. 412, 640 **4**
7. 36, 81 **9**
8. 140, 350 **70**
9. 72, 170 **2**
10. 12, 18, 42 **6**
11. 24, 56, 120 **8**
12. 48, 60, 84 **12**
13. 32, 80, 96 **16**
14. 14, 49, 70 **7**
15. 8, 10, 20 **2**

Find the GCF of each set of expressions.

16. $18b, 24b$ **$6b$**
17. $2a, 3a$ **a**
18. $5n, 5mn$ **$5n$**
19. $12cd, 24c$ **$12c$**
20. $30x, 50x^2$ **$10x$**
21. $15az, 25az$ **$5az$**
22. $2c, 4ac, 8a$ **2**
23. $d, 6c^2d, 12d$ **d**
24. $10ab, 15bc, 20b^2$ **$5b$**

Lesson 4-3
Pages 190–191

Use the *make a list* strategy to solve each problem.

1. **MEASUREMENT** Gabriel has to make deliveries to three neighbors. He lives at house *b* on the map. Find the shortest route to make the deliveries and return home?

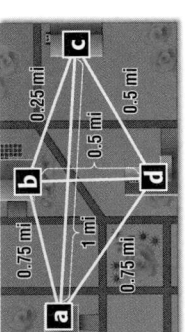

Sample answer: b–a–d–c–b; 2.25 mi

2. **FOOD** Daniel is making a peanut butter and jelly sandwich. His choices are creamy or crunchy peanut butter, white or wheat bread, and grape, apple, or strawberry jelly. How many different types of sandwiches can Daniel make? **12**

3. **GAMES** On the game board, you plan to move two spaces away from square A. You can move horizontally, vertically, or diagonally. How many different moves can you make from square A? List them.

A	B	C
D	E	F
G	H	I

3. 15; A–B–C, A–B–F, A–B–E, A–B–D, A–D–G, A–D–H, A–D–E, A–D–B, A–E–I, A–E–F, A–E–C, A–E–B, A–E–H, A–E–G, A–E–D

Lesson 4-4
Pages 192–195

Write each fraction in simplest form.

1. $\frac{14}{28}$ **$\frac{1}{2}$**
2. $\frac{15}{25}$ **$\frac{3}{5}$**
3. $\frac{100}{130}$ **$\frac{10}{13}$**
4. $\frac{14}{35}$ **$\frac{2}{5}$**
5. $\frac{9}{51}$ **$\frac{3}{17}$**
6. $\frac{54}{56}$ **$\frac{27}{28}$**
7. $\frac{75}{90}$ **$\frac{5}{6}$**
8. $\frac{24}{40}$ **$\frac{3}{5}$**
9. $\frac{180}{270}$ **$\frac{2}{3}$**
10. $\frac{312}{390}$ **$\frac{4}{5}$**
11. $\frac{240}{448}$ **$\frac{15}{28}$**
12. $\frac{71}{82}$ **$\frac{71}{82}$**
13. $\frac{333}{900}$ **$\frac{37}{100}$**
14. $\frac{85}{255}$ **$\frac{1}{3}$**
15. $\frac{84}{128}$ **$\frac{21}{32}$**
16. $\frac{64}{96}$ **$\frac{2}{3}$**
17. $\frac{99}{99}$ **1**
18. $\frac{3}{99}$ **$\frac{1}{33}$**
19. $\frac{44}{55}$ **$\frac{4}{5}$**
20. $\frac{57}{69}$ **$\frac{19}{23}$**
21. $\frac{15}{37}$ **$\frac{15}{37}$**
22. $\frac{144}{216}$ **$\frac{2}{3}$**
23. $\frac{5}{125}$ **$\frac{1}{25}$**
24. $\frac{204}{408}$ **$\frac{1}{2}$**
25. $\frac{15}{75}$ **$\frac{1}{5}$**

Lesson 4-5
Pages 196–200

Write each fraction or mixed number as a decimal. Use bar notation if the decimal is a repeating decimal.

1. $\frac{16}{20}$ **0.8**
2. $\frac{30}{120}$ **0.25**
3. $1\frac{7}{8}$ **1.875**
4. $\frac{1}{6}$ **$0.1\overline{6}$**
5. $\frac{11}{40}$ **0.275**
6. $5\frac{13}{50}$ **5.26**
7. $\frac{55}{300}$ **$0.18\overline{3}$**
8. $1\frac{1}{2}$ **1.5**
9. $\frac{5}{9}$ **$0.\overline{5}$**
10. $2\frac{3}{4}$ **2.75**
11. $\frac{9}{11}$ **$0.\overline{81}$**
12. $4\frac{1}{9}$ **$4.\overline{1}$**

Write each decimal as a fraction or mixed number in simplest form.

13. 0.26 **$\frac{13}{50}$**
14. 0.75 **$\frac{3}{4}$**
15. 0.4 **$\frac{2}{5}$**
16. 0.1 **$\frac{1}{10}$**
17. 4.48 **$4\frac{12}{25}$**
18. 9.8 **$9\frac{4}{5}$**
19. 0.91 **$\frac{91}{100}$**
20. 11.15 **$11\frac{3}{20}$**

Lesson 4-6

Pages 202–205

Write each ratio as a percent.

1. 39 out of 100 **39%**
2. $\frac{23}{100}$ **23%**
3. 17:100 **17%**
4. 72 per 100 **72%**
5. 4 to 100 **4%**
6. 98 in 100 **98%**

Write each fraction as a percent.

7. $\frac{1}{2}$ **50%**
8. $\frac{2}{5}$ **40%**
9. $\frac{60}{100}$ **60%**
10. $\frac{17}{20}$ **85%**
11. $\frac{7}{25}$ **28%**
12. $\frac{1}{20}$ **5%**
13. $\frac{8}{100}$ **8%**
14. $\frac{7}{7}$ **100%**
15. $\frac{9}{10}$ **90%**
16. $\frac{1}{100}$ **1%**
17. $\frac{50}{50}$ **100%**
18. $\frac{49}{50}$ **98%**

Write each percent as a fraction in simplest form.

19. 12% $\frac{3}{25}$
20. 23% $\frac{23}{100}$
21. 1% $\frac{1}{100}$
22. 94% $\frac{47}{50}$
23. 36% $\frac{9}{25}$
24. 4% $\frac{1}{25}$
25. 72% $\frac{18}{25}$
26. 100% **1**
27. 65% $\frac{13}{20}$
28. 47% $\frac{47}{100}$
29. 15% $\frac{3}{20}$
30. 48% $\frac{12}{25}$

Lesson 4-7

Pages 206–210

Write each percent as a decimal.

1. 42% **0.42**
2. 100% **1.0**
3. 8% **0.08**
4. 20% **0.2**
5. 35% **0.35**
6. 3% **0.03**
7. 62% **0.62**
8. 50% **0.5**
9. 28% **0.28**
10. 87% **0.87**
11. 7.5% **0.075**
12. 87.5% **0.875**
13. 1.8% **0.018**
14. 99.9% **0.999**
15. $85\frac{1}{4}$% **0.8525**
16. $24\frac{1}{2}$% **0.245**
17. $64\frac{4}{5}$% **0.648**
18. $36\frac{3}{4}$% **0.3675**
19. $1\frac{1}{5}$% **0.012**
20. $2\frac{1}{2}$% **0.025**

Write each decimal as a percent.

21. 0.16 **16%**
22. 0.1 **10%**
23. 0.5 **50%**
24. 0.98 **98%**
25. 0.31 **31%**
26. 0.76 **76%**
27. 0.07 **7%**
28. 0.8 **80%**
29. 0.07 **7%**
30. 0.10 **10%**
31. 0.90 **90%**
32. 1.00 **100%**
33. 0.666 **66.6%**
34. 0.725 **72.5%**
35. 0.138 **13.8%**
36. 0.899 **89.9%**
37. 0.256 **25.6%**
38. 0.038 **3.8%**
39. 0.0525 **5.25%**
40. 0.017 **1.7%**

Lesson 4-8

Pages 211–214

Find the LCM of each set of numbers.

1. 4, 9 **36**
2. 6, 16 **48**
3. 24, 36 **72**
4. 48, 84 **336**
5. 8, 9 **72**
6. 49, 56 **392**
7. 42, 66 **462**
8. 15, 39 **195**
9. 56, 64 **448**
10. 24, 42 **168**
11. 80, 250 **2,000**
12. 16, 24 **48**
13. 13, 14 **182**
14. 36, 48 **144**
15. 10, 100 **100**
16. 25, 200 **200**
17. 1, 2, 5 **10**
18. 2, 3, 7 **42**
19. 1, 9, 27 **27**
20. 2, 24, 36 **72**
21. 7, 21, 35 **105**
22. 12, 18, 28 **252**
23. 32, 80, 96 **480**
24. 5, 18, 45 **90**
25. 11, 22, 33 **66**
26. 35, 70, 140 **140**
27. 25, 200, 400 **400**
28. 100, 200, 300 **600**

Lesson 4-9

Pages 215–220

Replace each ● with <, >, or = to make a true sentence.

1. $-\frac{1}{5}$ ● $-\frac{3}{5}$ **>**
2. $-\frac{7}{8}$ ● $-\frac{5}{6}$ **<**
3. $-\frac{1}{6}$ ● $-\frac{5}{6}$ **>**
4. $-\frac{3}{4}$ ● $-\frac{1}{4}$ **<**
5. $-2\frac{1}{4}$ ● $-2\frac{2}{8}$ **=**
6. $-4\frac{3}{7}$ ● $-4\frac{2}{7}$ **<**
7. $-1\frac{4}{9}$ ● $-1\frac{8}{9}$ **>**
8. $-3\frac{4}{5}$ ● $-3\frac{2}{5}$ **<**
9. $\frac{7}{9}$ ● $\frac{3}{5}$ **>**
10. $\frac{14}{25}$ ● $\frac{3}{4}$ **<**
11. $\frac{8}{24}$ ● $\frac{20}{60}$ **=**
12. $\frac{5}{12}$ ● $\frac{4}{9}$ **<**
13. $\frac{18}{24}$ ● $\frac{10}{18}$ **>**
14. $\frac{4}{6}$ ● $\frac{5}{9}$ **>**
15. $\frac{11}{49}$ ● $\frac{12}{42}$ **<**
16. $\frac{5}{14}$ ● $\frac{2}{6}$ **>**

Order each set of numbers from least to greatest.

17. 70%, 0.6, $\frac{2}{3}$ **0.6, $\frac{2}{3}$, 70%**
18. 0.8, $\frac{17}{20}$, 17% **17%, 0.8, $\frac{17}{20}$**
19. $\frac{61}{100}$, 61.5%, 0.65 **$\frac{61}{100}$, 0.65, 61.5%**
20. $0.4\overline{2}$, $\frac{3}{7}$, 42% **42%, $0.4\overline{2}$, $\frac{3}{7}$**
21. 2.15, 2.105, $2\frac{7}{50}$ **2.105, $2\frac{7}{50}$, 2.15**
22. $7\frac{1}{8}$, 7.81, 7.18 **$7\frac{1}{8}$, 7.18, 7.81**

Lesson 5-1

Pages 230–235

Estimate. 1–21. Sample answers are given.

1. $\frac{3}{7} + \frac{6}{8}$ $\frac{1}{2} + 1 = 1\frac{1}{2}$
2. $\frac{3}{8} + \frac{7}{8}$ $\frac{1}{2} + 1 = 1\frac{1}{2}$
3. $\frac{1}{8} + \frac{8}{9}$ $0 + 1 = 1$
4. $3\frac{1}{8} + 7\frac{6}{7}$ $3 + 8 = 11$
5. $4\frac{2}{3} + 6\frac{7}{8}$ $5 + 7 = 12$
6. $3\frac{2}{3} \times 2\frac{1}{3}$ $4 \times 2 = 8$
7. $\frac{4}{5} \cdot 3$ $1 \cdot 3 = 3$
8. $9\frac{7}{8} - 6\frac{2}{3}$ $10 - 7 = 3$
9. $\frac{3}{7} - \frac{1}{15}$ $\frac{1}{2} - 0 = \frac{1}{2}$
10. $\frac{3}{4} \cdot \frac{7}{8}$ $1 \cdot 1 = 1$
11. $7\frac{1}{4} \div \frac{2}{3}$ $7 \div 1 = 7$
12. $\frac{5}{6} \div \frac{1}{3}$ $1 \div 1 = 1$
13. $9\frac{3}{8} + 3\frac{1}{8}$ $10 + 3 = 13$
14. $5\frac{1}{3} - 2\frac{3}{4}$ $5 - 3 = 2$
15. $13\frac{7}{8} - 2\frac{1}{3}$ $14 - 2 = 12$
16. $\frac{13}{15} \cdot 3$ $1 \cdot 3 = 3$
17. $\frac{1}{9} \div 2$ $0 \div 2 = 0$
18. $\frac{5}{8} - \frac{1}{16}$ $\frac{1}{2} - 0 = \frac{1}{2}$
19. $9\frac{2}{3} + 4\frac{7}{8}$ $10 + 5 = 15$
20. $\frac{1}{2} \cdot 25$ $\frac{1}{2} \cdot 26 = 13$
21. $35\frac{1}{3} \div 6\frac{3}{4}$ $35 \div 7 = 5$

Lesson 5-2

Pages 236–241

Add or subtract. Write in simplest form.

1. $\frac{5}{11} + \frac{9}{11}$ $1\frac{3}{11}$
2. $\frac{5}{8} - \frac{1}{8}$ $\frac{1}{2}$
3. $\frac{7}{10} + \frac{7}{10}$ $1\frac{2}{5}$
4. $\frac{9}{12} - \frac{5}{12}$ $\frac{1}{3}$
5. $\frac{2}{9} + \frac{8}{9}$ $1\frac{1}{9}$
6. $\frac{1}{2} + \frac{1}{4}$ $\frac{3}{4}$
7. $\frac{1}{3} - \frac{1}{12}$ $\frac{1}{4}$
8. $\frac{3}{7} + \frac{6}{14}$ $\frac{6}{7}$
9. $\frac{1}{4} + \frac{3}{5}$ $\frac{17}{20}$
10. $\frac{4}{9} + \frac{1}{2}$ $\frac{17}{18}$
11. $\frac{5}{7} - \frac{4}{21}$ $\frac{11}{21}$
12. $\frac{3}{4} - \frac{1}{6}$ $\frac{7}{12}$
13. $\frac{3}{5} + \frac{1}{4}$ $\frac{17}{20}$
14. $\frac{2}{3} - \frac{1}{8}$ $\frac{13}{24}$
15. $\frac{9}{10} + \frac{1}{3}$ $1\frac{7}{30}$

Evaluate each expression if $a = \frac{2}{3}$ and $b = \frac{7}{12}$.

16. $\frac{1}{5} + a$ $\frac{13}{15}$
17. $a - \frac{1}{6}$ $\frac{1}{2}$
18. $b + \frac{7}{8}$ $1\frac{11}{24}$
19. $\frac{7}{8} - a$ $\frac{5}{24}$
20. $a + \frac{1}{3}$ **1**
21. $a - b$ $\frac{1}{12}$

Lesson 5-3
Pages 242–246

Add or subtract. Write in simplest form.

1. $2\frac{1}{3} + 1\frac{1}{3}$ **$3\frac{2}{3}$**
2. $5\frac{2}{7} - 2\frac{3}{7}$ **$2\frac{6}{7}$**
3. $6\frac{3}{8} + 7\frac{1}{8}$ **$13\frac{1}{2}$**
4. $2\frac{3}{4} - 1\frac{1}{4}$ **$1\frac{1}{2}$**
5. $5\frac{1}{3} - 3\frac{1}{4}$ **$2\frac{1}{4}$**
6. $2\frac{2}{3} + 4\frac{1}{6}$ **$6\frac{7}{9}$**
7. $7\frac{4}{5} + 9\frac{3}{10}$ **$17\frac{1}{10}$**
8. $3\frac{3}{4} + 5\frac{5}{8}$ **$9\frac{3}{8}$**
9. $10\frac{2}{3} + 5\frac{6}{7}$ **$16\frac{11}{21}$**
10. $17\frac{2}{3} - 12\frac{1}{3}$ **$4\frac{8}{9}$**
11. $6\frac{5}{12} + 12\frac{5}{6}$ **$18\frac{5}{6}$**
12. $7\frac{1}{4} + 15\frac{5}{6}$ **$23\frac{1}{12}$**
13. $6\frac{1}{8} + 4\frac{2}{3}$ **$10\frac{19}{24}$**
14. $7 - 6\frac{4}{9}$ **$\frac{5}{9}$**
15. $8\frac{1}{12} + 12\frac{6}{11}$ **$20\frac{83}{132}$**
16. $7\frac{2}{8} + 8\frac{1}{4}$ **$15\frac{11}{12}$**
17. $12\frac{3}{11} + 14\frac{3}{13}$ **$26\frac{72}{143}$**
18. $21\frac{1}{3} + 15\frac{3}{8}$ **$36\frac{17}{24}$**
19. $19\frac{1}{7} + 6\frac{1}{4}$ **$25\frac{11}{28}$**
20. $9\frac{2}{5} - 8\frac{1}{3}$ **$1\frac{1}{15}$**
21. $18\frac{1}{4} - 3\frac{3}{8}$ **$14\frac{7}{8}$**
22. $1\frac{1}{8} + 2\frac{1}{12}$ **$3\frac{5}{24}$**
23. $2\frac{1}{12} - 1\frac{1}{8}$ **$\frac{23}{24}$**

Lesson 5-4
Pages 247–248

Eliminate possibilities to solve each problem.

1. **MEASUREMENT** Guillermo has a 3-gallon cooler with $1\frac{3}{4}$ gallons of juice in it. If he wants the cooler full for his soccer game, how much juice should he add? **C**

   A 4 gallons 　 C $1\frac{1}{4}$ gallons

   B $3\frac{1}{4}$ gallons 　 D $\frac{3}{4}$ gallon

2. **ELEPHANTS** An elephant in a zoo eats 58 cabbages in a week. About how many cabbages does an elephant eat in one year? **J**

   F 7 　 H 1,500

   G 700 　 J 3,000

3. **TRAVEL** Mr. Rollins drove 780 miles on a 5-day trip. He rented a car for \$23 per day plus \$0.15 per mile after 500 free miles. About how much did the rental car cost? **C**

   A \$100

   B \$130

   C \$160

   D \$180

Lesson 5-5
Pages 256–257

Multiply. Write in simplest form.

1. $\frac{2}{3} \times \frac{3}{5}$ **$\frac{2}{5}$**
2. $\frac{1}{2} \times \frac{2}{6}$ **$\frac{1}{15}$**
3. $\frac{4}{9} \times \frac{3}{7}$ **$\frac{4}{21}$**
4. $\frac{5}{12} \times \frac{6}{11}$ **$\frac{5}{22}$**
5. $\frac{3}{8} \times \frac{2}{9}$ **$\frac{3}{...}$**
6. $\frac{2}{5} \times \frac{5}{8}$ **$\frac{1}{4}$**
7. $\frac{7}{15} \times \frac{5}{21}$ **$\frac{1}{15}$**
8. $\frac{5}{6} \times \frac{15}{16}$ **$\frac{25}{32}$**
9. $\frac{2}{3} \times \frac{3}{13}$ **$\frac{2}{13}$**
10. $\frac{4}{9} \times \frac{1}{6}$ **$\frac{2}{27}$**
11. $3 \times \frac{1}{9}$ **$\frac{1}{3}$**
12. $5 \times \frac{6}{7}$ **$4\frac{2}{7}$**
13. $\frac{3}{5} \times 15$ **9**
14. $3\frac{1}{2} \times 4\frac{1}{3}$ **$15\frac{1}{6}$**
15. $4\frac{2}{5} \times 2\frac{3}{4}$ **$2\frac{1}{5}$**
16. $6\frac{1}{8} \times 5\frac{1}{7}$ **$31\frac{1}{2}$**
17. $2\frac{2}{3} \times 2\frac{1}{4}$ **6**
18. $\frac{7}{8} \times 16$ **14**
19. $5\frac{1}{5} \times 2\frac{1}{2}$ **13**
20. $7 \times \frac{1}{14}$ **$\frac{1}{2}$**
21. $22 \times \frac{3}{11}$ **6**
22. $8\frac{2}{3} \times 1\frac{1}{2}$ **13**
23. $4 \times 6\frac{1}{2}$ **26**
24. $\frac{1}{2} \times 10\frac{2}{3}$ **$5\frac{1}{3}$**
25. $\frac{2}{3} \times 21\frac{1}{3}$ **$14\frac{2}{9}$**
26. $\frac{7}{8} \times \frac{8}{7}$ **1**
27. $21 \times 1\frac{1}{2}$ **$10\frac{1}{2}$**
28. $11 \times \frac{1}{4}$ **$2\frac{3}{4}$**

Lesson 5-6
Pages 258–263

Find the multiplicative inverse of each number.

1. $2\frac{1}{3}$ **$\frac{3}{7}$ or $1\frac{1}{2}$**
2. $\frac{5}{4}$ **$\frac{4}{5}$**
3. 1 **$\frac{1}{1}$ or 1**
4. 10 **$\frac{1}{10}$**
5. $\frac{1}{7}$ **7**
6. $\frac{9}{16}$ **$\frac{16}{9}$ or $1\frac{7}{9}$**
7. $1\frac{1}{3}$ **$\frac{3}{4}$**
8. $3\frac{3}{4}$ **$\frac{4}{15}$**
9. $7\frac{3}{8}$ **$\frac{8}{59}$**
10. $6\frac{2}{5}$ **$\frac{5}{32}$**
11. $33\frac{1}{3}$ **$\frac{3}{100}$**
12. $66\frac{2}{3}$ **$\frac{3}{200}$**

Solve each equation. Check your solution.

13. $\frac{a}{13} = 2$ **26**
14. $\frac{8}{9}x = 24$ **27**
15. $\frac{3}{8}r = 36$ **96**
16. $\frac{3}{4}t = \frac{1}{2}$ **$\frac{2}{3}$**
17. $16 = \frac{h}{4}$ **64**
18. $\frac{m}{16} = 12$ **96**
19. $\frac{5}{8}n = 45$ **72**
20. $10 = \frac{b}{10}$ **100**
21. $\frac{1}{7}x = 7$ **49**
22. $5 = \frac{1}{5}y$ **25**
23. $\frac{4}{3}m = 28$ **21**
24. $\frac{2}{3}z = 20$ **30**
25. $\frac{c}{9} = 81$ **729**
26. $\frac{m}{9} = 9$ **81**
27. $16 = \frac{4}{9}f$ **36**
28. $\frac{15}{8}x = 225$ **120**

Lesson 5-7
Pages 265–270

Divide. Write in simplest form.

1. $\frac{2}{3} \div \frac{3}{2}$ **$\frac{4}{9}$**
2. $\frac{3}{5} \div \frac{2}{5}$ **$1\frac{1}{2}$**
3. $\frac{7}{10} \div \frac{3}{8}$ **$1\frac{13}{15}$**
4. $\frac{5}{9} \div \frac{5}{2}$ **$1\frac{7}{18}$**
5. $4 \div \frac{2}{3}$ **6**
6. $8 \div \frac{4}{5}$ **10**
7. $9 \div \frac{5}{9}$ **$16\frac{1}{5}$**
8. $\frac{2}{7} \div 2\frac{1}{7}$ **1**
9. $\frac{1}{14} \div 7$ **$\frac{1}{98}$**
10. $15 \div \frac{3}{5}$ **25**
11. $\frac{9}{14} \div \frac{3}{4}$ **$\frac{6}{7}$**
12. $\frac{7}{8} \div 10$ **$\frac{7}{80}$**
13. $16 \div 4\frac{3}{4}$ **$21\frac{1}{3}$**
14. $\frac{3}{8} \div 2\frac{1}{2}$ **$\frac{3}{20}$**
15. $5\frac{1}{2} \div 2\frac{1}{5}$ **$2\frac{1}{2}$**
16. $3\frac{1}{4} \div 5\frac{1}{2}$ **$\frac{13}{22}$**
17. $12\frac{5}{6} \div 2\frac{1}{6}$ **$5\frac{12}{13}$**
18. $7\frac{1}{2} \div 3\frac{1}{2}$ **$2\frac{1}{7}$**

Lesson 6-1
Pages 282–286

LUNCH Use the survey results to write each ratio as a fraction in simplest form.

Favorite School Lunch	Votes
Pizza	64
Hamburger	15
Macaroni and Cheese	14
Fish Sticks	4
Other	3

1. fish sticks:macaroni and cheese **$\frac{4}{14} = \frac{2}{7}$**
2. pizza:macaroni and cheese **$\frac{64}{14} = \frac{32}{7}$**
3. all votes:macaroni and cheese **$\frac{100}{14} = \frac{50}{7}$**
4. pizza:all votes **$\frac{64}{100} = \frac{16}{25}$**
5. other:hamburger **$\frac{3}{15} = \frac{1}{5}$**

6, 7. See Student Handbook Answer Appendix.

Determine whether the following ratios are equivalent. Explain.

6. 4 out of 6 balloons popped, 8 out of 12 balloons popped
7. 20 out of 25 students agree, 16 out of 30 students agree

Lesson 6-2

Pages 287–292

Find each unit rate. Round to the nearest hundredth if necessary.

1. $240 for 4 days **$60/day**
2. 250 people in 5 buses **50 people/bus**
3. 500 miles in 10 hours **50 mi/h**
4. 18 cups for 24 pounds **$\frac{3}{4}$ cup/pound**
5. 32 people in 8 cars **4 people/car**
6. $4.50 for 3 dozen **$1.50/dozen**
7. 245 tickets in 5 days **49 tickets/day**
8. 12 classes in 4 semesters **3 classes/semester**
9. 60 people in 4 rows **15 people/row**
10. 48 ounces in 3 pounds **16 oz/lb**
11. 20 people in 4 groups **5 people/group**
12. 1.5 pounds for $3.00 **0.5 lb/$**
13. 45 miles in 60 minutes **0.75 mi/min**
14. $5.50 for 10 disks **$0.55/disk**
15. 360 miles for 12 gallons **30 mi/gal**
16. $8.50 for 5 yards **$1.70/yd**
17. 24 cups for $1.20 **20 cups/dollar**
18. 160 words in 4 minutes **40 words/min**
19. $60 for 5 books **$12/book**
20. $24 for 6 hours **$4/h**

Lesson 6-3

Pages 293–297

For Exercises 1 and 2, find the rate of change for each table.

1.

Age (yr)	Height (in.)
9	54
10	56
11	58
12	60

2 in. per yr

2.

Time (h)	Temperature (°C)
0	0
4	3
8	6
12	9

3°C per 4h

3. **MOVIE RENTALS** The graph shows the cost of renting movies. Use the graph to find the rate of change. **cost increases by $5 for each movie rental**

Renting Movies

Lesson 6-4

Pages 298–303

Complete.

1. 4,000 lb = ■ T **2**
2. 5 T = ■ lb **10,000**
3. 5 lb = ■ oz **80**
4. 12,000 lb = ■ T **6**
5. $\frac{1}{4}$ lb = ■ oz **4**
6. 12 pt = ■ c **24**
7. 3 gal = ■ pt **24**
8. 24 fl oz = ■ c **3**
9. 8 pt = ■ c **16**
10. 10 pt = ■ qt **5**
11. $2\frac{1}{4}$ c = ■ fl oz **18**
12. 6 lb = ■ oz **96**
13. 10 gal = ■ qt **40**
14. 4 qt = ■ fl oz **128**
15. 4 pt = ■ c **8**
16. 13,200 ft = ■ mi **$2\frac{1}{2}$**
17. 120 oz = ■ lb **$7\frac{1}{2}$**
18. $9\frac{1}{4}$ gal = ■ qt **37**
19. 7,480 yd = ■ mi **$4\frac{1}{4}$**
20. $12\frac{1}{2}$ lb = ■ oz **200**
21. $7\frac{1}{2}$ qt = ■ pt **15**
22. $3\frac{1}{8}$ c = ■ fl oz **25**
23. $2\frac{1}{4}$ mi = ■ ft **11,880**
24. $3\frac{2}{3}$ T = ■ lb **$7,333\frac{1}{3}$**

Lesson 6-5

Pages 304–309

Complete. Round to the nearest hundredth if necessary.

1. 400 mm = ■ cm **40**
2. 4 km = ■ m **4,000**
3. 660 cm = ■ m **6.6**
4. 0.3 km = ■ m **300**
5. 30 mm = ■ cm **3**
6. 84.5 m = ■ km **0.0845**
7. ■ m = 54 cm **0.54**
8. 18 km = ■ cm **1,800,000**
9. ■ mm = 45 cm **450**
10. 4 kg = ■ g **4,000**
11. 632 mg = ■ g **0.632**
12. 4,497 g = ■ kg **4.497**
13. ■ mg = 0.51 kg **510,000**
14. 0.63 kg = ■ g **630**
15. ■ kg = 563 g **0.563**
16. 662 m = ■ km **0.662**
17. 5,283 mL = ■ L **5.283**
18. 0.24 cm = ■ mm **2.4**
19. 380 kL = ■ L **380,000**
20. 10.8 g = ■ mg **10,800**
21. 83,000 mL = ■ L **83**
22. 56 in. ≈ ■ cm **142.24**
23. 32.8 ft. ≈ ■ m **9.84**
24. 609 yd ≈ ■ m **554.19**
25. 21.78 mi ≈ ■ km **35.07**
26. 48 lb ≈ ■ kg **21,772.8**
27. 2.3 T ≈ ■ kg **2,086.56**
28. 8.5 c ≈ ■ mL **2,011.02**
29. 33 gal ≈ ■ L **125.07**
30. 1.8 qt ≈ ■ mL **1,703.43**

Lesson 6-6

Pages 310–315

Determine if the quantities in each pair of ratios are proportional. Explain. **1–3. See Student Handbook Answer Appendix.**

1. **MONEY** 2 coins for every 3 bills and 6 coins for every 9 bills
2. **SCALE** 3 feet for every 1 in and 15 feet for every 6 in
3. **FAMILY** 2 children for every 1 adult and 8 children for every 3 adults

Solve each proportion.

4. $\frac{u}{72} = \frac{2}{4}$ **36**
5. $\frac{12}{m} = \frac{15}{10}$ **8**
6. $\frac{36}{90} = \frac{16}{t}$ **40**
7. $\frac{g}{32} = \frac{8}{64}$ **4**
8. $\frac{5}{14} = \frac{10}{a}$ **28**
9. $\frac{k}{18} = \frac{5}{3}$ **30**
10. $\frac{15}{w} = \frac{60}{4}$ **1**
11. $\frac{81}{90} = \frac{y}{20}$ **18**
12. $\frac{45}{8} = \frac{36}{d}$ **6.4**
13. $\frac{125}{v} = \frac{20}{5}$ **31.25**
14. $\frac{4}{5} = \frac{x}{3}$ **2.4**
15. $\frac{45}{75} = \frac{j}{3}$ **1.8**

Lesson 6-7

Pages 318–319

Use the *draw a diagram* strategy to solve the following problems.

1. **TESTS** The scores on a test are found by adding or subtracting points as shown below. If Salazar's score on a 15-question test was 86 points, how many of his answers were correct, incorrect, and blank?

Answer	Points
Correct	+8
Incorrect	−4
No answer	−2

See Student Handbook Answer Appendix.

2. **GAMES** Six members of a video game club are having a tournament. In the first round, every player will play a video game against every other player. How many games will be in the first round of the tournament? **15 games**

3. **FAMILY** At Latrice's family reunion, $\frac{4}{5}$ of the people are 18 years of age or older. Half of the remaining people are under 12 years old. If 20 children are under 12 years old, how many people are at the reunion? **200 people**

Lesson 6-8

Pages 320–326

On a map, the scale is 1 inch = 50 miles. For each map distance, find the actual distance.

1. 5 inches **250 mi**
2. 12 inches **600 mi**
3. $2\frac{3}{8}$ inches **$118\frac{3}{4}$ mi**
4. $\frac{4}{5}$ inch **40 mi**
5. $2\frac{5}{6}$ inches **$141\frac{2}{3}$ mi**
6. 3.25 inches **162.5 mi**
7. 4.75 inches **237.5 mi**
8. 5.25 inches **262.5 mi**

On a scale drawing, the scale is $\frac{1}{2}$ inch = 2 feet. Find the dimensions of each room in the scale drawing.

9. 14 feet by 18 feet **$3\frac{1}{2}$ in. by $4\frac{1}{2}$ in.**
10. 32 feet by 6 feet **8 in. by $1\frac{1}{2}$ in.**
11. 3 feet by 5 feet **$\frac{3}{4}$ in. by $1\frac{1}{4}$ in.**
12. 20 feet by 30 feet **5 in. by $7\frac{1}{2}$ in.**

Lesson 6-9

Pages 328–332

Write each percent as a fraction in simplest form.

1. 32% $\frac{8}{25}$
2. 89% $\frac{89}{100}$
3. 72% $\frac{18}{25}$
4. 11% $\frac{11}{100}$
5. 1% $\frac{1}{100}$
6. 28% $\frac{7}{25}$
7. 55% $\frac{11}{20}$
8. 18.5% $\frac{37}{200}$
9. 22.75% $\frac{91}{400}$
10. 25.2% $\frac{63}{250}$
11. 75.5% $\frac{151}{200}$
12. 48.25% $\frac{193}{400}$
13. 6.5% $\frac{13}{200}$
14. 1.25% $\frac{1}{80}$
15. 88.9% $\frac{889}{1,000}$
16. $52\frac{1}{4}$% $\frac{209}{400}$
17. 895% $8\frac{19}{20}$
18. 480% $4\frac{4}{5}$
19. 0.78% $\frac{39}{5,000}$
20. 0.3% $\frac{3}{1,000}$

Write each fraction as a percent. Round to the nearest hundredth if necessary.

21. $\frac{14}{25}$ **56%**
22. $\frac{28}{50}$ **56%**
23. $\frac{14}{20}$ **70%**
24. $\frac{7}{10}$ **70%**
25. $\frac{17}{17}$ **100%**
26. $\frac{80}{125}$ **64%**
27. $\frac{9}{12}$ **75%**
28. $\frac{4}{6}$ **66.67%**
29. $\frac{11}{12}$ **91.67%**
30. $\frac{9}{16}$ **56.25%**
31. $\frac{8}{9}$ **88.89%**
32. $\frac{3}{16}$ **18.75%**
33. $\frac{5}{32}$ **15.63%**
34. $\frac{1}{16}$ **6.25%**
35. $\frac{8}{15}$ **53.33%**
36. $\frac{9}{11}$ **81.82%**
37. $\frac{1}{250}$ **0.4%**
38. $\frac{1}{500}$ **0.2%**
39. $12\frac{1}{2}$ **1,250%**
40. $18\frac{2}{5}$ **1,840%**

Lesson 7-1

Pages 344–348

Find each number. Round to the nearest tenth if necessary.

1. 5% of 40 **2**
2. 10% of 120 **12**
3. 12% of 150 **18**
4. 12.5% of 40 **5**
5. 75% of 200 **150**
6. 13% of 25.3 **3.3**
7. 250% of 44 **110**
8. 0.5% of 13.7 **0.1**
9. 600% of 7 **42**
10. 1.5% of $25 **$0.38**
11. 81% of 134 **108.5**
12. 43% of 110 **47.3**
13. 61% of 524 **319.6**
14. 100% of 3.5 **3.5**
15. 20% of 58.5 **11.7**
16. 45% of 125.5 **56.5**
17. 23% of 500 **115**
18. 80% of 8 **6.4**
19. 90% of 72 **64.8**
20. 32% of 54 **17.3**

Lesson 7-2

Pages 353–354

Find each number. Round to the nearest tenth if necessary.

1. What number is 25% of 280? **70**
2. 38 is what percent of 50? **76%**
3. 54 is 25% of what number? **216**
4. 24.5% of what number is 15? **61.2**
5. What number is 80% of 500? **400**
6. 12% of 120 is what number? **14.4**
7. Find 68% of 50. **34**
8. What percent of 240 is 32? **13.3%**
9. 99 is what percent of 150? **66%**
10. Find 75% of 1. **0.8**
11. What number is $33\frac{1}{3}$% of 66? **22**
12. 50% of 350 is what number? **175**
13. What percent of 450 is 50? **11.1%**
14. What number is $37\frac{1}{2}$% of 32? **12**
15. 95% of 40 is what number? **38**
16. Find 30% of 26. **7.8**
17. 9 is what percent of 30? **30%**
18. 52% of what number is 109.2? **210**
19. What number is 65% of 200? **130**
20. What number is 15.5% of 45? **7.0**

Lesson 7-3

Pages 355–360

Estimate by using fractions. 1–36. Sample answers are given.

1. 28% of 48 $\frac{1}{4} \cdot 48 = 12$
2. 99% of 65 $1 \cdot 65 = 65$
3. 445% of 20 $3 \cdot (4 \cdot 20) + (\frac{1}{2} \cdot 20) = 90$
4. 9% of 81 $\frac{1}{10} \cdot 80 = 8$
5. 73% of 240 $\frac{3}{4} \cdot 240 = 180$
6. 65.5% of 75 $\frac{2}{3} \cdot 75 = 50$
7. 48.2% of 93 $\frac{1}{2} \cdot 90 = 45$
8. 39.45% of 51 $\frac{2}{5} \cdot 50 = 20$
9. 287% of 122 $3 \cdot 120 = 360$
10. 53% of 80 $\frac{1}{2} \cdot 80 = 40$
11. 414% of 72 $4 \cdot 72 = 288$
12. 59% of 105 $\frac{3}{5} \cdot 105 = 63$

Estimate by using 10%. 13–24. See Student Handbook Answer Appendix.

13. 30% of 42
14. 70% of 104
15. 90% of 152
16. 67% of 70
17. 78% of 92
18. 12% of 183
19. 51% of 221
20. 23% of 504
21. 81% of 390
22. 41% of 60
23. 59% of 178
24. 22% of 450

Estimate.

25. 50% of 37 $\frac{1}{2} \cdot 40 = 20$
26. 18% of 90 $\frac{1}{5} \cdot 100 = 20$
27. 300% of 245 $3 \cdot 250 = 750$
28. 1% of 48 $\frac{1}{100} \cdot 50 = 0.5$
29. 70% of 300 $\frac{7}{10} \cdot 300 = 210$
30. 35% of 35 $\frac{2}{20} \cdot 40 = 14$
31. 60.5% of 60 $\frac{3}{5} \cdot 100 = 633$
32. $5\frac{1}{2}$% of 100 $\frac{50}{100} \cdot 100 = 6$
33. 40.01% of 16 $\frac{2}{5} \cdot 15 = 6$
34. 80% of 62 $\frac{4}{5} \cdot 60 = 48$
35. 45% of 119 $\frac{9}{20} \cdot 120 = 54$
36. 14.81% of 986 $\frac{3}{20} \cdot 1,000 = 150$

Lesson 7-4

Pages 361–365

Write an equation for each problem. Then solve. Round to the nearest tenth if necessary. 1–14. See Student Handbook Answer Appendix for equations.

1. Find 45% of 50. **22.5**
2. 75 is what percent of 300? **25%**
3. 16% of what number is 2? **12.5**
4. 75% of 80 is what number? **60**
5. 5% of what number is 12? **240**
6. Find 60% of 45. **27**
7. 90 is what percent of 95? **94.7%**
8. $28\frac{1}{2}$% of 64 is what number? **18.2**
9. Find 46.5% of 75. **34.9**
10. What number is 55.5% of 70? **38.9**
11. 80.5% of what number is 80.5? **100**
12. $66\frac{2}{3}$% of what number is 40? **60**
13. Find 122.5% of 80. **98**
14. 250% of what number is 75? **30**

Lesson 7-5
Pages 366–367

Solve each problem using the *reasonable answers* strategy.

1. **SKIING** Benito skied for 13.5 hours and estimated that he spent 30% of his time on the ski lift. Did he spend about 4, 6, or 8 hours on the ski lift? **about 4 h**

2. **CLASS TRIP** The class trip at Wilson Middle School costs $145 per student. A fundraiser earns 38% of this cost. Will each student have to pay about $70, $80, or $90? **$90**

3. **GAS MILEAGE** Miguel's car gets 38 miles per gallon and has 2.5 gallons of gasoline left in the tank. Can he drive for 85, 95, or 105 more miles before he runs out of gas? **95 mi**

4. **DINING** At a restaurant, the total cost of a meal is $87.50. Nadia wants to leave a 20% tip. Should she leave a total of $95, $105, or $115? **$105**

Lesson 7-6
Pages 369–374

Find each percent of change. Round to the nearest whole percent if necessary. State whether the percent of change is an *increase* or *decrease*. 1. **50% increase** 2. **160% increase** 11. **225% increase** 12. **96% decrease**

1. 450 centimeters to 675 centimeters
2. 77 million to 200.2 million
3. 500 albums to 100 albums **80% decrease**
4. 350 yards to 420 yards **20% increase**
5. 3.25 meters to 2.95 meters **9% decrease**
6. $65 to $75 **15% increase**
7. 180 dishes to 160 dishes **11% decrease**
8. 450 pieces to 445.5 pieces **1% decrease**
9. 700 grams 910 grams **30% increase**
10. 55 women to 11 women **80% decrease**
11. 412 children to 1,339 children
12. 464 kilograms to 20 kilograms
13. 24 hours to 86 hours **258% increase**
14. 16 minutes to 24 minutes **50% increase**

Lesson 7-7
Pages 375–378 1–12. See Student Handbook Answer Appendix.

Find the total cost or sale price to the nearest cent.

1. $45 sweater; 6% tax
2. $18.99 CD; 15% discount
3. $199 ring; 10% discount
4. $29 shirt; 7% tax
5. $19 purse; 25% discount
6. $145 coat; 6.25% tax
7. $12 meal; 4.5% tax
8. $899 computer; 20% discount
9. $105 skateboard; $7\frac{1}{2}\%$ tax
10. $599 TV; 12% discount
11. $12,500 car; $3\frac{3}{4}\%$ tax
12. $49.95 gloves; $5\frac{1}{4}\%$ tax

Find the percent of discount to the nearest percent.

13. sneakers: regular price, $72 sale price, $60 **17%**
14. dress shirt: regular price, $90 sale price, $22.50 **75%**
15. portable game player: regular price, $125 sale price, $100 **20%**
16. car: regular price, $25,000 sale price, $22,000 **12%**
17. hiking boots: regular price, $139 sale price, $113.98 **18%**
18. airline tickets: regular price, $556 sale price, $500.40 **10%**
19. CD: regular price, $15 sale price, $9 **40%**
20. computer: regular price, $600 sale price, $450 **25%**

Lesson 7-8
Pages 379–382

Find the simple interest earned to the nearest cent for each principal, interest rate, and time. 1–9. See Student Handbook Answer Appendix.

1. $2,000, 8%, 5 years
2. $500, 10%, 8 months
3. $750, 5%, 1 year
4. $175.50, $6\frac{1}{2}\%$, 18 months
5. $236.20, 9%, 16 months
6. $89, $7\frac{1}{2}\%$, 6 months
7. $800, 5.75%, 3 years
8. $225, $1\frac{1}{2}\%$, 2 years
9. $12,000, $4\frac{1}{2}\%$, 40 months

Find the simple interest paid to the nearest cent for each loan, interest rate, and time. 10–18. See Student Handbook Answer Appendix.

10. $750, 18%, 2 years
11. $1,500, 19%, 16 months
12. $300, 9%, 1 year
13. $4,750, 19.5%, 30 months
14. $2,345, 17%, 9 months
15. $689, 12%, 2 years
16. $390, 18.75%, 15 months
17. $1,250, 22%, 8 months
18. $3,240, 18%, 14 months

Lesson 8-1
Pages 395–400

Display each set of data in a line plot. Identify any clusters, gaps, or outliers. 1–4. See Student Handbook Answer Appendix.

1.

Number of Pets in the Home				
0	1	3	4	0
2	1	0	1	1
10	0	1	5	2

2.

High Temperatures for 18 Days (°F)					
75	81	75	65	76	81
77	80	65	65	80	80
76	85	66	75	80	75

3.

Number of Stories for Buildings in Denver				
56	43	36	42	29
54	42	32	34	
52	40	32	32	

Source: *The World Almanac and Book of Facts*

4.

Ages of Children at Sunny Day Care (years)					
4	1	6	4	5	3
4	5	1	2	5	4
3	2	4	1	3	3

Lesson 8-2
Pages 401–407

Find the mean, median, and mode for each set of data.

1. 1, 5, 9, 1, 2, 6, 8, 2 **4.25, 3.5, 1 and 2**
2. 2, 5, 8, 9, 7, 6, 3, 5, 1, 4 **5, 5**
3. 82, 79, 93, 91, 95, 81 **88, 91, 95**
4. 117, 103, 108, 120 **112, 112.5, no mode**
5. 256, 265, 247, 256 **256, 256, 256**
6. 47, 54, 66, 54, 46, 66 **55.5, 54, 54 and 66**
7.

```
              x
              x
      x       x x
      x x x   x x x x
x x x x x x x x x x x
10 11 12 13 14 15 16 17 18 19 20
```
15, 15, 15

8.

Number of Absences	Tally	Frequency
0	IIII	4
1	IIII IIII	9
2	IIII I	6
3	IIII	5

1.5, 1, 1

Lesson 8-3   Pages 409–413

1–4. See Student Handbook Answer Appendix.

Display each set of data in a stem-and-leaf plot.

1. 23, 15, 39, 68, 57, 42, 51, 52, 41, 18, 29

2. 189, 182, 196, 184, 197, 183, 196, 194, 184

3.
Average Monthly High Temperatures in Albany, NY (°F)

21	46	72	50
24	58	70	40
34	67	61	27

Source: *The World Almanac and Book of Facts*

4.
Super Bowl Winning Scores 1987–2004

39	55	52	27	34	20
42	20	30	35	23	48
20	37	49	31	34	32

Source: *The World Almanac and Book of Facts*

Lesson 8-4   Pages 414–420

1–4. See Student Handbook Answer Appendix.

Select the appropriate graph to display each set of data: bar graph or histogram. Then display the data in the appropriate graph.

1.
Longest Snakes

Snake Name	Length (ft)
Royal python	35
Anaconda	28
Indian python	25
Diamond python	21
King cobra	19
Boa constrictor	16

Source: *The Top 10 of Everything*

2.
Least Densely Populated States

State	People Per Square Mile
Alaska	1
Wyoming	5
Montana	6
North Dakota	9
South Dakota	10
New Mexico	15

Source: *The Top 10 of Everything*

3.
Cost of a Movie Ticket at Selected Theaters

$5.25	$6.50	$3.50	$3.75
$7.50	$9.25	$10.40	$4.75
$10.00	$4.50	$8.75	$7.25
$3.50	$6.70	$4.20	$7.50

4.
Highest Recorded Wind Speeds For Selected U.S. Cities (mph)

52	55	81	46	73	57
75	54	58	76	46	58
60	91	53	53	51	56
80	60	73	46	49	47

Source: *The World Almanac and Book of Facts*

Lesson 8-5   Pages 424–425

WEATHER For Exercises 1–3, solve by using the graph. **3. Sample answer: 88°F, 72°F**

Average High and Low Temperatures (Arlington, TX)

1. In which month is the average high temperature about twice as high as the average low temperature for January? **March**

2. What is the approximate difference between the average high temperature and the average low temperature each month? **about 20°F**

3. Predict the high and low temperatures for June based on the data given on the graph.

Lesson 8-6   Pages 426–431

For Exercises 1–3, refer to the graph at the right which shows Rachel's quiz scores for six quizzes.

Quiz Scores

1. Describe the trend in Rachel's quiz scores. **Sample answer: The scores are increasing.**

2. If the trend continues, predict Rachel's score on the seventh quiz. **Sample answer: 7**

3. If the trend continues, predict Rachel's score on the tenth quiz. **Sample answer: 10**

For Exercises 4–6, use the table which shows the average price paid to farmers per 100 pounds of sheep they sold.

Year	Price Per 100 Pounds ($)
1940	4
1950	12
1960	6
1970	8
1980	21
1990	23
2000	34

Source: *The World Almanac and Book of Facts*

4. Make a scatter plot of the data.

5. Describe the relationship, if any, between the two sets of data.

6. Predict the price per 100 pounds for 2010. Explain. **4–6. See Student Handbook Answer Appendix.**

Lesson 8-7   Pages 435–437

1. **SURVEYS** The table shows the results of a survey of students' favorite cookies. Predict how many of the 424 students at Scobey High School prefer chocolate chip cookies. **about 253 students**

Cookie	Number
chocolate chip	49
peanut butter	12
oatmeal	10
sugar	8
raisin	3

2. **VACATION** The circle graph shows the results of a survey of teens and where they would prefer to spend a family vacation. Predict how many of 4,000 teens would prefer to go to an amusement park. **1,800 teens**

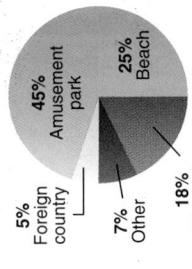

Vacation Survey
5% Foreign country; 45% Amusement park; 7% Other; 18% Mountains; 25% Beach

3. **TRAVEL** In 2000, about 29% of the foreign visitors to the U.S. were from Canada. If a particular hotel had 150,000 foreign guests in one year, how many would you predict were from Canada? **43,500 Canadians**

Lesson 8-8   1–3. See Student Handbook Answer Appendix.
Pages 438–443

Determine whether each conclusion is valid. Justify your answer.

1. To determine whether most students participate in after school activities, the principal of Humberson Middle School randomly surveyed 75 students from each grade level. Of these, 34% said they participate in after school activities. The principal concluded that about a third of the students at Humberson Middle School participate in after school activities.

2. To evaluate their product, the manager of an assembly line inspected the first 100 watches produced on Monday. Of these, 2 were defective. The manager concluded that about 2% of all watches produced are defective.

3. A television program asked its viewers to dial one of two phone numbers indicating their preference for one of two brands of shampoo. Of those that responded, 76% said they prefer Brand A. The program concluded that Brand A was the most popular brand of shampoo.

Lesson 8-9   1, 2. See Student Handbook Answer Appendix.
Pages 444–449

Which graph could be misleading? Explain your reasoning.

1. Both graphs show pounds of grapes sold to Westview School in one week.

Graph A   Graph B

2. Both graphs show commissions made by Mr. Turner for a four-week pay period.

Graph A   Graph B

Lesson 9-1
Pages 460–464

Use the spinner at the right to find each probability. Write as a fraction in simplest form.

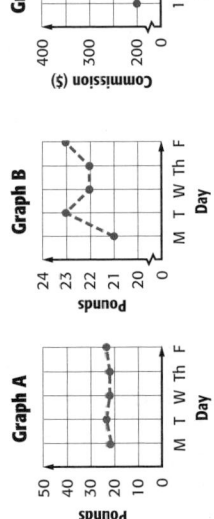

1. P(even number) $\frac{1}{2}$
2. P(prime number) $\frac{1}{2}$
3. P(factor of 12) $\frac{5}{8}$
4. P(composite number) $\frac{3}{8}$
5. P(greater than 10) 0
6. P(neither prime nor composite) $\frac{1}{8}$

A package of balloons contains 5 green, 3 yellow, 4 red, and 8 pink balloons. Suppose you reach in the package and choose one balloon at random. Find the probability of each event. Write as a fraction in simplest form.

7. P(red balloon) $\frac{1}{5}$
8. P(yellow balloon) $\frac{3}{20}$
9. P(pink balloon) $\frac{2}{5}$
10. P(orange balloon) 0
11. P(red or yellow balloon) $\frac{7}{20}$
12. P(not green balloon) $\frac{3}{4}$

Lesson 9-2
Pages 465–470

For each situation, find the sample space using a tree diagram.   1–5. See Student Handbook Answer Appendix for tree diagrams.

1. rolling 2 number cubes
2. choosing an ice cream cone from waffle, plain, or sugar and a flavor of ice cream from chocolate, vanilla, or strawberry
3. making a sandwich from white, wheat, or rye bread, cheddar or Swiss cheese and ham, turkey, or roast beef
4. tossing a penny twice
5. choosing one math class from Algebra and Geometry and one foreign language class from French, Spanish, or Latin

Lesson 9-3
Pages 471–474

Use the Fundamental Counting Principle to find the total number of outcomes in each situation.

1. choosing a local phone number if the exchange is 398 and each of the four remaining digits is different **5,040 outcomes**

2. choosing a way to drive from Millville to Westwood if there are 5 roads that lead from Millville to Miamisburg, 3 roads that connect Miamisburg to Hathaway, and 4 highways that connect Hathaway to Westwood **60 outcomes**

3. tossing a quarter, rolling a number cube, and tossing a dime **24 outcomes**

4. spinning the spinners shown below **96 outcomes**

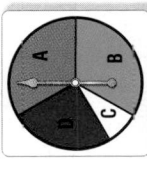 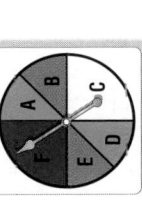 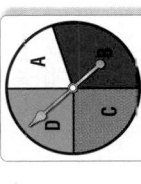

Lesson 9-4
Pages 475–478

1. **RACES** Eight runners are competing in a 100-meter sprint. In how many ways can the gold, silver, and bronze medals be awarded? **336 ways**

2. **LOCKERS** Five-digit locker combinations are assigned using the digits 1–9. In how many ways can the combinations be formed if no digit can be repeated? **15,120 ways**

3. **SCHEDULES** In how many ways can the classes math, language arts, science, and social studies be ordered on student schedules as the first four classes of their day? **24 ways**

4. **TOYS** At a teddy bear workshop, customers can select from black, brown, golden, white, blue, or pink for their bear's color. If a father randomly selects two bear colors, what is the probability that he will select a white bear for his son and a pink bear for his daughter? The father cannot pick the same color for both bears. **$\frac{1}{30}$**

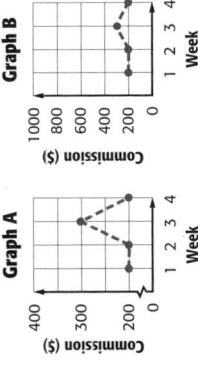

5. **WRITING** If you randomly select three of your last seven writing assignments to submit to an essay contest, what is the probability that you will select your first, fourth, and sixth essays in that order? **$\frac{1}{210}$**

Lesson 9-5
Pages 480–483

1. **EXERCISE** How many ways can you choose to exercise three days of a week? **35 ways**
2. **BOOKS** In how many ways can six books be selected from a collection of 12? **924 ways**
3. **REPORTS** In how many ways can you select three report topics from a total of 8 topics? **56 ways**
4. **GROUPS** How many ways can four students be chosen from a class of 26? **14,950 ways**
5. **ROLLER COASTERS** In how many ways can you ride five out of nine roller coasters if you don't care in what order you ride them? **126 ways**

Lesson 9-6
Pages 484–485

Use the *act it out* strategy to solve each problem.

1. **STAIRS** Lynnette lives on a certain floor of her apartment building. She goes up two flights of stairs to put a load of laundry in a washing machine on that floor. Then she goes down five flights to borrow a book from a friend who is ill. Next, she goes up 8 flights to visit another friend who is ill. How many flights up or down does Lynnette now have to go to take her laundry out of the washing machine? **3 flights up**

2. **LOGIC PUZZLE** Suppose you are on the west side of a river with a fox, a duck, and a bag of corn. You want to take all three to the other side of the river, but…
   - your boat is only large enough to carry you and either the fox, duck, or bag of corn.
   - you cannot leave the fox alone with the duck.
   - you cannot leave the duck alone with the corn.
   - you cannot leave the corn alone on the east side of the river because some wild birds will eat it. the wild birds are afraid of the fox.
   - you cannot leave the fox, duck, and the corn alone.
   - you can bring something across the river more than once.

   If there is no other way to cross the river, how do you get everything to the other side?

   First carry the duck across the river and bring the boat back empty. Then carry the fox across the river and carry the duck back. Then carry the corn across the river and bring the boat back empty. Finally carry the duck across the river.

Lesson 9-7
Pages 486–490

The frequency table shows the results of a fair number cube rolled 40 times.

Face	Frequency
1	5
2	9
3	2
4	8
5	12
6	4

1. Find the experimental probability of rolling a 4. $\frac{1}{5}$
2. Find the theoretical probability of *not* rolling a 4. $\frac{5}{6}$
3. Find the theoretical probability of rolling a 2. $\frac{1}{6}$
4. Find the experimental probability of *not* rolling a 6. $\frac{9}{10}$
5. Suppose the number cube was rolled 500 times. About how many times would it land on 5? **150**

Lesson 9-8
Pages 492–497

1. **COINS** Two evenly balanced nickels are tossed. Find the probability that one head and one tail result. $\frac{1}{4}$
2. **MONEY** A wallet contains four $5 bills, two $10 bills, and eight $1 bills. A bill is randomly selected. Find $P(\$5 \text{ or } \$1)$. $\frac{6}{7}$
3. **PROBABILITY** Two chips are selected from a box containing 6 blue chips, 4 red chips, and 3 green chips. The first chip selected is replaced before the second is drawn. Find $P(\text{red, green})$. $\frac{12}{169}$
4. **PROBABILITY** A bag contains 7 blue, 4 orange, 8 red, and 5 purple marbles. Suppose one marble is chosen and not replaced. A second marble is then chosen. Find $P(\text{purple, red})$. $\frac{5}{69}$

Lesson 10-1
Pages 510–513

Classify each angle as *acute, right, obtuse,* or *straight.*

1. 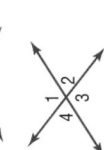 right
2. obtuse
3. straight
4. acute

5. Identify a pair of vertical angles in the diagram at the right. **∠1 and ∠3**

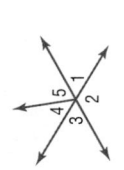

6. Identify a pair of adjacent angles in the diagram at the right. **Sample answer: ∠1 and ∠2**

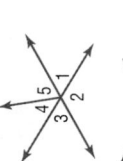

Lesson 10-2
Pages 514–517

Classify each pair of angles as *complementary, supplementary,* or *neither.*

1. complementary
2. supplementary
3. complementary

complementary

Find the value of x in each figure.

4. **40**
5. **55**
6. **160**

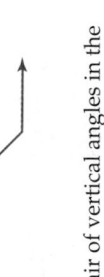

Lesson 10-3
Pages 518–523

1, 2. See Student Handbook Answer Appendix.

Display each set of data in a circle graph.

1.

Car Sales	
Style	Percent
sedan	45%
SUV	22%
pickup truck	9%
sports car	13%
compact car	11%

2.

Favorite Flavor of Ice Cream	
Flavor	Number
vanilla	11
chocolate	15
strawberry	8
mint chip	5
cookie dough	3

Lesson 10-4
Pages 524–529

Find the value of x.

1. **50**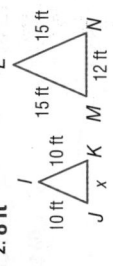

2. **135**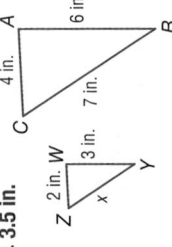

3. **20**

Classify each triangle by its angles and by its sides.

4. **acute, scalene**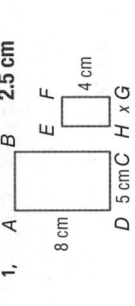

5. **right, scalene**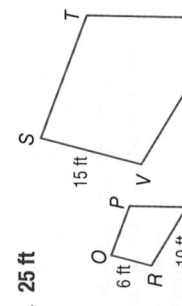

6. **acute, equilateral**

Lesson 10-5
Pages 530–531

1, 2. See Student Handbook Answer Appendix.

Use the *logical reasoning* strategy to solve each problem.

1. **GEOMETRY** Draw several isosceles triangles and measure their angles. What do you notice about the measures of the angles of an isosceles triangle.

2. **BASKETBALL** Placido, Dexter, and Scott play guard, forward, and center on a team, but not necessarily in that order. Placido and the center drove Scott to practice on Saturday. Placido does not play guard. Who is the guard?

Lesson 10-6
Pages 533–539

Classify each quadrilateral using the name that *best* describes it.

1. **square**

2. **parallelogram**

3. **quadrilateral**

Find the missing angle measure in each quadrilateral.

4. **94°**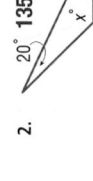

5. **103°**

6. **153°**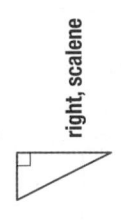

Lesson 10-7
Pages 540–545

Find the value of x in each pair of similar figures.

1. **2.5 cm**

2. **8 ft**

3. **25 ft**

4. **3.5 in.**

5. **40.5 cm**

6. **8.75 m**

Lesson 10-8
Pages 546–551

Determine whether each figure is a polygon. If it is, classify the polygon and state whether it is regular. If it is *not* a polygon, explain why.

1. **decagon, not regular**

2. **triangle, regular**

3. **not a polygon, sides are curved**

4. **not a polygon, sides are curved**

5. **octagon, not regular**

6. **not a polygon, figure is not closed**

Find the measure of an angle in each polygon if polygon is regular. Round to the nearest tenth of a degree if necessary.

7. triangle **60°**
8. 30-gon **168°**
9. 18-gon **160°**
10. 14-gon **154.3°**
11. hexagon **120°**
12. nonagon **140°**
13. 27-gon **166.7°**
14. octagon **135°**

Lesson 10-9 1, 2. See Student Handbook Answer Appendix.

Pages 553–557

1. Translate △ABC 2 units right and 1 unit down.

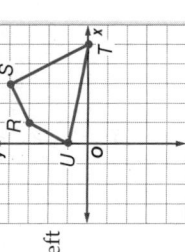

2. Translate quadrilateral *RSTU* 4 units left and 3 units down.

Triangle *TRI* has vertices $T(1, 1)$, $R(4, -2)$, and $I(-2, -1)$. Find the vertices of *T'R'I'* after each translation. Then graph the figure and its translated image. **3–6. See Student Handbook Answer Appendix for graphs.**

3. 2 units right, 1 unit down $T'(3, 0), R'(6, -3), I'(0, -2)$

4. 5 units left, 1 unit up $T'(-4, 2), R'(-1, -1), I'(-7, 0)$

5. 3 units right $T'(4, 1), R'(7, -2), I'(1, -1)$

6. 2 units up $T'(1, 3), R'(4, 0) I'(-2, 1)$

Lesson 10-10

Pages 558–562

Determine whether each figure has line symmetry. Write *yes* or *no*. If so, copy the figure and draw all lines of symmetry.

1. 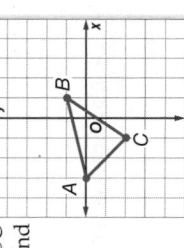 yes

2. no

3. yes

4. no

5. yes

6. yes

7. **See Student Handbook Answer Appendix.**
8. **See Student Handbook Answer Appendix for graph.**
Graph each figure and its reflection over the *x*-axis. Then find the coordinates of the vertices of the reflected image.

7. quadrilateral *QUAD* with vertices $Q(-1, 4), U(2, 2), A(1, 1),$ and $D(-2, 2)$

8. triangle △ABC with vertices $A(0, -1), B(4, -3),$ and $C(-4, -5)$ $A'(0, 1), B'(4, 3), C'(-4, 5)$

9, 10. **See Student Handbook Answer Appendix for graphs.**
Graph each figure and its reflection over the *y*-axis. Then find the coordinates of the vertices of the reflected image.

9. parallelogram *PARL* with vertices $P(3, 5), A(5, 4), R(5, 1),$ and $L(3, 2)$ $P'(-3, 5), A'(-5, 4), R'(-5, 1), L'(-3, 2)$

10. pentagon *PENTA* with vertices $P(-1, 3), E(1, 1), N(0, -2), T(-2, -2),$ and $A(-3, 1)$ $P'(1, 3), E'(-1, 1), N'(0, -2), T'(2, -2), A'(3, 1)$

Lesson 11-1

Pages 570–574

Find the area of each parallelogram. Round to the nearest tenth if necessary.

1. 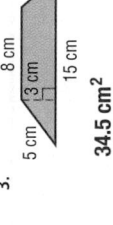 **12 m²**

2.  **108 m²**

3. 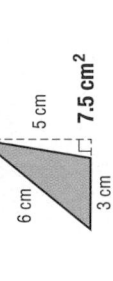 **437 ft²**

4. base = 19 m
height = 6 m **114 m²**

5. base = 135 in.
height = 15 in. **2,025 in²**

6. base = 8.2 m
height = 5.5 m **45.1 cm²**

7. base = 29.3 m
height = 10.1 m **295.9 m²**

Lesson 11-2

Pages 576–580

Find the area of each figure. Round to the nearest tenth if necessary.

1. 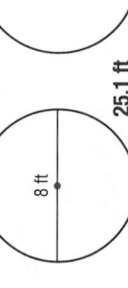 **20 ft²**

2. **7.5 cm²**

3. **34.5 cm²**

4. triangle: base = 5 in., height = 9 in. **22.5 in²**

5. trapezoid: bases = 3 cm and 8 cm, height = 12 cm **66 cm²**

6. trapezoid: bases = 10 ft and 15 ft, height = 12 ft **150 ft²**

7. triangle: base = 12 cm, height = 8 cm **48 cm²**

8. trapezoid: bases = 82.6 cm and 72.2 cm, height = 44.5 cm **3,444.3 cm²**

9. triangle: base = 500.5 ft, height = 254.5 ft **63,688.6 ft²**

Lesson 11-3

Pages 582–586

Find the circumference of each circle. Use 3.14 or $\frac{22}{7}$ for π. Round to the nearest tenth if necessary.

1. 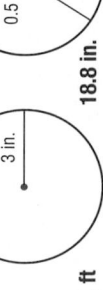 **25.1 ft**

2. 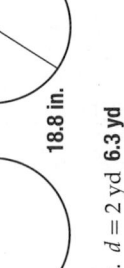 **18.8 in.**

3. 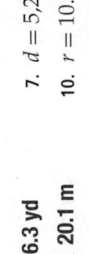 **1.6 m**

4.  **$26\frac{5}{7}$ ft**

5. $r = 1$ m **6.3 m**

6. $d = 2$ yd **6.3 yd**

7. $d = 5,280$ ft **16,579.2 ft**

8. $r = 0.5$ cm **3.1 cm**

9. $d = 6.4$ m **20.1 m**

10. $r = 10.7$ km **67.2 km**

11. $d = \frac{3}{16}$ in. **$\frac{33}{56}$ in.**

12. $r = 5\frac{1}{2}$ mi **$34\frac{4}{7}$ mi**

13. $d = 42\frac{3}{4}$ ft **$134\frac{5}{14}$ ft**

Lesson 11-4

Pages 587–591

Find the area of each circle. Round to the nearest tenth.

1. **28.3 cm²**

2. **12.6 yd²**

3. **3.1 in²**

4. radius = 8 in. **201.0 in²**
5. diameter = 5 ft **19.6 ft²**
6. **1,808.6 cm²**
6. radius = 24 cm
7. diameter = 2.3 m **4.2 m²**
8. diameter = 82 ft **5,278.3 ft²**
9. radius = 68 cm
10. radius = 9.8 mi **301.6 mi²**
11. diameter = 25.6 m
12. **12,35.8 in²**
12. diameter = 6.75 in.
13. radius = $1\frac{1}{4}$ ft **4.9 ft²**
14. diameter = $5\frac{2}{3}$ yd
15. diameter = $45\frac{1}{2}$ mi

9, 11, 14, 15. See Student Handbook Answer Appendix.

Lesson 11-5

Pages 592–593

Use the *solve a simpler problem* strategy to solve each problem.

1. **EARNINGS** Cedric makes $51,876 each year. If he is paid once every two weeks and actually takes home about 67% of his wages after taxes, how much does he take home each paycheck? Round to the nearest cent if necessary. **$1,336.80**

2. **CARS** Jorge plans to decorate the rims on his tires by putting a strip of shiny metal around the outside edge on each rim. The diameter of each tire is 17 inches, and each rim is 2.75 inches from the outside edge of each tire. If he plans to cut the four individual pieces for each tire from the same strip of metal, how long of a strip should he buy? Round to the nearest tenth. **144.5 in.**

3. **SAVINGS** Erin's aunt invested a total of $1,500 into three different savings accounts. She invested $450 into a savings account with an annual interest rate of 3.25% and $600 into a savings account with an annual interest rate of 4.75%. The third savings account had an annual interest rate of 4.375%. After 3 years, how much money will Erin's aunt have in the three accounts altogether if she made no more additional deposits or withdrawals? Round to the nearest cent. **$1,688.44**

BIOLOGY For Exercises 4–6, use the following information.
About five quarts of blood are pumped through the average human heart in one minute.

4. At this rate, how many quarts of blood are pumped through the average human heart in one year? (Use 365 days = 1 year) **2,628,000 qt**

5. If the average heart beats 72 times per minute, how many quarts of blood are pumped with each beat? Round to the nearest tenth. **0.1 qt**

6. About how many total gallons of blood are pumped through the average human heart in one week? **about 12,600 gal**

7. **LAND** A rectangular plot of land measures 1,450 feet by 850 feet. A contractor wishes to section off a portion of this land to build an apartment complex. If the complex is 425 feet by 550 feet, how many square feet of land will not be sectioned off to build it? **998,750 ft²**

Lesson 11-6

Pages 694–697

Find the area of each figure. Round to the nearest tenth if necessary.

1. **256 ft²**

2. **304 m²**

3. **300 in²**

4. **1,144.5 cm²**

5. **39.6 ft²**

6. **110.7 cm²**

7. **147.7 in²**

8. **993 m²**

9. **503.9 mm²**

Lesson 11-7

Pages 601–604

For each figure, identify the shape of the base(s). Then classify the figure.

1. **rectangle; rectangular prism**

2. **none; sphere**

3. **circle; cone**

4. **triangle; triangular pyramid**

5. **pentagon; pentagonal prism**

6. **square; square pyramid**

7. **SOUP** Classify the shape of a soup can as a three-dimensional figure. **cylinder**

8. **APPLIANCES** Classify the shape of a microwave oven as a three-dimensional figure. **rectangular prism**

Lesson 11-8

Pages 606–610

1–5. See Student Handbook Answer Appendix.

Draw a top, a side, and a front view of each solid.

1.

2.

3.

Draw each solid using the top, side, and front views shown.
Use isometric dot paper.

4.
top   side   front

5.
top   side   front

Lesson 11-9

Pages 611–616

Find the volume of each prism. Round to the nearest tenth if
necessary.

1. 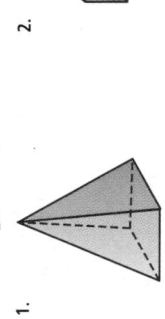 **24 ft³**
4 ft, 1 ft, 6 ft

2. 8.5 cm, 2 cm, 2 cm **34 cm³**

3. 12½ mm, 3 mm, 4 mm **150 mm³**

4. 2 yd, 2 yd, ½ yd **2 yd³**

5. 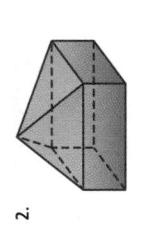 6 in., 18 in., 8 in. **432 in³**

6. 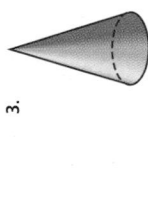 11 m, 5 m, 35 m **962.5 m³**

7. 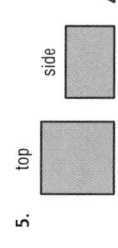 8 mm, 5 mm, 12 mm **240 mm³**

8. 8 yd, 15 yd, 11 yd, 17 yd, 5 mm **660 yd³**

Find the volume of each rectangular prism. Round to the nearest tenth
if necessary.

9. length = 3 ft
width = 10 ft
height = 2 ft **60 ft³**

10. length = 18 cm
width = 23 cm
height = 15 cm **6,210 cm³**

11. length = 25 mm
width = 32 mm
height = 10 mm **8,000 mm³**

12. length = 1.5 in.
width = 3 in.
height = 6 in. **27 in³**

13. length = 4.5 cm
width = 6.75 cm
height = 2 cm **60.8 cm³**

14. length = 16 mm
width = 0.7 mm
height = 12 mm **134.4 mm³**

15. length = 3½ ft
width = 10 ft
height = 6 ft **210 ft³**

16. length = 5½ in.
width = 12 in.
height = 3⅜ in. **222.8 in³**

17. Find the volume of a rectangular prism with a length of 3 yards, a width of 5 feet,
and a height of 12 feet. **540 ft³**

18. Find the volume of a triangular prism whose base has an area of 416 square feet
and whose height is 22 feet. **9,152 ft³**

Lesson 11-10

Pages 617–621

Find the volume of each cylinder. Round to the nearest tenth. Use 3.14 for π.

1. 2 cm, 4 cm **50.2 cm³**

2. 2 cm, 3 yd **45.9 yd³**

3. 16 mm, 7.5 mm **2,826 mm³**

4. 4.5 in., 1.5 in. **23.8 in³**

5. radius = 6 in.
height = 3 in. **339.1 in³**

6. radius = 8 ft
height = 10 ft **2,009.6 ft³**

7. radius = 6 km
height = 12 km **1,356.5 km³**

8. radius = 8.5 cm
height = 3 cm **680.6 cm³**

9. diameter = 16 yd
height = 4.5 yd **904.3 yd³**

10. diameter = 3.5 mm
height = 2.5 mm **24.0 mm³**

11. diameter = 12 m
height = 4.75 m **536.9 m³**

12. diameter = ⅝ in.
height = 4 in. **1.2 in³**

13. diameter = 100 ft
height = 35 ft **274,750 ft³**

14. radius = 40.5 m
height = 65.1 m **335,290.1 m³**

15. radius = 0.5 cm
height = 1.6 cm **1.3 cm³**

16. diameter = 8¾ in.
height = 5½ in. **330.6 in³**

17. Find the volume of a cylinder whose diameter is 6 inches and height is 2 feet.
Round to the nearest tenth. **0.4 ft³ or 678.2 in³**

18. How tall is a cylinder that has a volume of 2,123 cubic meters and a radius of
13 meters? Round to the nearest tenth. **4.0 m**

19. A cylinder has a volume of 310.2 cubic yards and a radius of 2.9 yards. What is the
height of the cylinder? Round to the nearest tenth. **11.7 yd**

20. Find the height of a cylinder whose diameter is 25 centimeters and volume is
8,838 cubic centimeters. Round to the nearest tenth. **18.0 cm**

Lesson 12-1

Pages 634–637

16–30. See Student Handbook Answer Appendix.

Estimate each square root to the nearest whole number.

1. $\sqrt{27}$ **5**

2. $\sqrt{112}$ **11**

3. $\sqrt{249}$ **16**

4. $\sqrt{88}$ **9**

5. $\sqrt{1,500}$ **39**

6. $\sqrt{612}$ **25**

7. $\sqrt{340}$ **18**

8. $\sqrt{495}$ **22**

9. $\sqrt{264}$ **16**

10. $\sqrt{350}$ **19**

11. $\sqrt{834}$ **29**

12. $\sqrt{3,700}$ **61**

13. $\sqrt{298}$ **17**

14. $\sqrt{101}$ **10**

15. $\sqrt{800}$ **28**

Graph each square root on a number line.

16. $\sqrt{58}$

17. $\sqrt{750}$

18. $\sqrt{1,200}$

19. $\sqrt{1,000}$

20. $\sqrt{5,900}$

21. $\sqrt{999}$

22. $\sqrt{374}$

23. $\sqrt{512}$

24. $\sqrt{3,750}$

25. $\sqrt{255}$

26. $\sqrt{83}$

27. $\sqrt{845}$

28. $\sqrt{200}$

29. $\sqrt{500}$

30. $\sqrt{10,001}$

31. **ALGEBRA** Evaluate $\sqrt{a-b}$ to the nearest tenth if $a = 16$ and $b = 4$. **3.5**

32. **ALGEBRA** Estimate the value of $\sqrt{x+y}$ to the nearest whole number if $x = 64$ and
$y = 25$. **9**

Lesson 12-2

Pages 638–643

Find the missing measure of each triangle. Round to the nearest tenth if necessary.

1. 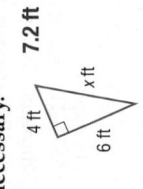 **7.2 ft**
2. 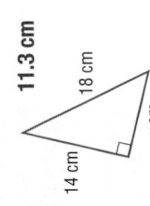 **11.3 cm**
3. 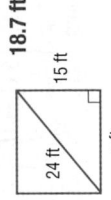 **18.7 ft**

4. $a = 12$ cm, $b = 25$ cm **27.7 cm**
5. $a = 5$ yd, $c = 10$ yd **8.7 yd**
6. $b = 12$ mi, $c = 20$ mi **16 mi**
7. $a = 15$ yd, $b = 24$ yd **28.3 yd**
8. $a = 4$ m, $c = 12$ m **11.3 m**
9. $a = 8$ mm, $b = 11$ mm **13.6 mm**
10. $a = 1$ mi, $c = 3$ mi **2.8 mi**
11. $a = 5$ yd, $b = 8$ yd **9.4 yd**
12. $b = 7$ in., $c = 19$ in., **17.7 in.**
13. $a = 50$ km, $c = 75$ km **55.9 km**
14. $b = 82$ ft, $c = 100$ ft **57.2 ft**
15. $a = 100$ m, $b = 200$ m **223.6 m**

Lesson 12-3

Pages 644–645

Use the *make a model* strategy to solve each problem.

1. **ARCHITECTURE** An architect is designing a large skyscraper for a local firm. The skyscraper is to be 1,200 feet tall, 500 feet long, and 400 feet wide. If his model has a scale of 80 feet = 1 inch, find the volume of the model. **468.75 in³**

2. **STACKING BOXES** Box A has twice the volume of Box B. Box B has a height of 10 centimeters and a length of 5 centimeters. Box A has a width of 20 centimeters, a length of 10 centimeters, and a width of 5 centimeters. What is the width of Box B? **10 cm**

3. **TRAVEL** On Monday, Mara drove 400 miles as part of her journey to see her sister. She drove 60% of this distance on Tuesday. If the distance she drove on Tuesday represents one third of her total journey, how many more miles does she still need to drive? **80 mi**

4. **PIZZA** On Monday, there was a whole pizza in the refrigerator. On Tuesday, Enrico ate $\frac{1}{3}$ of the pizza. On Wednesday, he ate $\frac{1}{3}$ of what was left. On Thursday, he ate $\frac{1}{2}$ of what remained. What fractional part of the pizza is left? $\frac{2}{9}$

5. **GARDENS** Mr. Blackwell has a circular garden in his backyard. He wants to build a curved brick pathway around the entire garden. The garden has a radius of 18 feet. The distance from the center of the garden to the outside edge of the brick pathway will be 21.5 feet. Find the area of the brick pathway. Round to the nearest tenth. **434.3 ft²**

Lesson 12-4

Pages 647–651

Find the surface area of each rectangular prism. Round to the nearest tenth if necessary. 8, 11, 12, 14–16. See Student Handbook Answer Appendix.

1. 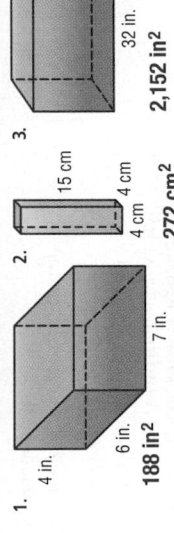 **188 in²**
2. 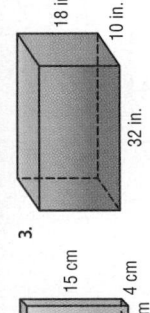 **272 cm²**
3. 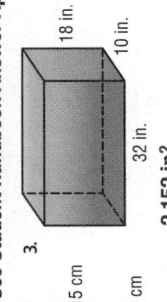 **2,152 in²**
4. 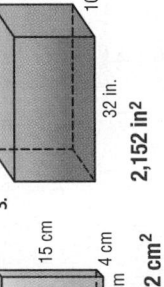 **1,724 yd²**

5. length = 10 m, width = 6 m, height = 7 m **344 m²**
6. length = 20 mm, width = 15 mm, height = 25 mm **2,350 mm²**
7. length = 16 ft, width = 20 ft, height = 12 ft **1,504 ft²**
8. length = 52 cm, width = 48 cm, height = 45 cm
9. length = 8 ft, width = 6.5 ft, height = 7 ft **307 ft²**
10. length = 9.4 m, width = 2 m, height = 5.2 m **156.2 m²**
11. length = 20.4 cm, width = 15.5 cm, height = 8.8 cm
12. length = 8.5 mi, width = 3 mi, height = 5.8 mi
13. length = $7\frac{1}{4}$ ft, width = 5 ft, height = $6\frac{1}{2}$ ft **231.8 ft²**
14. length = $15\frac{2}{3}$ yd, width = $7\frac{1}{3}$ yd, height = 9 yd
15. length = $4\frac{1}{2}$ in., width = 10 in., height = $8\frac{3}{4}$ in.
16. length = 12.2 mm, width = 7.4 mm, height = 7.4 mm

17. Find the surface area of an open-top box with a length of 18 yards, a width of 11 yards, and a height of 14 yards. **1,010 yd²**

18. Find the surface area of a rectangular prism with a length of 1 yard, a width of 7 feet, and a height of 2 yards. **162 ft² or 18 yd²**

Lesson 12-5

Pages 654–657

9–12. See Student Handbook Answer Appendix.

Find the surface area of each cylinder. Round to the nearest tenth.

1. 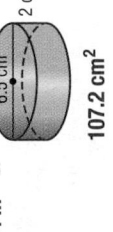 **188.4 in²**
2.  **107.2 cm²**
3.  **31.8 m²**
4.  **19.6 ft²**

5. height = 6 cm, radius = 3.5 cm **208.8 cm²**
6. height = 16.5 mm, diameter = 18 mm **1,441.3 mm²**
7. height = 22 yd, radius = 10.5 yd **2,143.1 yd²**
8. height = 6 ft, radius = 18.5 ft **2,846.4 ft²**
9. height = 10.2 mi, diameter = 4 mi
10. height = 8.6 cm, diameter = 8.2 cm
11. height = 5.8 km, diameter = 3.6 km
12. height = 32.7 m, radius = 21.5 m
13. height = $2\frac{2}{3}$ yd, diameter = 6 yd **106.8 yd²**
14. height = $12\frac{3}{4}$ ft, radius = $7\frac{1}{4}$ ft **910.6 ft²**
15. height = $5\frac{1}{5}$ mi, radius = $18\frac{1}{3}$ mi **2,709.4 mi²**
16. height = $5\frac{1}{2}$ in., diameter = 3 in. **65.9 in²**

Mixed Problem Solving

Chapter 1 Introduction to Algebra and Functions

Pages 22–77

1. **HISTORY** In 1932, Amelia Earhart flew 2,026 miles in 14 hours 56 minutes. To the nearest mile, what was her speed in miles per minute? (Lesson 1-1) **2 mi/min**

2. **LIGHT** The speed of light is about 67^3 kilometers per second. How many kilometers per second is this? (Lesson 1-2) **300,763 km/s**

3. **FARMING** Find the length of one side of a square field with an area of 180,625 square feet. (Lesson 1-3) **425 ft**

4. **SALES** A department store is having a back-to-school sale. The table shows the prices of three popular items.

Item	Price ($)
Jeans	37.99
Sweatshirt	19.88
Polo Shirt	22.50

Latonia wants to buy 2 pairs of jeans, 3 sweatshirts, and 1 polo shirt. Write and evaluate a numerical expression that represents the total cost of all three items. (Lesson 1-4)
$2(37.99)$
$+ 3(19.88)$
$+ 1(22.50);$
$158.12

5. **MONEY** Mateo has $2.58 in coins. If he has quarters, dimes, nickels, and pennies, how many of each coin does he have? Use the *guess and check* strategy. (Lesson 1-5) **Sample answer: 7 quarters, 6 dimes, 3 nickels, 8 pennies**

6. **FITNESS** You can estimate how fast you walk in miles per hour by evaluating the expression $\frac{n}{30}$, where n is the number of steps you take in one minute. Find your speed in miles per hour if you take 96 steps in one minute. (Lesson 1-6) **3.2 mi/h**

7. **BASEBALL** Last year, Scott attended 13 Minnesota Twins baseball games. This year, he attended 24. Solve $13 + n = 24$ to find how many more games he attended this year than last. (Lesson 1-7) **7. 11 games**

8. **HOT AIR BALLOONS** Miyoki paid $140 for a four-hour hot air balloon ride over the Bridger Mountains. Solve $4h = 140$ to find the cost per hour of the ride. (Lesson 1-7) **$35**

ENTERTAINMENT For Exercises 9 and 10, use the following information.
The five members of the Wolff family went to an amusement park. They each purchased an all-day ride pass and a water park pass, as shown below. (Lesson 1-8)

Item	Price ($)
All-Day Ride Pass	14.95
Water Park Pass	6.50

$5(14.95 + 6.50); 5(14.95) + 5(6.50)$

9. Use the Distributive Property to write two different expressions that represent the total cost for the family. **$5(14.95 + 6.50); 5(14.95) + 5(6.50)$**

10. Find the total cost of the passes. **$107.25**

11. **NUMBER THEORY** Numbers that can be represented by a square arrangement of dots are called *square numbers*. The first four square numbers are shown below. (Lesson 1-9)

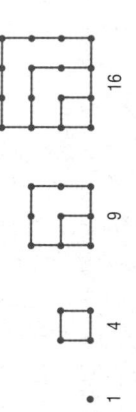

1 4 9 16

Write a sequence formed by the area of the first eight square numbers. **1, 4, 9, 16, 25, 36, 49, 64**

12. **TIME** Copy and complete the function table showing how many days y there are in various number of weeks x. Then identify the domain and range. (Lesson 1-10)

x	$7x$	y
1	7(1)	7
2	7(2)	14
3	7(3)	21
4	7(4)	28

Domain: **{1, 2, 3, 4}**
Range: **{7, 14, 21, 28}**

Chapter 2 Integers

Pages 78–125

1. **AIR CONDITIONING** Jacob turned on the air conditioning and the temperature in his apartment decreased 8 degrees. Write an integer to represent the change in temperature. (Lesson 2-1) **−8**

EARTH SCIENCE For Exercises 2 and 3, use the table below. It describes the deepest land depressions in the world in feet below sea level.
2, 3. **See Student Handbook Answer Appendix.**

Depth (ft)			
220	436	511	282
383	505	235	230

Source: *The Top 10 Everything*

2. Write an integer to represent each depth. (Lesson 2-1)

3. Order the integers from greatest depth to least depth. (Lesson 2-2)

ENTERTAINMENT For Exercises 4–8, use the diagram below. It shows the locations of several rides at the Outlook Amusement Park. (Lesson 2-3)

4. Which ride(s) is located in quadrant III? **Zip Master**

5. Which ride(s) is located on the y-axis? Name the coordinates. **See Student Handbook Answer Appendix.**

6. Which ride(s) has coordinates in which the x-coordinates and y-coordinates are equal? **Wild Thing, Zip Master**

7. In which quadrant is the Hurricane located? **Quadrant II**

8. A new ride is built with a location on the x-axis and 5 units left of the origin. Name the coordinates of this point. **(−5, 0)**

9. **CAVERNS** Adriana is 52 feet underground touring the Lewis and Clark Caverns. She climbs a ladder up 15 feet. What is her new location? (Lesson 2-4) **37 ft underground or −37 ft**

10. **RECORDS** The lowest temperature recorded in Verkhoyansk, Russia, was about −90°F. The highest temperature was about 99°F. What is the difference between these temperatures? (Lesson 2-5) **189° F**

11. **EARTH SCIENCE** The highest and lowest points in California are shown in the table. What is the difference in elevations? (Lesson 2-5) **14,776 ft**

Location	Elevation
Mount Whitney	14,494 ft above sea level
Death Valley	282 ft below sea level

Source: *The World Almanac of the U.S.A.*

12. **RIDES** A glider ride over the Crazy Mountains has a maximum altitude of 12,000 feet. It is descending at a rate of about 300 feet per minute. At what altitude will the glider be 20 minutes later? (Lesson 2-6) **6,000 ft**

13. **SPORTS** Every 12 times at bat, Simon hits the ball 3 times. About how many times will he hit the ball after 20 times at bat? 40? 84? Use the *look for a pattern* strategy. (Lesson 2-7)

Times at Bat	Number of Hits
12	3
20	5
40	10
84	21

14. **TEMPERATURE** A temperature of −89°C was recorded in Antarctica. Use the expression $\frac{9C}{5} + 32$, where C is the temperature in degrees Celsius, to find the temperature in degrees Fahrenheit. (Lesson 2-8) **about −128.2°F**

Chapter 3 Algebra: Linear Equations and Functions

Pages 126–175

1. **TOURISM** The Statue of Liberty in New York, New York, and the Eiffel Tower in Paris, France, were designed by the same person. The Statue of Liberty is 152 feet tall. It is 732 feet shorter than the Eiffel Tower, x. Write an equation that models this situation. (Lesson 3-1) **$152 = x - 732$**

ELECTIONS For Exercises 2 and 3, use the table below and the following information. New York has one more electoral vote than Texas. Pennsylvania has 9 fewer electoral votes than Texas. (Lesson 3-2)

Number of Electoral Votes 2000	
California	54
New York	33
Texas	▨
Florida	25
Pennsylvania	23

$33 = n + 1; 23 = n - 9$

2. Write two different equations to find the number of electoral votes in Texas, n.

3. Find the number of electoral votes in Texas. **32 votes**

4. **ROLLER COASTERS** The track length of a popular roller coaster is 5,106 feet. The roller coaster has an average speed of about 2,000 feet per minute. At that speed, how long will it take to travel its length of 5,106 feet? Use the formula $d = rt$. (Lesson 3-3) **about 2.553 min**

5. **NUMBERS** A number is halved. Then three is subtracted from the quotient, and 5 is multiplied by the difference. Finally, 1 is added to the product. If the ending number is 26, what was the beginning number? Use the *work backward* strategy. (Lesson 3-4) **16**

6. **BUSINESS** Carla's Catering charges a $25 fee to serve 15 or fewer people. In addition to that fee, they charge $10 per appetizer. You are having a party for 12 people and can spend a total of $85. How many appetizers can you order from Carla's Catering? (Lesson 3-5) **6 appetizers**

CHESS For Exercises 7–10, use the chess board below. (Lesson 3-6)

12 in.

12 in.

7. What is the perimeter of the chess board? **48 in.**

8. What is the area of the chess board? **144 in²**

9. What is the area of each small square? **2.25 in²**

10. A travel chess board has half the length and width of the board shown. What is the perimeter and area? **24 in; 36 in²**

11. **FENCING** Mr. Hernandez will build a fence to enclose a rectangular yard for his horse. If the area of the yard to be enclosed is 1,944 square feet, and the length of the yard is 54 feet, how much fencing is needed? (Lesson 3-6) **180 ft**

12. **GEOMETRY** The formula for the perimeter of a square is $P = 4s$, where P is the perimeter and s is the length of a side. Graph the equation. (Lesson 3-7) **See Student Handbook Answer Appendix.**

AGES For Exercises 13–16, use the table below. It shows how Jared's age and his sister Emily's age are related. (Lesson 3-7)

Jared's age (yr)	1	2	3	4	5
Emily's age (yr)	7	8	9	10	11

13. Write a verbal expression to describe how the ages are related. **Emily is 6 years older than Jared.**

14. Write an equation for the verbal expression. Let x represent Jared's age and y represent Emily's age. **$y = x + 6$**

15. Predict how old Emily will be when Jared is 10 years old. **16 years**

16. Graph the equation. **See Student Handbook Answer Appendix.**

Chapter 4 Fractions, Decimals, and Percents

Pages 178–227

LAND For Exercises 1–3, use the information below.

A section of land is one mile long and one mile wide. (Lesson 4-1) **$1. 2^5 \times 3 \times 5 \times 11$**
$2. 27,878,400 \ ft^2$

1. Write the prime factorization of 5,280.

2. Find the area of the section of land in square feet. (*Hint*: 1 mile = 5,280 feet)

3. Write the prime factorization of the area that you found in Exercise 2. **$2^{10} \times 3^2 \times 5^2 \times 11^2$**

DECORATIONS For Exercises 4 and 5, use the information below.

Benito is cutting streamers from crepe paper for a party. He has a red roll of crepe paper 144 inches long, a white roll 192 inches long, and a blue roll 360 inches long. (Lesson 4-2)

4. If he wants to have all colors of streamers the same length, what is the longest length that he can cut? **24 in.**

5. If he cuts the longest possible length, how many streamers can he cut? **29 streamers**

6. **PRIZES** By reaching into a bag that has the letters A, B, and C, George will select three winners in order. How many possible combinations are there of the people who could win? Use the *make an organized list* strategy. (Lesson 4-3)
6 combinations; ABC; ACB; BAC; BCA; CAB; CBA

OLYMPICS For Exercises 7 and 8, refer to the table below. It shows the medals won by the top three countries in the 2000 Summer Olympics.

Country	Medals		
	Gold	Silver	Bronze
United States	40	24	33
Russia	32	28	28
China	28	16	15

Source: *The World Almanac*

7. Write the number of gold medals that Russia won as a fraction of the total number that Russia won in simplest form. (Lesson 4-4) **$\frac{4}{11}$**

8. Write the fraction that you wrote in Exercise 7 as a decimal. (Lesson 4-5) **$0.\overline{36}$**

9. **SPORTS** At Belgrade Intermediate School, 75 out of every 100 students participate in sports. What percent of students do *not* participate in sports? (Lesson 4-6) **25%**

ADVERTISING For Exercises 10–13, use the table below. It shows the results of a survey in which teens were asked which types of advertising they pay attention to.

Type of Advertising	Percent of Teens
Television	80%
Magazine	62%
Product in a Movie	48%
Ad in an E-Mail	24%

Source: *E-Poll*

Write each percent as a fraction in simplest form. (Lesson 4-6) **13. $\frac{6}{25}$**

10. television **$\frac{4}{5}$**   11. magazine **$\frac{31}{50}$**

12. product in a movie **$\frac{12}{25}$**   13. ad in an e-mail

GEOMETRY For Exercises 14–16, refer to the grid at the right. (Lesson 4-7)

14. Write a decimal and a percent to represent the "T" shaded area. **0.4; 40%**

15. Write a decimal and a percent to represent the area shaded pink. **0.05; 5%**

16. What percent of the grid is *not* shaded? **55%**

17. **FLOWERS** Roses can be ordered in bunches of 6 and carnations in bunches of 15. If Ingrid wants to have the same number of roses as carnations for parent night, what is the least number of each flower that she must order? (Lesson 4-8) **30**

18. **Alaska, Wisconsin, Michigan**

18. **WATER** The table at the right shows the fraction of each state that is water. Order the states from least to greatest fraction of water. (Lesson 4-9)

What Part is Water?	
State	Fraction
Alaska	$\frac{3}{41}$
Michigan	$\frac{40}{97}$
Wisconsin	$\frac{1}{6}$

Source: *The World Almanac of the U.S.A*

Mixed Problem Solving

Chapter 5 Applying Fractions

1. **MEALS** A box of instant potatoes contains 20 cups of flakes. A family-sized bowl of potatoes uses $3\frac{2}{3}$ cups of the flakes. Estimate how many family-sized bowls can be made from one box. (Lesson 5-1) **Sample answer: 20 ÷ 4 or 5 bowls**

2. **BAKING** A recipe calls for $2\frac{1}{3}$ cups of flour. Theo wants to make six batches of this recipe. About how much flour should he have available to use? (Lesson 5-1) **about 2 × 6 + $\frac{1}{3}$ × 6 or 12 + 2 or 14 c**

3. **CRAFTS** Kyle bought $\frac{5}{6}$ yard of fabric to make a craft item. He used $\frac{3}{4}$ yard in making the item. How much fabric was left over? (Lesson 5-2) **$\frac{1}{12}$ yd**

RAINFALL For Exercises 4 and 5, use the table. It shows the average annual precipitation for three of the driest locations on Earth. (Lesson 5-2)

Location	Precipitation (in.)
Arica, Chile	$\frac{3}{100}$
Iquique, Chile	$\frac{1}{5}$
Callao, Peru	$\frac{12}{25}$

Source: *The Top 10 Everything*

4. How much more rain does Iquique get per year than Arica? $\frac{17}{100}$ **in.**

5. How much more annual rain does Callao get than Iquique? $\frac{7}{25}$ **in.**

6. **INTERIOR DESIGN** A living room wall is $16\frac{1}{4}$ feet long. A window runs from the floor to the ceiling and has a length along the floor of $6\frac{3}{8}$ feet. How long is the wall without the window? (Lesson 5-3) $9\frac{7}{8}$ **ft**

7. **HEALTH** The human body is about $\frac{7}{10}$ water. About how much would a person weigh if they had 70 pounds of water weight? Use the *eliminate possibilities* strategy. (Lesson 5-4) **B**

A 200 pounds   C 150 pounds

B 100 pounds   D 70 pounds

8. **FOOD** The table below shows the carry-out menu for a Benito's Restaurant.

Take-out	Price ($)
Main Dish	5.00
Side Dishes	1.00
Dessert	2.00

A family of four spent $24.00 dollars for a take-home meal. What combination is possible for their meal? Use the *eliminate possibilities* strategy. (Lesson 5-4) **H**

F 3 main dishes and 2 side dishes

G 4 main dishes and 3 side dishes

H 3 main dishes, 3 side dishes, and 3 desserts

J 4 main dishes and 4 desserts

9. **STARS** The star Sirius is about $8\frac{7}{10}$ light years from Earth. Alpha Centauri is half this distance from Earth. How far is Alpha Centauri from Earth? (Lesson 5-5) $4\frac{7}{20}$ **light years**

10. **LIFE SCIENCE** Use the table below. It shows the average growth per month of hair and fingernails. Solve $3 = \frac{1}{2}t$ to find how long it takes hair to grow 3 inches. (Lesson 5-6) **6 mo**

Average Monthly Growth	
Hair	$\frac{1}{2}$ in.
Fingernails	$\frac{2}{25}$ in.

11. **SEWING** Jocelyn has nine yards of fabric to make table napkins for a senior citizens' center. She needs $\frac{3}{8}$ yard for each napkin. Use $\frac{3}{8}c = 9$ to find the number of napkins that she can make with this amount of fabric. (Lesson 5-6) **24 napkins**

12. **WHALES** During the first year, a baby whale gains about $27\frac{3}{5}$ tons. What is the average weight gain per month? (Lesson 5-7) **12. $2\frac{3}{10}$ T/mo**

Chapter 6 Ratios and Proportions

1. **SCHOOLS** In a recent year, Oregon had 924 public elementary schools and 264 public high schools. Write a ratio in simplest form comparing the number of public high schools to elementary schools. (Lesson 6-1) $\frac{2}{7}$

2. **MONTHS** Write a ratio in simplest form comparing the number of months that begin with the letter J to the total number of months in a year. (Lesson 6-1) $\frac{1}{4}$

3. **EXERCISE** A person jumps rope 14 times in 10 seconds. What is the unit rate in jumps per second? (Lesson 6-2) **1.4 jumps per s**

4. **FOOD** A 16-ounce box of cereal costs $3.95. Find the unit price to the nearest cent. (Lesson 6-2) **$0.25 per oz**

5. **MARKERS** The table below shows the number of markers per box. Graph the data. Then find the slope of the line. Explain what the slope represents. (Lesson 6-3) **See Student Handbook Answer Appendix.**

Markers	8	16	24	32
Boxes	1	2	3	4

6. **TEMPERATURE** At 2:00, the temperature is 78°F. At 3:00, the temperature is 81°F. What is the rate of change? (Lesson 6-3) **3° per h**

7. **LIFE SCIENCE** An adult has about 5 quarts of blood. If a person donates 1 pint of blood, how many pints are left? (Lesson 6-4) **9 pt**

8. **COFFEE** In Switzerland, the average amount of coffee consumed per year is 1,089 cups per person. How many pints is this? (Lesson 6-4) **544.5 pt**

9. **BUILDINGS** A skyscraper is 0.484 kilometers tall. What is the height of the skyscraper in meters? (Lesson 6-5) **484 m**

10. **WATER** A bottle contains 1,065 milliliters of water. About how many cups of water does the bottle hold? (Lesson 6-5) **about 4.5 c**

11. **PHOTOGRAPHS** Mandy is enlarging a photograph that is 3 inches wide and 4.5 inches long. If she wants the width of the enlargement to be 10 inches, what will be the length? (Lesson 6-6) **15 in.**

12. **TILES** A kitchen is 10 feet long and 8 feet wide. If kitchen floor tiles are $2\frac{1}{2}$ inches by 3 inches, how many tiles are needed for the kitchen? Use the *draw a diagram* strategy. (Lesson 6-7) **1,536**

13. **MAPS** Washington, D.C., and Baltimore, Maryland, are $2\frac{7}{8}$ inches apart on a map. If the scale is $\frac{1}{2}$ inch : 6 miles, what is the actual distance between the cities? (Lesson 6-8) $34\frac{1}{2}$ **mi**

14. **MODELS** Ian is making a miniature bed for his daughter's doll house. The actual bed is $6\frac{3}{4}$ feet long. If he uses the scale $\frac{1}{2}$ inch = $1\frac{1}{2}$ feet, what will be the length of the miniature bed? (Lesson 6-8) $2\frac{1}{4}$ **in.**

15. **POPULATION** According to the U.S. Census Bureau, 6.6% of all people living in Florida are 10–14 years old. What fraction is this? Write in simplest form. (Lesson 6-9) $\frac{33}{500}$

COINS For Exercises 16 and 17, use the table below. It shows the fraction of a quarter that is made up of the metals nickel and copper. Write each fraction as a percent. Round to the nearest hundredth if necessary. (Lesson 6-9)

Metal	Fraction of Quarter
Nickel	$\frac{1}{12}$
Copper	$\frac{11}{12}$

16. nickel **8.33%**

17. copper **91.67%**

Chapter 7 Applying Percents

1. **SEEDS** A packet of beans guarantees that 95% of its 200 seeds will germinate. How many seeds are expected to germinate? (Lesson 7-1) **190 seeds**

2. **SKIS** Toshiro spent $520 on new twin-tip skis. This was 40% of the money he earned at his summer job. How much did he earn at his summer job? (Lesson 7-2) **$1,300**

3. **GEOGRAPHY** In Washington, about 5.7% of the total area is water. If the total area of Washington is 70,637 square miles, estimate the number of square miles of water by using 10%. (Lesson 7-3) **See Student Handbook Answer Appendix.**

4. **GOVERNMENT** Of the 435 members in the U.S. House of Representatives, 53 are from California and 13 are from North Carolina. To the nearest whole percent, what percent of the representatives are from California? from North Carolina? (Lesson 7-4) **12%; 3%**

FOOD For Exercises 5 and 6, use the graph below. It shows the results of a survey in which 1,200 people were asked how they determine how long food has been in their freezer. (Lesson 7-4)

Frozen Foods

- Guess 44%
- Label the Containers 35%
- Arrange by Date 12%
- Other 9%

Source: Opinion Research Corporation

5. How many of the 1,200 surveyed guess to determine how long food has been in their freezer? **528 people**

6. How many of the 1,200 surveyed label their freezer containers? **420 people**

7. **DVDs** A store has 1,504 DVDs in stock. The store sold 19.8% of the DVDs last month. About how many DVDs did they sell last month? Use the *reasonable answers* strategy. (Lesson 7-5) **300**

SPORTS For Exercises 8 and 9, use the table below. It shows the number of participants ages 7 to 17 in the sports listed. (Lesson 7-6)

Sport	Number (millions)	
	1990	2000
In-Line Skating	3.6	21.8
Snowboarding	1.5	4.3
Roller Hockey	1.5	2.2
Golf	23.0	26.4

Source: National Sporting Goods Association

8. What is the percent of change in in-line skaters 7 to 17 years old from 1990 to 2000? Round to the nearest percent and state whether the percent of change is an *increase* or *decrease*. **506% increase**

9. Find the percent of change from 1990 to 2000 in the number of children and teens who played roller hockey. Round to the nearest percent. **47% increase**

COMPUTERS For Exercises 10 and 11, use the following information.
The Wares want to buy a new computer with a regular price of $1,049. (Lesson 7-7) **10. $839.20**

10. If the store is offering a 20% discount, what will be the sale price of the computer?

11. If the sales tax on the computer is 5.25%, what will be the total cost with the discount? **$883.26**

BANKING For Exercises 12–15, complete the table below. The interest earned is simple interest. (Lesson 7-8)

	Principal	Rate	Time (yr)	Interest Earned
12.	$1,525.00	5%	$2\frac{1}{2}$	$190.63
13.	$2,250.00	4%		$337.50 $3.75
14.		3.5%	4	$498.40 $3,560
15.	$5,080.00		3	$952.50 6.25%

Chapter 8 Statistics: Analyzing Data

NUTRITION For Exercises 1–3, use the data below, that gives the grams of carbohydrates in fifteen different energy bars.
24, 16, 16, 2, 20, 26, 14, 20, 20, 16, 16, 15, 20

1. Make a line plot of the data. (Lesson 8-1)

2. What is the range of the data? (Lesson 8-1) **24**

3. Identify any clusters, gaps, or outliers and explain what they represent. (Lesson 8-1)

1, 3. See Student Handbook Answer Appendix.

BASKETBALL For Exercises 4–5, refer to the table below. It shows the number of games played by Michael Jordan each year from 1986–1987 to 2001–2002.

Number of Games Played

82	81	82	82	80	78	0	60
17	82	82	82	0	0	60

4. Find the mean, median, and mode of the data. (Lesson 8-2) **55.625; 80.5; 82**

5. Make a stem-and-leaf plot of the data. (Lesson 8-3)

5–6. See Student Handbook Answer Appendix.

6. **TOURISTS** The table shows the countries from which the most tourists in the United States came. Make a bar graph of the data. (Lesson 8-4)

Country	Visitors (millions)
Canada	14.6
Mexico	10.3
Japan	5.0
United Kingdom	4.7

7. **LUNCHES** Use the bar graph to determine on what day about twice as many lunches were sold as on Wednesday. (Lesson 8-5) **Friday**

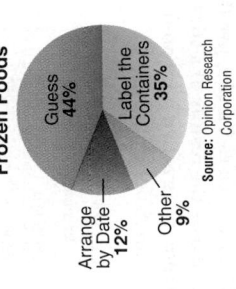

Number of Lunches Sold at ABC Junior High

SWIMMING For Exercises 8 and 9, refer to the table. It shows the winning Olympic times for the Women's 4 × 100-meter Freestyle Relay in swimming. (Lesson 8-6)

Year	Time (s)
1976	225
1980	223
1984	224
1988	221
1992	220
1996	219
2000	217

Source: ESPN Sports Almanac

8. Make a line graph of the data. **See Student Handbook Answer Appendix.**

9. Predict the winning time in 2008. **Sample answer: 215 s**

10. **SURVEYS** A survey of randomly selected teens revealed that 68% have a personal cell phone. If there are 1,200 teens at Harrisburg Middle School, about how many have a personal cell phone? (Lesson 8-7) **about 816 teens**

11. **CATS** To determine what type of cat most customers prefer, the president of a cat food company mailed 250 surveys to cat owners. Of the 185 surveys that were returned, 52% preferred calico cats. The president concluded that about half of cat owners prefer calico cats. Determine whether this conclusion is valid. Justify your answers. (Lesson 8-8)

11, 12. See Student Handbook Answer Appendix.

12. **CELL PHONES** The table shows the number of monthly minutes Mallory used on her cell phone during the past year. She claims that the average number of minutes used is about 324. Explain how this is misleading. (Lesson 8-9)

284	322	286	359	318	294
602	278	292	267	299	285

Chapter 9 Probability

Pages 458–505

1. **DENTISTS** A dental hygienist randomly chooses a toothbrush in a drawer containing 17 white, 12 green, and 5 blue toothbrushes. What is the probability that she chooses a green toothbrush? Write as a fraction in simplest form. (Lesson 9-1) $\frac{6}{17}$

SURVEYS For Exercises 2 and 3, use the table below. It shows the results of a survey in which adults were asked how proud they were to be an American. (Lesson 9-1)

How Proud Are You?	
Response	Number
Extremely	650
Very	250
Moderately	60
Little/Not at All	30
No Opinion	10

Source: Gallup Poll

2. If one person participating in the survey is chosen at random, what is the probability that the person is extremely patriotic? Write as a fraction in simplest form? $\frac{13}{20}$

3. If one person participating in the survey is chosen at random, what is the probability that he is *not* moderately patriotic? Write as a fraction in simplest form. $\frac{47}{50}$

RANCHING For Exercises 4 and 5, use the following information.
For Roger to reach his cattle pasture, he must pass through three consecutive gates. Any of the three gates can be either *open* or *closed*. (Lesson 9-2)

4. **See Student Handbook Answer Appendix.** Make a tree diagram to show all of the possible positions of the gates.

5. What is the probability that all three gates will be closed when Roger visits this pasture? Write as a fraction. $\frac{1}{8}$

6. **SKATEBOARDS** World Sports makes skateboards with different deck patterns. You can choose one of four deck lengths and one of six types of wheels. If they have 120 different skateboards, how many deck patterns are there? (Lesson 9-3) **5 patterns**

7. **READING** Mr. Steadman plans to read eight children's novels to his second graders during the school year. In how many ways can he arrange the books to be read? (Lesson 9-4) **40,320 ways**

8. **CRAFTS** Marina has print fabric in pink, blue, magenta, green, yellow, and tan. How many different stuffed bears can she make if each bear has only four different fabrics, and the order of the fabrics is not important? (Lesson 9-5) **15 bears**

9. **TRAVEL** There are four seats in Pedro's car: two in the front and two in the back. If Benny, Carlita, and Juanita are all in the car with Pedro, how many ways can they be seated in the car if Pedro is driving? Use the *act it out* strategy. (Lesson 9-6) **6 ways**

10. **FOOD** The graph shows the results of a survey in which 7th graders at Plentywood Middle School were asked to name their favorite fruit. If a 7th grader at the school is randomly selected, what is the probability that they chose bananas as their favorite? Write as a fraction in simplest form. (Lesson 9-7) $\frac{1}{4}$

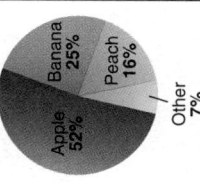

Favorite Fruits
Apple 52%, Banana 25%, Peach 16%, Other 7%

MARBLES For Exercises 11 and 12, refer to the table. (Lesson 9-8)

Color	Number
Red	10
Blue	6
Purple	10
Yellow	4
Green	2

11. What is the probability of randomly selecting one yellow marble and then one purple marble? Assume that the first marble is not replaced. $\frac{5}{128}$

12. What is the probability of randomly selecting two red marbles? Assume that the first marble is replaced. $\frac{25}{256}$

Pages 508–569

Chapter 10 Geometry: Polygons

ART For Exercises 1 and 2, use the diagram of the Native American artifact.

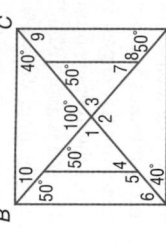

1. Name a right angle and a straight angle. (Lesson 10-1)

2. If $m\angle AOB = 90°$, what is $m\angle DOC$? (Lesson 10-2) **90°**

1. Sample answer: $\angle AOB$; $\angle AOC$

TELEVISION For Exercises 3 and 4, use the survey results shown in the table below. (Lesson 10-3)

Channels Families Watch	
Number	Percent
5 or fewer	30%
6–12	33%
13–25	19%
26 or more	14%

3. The fifth category in the survey is *no TV or no opinion*. What percent of the people surveyed were in this category? **4%**

4. Make a circle graph of the data.

4, 5. See Student Handbook Answer Appendix.

5. **ART** Victor drew a right triangle so that one of the acute angles measures 55°. Without measuring, describe how Victor can determine the measure of the other acute angle in the triangle. Then find the angle measure. (Lesson 10-4)

6. **Mr. Sanchez can increase the width to 11 m.** **GARDENING** Mr. Sanchez has a flower bed with a length of 10 meters and a width of 5 meters. If he can only change the width of the flower bed, describe what he can do to increase the perimeter by 12 meters. Use the *logical reasoning* strategy. (Lesson 10-5)

7. **Mitchell, Deidre, Carlos, Tramaine** **RUNNING** Four friends are entered in a race. Deirdre finishes directly ahead of Carlos. Mitchell finishes three places ahead of Tramaine and directly ahead of Deirdre. If Tramaine finishes fourth, place the runners in order from first to last. Use *logical reasoning*. (Lesson 10-5)

For Exercises 8 and 9, use the figure below.

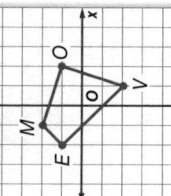

8, 9. See Student Handbook Answer Appendix.

8. Find the measure of each angle numbered from 1–10. (Lesson 10-4)

9. Find the *best* name to classify quadrilateral *ABCD*. Explain your reasoning. (Lesson 10-6)

10. **CRAFTS** Priscilla makes porcelain dolls that are proportional to a real child. If Jody is $4\frac{2}{3}$ feet tall with a 23-inch waist, what should be the waist measure of a doll that is 13 inches tall? Round to the nearest inch. (Lesson 10-7) **5 in.**

11. **ART** Draw a tessellation using two of the polygons listed at the right. Identify the polygons and explain why the tessellation works. (Lesson 10-8)

regular triangles
quadrilaterals
pentagons
hexagons
octagons

11–13. See Student Handbook Answer Appendix.

For Exercises 12 and 13, use the quadrilateral *MOVE* shown below.

12. Describe the translation that will move *M* to the point at (2, −2). Then graph quadrilateral *M'O'V'E'* using this translation. (Lesson 10-9)

13. Find the coordinates of the vertices of quadrilateral *MOVE* after a reflection over the y-axis. Then graph the reflection. (Lesson 10-10)

Chapter 11 Measurement: Two- and Three-Dimensional Figures

Pages 568–631

1. **CRAFTS** A quilt pattern uses 25 parallelogram-shaped pieces of fabric, each with a base of 4 inches and a height of $2\frac{1}{2}$ inches. How much fabric is used to make the 25 pieces? (Lesson 11-1) **250 in²**

2. **FURNITURE** A corner table is in the shape of a right triangle. If the side lengths of the tabletop are 3.5 feet, 3.5 feet, and 4.9 feet, what is the area? Round to the nearest tenth if necessary. (Lesson 11-2) **6.1 ft²**

3. **PUZZLES** Find the area of each small and large shaded triangle. Round to the nearest whole. (Lesson 11-2)
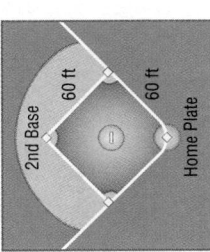
small: 13 cm²,
large: 25 cm²

4. **EARTH SCIENCE** Earth has a diameter of 7,926 miles. Use the formula for the circumference of a circle to estimate the circumference of Earth at its equator. (Lesson 11-3) **about 24,900 mi**

5. **COOKIES** In New Zealand, a giant circular chocolate chip cookie was baked with a diameter of 81 feet 8 inches. To the nearest square foot, what was the area of the cookie? (Lesson 11-4) **5,236 ft²**

6. **SPORTS PROFIT** A stadium seats 1,001,800 people. 22% of the tickets cost $134.87 each. 45% of the tickets cost $67.99 each. The remaining 33% cost only $35.87 each. About how much revenue is made from one game when each seat is sold out? Use the *solve a simpler problem strategy.* (Lesson 11-5) **about $72,000,000**

7. **LANDSCAPING** Find the area of the flower garden shown in the diagram at the right. Round to the nearest square foot. (Lesson 11-6)
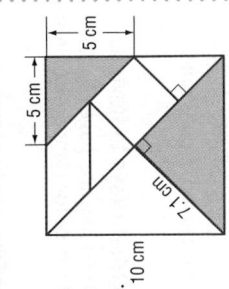
3,148 ft²

8. **GEOMETRY** A certain three-dimensional figure has four triangular faces and one square face. Classify this figure. (Lesson 11-7) **square pyramid**

9. **RECORDS** According to the *Guinness Book of World Records*, the tallest hotel in the world is the 1,053-foot sail-shaped Burj Al Arab in Dubai, United Arab Emirates.
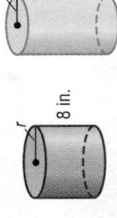
Draw possible sketches of the top, side, and front views of the hotel. (Lesson 11-8) **See Student Handbook Answer Appendix.**

OCEANS For Exercises 10 and 11, use the following information.
The Atlantic Ocean has an area of about 33,420,000 square miles. Its average depth is 11,730 feet. (Lesson 11-9)

10. To the nearest hundredth, what is the average depth of the Atlantic Ocean in miles? (*Hint:* 1 mi = 5,280 ft) **2.22 mi**

11. What is the approximate volume of the Atlantic Ocean in cubic miles? **74,192,400 mi³**

WATER For Exercises 12–13, use the cylinder-shaped water tank. (Lesson 11-10)
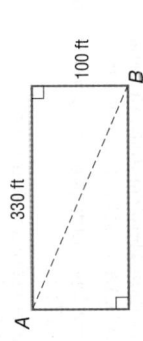

12. Find the volume of the tank. Round to the nearest cubic foot. **15,700 ft³**

13. One cubic foot is approximately 7.48 gallons. Find the approximate volume of the water tank to the nearest gallon. **13. 117,436 gal**

714 Mixed Problem Solving

Chapter 12 Extending Geometry and Measurement

Pages 634–663

1. **OMELETS** In Japan, a gigantic omelet was made with an area of 1,383 square feet. If the omelet was a square, what would be its side lengths? Round to the nearest tenth. (Lesson 12-1) **37.2 ft**

2. **SOFTBALL** A softball diamond is a square measuring 60 feet on each side.
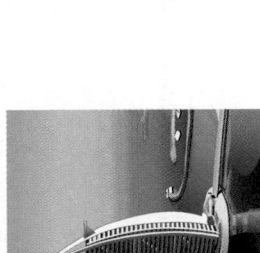
How far does a player on second base throw when she throws from second base to home? Round to the nearest tenth. (Lesson 12-2) **84.9 ft**

3. **BANDS** Mr. Garcia is planning a band formation at a football game. The diagram shows the dimensions of the field.
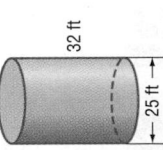
To the nearest foot, what is the distance from *A* to *B*? (Lesson 12-2) **345 ft**

4. **GEOMETRY** Two right triangles are side by side such that they form a larger isosceles triangle. If the two right triangles are congruent and each have angle measures of 90°, 45°, and 45°, what type of triangle will the new isosceles triangle be? Use the *make a model strategy.* (Lesson 12-3) **right triangle**

5. **CUBES** A rectangular prism is formed from 48 centimeter cubes such that the height of the prism is one half of the width and one third of the length of the prism. Find the dimensions of the rectangular prism. Use the *make a model strategy.* (Lesson 12-3) **6 cm by 4 cm by 2 cm**

For Exercises 6 and 7, use the following information.
Liz is designing some gift boxes. The small box is 6 inches long, 4 inches wide, and 2.5 inches high. The medium box has dimensions that are each 3 times the dimensions of the small box. (Lesson 12-4)

6. Find the surface area of the small box. **6.98 in²**

7. What are the dimensions of the medium box? Then find the surface area of the medium box. **18 in. by 12 in. by 7.5 in.; 882 in²**

STORAGE For Exercises 8–10, use the following information.
The two canisters shown below each have a volume of about 628.3 cubic inches. (Lesson 12-5)
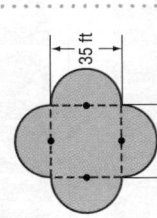

8. What is the radius of the blue canister? Round to the nearest tenth. **5.0 in.**

9. What is the height of the yellow canister? Round to the nearest tenth. **12.5 in.**

10. What is the difference between the surface areas of the two canisters? **6.3 in²**

HATS For Exercises 11–13, use the following information. (Lesson 12-5)
A certain cylinder-shaped hat box has a height of 9 inches and a radius of 5.5 inches. Its lid is also shaped as a cylinder, with a slightly larger diameter so that the lid fits over the box.

11. How many square inches of material are needed to make the hat box, not including the lid? Round to the nearest tenth. **405.8 in²**

12. If the lid has a height of 3.5 inches and a diameter of 11.8 inches, how many square inches of material are needed to make the lid? Round to the nearest tenth. **239.0 in²**

13. How many times more material is needed to make the hat box than the lid? Round to the nearest tenth. **1.7**

Mixed Problem Solving 715

Preparing for Standardized Tests

Throughout the school year, you may be required to take several standardized tests, and you may have many questions about them. Here are some answers to help you get ready.

How Should I Study?

The good news is that you've been studying all along—a little bit every day. Here are some of the ways your textbook has been preparing you.

- **Every Day** Each lesson had multiple-choice practice questions.

- **Every Week** The Mid-Chapter Quiz and Practice Test also had several practice questions.

- **Every Month** The Test Practice pages at the end of each chapter had even more questions, including short-response/grid-in and extended-response questions.

Are There Other Ways to Review?

Absolutely! The following pages contain even more practice for standardized tests.

Tips for SUCCESS

Prepare

- Go to bed early the night before the test. You will think more clearly after a good night's rest.
- Become familiar with common formulas and when they should be used.
- Think positively.

During the Test

- Read each problem carefully. Underline key words and think about different ways to solve the problem.
- Watch for key words like *not*. Also look for order words like *least*, *greatest*, *first*, and *last*.
- Answer questions you are sure about first. If you do not know the answer to a question, skip it and go back to that question later.
- Check your answer to make sure it is reasonable.
- Make sure that the number of the question on the answer sheet matches the number of the question on which you are working in your test booklet.

Whatever you do...

- Don't try to do it all in your head. If no figure is provided, draw one.
- Don't rush. Try to work at a steady pace.
- Don't give up. Some problems may seem hard to you, but you may be able to figure out what to do if you read each question carefully or try another strategy.

717

Multiple-Choice Questions

Multiple-choice questions are the most common type of question on standardized tests. These questions are sometimes called *selected-response questions*. You are asked to choose the best answer from four or five possible answers.

To record a multiple-choice answer, you may be asked to shade in a bubble that is a circle or an oval or just to write the letter of your choice. Always make sure that your shading is dark enough and completely covers the bubble.

Incomplete shading
(A) (B) (C) (D)

Too light shading
(A) (B) (C) (D)

Correct shading
(A) (B) ● (D)

The answer to a multiple-choice question may not stand out from the choices. However, you may be able to eliminate some of the choices. Another answer choice might be that the correct answer is not given.

TEST EXAMPLE

1. Mrs. Hon's seventh grade students are purchasing stuffed animals to donate to a charity. They bought 3 boxes containing eight animals each and 2 boxes containing twelve animals each. Which expression *cannot* be used to find the total number of animals they bought to give to the charity?

A $8 + 8 + 8 + 12 + 12$ C $3(8) + 2(12)$

B $3 \times 8 + 2 \times 12$ D $5 \times (8 + 12)$

Notice that the problem asks for the expression that *cannot* represent the situation.

Read the problem carefully and locate the important information. There are 3 boxes that have eight animals, so that is 3×8, or 24 animals. There are 2 boxes of twelve animals, so that is 2×12, or 24 animals. The total number of animals is $24 + 24$, or 48.

You know from reading the problem that you are looking for the expression that *does not* simplify to 48. Simplify each expression to find the answer.

A $8 + 8 + 8 + 12 + 12 = (8 + 8 + 8) + (12 + 12)$
$= 24 + 24$
$= 48$

B $3 \times 8 + 2 \times 12 = 24 + 24$
$= 48$

C $3(8) + 2(12) = 24 + 24$
$= 48$

D $5 \times (8 + 12) = 5 \times 20$
$= 100$

The only expression that *does not* simplify to 48 is D. The correct choice is D.

Some problems are easier to solve if you draw a diagram. If you cannot write in the test booklet, draw a diagram on scratch paper.

TEST EXAMPLE

2. On a hiking trip, Grace and Alicia traveled 10 miles south and 4 miles west. If they take the shortest return route, how far will the hike be back to their starting point? Round to the nearest tenth of a mile.

A 6.0 mi   B 9.2 mi   C 10.8 mi   D 14.0 mi

STRATEGY
Diagrams
Draw a diagram for the situation.

To solve this problem, you need to draw a diagram of the situation. Label the directions and the important information from the problem.

Use the Pythagorean Theorem to find the distance that they will hike back to their starting point.

$c^2 = a^2 + b^2$ Pythagorean Theorem
$c^2 = 4^2 + 10^2$ Replace a with 4 and b with 10.
$c^2 = 16 + 100$ Simplify.
$c^2 = 116$ Add.
$\sqrt{c^2} = \sqrt{116}$ Take the square root of each side.
$c \approx 10.8$ Use a calculator to simplify.

The hike back will be about 10.8 miles. The correct choice is C.

Round the answer to the correct decimal place.

Some problems give you more information than you need to solve the problem. Read the question carefully to determine the information you need.

TEST EXAMPLE

3. One of the biggest pieces of cheese ever produced was made in 1866 in Ingersoll, Canada. It weighed 7,300 pounds. It was shaped as a cylinder with a diameter of 7 feet and a height of 3 feet. To the nearest cubic foot, what was the volume of the cheese? Use 3.14 for π.

A 462 ft³   B 143 ft³   C 115 ft³   D 63 ft³

STRATEGY
Formulas
Use the reference sheet to find the correct formula.

You need to use the formula for the volume of a cylinder. The diameter is 7 feet, so the radius is $\frac{7}{2}$ or 3.5 feet. The height is 3 feet.

$V = \pi r^2 h$ Volume of a cylinder
$V \approx (3.14)(3.5)^2(3)$ Replace π with 3.14, r with 3.5, and h with 3.
$V \approx 115.395$ Simplify.

The volume of the cheese is about 115 cubic feet. The correct choice is C.

Preparing for
Standardized Tests

Multiple-Choice Practice

Choose the best answer.

Number and Operations

1. The world's smallest fruit is the fruit of a wolffia plant, which measures about 0.01 inch in length. Another small fruit is the eye of a sewing needle, with a length of 0.20 inch. How many times longer is the eye of a sewing needle fruit than a wolffia fruit? **D**

   A 0.002 C 2
   B 0.005 D 20

2. The table shows what types of trash fill landfills in the United States. What fraction of the trash in landfills is plastic? **J**

Type of Trash	Percent in Landfills
metal	8%
plastic	24%
food, yard waste	11%
rubber, leather	6%
paper	21%
other trash	30%

   Source: *The World Almanac for Kids*

   F $\frac{1}{100}$ H $\frac{1}{6}$
   G $\frac{1}{24}$ J $\frac{6}{25}$

3. A recent movie earned 317 million dollars in ticket sales. What is this value in scientific notation? **C**

   A 3.17
   B 317×10^6
   C 3.17×10^8
   D 3.17×10^{11}

4. Mercury orbits the sun at 29.75 miles per second. Earth orbits the sun at 18.51 miles per second. How many more miles does Mercury travel in one minute than Earth? **H**

   F 11.24 mi H 674.4 mi
   G 269.76 mi J 40,464 mi

Algebra

5. The table shows the population growth of a certain bacteria. How many bacteria will there be after 5 hours? **C**

Hours	0	1	2	3	4	5
Number of Bacteria	32	48	72	104	144	?

   A 243 B 200 C 192 D 178

6. Which function rule describes the relationship between distance from home y and hours traveled x? **J**

Time (h) x	Distance from Home (mi) y
0	0
1	65
2	130
3	195

   F $65y = x$ H $y = x + 65$
   G $y = 65 \div x$ J $y = 65x$

7. For a family portrait, a photographer charges a sitting fee and an amount of money per portrait ordered. Which function rule describes the relationship between the total cost y and number of portraits x? **C**

   Family Portrait

   [graph of Total Cost ($) vs Number of Portraits with points (0, 40), (1, 50), (2, 60), (3, 70), (4, 80), (5, 90)]

   A $y = 10 + 40x$ C $y = 40 + 10x$
   B $y = 40x + 10x$ D $y = 10x$

TEST-TAKING TIP

Question 11 Most standardized tests will include any commonly used formulas at the front of the test booklet. Quickly review the list before you begin so that you know what formulas are available.

Geometry

8. The three towns on the map form a triangle. Which term *best* describes the angle with vertex at Worthington? **F**

   [map showing Pipestone, 30°, 55°, Windom, Worthington]

   F obtuse H acute
   G right J straight

9. Pedro is using a triangle in a computer graphics design. On a coordinate plane, the vertices of the triangle are $A(-1, 1)$, $B(0, 2)$, and $C(5, -1)$. If Pedro translates the triangle 4 units left and 3 units down, what will be the coordinates of B'? **D**

   A $(-1, -4)$ C $(4, 5)$
   B $(4, -1)$ D $(-4, -1)$

10. Jasmine is using this polygon on a poster she is making for the basketball team. Which term *best* describes the polygon? **J**

    [arrow-shaped polygon labeled "All the way to the top!"]

    F quadrilateral H hexagon
    G decagon J heptagon

Measurement

11. Crispy Crackers are packaged in a box that measures 6 inches by 2.5 inches by 10 inches. Which dimensions are of a prism that has the same volume as the Crispy Crackers box? **B**

    A 6.5 in. by 2 in. by 10 in.
    B 6.25 in. by 3 in. by 8 in.
    C 7.25 in. by 2 in. by 9.5 in.
    D 4 in. by 7.5 in. by 6 in.

12. The Crab nebula is a cloud of gas and dust particles in space that is expanding at a rate of 930 miles per second. What is its rate of expansion in miles per hour? **J**

    F 22,320 mph H 1,339,200 mph
    G 55,800 mph J 3,348,000 mph

13. Super Toys makes two sizes of building blocks shaped as cubes. The large block has side length four times the length of the small block. What is the ratio of the surface area of the small block to the surface area of the large block? **C**

    A 1 to 4 C 1 to 16
    B 1 to 6 D 1 to 32

Data Analysis and Probability

14. The table shows the number of students playing each sport at Wilson Junior High. Find the mean of the data. **H**

Sport	Number of Students
baseball/softball	49
basketball	74
soccer	82
swimming	21
track and field	115
volleyball	25

    F 23 G 49 H 61 J 94

15. The spinner is divided into four equal-sized sections. If you spin the spinner 62 times, which is the *best* estimate for the number of times you will land on 2? **A**

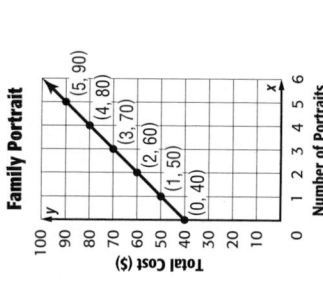

    A 15 B 30 C 40 D 50

Gridded-Response Questions

Gridded-response questions are another type of question on standardized tests. These questions are sometimes called *student-produced response* or *grid in*.

For gridded response, you must mark your answer on a grid printed on an answer sheet. The grid contains a row of four or five boxes at the top, two rows of ovals or circles with decimal and fraction symbols, and four or five columns of ovals, numbered 0–9. An example of a grid from an answer sheet is shown.

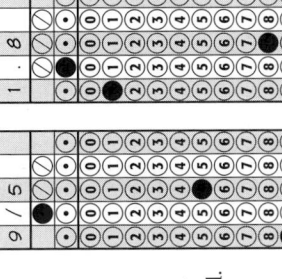

TEST EXAMPLE

1 Mr. Byrd builds and sells storage buildings. The dimensions of his most popular model are shown in the diagram. What is the volume of the building in cubic feet?

[diagram: rectangular box labeled 8 ft, 10 ft, 12 ft]

What do you need to find?

You need to find the volume of a rectangular prism. Use the formula and the dimensions given in the diagram.

$V = \ell wh$ Volume of a rectangular prism

$V = 12 \cdot 10 \cdot 8$ Replace ℓ with 12, w with 10, and h with 8.

$V = 960$ Multiply.

The volume is 960 cubic feet.

How do you fill in the grid for the answer?

- Write your answer in the answer boxes.
- Write only one digit or symbol in each answer box.
- Do not write any digits or symbols outside the answer boxes.
- You may write your answer with the first digit in the left answer box, or with the last digit in the right answer box. You may leave blank any boxes you do not need on the right or the left side of your answer.
- Fill in only one bubble for every answer box that you have written in. Be sure not to fill in a bubble under a blank answer box.

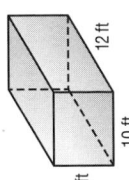

STRATEGY
Formulas
Use the reference sheet to find the formula you need.

Many gridded-response questions result in an answer that is a fraction or a decimal. These values can also be filled in on the grid.

TEST EXAMPLE

2 A prize box contains 12 glitter pencils, 5 fluorescent pens, and 13 mechanical pencils. If Alex randomly selects a prize, what is the probability that he will choose a glitter pencil?

$P(\text{glitter pencil}) = \dfrac{\text{number of favorable outcomes}}{\text{number of possible outcomes}}$

$= \dfrac{12}{12 + 5 + 13} = \dfrac{12}{30} = \dfrac{2}{5}$

You can either grid the fraction $\frac{12}{30}$ or $\frac{2}{5}$. You also can rewrite the fraction as a decimal and grid 0.4. Be sure to write the decimal point or fraction bar in the answer box. The following are acceptable answers.

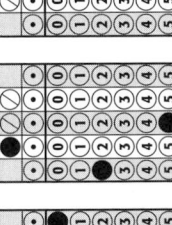

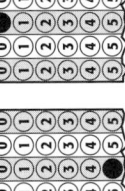

Any equivalent fraction that fits the grid will be counted as correct.

Do not leave a blank answer box in the middle of an answer.

If the answer is a mixed number, change it to an equivalent improper fraction or decimal.

TEST EXAMPLE

3 A hummingbird measures $2\frac{1}{2}$ inches in length. A sandpiper, measures $4\frac{1}{2}$ inches in length. How many times as long is the sandpiper as the hummingbird?

Divide the length of the sandpiper by the length of the hummingbird.

$4\frac{1}{2} \div 2\frac{1}{2} = \dfrac{9}{2} \div \dfrac{5}{2}$ Rename $2\frac{1}{2}$ as $\frac{5}{2}$

$\qquad = \dfrac{9}{2} \cdot \dfrac{2}{5}$ Multiply by the reciprocal of $\frac{5}{2}$, which is $\frac{2}{5}$

$\qquad = \dfrac{9}{5}$

You can either grid the improper fraction $\frac{9}{5}$, or rewrite it as 1.8 and grid the decimal. Do not enter 14/5, as this will be interpreted as $\frac{14}{5}$.

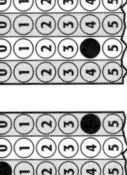

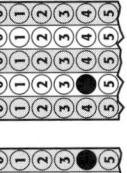

Preparing for Standardized Tests

Gridded-Response Practice

Solve each problem. Then copy and complete a grid like the one shown on page 722.

Number and Operations

1. The seventh-grade class at Willow Creek Middle School is planning a class trip. Each student will need to pay $4.50 for the bus ride, $8.00 for a ticket to the museum, and $5.25 for lunch. If there are 52 students in the class, what will be the total cost in dollars of the trip? **923**

2. The highest point in Louisiana is Driskill Mountain at 585 feet. The lowest point is −8 feet in New Orleans. What is the difference in feet between the highest and lowest elevation points? **593**

3. People in the United States own about 204 million cars. If the number of cars is written in scientific notation, what is the exponent of the 10 in the expression? **8**

4. Ashlee has $5\frac{1}{4}$ cups of cocoa powder. If each batch of chocolate cookies uses $\frac{1}{2}$ cup of cocoa powder, how many batches could she make? **$2\frac{1}{2}$ or 10.5**

Algebra

5. The number of televisions per 1,000 people in France is 598. The number of televisions per 1,000 people in the United States is 208 greater than the number in France. How many televisions are there in the United States per 1,000 people? **806**

6. The table shows the number of white beads that Carmen uses in each row for a particular pattern in a necklace that she designed. How many white beads will there be in the sixth row? **32**

Row	1	2	3	4	5
Beads	1	2	4	8	16

7. The table shows the cost of renting a booth at the week-long Fall Festival. There is an initial charge for reserving a booth and a fee per day. What is the cost in dollars of renting a booth for the 7 days of the festival? **330**

Days	0	1	2	3
Cost ($)	50	90	130	170

8. The graph shows the cost to rent a power paint sprayer. Let x be the number of hours the sprayer is rented and y be the total cost of the rental. Suppose an equation of the form $y = ax$ represents the data in the graph. What is the value of a? **2.5 or 2.50**

Renting a Power Paint Sprayer

Cost ($): 30, 25, 20, 15, 10, 5 — Time (h): 0 1 2 3 4 5 6 7

9. The temperature on a January morning is −18°F. The temperature is expected to rise at a rate of 5° each hour for the next several hours. In how many hours will the temperature be 7°F? **5**

Geometry

10. Triangle ABC is similar to triangle XYZ. What is the measure of $\angle Z$ in degrees? **75**

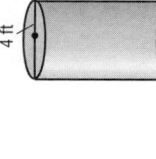

11. Triangle DEF has vertices $D(1, 1)$, $E(4, −2)$, and $F(0, −3)$. Find the y-coordinate of point E after the triangle is reflected over the x-axis. **2**

12. In the diagram, $\angle 1$ and $\angle 2$ are supplementary. Find the measure of $\angle 3$ in degrees. **62**

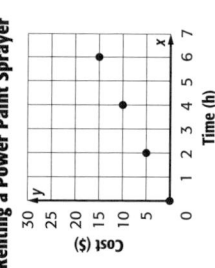

13. Rectangle B has width and length 3 times the width and length of Rectangle A. As a fraction, what is the ratio of the area of Rectangle A to the area of Rectangle B? **1/9**

Measurement

14. In the United States, the average amount of meat eaten per person is 261 pounds per year. If there are 365 days in a year, what is the average number of ounces of meat eaten per day? Round to the nearest ounce. **11**

TEST-TAKING TIP

Question 14 The units of measure given in a question may not be the same as the units of measure asked for in the answer. Check that your solution is in the correct unit.

15. A rectangle has an area of 318 square centimeters and a width of 12 centimeters. What is the length of the rectangle in centimeters? **26.5**

16. The circle graph shows the results of a survey in Ms. Chen's fifth period math class. What is the exact degree measure of the section of the circle graph representing soccer? **162**

Favorite Sports of Ms. Chen's Students

Soccer 45%, Basketball 25%, Baseball 20%, Other 10%

17. One acre of land is 43,560 square feet. How many square yards are in one acre? **4840**

Data Analysis and Probability

18. The Browns plan to paint the top, bottom, and sides of the cylinder-shaped barrel with a waterproof coating. What is the surface area in square feet of the barrel? Round to the nearest square foot. **113**

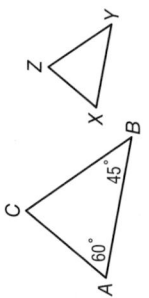

4 ft, 7 ft

19. The table shows the world's highest dams and the countries in which they are located. Find the range of the data. **128**

Country	Height (ft)
Tajikistan	984
Switzerland	935
Georgia	892
Italy	859
Mexico	856

Source: *Scholastic Book of World Records*

20. The table shows the prices in dollars that Mike spent on his college textbooks. What is the mean of the data? **53.50**

66.00	51.25	50.00	63.00
56.25	9.00	82.00	50.50

21. Kaya has the following scores for the first four tests in her science class: 82%, 95%, 100%, and 90%. She wants the mean of her first five tests to be 93%. What score as a percent must she earn on the fifth test? **98**

22. In a carnival game, the probability of winning is 0.005. As a percent, what is the probability of losing? **99.5**

23. A beverage cooler contains 6 regular colas, 5 orange drinks, 7 iced teas, and 7 diet colas. James reaches into the cooler and randomly takes two drinks, one after the other. Find the probability that he will choose a regular cola and then an orange drink. **1/20 or 0.05**

Short-Response Questions

Short-response questions require you to provide a solution to the problem as well as any method, explanation, and/or justification you used to arrive at the solution. These are sometimes called *constructed-response, open-response, open-ended, free-response,* or *student-produced questions.*

The following is a sample **rubric**, or scoring guide.

Credit	Score	Criteria
Full	2	Full credit: The answer is correct and a full explanation is provided that shows each step in arriving at the final answer.
Partial	1	Partial credit: There are two different ways to receive partial credit. • The answer is correct, but the explanation provided is incomplete or incorrect. • The answer is incorrect, but the explanation and method of solving the problem is correct.
None	0	No credit: Either an answer is not provided or the answer does not make sense.

On some standardized tests, no credit is given for a correct answer if your work is not shown.

TEST EXAMPLE

STRATEGY
Reread the Problem
Look for the important information in the problem.

1 Hanna is deciding between a desktop and a laptop that are on sale. The desktop costs $609.00 with a 10% discount. The laptop costs $725.00 with a 25% discount. There is also a 6.75% sales tax on all purchases. Which computer is less expensive? What will be the total cost of the computer including discount and sales tax?

Full Credit Solution

Since there are two computers to compare, I will first find the discounted price of each computer. I will change each percent to a decimal to make the calculations.

desktop
$609.00 \times 0.10 = 60.90$
$609.00 - 60.90 = 548.10$

laptop
$725.00 \times 0.25 = 181.25$
$725.00 - 181.25 = 543.75$

The laptop is less expensive after the discount.
I still need to find the cost of the laptop computer with tax.

543.75×0.0675 6.75% = 0.0675
$= 36.703125$ Use a calculator.
≈ 36.70

Now I will add the sales tax to the cost of the laptop.
$543.75 + 36.70 = 580.45$

The laptop will cost Hanna $580.45, including sales tax.

The steps, calculations, and reasoning are clearly stated.

Partial Credit Solution

In this sample solution, the calculations are correct and the answer is correct. However, there is no explanation for any of the calculations.

$609.00 \times 0.10 = 60.90$
$609.00 - 60.90 = 548.10$
$548.10 \times 1.0675 = 585.09675$

$725.00 \times 0.25 = 181.25$
$725.00 - 181.25 = 543.75$
$543.75 \times 1.0675 = 580.453125$
The laptop is cheaper for $580.45.

Notice that the student multiplies the discounted price by 1.0675 since the cost is 1 and the tax is 0.0675. So, the total is then 1.0675.

Partial Credit Solution

In this sample solution, the answer is partially incorrect because the student does not add the sales tax.

I will find the discount price for each set.

Desktop: Since the current price is 100% and the discount is 10%, the sale price will be
$100 - 10 = 90\%$ or 0.9.
$609.00 \times 0.9 = 548.10$

Laptop: Since the current price is 100% and the discount is 25%, the sale price will be
$100 - 25 = 75\%$ or 0.75.
$725.00 \times 0.75 = 543.75$

Hanna should get the laptop for $543.75.

The student does not add the cost of the tax.

No Credit Solution

In this sample solution, the student does not understand how to find discounted prices and the sales tax. There are just some calculations using the numbers in the problem.

$609.00 - 10\% = 602.91$
$725.00 - 25\% = 625.00$
$602.91 + 6.75\% = 609.66$
$625.00 + 6.75 = 631.75$
I think Hanna should buy the desktop for $609.66.

Preparing for
Standardized Tests

Short-Response Practice

Solve each problem. Show all your work.

Number and Operations

1. A main unit of currency in Egypt is the pound. One U.S. dollar is equal to $3\frac{4}{5}$ pounds. How many pounds are equivalent to $10.00 in the U.S.? **38 pounds**

2. The average daytime temperature on Venus is 870°F. The average temperature on Jupiter is −160°F. What is the difference between the average temperatures on Venus and Jupiter? **1,030°F**

3. A bag of chocolate candies has a nutrition label stating that each serving contains 20% of the recommended daily amount of fat. A serving has 13 grams of fat. Using this information, what is the total recommended daily amount of fat in grams? **65 g**

4. The Montana Department of Fish, Wildlife, and Parks raised the price of a tag to catch a paddlefish from $2.50 to $5.00 for residents and from $7.50 to $15.00 for nonresidents. Which percent of increase is greater, the increase for residents or for nonresidents? **They are the same with both being a 100% increase.**

5. A recent article in the newspaper said that there were 75 cell phones for every 100 people in Finland. The number of cell phones in Finland was given to be 3,893,000. Estimate the population of Finland using this information. **about 5,000,000 people**

Algebra

6. Florida has 8,426 miles of shoreline. Alaska has 25,478 more miles of shoreline than Florida. Write and solve an equation to find the number of miles of shoreline for Alaska. $a = 8,426 + 25,478$; $a = 33,904$ **mi**

7. Juana is saving money to buy a skateboard that costs $95. She has $25 and plans to save $5 per week. In how many weeks will she have enough money for the skateboard? **14 weeks**

8. Tyler delivers televisions for Electronics Depot. The graph shows the amount Tyler charges for delivery based on distance. Name the slope and y-intercept of the graph and describe what they mean in this situation. **See Student Handbook Answer Appendix.**

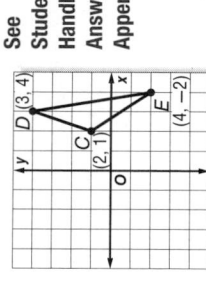

Charge for Delivery

9. Solve $\frac{2}{3}b = \frac{8}{7}$. $\frac{12}{7}$

Geometry

10. The formula for the area of a trapezoid is $A = \frac{1}{2}h(b_1 + b_2)$. Find the area of the trapezoid. **70 ft²**

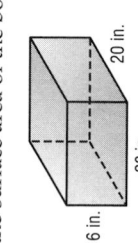

$b_1 = 6$ ft
$h = 7$ ft
$b_2 = 14$ ft

11. Angles MNP and PNO are supplementary. Find $m\angle PNO$. **155°**

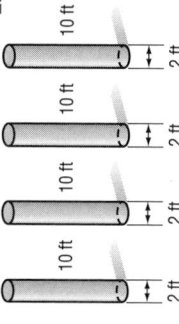

12. What is the value of x? **62**

13. Colby is planning to use $\triangle CDE$ for a design by using transformations. He plans to reflect it over the y-axis. Find the coordinates of $\triangle CDE$ after this reflection. Graph the reflected image of the triangle. **See Student Handbook Answer Appendix.**

> **TEST-TAKING TIP**
> **Questions 17 and 18** After finding the solution, always go back and read the problem again to make sure your solution answers what the problem is asking.

Data Analysis and Probability

19. The stem-and-leaf plot shows the scores on the last math test in Mr. Hill's class. What is the range of the data? **39**

Stem	Leaf
9	1 2 3 5 6 9
8	0 2 5 6 6 7 8 8
7	1 2 3 5 7 9 9
6	0 5 8 9 9 8|2 = 82 points

20. The table shows the heights of the world's largest flightless birds. Make a bar graph of the data. **See Student Handbook Answer Appendix.**

Bird	Height (in.)
Ostrich	96
Emu	60
Cassowary	60
Rhea	54
Emperor Penguin	45

21. The table shows the average precipitation in inches for each month in Syracuse, New York. Make a scatter plot of the data. Use the months on the horizontal axis and the precipitation on the vertical axis. Describe the graph. **See Student Handbook Answer Appendix.**

Month	Precipitation (in.)	Month	Precipitation (in.)
Jan	2.34	July	3.81
Feb	2.15	Aug	3.51
Mar	2.77	Sep	3.79
Apr	3.33	Oct	3.24
May	3.28	Nov	3.72
June	3.79	Dec	3.2

22. Two number cubes each marked with 1, 2, 3, 4, 5, 6 on their faces are rolled. List all the possible outcomes. **There are 36 possible outcomes: 1, 1; 1, 2; 1, 3; … 6, 6.**

Measurement

14. Diego ran in a 10-kilometer race. What is the distance of this race in meters? **10,000 m**

15. What is the surface area of the box? **2,656 in²**

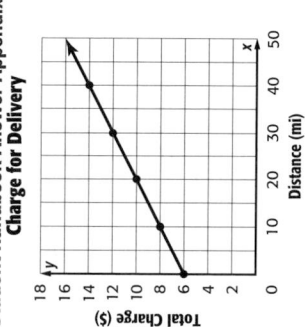

16 in.
20 in.
28 in.

16. A certain aircraft uses 350 gallons of fuel per hour. If the plane used 1,925 gallons of fuel on a flight between two cities, how many hours long was the flight? **5.5 h**

17. Curtis is painting the four columns for the set of a school play. What is the surface area that needs to be painted? Assume that the tops and bottoms of the columns do *not* need to be painted. **251.3 ft²**

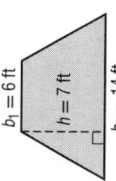 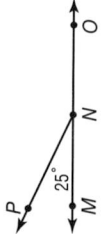 

10 ft
2 ft

18. The record for women running the Boston Marathon was set in 2002 when Margaret Okayo of Kenya ran the 26.2-mile course in approximately 2 hours and 21 minutes. What was her average speed in miles per hour? **about 11.15 mph**

Extended-Response Questions

Extended-response questions are often called *open-ended* or *constructed-response questions*. Most extended-response questions have multiple parts. You must answer all parts to receive full credit.

Extended-response questions are similar to short-response questions in that you must show all of your work in solving the problem and a rubric is used to determine whether you receive full, partial, or no credit. The following is a sample rubric for scoring extended-response questions.

Credit	Score	Criteria
Full	4	Full credit: A correct solution is given that is supported by well-developed, accurate explanations.
Partial	3, 2, 1	Partial credit: A generally correct solution is given that may contain minor flaws in reasoning or computation, or an incomplete solution is given. The more correct the solution, the greater the score.
None	0	No credit: An incorrect solution is given indicating no mathematical understanding of the concept, or no solution is given.

On some standardized tests, no credit is given for a correct answer if your work is not shown.

Make sure that when the problem says to *Show your work*, you show every aspect of your solution including figures, sketches of graphing calculator screens, or the reasoning behind computations.

TEST EXAMPLE

1. Each fall, the community pool is drained. The pool contains 100,000 gallons of water. The pool has two drains that together drain the pool at a rate of 10,000 gallons per hour.

   a. Make a function table for this situation. Let x represent the time in hours the pool drains. Let y represent the gallons of water left in the pool.

   b. Make a graph of the data in the function table.

   c. Predict how many hours it will take for the pool to drain.

Full Credit Solution

Part a A complete table includes labeled columns.

Every 2 hours there will be 20,000 gallons less water.

Hours (x)	Water Left (y)	(x, y)
2	80,000	(2, 80,000)
4	60,000	(4, 60,000)
6	40,000	(6, 40,000)
8	20,000	(8, 20,000)
10	0	(10, 0)

Part b A complete graph includes a title for the graph, appropriate scales and labels for the axes, and correctly graphed points.

To make a graph, I graphed the ordered pairs from my table and decided to connect them with a line.

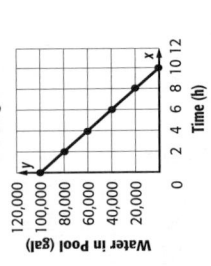

Draining a Pool

The student gives reasoning in graphing the ordered pairs.

Part c

The pool is drained when the y-value is 0. That is at 10 hours. It will take 10 hours to drain the pool.

Partial Credit Solution

Part a This sample answer has an incomplete table.

1	90,000
2	80,000
3	70,000

Part b Partial credit is given because the points are graphed correctly, but the scale on the y-axis jumps from 0 to 70,000 with no break.

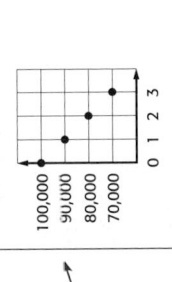

Water in the Pool

Partial credit can be given if parts of the table and graph are missing.

Part c

I wrote a function rule to find how long it will take to drain the pool. I let $y = 0$ to find the number of hours.

$$y = 100,000 - 10,000x$$
$$0 = 100,000 - 10,000x$$
$$10,000x = 100,000$$
$$x = 10 \quad \text{It will take 10 hours to drain the pool.}$$

Full credit is given for Part c.

No Credit Solution

If the student demonstrates no understanding of making a table or graph or making a prediction, then no credit is given.

Extended-Response Practice

Solve each problem. Show all your work.

Number and Operations

1. The table shows the land area and water area of five states.
a–c. See Student Handbook Answer Appendix.

Land and Water Area of Five States

State	Land Area (mi²)	Water Area (mi²)
Florida	53,937	5991
Colorado	103,729	371
Alaska	570,374	44,856
Iowa	55,875	401
Rhode Island	1,045	186

a. Find the percent of each state that is water. The entire state area is the sum of the land and water areas.

b. Order the states from the state with the least percent water to the greatest percent water.

c. Suppose a state had land and water areas such that the water area was 20% of the total area. Give a possible land and water area, with land area greater than 1,000 square miles, such that this is true.

Algebra

2. The table shows the rental rates for a crane rental service. There is an initial fee to reserve the crane and a daily fee.
a–c. See Student Handbook Answer Appendix.

Days	Cost	Days	Cost
0	$100	4	$280
1	$145	5	$325
2	$190	6	$370
3	$235		

a. Graph the data. Let x = number of days and y = cost. Connect the points.

b. What is the slope of the line? What does the slope represent?

c. What would be the charge for renting the crane for 10 days?

3. A long-distance phone company charges 40¢ per call plus 4¢ per minute.

a. Write and solve an equation to find the number of minutes used for a call that costs $2.80.

b. Another long-distance company charges 6¢ per minute and no connection fee. What is the cost of a 60-minute call?

c. Which service would charge less for a 90-minute call?
a–c. See Student Handbook Answer Appendix.

Geometry

4. Ava and Bryn are making rectangular fleece blankets. Ava is making her blanket 40 inches by 60 inches. Bryn says she wants to make her blanket "twice as big."

a. What is the area of Ava's blanket?

b. Bryn makes her blanket such that both the length and width are each twice the length and width of Ava's blanket. What will be the area of Bryn's blanket?

c. What is the ratio of the area of Bryn's blanket in Part b to the area of Ava's blanket in Part a?

d. Ava tells Bryn that a blanket is "twice as big" if the area is twice the area of the other. Give a possible length and width for a blanket twice as big as Ava's using this idea of "twice as big."
a–d. See Student Handbook Answer Appendix.

5. The map shows five towns and the angle measures for roads connecting them.

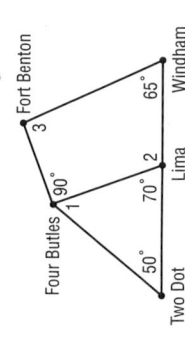

a. Find the measure of ∠1. Explain.

b. Find the measures of ∠2 and ∠3. Explain.

Measurement

6. City planners are considering enlarging the circular manholes in their streets. Currently, the diameter of a manhole cover is 24 inches. The new size being considered is 2 inches greater all the way around.
a–c. See Student Handbook Answer Appendix.

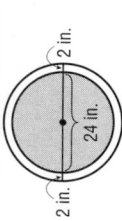

a. Find the area of a current manhole cover with diameter of 24 inches. Round to the nearest square inch.

b. Find the area of a new manhole cover. Round to the nearest square inch.

c. What would be the percent increase in the area of a manhole cover if the new covers are made?

TEST-TAKING TIP

Question 6 Be sure to completely and carefully read the problem before beginning any calculations. If you read too quickly, you may miss a key piece of information.

7. A company that sells beads for craft projects has the two containers shown for packaging the beads.
a–c. See Student Handbook Answer Appendix.

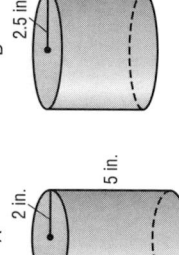

a. Find the volume of each container. Round to the nearest tenth of a cubic inch.

b. Find the ratio of the volume of container A to the volume of container B.

c. The company wants to make a container shaped as a rectangular prism. Find a possible length, width, and height for the container such that its volume is twice the volume of container B.

Data Analysis and Probability

8. The table shows the normal monthly temperatures in degrees Fahrenheit for Honolulu, Hawaii, and Minneapolis, Minnesota.
a–c. See Student Handbook Answer Appendix.

Month	Honolulu	Minneapolis
Jan	73	13
Feb	73	20
Mar	74	32
Apr	76	47
May	77	59
Jun	80	68
Jul	81	73
Aug	82	71
Sep	82	61
Oct	80	49
Nov	78	33
Dec	75	19

Source: *The World Almanac*

a. Make a scatter plot of the data for Honolulu. Place the months on the x-axis and the temperatures on the y-axis. Describe the graph.

b. Make a scatter plot of the data for Minneapolis. Place the months on the x-axis and the temperatures on the y-axis. Describe the graph.

c. Compare the range for each city's temperature data. Explain a possible reason for the difference in the data.

9. Two 4-sided number cubes are rolled for a game, one white and one black. Each number cube has faces numbered 1 through 4.
a–c. See Student Handbook Answer Appendix.

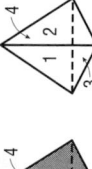

a. List the sample space for rolling the two number pieces.

b. What is the theoretical probability that a player will roll a sum of 8?

c. If you played this game 50 times, how many times would you expect to get a sum of 4?

Concepts and Skills Bank

 Divisibility Patterns

Concepts and Skills Bank

 Divisibility Patterns

In $54 \div 6 = 9$, the quotient, 9, is a whole number. So, we say that 54 is **divisible** by 6. You can use the following rules to determine whether a number is by 2, 3, 4, 5, 6, 9, and 10.

A number is divisible by:

- 2 if the ones digit is divisible by 2.
- 3 if the sum of the digits is divisible by 3.
- 4 if the number formed by the last two digits is divisible by 4.
- 5 if the ones digit is 0 or 5.
- 6 if the number is divisible by both 2 and 3.
- 9 if the sum of the digits is divisible by 9.
- 10 if the ones digit is 0.

1 Focus

Objective

- Use divisibility rules to determine whether a number is divisible by a given number.

Vocabulary

- divisible

Teaching Tip

You may choose to review these divisibility rules with students prior to Lesson 4-1. They will be helpful to students as they find the prime factorization of a number.

EXAMPLE **Use Divisibility Rules**

Determine whether 972 is divisible by 2, 3, 4, 5, 6, 9, or 10.

2: Yes; the ones digit, 2, is divisible by 2.

3: Yes; the sum of the digits, $9 + 7 + 2 = 18$, is divisible by 3.

4: Yes; the number formed by the last two digits, 72, is divisible by 4.

5: No; the ones digit is not 0 or 5.

6: Yes; the number is divisible by 2 and 3.

9: Yes; the sum of the digits, 18, is divisible by 9.

10: No; the ones digit is not 0.

2 Teach

Scaffolding Questions

Write the numbers shown below on the chalkboard.

1	2	3	4	5	6	7	8	9	10
11	12	13	14	15	16	17	18	19	20
21	22	23	24	25	26	27	28	29	30
31	32	33	34	35	36	37	38	39	40
41	42	43	44	45	46	47	48	49	50

Ask:

- Which numbers can evenly be divided by 2? (Underline these numbers.) All those with a last digit that is 0, 2, 4, 6, or 8.

- Which numbers can evenly be divided by 5? (Circle these numbers.) All those with a last digit that is 0 or 5.

- What numbers can evenly be divided by 10? (Place a checkmark next to these numbers.) All those with a last digit that is 0.

- Which numbers can evenly be divided by 3? (Hint: Look at both digits. Place a star next to these numbers.) All those where the sum of the digits can be divided evenly by 3.

Exercises

Use divisibility rules to determine whether the first number is divisible by the second number.

1. 447; 3 **yes**
2. 135; 6 **no**
3. 240; 4 **yes**
4. 419; 3 **no**
5. 831; 3 **yes**
6. 4,408; 4 **yes**
7. 7,110; 5 **yes**
8. 1,287; 9 **yes**
9. 2,984; 9 **no**
10. 7,026; 6 **yes**
11. 1,260; 10 **yes**
12. 8,903; 6 **no**

Determine whether each number is divisible by 2, 3, 4, 5, 6, 9, or 10.

13. 712 **2, 4**
14. 1,035 **3, 5, 9**
15. 8,901 **3, 9**
16. 462 **2, 3, 6**
17. 270 **2, 3, 5, 6, 9, 10**
18. 1,005 **3, 5**
19. 32,221 **none**
20. 8,340 **2, 3, 4, 5, 6, 10**
21. 920 **2, 4, 5, 10**
22. 50,319 **3, 9**
23. 64,042 **2**
24. 3,498 **2, 3, 6**

25. **MEASUREMENT** Jordan has 5,280 feet of rope. Can he cut the rope into 9-foot pieces and use all of the rope? Explain. **No; 5,280 is not divisible by 9.**

3 Practice

✓ Formative Assessment

Use Exercises 1-25 to determine whether students comprehend how to determine if a number is divisible by 2, 3, 4, 5, 6, 9, and 10.

4 Assess

Higher-Level Thinking

Challenge students to find a number that is divisible by 3, 6, 9, and 10. Sample answer: 270 Have students create other similar problems to share with one another.

Estimating with Decimals

Estimation can be used to provide quick answers when an exact answer is not necessary. It is also an excellent way to check whether your answer is reasonable. One method of estimating is to use rounding. Round numbers to any place value that makes estimation easier.

EXAMPLES Estimate by Rounding

Estimate by rounding.

1 23.485 − 9.757

$$
\begin{array}{ll}
23.485 \rightarrow & 23 \\
-9.757 \rightarrow & -10 \\
\hline
& 13
\end{array}
$$
Round to the nearest whole numbers.

The difference is about 13.

2 6.43 + 2.17 + 9.1 + 4.87

$$
\begin{array}{ll}
6.43 \rightarrow & 6 \\
2.17 \rightarrow & 2 \\
9.1 \rightarrow & 9 \\
+4.87 \rightarrow & +5 \\
\hline
& 22
\end{array}
$$
Round to the nearest whole numbers.

The sum is about 22.

Another way to estimate sums is to use **clustering**. This strategy is used when all the numbers are close to a common value.

EXAMPLE Estimate by Clustering

3 Estimate 9.775 + 9.862 + 9.475 + 9.724 by clustering.

All of the numbers are clustered around 10. There are four numbers.

So, the sum is about 4 × 10 or 40.

Exercises

Estimate by rounding. **1–15. Sample answers are given.**

1. 8.56 + 5.34 **9 + 5 = 14**
2. 34.84 − 17.69 **2. 35 − 18 = 17**
3. 6.8 + 2.4 **7 + 2 = 9**
4. 40.79 − 6.8 **41 − 7 = 34**
5. 6.9 + 5.2 **7 + 5 = 12**
6. 23.84 + 12.13 **24 + 12 = 36**
7. 34.3 − 18.9 **34 − 19 = 15**
8. 7.5 + 8.4 **8 + 8 = 16**
9. 65.48 − 9.3 **65 − 9 = 56**
10. 26.3 + 9.7 **26 + 10 = 36**
11. 33.21 − 8.23 **33 − 8 = 25**
12. 67.86 − 24.35 **68 − 24 = 44**
13. 8.99 − 2.6 **9 − 3 = 6**
14. 121.5 + 487.8 **14. 122 + 488 = 610**
15. 32.5 + 81.4 **33 + 81 = 114**

Estimate by clustering. **16–23. See Student Handbook Answer Appendix.**

16. 18.4 + 22.5 + 20.7
17. 56.9 + 63.2 + 59.3 + 61.1
18. 42.3 + 41.5 + 39.8 + 40.4
19. 77.8 + 75.6 + 81.2 + 79.9
20. 239.8 + 242.43 + 236.20 + 240.77
21. 9.9 + 10.0 + 10.3 + 11.1 + 9.8 + 11.2
22. 50.4 + 51.1 + 48.9 + 49.5 + 50.8
23. 100.5 + 97.8 + 101.6 + 100.2 + 99.3

Concepts and Skills Bank **735**

Concepts and Skills Bank

Concepts and Skills Bank

 Estimating with Decimals

1 Focus

Objective
- Use estimation methods to add and subtract decimals.

Vocabulary
- estimation
- clustering

Teaching Tip
You may choose to review these estimation methods with decimals prior to solving equations in Chapter 3.

2 Teach

Communication
Have students discuss real-world situations in which it may be necessary to estimate the sum or difference of decimals. Some examples may include determining an approximate amount spent while shopping or figuring the approximate difference in time of two runners in a race.

Scaffolding Questions
As you ask the following questions, write each number on the board.

Ask:
- What is 26.79 rounded to the nearest whole number? 27
- What is 13.48 rounded to the nearest whole number? 13
- What is the approximate sum of 26.79 and 13.48? 40
- What is the approximate difference of 26.79 and 13.48? 14

Concepts and Skills Bank

 Practice

Formative Assessment
Use Exercises 1-15 to determine whether students comprehend how to estimate using rounding. Use Exercises 16-23 to determine whether students comprehend how to estimate using clustering.

4 Assess

Ticket Out the Door
Write a problem such as 27.31 million + 5.9 million on the board. Have students write their estimates of the sum on a piece of a paper.

Concepts and Skills Bank **735**

Concepts and Skills Bank

3 Multiplying Decimals

1 Focus

Objective

- Multiply decimals.

Teaching Tip

You may choose to review multiplying decimals prior to solving equations in Chapter 3.

2 Teach

Hands-On Activity

Have students use a 10-by-10 grid to model the multiplication of 0.2 × 0.6. Tell students that the 10-by-10 grid represents 1. Students should shade 2 rows one color to represent 0.2. Then they should use another color to shade 6 columns to represent 0.6. The overlapping region represents the product, 0.12.

Scaffolding Questions

As you ask the following questions, write each number on the board.

Ask:

- What is the place value of the 5 in 0.5? 5 tenths

- What is the place value of the 3 in 0.23? 3 hundredths

- What is the place value of the 7 in 1.467? 7 thousandths

- How many decimal places are in 82.015? 3

- How many decimal places are in 660.4? 1

3 Practice

Formative Assessment

Use Exercises 1-38 to determine whether students comprehend how to multiply decimals.

736 Concepts and Skills Bank

---

3 Multiplying Decimals

To multiply decimals, multiply as with whole numbers. The product has the same number of decimal places as the sum of the decimal places of the factors. Use estimation to determine whether your answers are reasonable.

EXAMPLES **Multiply Decimals**

Multiply.

(1) **1.3 × 0.9**   **Estimate** $1 \times 1 = 1$

$$
\begin{array}{rl}
1.3 & \leftarrow \text{1 decimal place} \\
\times\ 0.9 & \leftarrow \text{1 decimal place} \\
\hline
1.17 & \leftarrow \text{2 decimal places}
\end{array}
$$

The product is reasonable.

(2) **0.054 × 1.6**   **Estimate** $0 \times 2 = 0$

$$
\begin{array}{rl}
0.054 & \leftarrow \text{3 decimal places} \\
\times\ 1.6 & \leftarrow \text{1 decimal place} \\
\hline
324 & \\
540 & \\
\hline
0.0864 &
\end{array}
$$
Annex a zero on the left so the answer has four decimal places. Compare to the estimate.

Exercises

Place the decimal point in each product. Add zeros if necessary.

1. $1.32 \times 4 = 528$ **5.28**
2. $0.07 \times 1.1 = 77$ **0.077**
3. $0.4 \times 0.7 = 28$ **0.28**
4. $1.9 \times 0.6 = 114$ **1.14**
5. $1.4 \times 0.09 = 126$ **0.126**
6. $5.48 \times 3.6 = 19728$ **19.728**
7. $4.5 \times 0.34 = 153$ **1.53**
8. $0.45 \times 0.02 = 9$ **0.009**
9. $150.2 \times 32.75 = 4919050$ **4,919.050**

Multiply.

10.
$$
\begin{array}{r}
0.2 \\
\times\ 6 \\
\hline
1.2
\end{array}
$$
11.
$$
\begin{array}{r}
0.3 \\
\times\ 0.9 \\
\hline
0.27
\end{array}
$$
12.
$$
\begin{array}{r}
0.45 \\
\times\ 0.12 \\
\hline
0.054
\end{array}
$$
13.
$$
\begin{array}{r}
0.0023 \\
\times\ 32 \\
\hline
0.0736
\end{array}
$$
14.
$$
\begin{array}{r}
1.5 \\
\times\ 2.7 \\
\hline
4.05
\end{array}
$$

15.
$$
\begin{array}{r}
10.1 \\
\times\ 9 \\
\hline
90.9
\end{array}
$$
16.
$$
\begin{array}{r}
2 \\
\times\ 0.3 \\
\hline
0.6
\end{array}
$$
17.
$$
\begin{array}{r}
6.78 \\
\times\ 1.3 \\
\hline
8.814
\end{array}
$$
18.
$$
\begin{array}{r}
200 \\
\times\ 0.004 \\
\hline
0.8
\end{array}
$$
19.
$$
\begin{array}{r}
0.0023 \\
\times\ 0.35 \\
\hline
0.000805
\end{array}
$$

20. 15.8×11 **173.8**
21. 88×2.5 **220**
22. 33×0.03 **0.99**
23. 36×0.46 **16.56**
24. 0.003×482 **1.446**
25. 1.88×1.11 **2.0868**
26. 0.6×2 **1.2**
27. 38.3×29.1 **1,114.53**
28. 0.7×18 **12.6**
29. 8×0.3 **2.4**
30. 12.2×12.4 **151.28**
31. 380×1.25 **475**
32. 42×0.17 **7.14**
33. 0.4×16 **6.4**
34. 0.23×0.2 **0.046**
35. 0.44×0.5 **0.22**
36. 0.44×55 **24.2**
37. 44×0.55 **24.2**

38. **JOBS** Antonia earns $10.75 per hour. What are her total weekly earnings if she works 34.5 hours? Round to the nearest cent. **$370.88**

---

4 Assess

Higher-Level Thinking

Ask students to determine whether the following statements are *sometimes, always,* or *never* true. Have students provide an example or counterexample with each.

- When two decimals, both less than 1, are multiplied, the product is less than 1. always; $0.5 \times 0.6 = 0.3$

- When two decimals, both greater than 1, are multiplied, the product is less than both of the factors. never; $1.5 \times 2.3 = 3.45$ and $3.45 > 1.5$ and $3.45 > 2.3$

4 **Powers of Ten**

You can use a pattern to mentally find the product of any number and a power of 10 that is greater than 1. Count the number of zeros in the power of 10 or use the exponent. Then move the decimal point that number of places to the right.

Decimal Power of 10	Product
19.7×10^1 (or 10)	$= 197$
19.7×10^2 (or 100)	$= 1,970$
19.7×10^3 (or 1,000)	$= 19,700$
19.7×10^4 (or 10,000)	$= 197,000$

EXAMPLES **Use Mental Math to Multiply**

Multiply mentally.

1 12.562×100

$12.562 \times 100 = 12.562$ Move the decimal point two places
          $= 1,256.2$ to the right, since 100 has two zeros.

2 0.59×10^4

$0.59 \times 10^4 = 0.5900$ Move the decimal point four places
          $= 5,900$ to the right, since the exponent is 4.

To mentally multiply by a power of ten that is less than 1, count the number of decimal places. Or, if the power is written as a fraction, use the exponent in the denominator. Then move the decimal point that number of places *to the left*.

Decimal Power of 10	Product
$19.7 \times 0.1 \left(\text{or } \frac{1}{10^1}\right)$	$= 1.97$
$19.7 \times 0.01 \left(\text{or } \frac{1}{10^2}\right)$	$= 0.197$
$19.7 \times 0.001 \left(\text{or } \frac{1}{10^3}\right)$	$= 0.0197$

EXAMPLES **Use Mental Math to Multiply**

Multiply mentally.

3 10.5×0.01

$10.5 \times 0.01 = 10.5$ Move the decimal point
          $= 0.105$ two places to the left.

4 $5,284 \times 0.00001$

$5,284 \times 0.00001 = 05284$ Move the decimal point
          $= 0.05284$ five places to the left.

Exercises

Multiply mentally.

1. 12.53×10 **125.3**
2. 4.6×10^3 **4,600**
3. 78.4×0.01 **0.784**
4. 0.05×100 **5**
5. 4.527×100 **452.7**
6. $2.78 \times 1,000$ **2,780**
7. 13.58×0.01 **0.1358**
8. 5.49×10^3 **5,490**
9. 0.1×0.8 **0.08**
10. 0.925×10 **9.25**
11. 99.44×10^2 **9,944**
12. 0.01×16 **0.16**
13. 1.32×10^3 **1,320**
14. $0.56 \times 10,000$ **5,600**
15. 1.4×0.001 **0.0014**
16. 11.23×10^5 **1,123,000**
17. 68.94×0.01 **0.6894**
18. 0.8×10^4 **8,000**
19. 28.1×0.01 **0.281**
20. 9.3×10^7 **93,000,000**
21. $625,799 \times 0.0001$ **62.5799**

Concepts and Skills Bank

 Concepts and Skills Bank

Concepts and Skills Bank

4 **Powers of Ten**

1 **Focus**

Objective

- Multiply decimals mentally by powers of ten.

Teaching Tip

You may choose to review multiplying decimals by powers of ten prior to changing metric units in Lesson 6-5.

2 **Teach**

Communication

Write 10^1, 10^2, 10^3, and 10^4 on the board. Ask students how the exponent is related to the number of zeros when each number is written in standard form. The number of zeros is the same as the exponent.

Scaffolding Questions

Remind students that exponents such as 4^5 are read *four to the fifth* power, because the base 4 is used as a factor 5 times. As you ask the following questions, write each exponent on the board without naming it.

Ask:

- How do you read...3^2? three squared, or three to the second power
- How do you read...2^6? two to the sixth power
- How do you read...10^3? ten to the third power, or ten cubed

3 **Practice**

 Formative Assessment

Use Exercises 1–21 to determine whether students comprehend how to multiply decimals by powers of ten.

4 **Assess**

Higher-Level Thinking

Write problems such as 0.0006×0.00001 or $86 \times 100,000$ on the board. Have students write the product of one of the problems on a piece of paper.

Concepts and Skills Bank

 Dividing Decimals

Focus

Objective

- Divide decimals.

Teaching Tip

You may choose to review dividing decimals prior to solving multiplication equations in Lesson 3-3.

2 Teach

Hands-On Activity

Have students work in groups of three or four. Give each group two straws, one that is 12 inches long and one that is 1.2 inches long. Have each group cut each straw into three pieces of equal length. Have each group describe their method to the class.

Scaffolding Questions

Ask:

- I have $10. How many drinks can I buy, if each drink costs $2.50? 4
- I have $3. How many hot dogs can I buy, if each hot dog costs $1.50? 2
- I have $2.40. How many apples can I buy, if each apple costs $0.80? 3

3 Practice

✔ Formative Assessment

Use Exercises 1-33 to determine whether students comprehend how to divide decimals.

4 Assess

Open-Ended Assessment

Ask each student to write a five-question quiz on dividing decimals. They should also provide a complete answer key.

738 Concepts and Skills Bank

Dividing Decimals

To divide two decimals, use the following steps.

- If necessary, change the divisor to a whole number by moving the decimal point to the right. You are multiplying the divisor by a power of ten.
- Move the decimal point in the dividend the same number of places to the right. You are multiplying the dividend by the same power of ten.
- Divide as with whole numbers.

EXAMPLES Divide Decimals

Divide.

(1) $25.8 \div 2$ **Estimate** $26 \div 2 = 13$

$$\begin{array}{r} 12.9 \\ 2\overline{)25.8} \\ -2 \\ \hline 5 \\ -4 \\ \hline 18 \\ -18 \\ \hline 0 \end{array}$$

The divisor, 2, is already a whole number, so you do not need to move the decimal point. Divide as with whole numbers. Then place the decimal directly above the decimal point in the dividend.

Compared to the estimate, the quotient, 12.9, is reasonable.

(2) $199.68 \div 9.6$ **Estimate** $200 \div 10 = 20$

$$\begin{array}{r} 20.8 \\ 9.6\overline{)199.68} \\ -192 \\ \hline 7\,68 \\ -7\,68 \\ \hline 0 \end{array}$$

Move each decimal point one place to the right.

Compare the answer to the estimate.

Exercises

Divide.

1. $0.3\overline{)9.81}$ **32.7**
2. $12\overline{)0.12}$ **0.01**
3. $3.2\overline{)5.76}$ **1.8**
4. $0.22\overline{)0.0132}$ **0.06**
5. $0.04\overline{)0.008}$ **0.2**
6. $3.18\overline{)0.636}$ **0.2**
7. $0.2\overline{)8.24}$ **41.2**
8. $82.3\overline{)823}$ **10**
9. $12.02\overline{)24.04}$ **2**
10. $0.5\overline{)85}$ **170**
11. $74.9\overline{)5.992}$ **0.08**
12. $19.2\overline{)4.416}$ **0.23**
13. $1.9\overline{)38.57}$ **20.3**
14. $13.8\overline{)131.1}$ **9.5**
15. $6.48\overline{)259.2}$ **40**
16. $812 \div 0.4$ **2,030**
17. $0.34 \div 0.2$ **1.7**
18. $14.4 \div 0.12$ **120**
19. $90.175 \div 2.5$ **36.07**
20. $39.95 \div 799$ **0.05**
21. $88.8 \div 444$ **0.2**
22. $613.8 \div 66$ **9.3**
23. $2,445.3 \div 33$ **74.1**
24. $20.24 \div 2.3$ **8.8**
25. $45 \div 0.09$ **500**
26. $2.475 \div 0.03$ **82.5**
27. $4.6848 \div 0.366$ **12.8**
28. $180 \div 0.36$ **500**
29. $97.812 \div 1.1$ **88.92**
30. $23 \div 0.023$ **1,000**
31. $1,680.042 \div 44.2$ **38.01**

32. **OLYMPICS** In the 2000 Olympics, Michael Johnson of the U.S. ran the 400-meter run in 43.84 seconds. To the nearest hundredth, find his speed in meters per second. **9.12 m/s**

33. **SCIENCE** It takes Pluto 247.69 Earth years to revolve once around the Sun. It takes Jupiter 11.86 Earth years to revolve once around the Sun. About how many times longer does it take Pluto than Jupiter to revolve once around the Sun? **about 21 times**

6 Converting Currencies

Countries around the world use different types of currency. By using an exchange rate table, proportions, and a calculator, you can convert from one type of currency to another.

Examine the following exchange rate table. All values in the same column are equivalent to each other.

Exchange Rates					
United States Dollars	1	2.020590	0.999950	1.407465	0.864699
British Pounds	0.494905	1	0.494880	0.696562	0.427944
Canadian Dollars	1.000050	2.020691	1	1.407536	0.864742
Euros	0.710497	1.435623	0.710461	1	0.614366
Australian Dollars	1.156472	2.336756	1.156414	1.627694	1

*Exchange rates as of September 21, 2007

You can use proportions to convert any amount of money from one currency to another.

EXAMPLE

Julian has 16 United States dollars to exchange for euros. How many euros will he receive?

U.S. dollar $\longrightarrow$
euros $\longrightarrow$ $\dfrac{1}{0.710497} = \dfrac{16}{x}$ Set up a proportion.

$1(x) = 16(0.710497)$ Cross multiply.

$x = 11.367952$ Simplify.

He will receive about 11.37 euros in exchange for 16 United States dollars.

Exercises

Fill in the blanks by converting each currency. Round to the nearest hundredth.

1. 26.41 Canadian dollars = __**18.76**__ euros
2. 46.82 British pounds = __**94.60**__ United States dollars
3. 4.7 Australian dollars = __**2.89**__ euros
4. 285.31 United States dollars = __**141.20**__ British pounds
5. 567.31 Canadian dollars = __**656.05**__ Australian dollars
6. 91.67 euros = __**129.03**__ Canadian dollars
7. 6 Australian dollars = __**2.57**__ British pounds
8. 37.24 euros = __**52.41**__ United States dollars
9. 64.28 British pounds = __**129.89**__ Canadian dollars
10. 74.28 United States dollars = __**85.90**__ Australian dollars

4 Assess

Open-Ended Assessment
Have students find the current exchange rate for the U.S. dollar and another country's currency. Then have them write and solve a problem that can be solved using the exchange rate.

Concepts and Skills Bank

6 Converting Currencies

1 Focus

Objective

- Use proportions to convert currencies.

Teaching Tip
You may choose to introduce converting currencies as an extension to solving proportions in Lesson 6-6.

2 Teach

Scaffolding Questions
Have students use the exchange rate table given on page 739.

Ask:
- What fraction would you use to convert British pounds to Australian dollars? $\dfrac{1}{2.336756}$ or $\dfrac{2.336756}{1}$
- What fraction would you use to convert euros to United States dollars? $\dfrac{1}{1.407465}$ or $\dfrac{1.407465}{1}$
- When setting up a proportion to convert currency rates, what must be true of the numerators and denominators of the fractions? Sample answer: Both numerators should represent the same currency, and both denominators should represent the same currency.

3 Practice

Formative Assessment

Use Exercises 1-10 to determine whether students comprehend how to convert currencies.

Concepts and Skills Bank

 7 Solving Inequalities

1 Focus

Objective

- Solve and graph inequalities.

Vocabulary

- inequalities

Teaching Tip

You may choose to introduce inequalities and solving inequalities as an extension to solving equations in Lessons 3-2, 3-3, and 3-5.

2 Teach

Reading Mathematics

Ask students to read the following problems and to indicate whether they are true or false.

$6 > 2$ true
$3(6) > 3(2)$ true
$7 \le 3$ false
$7 \le 3 + 4$ true

Scaffolding Questions

Write the inequality $4x \ge 20$ on the board.

Ask:

- What does the sentence mean in words? The product of 4 and a number x is greater than or equal to 20.

- Does the value 6 make this inequality true? Explain. Yes; $4 \times 6 = 24$, which is greater than 20.

- Does the value −6 make this inequality true? Explain. No; $4 \times (-6) = -24$, which is not greater than or equal to 20.

- Does the value 5 make this inequality true? Explain. Yes; $4 \times 5 = 20$, which is equal to 20.

---

7 Solving Inequalities

You have already solved one- and two-step equations. You can apply what you learned about equations to solve one- and two-step inequalities. **Inequalities** are sentences that compare quantities that are not equal. The symbols used are $<, >, \le, \ge,$ and $\ne$.

Inequality Symbols
Key Concept

Symbols	<	>	≤	≥	≠
Words	• less than • fewer than	• greater than • more than	• less than or equal to • no more than • at most	• greater than or equal to • no less than • at least	• not equal to

EXAMPLE Solve a One-Step Inequality

1 Solve $s + \frac{3}{4} \le 1\frac{1}{4}$.

$$s + \frac{3}{4} \le 1\frac{1}{4} \qquad \text{Write the inequality.}$$

$$s + \frac{3}{4} - \frac{3}{4} \le 1\frac{1}{4} - \frac{3}{4} \qquad \text{Subtract } \frac{3}{4} \text{ from each side.}$$

$$s + \frac{3}{4} - \frac{3}{4} \le \frac{5}{4} - \frac{3}{4} \qquad \text{Change } 1\frac{1}{4} \text{ to an improper fraction, } \frac{5}{4}.$$

$$s \le \frac{2}{4} \text{ or } \frac{1}{2} \qquad \text{Subtract.}$$

The solution is $s \le \frac{1}{2}$.

EXAMPLE Solve a Two-Step Inequality

2 Solve $7p + 21 \le 49$.

$$7p + 21 \le 49 \qquad \text{Write the inequality.}$$

$$7p + 21 - 21 \le 49 - 21 \qquad \text{Subtract 21 from each side.}$$

$$7p \le 28 \qquad \text{Simplify.}$$

$$p \le \frac{28}{7} \qquad \text{Divide each side by 7.}$$

$$p \le 4 \qquad \text{Simplify.}$$

The solution is $p \le 4$.

Unlike the solution to an equation, the solution $p \le 4$ reflects a set of numbers. One way to show this is in a number line graph.

---

3 Practice

✓ Formative Assessment

Use Exercises 1-15 to determine whether students comprehend how to solve and graph an inequality.

4 Assess

Yesterday's News

Have students write about how the skills they learned in Chapter 3 on solving equations helped them in learning about solving inequalities.

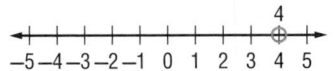

EXAMPLE Graph an Inequality

3 Graph $p \leq 4$.

Draw a number line and label the integers. Draw a circle at 4. The circle on the graph shows that the numbers up to 4 but not including 4 are included in the solution.

number line from -5 to 5 with open circle at 4, labeled 4

When $\geq$ or $\leq$ is used, the circle on the graph is filled in to show that the number is included in the solution.

Test numbers on either side of 4 to determine the direction of the graph. Draw an arrow pointing in the direction of 2. Use other numbers in this set to check the solution.

p	$7p + 21 \leq 49$	Solution
5	$7 \times 5 + 21 \overset{?}{\leq} 49$	
	$35 + 21 \overset{?}{\leq} 49$	No
	$56 \nleq 49$	
3	$7 \times 3 + 21 \overset{?}{\leq} 49$	
	$21 + 21 \leq 49$	Yes
	$42 \leq 49$	

Exercises

Solve each inequality. Graph each solution on a number line. Round to the nearest tenth if necessary. **1–12. See Student Handbook Answer Appendix.**

1. $2x \geq -14$

2. $30n < 160$

3. $y + 51 \leq 85$

4. $2.5 + 1.5a \leq 7.5$

5. $8.1h + 6.3 \geq 22.5$

6. $0.75g + 23 < 34$

7. $2m + 6.2 \geq 15.6$

8. $3.3(f + 2) > 36.3$

9. $\frac{1}{2}(p + 8) \geq 12$

10. $\frac{1}{3}r - \frac{2}{3} \geq 1$

11. $2n - \frac{1}{5} < 9\frac{4}{5}$

12. $\frac{1}{14}d + \frac{3}{14} \leq \frac{2}{7}$

13. **SAVINGS** Trisha wants to save up to buy a new cell phone that costs less than $150. She already has $75 saved. She also makes $10 a week doing her chores. Write and solve an inequality to find the number of weeks worked that would allow Trisha to buy a new cell phone. $10w + 75 \geq 150; w \geq 7.5$

14. **TEXT MESSAGING** Joshua spends $0.25 every time he sends a text message through his cell phone. Write and solve an inequality that shows the number of text messages he can send with $3.00. $0.25t \leq 3; t \leq 12$

15. **SPORTS** Allyson spends $7\frac{1}{2}$ hours playing sports each week. Softball takes a total of $3\frac{1}{4}$ hours each week. If she plays sports 4 days a week, write and solve an inequality that shows the average amount of time per day she spends on other sports. $4h + 3\frac{1}{4} \geq 7\frac{1}{2}; h \geq 1\frac{1}{16}$

Concepts and Skills Bank (tab)

Concepts and Skills Bank (tab)

Concepts and Skills Bank

(8) Monomials and Polynomials

1 Focus

Objective

- Classify and simplify polynomials.

Vocabulary

- polynomial
- monomial

Teaching Tip

You may choose to introduce monomials and polynomials as an extension to linear equations and functions in Chapter 3.

2 Teach

Scaffolding Questions

Tell students that one box contains 4 packages of pencils and 3 packages of highlighters and a second box contains 6 packages of pencils and 5 packages of highlighters.

Ask:

- How many packages of pencils are there altogether? How many packages of highlighters are there altogether? 10 packages of pencils; 8 packages of highlighters

- If you let p represent the number of pencils in each package and h represent the number of highlighters in each package, what expression can you write for the number of pencils and highlighters in the first box? the second box? $4p + 3h$; $6p + 5h$

- What expression can you write to represent the total number of pencils and the total number of highlighters? $10p + 8h$

---

(8) Monomials and Polynomials

A **polynominal** is an algebraic expression that includes real numbers and variables. In a polynomial, there are no terms with variables in the denominator and no terms with variables under a radical sign.

polynomial: $2x^2 - 3x + 4$ not a polynomial: $x^2 - \frac{8}{x}$

A specific kind of polynomial is a **monomial.** Since the prefix *mono-* means one, a monomial is a polynomial that contains only one term, like $7x$. Monomials that contain the same variables to the same power are *like terms*.

EXAMPLES Classify Polynomials

Determine whether each expression is a polynomial. Explain your reasoning. If it is a polynomial, state the number of terms in the expression.

(1) $3x^3 + 8x + 7$

This is a polynomial because it is the sum of three monomials. There are three terms.

(2) $m - \frac{1}{m}$

This is *not* a polynomial because $\frac{1}{m}$ has a variable in the denominator.

EXAMPLE Simplify Polynomials

(3) Find $8x + 7 + 3x + 2$.

$8x + 7 + 3x + 2$	Write the expression.
$= (8x + 3x) + (7 + 2)$	Group like terms.
$= 11x + 9$	Simplify by combining like terms.

Exercises

Determine whether each expression is a polynomial. Explain your reasoning. If it is a polynomial, state the number of terms in the expression. **1–18. See Student Handbook Answer Appendix.**

1. $\frac{t^2}{5}$ 2. $5 + \sqrt{b}$ 3. $p^4 + 5p - 2$ 4. $-5y^4z$

5. $4a^2 - 2a + \sqrt{90}$ 6. $\frac{6}{n^4} + \frac{n^2}{3} - 5$ 7. $-8c^5d^3 - 4cd + 3d$ 8. $15r^2s^3 - 9r + \sqrt{s}$

Simplify each expression.

9. $12r + 8s + 4r + s$ 10. $4a + 5b + 10 + 6a$ 11. $7f + 8g + 2f + g$

12. $16x + 12y + 21y + 12x$ 13. $5t + 7 + u + 3$ 14. $13c + 10d + 4c + 7d$

15. $4j + 6 + 9j + 3$ 16. $11p + 12q + 4p + 9q$ 17. $15mn + 12m + 4n + 7mn$

18. **GEOMETRY** The sides of a hexagon measure $3x$, $7y$, $6y$, $8x$, y, and $4x$. Write the perimeter of the figure in simplest form.

3 Practice

Formative Assessment

Use Exercises 1-8 to determine whether students comprehend how to classify polynomials.

Use Exercises 9-18 to determine whether students comprehend how to simplify polynomials.

4 Assess

Open-Ended Assessment

Challenge students to write a polynomial with four terms that simplifies to $5x + 11y$.

9 Rotations

A **rotation** occurs when a figure is rotated around a point. A rotation does not change the size or shape of the figure. The rotations shown below are clockwise around the origin.

90° Rotation

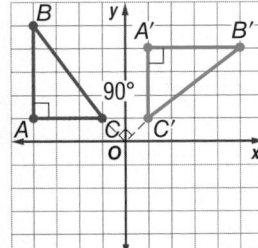

180° Rotation

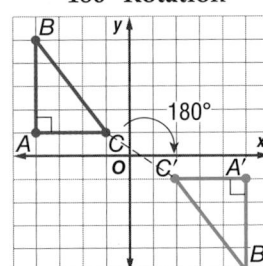

270° Rotation

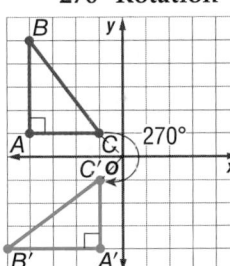

EXAMPLE Rotate a Figure About the Origin

① Triangle *ABC* has vertices *A*(−4, 4), *B*(−1, 2), and *C*(−3, 1). Graph the figure and its rotated image after a clockwise rotation of 90° about the origin. Then give the coordinates of the vertices for △*A′B′C′*.

STEP 1 Graph △*ABC* on a coordinate plane.

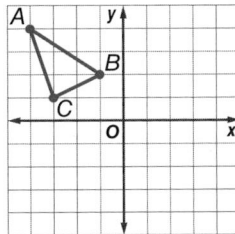

STEP 2 Sketch segment $\overline{BO}$ connecting point *B* to the origin. Sketch another segment, $\overline{BO}$ so that the angle between point *B*, *O*, and *B′* measures 90° and the segment is congruent to $\overline{BO}$.

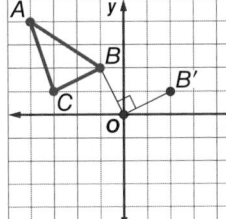

STEP 3 Repeat Step 2 for points *A* and *C*. Then connect the vertices to form △*A′B′C′*.

So, the coordinates of the vertices of △*A′B′C′* are *A′*(4, 4), *B′*(2, 1), and *C′*(1, 3).

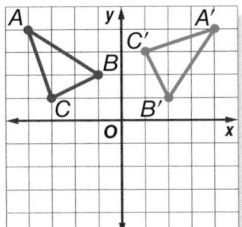

Concepts and Skills Bank **743**

---

3 Practice

 Formative Assessment

Use Exercises 1-12 to determine whether students comprehend how to graph rotations.

4 Assess

Yesterday's News

Have students write about how the skills they learned in Lessons 10-9 and 10-10 on transformations helped them in graphing rotations.

Concepts and Skills Bank

9 Rotations

1 Focus

Objective

• Graph rotations on a coordinate plane.

Vocabulary

• rotation

Teaching Tip

You may choose to introduce rotations as an extension to the study of transformations in Lessons 10-9 and 10-10.

2 Teach

Communication

Draw the following tessellations on the board. Have students discuss how rotations were used in creating these tessellations.

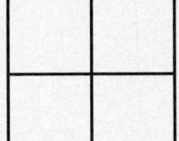 

Scaffolding Questions

Draw the following figure on the board.

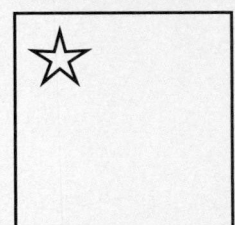

Ask:

• In which corner will the star be after a 90° rotation? upper-right corner

• In which corner will the star be after a 270° rotation? lower-left corner

• What degree of rotation will result in the star being in the lower-right corner of the figure? 180°

Concepts and Skills Bank **743**

② Triangle *LMN* has vertices *L*(5, 4), *M*(5, 7), and *N*(8, 7). Graph the figure and its rotated image after a counterclockwise rotation of 180° about vertex *L*. Then give the coordinates of the vertices for △*L′M′N′*.

 STEP 1 Graph the original triangle.   **STEP 2** Graph the rotated image.

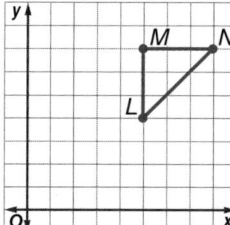   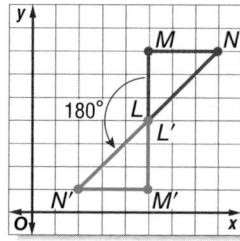

So, the coordinates of the vertices of △*L′M′N′* are *L′*(5, 4), *M′*(5, 1), and *N′*(2, 1).

Exercises 1–6. See Student Handbook Answer Appendix.

Graph △*XYZ* and its rotated image after each rotation. Then give the coordinates of the vertices for △*X′Y′Z′*.

1. 180° clockwise about the origin

2. 270° counterclockwise about vertex *X*

3. 90° counterclockwise about the origin

4. 270° clockwise about vertex *Y*

5. 180° counterclockwise about vertex *Z*

6. 90° clockwise about the origin

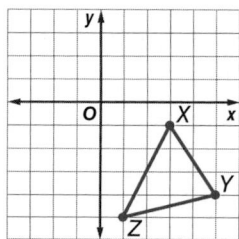

Graph quadrilateral *ABCD* and its rotated image after each rotation. Then give the coordinates of the vertices for quadrilateral *A′B′C′D′*. 7–12. See Student Handbook Answer Appendix.

7. 90° counterclockwise about the origin

8. 90° clockwise about vertex *A*

9. 180° counterclockwise about vertex *D*

10. 270° clockwise about the origin

11. 90° clockwise about the origin

12. 180° clockwise about vertex *B*

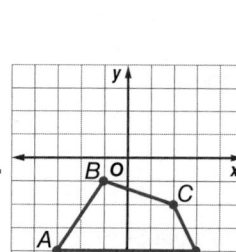

Concepts and Skills Bank

10 Cross Sections of Three-Dimensional Figures

The intersection of a solid and a plane is called a **cross section** of the solid.

Inequality Symbols

Key Concept

Vertical Slice	Angled Slice	Horizontal Slice
The cross section is a rectangle.	The cross section is an oval.	The cross section is a circle.

EXAMPLE — Describe Cross Sections

1. Draw and describe the shape resulting from a vertical, angled, and horizontal cross section of a square pyramid.

Slice	Drawing	Description
Vertical		The cross section is a triangle.
Angled		The cross section is a trapezoid.
Horizontal		The cross section is a square.

Concepts and Skills Bank

10 Cross Sections of Three-Dimensional Figures

1 Focus

Objective

- Draw and describe cross sections of three-dimensional figures.

Vocabulary

- cross section

Teaching Tip

You may choose to introduce cross sections of three-dimensional figures as an extension to the study of three-dimensional figures in Lessons 11-7 and 11-8.

2 Teach

Hands-On Activity

Have students work in groups of three. Give each group three pieces of construction paper. Challenge students to arrange the paper so that one piece is a cross section and the other two pieces form a three-dimensional figure. Have students outline where the three-dimensional figure meets the cross section. Then have students show the class their figure and the shape formed by the cross section.

Scaffolding Questions

Show students a soda can, a tissue box, and a ball.

Ask:

- Which object(s) could result in a circle when a cross section is taken? soda can and ball

- Which object(s) could result in a rectangle when a cross section is taken? tissue box and soda can

- Which object(s) could result in an oval when a cross section is taken? soda can and ball

3 Practice

Formative Assessment

Use Exercises 1-13 to determine whether students comprehend how to draw and describe a cross section of a three-dimensional figure.

4 Assess

Open-Ended Assessment

Challenge students to draw a triangular prism and to describe the different cross sections of the figure.

Exercises 1–13. See Student Handbook Answer Appendix.

Draw and describe the shape resulting from each cross section.

1. cone

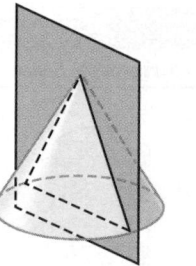

2. triangular pyramid

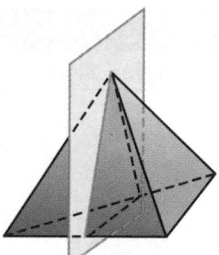

3. rectangular prism

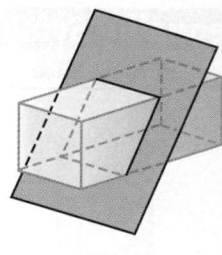

4. cone

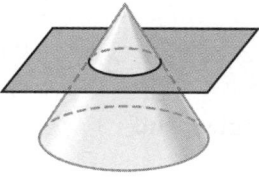

5. rectangular prism

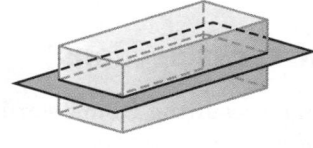

6. cone

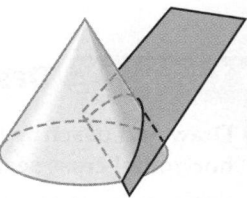

7. triangular pyramid

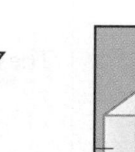

8. rectangular prism

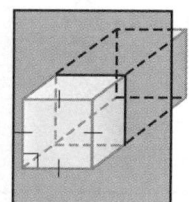

9. triangular prism

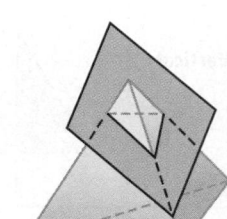

SPORTS For Exercises 10 and 11, use the following information.

A standard basketball is shaped like a sphere.

10. Draw a basketball with a vertical, angled, and horizontal slice.

11. Draw and describe the cross section made by each slice.

SPORTS For Exercises 12 and 13, use the following information.

A soup can is shaped like a cylinder.

12. Draw a soup can with a vertical, angled, and horizontal slice.

13. Draw and describe the cross section made by each slice.

Converting Between Measurement Systems

Dimensional analysis is the process of including units of measurement as factors when you compute. You can use ratios to convert measurements between the two common measurement systems. For example, since 1 in. ≈ 2.54 cm, the ratio $\frac{1 \text{ in.}}{2.54 \text{ cm}} \approx 1$. So, you can multiply a measurement by this ratio without changing its value.

Conversion Factors for Length	
1 in. ≈ 2.54 cm	1 yd ≈ 0.914 m
1 ft ≈ 0.305 m	1 mi ≈ 1.609 km
Conversion Factors for Capacity and Mass or Weight	
1 fl oz ≈ 29.574 mL	1 qt ≈ 0.946 L
1 pt ≈ 0.473 L	1 gal ≈ 3.785 L
1 oz ≈ 28.35 g	1 lb ≈ 0.454 kg

EXAMPLES **Convert Between Systems**

1 **15 feet to meters**

Use 1 ft ≈ 0.305 meters.

$15 \text{ ft} \approx 15 \text{ ft} \cdot \frac{0.305 \text{ m}}{1 \text{ ft}}$ Since 1 ft ≈ 0.305 m, multiply by $\frac{0.305 \text{ m}}{1 \text{ ft}}$.

$\approx 15 \cancel{\text{ ft}} \cdot \frac{0.305 \text{ m}}{1 \cancel{\text{ ft}}}$ Divide out common units, leaving the desired unit, meter.

$\approx 15 \text{ ft} \cdot 0.305$ or 4.58 m   Multiply.

So, 15 feet is approximately 4.58 meters.

2 **22 kilograms to pounds.**

Use 1 lb ≈ 0.454 kg.

$22 \text{ kg} \approx 22 \text{ kg} \cdot \frac{1 \text{ lb}}{0.454 \text{ kg}}$ Since 1 qt ≈ 0.946 L, multiply by $\frac{1 \text{ lb}}{0.454 \text{ kg}}$.

$\approx 22 \cancel{\text{ kg}} \cdot \frac{1 \text{ lb}}{0.454 \cancel{\text{ kg}}}$ Divide out common units, leaving the desired unit, pound.

$\approx \frac{22}{0.454}$ or 48.46 pounds.   Divide.

So, 22 kilograms is approximately 48.46 pounds.

Exercises 1–16. See Student Handbook Answer Appendix.

Complete each conversion. Round to the nearest hundredth.

1. 17 in. ≈ ■ cm
2. 13 L ≈ ■ gal
3. 15 oz ≈ ■ g
4. 12 m ≈ ■ ft
5. 10 L ≈ ■ pt
6. 150 cm ≈ ■ in.
7. 18 fl oz ≈ ■ mL
8. 15 km ≈ ■ mi
9. 8 yd ≈ ■ m
10. 25 mi ≈ ■ km
11. 200 mL ≈ ■ fl oz
12. 12 L ≈ ■ qt
13. 32 ft ≈ ■ m
14. 12 gal ≈ ■ L
15. 575 g ≈ ■ oz
16. 55 lb ≈ ■ kg

17. **ANIMALS** A peregrine falcon can reach a speed of 250 kilometers per hour. How many miles is this per hour? **155.38 miles per hour**

18. **FOOD** The heaviest apple ever picked weighed about 4 pounds. About how many kilograms did the apple weigh? **1.82 kg**

Concepts and Skills Bank **747**

(side tab) Concepts and Skills Bank

Concepts and Skills Bank

 Converting Between Measurement Systems

1 Focus

Objective

- Use dimensional analysis to convert units of measurement between the metric system and customary system.

Vocabulary

- dimensional analysis

Teaching Tip

You may choose to introduce converting units of measurement between systems as an extension to converting measurements within a system in Lessons 6-4 and 6-5.

2 Teach

Scaffolding Questions

Have students measure the width of your classroom to the nearest foot. Write this measurement on the board.

Ask:

- What ratio can we use to convert this measurement to meters? $\frac{0.305 \text{ m}}{1 \text{ ft}}$
- What units cancel out when converting the measurement? feet
- About how many meters wide is our classroom? See students' work.
- How can we verify our calculation? Use a meter stick to measure the width of the classroom.

(side tab) Concepts and Skills Bank

---

3 Practice

 Formative Assessment

Use Exercises 1-18 to determine whether students comprehend how to use dimensional analysis to convert units of measurement between the metric system and customary system.

4 Assess

Open-Ended Assessment

Ask students to write a five-question quiz on converting between measurement systems. They should also provide a complete answer key.

Concepts and Skills Bank

12 Volume and Surface Area of Composite Figures

1 Focus

Objective

- Find the volume and surface area of composite figures.

Teaching Tip

You may choose to introduce finding the volume and surface area of composite figures as an extension to finding the volume and surface area of three-dimensional figures in Chapter 11.

2 Teach

Communication

Have students look at the composite figures on pages 748 and 749. Ask students to describe possible real-world objects that these figures could represent. Answers may include a house, building blocks, a washer, or a desk.

Scaffolding Questions

Draw the figure below on the chalkboard.

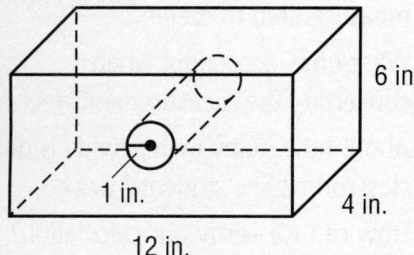

Ask:
- What two figures do you notice in the drawing? a rectangular prism and a cylinder
- What formulas would you use to find the volume of the figure? $V = \ell wh$ and $V = \pi r^2 h$
- What is the volume of the rectangular prism? 288 in^3

---

12 Volume and Surface Area of Composite Figures

Volume is the measure of space occupied by a three-dimensional figure. The volume of a composite figure can be found by separating the figure into solids whose volumes you know how to find.

EXAMPLE Find the Volume of a Composite Figure

1 Find the volume of the toy house shown at the right.

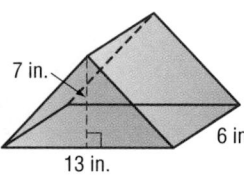

The toy house is made of one rectangular prism and one triangular prism. Find the volume of each prism.

Rectangular Prism

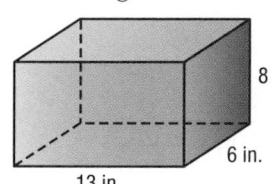

Triangular Prism

$V = Bh$
$V = (13 \cdot 6)\ 8$ or 624

$V = Bh$
$V = \left(\frac{1}{2} \cdot 13 \cdot 7\right) 6$ or 273

The volume of the toy house is $624 + 273$ or 897 cubic inches.

EXAMPLE Find the Surface Area of a Composite Figure

2 Max is painting the mailbox shown. What is the area of the surface that is to be painted? Round to the nearest tenth.

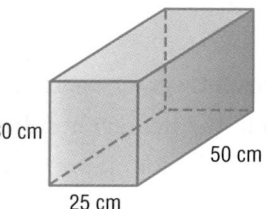

The mailbox is made of one half of one cylinder and one rectangular prism.

Cylinder

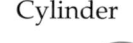
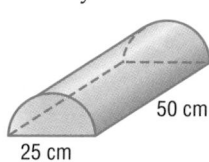

Rectangular Prism

There is only one base needed. The top is covered by the half cylinder.

$S = \dfrac{2\pi r^2 + 2\pi rh}{2}$

$S = \dfrac{2\pi(12.5)^2 + 2\pi(12.5)(50)}{2}$

$S \approx 2{,}454.4$

$S = 2\ell w + \ell h + 2wh$

$S = 2 \cdot 25 \cdot 30 \cdot 25 \cdot 50 + 2 \cdot 30 \cdot 50$

$S = 5{,}750$

So, the area to be painted is equal to $2{,}454.4 + 5{,}750$ or $8{,}204.4$ square centimeters.

- What is the volume of the cylinder to the nearest tenth? 12.6 in^3
- What is the volume of the composite figure to the nearest tenth? 275.4 in^3

Exercises

Find the volume of each figure. Round to the nearest tenth if necessary.

1.
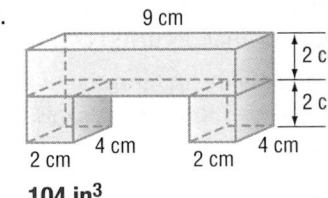
2 in.
6 in.
8 in.
4 in.
224 in³

2.

9 cm
2 cm
2 cm
2 cm   4 cm   2 cm   4 cm
104 in³

3.
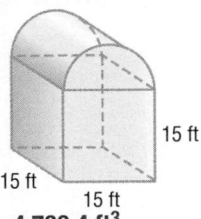
15 ft
15 ft
15 ft
4,700.4 ft³

4.
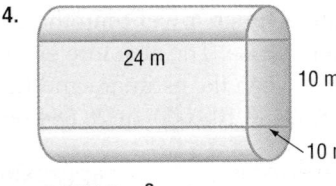
24 m
10 m
10 m
4,285.0 m³

Find the surface area of each figure. Round to the nearest tenth if necessary.

5.
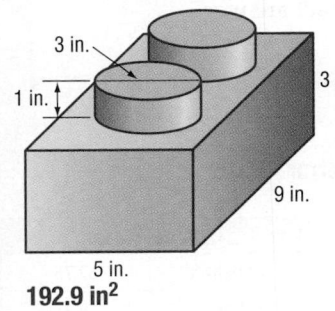
3 in.
1 in.
3 in.
9 in.
5 in.
192.9 in²

6.
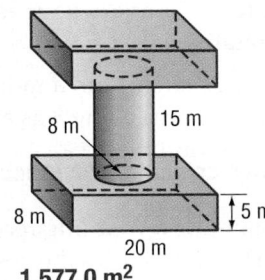
8 m
15 m
8 m
5 m
20 m
1,577.0 m²

7.
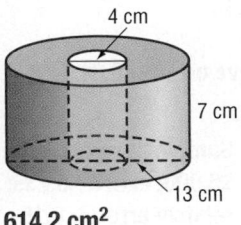
4 cm
7 cm
13 cm
614.2 cm²

8.
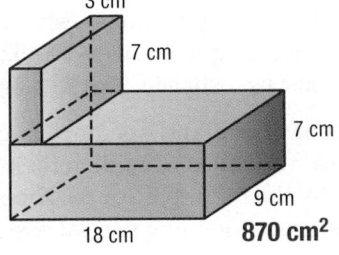
3 cm
7 cm
7 cm
9 cm
18 cm
870 cm²

Concepts and Skills Bank **749**

3 Practice

Formative Assessment

Use Exercises 1-4 to determine whether students comprehend how to find the volume of composite figures.

Use Exercises 5-8 to determine whether students comprehend how to find the surface area of composite figures.

4 Assess

Yesterday's News
Have students write about how the skills they learned in Chapter 11 on finding the volume and surface area of three-dimensional figures helped them in finding the volume and surface area of composite figures.

Concepts and Skills Bank

Concepts and Skills Bank

 **Relative Error and Magnitude**

1 Focus

Objective

- Calculate the relative error of problems by finding an estimated answer and an exact answer.

Vocabulary

- absolute error
- relative error

Teaching Tip

You may choose to introduce relative error and magnitude as an extension to Looking Ahead Lesson 1 on scientific notation. You may point out how relative error can be useful when estimating with such large numbers, such as those written in scientific notation.

2 Teach

Scaffolding Questions

Copy the following table on the board.

World's Top 5 Tallest Mountains	
Mt. Everest	29,035 ft
Qogir (K2)	28,250 ft
Kangchenjunga	28,169 ft
Lhotse	27,920 ft
Makalu I	27,765 ft

Ask:

- About how much taller is Mt. Everest than Makalu I? 1,000 ft
- What is the exact difference in the height of Mt. Everest and Makalu I? 1,270 ft
- What is the absolute error of this calculation? 270 ft
- What is the relative error of this calculation as a percent? 21%

Concepts and Skills Bank

13 Relative Error and Magnitude

Significant error can occur when estimating or making predictions using large numbers. By comparing estimates to exact calculations, you can identify the amount of error that occurred as a result of rounding or estimating.

The **absolute error** is the magnitude of the difference between the estimate and the actual answer. **Relative error** is the absolute error in estimating a quantity divided by the magnitude of the exact value.

EXAMPLE

Estimate the population increase for New York City from 2003 to 2006. Then find the exact population increase and compare.

New York City	
Year	Population
2006	8,214,426
2005	8,143,197
2004	8,104,079
2003	8,085,742

Estimate: $8,200,000 - 8,100,000 = 100,000$

Exact: $8,214,426 - 8,085,742 = 128,684$

The estimate is much lower than the exact population increase. The absolute error is the difference between the estimate and the exact answer: $128,684 - 100,000$, or 28,684 people.

The relative error is $\frac{28,684}{128,684}$ or approximately 0.22 or 22%.

Exercises

Solve each problem. Compare your estimate to the exact answer by finding the relative error.

1. Find the area of a circle with a radius of 14 centimeters. First calculate the area using 3 as an estimate for π. Then use 3.14 to find the area.
   Sample answer: estimate: 126; exact: 138.03; relative error ≈ 0.09

2. Jennifer is planning a wedding reception for 300 guests. The table shows the cost per person for each part of the meal. She needs to know the total approximate cost of the food for the reception.
   Sample answer: estimate: $4,500; exact: $4,185; relative error ≈ 0.07

Cost (per person)	
Appetizer	$2.75
Entrée	$6.75
Beverage	$1.55
Cake	$2.90

3. Antonio is driving 2,452 miles from Albany, New York, to Los Angeles, California. He drives about 68 miles per hour for most of the trip. Antonio estimates how long his trip will take by rounding 68 to 70 and 2,452 to 2,500.
   Sample answer: estimate: 35 h 43 min; exact: 36 h 4 min; relative error ≈ 0.01

4. As part of their grand opening, a new grocery store decides to give a free gallon of milk to their first 1,500 customers. Normally the milk sells for $3.49 per gallon. How much will the grand-opening special cost the grocery store?
   Sample answer: estimate: $6,000; exact: $5,235; relative error ≈ 0.15

---

3 Practice

 Formative Assessment

Use Exercises 1-4 to determine whether students comprehend how to calculate the relative error of a problem.

4 Assess

Higher-Level Thinking

Have students search through a newspaper or magazine to find a table or graphic that uses estimations. Have students describe how relative error could possibly impact the results shown in the table or graphic.

Extra Practice

Page 670, Extra Practice, (Lesson 1-8)

13. Distributive   **14.** Commutative ($\times$)

15. Associative ($+$)   **16.** Commutative ($+$)

17. Distributive   **18.** Identity ($\times$)

19. Associative ($\times$)   **20.** Associative ($+$)

21. Associative ($\times$)   **22.** Identity ($+$)

23. Commutative ($\times$)   **24.** Commutative ($+$)

Page 670, Extra Practice, (Lesson 1-9)

1. 4 is added to each term; 21, 25, 29

2. 2 is added to each term; 11, 13, 15

3. 5 is added to each term; 30, 35, 40

4. 3 is added to each term; 102, 105, 108

5. 6 is added to each term; 32, 38, 44

6. 0.9 is added to each term; 8.1, 9.0, 9.9

7. 0.1 is added to each term; 0.6, 0.7, 0.8

8. 1.1 is added to each term; 6.7, 7.8, 8.9

9. 0.2 is added to each term; 9.7, 9.9, 10.1

10. 8 is added to each term; 35, 43, 51

11. 25 is added to each term; 450, 475, 500

12. 15 is added to each term; 680, 695, 710

13. 5 is added to each term; 22, 27, 32

14. 7 is added to each term; 38, 45, 52

15. 7 is added to each term; 28, 35, 42

16. 6 is added to each term; 25, 31, 37

17. 6 is added to each term; 119, 125, 131

18. 81 is added to each term; 333, 414, 495

19. 0.2 is added to each term; 3.4, 3.6, 3.8

20. 0.5 is added to each term; 6.1, 6.6, 7.1

21. 1.1 is added to each term; 11.0, 12.1, 13.2

22. 1.5 is added to each term; 25.5, 27, 28.5

23. 0.3 is added to each term; 15.7, 16.0, 16.3

24. 0.3 is added to each term; 1.3, 1.6, 1.9

Page 671, Extra Practice, (Lesson 2-1)

7.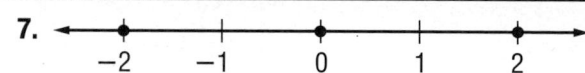

8.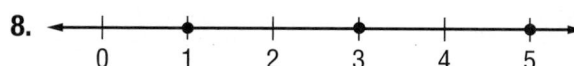

9.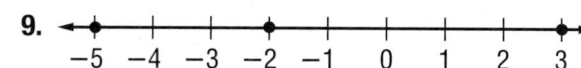

10.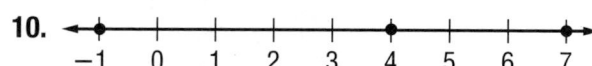

Page 672, Extra Practice, (Lesson 2-3)

13–24.

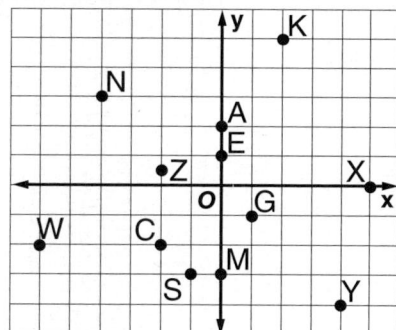

Page 674, Extra Practice, (Lesson 3-1)

1. $p - 6$ **2.** $20 + c$

3. $\dfrac{a}{b}$ **4.** $a + 6$

5. $x + 12$ **6.** $\dfrac{\$1,000}{z}$

7. $\dfrac{y}{3}$ **8.** $7m$

9. $f - 9$ **10.** $26 - q$

11. $19 - z$ **12.** $x - 2$

13. $3x - 4 = 17$ **14.** $n + 6 = 5$

15. $20 + 2n = -30$ **16.** $\dfrac{n}{-2} = -42$

17. $4 + 3n = 18$ **18.** $5n - 15 = 92$

19. $8n + 12 = 36$ **20.** $n - 24 = -30$

Page 675, Extra Practice, (Lesson 3-4)

3. Greg rented 9 videos, Paloma rented 5, Grace rented 1, and Jack rented 10.

Page 675, Extra Practice, (Lesson 3-6)

6. 13.5 km; 7.875 km^2 **8.** 50 m; 96.1875 m^2

Page 676, Extra Practice, (Lesson 3-7)

1.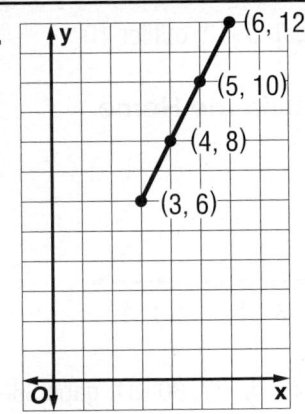
(6, 12)
(5, 10)
(4, 8)
(3, 6)

7.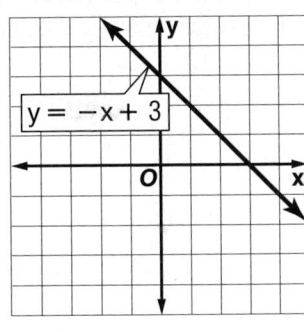
$y = -x + 3$

2.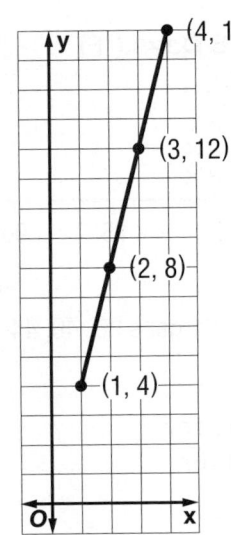
(4, 16)
(3, 12)
(2, 8)
(1, 4)

8.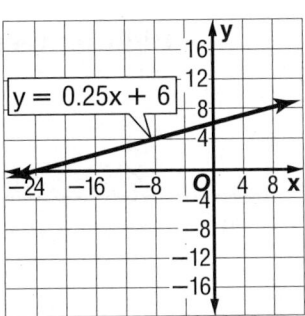
$y = 0.25x + 6$

3.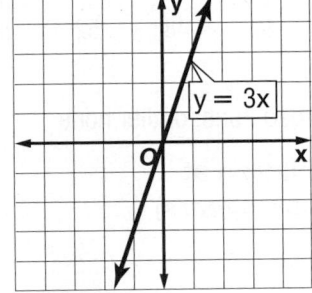
$y = 3x$

9.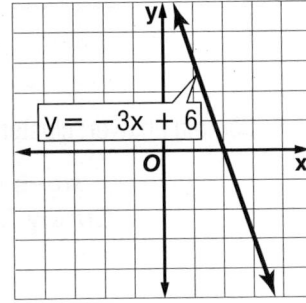
$y = -3x + 6$

4.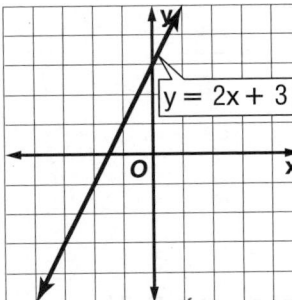
$y = 2x + 3$

10.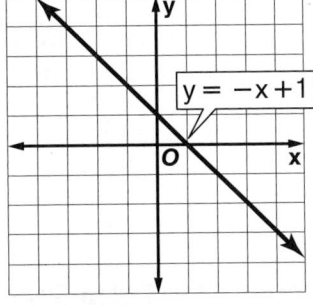
$y = -x + 1$

5.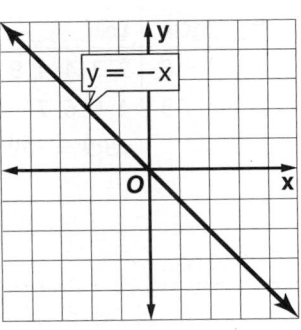
$y = -x$

11.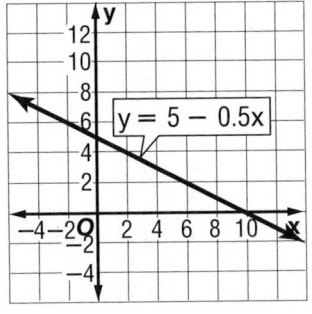
$y = 5 - 0.5x$

6.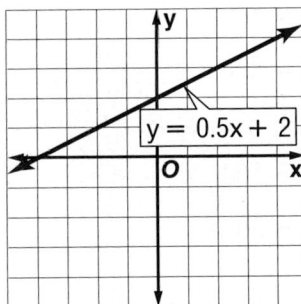
$y = 0.5x + 2$

Page 676, Extra Practice, (Lesson 4-1)

19. $5 \times 7 \times x \times y$ **20.** $2 \times 7 \times a \times a$

21. $2 \times 3 \times 5 \times n$ **22.** $3 \times 3 \times 3 \times c \times d \times d$

23. $2 \times 2 \times s \times s \times t \times t$ **24.** $2 \times 2 \times 3 \times 5 \times p \times p \times q \times r$

Page 681, Extra Practice, (Lesson 6-1)

7. yes; $\frac{4}{6} = \frac{2}{3}$ and $\frac{8}{12} = \frac{2}{3}$, so $\frac{4}{6} = \frac{8}{12}$

8. no; $\frac{20}{25} \neq \frac{16}{30}$ since $\frac{20}{25} = \frac{4}{5}$ and $\frac{16}{30} = \frac{8}{15}$

9. no; $\frac{20}{15} \neq \frac{30}{25}$ since $\frac{20}{15} = \frac{4}{3}$ and $\frac{30}{25} = \frac{6}{5}$

10. yes; $\frac{36}{63} = \frac{4}{7}$ since $\frac{28}{49} = \frac{4}{7}$, so $\frac{36}{63} = \frac{28}{49}$

Page 682, Extra Practice, (Lesson 6-2)

8. 3 classes/semester

Page 683, Extra Practice, (Lesson 6-6)

1. yes; $\frac{2}{3} = \frac{6}{9}$ since $2 \times 9 = 18$ and $3 \times 6 = 18$

2. no; $\frac{3}{1} \neq \frac{15}{6}$ since $3 \times 6 = 18$ but $1 \times 15 \neq 18$

3. no; $\frac{2}{1} \neq \frac{8}{3}$ since $2 \times 3 = 6$, but $1 \times 8 \neq 6$

Page 683, Extra Practice, (Lesson 6-7)

1. Multiplication followed by subtraction; $12 \times 8 = 96$, $96 - 8 = 88$, $88 - 2 = 86$, 12 correct, 2 incorrect, 1 no answer

Page 685, Extra Practice, (Lesson 7-3)

13. $0.1 \times 40 = 4$ and $3 \times 4 = 12$

14. $0.1 \times 100 = 10$ and $7 \times 10 = 70$

15. $0.1 \times 150 = 15$ and $9 \times 15 = 135$

16. $0.1 \times 70 = 7$ and $7 \times 7 = 49$

17. $0.1 \times 90 = 9$ and $8 \times 9 = 72$

18. $0.1 \times 180 = 18$

19. $0.1 \times 220 = 22$ and $5 \times 22 = 110$

20. $0.1 \times 500 = 50$ and $2 \times 50 = 100$

21. $0.1 \times 400 = 40$ and $8 \times 40 = 320$

22. $0.1 \times 60 = 6$ and $4 \times 6 = 24$

23. $0.1 \times 180 = 18$ and $6 \times 18 = 108$

24. $0.1 \times 450 = 45$ and $2 \times 45 = 90$

Page 685, Extra Practice, (Lesson 7-4)

1. $n = 0.45 \times 50$; 22.5

2. $75 = p \times 300$; 25%

3. $2 = 0.16 \times w$; 12.5

4. $n = 0.75 \times 80$; 60

5. $12 = 0.05 \times w$; 240

6. $n = 0.60 \times 45$; 27

7. $90 = p \times 95$; 94.7%

8. $n = 0.285 \times 64$; 18.2

9. $n = 0.465 \times 75$; 34.9

10. $n = 0.555 \times 70$; 38.9

11. $80.5 = 0.805 \times w$; 100

12. $40 = \frac{2}{3} \times w$; 60

13. $n = 1.225 \times 80$; 98

14. $75 = 2.5 \times w$; 30

Page 686, Extra Practice, (Lesson 7-7)

1. $47.70

2. $16.14

3. $179.10

4. $31.03

5. $14.25

6. $154.06

7. $12.54

8. $719.20

9. $112.88

10. $527.12

11. $12,968.75

12. $52.57

Page 687, Extra Practice, (Lesson 7-8)

1. $800

2. $33.33

3. $37.50

4. $17.11

5. $28.34

6. $3.34

7. $138

8. $6.75

9. $1,800

10. $270

11. $380

12. $27

13. $2,315.63

14. $298.99

15. $165.36

16. $91.41

17. $183.33

18. $680.40

Page 687, Extra Practice, (Lesson 8-1)

1. Sample answer: cluster 0–2; gap 5–10; outlier 10

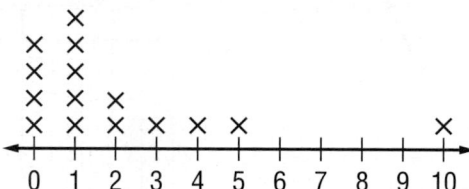

Number of Pets in the Home

2. Sample answer: clusters 65–66, 75–77, 80–81; gaps 66–75, 77–80, 81–85; outlier 85

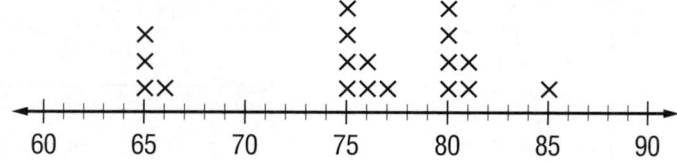

High Temperature for 18 Days (°F)

3. Sample answer: clusters 32–36, 40–43; gaps 36–40, 44–52; outlier none

Number of Stories for Buildings in Denver

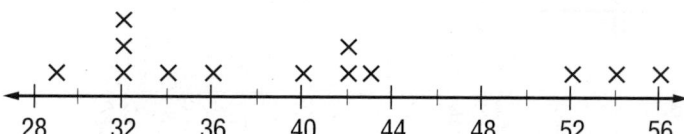

4. Sample answer: cluster 1–9; gap none; outlier none

Ages of Children at Sunny Day Care (years)

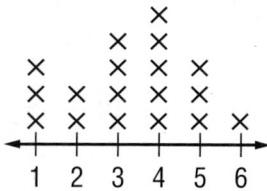

Page 688, Extra Practice, (Lesson 8-3)

1.

Stem	Leaf
1	5 8
2	3 9
3	9
4	1 2
5	1 2 7
6	8

$1|5 = 15$

2.

Stem	Leaf
18	2 3 4 4 9
19	4 6 6 7

$18|9 = 189$

3.

Stem	Leaf
2	1 4 7
3	4
4	0 6
5	0 8
6	1 7
7	0 2

$3|4 = 34$

4.

Stem	Leaf
2	0 0 0 3 7
3	0 1 2 4 4 4 5 7 9
4	2 8 9
5	2 5

$2|0 = 20$

4. Histogram

Highest Recorded Wind Speeds

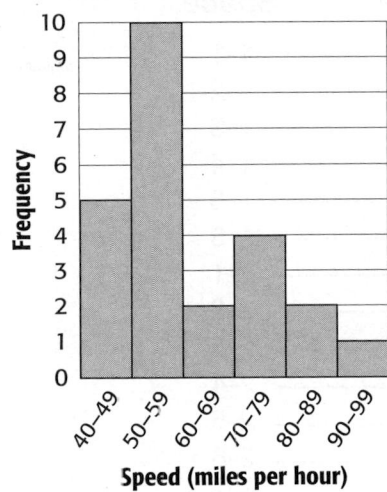

Page 688, Extra Practice, (Lesson 8-4)

1. **Longest Snakes**

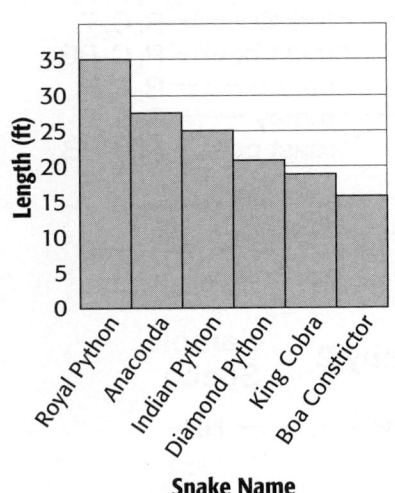

2. **Least Densely Populated States**

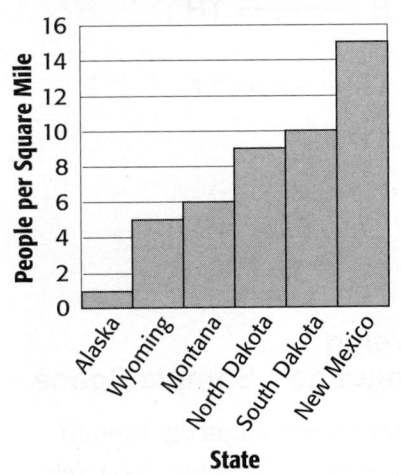

3. Histogram

Cost of a Movie Ticket

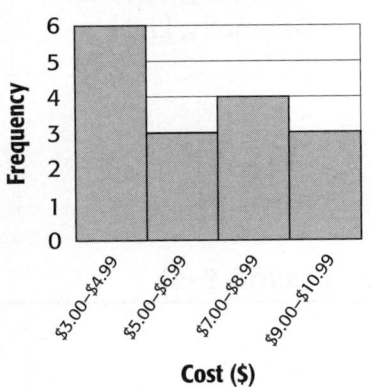

Page 689, Extra Practice, (Lesson 8-6)

4.

Price for Sheep

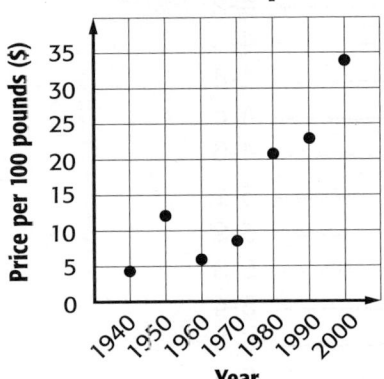

5. Sample answer: Except for the interval from 1950 to 1960, the price increases during each ten-year period.

6. Sample answer: about $40; if you draw a line lying close to the points from 1960 to 2000, 40 lies at 2010.

Page 690, Extra Practice, (Lesson 8-8)

1. The conclusion is valid; Sample answer: The sample is a simple random sample.

2. The conclusion is not valid; Sample answer: The sample is a convenience sample.

3. The conclusion is not valid; Sample answer: The sample is a voluntary response sample.

Page 690, Extra Practice, (Lesson 8-9)

1. Graph B is misleading. The change is the vertical scale makes it seem as if the pounds of grapes sold made drastric changes over the course of the week.

2. Graph A is misleading. The change in the vertical scale makes it seem as if Mr. Turner made a lot more money in the third week.

Page 691, Extra Practice, (Lesson 9-2)

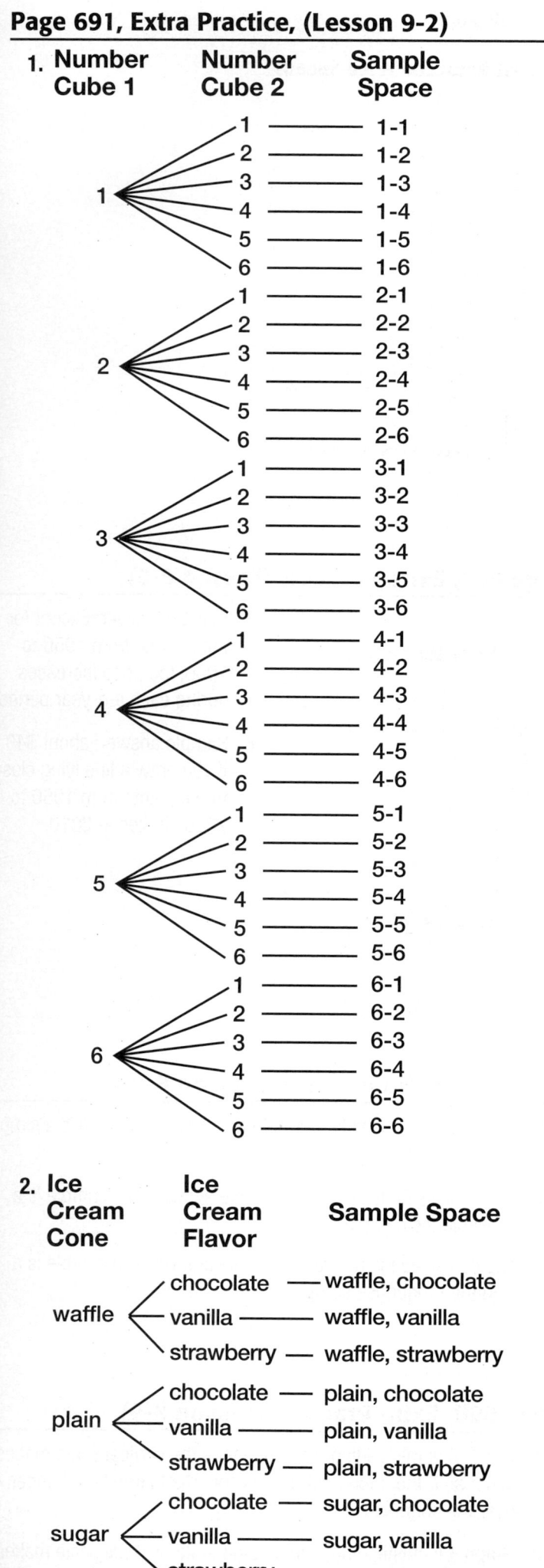

1. Number Cube 1 / Number Cube 2 / Sample Space

Cube 1	Cube 2	Sample Space
1	1	1-1
	2	1-2
	3	1-3
	4	1-4
	5	1-5
	6	1-6
2	1	2-1
	2	2-2
	3	2-3
	4	2-4
	5	2-5
	6	2-6
3	1	3-1
	2	3-2
	3	3-3
	4	3-4
	5	3-5
	6	3-6
4	1	4-1
	2	4-2
	3	4-3
	4	4-4
	5	4-5
	6	4-6
5	1	5-1
	2	5-2
	3	5-3
	4	5-4
	5	5-5
	6	5-6
6	1	6-1
	2	6-2
	3	6-3
	4	6-4
	5	6-5
	6	6-6

2. Ice Cream Cone / Ice Cream Flavor / Sample Space

- waffle
  - chocolate — waffle, chocolate
  - vanilla — waffle, vanilla
  - strawberry — waffle, strawberry
- plain
  - chocolate — plain, chocolate
  - vanilla — plain, vanilla
  - strawberry — plain, strawberry
- sugar
  - chocolate — sugar, chocolate
  - vanilla — sugar, vanilla
  - strawberry — sugar, strawberry

3. Bread / Cheese / Meat / Sample Space

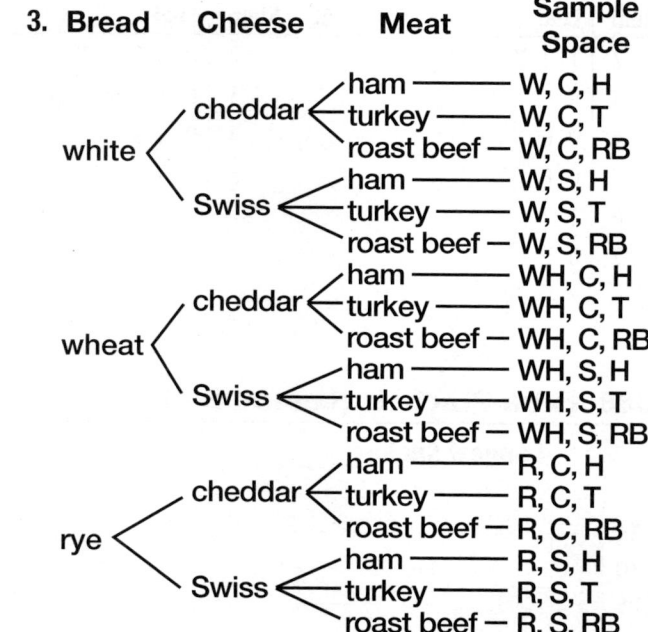

- white
  - cheddar
    - ham — W, C, H
    - turkey — W, C, T
    - roast beef — W, C, RB
  - Swiss
    - ham — W, S, H
    - turkey — W, S, T
    - roast beef — W, S, RB
- wheat
  - cheddar
    - ham — WH, C, H
    - turkey — WH, C, T
    - roast beef — WH, C, RB
  - Swiss
    - ham — WH, S, H
    - turkey — WH, S, T
    - roast beef — WH, S, RB
- rye
  - cheddar
    - ham — R, C, H
    - turkey — R, C, T
    - roast beef — R, C, RB
  - Swiss
    - ham — R, S, H
    - turkey — R, S, T
    - roast beef — R, S, RB

4. Penny 1 / Penny 2 / Sample Space

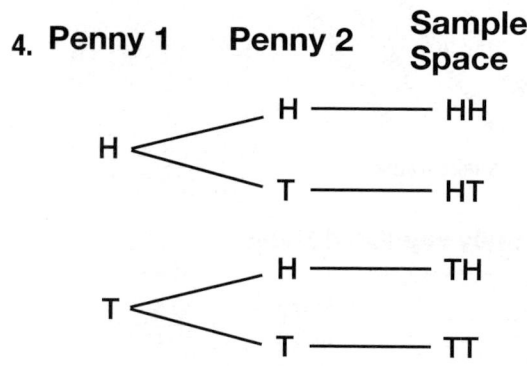

- H
  - H — HH
  - T — HT
- T
  - H — TH
  - T — TT

5. Math / Foreign Language / Sample Space

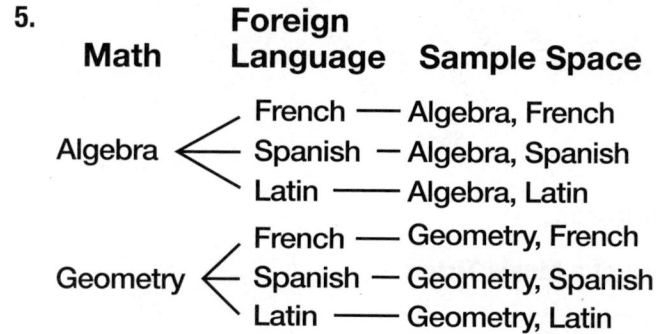

- Algebra
  - French — Algebra, French
  - Spanish — Algebra, Spanish
  - Latin — Algebra, Latin
- Geometry
  - French — Geometry, French
  - Spanish — Geometry, Spanish
  - Latin — Geometry, Latin

Page 692, Extra Practice, (Lesson 9-5)

2. 924 ways

3. 56 ways

Page 694, Extra Practice, (Lesson 10-3)

1. **Car Sales**

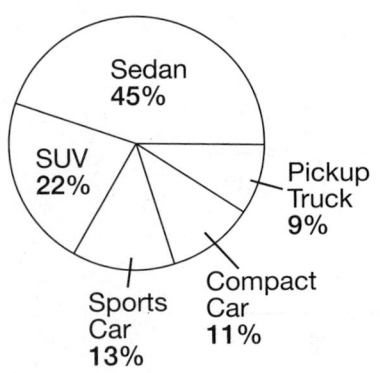

2. **Favorite Flavor of Ice Cream**

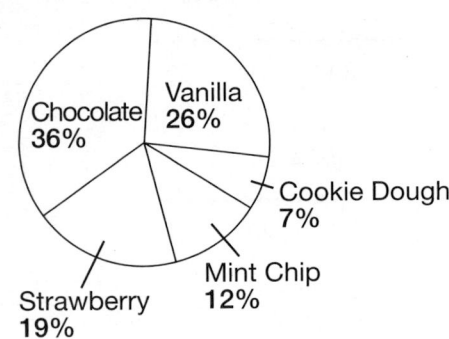

Page 694, Extra Practice, (Lesson 10-5)

1. See students' drawings; Sample answer: Two of the angles in an isosceles triangle are congruent.

2. Scott

Page 696, Extra Practice, (Lesson 10-9)

1.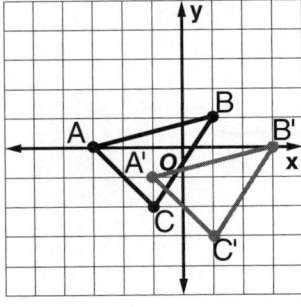

2.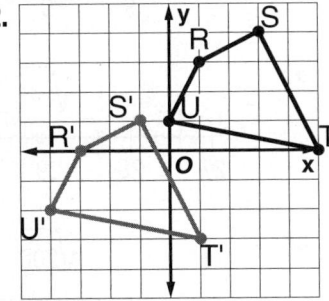

3.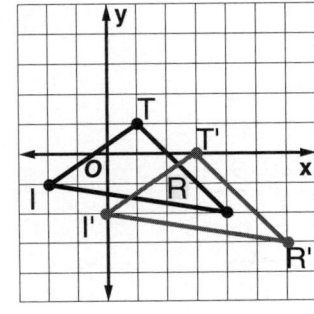

4.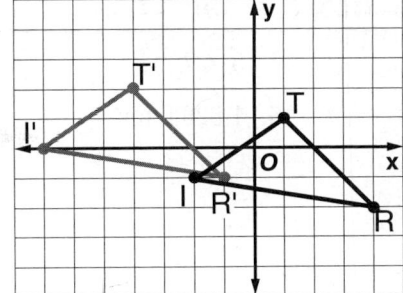

5.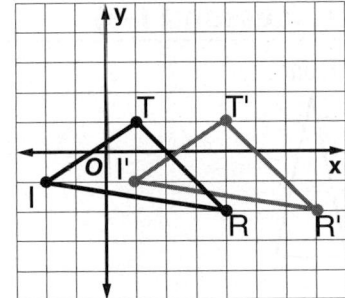

6.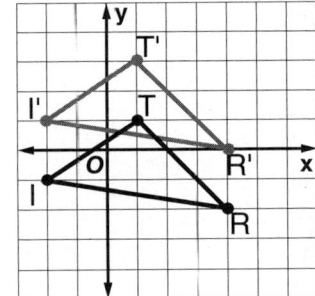

Page 696, Extra Practice, (Lesson 10-10)

7. $Q'(-1, -4)$, $U'(2, -2)$, $A'(1, -1)$, $D'(-2, -2)$

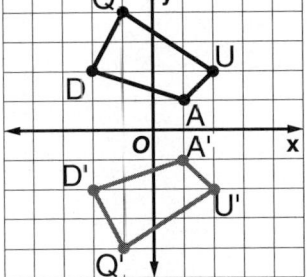

9.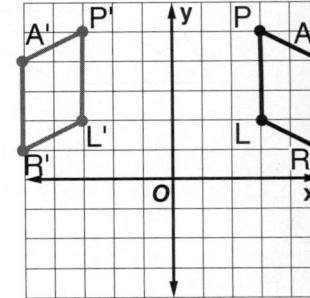

8.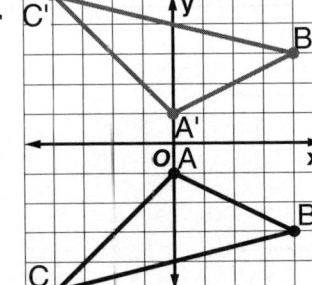

10.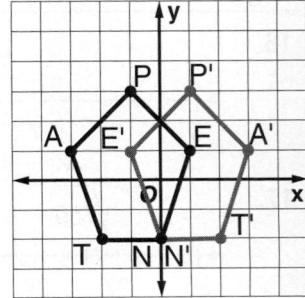

Page 698, Extra Practice, (Lesson 11-4)

9. 14,526.7 cm^2 **11.** 514.7 m^2

14. 25.2 yd^2 **15.** 1,626.0 mi^2

Page 700, Extra Practice, (Lesson 11-8)

1. Top   Side   Front

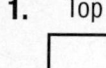  

2. Top   Side   Front

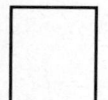 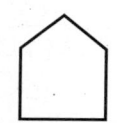 

3. Top   Side   Front

4.

5.

Page 701, Extra Practice, (Lesson 12-1)

16.

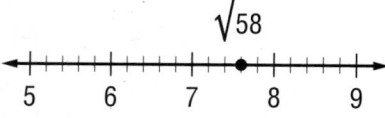

17.

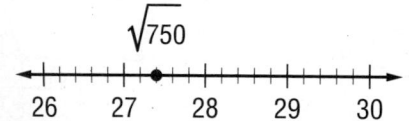

18.

19.

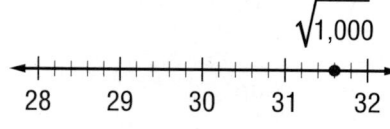

20.

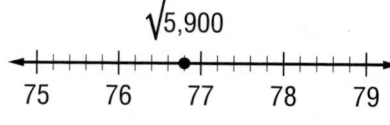

21.

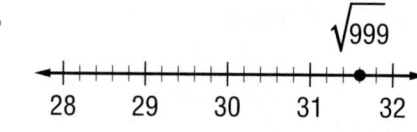

22.

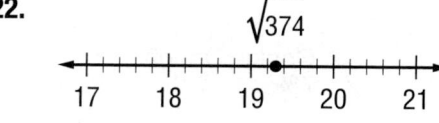

23.

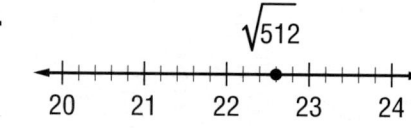

24.

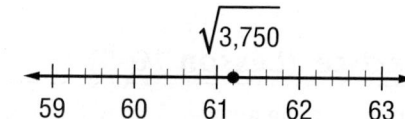

25.

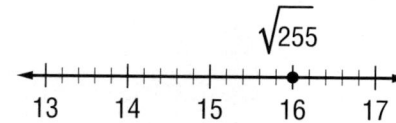

26.

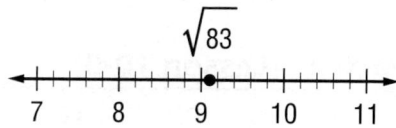

27.

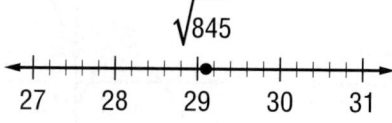

28.

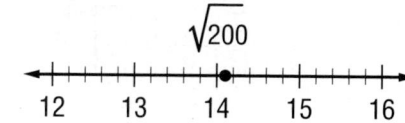

29.

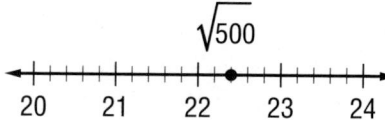

30.

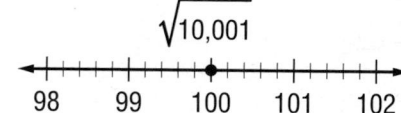

Page 703, Extra Practice, (Lesson 12-4)

8. $13,992 \text{ cm}^2$ **11.** $1,264.2 \text{ cm}^2$

12. 184.4 mi^2 **14.** 643.8 yd^2

15. 343.8 in^2 **16.** 470.6 mm^2

Page 703, Extra Practice, (Lesson 12-5)

9. 153.3 mi^2 **10.** 327.2 cm^2

11. 86.0 km^2 **12.** $7,321.8 \text{ m}^2$

Mixed Problem Solving

Page 705, Mixed Problem Solving, (Chapter 2)

2. $-220, -436, -511, -282, -383, -505, -235, -230$

3. $-511, -505, -436, -383, -282, -235, -230, -220$

5. Hot Tower $(0, 3)$; Ferris Wheel $(0, -4)$

Page 706, Mixed Problem Solving, (Chapter 3)

12.

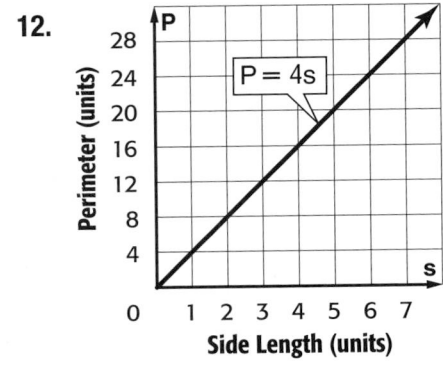

16.

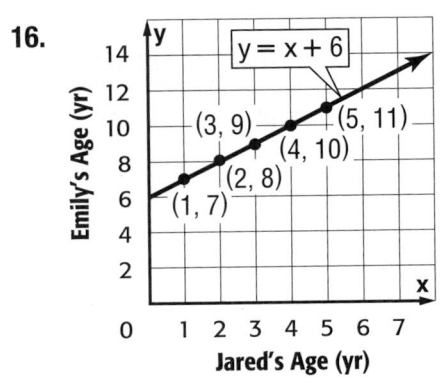

Page 709, Mixed Problem Solving, (Chapter 6)

5.

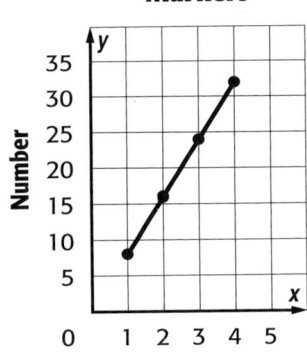

Page 710, Mixed Problem Solving, (Chapter 7)

3. Sample answer: $0.1 \times 70,000 = 7,000$ and $\frac{1}{2} \times 7,000 = 3,500 \text{ mi}^2$

Page 711, Mixed Problem Solving, (Chapter 8)

1.

```
                        ×
                        ×
                        ×       ×
                        ×       ×
                        ×       ×
    ×               ×××  ××        ×   ×
  ──┼──┼──┼──┼──┼──┼──┼──┼──┼──┼──┼──┼──┼──
    2  4  6  8 10 12 14 16 18 20 22 24 26 28
```

3. Sample answer: cluster 14–16: most of the energy bars have 14–16 grams of carbohydrates; gaps 2–14 and 16–20: outlier 2: one bar has 2 grams which is much less than the rest of the bars.

5.

Stem	Leaf
0	0 0 0 0
1	7
2	
3	
4	
5	
6	0
7	8
8	0 1 2 2 2 2 2 2 2

$7|8 = 78 \text{ games}$

6.

Tourists in U.S.

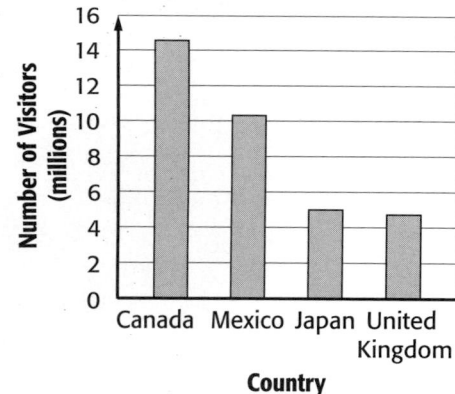

8.

Winning Times

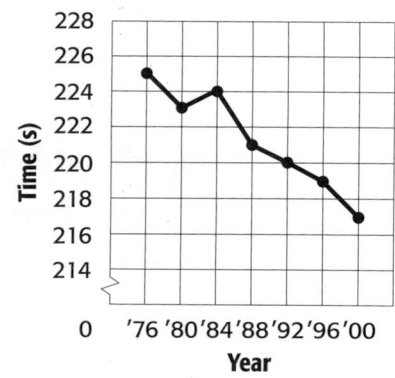

11. The conclusion is not valid; Sample answer: The sample is a voluntary response sample.

12. Sample answer: Mallory used the mean to calculate her average number number of monthly minutes. This is misleading because of the outliner, 602. A more appropriate measure to use to describe the data would be the median.

Page 712, Mixed Problem Solving, (Chapter 9)

4.

| Gate 1 | Gate 2 | Gate 3 | Sample Space |

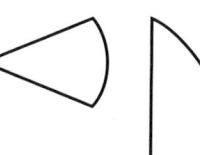

O, O, O
O, O, C
O, C, O
O, C, C
C, O, O
C, O, C
C, C, O
C, C, C

O = Open   C = Closed

Page 713, Mixed Problem Solving, (Chapter 10)

4. **Channels that Families Watch**

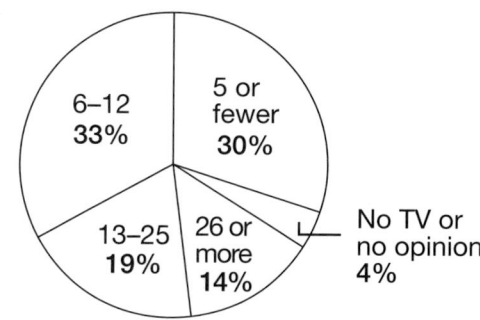

5. Sample answer: Victor could subtract 90° and 55° from 180°, leaving 35°. Thus, the measure of the third angle is 35°.

8. $m\angle1 = 80°$, $m\angle2 = 100°$, $m\angle3 = 80°$, $m\angle4 = 50°$, $m\angle5 = 130°$, $m\angle6 = 50°$, $m\angle7 = 50°$, $m\angle8 = 130°$, $m\angle9 = 50°$, $m\angle10 = 40°$.

9. Rectangle; sample answer: it was four right angles, but the four sides may not be congruent.

11. Sample answer: triangles and quadrilaterials; the sum of the angles where the vertices meet is 360°.

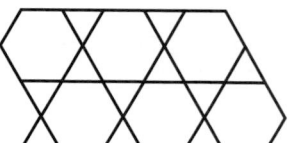

12. 3 units right, 4 units down

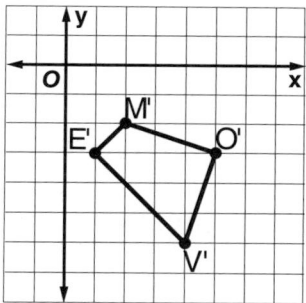

13. $M'(1, 2)$, $O'(-2, 1)$, $V'(-1, -2)$, $E'(2, 1)$

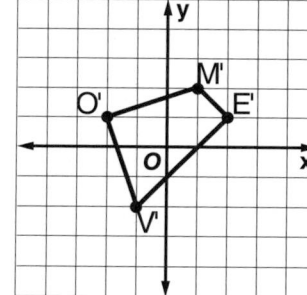

Page 714, Mixed Problem Solving, (Chapter 11)

9. Sample answer: top   side   front

Preparing for Standardized Tests

Page 728, Short-Response Practice

8. The slope is 0.2. It means that Tyler charges $0.20 per mile. The *y*-intercept is $6. It means that there is an initial charge of $6 for any delivery in addition to the miles driven.

13. $C'(-2, 1)$, $D'(-3, 4)$, $E'(-4, -2)$

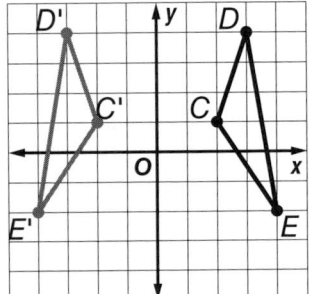

20. World's Largest Flightless Birds

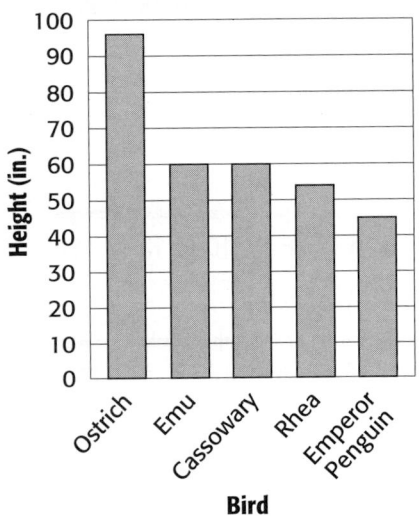

21. Precipitation in Syracuse

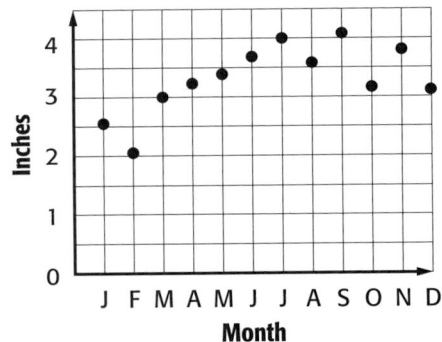

Sample answer: The amount of precipitation is lowest in February and then increases until July.

Page 732, Extended Response Practice

1a. Florida: about 10.0%; Colorado: about 0.4%; Alaska: about 7.3%; Iowa: about 0.7%; Rhode Island: about 15.1%

1b. Colorado, Iowa, Alaska, Florida, Rhode Island

1c. Sample answer: land area of 2,000 square miles, water area of 500 square miles, percent comparing water to total $= 500 \div 2,500 \times 100 = 20\%$

2a. Cost to Rent a Crane

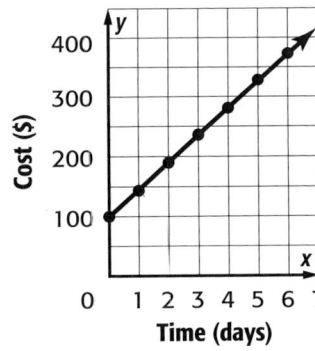

2b. The slope of the line is 45. That is the rental fee per day.

2c. $550

3a. $2.80 = 0.40 + 0.04x$; 60 minutes.

3b. $3.60

3c. Use the service that charges 40 cents per connection and 4 cents per minute.

4a. The area is 2,400 square inches.

4b. The dimensions are 80 inches by 120 inches. The area is 9,600 square inches.

4c. The ratio of the areas is 4 to 1.

4d. Sample answer: 60 inches by 80 inches

5a. The measure of ∠1 is 60° since the sum of the measures of the angles of any triangle is 180°.

5b. The measure of ∠2 is 110° because the two angles are supplementary. The measure of ∠3 is 95° since the sum of the measures of the angles of a quadrilateral is always 360°.

6a. The area is about 452 square inches.

6b. The area is about 616 square inches.

6c. The percent increase in area is about 36%.

7a. A: 62.8 in³; B: 78.5 in³

7b. 0.8

7c. Sample answer: 5 in. by 4 in. by 7.85 in.

8a. Normal Temperatures for Honolulu

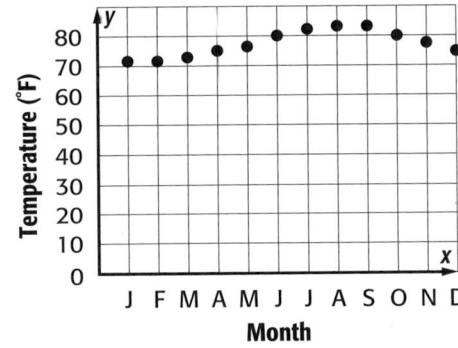

Sample answer: The points suggest a curve if connected. The curve is very slight but goes to its highest point during August and September and then curves downward again.

8b.

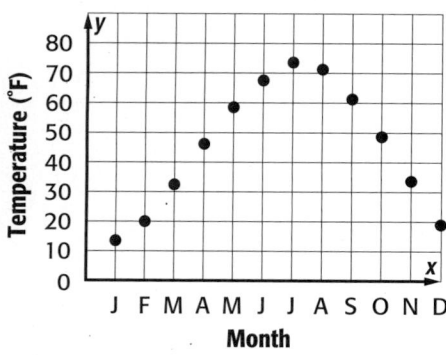

Normal Temperatures for Minneapolis

Sample answer: The points suggest a curve if connected. The curve is fairly steep as it goes up from January to July and then goes back downward to December.

8c. The range for Honolulu is 9, while the range for Minneapolis is 60. Sample reasons: Honolulu is close to the equator and is also an island, which affects the climate. Minneapolis is in the northern portion of the continental United States, so will have more varied temperatures.

9a.

	1	2	3	4
1	1, 1	1, 2	1, 3	1, 4
2	2, 1	2, 2	2, 3	2, 4
3	3, 1	3, 2	3, 3	3, 4
4	4, 1	4, 2	4, 3	4, 4

9b. $\frac{1}{16}$

9c. Using theoretical probability, you would get a sum of 4 threes out of sixteen times. So, $50 \cdot \frac{3}{16} \approx 9$ times

Concepts and Skills Bank

Page 735, Concepts and Skills Bank

16–23. Sample answers are given.

16. $3 \times 20 = 60$

17. $4 \times 60 = 240$

18. $4 \times 40 = 160$

19. $4 \times 80 = 320$

20. $4 \times 240 = 960$

21. $6 \times 10 = 60$

22. $5 \times 50 = 250$

23. $5 \times 100 = 500$

Page 741, Concepts and Skills Bank

1. $x \geq -7$

2. $n < 5.3$

3. $y \leq 34$

4. $a \leq 3.3$

5. $h \geq 2$

6. $g < 14.7$

7. $m \leq 4.7$

8. $f > 9$

9. $p \geq 16$

10. $r \geq 5$

11. $n < 5$

12. $d \leq 1$

Page 742, Concepts and Skills Bank

1. Yes, there are no denominator variables and no variables under radical signs.; 1 term

2. No, the variable b is under a radical sign.

3. Yes, there are no denominator variables and no variables under radical signs.; 3 terms

4. Yes, there are no denominator variables and no variables under radical signs.; 1 term

5. Yes, there are no denominator variables and no variables under radical signs.; 3 terms

6. No, the variable n is in the denominator.

7. Yes, there are no denominator variables and no variables under radical signs.; 3 terms

8. No, the variable s is under a radical sign.

9. $16r + 9s$

10. $10a + 5b + 10$

11. $9f + 9g$

12. $28x + 33y$

13. $5t + u + 10$

14. $17c + 17d$

15. $13j + 9$

16. $15p + 21q$

17. $22mn + 12m + 4n$

18. $15x + 14y$

Page 744, Concepts and Skills Bank

1. $X'(-3, 1)$, $Y'(-5, 4)$, and $Z'(-1, -5)$

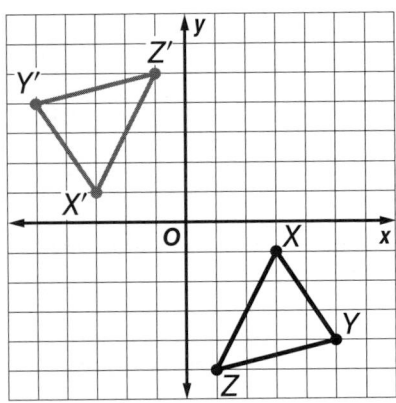

2. $X'(3, -1)$, $Y'(0, -3)$, and $Z'(-1, 1)$

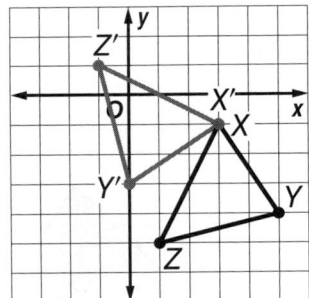

3. $X'(1, 3)$, $Y'(4, 5)$, and $Z'(5, 1)$

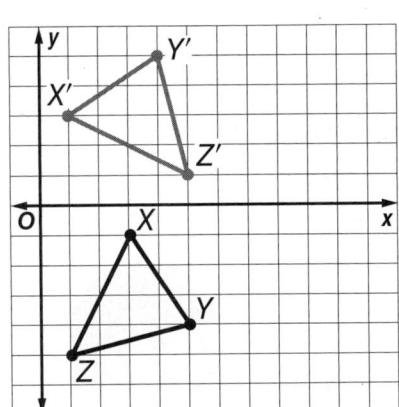

4. $X'(2, -6)$, $Y'(5, -4)$, and $Z'(5, -8)$

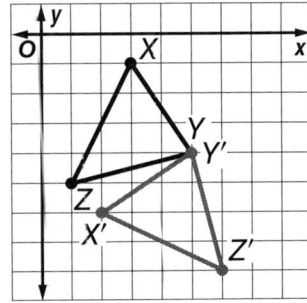

5. $X'(-1, -9)$, $Y'(-3, -6)$, and $Z'(1, -5)$

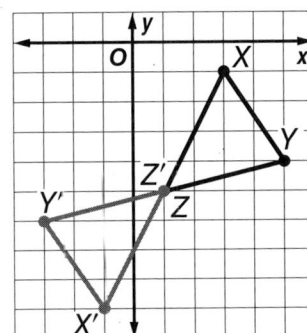

6. $X'(-1, -3)$, $Y'(-4, -5)$, and $Z'(-5, -1)$

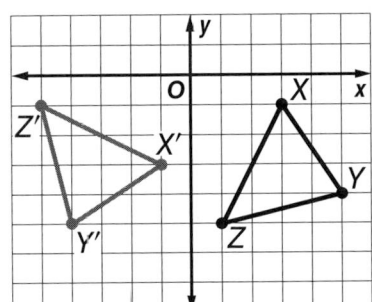

7. $A'(4, -3)$, $B'(1, -1)$, $C'(2, 2)$, and $D'(4, 3)$

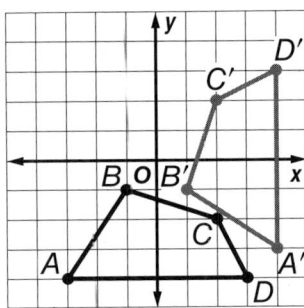

8. $A'(-3, -4)$, $B'(0, -6)$, $C'(-1, -9)$, and $D'(-3, -10)$

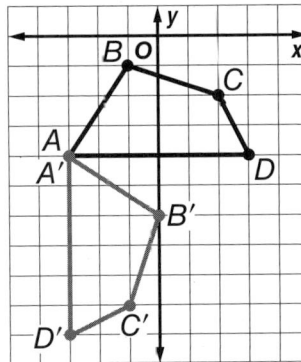

9. $A'(9, -4)$, $B'(7, -7)$, $C'(4, -6)$, and $D'(3, -4)$

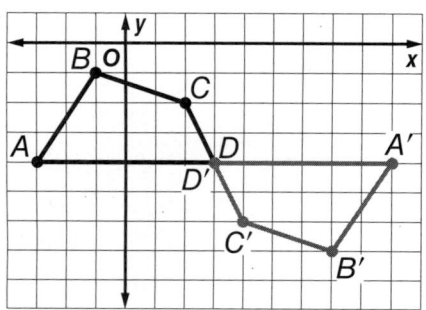

10. $A'(4, -3)$, $B'(1, -1)$, $C'(2, 2)$, and $D'(4, 3)$

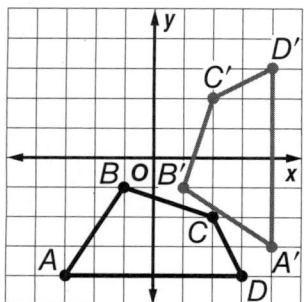

11. $A'(-4, 3)$, $B'(-1, 1)$, $C'(-2, -2)$, and $D'(-4, -3)$

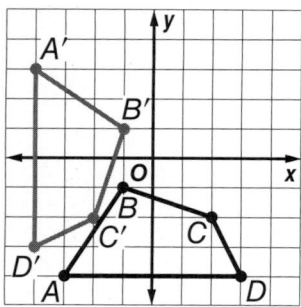

12. $A'(1, 2)$, $B'(-1, -1)$, $C'(-4, 0)$, and $D'(-5, 2)$

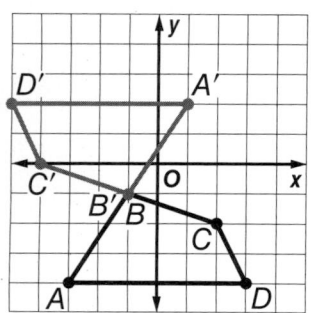

Page 746, Concepts and Skills Bank

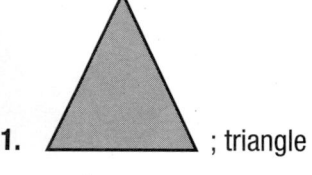

1. ; triangle

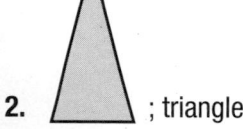

2. ; triangle

3. ; square

4. 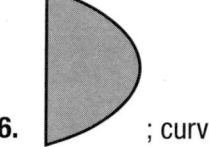 ; circle

5. 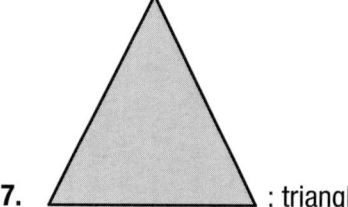 ; rectangle

6. ; curve

7. ; triangle

8. ; square

9. 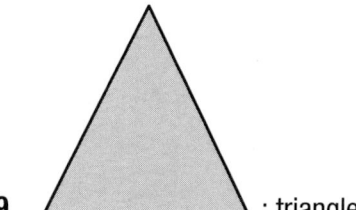 ; triangle

10. vertical: 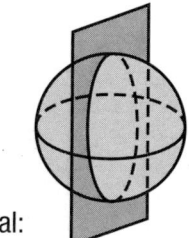 ; angled: 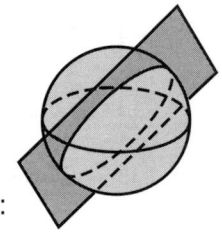 ;

horizontal: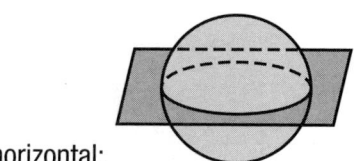

11. All three cross sections are circles.;

12. vertical: 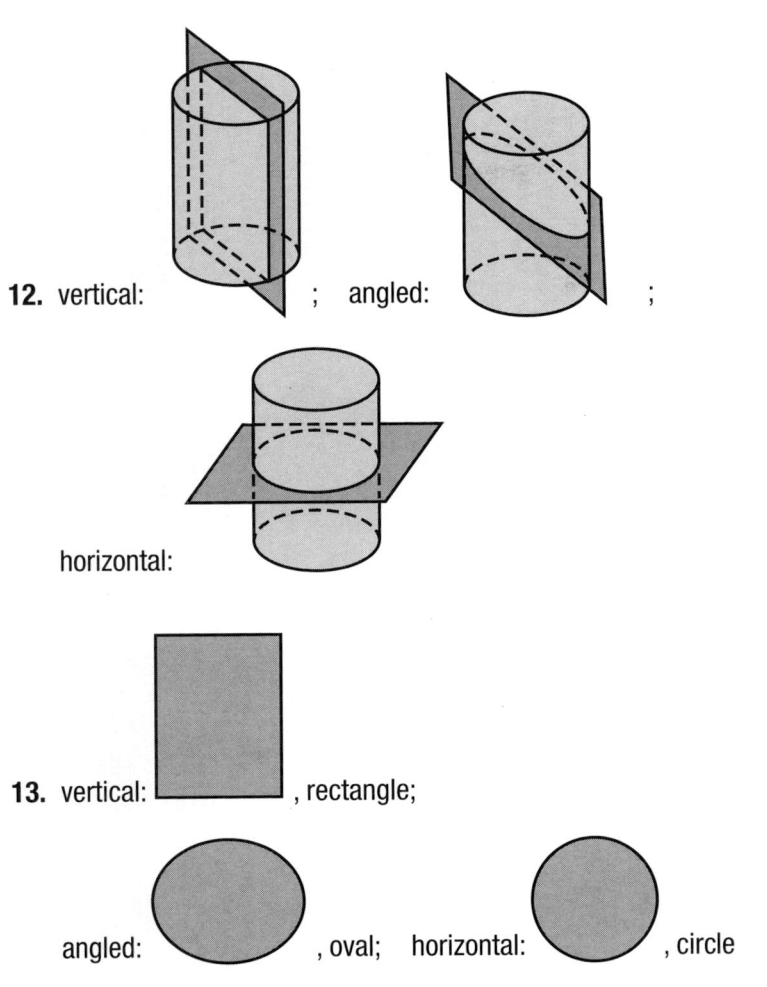 ; angled: ;

horizontal:

13. vertical: , rectangle;

angled: , oval; horizontal: , circle

Page 747, Concepts and Skills Bank

  1. 43.15

  2. 3.43

  3. 425.25

  4. 39.34

  5. 21.14

  6. 59.06

  7. 532.33

  8. 9.32

  9. 7.31

10. 40.22

11. 6.76

12. 12.68

13. 9.76

14. 45.42

15. 20.28

16. 24.97

Photo Credits

Cover: (t)Created by Michael Trott with Mathematica. From *Graphica 1*, Copyright 1999 Wolfram Media, Inc., (b); Richard Hutchings/Digital Light Source, shot on location courtesy of Busch Gardens/ Adventure Island, Tampa Florida; **iv** File Photo; **v** Digital Vision/Getty Images; **vi** Aaron Haupt; **vii** (bl)File Photo, (others) Aaron Haupt; **x-xi** David Frazier/ CORBIS; **xii-xiii** Robert Glusic/Photodisc/Getty Images; **xiv-xv** Brand X Pictures/PunchStock; **xvi-xvii** Eastcott Momatiuk/Photodisc/Getty Images; **xviii-xix** Michael Ventura/Alamy Images; **xx-xxi** Kim Karpeles/Alamy Images; **xxii-xxiii** W.A.Hamilton/Alamy; **001** Digital Vision/ PunchStock; **003** Reuters/CORBIS; **004** David Frazier/ CORBIS; **005** curved-light/Alamy Images; **006** Jonathan Ferrey/Getty Images; **007** Robert Laberge/Getty Images; **008** William Manning/www.williammanning.com/CORBIS; **009** Krista Kennell/ZUMA/CORBIS; **010** Arcaid/CORBIS; **011** Momatiuk-Eastcott/CORBIS; **012** Royalty-Free/CORBIS; **013** PhotoLink/Photodisc/Getty Images; **014** Joe McDonald/ Animals Animals; **015** Masterfile; **016** (t)Joel A. Rogers/www. CoasterGallery.com, (b)Daniel Dempster Photography/Alamy Images; **017** (t)Chuck Pefley/Alamy images, (c)Penny Boyd/ Alamy Images, (b)Goodshoot/CORBIS, (br)Marie Read/ Animals Animals; **018** (t)Marian Bacon/Animals Animals, (c)Scott Smith/CORBIS, (b)kansastravel.org; **019** (t)Volkmar Wentzel/Getty Images, (cl)John December, (cr)M. Timothy O'Keefe/Alamy Images, (b)Steve Hamblin/Alamy Images; **020-021** JG Photography/Alamy Images; **022** Andre Jenny/ Alamy Images; **026** Jose Luis Pelaez, Inc./Blend Images/Getty Images; **032** Stefano Bianchetti/CORBIS; **035** Lawrence Manning/CORBIS; **039** The McGraw-Hill Companies Inc.; **041** (t)Michael Newman/PhotoEdit, (r)David Young-Wolff/ PhotoEdit; **042** Kevin Peterson/Photodisc/Getty Images; **045** SW Productions/Photodisc/Getty Images; **049** Photo courtesy of BGSU Photo Services; **052** (l)David Young-Wolff/ PhotoEdit, (r)Tony Freeman/PhotoEdit; **054** Tim de Waele/ CORBIS; **064** (l)Noel Hendrickson/Digital Vision/Getty Images, (r)Eric and David Hosking/CORBIS; **066** Herbert Kehrer/zefa/CORBIS; **078** SW Productions/Brand X/CORBIS; **080** Chase Jarvis/CORBIS; **090** Kevin Schafer/Photographer's Choice RF/Getty Images; **099** (l)Myrleen Ferguson Cate/ PhotoEdit, (r)David Young-Wolff/PhotoEdit; **104** NASA/ Photodisc/Getty Images; **106** (l)Cleve Bryant/PhotoEdit, (r)David Young-Wolff/PhotoEdit; **109** Ralph White/CORBIS; **112** John Evans; **116** Lothar Lenz/zefa/CORBIS; **126** Sarah Hadley/Alamy Images; **128** JPL/NASA; **129** Photo by Brad Kuntz; **132** (t)David Siccardi/CORBIS, (b)Comstock/CORBIS, (br)Dann Tardif/LWA/Blend Images/Getty Images; **137** Stephen Frink/zefa/CORBIS; **139** Eddie Adams/Sygma/ CORBIS; **140** Streeter Lecka/Stringer/Getty Images; **143** Jose Luis Pelaez, Inc./Blend Images/Getty Images; **146** (l)Ryan McVay/Photodisc/Getty Images, (r)Comstock/CORBIS; **148** John Evans; **153** John Eder/Stone/Getty Images; **154** Robert Glusic/Photodisc/Getty Images; **160** David Young-Wolff/PhotoEdit; **176-177** Brand X Pictures/PunchStock; **178** Robert Marien/CORBIS; **183** Zigmund Leszcynski/ Animals Animals; **184** Mark Duffy/Alamy Images; **185** Raymond K Gehman/National Geographic/Getty Images; **190** Matt Meadows; **193** Jose Luis Pelaez Inc/Blend Images/ Getty Images; **195** (l)Seth Kushner/Taxi/Getty Images, (r)Image Source/SuperStock; **198** Comstock/SuperStock; **203** Bäumle Studios/Alamy Images; **208** Steve Bloom/Taxi/ Getty Images; **210** (l)RubberBall/SuperStock, (r)RubberBall/ SuperStock; **212** Roy Ooms/Masterfile; **216** John Wilkes/ SuperStock; **218** United States coin images from the United States Mint; **219** Yiorgos Karahalis/Reuters/CORBIS; **228** Eclipse Studios; **230** Eastcott Momatiuk/Photodisc/Getty Images; **232** Michael Newman/PhotoEdit; **234** Russell Kightley/Photo Researchers; **239** David R. Frazier Photolibrary, Inc./Alamy Images; **240** (l)George Doyle/ Stockbyte/Getty Images, (r)Michael Newman/PhotoEdit; **242** Diane Macdonald/Stockbyte/Getty Images; **244** Stockbyte/Getty Images; **248** Getty Images; **254** Garry Black/Masterfile; **256** Rob Lewine/CORBIS; **262** Jeff Greenberg/Alamy Images; **268** Phyllis Greenberg/Animals Animals; **270** (t)Jack Hollingsworth/CORBIS, (r)Barbara Penoyar/Photodisc/Getty Images; **278-279** Christie's Images/ CORBIS; **280** Alan Schein/zefa/CORBIS; **283** Brian Snyder/ Reuters/CORBIS; **285** (l)Tom Brakefield/CORBIS, (r)Judith Collins/Alamy Images; **286** (l)Donna Day/ImageState, (r)JupiterImages/Thinkstock/Alamy Images; **287** David

Young-Wolff/PhotoEdit; **289** Doug Menuez/Photodisc/Getty Images; **290** Ryan McVay/Stone+/Getty Images; **291** Don Emmert/AFP/Getty Images; **295** Thomas Allen/Digital Vision/Getty Images; **298** John Lambert/Brand X/CORBIS; **300** Norbert Wu/Minden Pictures; **305** age fotostock/ SuperStock; **307** Lawrence Lawry/Photodisc/Getty Images; **308** (t)Bruce Edwards/America 24-7/Getty Images, (bl)Jonathan Nourok/PhotoEdit, (br)Michael Newman/ PhotoEdit; **312** CORBIS; **314** Alley Cat Productions/Brand X/ CORBIS; **318** KS Studios; **319** Michael Newman/PhotoEdit; **325** Bilderbuch/Design Pics/CORBIS; **331** Franz Marc Frei/ CORBIS; **340** Masterfile; **344** DLILLC/CORBIS; **347** G. Biss/ Masterfile; **350** Ingemar Edfalk/Pixonnet.com/Alamy Images; **352** Donna Ikenberry/Animals Animals; **354** Digital Vision/ Getty Images; **356** Big Cheese Photo/SuperStock; **358** D. Robert & Lorri Franz/CORBIS; **359** (l)FIRST LIGHT ASSOCIATED PHOTOGRAPHERS, (r)Flying Colours Ltd/ Digital Vision/Getty Images; **363** Alaskastock; **366** Adrian Peacock/Digital Vision/Getty Images; **374** (l)RubberBall/ ImageState, (r)Barbara Penoyar/Photodisc/Getty Images; **376** Gregor Schuster/Photographer's Choice RF/Getty Images; **380** Don Mason/Blend Images/Getty Images; **392-393** Matthias Kulka/zefa/CORBIS; **394** Michael Ventura/ Alamy Images; **399** Harald Sund/Photographer's Choice/ Getty Images; **400** (l)MedioImages/Alamy Images, (r)Tony Freeman/PhotoEdit; **406** CORBIS; **410** Barbara Peacock/Taxi/ Getty Images; **411** JUPITERIMAGES/Liquid Library Value/ Alamy; **413** Brandon D. Cole/CORBIS; **419** Daryl Balfour/The Image Bank/Getty Images; **424** Gabe Palmer/Alamy Images; **431** Bob Daemmrich/Stock Boston; **438** Paul Costello/Getty Images; **441** photocuisine/CORBIS; **446** Andrew J.G. Bell; Eye Ubiquitous/CORBIS; **458** Robert Michael/CORBIS; **461** Bettmann/ CORBIS; **468** Ariel Skelley/CORBIS; **469** Tom Hauck/Getty Images; **473** O'Brien Productions/CORBIS; **476** Shenval/Alamy Images; **477** Tetra Images/Alamy Images; **481** Doug Menuez/Getty Images; **483** (l)George Doyle/ Stockbyte Platinum/Alamy Images, (r)Jose Luis Pelaez Inc/ Blend Images/Getty Images; **484** Laura Sifferlin; **488** Zefa RF/ Alamy Images; **492** United States coin images from the United States Mint; **506-507** Oberto Gill/Beateworks/CORBIS; **508** Dennis MacDonald/Alamy Images; **510** Kelly-Mooney Photography/CORBIS; **519** Stephen Dalton/Animals Animals; **526** Jeff Greenberg/PhotoEdit; **528** Damir Frkovic/Masterfile; **530** Ryan McVay/Photodisc/Getty Images; **537** (l)Michael Newman/PhotoEdit, (r)Michelle Pedone/zefa/CORBIS; **544** Martin Shields/Alamy Images; **548** (t)Andriy Doriy Textures/Alamy Images, (b)Somos/Veer/Getty Images; **550** (l)Jeff Greenberg/PhotoEdit, (r)Todd Gipstein/National Geographic/Getty Images; **556** Artwork courtesy of Marjorie Rice; **560** Robert Spoenlein/zefa/CORBIS; **561** (t)Jose Fuste Raga/CORBIS, (b)Allen Wallace/Photonica/Getty Images; **570** Kim Karpeles/Alamy Images; **573** Don Farrall/Photodisc/ Getty Images; **575** Jules Frazier/Photodisc/Getty Images; **580** Byron Schumaker/Alamy; **583** Getty Images; **584** Iconotec/Alamy Images; **587** (l)BananaStock/ PictureQuest/Jupiter Images, (t)Studio Wartenberg/zefa/ CORBIS, (cr)Klaus Leidorf/zefa/CORBIS, (r)BananaStock/ PunchStock; **590** United States coin images from the United States Mint; **592** (l)MedioImages/CORBIS, (r)Michael Newman/PhotoEdit; **594** Jim Esposito Photography LLC/ Photodisc/Getty Images; **604** Judith Collins/Alamy Images; **605** (t)C Squared Studios/Photodisc/Getty Images, (c)Glencoe, (b)PhotoLink/Photodisc/Getty Images; **608** Phil Degginger/ Alamy Images; **610** Chris Bell/Taxi/Getty Images; **611** (t)Mark Karrass/CORBIS, (t)Ryan McVay/Photodisc/Getty Images; **(b)Lew Robertson/CORBIS; 614** Charles Gupton/CORBIS; **617** Keate/Masterfile; **620** Tony Freeman/PhotoEdit; **621** Duncan Usher/Foto Natura/Minden Pictures; **629** Gregor Schuster/zeta/CORBIS; **634** Horizons Companies; **638** Myrleen Ferguson Cate/PhotoEdit; **641** Steve Bly/Alamy Images; **645** (l)Comstock/SuperStock, (r)Stockbyte/ SuperStock; **646** Michael Newman/PhotoEdit; **652** Daly & Newton/Getty Images; **657** W.A.Hamilton/Alamy; **666** Eclipse Studios; **LA0-LA1** Brand X Pictures/Punchstock; **LA2** Charles O'Rear/CORBIS; **LA3** Chris A Crumley/Alamy Images; **LA9** Doug Menuez/Getty Images; **LA13** allOver photography/Alamy Images; **LA14** Brand X Pictures/ PunchStock; **LA17** Royalty-Free-CORBIS; **LA18** dbphotos/ Alamy Images; **LA21** Merlin D. Tuttle, Bat Conservation International; **LA24** Royalty-Free-CORBIS

Glossary/Glosario

Math Online A mathematics multilingual glossary is available at glencoe.com.

The glossary includes the following languages.

Arabic	Cantonese	Korean	Tagalog
Bengali	English	Russian	Urdu
Brazilian Portuguese	Haitian Creole	Spanish	Vietnamese
	Hmong		

English

absolute value (p. 81) The distance the number is from zero on a number line.

acute angle (p. 511) An angle with a measure greater than 0° and less than 90°.

acute triangle (p. 525) A triangle having three acute angles.

Addition Property of Equality (p. 138) If you add the same number to each side of an equation, the two sides remain equal.

additive inverse (p. 96) The opposite of an integer. The sum of an integer and its additive inverse is zero.

adjacent angles (p. 511) Angles that have the same vertex, share a common side, and do not overlap.

algebra (p. 44) The branch of mathematics that involves expressions with variables.

algebraic expression (p. 44) A combination of variables, numbers, and at least one operation.

analyze (p. 397) To describe, summarize, and compare data.

Español

valor absoluto Distancia a la que se encuentra un número de cero en la recta numérica.

ángulo agudo Ángulo que mide más de 0° y menos de 90°.

triángulo acutángulo Triángulo con tres ángulos agudos.

propiedad de adición de la igualdad Si sumas el mismo número a ambos lados de una ecuación, los dos lados permanecen iguales.

inverso aditivo El opuesto de un entero. La suma de un entero y su inverso aditivo es cero.

ángulos adyacentes Ángulos que comparten el mismo vértice y un común lado, pero no se sobreponen.

álgebra Rama de las matemáticas que involucra expresiones con variables.

expresión algebraica Combinación de variables, números y por lo menos una operación.

analizar Describir, resumir o comparar datos.

angle (p. 510) Two rays with a common endpoint form an angle. The rays and vertex are used to name the angle.

∠ABC, ∠CBA, or ∠B

area (p. 157) The number of square units needed to cover a surface enclosed by a geometric figure.

arithmetic sequence (p. 57) A sequence in which each term is found by adding the same number to the previous term.

Associative Property (p. 54) The way in which three numbers are grouped when they are added or multiplied does not change their sum or product.

average (p. 402) The mean of a set of data.

bar graph (p. 415) A graphic form using bars to make comparisons of statistics.

Students' Favorite Pastime

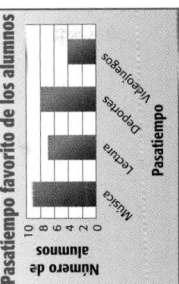

bar notation (p. 197) In repeating decimals, the line or bar placed over the digits that repeat. For example, 2.63 indicates that the digits 63 repeat.

base (p. 30) In a power, the number used as a factor. In 10^3, the base is 10. That is, $10^3 = 10 \times 10 \times 10$.

base (p. 572) The base of a parallelogram or triangle is any side of the figure. The bases of a trapezoid are the parallel sides.

base (p. 603) The top or bottom face of a three-dimensional figure.

biased sample (p. 439) A sample drawn in such a way that one or more parts of the population are favored over others.

ángulo Dos rayos con un extremo común forman un ángulo. Los rayos y el vértice se usan para nombrar el ángulo.

∠ABC, ∠CBA o ∠B

área El número de unidades cuadradas necesarias para cubrir una superficie cerrada por una figura geométrica.

sucesión aritmética Sucesión en que cada término se encuentra sumando el mismo número al término anterior.

propiedad asociativa La manera de agrupar tres números al sumarlos o multiplicarlos no cambia su suma o producto.

promedio La media de un conjunto de datos.

gráfica de barras Forma gráfica que usa barras para hacer comparaciones estadísticas.

Pasatiempo favorito de los alumnos

notación de barra Línea o barra que se coloca sobre los dígitos que se repiten en decimales periódicos. Por ejemplo, 2.63 indica que los dígitos 63 se repiten.

base En una potencia, el número usado como factor. En 10^3, la base es 10. Es decir, $10^3 = 10 \times 10 \times 10$.

base La base de un paralelogramo o triángulo es el lado de la figura. Las bases de un trapecio son los lados paralelos.

base La cara inferior o superior de una figura tridimensional.

muestra sesgada Muestra en que se favorece una o más partes de una población.

Cómo usar el glosario en español:
1. Busca el término en inglés que desees encontrar.
2. El término en español, junto con la definición, se encuentran en la columna de la derecha.

C

center (p. 584) The given point from which all points on a circle or sphere are the same distance.

centro (p. 584) Un punto dado del cual equidistan todos los puntos de un círculo o de una esfera.

circle (p. 584) The set of all points in a plane that are the same distance from a given point called the center.

círculo (p. 584) Conjunto de todos los puntos en un plano que equidistan de un punto dado llamado centro.

circle graph (p. 518) A type of statistical graph used to compare parts of a whole.

gráfica circular (p. 518) Tipo de gráfica estadística que se usa para comparar las partes de un todo.

Area of Oceans

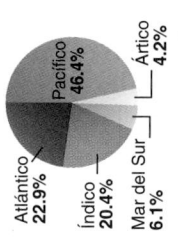

Pacific 46.4%
Atlantic 22.9%
Indian 20.4%
Southern 6.1%
Arctic 4.2%

Área de superficie de los océanos

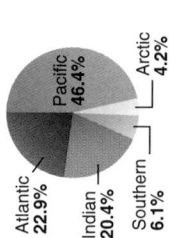

Pacífico 46.4%
Atlántico 22.9%
Índico 20.4%
Mar del Sur 6.1%
Ártico 4.2%

circumference (p. 584) The distance around a circle.

circunferencia (p. 584) La distancia alrededor de un círculo.

cluster (p. 397) Data that are grouped closely together.

agrupamiento (p. 397) Datos estrechamente agrupados.

coefficient (p. 45) The numerical factor of a term that contains a variable.

coeficiente El factor numérico de un término que contiene una variable.

combination (p. 480) An arrangement, or listing, of objects in which order is not important.

combinación Arreglo o lista de objetos donde el orden no es importante.

common denominator (p. 215) A common multiple of the denominators of two or more fractions. 24 is a common denominator for $\frac{1}{3}$, $\frac{5}{8}$, and $\frac{3}{4}$ because 24 is the LCM of 3, 8, and 4.

común denominador (p. 215) El múltiplo común de los denominadores de dos o más fracciones. 24 es un denominador común para $\frac{1}{3}$, $\frac{5}{8}$ y $\frac{3}{4}$ porque 24 es el mcm de 3, 8 y 4.

Commutative Property (p. 54) The order in which two numbers are added or multiplied does not change their sum or product.

propiedad commutativa El orden en que se suman o multiplican dos números no afecta su suma o producto.

complementary angles (p. 514) Two angles are complementary if the sum of their measures is 90°.

ángulos complementarios Dos ángulos son complementarios si la suma de sus medidas es 90°.

∠1 and ∠2 are complementary angles.

∠1 y ∠2 son complementarios.

---

complementary events (p. 462) The events of one outcome happening and that outcome not happening are complementary events. The sum of the probabilities of complementary events is 1.

eventos complementarios Se dice de los eventos de un resultado que ocurren y el resultado que no ocurre. La suma de las probabilidades de eventos complementarios es 1.

complex figure (p. 596) A figure made of circles, rectangles, squares, and other two-dimensional figures.

figura compleja Una figura compuesta por círculos, rectángulos, cuadrados y otras dos figuras bidimensionales.

composite number (p. 181) A whole number greater than 1 that has more than two factors.

número compuesto Un número entero mayor que 1 que tiene más de dos factores.

compound event (p. 492) An event consisting of two or more simple events.

evento compuesto Un evento que consiste en dos o más eventos simples.

cone (p. 604) A three-dimensional figure with a curved surface and a circular base.

cono Figura tridimensional con una superficie curva y una base circular.

congruent angles (p. 511) Angles that have the same measure.

ángulos congruentes Ángulos que tienen la misma medida.

∠1 and ∠2 are congruent angles.

∠1 y ∠2 son congruentes.

congruent figures (p. 554) Figures with equal corresponding sides of equal length and corresponding angles of equal measure.

figuras congruentes Figuras cuyos lados y ángulos correspondientes son iguales.

congruent segments (p. 525) Segments having the same measure.

segmentos congruentes Segmentos que tienen la misma medida.

Side $\overline{AB}$ is congruent to side $\overline{BC}$.

$\overline{AB}$ es congruente a $\overline{BC}$.

convenience sample (p. 439) A sample which includes members of the population that are easily accessed.

muestra de conveniencia Muestra que incluye miembros de una población fácilmente accesibles.

coordinate plane (p. 88) A plane in which a horizontal number line and a vertical number line intersect at their zero points. Also called a coordinate grid.

plano de coordenadas Plano en el cual se han trazado dos rectas numéricas, una horizontal y una vertical, que se intersecan en sus puntos cero. También conocido como sistema de coordenadas.

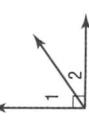
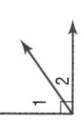

corresponding angles (p. 540) Congruent angles of similar figures.

ángulos correspondientes Ángulos iguales de figuras semejantes.

corresponding sides (p. 540) Congruent or proportional sides of similar figures.

lados correspondientes Lados iguales o proporcionales de figuras semejantes.

counterexample (p. 56) An example showing that a statement is not true.

contraejemplo Ejemplo que demuestra que un enunciado no es verdadero.

cross product (p. 310) In a proportion, a cross product is the product of the numerator of one ratio and the denominator of the other ratio.

productos cruzados En una proporción, un producto cruzado es el producto del numerador de una razón y el denominador de la otra razón.

cubed (p. 30) The product in which a number is a factor three times. Two cubed is 8 because $2 \times 2 \times 2 = 8$.

al cubo El producto de un número por sí mismo, tres veces. Dos al cubo es 8 porque $2 \times 2 \times 2 = 8$.

cylinder (p. 604) A three-dimensional figure with two parallel congruent circular bases.

cilindro Figura tridimensional que tiene dos bases circulares congruentes y paralelas.

D

data (p. 376) Pieces of information, which are often numerical.

datos Información, la cual a menudo se presenta de manera numérica.

decagon (p. 546) A polygon having ten sides.

decágono Un polígono con diez lados.

defining the variable (p. 50) Choosing a variable to represent an unknown value in a problem, and using it to write an expression or equation to solve the problem.

definir una variable El elegir una variable para representar un valor desconocido en un problema y usarla para escribir una expresión o ecuación para resolver el problema.

degrees (p. 510) The most common unit of measure for angles. If a circle were divided into 360 equal-sized parts, each part would have an angle measure of 1 degree.

grados La unidad más común para medir ángulos. Si un círculo se divide en 360 partes iguales, cada parte tiene una medida angular de 1 grado.

dependent events (p. 493) Two or more events in which the outcome of one event affects the outcome of the other event(s).

eventos dependientes Dos o más eventos en que el resultado de un evento afecta el resultado de otro u otros eventos.

diameter (p. 584) The distance across a circle through its center.

diameter

diámetro La distancia a través de un círculo pasando por el centro.

diámetro

disjoint events (p. 494) Events that cannot happen at the same time.

eventos disjuntos Eventos que no pueden ocurrir al mismo tiempo.

Distributive Property (p. 53) To multiply a sum by a number, multiply each addend of the sum by the number outside the parentheses.

propiedad distributiva Para multiplicar una suma por un número, multiplica cada sumando de la suma por el número fuera del paréntesis.

Division Property of Equality (p. 142) If you divide each side of an equation by the same nonzero number, the two sides remain equal.

propiedad de igualdad de la división Si divides ambos lados de una ecuación entre el mismo número no nulo, los lados permanecen iguales.

domain (p. 63) The set of input values for a function.

dominio El conjunto de valores de entrada de una función.

E

edge (p. 603) The segment formed by intersecting faces of a three-dimensional figure.

arista Segmento de recta formado por la intersección de las caras en una figura tridimensional.

equation (p. 49) A mathematical sentence that contains an equals sign, =.

ecuación Enunciado matemático que contiene un signo de igualdad, =.

equilateral triangle (p. 525) A triangle having three congruent sides.

triángulo equilátero Triángulo con tres lados congruentes.

equivalent expressions (p. 53) Expressions that have the same value.

expresiones equivalentes Expresiones que tienen el mismo valor.

equivalent fractions (p. 192) Fractions that have the same value. $\frac{2}{3}$ and $\frac{4}{6}$ are equivalent fractions.

fracciones equivalentes Fracciones que tienen el mismo valor. $\frac{2}{3}$ y $\frac{4}{6}$ son fracciones equivalentes.

equivalent ratios (p. 288) Two ratios that have the same value.

razones equivalentes Dos razones que tienen el mismo valor.

evaluate (p. 31) To find the value of an expression.

evaluar Calcular el valor de una expresión.

experimental probability (p. 486) An estimated probability based on the relative frequency of positive outcomes occurring during an experiment.

probabilidad experimental Estimado de una probabilidad que se basa en la frecuencia relativa de los resultados positivos que ocurren durante un experimento.

exponent (p. 30) In a power, the number that tells how many times the base is used as a factor. In 5^3, the exponent is 3. That is, $5^3 = 5 \times 5 \times 5$.

exponente En una potencia, el número que indica las veces que la base se usa como factor. En 5^3, el exponente es 3. Es decir, $5^3 = 5 \times 5 \times 5$.

exponential form (p. 31) Numbers written with exponents.

forma exponencial Números escritos usando exponentes.

F

face (p. 603) The flat surface of a three-dimensional figure.

cara Superficies planas de una figura tridimensional.

factors (p. 30) Two or more numbers that are multiplied together to form a product.

factores Dos o más números que se multiplican entre sí para formar un producto.

factor tree (p. 182) A diagram showing the prime factorization of a number. The factors branch out from the previous factors until all of the factors are prime numbers.

diagrama de árbol Diagrama que muestra la factorización prima de un número. Los factores se ramifican a partir de los factores previos hasta que todos los factores son números primos.

formula (p. 144) An equation that shows the relationship among certain quantities.

fórmula Ecuación que muestra la relación entre ciertas cantidades.

function (p. 63) A relation in which each element of the input is paired with exactly one element of the output according to a specified rule.

función Relación en que cada elemento de entrada es apareado con un único elemento de salida, según una regla específica.

function rule (p. 63) The operation performed on the input of a function.

regla de función Operación que se efectúa en el valor de entrada.

function table (p. 63) A table used to organize the input numbers, output numbers, and the function rule.

tabla de funciones Tabla que organiza las entradas, la regla y las salidas de una función.

Fundamental Counting Principle (p. 471) Uses multiplication of the number of ways each event in an experiment can occur to find the number of possible outcomes in a sample space.

Principio Fundamental de Contar Este principio usa la multiplicación del número de veces que puede ocurrir cada evento en un experimento para calcular el número de posibles resultados en un espacio muestral.

G

gram (p. 304) A unit of mass in the metric system equivalent to 0.001 kilogram.

gramo Unidad de masa del sistema métrico. Un gramo equivale a 0.001 kilogramo.

graph (p. 80) The process of placing a point on a number line at its proper location.

graficar Proceso de dibujar o trazar un punto en una recta numérica en su ubicación correcta.

greatest common factor (GCF) (p. 186) The greatest of the common factors of two or more numbers. The GCF of 18 and 24 is 6.

máximo común divisor (MCD) El mayor factor común de dos o más números. El MCD de 18 y 24 es 6.

H

height (p. 572) The length of the segment perpendicular to the base with endpoints on opposite sides. In a triangle, the distance from a base to the opposite vertex.

altura Longitud del segmento perpendicular a la base y con extremos en lados opuestos. En un triángulo, es la distancia desde una base al vértice opuesto.

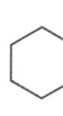

---

heptagon (p. 546) A polygon having seven sides.

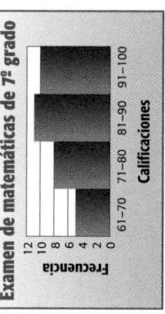

heptágono Polígono con siete lados.

hexagon (p. 546) A polygon having six sides.

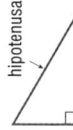

hexágono Polígono con seis lados.

histogram (p. 416) A special kind of bar graph in which the bars are used to represent the frequency of numerical data that have been organized in intervals.

histograma Tipo especial de gráfica de barras que usa barras para representar la frecuencia de los datos numéricos, los cuales han sido organizados en intervalos iguales.

hypotenuse (p. 640) The side opposite the right angle in a right triangle.

hipotenusa El lado opuesto al ángulo recto en un triángulo rectángulo.

I

Identity Property (p. 54) The sum of an addend and 0 is the addend. The product of a factor and 1 is the factor.

propiedad de identidad La suma de un sumando y 0 es el sumando mismo. El producto de un factor y 1 es el factor mismo.

independent events (p. 492) Two or more events in which the outcome of one event does not affect the outcome of the other event(s).

eventos independientes Dos o más eventos en los cuales el resultado de uno de ellos no afecta el resultado de los otros eventos.

indirect measurement (p. 542) Finding a measurement by using similar triangles and writing a proportion.

medida indirecta Técnica que se usa para calcular una medida a partir de triángulos semejantes y proporciones.

integer (p. 80) Any number from the set $\{\dots, -4, -3, -2, -1, 0, 1, 2, 3, 4, \dots\}$

entero Todo número del conjunto $\{\dots, -4, -3, -2, -1, 0, 1, 2, 3, 4, \dots\}$

inverse operations (p. 136) Operations that "undo" each other. Addition and subtraction are inverse operations.

operaciones inversas Operaciones que se "anulan" mutuamente. La adición y la sustracción son operaciones inversas.

irrational number (p. 637) A number that cannot be expressed as the quotient of two integers.

número irracional Número que no se puede expresar como el cociente de dos enteros.

isosceles triangle (p. 525) A triangle having at least two congruent sides.

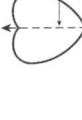

triángulo isósceles Triángulo que tiene por lo menos dos lados congruentes.

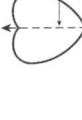

K

kilogram (p. 304) The base unit of mass in the metric system equivalent to 1,000 grams.

kilogramo Unidad fundamental de masa del sistema métrico. Un kilogramo equivale a mil gramos.

L

lateral face (p. 603) One side of a three-dimensional figure.

cara lateral Lado de una figura tridimensional.

leaf (p. 410) The second greatest place value of data in a stem-and-leaf plot.

hoja El segundo valor de posición mayor en un diagrama de tallo y hojas.

least common denominator (LCD) (p. 215) The least common multiple of the denominators of two or more fractions.

mínimo común denominador (mcd) El menor múltiplo común de los denominadores de dos o más fracciones.

least common multiple (LCM) (p. 211) The least of the common multiples of two or more numbers. The LCM of 2 and 3 is 6.

mínimo común múltiplo (mcm) El menor múltiplo común de dos o más números. El mcm de 2 y 3 es 6.

leg (p. 640) Either of the two sides that form the right angle of a right triangle.

cateto Cualquiera de los lados que forman el ángulo recto de un triángulo rectángulo.

like fractions (p. 236) Fractions that have the same denominator.

fracciones semejantes Fracciones con el mismo denominador.

line graph (p. 426) A type of statistical graph using lines to show how values change over a period of time.

6-Mile Hike

gráfica lineal Tipo de gráfica estadística que usa segmentos de recta para mostrar cómo cambian los valores durante un periodo de tiempo.

Caminata de 6 millas

line of reflection (p. 559) The line over which a figure is reflected.

eje de reflexión La línea sobre la cual se refleja una figura.

line of symmetry (p. 558) A line that divides a figure into two halves that are reflections of each other.

line of symmetry

eje de simetría Recta que divide una figura en dos mitades que son reflexiones entre sí.

eje de simetría

line plot (p. 396) A diagram that shows the frequency of data. An × is placed above a number on a number line each time that number occurs in a set of data.

5 10 15 20 25 30 35 40

esquema lineal Gráfica que muestra la frecuencia de datos. Se coloca una × sobre la recta numérica, cada vez que el número aparece en un conjunto de datos.

5 10 15 20 25 30 35 40

line symmetry (p. 558) Figures that match exactly when folded in half have line symmetry.

simetría lineal Exhiben simetría lineal las figuras que coinciden exactamente al doblarse una sobre otra.

linear equation (p. 164) An equation for which the graph is a straight line.

ecuación lineal Ecuación cuya gráfica es una recta.

liter (p. 304) The base unit of capacity in the metric system. A liter is a little more than a quart.

litro Unidad básica de capacidad del sistema métrico. Un litro es un poco más de un cuarto de galón.

M

mean (p. 402) The sum of the data divided by the number of items in the data set.

media La suma de los datos dividida entre el número total de artículos en el conjunto de datos.

measures of central tendency (p. 402) Numbers that are used to describe the center of a set of data. These measures include the mean, median, and mode.

medidas de tendencia central Números que se usan para describir el centro de un conjunto de datos. Estas medidas incluyen la media, la mediana y la moda.

median (p. 403) The middle number in a set of data when the data are ordered from least to greatest. If the data has an even number of items, the median is the mean of the two numbers closer to the middle.

mediana El número del medio en un conjunto de datos cuando los datos se ordenan de menor a mayor. Si los datos tienen un número par de artículos, la mediana es la media de los dos números más cercanos al medio.

meter (p. 304) The base unit of length in the metric system.

metro Unidad fundamental de longitud del sistema métrico.

metric system (p. 304) A base-ten system of measurement using the base units: meter for length, kilogram for mass, and liter for capacity.

sistema métrico Sistema de medidas de base diez que usa las unidades fundamentales: metro para longitud, kilogramo para masa y litro para capacidad.

octagon (p. 546)   A polygon having eight sides.

octágono   Polígono que tiene ocho lados.

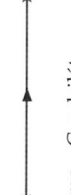

opposites (p. 96)   Two integers are opposites if they are represented on the number line by points that are the same distance from zero, but on opposite sides of zero. The sum of two opposites is zero.

opuestos   Dos enteros son opuestos si, en la recta numérica, están representados por puntos que equidistan de cero, pero en direcciones opuestas. La suma de dos opuestos es cero.

order of operations (p. 38)   The rules to follow when more than one operation is used in a numerical expression.
1. Evaluate the expressions inside grouping symbols
2. Evaluate all powers
3. Multiply and divide in order from left to right.
4. Add and subtract in order from left to right.

orden de operaciones   Reglas a seguir cuando se usa más de una operación en una expresión numérica.
1. Primero ejecuta todas las operaciones dentro de los símbolos de agrupamiento
2. Evalúa todas las potencias antes que las otras operaciones.
3. Multiplica y divide en orden de izquierda a derecha.
4. Suma y resta en orden de izquierda a derecha.

ordered pair (p. 88)   A pair of numbers used to locate a point in the coordinate plane. An ordered pair is written in the form (x-coordinate, y-coordinate).

par ordenado   Par de números que se utiliza para ubicar un punto en un plano de coordenadas. Se escribe de la siguiente forma: (coordenada x, coordenada y).

origin (p. 88)   The point at which the x-axis and the y-axis intersect in a coordinate plane.

origen   Punto en que el eje x y el eje y se intersecan en un plano de coordenadas.

outcome (p. 460)   One possible result of a probability event. For example, 4 is an outcome when a number cube is rolled.

resultado   Uno de los resultados posibles de un evento probabilístico. Por ejemplo, 4 es un resultado posible cuando se lanza un dado.

outlier (p. 397)   A piece of data that is quite separated from the rest of the data.

valor atípico   Dato que se encuentra muy separado del resto de los datos.

P

parallel lines (p. 533)   Lines in a plane that do not intersect.

líneas paralelas   Rectas situadas en un mismo plano y que no se intersecan.

parallelogram (p. 533)   A quadrilateral with opposite sides parallel and opposite sides congruent.

paralelogramo   Cuadrilátero cuyos lados opuestos son paralelos y congruentes.

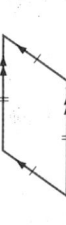

part (p. 350)   In a percent proportion, the number that is compared to the whole quantity.

parte   En una proporción porcentual, el número que se compara con la cantidad total.

---

mode (p. 403)   The number or numbers that appear most often in a set of data. If there are two or more numbers that occur most often, all of them are modes.

moda   El número o números que aparece con más frecuencia en un conjunto de datos. Si hay dos o más números que ocurren con más frecuencia, todos ellos son modas.

multiple (p. 211)   The product of a number and any whole number.

múltiplo   El producto de un número y cualquier número entero.

Multiplication Property of Equality (p. 259)   If you multiply each side of an equation by the same nonzero number, the two sides remain equal.

propiedad de multiplicación de la igualdad   Si multiplicas ambos lados de una ecuación por el mismo número no nulo, lo lados permanecen iguales.

multiplicative inverse (p. 258)   The product of a number and its multiplicative inverse is 1. The multiplicative inverse of $\frac{2}{3}$ is $\frac{3}{2}$.

inverso multiplicativo   El producto de un número y su inverso multiplicativo es 1. El inverso multiplicativo de $\frac{2}{3}$ es $\frac{3}{2}$.

N

negative integer (p. 80)   An integer that is less than zero.

entero negativo   Un entero menor que cero.

net (p. 600)   A two-dimensional figure that can be used to build a three-dimensional figure.

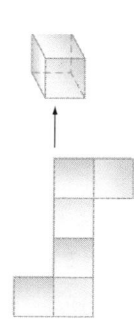

red   Figura bidimensional que sirve para hacer una figura tridimensional.

nonagon (p. 546)   A polygon having nine sides.

enágono   Polígono que tiene nueve lados.

numerical expression (p. 38)   A combination of numbers and operations.

expresión numérica   Combinación de números y operaciones.

O

obtuse angle (p. 511)   Any angle that measures greater than 90° but less than 180°.

ángulo obtuso   Cualquier ángulo que mide más de 90° pero menos de 180°.

obtuse triangle (p. 525)   A triangle having one obtuse angle.

triángulo obtusángulo   Triángulo que tiene un ángulo obtuso.

pentagon (p. 546) A polygon having five sides.

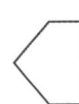

percent (p. 202) A ratio that compares a number to 100.

percent equation (p. 361) An equation that describes the relationship between the part, whole, and percent.
part = percent • whole

percent of change (p. 369) A ratio that compares the change in a quantity to the original amount.

percent of decrease (p. 369) A percent of change when the original quantity decreased.

percent of increase (p. 369) A percent of change when the original quantity increased.

percent proportion (p. 350) Compares part of a quantity to the whole quantity using a percent.
$$\frac{part}{whole} = \frac{percent}{100}$$

perfect squares (p. 34) Numbers with square roots that are whole numbers. 25 is a perfect square because the square root of 25 is 5.

perimeter (p. 156) The distance around a closed geometric figure.

permutation (p. 475) An arrangement, or listing, of objects in which order is important.

perpendicular lines (p. 512) Lines that meet to form right angles.

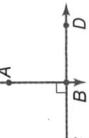

pi (π) (p. 584) The ratio of the circumference of a circle to its diameter. An approximation often used for π is 3.14.

polygon (p. 546) A simple closed figure in a plane formed by three or more line segments.

---

pentágono Polígono que tiene cinco lados.

por ciento Razón que compara un número con 100.

ecuación porcentual Ecuación que describe la relación entre la parte, el todo y el por ciento.
parte = por ciento • todo

porcentaje de cambio Razón que compara el cambio en una cantidad, con la cantidad original.

porcentaje de disminución Porcentaje de cambio cuando disminuye la cantidad original.

porcentaje de aumento Porcentaje de cambio cuando aumenta la cantidad original.

proporción porcentual Comparar partes de una cantidad, a la cantidad entera, usando un porcentaje.
$$\frac{parte}{todo} = \frac{porcentaje}{100}$$

cuadrados perfectos Números cuya raíz cuadrada es un número entero. 25 es un cuadrado perfecto porque la raíz cuadrada de 25 es 5.

perímetro La distancia alrededor de una figura geométrica cerrada.

permutación Arreglo o lista en que el orden es importante.

rectas perpendiculares Rectas que al encontrarse forman ángulos rectos.

pi (π) Razón entre la circunferencia de un círculo y su diámetro. A menudo, se usa 3.14 como aproximación del valor de π.

polígono Figura simple cerrada en un plano, formada por tres o más segmentos de recta.

---

population (p. 434) The entire group of items or individuals from which the samples under consideration are taken.

positive integer (p. 80) An integer that is greater than zero.

powers (p. 30) Numbers expressed using exponents. The power 3² is read *three to the second power, or three squared.*

prime factorization (p. 182) Expressing a composite number as a product of prime numbers. For example, the prime factorization of 63 is 3 × 3 × 7.

prime number (p. 181) A whole number greater than 1 that has exactly two factors, 1 and itself.

principal (p. 379) The amount of money deposited or invested.

prism (p. 601) A three-dimensional figure with at least three rectangular lateral faces and top and bottom faces parallel.

probability (p. 460) The chance that some event will happen. It is the ratio of the number of ways a certain event can occur to the number of possible outcomes.

properties (p. 54) Statements that are true for any number or variable.

proportion (p. 310) An equation that shows that two ratios are equivalent.

proportional (p. 310) The relationship between two ratios with a constant rate or ratio.

protractor (p. 680) An instrument used to measure angles.

pyramid (p. 603) A three-dimensional figure with at least three lateral faces that are triangles and only one base.

Pythagorean Theorem (p. 640) In a right triangle, the square of the length of the hypotenuse is equal to the sum of the squares of the lengths of the legs. $c^2 = a^2 + b^2$

---

población El grupo total de individuos o de artículos del cual se toman las muestras bajo estudio.

entero positivo Un entero mayor que cero.

potencias Números que se expresan usando exponentes. La potencia 3² se lee *tres a la segunda potencia o tres al cuadrado.*

factorización prima Escritura de un número compuesto como el producto de números primos. La factorización prima de 63 es 3 × 3 × 7.

número primo Número entero mayor que 1 que sólo tiene dos factores, 1 y sí mismo.

capital La cantidad de dinero depositada o invertida.

prisma Figura tridimensional que tiene por lo menos tres caras laterales rectangulares y caras paralelas superior e inferior.

probabilidad La posibilidad de que suceda un evento. Es la razón del número de maneras en que puede ocurrir un evento al número total de resultados posibles.

propiedades Enunciados que se cumplen para cualquier número o variable.

proporción Ecuación que muestra que dos razones son equivalentes.

proporcional Relación entre dos razones con una tasa o razón constante.

transportador Instrumento que sirve para medir ángulos.

pirámide Figura tridimensional que tiene por lo menos tres caras laterales triangulares que son triángulos y una sola base.

Teorema de Pitágoras En un triángulo rectángulo, el cuadrado de la longitud de la hipotenusa es igual a la suma de los cuadrados de las longitudes de los catetos. $c^2 = a^2 + b^2$

Q

quadrant (p. 88) One of the four regions into which the two perpendicular number lines of the coordinate plane separate the plane.

cuadrante Una de las cuatro regiones en que dos rectas numéricas perpendiculares dividen el plano de coordenadas.

quadrilateral (p. 533) A closed figure having four sides and four angles.

cuadrilátero Figura cerrada que tiene cuatro lados y cuatro ángulos.

R

radical sign (p. 35) The symbol used to indicate a nonnegative square root, $\sqrt{}$.

signo radical Símbolo que se usa para indicar una raíz cuadrada no negativa, $\sqrt{}$.

radius (p. 584) The distance from the center of a circle to any point on the circle.

radio Distancia desde el centro de un círculo hasta cualquier punto del mismo.

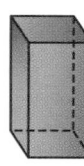

radius

random (p. 461) Outcomes occur at random if each outcome is equally likely to occur.

aleatorio Un resultado ocurre al azar si la posibilidad de ocurrir de cada resultado es equiprobable.

range (p. 63) The set of output values for a function.

rango Conjunto de los valores de salida de una función.

range (p. 397) The difference between the greatest and least numbers in a data set.

rango La diferencia entre el número mayor y el menor en un conjunto de datos.

rate (p. 287) A ratio that compares two quantities with different kinds of units.

tasa Razón que compara dos cantidades que tienen distintas unidades de medida.

rate of change (p. 293) A ratio that shows a change in one quantity with respect to a change in another quantity.

tasa de cambio Razón que representa el cambio en una cantidad con respecto al cambio en otra cantidad.

ratio (p. 202) A comparison of two numbers by division. The ratio of 2 to 3 can be written as 2 out of 3, 2 to 3, 2 : 3, or $\frac{2}{3}$.

razón Comparación de dos números mediante división. La razón de 2 a 3 puede escribirse como 2 de cada 3, 2 a 3, 2:3 ó $\frac{2}{3}$.

---

rational number (p. 216) A number that can be expressed as a fraction.

número racional Número que puede expresarse como fracción.

reciprocal (p. 258) The multiplicative inverse of a number.

recíproco El inverso multiplicativo de un número.

rectangle (p. 533) A parallelogram having four right angles.

rectángulo Paralelogramo con cuatro ángulos rectos.

rectangular prism (p. 611) A solid figure that has two parallel and congruent bases that are rectangles.

prisma rectangular Figura sólida con dos bases paralelas y congruentes que son rectángulos.

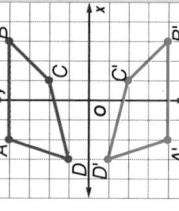

reflection (p. 559) A type of transformation in which a figure is flipped over a line of symmetry.

reflexión Tipo de transformación en el que se da vuelta a una figura sobre un eje de simetría.

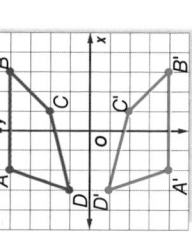

regular polygon (p. 546) A polygon that has all sides congruent and all angles congruent.

polígono regular Polígono con todos los lados y todos los ángulos congruentes.

repeating decimals (p. 197) A decimal whose digits repeat in groups of one or more. Examples are 0.181818... and 0.83333....

decimales periódicos Decimal cuyos dígitos se repiten en grupos de uno o más. Por ejemplo: 0.181818... y 0.83333....

rhombus (p. 533) A parallelogram having four congruent sides.

rombo Paralelogramo que tiene cuatro lados congruentes.

right angle (p. 511) An angle that measures 90°.

ángulo rect Ángulo que mide exactamente 90°.

right triangle (p. 525) A triangle having one right angle.

triángulo rectángulo Triángulo que tiene un ángulo recto.

sample (p. 438) A randomly selected group chosen for the purpose of collecting data.

muestra Grupo escogido al azar o aleatoriamente que se usa con el propósito de recoger datos.

sample space (p. 465) The set of all possible outcomes of a probability experiment.

espacio muestral Conjunto de todos los resultados posibles de un experimento probabilístico.

sampling (p. 312) A practical method used to survey a representative group.

muestreo Método conveniente que facilita la elección y el estudio de un grupo representativo.

scale (p. 320) On a map, intervals used representing the ratio of distance on the map to the actual distance.

escala En un mapa, los intervalos que se usan para representar la razón de las distancias en el mapa a las distancias verdaderas.

scale drawing (p. 320) A drawing that is similar but either larger or smaller than the actual object.

dibujo a escala Dibujo que es semejante, pero más grande o más pequeño que el objeto real.

scale factor (p. 322) A scale written as a ratio in simplest form.

factor de escala Escala escrita como una razón en forma reducida.

scale model (p. 320) A model used to represent something that is too large or too small for an actual-size model.

modelo a escala Réplica de un objeto real, el cual es demasiado grande o demasiado pequeño como para construirlo de tamaño natural.

scalene triangle (p. 525) A triangle having no congruent sides.

triángulo escaleno Triángulo sin lados congruentes.

scatter plot (p. 427) In a scatter plot, two sets of related data are plotted as ordered pairs on the same graph.

diagrama de dispersión Diagrama en que dos conjuntos de datos relacionados aparecen graficados como pares ordenados en la misma gráfica.

School Commute

Tiempo para llegar a la escuela

S

semicircle (p. 696) Half of a circle.

semicírculo Mitad de un círculo con el mismo diámetro.

sequence (p. 57) A list of numbers in a certain order, such as 0, 1, 2, 3, or 2, 4, 6, 8.

sucesión Lista de números en cierto orden, tales como 0, 1, 2, 3 ó 2, 4, 6, 8.

similar figures (p. 540) Figures that have the same shape but not necessarily the same size.

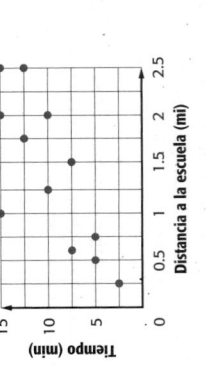

figuras semejantes Figuras que tienen la misma forma, pero no necesariamente el mismo tamaño.

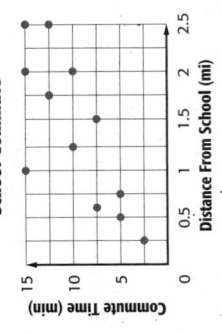

simple event (p. 460) One outcome or a collection of outcomes.

eventos simples Un resultado o una colección de resultados.

simple interest (p. 425) The amount paid or earned for the use of money. The formula for simple interest is $I = prt$.

interés simple Cantidad que se paga o que se gana por el uso del dinero. La fórmula para calcular el interés simple es $I = prt$.

simple random sample (p. 438) A sample where each item or person in the population is as likely to be chosen as any other.

muestra aleatoria simple Muestra de una población que tiene la misma probabilidad de escogerse que cualquier otra.

simplest form (p. 192) A fraction is in simplest form when the GCF of the numerator and the denominator is 1.

forma reducida Una fracción está escrita en forma reducida si el MCD de su numerador y denominador es 1.

simulate (p. 491) A way of acting out or modeling a problem situation.

simulación Manera de modelar o representar un problema.

slope (p. 293) The rate of change between any two points on a line. The ratio of vertical change to horizontal change.

pendiente Razón de cambio entre cualquier par de puntos en una recta. La razón del cambio vertical al cambio horizontal.

solution (p. 49) A value for the variable that makes an equation true. The solution of $12 = x + 7$ is 5.

solución Valor de la variable de una ecuación que hace verdadera la ecuación. La solución de $12 = x + 7$ es 5.

solving an equation (p. 49) The process of finding a solution to an equation.

resolver una ecuación Proceso de encontrar el número o números que satisfagan una ecuación.

sphere (p. 604) A three-dimensional figure in which all points are equal distance from the center.

esfera Figura tridimensional en que todos los puntos están equidistantes del centro.

square (p. 34) The product of a number and itself. 36 is the square of 6.

cuadrado El producto de un número por sí mismo. 36 es el cuadrado de 6.

square (p. 533) A parallelogram having four right angles and four congruent sides.

cuadrado Paralelogramo con cuatro ángulos rectos y cuatro lados congruentes.

square root (p. 35) One of the two equal factors of a number. The square root of 9 is 3.

raíz cuadrada Uno de los dos factores iguales de un número. La raíz cuadrada de 9 es 3.

standard form (p. 31) Numbers written without exponents.

forma estándar Números escritos sin exponentes.

Glossary/Glosario

statistics (p. 396) The branch of mathematics that deals with collecting, organizing, and interpreting data.

stem (p. 410) The greatest place value common to all the data values is used for the stem of a stem-and-leaf plot.

stem-and-leaf plot (p. 410) A system used to condense a set of data where the greatest place value of the data forms the stem and the next greatest place value forms the leaves.

straight angle (p. 511) An angle that measures exactly 180°.

Subtraction Property of Equality (p. 136) If you subtract the same number from each side of an equation, the two sides remain equal.

supplementary angles (p. 514) Two angles are supplementary if the sum of their measures is 180°.

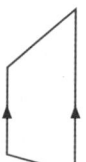

∠1 and ∠2 are supplementary angles.

surface area (p. 649) The sum of the areas of all the surfaces (faces) of a three-dimensional figure.

survey (p. 434) A question or set of questions designed to collect data about a specific group of people.

term (p. 57) Each number in a sequence.

terminating decimals (p. 197) A decimal whose digits end. Every terminating decimal can be written as a fraction with a denominator of 10, 100, 1,000, and so on.

tessellation (p. 548) A repetitive pattern of polygons that fit together with no holes or gaps.

estadística Rama de las matemáticas cuyo objetivo primordial es la recopilación, organización e interpretación de datos.

tallo El mayor valor de posición común a todos los datos es el que se usa como tallo en un diagrama de tallo y hojas.

diagrama de tallo y hojas Sistema que se usa para condensar un conjunto de datos y en el cual el mayor valor de posición de los datos forma el tallo y el segundo mayor valor de posición de los datos forma las hojas.

ángulo llano Ángulo que mide exactamente 180°.

propiedad de sustracción de la igualdad Si restas el mismo número de ambos lados de una ecuación, los dos lados permanecen iguales.

ángulos suplementarios Dos ángulos son suplementarios si la suma de sus medidas es 180°.

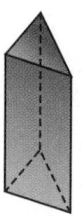

∠1 y ∠2 son suplementarios.

área de superficie La suma de las áreas de todas las superficies (caras) de una figura tridimensional.

encuesta Pregunta o conjunto de preguntas diseñadas para recoger datos sobre un grupo específico de peronas.

término Cada número en una sucesión.

decimales terminales Decimal cuyos dígitos terminan. Todo decimal terminal puede escribirse como una fracción con un denominador de 10, 100, 1,000, etc.

teselado Un patrón repetitivo de polígonos que coinciden perfectamente, sin dejar huecos o espacios.

theoretical probability (p. 486) The ratio of the number of ways an event can occur to the number of possible outcomes.

three-dimensional figures (p. 603) A figure with length, width, and depth (or height).

transformation (p. 553) A movement of a geometric figure.

translation (p. 553) One type of transformation where a geometric figure is slid horizontally, vertically, or both.

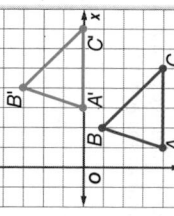

trapezoid (p. 533) A quadrilateral with one pair of parallel sides.

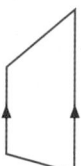

tree diagram (p. 466) A diagram used to show the total number of possible outcomes in a probability experiment.

triangle (p. 524) A polygon that has three sides and three angles.

triangular prism (p. 615) A prism that has bases that are triangles.

two-step equation (p. 151) An equation having two different operations.

probabilidad teórica La razón del número de maneras en que puede ocurrir un evento al número total de resultados posibles.

figuras tridimensionales Figuras que poseen largo, ancho y profundidad (o altura).

transformación Movimientos de figuras geométricas.

traslación Tipo de transformación en que una figura se desliza horizontal o verticalmente o de ambas maneras.

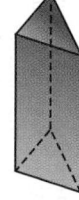

trapecio Cuadrilátero con un único par de lados paralelos.

diagrama de árbol Diagrama que se usa para mostrar el número total de resultados posibles en experimento probabilístico.

triángulo Polígono que posee tres lados y tres ángulos.

prisma triangular Prisma cuyas bases son triángulos.

ecuación de dos pasos Ecuación que contiene dos operaciones distintas.

U

unbiased sample (p. 438) A sample representative of the entire population.
muestra no sesgada Muestra que se selecciona de modo que sea representativa de la población entera.

unit rate (p. 287) A rate with denominator of 1.
tasa unitaria Una tasa con un denominador de 1.

unit ratio (p. 298) A unit rate where the denominator is one unit.
razón unitaria Tasa unitaria en que el denominador es la unidad.

unlike fractions (p. 237) Fractions with different denominators.
fracciones con distinto denominador Fracciones cuyos denominadores son diferentes.

V

variable (p. 44) A placeholder, usually a letter, used to represent an unspecified value in mathematical expressions or sentences. In $3 + a = 6$, a is a variable.
variable Marcador de posición, por lo general, una letra, que se usa para representar un valor desconocido en expresiones o enunciados matemáticos. En $3 + a = 6$, a es una variable.

Venn diagram (p. 186) A diagram that uses overlapping circles to show how elements among sets of numbers or objects are related.
diagrama de Venn Diagrama que usa círculos para mostrar la relación entre los elementos en un conjunto de números u objetos

vertex (p. 510) A vertex of an angle is the common endpoint of the rays forming the angle.
vértice El vértice de un ángulo es el extremo común de los rayos que lo forman.

vertex

vértice

vertex (p. 603) The point where the edges of a three dimensional figure intersect.
vértice Punto donde se intersecan las aristas de una figura tridimensional.

vertical angles (p. 511) Opposite angles formed by the intersection of two lines.
ángulos opuestos por el vértice Ángulos opuestos que se forman de la intersección de dos rectas.

$\angle 1$ and $\angle 2$ are vertical angles.

$\angle 1$ y $\angle 2$ son ángulos opuestos por el vértice.

volume (p. 613) The number of cubic units needed to fill the space occupied by a solid.
volumen Número de unidades cúbicas que se requieren para llenar el espacio que ocupa un sólido.

voluntary response sample (p. 439) A sample which involves only those who want to participate in the sampling.
muestra de respuesta voluntaria Muestra que involucra sólo aquellos que quieren participar en el muestreo.

W

whole (p. 350) In a percent proportion, the number to which the part is being compared.
todo En una proporción porcentual, el número con que se compara la parte.

X

x-axis (p. 88) The horizontal number line in a coordinate plane.
eje x La recta numérica horizontal en el plano de coordenadas.

x-coordinate (p. 88) The first number of an ordered pair. It corresponds to a number on the x-axis.
coordenada x El primer número de un par ordenado. Corresponde a un número en el eje x.

Y

y-axis (p. 88) The vertical number line in a coordinate plane.
eje y La recta numérica vertical en el plano de coordenadas.

y-coordinate (p. 88) The second number of an ordered pair. It corresponds to a number on the y-axis.
coordenada y El segundo número de un par ordenado. Corresponde a un número en el eje y.

Z

zero pair (p. 93) The result when one positive counter is paired with one negative counter.
par nulo Resultado que se obtiene cuando una ficha positiva se aparea con una ficha negativa.

Selected Answers

Chapter 1 Introduction to Algebra and Functions

Page 23

1. 105.8   3. 60.64   5. $72.94   7. 2.5   9. 6.2   11. 29.4
13. 10.2   15. 5.3   17. 4.46

Pages 27–29   Lesson 1-1

1. Sample answer: 4 times; 16,000 ÷ 4,000 = 4
3. 3,000   5. $763.75
7.

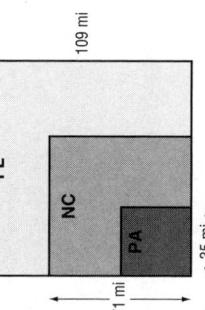

9. every 45 minutes   11. 5:10 P.M.   15. 13 wk
17. Sample answer: For the school bake sale, Samantha bakes 79 cookies and 42 brownies. If two other students baked the same amount of cookies and brownies, how many items did they bake altogether?   19. C   21. 100   23. 625

Pages 31–33   Lesson 1-2

1. $9 \cdot 9 \cdot 9$ 3. $8 \cdot 8 \cdot 8 \cdot 8$ 5. 49   7. Sample answer: 9,765,625 people   9. 1^4 11. $1 \cdot 1 \cdot 1 \cdot 1$
13. $3 \cdot 3 \cdot 3 \cdot 3 \cdot 3 \cdot 3$ 15. $9 \cdot 9 \cdot 9$ 17. 64
19. 2,401   21. 1   23. 1,000,000   25. 3^2 27. 1^8
29. $4 \cdot 4 \cdot 4 \cdot 4 \cdot 4$ 31. 1,296   33. 3^3 35. $5^4 \cdot 4^3$
37. $1^{14}, 17^3, 6^5, 4^{10}$ 39. $7^2, 5^3, 2^{11}, 4^6$ 41. $8^2 = 64$ and $4^3 = 64$ 43. Sample answer: The pattern is that each successive term is $\frac{1}{2}$ of the previous one, so $2^0 = 1$ and
$2^{-1} = \frac{1}{2}$.   45. 7 wins   47. 4   49. 25

Pages 36–37   Lesson 1-3

1. 36   3. 289   5. 3   7. 11   9. 24 in. by 24 in.   11. 1
13. 121   15. 400   17. 1,156   19. 4   21. 10   23. 16
25. 25   27. 40 ft   29. 361   31. 53,824 mi^2

33.

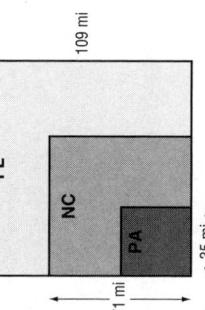

35. 41m^2 greater; The area of a 7 by 7 square has an area of 49 m^2.   37. Yes; for example, a pen that measures 10 feet by 10 feet has the same perimeter, but its area is 100 square feet, which is greater than 84 square feet.   39. Sample answer: It is called squaring the number because the area of a square is found by multiplying the two side lengths together.   41. J
43. $8 \cdot 8 \cdot 8 \cdot 8$ 45. $2 \cdot 2 \cdot 2 \cdot 2 \cdot 2$ 47. 21   49. 30

Pages 40–41   Lesson 1-4

1. 11; Sample answer: Subtract first since 5 − 2 is in parentheses. Then add 8.   3. 11; Sample answer: Multiply 2 by 6 first since multiplication comes before addition or subtraction. Then subtract and add in order from left to right.   5. 400; Sample answer: Evaluate 10^2 first since it is a power. Then multiply by 4.   7. 11; Sample answer: Subtract first since 6 − 3 is in parentheses. Then multiply the difference by 2 and multiply 3 by 4 since multiplication comes before addition or subtraction. Finally, add 17 + 6 and subtract 12 in order from left to right.   9. 3(0.05) + 2(0.25) + 2(0.10) + 7(0.01); $0.92   11. 3; Sample answer: Add first since 3 + 4 is in parentheses. Then subtract.   13. 1; Sample answer: Subtract first since 11 − 2 is in parentheses. Then divide.   15. 8; Sample answer: Divide first since division comes before addition or subtraction. Then subtract 1 and add 7 in order from left to right.   17. 5; Sample answer: Multiply first since multiplication comes before addition or subtraction. Then subtract the product from 118 and add 5.   19. 30,000; Sample answer: Evaluate 10^4 first since it is a power. Then multiply by 3.   21. 386; Sample answer: Evaluate 7^2 first since it is a power. Then multiply by 8 since multiplication comes before addition or subtraction. Finally, subtract.   23. 75; Sample answer: Evaluate 9^2 since it is a power. Then divide 14 by 7 and multiply the quotient by 3 since multiplication and division occur from left to right. Finally, subtract.   25. 22; Sample answer: Add first since 6 + 5 is in parentheses. Then subtract 6 from 8 since 8 − 6 is in parentheses. Finally, multiply.   27. 23; Sample answer: Add first since 4 + 7 is in parentheses. Then multiply the sum by 3. Next, multiply 5 by 4 and divide the product by 2 since multiplication and division occur in order from left to right. Finally, subtract.   29. $3.25   31. 19; Sample answer: Evaluate 3^3 first since it is a power. Then add 8. Next subtract 6 from 10 since 10 − 6 is in parentheses. Then square the difference since the power is 2. Finally subtract 16 from 35.   33. 64; Sample answer: Subtract first since 4 − 3.2 is in parentheses. Multiply 7 by 9 next since multiplication occurs from left to right. Then subtract 0.8 from the product, 63, and add 1.8 since addition and subtraction occur from left to right.   35. Peggy; the first step is to do the division 24 ÷ 6. Phoung incorrectly multiplied 6 and 2 first.   37. Yes; For example, a pen that measures 10 feet by 10 feet has the same perimeter, but its area is 100 square feet, which is greater than 84 square feet.   39. H   41. 8   43. 28   45. 968

Pages 42–43   Lesson 1-5

1. Sample answer: You need to keep track of what numbers you have already guessed, so that you do not make the same guess twice. You also need to know what numbers produce answers that are too large or

too small, so you can make better guesses. **3.** 125 adult tickets and 250 student tickets **5.** birthday, holiday, vacation **7.** The circumference of Earth is 24,900 miles long at the Equator. **9.** 512 and 1,024 **11.** 324.8 in. of snow. **13.** 2, 3, 6

Pages 46–47   Lesson 1-6
1. 10 **3.** 2 **5.** 32 **7.** 22 **9.** 7 **11.** 3 **13.** 4 **15.** 7 **17.** 5 **19.** 12 **21.** 48 **23.** 4 **25.** 18 **27.** 36 **29.** 5 **31.** 4 quarts **33.** 5.1 **35.** $19.99d + 0.17m$ **37.** 64 ft **39.** Sample answer: $5x - 37$ if $x = 8$ **41.** Sample answer: Sometimes; $x - 3$ and $y - 3$ represent the same value only when $x = y$ **43.** G **45.** 28 **47.** 56 **49.** 19 **51.** false

Pages 51–52   Lesson 1-7
1. 3 **3.** 54 **5.** $2.25 **7.** 7 **9.** 28 **11.** 46 **13.** 33 **15.** 64 **17.** 7 **19.** 11 **21.** $m =$ the number of miles Derrick walked on Monday; $m + 2.5 = 6.3$; 3.8 mi **23.** 5.4 **25.** 4.4 **27.** 1.2 **29.** $\$1.75 + c = \$6.25; c = \$4.50$ **31.** Antonio; $105 - 35 = 70$ is a true statement. $35 - 35 \neq 70$ **33.** A **35.** J **37.** 31 **39.** 19 **41.** 28 **43.** 150

Pages 55–56   Lesson 1-8
1. $7(4) + 7(3)$; 49 **3.** $3(9 + 6)$; 45 **5.** $4(12 + 5)$; $68; Sample answer: The expression $12 + 5$ represents the cost of one ticket and one hot dog. The expression $4(12 + 5)$ represents the cost of four tickets and four hot dogs. Since $4 \times 12 = 48$ and $4 \times 5 = 20$, find $48 + 20$, or 68, to find the total cost of four tickets and four hot dogs. **7.** Sample answer: Rewrite $44 + (23 + 16)$ as $44 + (16 + 23)$ using the Commutative Property of Addition. Rewrite $44 + (16 + 23)$ as $(44 + 16) + 23$ using the Associative Property of Addition. Find $44 + 16$, or 60, mentally. Then find $60 + 23$, or 83, mentally. **9.** $2(6) + 2(7)$; 26 **11.** $4(3 + 8)$; 44 **13.** Sample answer: Rewrite $(8 + 27) + 52$ as $(27 + 8) + 52$ using the Commutative Property of Addition. Rewrite $(27 + 8) + 52$ as $27 + (8 + 52)$ using the Associative Property of Addition. Find $8 + 52$, or 60, mentally. Then find $60 + 27$, or 87, mentally. **15.** Sample answer: Rewrite $91 + (15 + 9)$ as $91 + (9 + 15)$ using the Commutative Property of Addition. Rewrite $91 + (9 + 15)$ as $(91 + 9) + 15$ using the Associative Property of Addition. Find $91 + 9$, or 100, mentally. Then find $100 + 15$, or 115, mentally. **17.** Sample answer: Rewrite $(4 \cdot 18) \cdot 25$ as $(18 \cdot 4) \cdot 25$ using the Commutative Property of Multiplication. Rewrite $(18 \cdot 4) \cdot 25$ as $18 \cdot (4 \cdot 25)$ using the Associative Property of Multiplication. Find $4 \cdot 25$, or 100, mentally. Then find $100 \cdot 18$, or 1,800, mentally. **19.** Sample answer: Rewrite $15 \cdot (8 \cdot 2)$ as $15 \cdot (2 \cdot 8)$ using the Commutative Property of Multiplication. Rewrite $15 \cdot (2 \cdot 8)$ as $(15 \cdot 2) \cdot 8$ using the Associative Property of Multiplication. Find $15 \cdot 2$, or 30, mentally. Then find $30 \cdot 8$, or 240, mentally. **21.** Sample answer: Rewrite $5 \cdot (30 \cdot 12)$ as $5 \cdot (12 \cdot 30)$ using the Commutative Property of Multiplication. Rewrite $5 \cdot (12 \cdot 30)$ as $(5 \cdot 12) \cdot 30$ using the Associative Property

of Multiplication. Find $5 \cdot 12$, or 60, mentally. Then find $60 \cdot 30$, or 1,800, mentally. **23.** $5(20 + 7)$; 135 million **25.** $7(9 - 3)$; 42 **27.** $9(7 - 3)$; 36 **29.** $y + 5$ **31.** $32b$ **33.** $2x + 6$ **35.** $6c + 6$ **37.** $55 + 184 = 184 + 55$ **39.** Sample answer: $(5 + z) + 9 = 5 + (z + 9)$ **41.** Sample answer: Since $24 \div (12 \div 2) = 4$ and $(24 \div 12) \div 2 = 1$, $24 \div (12 \div 2) \neq (24 \div 12) \div 2$. **43.** B **45.** 11.3 **47.** 75 yr **49.** 10 **51.** 4.6

Pages 59–61   Lesson 1-9
1. 9 is added to each term; 36, 45, 54 **3.** 0.1 is added to each term; 1.4, 1.5, 1.6 **5.** $3n$; 36 in. **7.** 6 is added to each term; 25, 31, 37 **9.** 12 is added to each term; 67, 79, 91 **11.** 5 is added to each term; 53, 58, 63 **13.** 0.8 is added to each term; 5.6, 6.4, 7.2 **15.** 1.5 is added to each term; 10.5, 12.0, 13.5 **17.** 4 is added to each term; 20.6, 24.6, 28.6 **19.** $7n$; 42 laps **21.** 25 is added to each term; 120, 145, 170 **23.** 256, 1,024, 4,096 **25.** 324, 972, 2,916 **27.** 1,200 **29.** 4,950 **31.** The Fibonacci sequence is 1, 1, 2, 3, 5, 8, 13, …. In this sequence, each term after the second term is the sum of the two terms before it. Fibonacci numbers occur in many areas of nature, including pine cones, shell spirals, and branching plants. **33.** $8 + 2, + 4, + 6, + 8, …$; 30, 42, 56 **35.** Sample answer: paper/pencil; Write the equation that represents this situation, $15n$. Since 2 years = 24 months, evaluate the expression when n is 24. $15(24) = 360$. So, after 2 years, $360 will be saved. **37.** D **39.** 48; Sample answer: Rewrite $(23 + 18) + 7$ as $(18 + 23) + 7$ using the Commutative Property of Addition. Rewrite $(18 + 23) + 7$ as $18 + (23 + 7)$ using the Associative Property of Addition. Find $23 + 7$, or 30, mentally. Then find $18 + 30$, or 48, mentally. **41.** 29 **43.** 20 **45.** 8 **47.** 3

Pages 65–67   Lesson 1-10

1.

x	3x	y
1	3·1	3
2	3·2	6
3	3·3	9
4	3·4	12

; domain: {1, 2, 3, 4}; range: {3, 6, 9, 12}

3.

x	8x	y
1	8·1	8
2	8·2	16
3	8·3	24
4	8·4	32

; domain: {1, 2, 3, 4}; range: {8, 16, 24, 32}

5. 693 mi; Sample answer: Replace h with 3 in the equation $m = 231h$ to find the distance in miles the race car travels in 3 hours.

7.

x	6x	y
1	6·1	6
2	6·2	12
3	6·3	18
4	6·4	24

; domain: {1, 2, 3, 4}; range: {6, 12, 18, 24}

9.

x	25x	y
1	25·1	25
2	25·2	50
3	25·3	75
4	25·4	100

; domain: {1, 2, 3, 4}; range: {25, 50, 75, 100}

11. $c = 40m$ **13.** $t = 35m$

15.

x	x − 1	y
1	1 − 1	0
2	2 − 1	1
3	3 − 1	2
4	4 − 1	3

; domain: {1, 2, 3, 4}; range: {0, 1, 2, 3}

17.

x	x + 0.25	y
0	0 + 0.25	0.25
1	1 + 0.25	1.25
2	2 + 0.25	2.25
3	3 + 0.25	3.25

; domain: {0, 1, 2, 3}; range: {0.25, 1.25, 2.25, 3.25}

19.

Width (units)	6w	Area (sq units)
2	6·2	12
3	6·3	18
4	6·4	24
5	6·5	30

21. $m = 8s$ **23.** 480 mi; 1,140 mi; Sample answer: Replace s with 60 in the equation $m = 8s$ and in the equation $m = 19s$ to find the number of miles Jupiter travels in 1 minute the number of miles Earth travels in 1 minute, respectively. **25.** $y = 3x$ **27.** Sample answer: Sam charges $3 for each dog that he walks. In the equation $y = 3x$, x represents the number of dogs and y represents the total amount of money earned. **29.** C **31.** 63, 72, 81 **33.** $(12)4 + (4)4$; 64 **35.** $10(6 - 5)$; 10 **37.** 7 **39.** 7

Pages 70–74   Chapter 1   Study Guide and Review
1. false, equivalent expressions **3.** false, domain **5.** true **7.** false, square **9.** 60 ft **11.** $3 \cdot 3 \cdot 3 \cdot 3$ **13.** 5 **15.** $5 \cdot 5 \cdot 5 \cdot 5$ **17.** 40,353,607 **19.** 324 **21.** 100 **23.** 8 **25.** 169 **27.** 18 **29.** 25 **31.** 33 **33.** $36 \div 4 + 12 \div 3$; 13 **35.** 22 **37.** 5 **39.** 48 **41.** 8 **43.** 108 **45.** $9 + x = 15$; 6 tickets **47.** 68; Sample answer: Rewrite $14 + (38 + 16)$ as $14 + (16 + 38)$ using the Commutative Property of Addition. Rewrite $14 + (16 + 38)$ as $(14 + 16) + 38$ using the Associative Property of Addition. Find $14 + 16$, or 30, mentally. Then find $30 + 38$, or 68, mentally. **49.** $\$2(15 + 12)$; $54; Sample answer: The expression $15 + 12$ represents the total number of roses Wesley sold. The expression $\$2(15 + 12)$ represents the total amount of money Wesley earned. Since $\$2 \times 15 = \$30$ and $\$2 \times 12 = \$24$, find $\$30 + \$24$, or $54, to find the total amount Wesley earned. **51.** Each term is found by adding 0.8 to the previous term; 6.6, 7.4, 8.2 **53.** $\$4.50n$

55.

x	4x	y
5	4(5)	20
6	4(6)	24
7	4(7)	28
8	4(8)	32

; domain: {5, 6, 7, 8}; range: {20, 24, 28, 32}

Chapter 2 Integers

Page 79   Chapter 2   Getting Ready
1. < **3.** < **5.** Garrett **7.** 20 **9.** 9 **11.** 216 **13.** 29 **15.** 1,900 mi

Pages 82–83   Lesson 2-1
1. −11 **3.** 16 **5.** −15

7. [number line]

9. 8 **11.** 9 **13.** −53 **15.** −2 **17.** 12 **19.** −7

21. [number line] −3 −2 −1 0 1

23. [number line]

25. 10 **27.** 2 **29.** 14 **31.** 25 **33.** 5 **35.** 17 positive charges; 17; 25 negative charges: −25 **37.** false; 0 **39.** C

41.

x	x − 4	y
4	4 − 4	0
5	5 − 4	1
6	6 − 4	2
7	7 − 4	3

; domain: {4, 5, 6, 7}; range: {0, 1, 2, 3}

43.

x	5x + 1	y
1	5·1 + 1	6
2	5·2 + 1	11
3	5·3 + 1	16
4	5·4 + 1	21

; domain: {1, 2, 3, 4}; range: {6, 11, 16, 21}

45. > **47.** >

Pages 85–87   Lesson 2-2
1. > **3.** > **5.** {−18, −16, −10, 12, 19} **7.** < **9.** > **11.** > **13.** < **15.** {−8, −5, −3, 6, 11} **17.** {−7, −6, −4, 1, 3, 5} **19.** Sunlight, Twilight, Midnight, Abyssal, Hadal **21.** < **23.** < **25.** −5, −2, 5, 10, 20 **27.** 5° with a 10-mile-per-hour wind **29.** true **31.** true **33.** −1 **35.** C **37.** −9 **39.** $r = 6t$

41–44. [number line]

For Homework Help, go to Hotmath.com

Pages 90–92 — Lesson 2-3

1. (−2, −4), III 3. (0, 3), y-axis

5–8.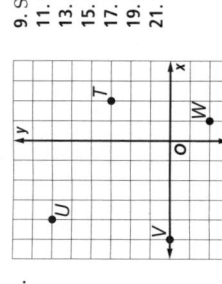

9. Sea Cliffs
11. (−2, 2), II
13. (−5, 0), x-axis
15. (2, −2), IV
17. (−4, −1), III
19. (2, 2), I
21. (0, 4), y-axis

23–34.

35. Africa 37. South America

39–41.

43. Sample answer: Rene Descarte is often credited with inventing the coordinate plane and so the coordinate plane is sometimes called the Cartesian plane, in his honor. The myth is that while a child, Descarte lay in bed one day watching a fly crawling around on the ceiling. In wondering how to tell someone else where the fly was, he realized that he could describe its position by its distance from the walls of the room. 45. Sample answer: Sometimes; both (0, −2) and (0, 2) lie on the y-axis.

47. Sample answer: Using the graphic, you can see that an ordered pair such as (−5, −4) is in Quadrant III.

49. Sample answer: Point A is 1 unit to the right and 2 units down from the origin, in quadrant IV. Point B is 2 units to the left and 1 unit up from the origin, in quadrant II. 51. G 53. > 55. < 57. 41 mi
59. 1,326 61. 11,737

Pages 98–99 — Lesson 2-4

1. −14 3. 7 5. −4 7. 0 9. −$25 + $18; −$7; Camilia still owes her brother $7. 11. −25 13. 28
15. −6 17. −13 19. −2 21. 2 23. 0 25. 22
27. −19 29. 60 + (−60); 0; The pelican is now at sea level. 31. −5 + (−15) + 12; The team has lost a total of 8 yards. 33. 4 35. −3 39. a 41. $m + (−15)$
43. Sample answer: Look at the signs. If the numbers being added are both positive, the sum is positive. If the numbers being added are both negative, the sum is negative. If the numbers being added have different signs, subtract their absolute values and give the sum the sign of the number with the greatest absolute value. If the numbers being added are opposites, the sum is zero. 45. B 47. (−2, 4); 11 49. (−3, −1); 111 51. −8, −4, −3, 0, 1, 4, 6 53. 103 55. 3,109

Pages 105–106 — Lesson 2-5

1. −3 3. −12 5. 24 7. −2 9. −21 11. 22 13. −10
15. −14 17. 23 19. 31 21. −14 23. −30 25. 104
27. 6 29. 0 33. 15 35. 11 37. 8,757 ft
39. 5,066 ft 41. −31 43. 23 45. Mei; Alicia did not add the additive inverse of −18. 47. Sample answer: To subtract an integer, add its additive inverse. 49. J
51. −11 53. −14 55. 8 57. −33 59. −24

Pages 109–111 — Lesson 2-6

1. −60 3. −28 5. 45 7. 64 9. −12 11. 100(−3) = −300; Tamera's investment is now worth $300 less than it was before the price of the stock dropped.
13. 70 15. −220 17. −70 19. −50 21. 80
23. −125 25. 81 27. −45 29. 49 31. −24 33. 24
35. 64 37. −160 39. 5(−650) = −3,250; Ethan burns 3,250 Calories each week. 41. −243 43. 88

47.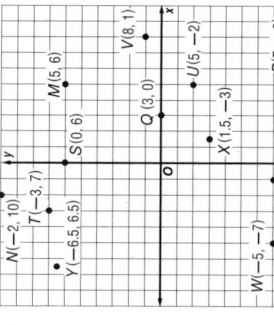

49. Sample answer: −6 × 3 = −18 51. Sample answer: 1; (−1)(−1) = 1. Since there are 50 ÷ 2 = 25 pairs of (−1) factors, $(−1)^{50} = 1^{25}$. One raised to any power is still 1. 53. Sample answer: The product of three integers is positive when exactly two integers are negative or all three integers are positive. 55. J 57. 8
59. −21 61. −6 63. −9 65. 18 + x = 51; x = 33

Pages 112–113 — Lesson 2-7

1. Sample answer: Use the look for a pattern strategy when there is a data table, a series of numbers, or a geometric pattern as part of the problem. 3. Sample answer: Amanda has $2 in change in her bank. If she adds $0.50 each week for 7 weeks, how much money will be in her bank? $5.50 5. 8 months 7. Sample answer: 3 quarters, 2 nickels, and 1 penny 9. 2 letters and 10 postcards 11. 8,914,113 13. 84 cm

Pages 116–118 — Lesson 2-8

1. −4 3. −6 5. 5 7. −3 9. −48.3°C 11. −7
13. −9 15. 10 17. −7 19. −9 21. 9 23. 5
25. −12 27. −3 29. 2 31. −1 33. −10°F 35. 8
37. 1 39. −53 ft 41. −32 ÷ (−4) has a positive quotient; the others have negative quotients
43. −20, −10, −5, −4, −2, −1, 1, 2, 4, 5, 10, 20 45. A
47. 49. 60 51. 81 53. −10 55. 30

Pages 119–122 — Chapter 2 Study Guide and Review

1. false, negative 3. false; opposite
5. false, y-coordinate 7. true 9. false, positive
11. 350 ft 13. −12° 15. 32 17. −48 mL
19. > 21. < 23. < 25. {−32, −23, −21, 14, 19, 25}
27. −10, −6, −5, 0, 2, 5, 10, 12, 20, 25

28–31.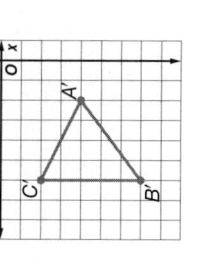

33. 2 35. −5
37. 123 ft 39. −3
41. 4 43. −12
45. 35 47. 28
49. −35
51. 17,280
53. 576 ft
55. −3 57. 9

Chapter 3 Algebra: Linear Equations and Functions

Page 127 — Chapter 3 Getting Ready

1. 4 3. −11

5.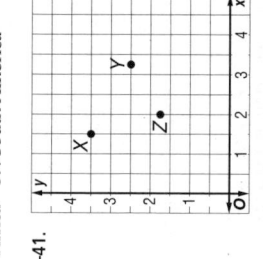

7. −8 9. 4
11. −11 13. 14
15. 2 17. −2

Pages 131–133 — Lesson 3-1

1. n + 8 3. n − 9 = 24 5. 2m = 18 7. x − 1 = 34.3
9. 15 + t 11. n − 10 13. 8r 15. $\frac{a}{3}$ 17. n + 4 = −8
19. 5d = −20 21. h − 10 = 26 23. $\frac{a}{4}$ + 3.5 = 5.5
25. the length is 4 times the width 27. the width is 5

---

less than the length 29. 2b + 2 31. 3(a − 43)
33. $13k^2$ 35. American toad 37. 3 less than a number is 6. 39. x + 2; x − 2 41. C 43. −7 45. 15
47. 25 49. 49 51. Plan A 53. −11 55. −8

Pages 139–141 — Lesson 3-2

1. 2 3. −2 5. d + 120 = 364; 244 ft 7. 5 9. 7 11. 7
13. −3 15. −9 17. 17 19. 7 21. 7 = w + 2; 5
23. 15 = t − 3; 18 years old 25. 61 27. −5 29. −12
31. 18.4 33. 6.4 35. −0.68 37. d − 5 = 18; $23
39. 35 + 45 + x = 180; 100° 41. 1 − 1 + s = −5; −5
43. s − 65 = 13; 78 mph 45. n − 13 = 163; 176 ft
47. The value of y decreases by 2. 49. C 51. p + 180
53. 46 pages 55. 2.6 57. 1.52

Pages 144–146 — Lesson 3-3

1. 3 3. −3 5. 8 h 7. 7 9. −3 11. 7 13. −9
15. 4 17. −8 19. 15w = 300; 20 weeks 21. 3h
23. 23 25. 18 27. 4.7 29. Sample answer: Evelyn Ashford has the faster average speed. Her race is half the distance as Sanya Richards, and it took her less than half the time as Sanya Richards to complete her race. 31. 20.88h = 145; h ≈ 6.94 33. Steve; the variable is multiplied by −6. To solve for x, you need to divide each side of the equation by the entire coefficient, −6. 35. Sample answer: Billie has twice as many cards as Tyree. If Billie has 16 cards, how many does Tyree have? 37. Sample answer: If it takes a scuba diver 4 seconds to swim 8 meters below the surface of the water, what is the rate of descent?
39. 8 41. 5 43. −3y

45.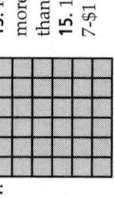

Pages 148–149 — Lesson 3-4

1. When you are given the final result and asked to find an earlier amount. 3. Sample answer: In the first four games, Hannah scored a total of 83 points. In the first game she scored 19 points. In game three, she scored 27 points and in the second game she scored 22 points. How many points did she score in the first game? To solve, first subtract 19 from 83, which is 64. Then subtract 27 from 64 to get 37. Finally, subtract 22 from 37. So, Hannah scored 15 points in her first game.
5. 4 7. 19,200 tennis balls 9. Brie is 14 years old.
11.   13. Raquel's car gets 1,774,074 more inches per gallon than an aircraft carrier.
15. 1-$10 bill, 2-$5 bills, and 7-$1 bills

Pages 153–155 — Lesson 3-5

1. 2 3. 3 5. 3 7. 14c + 23 = 65; 3 CDs 9. 3
11. −4 13. 4 15. 9 17. 8 19. 11 21. 2c + 10 = 14;

Left physical page (R30)

2 cups 23. 2.25 25. 2.1 27. 28 29. $8 + 47.6d = 960$; 20 days 31. 92.2°F 33. $\frac{1}{2}(20x) - 18 = 200$; $x = 21.8$; They must sell at least 22 subscriptions. 35. Sample answer: A flower shop charges $2 for each flower in a vase and $5 for the vase. How many flowers can you place in a vase if you have $15 to spend? 37. G 39. 7 41. 41 43. 213 ft 45. 14 47. 16

Pages 158–161 **Lesson 3-6**
1. 18 yd 3. 7 in. 5. 26.25 ft² 7. 36 ft 9. 14.8 mm 11. 11 ft 13. 18 in. 15. 78 ft² 17. 183.6 m² 19. 6.5 in² 21. 5 squares 23. $\ell = 33$ ft 25. 3,200 yd² 27. perimeter; 4 mi 29. area; 13 ft 31. 270 m²

35. 9;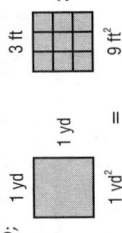

37. 144;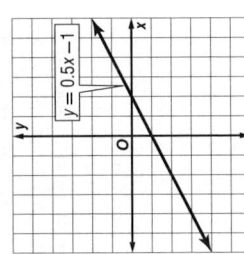

39. When the width of a rectangle is doubled, the perimeter becomes $2\ell + 4w$ and the area becomes $2\ell w$, or in other words, the area is doubled. 41. $P = 2(3w + 1) + 2w$ or $P = 8w + 2$ 43. A 45. −2 47. 3.5 49. $5x = 11.25$; $2.25 51. −27 53. 11 years old

55.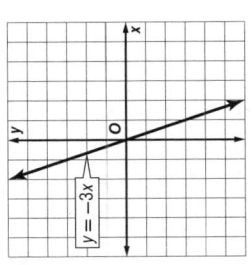

57.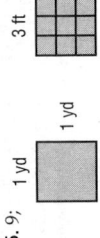

Pages 166–167 **Lesson 3-7**
1. **Total Cost of Baseballs**
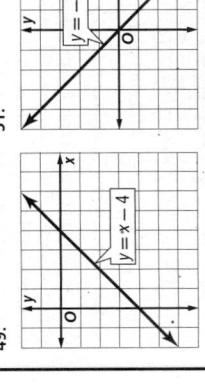

3.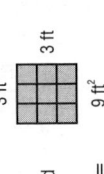

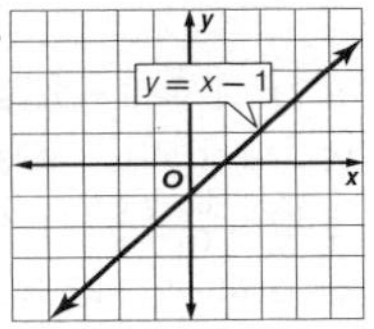

5.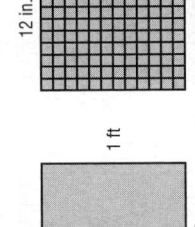

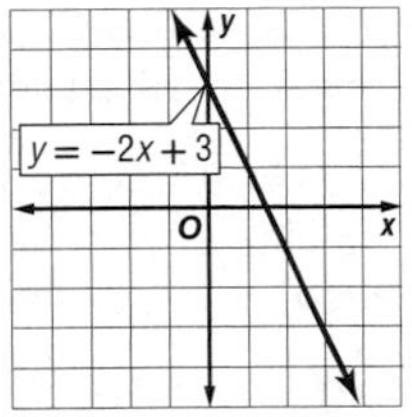

7. **Total Phone Bill**
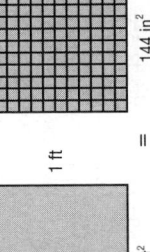

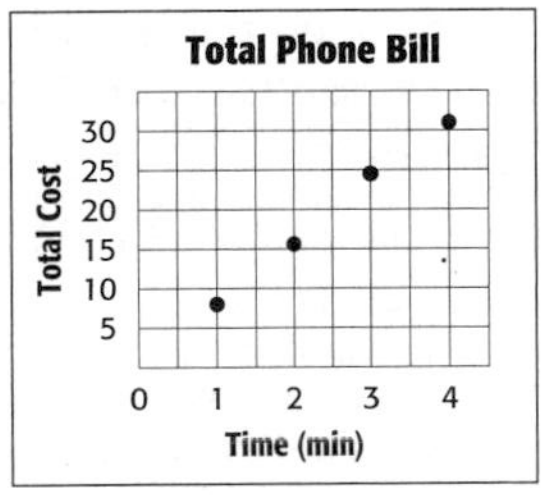

9.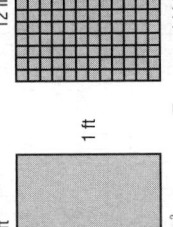

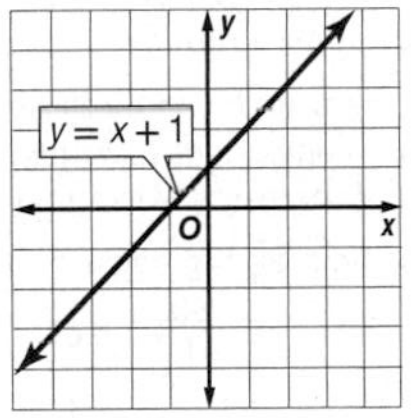

11.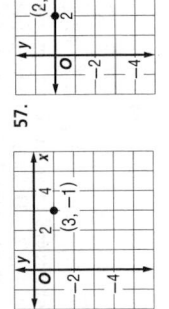

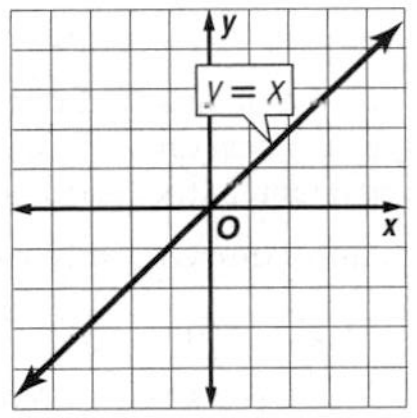

13.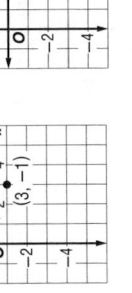

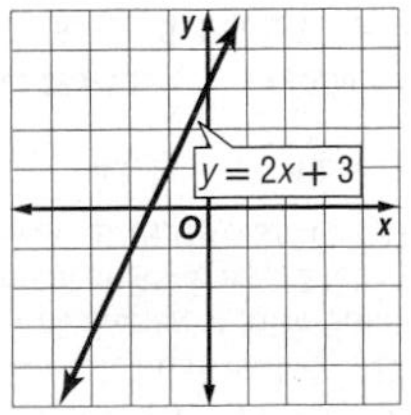

15.
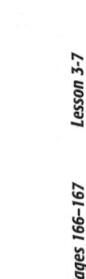

R30 Selected Answers

Right physical page (R31)

53.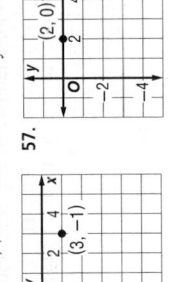

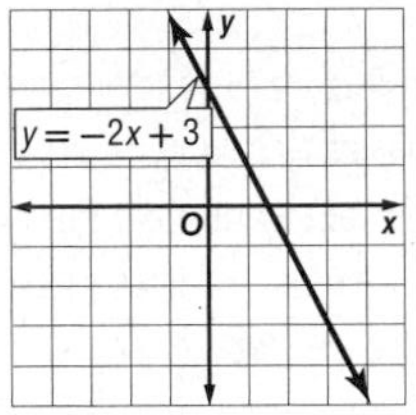

55. $y = 9x$

Chapter 4 Fractions, Decimals, and Percents

Page 179 **Chapter 4** **Getting Ready**
1. 0.61 3. 0.33 5. Kirsten 7. 2, 3, 6 9. Yes; the sum of the digits, 6, is divisible by 3. 11. 6 13. 0.75 15. $5 \times 5 \times 5 \times 5 \times 5$ 17. $9 \times 9 \times 9 \times 9$

Pages 183–184 **Lesson 4-1**
1. prime 3. prime 5. 2×17 7. $2^2 \times 3$ 9. $2 \cdot 2 \cdot 2 \cdot 2 \cdot x \cdot x$ 11. composite 13. prime 15. composite 17. prime 19. $2^5 \times 3$ 21. $3^2 \times 11$ 23. $2 \times 3 \times 5 \times 7$ 25. $2 \times 3^2 \times 7$ 27. $2 \cdot 5^2$ 29. $3 \cdot 5 \cdot m \cdot n$ 31. $2 \cdot 17 \cdot j \cdot k \cdot m$ 33. $2 \cdot 2 \cdot 13 \cdot g \cdot h \cdot h$ 35. 7 37. 5^2 39. $2 \times 5^2 \times 29$ 41. prime 43. 81: 9×9, 3×27; 225: 9×25, 5×45; 441: 9×49; 7×63 45. 36 47. If $n = 1$, $2n$ is a prime number. If $n > 1$, $2n$ is a composite number with at least three factors. 49. H 51. 36 ft; 65 ft² 53. −4 55. 0 57. 2, 5, 10 59. 3, 9

Pages 188–189 **Lesson 4-2**
1. 6 3. 10 5. 4 7. 9 9. 6 11. 5 13. 24 15. 8 17. 6 19. 7 21. 8 students 23. 6 care packages 25. 25¢ 27. $6a$ 29. $5y$ 31. Sample answer: 60 and 90 35. Sample answer: 24 and 36 33. Sample answer: The first prism is 8 in. high, 3 in. long, and 4 in. wide. The second prism is 8 in. high, 6 in. long, and 5 in. wide. The third prism is 8 in. high, 5 in. long, and 5 in. wide. 37. always 39. Sample answer: 4 and 12 are factors of 24. The greatest common factor of 4, 12, and 24 is 4. 41. G

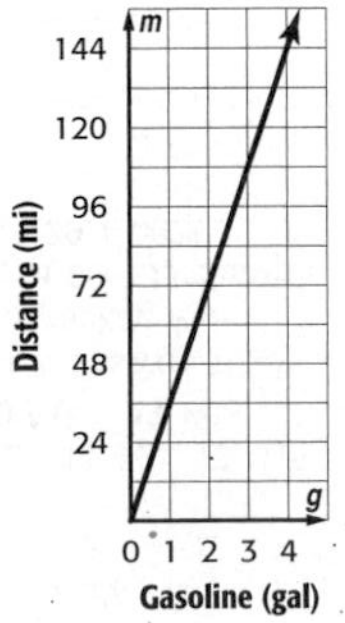

17.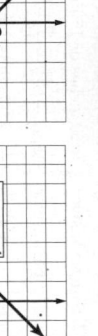

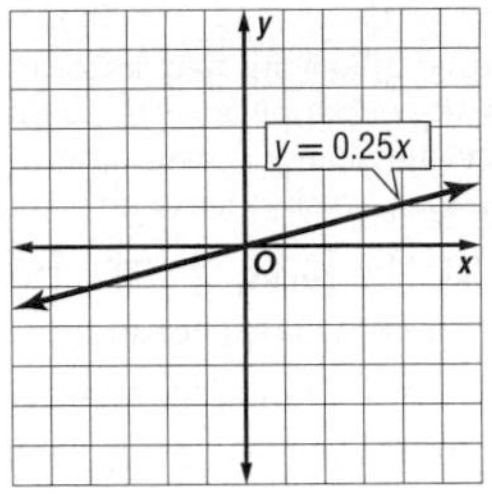

19.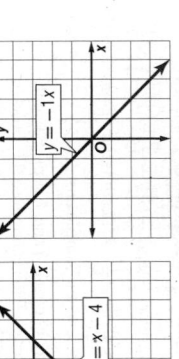

23.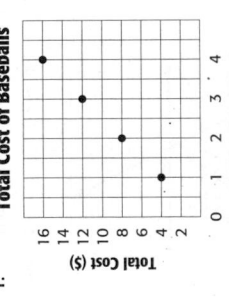

25. C 27. −3 29. 4 31. 15

Pages 169–172 **Chapter 3** **Study Guide and Review**
1. true 3. true 5. true 7. False; subtract 3 from each. 9. true 11. false; perimeter 13. $x + 5$ 15. $2a$ 17. $n - 4 = 19$ 19. $f + \$8.75$ 21. −6 23. 23 25. 37 27. 4 29. −9 31. $14w = 98$; 7 weeks 33. $146.70 35. 4 37. −2 39. 5 41. 53.4 in.; 142.82 in² 43. 7 mi 45. 16 yd 47. 12 ft

49.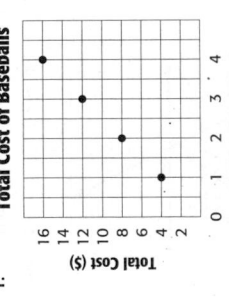

51.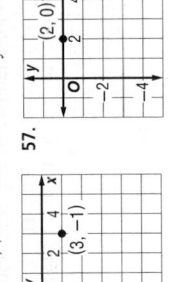

For Homework Help, go to Hotmath.com

43.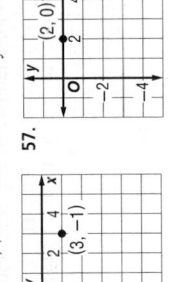

Selected Answers R31

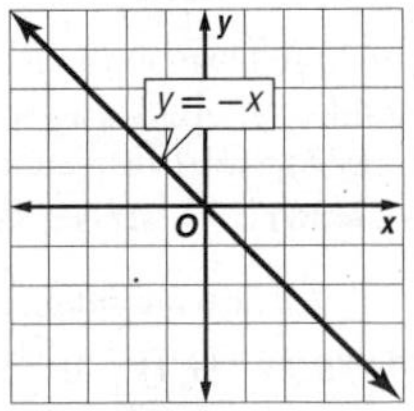

45.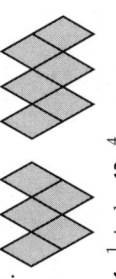

Pages 190–191   Lesson 4-3

1. Sample answer: By making an organized list, you can show all the possible pizza combinations. Count the number of pizzas to determine the answer. 3. 6 outfits   5. 6 ways   7. 27, 29   9. Paul: 9; Angelina: 5; Bret: 9; Jill: 1   11. 7 in.   13. 0.5m

Pages 194–195   Lesson 4-4

1. $\frac{1}{3}$ 3. $\frac{2}{5}$ 5. $\frac{1}{2}$ 7. $\frac{5}{9}$ 9. $\frac{1}{7}$ 11. $\frac{4}{7}$ 13. $\frac{6}{7}$ 15. 1   17. $\frac{5}{6}$ 19. $\frac{5}{7}$ 21. $\frac{5}{2}$ 23. $\frac{1}{5}$ 25. $\frac{4}{3}$ 27. $\frac{1}{3}$ 31. No, because both the numerator and denominator can be divided by 2.   33. Sample answer: A fraction is in simplest form if the GCF of the numerator and denominator is 1.   35. F   37. 9   39. 5   41. 0.5   43. 0.7

Pages 199–200   Lesson 4-5

1. 0.4   3. 7.5   5. 0.125   7. 0.$\overline{5}$ 9. $\frac{11}{50}$ 11. $4\frac{3}{5}$ 13. 0.8   15. 4.16   17. 0.3125   19. 0.66   21. 5.875   23. 0.$\overline{4}$ 25. 0.$\overline{16}$ 27. 5.3   29. $\frac{5}{9}$ 31. $\frac{11}{20}$ 33. $\frac{24}{25}$ 35. $30\frac{1}{2}$ cm   39. $\frac{22}{3}$ 41. $\frac{-16}{5}$ 43. Felisa; Sample answer: Felisa's batting average is about 0.286. Harmony's batting average is about 0.263. 0.286 > 0.263, so Felisa's average is better than Harmony's.   45. Felisa's answer: $3\frac{5}{11} \approx 3.14286...$ and $3\frac{10}{71} \approx 3.14085$; Since 3.1415927... is between $3\frac{5}{11}$ and $3\frac{10}{71}$, Archimedes was correct.   47. B   49. $\frac{5}{12}$ 51. $\frac{5}{7}$ 53. 9 pizzas   55. $\frac{3}{9}$ or $\frac{1}{3}$ 57. $\frac{4}{12}$ or $\frac{1}{3}$

Pages 204–205   Lesson 4-6

1. 57%   3. 25%   5. 85%   7. $\frac{7}{10}$ 9. $\frac{11}{50}$ 11. 42%   13. 99.9%   15. $66\frac{2}{3}$%   17. 80%   19. 26%   21. 60%   23. 100%   25. 30%   27. $\frac{7}{10}$ 29. $\frac{22}{25}$ 31. $\frac{13}{100}$ 33. 3   35. <   37. =   39. >   41. 64%   43. 5%; the other ratios equal 25%   45. C   47. $\frac{3}{5}$ 49. $2\frac{4}{5}$ 51. 3   53. 4   55. 71   57. 0.791

Pages 208–210   Lesson 4-7

1. 0.68   3. 0.276   5. 9%   7. 73%   9. 0.027   11. 0.06   13. 0.185   15. 0.022   17. 0.277   19. 0.3025   21. 0.686   23. 70%   25. 580%   27. 95%   29. 17%   31. 67.5%   33. 1.2%   35. 34.7%   37. 33.9%   39. <   41. >   43. <   45. 0.01389; 0.04167; 0.02083; 0.05; 0.03125   47. 1.2 ft   49. Sample answer: 0.25, $\frac{1}{4}$, 25%

47. 20 songs

51. 37.5%   53. 3.125%   55. D   57. 72%   59. 3.1%   61. −125   63. $2 \times 5 \times 5$ 65. $2 \times 2 \times 19$

Pages 213–214   Lesson 4-8

1. 28   3. 60   5. 60   7. 2020   9. 72   11. 72   13. 315   15. 72   17. 420   19. 144   21. 6:00 P.M.   23. 50¢   25. Sample answer: 5, 7   27. Sample answer: 10, 35   29. 4 packages of juice boxes and 5 packages of oatmeal snack bars   31. $2^2 \cdot 3 \cdot 5$, or 60   33. Sample answer: 3, 10, 15   35. C   37. 0.55   39. 0.0025   41. $\frac{17}{25}$ 43. $2s + 7$ 45. <

Pages 218–220   Lesson 4-9

1. >   3. <   5. Eliot; 3 out of 4 has an average of 0.75; 7 out of 11 has an average of 0.64   7. C   9. <   11. =   13. <   15. >   17. >   19. <   21. >   23. =   25. Jim; $\frac{10}{16} > \frac{4}{15}$ 27. $\frac{8}{10}$, 0.805, 81%   29. −1.4, −1.25, −1$\frac{1}{20}$ 31. $3.47, \frac{3}{7}, 3\frac{3}{5}$ 33. >   35. <   37. 6c, $6\frac{3}{4}$c, 6.5c   39. $\frac{5}{8}$g, 1.5g, 5g   41. Eastern Chipmunk   43. Bustos: 0.346; Kretschman: 0.333; Nuveman: 0.313; Watley: 0.400; Watley   45. 0.08; 0.08 equals 8% and the other ratios equal 80%.   47. Sample answer: Gwen needs $\frac{2}{5}$ yard of fabric and $\frac{3}{8}$ yard of ribbon to make a pillow. Which item does she need more, fabric or ribbon? Answer: fabric   49. H   51. 42   53. 48   55. 0.06   57. 18   59. 4   61. 12

---

43. Sample answer: $\frac{1}{4} \times 60$ inches or 15 inches   45. Sample answer: $\frac{11}{12}$ and $\frac{7}{15}$; $\frac{11}{12} - \frac{7}{15} \approx 1 - \frac{1}{2}$ or $\frac{1}{2}$ 47. Estimation; Dion doesn't need an exact answer. Sample answer: $3\frac{1}{4} + 1\frac{3}{4} + 1\frac{3}{4}$ is about halfway between 6 and 7 cups. Since this is more than 6 cups, Dion cannot use this bowl to mix the ingredients.   49. 38 cups   51. >   53. <   55. 5 pkg. of necklaces and 3 pkg. of bracelets   57. 37.5%   59. 1.9%   61. 10   63. 15

Pages 238–241   Lesson 5-2

1. $\frac{2}{5}$ 3. $\frac{1}{4}$ 5. $\frac{13}{24}$ 7. $\frac{1}{4}$ 9. addition; Sample answer: To find how much smaller the total height of the photo is now, add $\frac{5}{16}$ and $\frac{3}{8}$.   11. $\frac{4}{7}$ 13. $\frac{2}{3}$ 15. $\frac{2}{3}$ 17. $\frac{13}{24}$ 19. $\frac{5}{6}$ 21. $\frac{14}{45}$ 23. addition; Sample answer: To find the smallest width to make the shelf, add $\frac{4}{5}$ and $\frac{3}{4}$; $1\frac{11}{20}$ ft   25. subtraction; Sample answer: To find how much more turkey Makayla bought, subtract $\frac{1}{4}$ from $\frac{5}{8}$; $\frac{3}{8}$ 27. $\frac{23}{28}$ 29. $\frac{7}{12}$ 31. $1\frac{1}{4}$ 33. $2\frac{2}{3}$ 35. $\frac{11}{15}$ 37. $1\frac{1}{4}$ 39. $\frac{1}{12}$ 41. $\frac{1}{3} - (\frac{1}{6} + \frac{1}{4}) = \frac{1}{4}$ 43. $\frac{3}{4}$ 45. Sample answer: The sum of two unit fractions $\frac{1}{a}$ and $\frac{1}{b}$, where a and b are not 0, is $\frac{a+b}{a \cdot b}$.

Rename each fraction using the LCD, ab.

$\frac{1}{a} + \frac{1}{b} = \frac{1 \cdot b}{a \cdot b} + \frac{1 \cdot a}{b \cdot a}$ Simplify.

$= \frac{b}{ab} + \frac{a}{ab}$ Add the numerators.

$= \frac{b+a}{ab}$

$= \frac{a+b}{ab}$ Commutative Property

So, $\frac{1}{99} + \frac{1}{100} = \frac{99+100}{99 \cdot 100}$ or $\frac{199}{9,900}$ 47. Lourdes; Meagan did not rename the fractions using the LCD.   49. A   51. D   53. Sample answer: $4 + 4 = 8$ 55. Sample answer: $6 \cdot 3 = 18$ 57. 24.8%   59. −5   61. $\frac{1}{3}$ 63. 5

Pages 244–246   Lesson 5-3

1. $9\frac{6}{7}$ 3. $4\frac{2}{3}$ 5. $1\frac{7}{12}$ 7. $4\frac{5}{8}$ 9. $3\frac{3}{20}$ gal   11. $7\frac{5}{7}$ 13. $2\frac{1}{7}$ 15. $7\frac{5}{12}$ 17. $18\frac{17}{24}$ 19. $3\frac{1}{2}$ 21. $2\frac{11}{20}$ 23. $5\frac{7}{12}$ 25. $7\frac{5}{6}$ 27. addition; Sample answer: To find the length of the necklace, add $7\frac{1}{4}$ in. and $10\frac{5}{8}$ in.; $17\frac{7}{8}$ in.   29. subtraction; Sample answer: To find how many inches Alameda had cut, subtract $6\frac{1}{2}$ from $9\frac{3}{4}$; $3\frac{1}{4}$ in.   31. $15\frac{1}{4}$ 33. $1\frac{3}{8}$ 35. $7\frac{1}{8}$ yd   37. Estimation; You do not need an exact answer; Less than; $7 + 1 < 2 + 7$ 39. Sample answer: Since the garden is a rectangle, the length of one side added to the length of the other side would equal half the length of the perimeter. If one

---

side of the garden is $2\frac{5}{12}$ ft long, find 6 ft − $2\frac{5}{12}$ ft, or $3\frac{7}{12}$ ft.   41. H   43. Sample answer: $9 \times 7 = 63$ 45. Sample answer: $9 \div 1 = 1$ 47. 15 ft

Pages 248–249   Lesson 5-4

1. Sample answer: Use estimation, look for a pattern, work backward.   3. Sample answer: A fishbowl holds $1\frac{1}{2}$ gallons of water. If there is $\frac{1}{3}$ gallon of water in the bowl, how many more gallons are needed to fill the bowl; $\frac{2}{3}$ gallons, $1\frac{1}{6}$ gallons, or $2\frac{1}{6}$ gallons. Answer: $\frac{2}{3}$ gallon is not enough because that would make exactly 1 gallon of water in the tank. $2\frac{1}{6}$ gallons is too much, since the tank only holds $1\frac{1}{2}$ gallons. The answer is $1\frac{1}{6}$ gallons.   5. J   7. $\frac{1}{8}$ in.

9.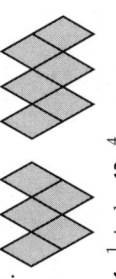

11. $\frac{1}{49}$ inch   13. $\frac{4}{15}$

Pages 255–257   Lesson 5-5

1. $\frac{2}{9}$ 3. $\frac{2}{3}$ 5. $1\frac{2}{3}$ 7. 32 pounds   9. $\frac{4}{15}$ 11. $4\frac{4}{5}$ 13. $\frac{1}{9}$ 15. $\frac{11}{20}$ 17. $\frac{3}{8}$ 19. $\frac{3}{4}$ 21. $\frac{3}{16}$ 23. 14 c   25. $\frac{1}{9}$ 27. 30   29. $31\frac{1}{3}$ 31. 20   33. $7\frac{1}{10}$ mi   35. $\frac{8}{21}$ 37. $\frac{11}{48}$ 39. $16\frac{1}{2}$ yd; $10\frac{5}{6}$ yd^2 41. one pint   43. one centimeter   45. $15\frac{3}{4}$ 47. $28\frac{3}{4}$ 49. broccoli: $1\frac{7}{8}$ c, pasta: $5\frac{5}{8}$ c, salad dressing: 1 c, cheese: 2 c; Multiply each amount by $1\frac{1}{2}$.   51. $\frac{2}{5} \times \frac{3}{5}$; Sample answer: The model shows that $\frac{3}{5}$ of the rectangle is 15 sections out of 25 sections. Since $\frac{2}{5}$ of 15 sections is six sections, $\frac{2}{5}$ of $\frac{3}{5}$ is $\frac{6}{25}$.   53. Always; Sample answer: Improper fractions are always greater than 1.   55. Sample answer: The model shows that $\frac{3}{4}$ of one rectangle is 3 sections out of 4 sections shaded since 2 sets of rectangles with 3 sections out of 4 sections is $\frac{6}{4}$, 2 of $\frac{3}{4}$ is $\frac{6}{4}$, or $1\frac{1}{2}$.   57. H   59. $2\frac{1}{10}$ in.   61. >   63. 4.95 + 0.6x = 22.95; 300 min   65. 3

Pages 261–263   Lesson 5-6

1. $\frac{1}{5}$ 3. $\frac{5}{29}$ 5. 32   7. 20.5   9. $\frac{4}{1}$ 11. 32   13. $\frac{6}{5}$ or $1\frac{1}{5}$ 15. $\frac{1}{6}$ or 6   17. $\frac{1}{4}$ 19. $\frac{8}{41}$ 21. 36   23. 14.4   25. 2.88   27. $\frac{6}{5}$ 29. $\frac{20}{21}$ 31. $6\frac{2}{3}$ 33. 195 mi   35. −75   37. 41.4   39. $1\frac{1}{2}$ 41. x = elevation change of the Wild Cave Tour; $140 = \frac{7}{15}x$; 300ft   43. x = number of servings; $\frac{3}{4} = 16\frac{1}{2}x$; 22 servings   45. x = the person's age; $\frac{2}{3}x = 26$; 78 years old

Chapter 5   Applying Fractions

Page 229   Chapter 5   Getting Ready

1. 35   3. 30   5. 21.6   7. 0.83   9. 4   11. $2\frac{6}{5}$ 13. $5\frac{5}{3}$ 15. $\frac{5}{3}$ or $1\frac{2}{3}$ c

Pages 233–235   Lesson 5-1

1–41. Sample answers are given.   1. 8 ÷ 2 = 10   3. 6 × 3 = 18   5. 0 + $\frac{1}{2}$ = $\frac{1}{2}$ 7. $\frac{1}{2}$ × 1 = $\frac{1}{2}$ 9. $\frac{1}{4}$ + $\frac{1}{4}$ = $\frac{1}{2}$ 11. $\frac{1}{2}$ of 6 ≈ 4ft   13. 1 + 6 = 7   15. 4 − 2 = 2   17. 2 · 3 = 6   19. 9 ÷ 3 = 3   21. $\frac{1}{2}$ ÷ $\frac{1}{2}$ = 1   23. 1 − $\frac{1}{2}$ = $\frac{1}{2}$ 25. $\frac{1}{2}$ · 1 = $\frac{1}{2}$ 27. 0 ÷ 1 = 0   29. 16 + 1 or 17 in.   31. $\frac{1}{6} \times 36 = 6$ 33. 25 ÷ 5 = 5   35. 24 ÷ 2 = 12   37. 39   39. 24   41. $\frac{1}{2} \times 200$ or 100

Pages 221–224   Chapter 4   Study Guide and Review

1. false; division   3. true   5. false; least common multiple   7. true   9. 2^7 11. 5 × 19   13. 65 = 5 · 13   15. 6   17. 21   19. $12   21. 15 different plans   23. $\frac{7}{12}$ 25. $\frac{5}{2}$ 27. $\frac{1}{2}$ 29. 0.75   31. 0.5   33. 6.4   35. $\frac{7}{10}$ 37. $\frac{1}{50}$ 39. $\frac{27}{50}$ 41. $5.1\overline{3}$ min   43. 44%   45. 40%   47. $\frac{19}{20}$ 49. $\frac{4}{25}$ 51. 0.48   53. 0.125   55. 61%   57. 19%   59. 0.12   61.8   63. 24   65. 120   67. <   69. >   71. English

For Homework Help, go to Hotmath.com

Chapter 6 Ratios and Proportions (left page R34)

47. 20; Sample answer: By solving $8 = \frac{m}{4}$, you find that $m = 32$. So, replace m with 32 to find $32 - 12 = 20$. Then **51.** A
49. Sample answer: Multiply each side by 2. Then divide each side by $(b_1 + b_2)$. So, $\frac{2A}{b_1+b_2} = h$. **61.** 1.23
53. $\frac{1}{6}$ **55.** $\frac{2}{5}$ **57.** $3\frac{5}{12}$ c **59.** 0.08
63. -1 **65.** -8 **67.** Sample answer: $18 \div 3 = 6$
69. Sample answer: $0 \div 1 = 0$

Pages 267–270   Lesson 5-7
1. $\frac{3}{8}$ **3.** $3\frac{1}{3}$ **5.** $\frac{1}{15}$ **7.** $1\frac{1}{5}$ **9.** 56 segments **11.** $\frac{7}{16}$
13. $1\frac{1}{5}$ **15.** 12 **17.** $\frac{2}{15}$ **19.** 12 **21.** $\frac{4}{15}$ **23.** $\frac{2}{3}$ **25.** $2\frac{17}{20}$
27. $7\frac{4}{5}$ **29.** 36 **31.** $3\frac{34}{35}$

33. $1\frac{1}{4}$;

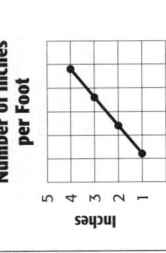

35. $2\frac{3}{4}$;

Pages 271–274   Chapter 5 Study Guide and Review
1. numerators **3.** reciprocal **5.** unlike **7.** $1\frac{11}{7}$ **9.** 3
11. reciprocal **13.** Sample answer: $3 \div 1 = 3$
15. Sample answer: $1 \times 0 = 0$ **17.** Sample answer: $\frac{1}{2} \times 26 = 13$ **19.** Sample answer: 19×10 or about 190 ft² **21.** $\frac{1}{6}$ **23.** $\frac{2}{5}$ **25.** $\frac{5}{24}$ **27.** $\frac{5}{8}$ in. **29.** $9\frac{11}{15}$
31. $10\frac{1}{2}$ **33.** $\frac{4}{15}$ **35.** $15\frac{1}{4}$ **37.** $7\frac{11}{12}$ h **39.** G **41.** $\frac{5}{27}$
43. $2\frac{3}{5}$ **45.** $9\frac{3}{8}$ **47.** $\frac{12}{7}$ or $1\frac{5}{7}$ **49.** $\frac{3}{10}$ **51.** 15 **53.** 0.75
55. $\frac{7}{10}$ **57.** $3\frac{3}{10}$ **59.** $1\frac{21}{22}$ **61.** 54

Getting Ready   Chapter 6
1. 3 **3.** $3\frac{1}{3}$ **5.** $\frac{3}{11}$ **7.** $\frac{1}{22}$ **9.** $\frac{2}{9}$ **11.** $\frac{1}{50}$ **13.** 450

37. 25 **39.** $\frac{1}{22}$ **41.** $3\frac{1}{3}$ **43.** 4 **45.** $7\frac{9}{10}$ times as many
47. 6:30 P.M.; Sample answer: $105 \div 35 = 3$, The storm will travel 105 miles in 3 sets of $\frac{1}{2}$ hour, or $1\frac{1}{2}$ hours. Adding $1\frac{1}{2}$ hours to 5:00 P.M. will make it 6:30 P.M.
49. Yes; Sample answer: You could use paper and pencil; $\frac{3}{4}$ of what number is $1\frac{1}{2}$? $1\frac{1}{2}$ feet $\div \frac{3}{4} = \frac{3}{2}$ feet $\cdot \frac{4}{3} = 2$ feet.
51. Yes. If the first proper fraction is larger than the second proper fraction then the resulting quotient will be a whole number or mixed number. **53.** H
55. $\frac{13}{4}$ or $3\frac{1}{4}$ **57.** $\frac{4}{21}$ **59.** 4.5 ft

Page 281
1. 48.1 **3.** 7.4 **5.** $\frac{1}{5}$ **7.** $\frac{2}{3}$ **9.** $\frac{39}{50}$ **11.** $\frac{1}{50}$ **13.** 450
15. 2,200

Lesson 6-1   Pages 284–286
1. $\frac{2}{15}$ **3.** $\frac{1}{51}$ **5.** yes; $\frac{12}{20} = \frac{3}{5}$ and $\frac{6}{10} = \frac{3}{5}$ **7.** no; but $5 \cdot 3 \neq 20$ **9.** $\frac{3}{2}$ **11.** $\frac{1}{3}$ **13.** $\frac{2}{5}$ **15.** $\frac{21}{1,600}$ **17.** $\frac{21}{32}$
19. yes; $\frac{4}{16} = \frac{1}{4}$ and $\frac{10}{40} = \frac{1}{4}$ so $\frac{4}{16} = \frac{10}{40}$ **21.** no; $\frac{8}{6} = \frac{4}{3}$ and $\frac{12}{10} = \frac{6}{5}$, so $\frac{8}{6} \neq \frac{12}{10}$ **23.** no; Sample answer: $\frac{12\text{ in.}}{3\text{ in.}} = \frac{4}{1}$ and $\frac{6\text{ in.}}{1\text{ in.}} = \frac{6}{1}$ so $\frac{12\text{ in.}}{3\text{ in.}} \neq \frac{6\text{ in.}}{1\text{ in.}}$ **25.** no; $\frac{71}{42} \neq \frac{16}{9}$ **27.** 9 lb **29.** yes; $\frac{330}{396} = \frac{5}{6}$, **31.** Areas A and C; both ratios simplify to a growth-to-removal ratio of $\frac{11}{30}$
33. 80; Sample answer: $440 + 80 = 520$; $\frac{520}{1,200} = \frac{13}{30}$ which is the same ratio as area B **35.** 2,400; The denominator of the ratios increases by 1. $\frac{20}{40} = \frac{1}{2}$, $\frac{40}{120} = \frac{1}{3}$, $\frac{120}{480} = \frac{1}{4}$ **37.** B **39.** $\frac{6}{7}$ **41.** $1\frac{2}{3}$ **43.** $5\frac{2}{3}$ **45.** 4.9 **47.** $0.31

Pages 289–292   Lesson 6-2
1. 6 mi per gal **3.** $0.50 per lb **5.** C **7.** 60 mi/h **9.** 30.4 people per class **11.** 3.5 m/s **13.** $0.14/oz **15.** about $0.50 per pair **17.** Susanna; 1.78 m/s > 1.66 m/s > 1.23 m/s **19.** Soft drinks A and B have about 3 grams of sodium per ounce and Soft drink C has about 6 grams per ounce. **21.** 510 words **23.** Sample answer: about 60 **25.** 182.7 **27.** 38¢ per lb; $1.89 \div 5 \approx$ $1.90 $\div 5$ or $0.38 **29.** 3 c **31.** about 1 h 29 min 49 s **33.** The bear's heart beats 120 times in 2 minutes when it is active. **35.** the bear's heart rate in beats per minute **37.** when it is active; Sample answer: The active line increases faster than the hibernating line when read from left to right. **41.** Always; every rate is a ratio, because it is a comparison of two quantities by division. **43.** Sample answer: a; $\frac{30\text{ ft}}{2\text{ min}} = 15$ ft/min, $\frac{40\text{ ft}}{2\text{ min}} = 20$ ft/min **45.** C **47.** $\frac{2}{9}$ **49.** $\frac{9}{14}$ **51.** 8 subs **53.** $\frac{1}{2}$ **55.** $\frac{1}{4}$

Pages 295–297   Lesson 6-3
1. 1.5°F every hour **3.** slope: $\frac{8}{1}$ or 8; There are 8 packs of fruit snacks in each box.

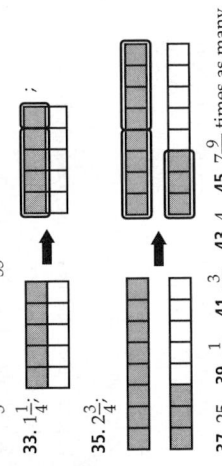

Fruit Snacks

Right page (R35)

47. slope: $\frac{12}{1}$ or 12; There are 12 inches in 1 foot.

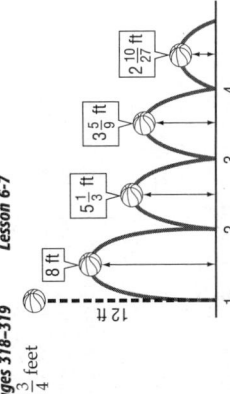

Number of Inches per Foot

49. $6\frac{1}{5}$ **51.** $5\frac{19}{20}$ **53.** 10 **55.** 3.2

Pages 313–315   Lesson 6-6
1. No; sample answer: $\frac{10\text{ children}}{2\text{ adults}} = \frac{5\text{ children}}{1\text{ adult}}$; $\frac{12\text{ children}}{3\text{ adults}} = \frac{4\text{ children}}{1\text{ adult}}$. The unit rates are not equal. **3.** Yes; sample answer: The cross products of the ratios $\frac{8}{21}$ and $\frac{12}{31.5}$, 8×31.5 and 21×12, are both equal to 252.
5. 15 **7.** 29.4 **9.** 20 **11.** $8.33 **13.** No; sample answer: The cross products of the ratios $\frac{20}{16}$ and $\frac{5}{4}$, 20×5 or 100 and 6×16 or 96, are not equal. **15.** Yes; sample answer: The cross products of the ratios $\frac{16}{200}$ and $\frac{28}{350}$, 16×350 and 200×28, are both equal to 5,600.
17. No; sample answer: The cross products of the ratios $\frac{1.4\text{ T}}{18\text{ days}}$ and $\frac{10.5\text{ T}}{60\text{ days}}$, 1.4×60 or 84 and 18×10.5 or 189, are not equal. **19.** No; $\frac{45\text{ min}}{25\text{ pages}} = \frac{1.8\text{ min}}{1\text{ page}}$ and $\frac{60\text{ min}}{30\text{ pages}} = \frac{2\text{ min}}{1\text{ page}}$. These rates are not equivalent. **21.** 15
23. 3 **25.** 1.5 **27.** 63 **29.** 2.4 **31.** 13.5 **33.** 4.2 lb
35. 1.6 oz **37.** (3, 15) represents 3 pizzas cost $15. (5, 25) represents 5 pizzas cost $25. Yes, as the number of pizzas increases by 1, the cost increases by $5. **39.** 5, with delivery fee; 5 no delivery fee; the slope represents the cost per pizza **41.** $19.50 **43.** $\frac{325}{13} = \frac{100}{x}$, 4 **45.** $5.70 for 6 lb; Sample answer: This ratio has a unit rate of 0.95/lb, while all of the other ratios have a unit rate of $0.90/lb. **47.** Sample answer: Mental math; $10 is 4 times more than $2.50, so the number of ears is 4 times more than a dozen, which is 4 dozen or 48 ears of corn.
49. B **51.** about 2.27 kg **53.** 56 **55.** $20\frac{9}{16}$ **57.** $17\frac{5}{32}$

Pages 318–319   Lesson 6-7
1. $\frac{3}{4}$ feet

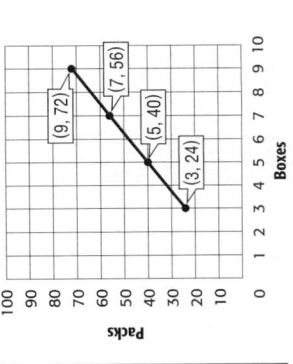

5. $9 per h **7.** $9 per shirt **9.** 0.45 mi/min

Cycling

(20, 180), (15, 135), (10, 90), (5, 45)

Distance (km)

11. $\frac{1}{6}$ inch per minute

13.

Length of Poster (ft)	Ribbon Needed (in.)
3	18
6	36
9	54
12	72

15. A **17.** $11.90 **19.** $\frac{18}{1}$ **21.** 50 **23.** 6.5

Pages 301–303   Lesson 6-4
1. 48 **3.** 52 **5.** 3 **7.** $7\frac{1}{2}$ **9.** 0.0075 mi/s **11.** $4\frac{1}{2}$
13. 16 **15.** 24 **17.** 6,600 **19.** $6\frac{1}{2}$ **21.** 6,750
23. 3,520 ft **25.** $17\frac{1}{2}$ qt **27.** 1,056,000 ft/h **29.** No; 15 in. $+ 4\frac{1}{2}$ in. $+ 6\frac{3}{4}$ in. $= 26\frac{1}{4}$ in. and $26\frac{1}{4} \div 12 = 2\frac{3}{16}$. So, it snowed a total of $2\frac{3}{16}$ ft or about 2 ft, not $2\frac{1}{4}$ ft.
31. $\frac{1}{2}$ **33.** about $8\frac{1}{2}$ mi **35.** $\frac{1}{4}$ **37.** 3 gal; Sample answer: the graph increases by 1 gallon for every 4 quarts. **39.** $\div$ **41.** = **43.** 720 in², Square feet mean a unit of feet × feet. To divide out each unit, you must multiply by two conversion factors that have feet in the denominator and inches in the numerator. 5 ft² $\cdot \frac{12\text{ in.}}{1\text{ ft}} \cdot \frac{12\text{ in.}}{1\text{ ft}} = 720$ in² **45.** G **47.** $9 per h
49. 8 ft **51.** $2v$ **53.** 118.9 **55.** 142.127

Pages 307–309   Lesson 6-5
1. 370 **3.** 1.46 **5.** 8.52 **7.** 128.17 **9.** about 5,333.33 ft **11.** 0.98 **13.** 3.0 **15.** 0.08 **17.** 130,500 **19.** 106.17 **21.** 36.01 **23.** 15.75 **25.** 0.51 kg **27.** about 35,420 meters per hour **29.** 16,582.42 **31.** 403,704 **33.** 0.06 L, 660 mL, 6.6 kL **35.** 130 cm, 2650 mm, 5 m **37.** 50 cm **39.** Jake; Gerardo divided 3.25 by 1,000; he should have multiplied. **41.** about 621,118.01 mi **43.** There are a greater number of smaller units. **45.** H

R36 — Left column

3. 30 miles 5. 125 minutes 7. 28 games
9. Mary, Isabela, Anna, Pilar

Pages 323–326   Lesson 6-8
1. 50 km 3. 130 km 5. 14 feet 7. $16\frac{2}{3}$ in. 9. $\frac{1}{48}$
11. $\frac{1}{63,360}$ 13. 81 mi 15. 40 mi 17. 12 ft by 9 ft
19. $11\frac{1}{5}$ in.; $\frac{1}{90}$ 21. 6 in.; $\frac{1}{720}$ 23. 26 mi 25. $\frac{1}{3}$; about
6.33 feet 29. $\frac{5,000}{1}$ 31a. A; 0.5 cm is larger than 1 mm.
If 0.5 cm on the model is equal to 1 mm on the actual
figure, then model A must be larger than the actual
figure. 31b. 1.5 mm is smaller than 4 cm. If 1.5 mm
on the model is equal to 4 cm on the actual figure, then
model B must be smaller than the actual figure. 31c. C;
0.25 cm is equal to 2.5 mm. If 0.25 cm is equal to 2.5 mm
on the actual figure, then model C must be the same
size as the actual figure. 33. Sample answer: Using the
scale given on the map, look at the distance between the
two cities on the map and then estimate the actual
distance based on the distance given in the scale.
35. F 37. 200 people 39. 15 41. Sample answer:
$7 + 9 + 10 + 12 + 7$ or 45 mi 43. 24 45. 30 47. 60
49. $\frac{13}{30}$ 51. $\frac{7}{8}$

Pages 331–332   Lesson 6-9
1. $\frac{27}{100}$ 3. $\frac{3}{40}$ 5. $\frac{5}{8}$ 7. 0.16% 9. 11.11% 11. $\frac{5}{8}$
13. 0.13% 15. $\frac{1}{3}$ 17. $\frac{15}{16}$ 19. $\frac{1}{1000}$ 21. 555%
23. 375% 25. 96.67% 27. 71.43% 29. 0.13%
31. 0.42% 33. 140% 35. < 37. > 39. $\frac{1}{2}, \frac{2}{5}$, 0.48,
0.5 43. Less than; $\frac{26}{125} = 20.8\%$ 45. Sample answer:
Since a percent is a ratio that compares a number to
100, 80% is the ratio $\frac{80}{100}$. The ratio $\frac{80}{100}$ can be read as
eighty-hundredths or written as a decimal, 0.80 or 0.8.
The ratio $\frac{80}{100}$ also simplifies to $\frac{4}{5}$ if you divide the
numerator and denominator by the same number, 20.
47. G 49. 2 51. $\frac{9}{20}$ 53. $1\frac{3}{4}$

Pages 333–336   Chapter 6   Study Guide and Review
1. ratio 3. rate 5. scale drawing 7. scale factor
9. unit rate 11. $\frac{4}{1}$ 13. $\frac{2}{1}$ 15. no; $\frac{18}{24} = \frac{3}{4}, \frac{20}{24} = \frac{5}{4}$,
and $\frac{3}{4} \neq \frac{4}{4}$ 17. 90 mi per day
19.

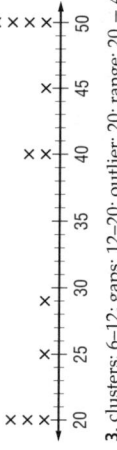

José's Savings

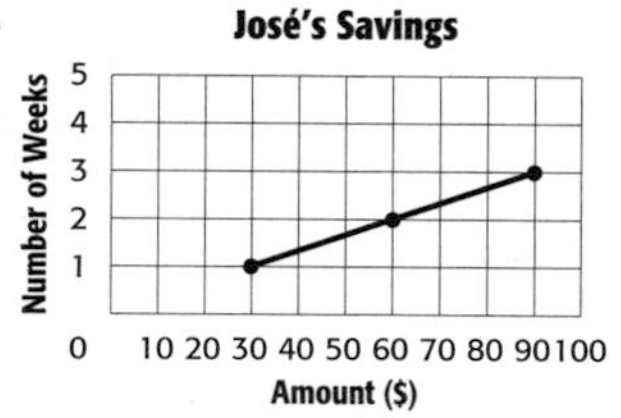

slope: $\frac{30}{1}$ or 30; José saved $30 every week.
21. 24 23. $4\frac{1}{2}$ 25. 50 bushels 27. 51,528.96

R36 Selected Answers

R36 — Right column

29. 18.43 31. about 345 lb 33. 54 35. 9 37. $2\frac{1}{3}$
39. 27 feet 41. 24 mi 43. $\frac{11}{40}$ 45. $\frac{181}{400}$ 47. 91.67%

Chapter 7 Applying Percents

Page 341   Chapter 7   Getting Ready
1. 48 3. 1,512 5. $54.75 7. 0.34 9. 0.75 11. 75
13. 38.9 15. 0.17 17. 1.57 19. 0.075

Pages 346–348   Lesson 7-1
1. 4 3. 110.5 5. 23 7. $3.25 9. $194.40 11. 45.9
13. 14.7 15. 17.5 17. 62.5 19. $290 21. 3.5
23. 97.8 25. 92.5 27. about 19.5 million 29. 3.3
31. 990 33. 520 35. 0.24 37. $9.75 39. $297
41. about 316 43. Sample answer: 53% of 60 → 50%
$\times$ 60 or $\frac{1}{2} \times 60 = 30$ 45. Sample answer: 75% of 19 →
75% $\times$ 20 or $\frac{3}{4} \times 20 = 15$ 47. 80 49. Sample answer:
24% $\times$ 250 or 60 people prefer cherries. So, 250 − 60
or 190 people did not prefer cherries. 51. 15
53. Sample answer: Determine the number of
questions answered correctly on a test and find how
much to tip a restaurant server. 55. Less than the
original number; you are subtracting 10% of a greater
number. 57. C 59. 71% 61. $\frac{3}{5}$ 63. $\frac{17}{24}$ 65. 1267.81

Pages 353–354   Lesson 7-2
1. 36% 3. 0.7 5. 75 7. 3 c 9. 7.5% 11. 8.6
13. 375 15. 24 17. 40% 19. 4.1 21. 192
23. 0.2% 25. $8 27. about 3.4% 29. about 6,378 km
31. 20% of 500, 20% of 100, 5% of 100; If the percent is
the same but the base is greater, then the part is
greater. If the base is the same but the percent is
greater, then the part is greater. 33. B 35. 30
37. 2.75 39. 3 41. 30 43. 18

Pages 357–360   Lesson 7-3
1. $5; \frac{1}{2} \cdot 10 = 5$; $0.1 \cdot 10 = 1$ and $5 \cdot 1 = 5$ 3. $24; \frac{2}{5} \cdot 60$
$= 24$; $0.1 \cdot 60 = 6$ and $4 \cdot 6 = 24$ 5. $(1 \cdot 70) + (\frac{1}{5} \cdot 70)$
$= 105$ 7. about $50; \frac{1}{4} \cdot 200 = $50; 0.1 \cdot 200 = 20$ and
$2.5 \cdot 20 = 50 9. about 160,000 acres; 0.1 · 20,000,000
$= 200,000$ and $\frac{4}{5}$ of 200,000 = 160,000 11. $18; \frac{1}{5} \cdot 90 =$
$18; 0.1 \cdot 90 = 9$ and $2 \cdot 9 = 18$ 13. $135; \frac{3}{4} \cdot 180 = 135$;
$0.1 \cdot 180 = 18$ and $7.5 \cdot 18 = 135$ 15. $90; \frac{9}{10} \cdot 100 = 90$;
$0.1 \cdot 100 = 10$ and $9 \cdot 10 = 90$ 17. $36; \frac{3}{10} \cdot 120 = 36$;
$0.1 \cdot 120 = 12$ and $3 \cdot 12 = 36$ 19. $90; \frac{7}{10} \cdot 150 = 90$; 0.1
$\cdot 150 = 15$ and $6 \cdot 15 = 90$ 21. $168; \frac{7}{10} \cdot 240 = 168$; 0.1
$\cdot 240 = 24$ and $7 \cdot 24 = 168$ 23. about 12 muscles;
$\frac{3}{10} \cdot 40 = 12$ 25. $(2 \cdot 300) + (\frac{1}{4} \cdot 300) = 675$ 27. $0.01 \cdot$
$200 = 2$ and $\frac{3}{4} \cdot 2 = 1.5$ 29. $0.01 \cdot 70 = 0.7$ 31. about
2,700 birds; $0.01 \cdot 450,000 = 4,500$ and $\frac{3}{5} \cdot 4,500 = 2,700$
33. $\frac{1}{2} \cdot 80 = 40$ 35. $\frac{1}{10} \cdot 240 = 24$ 37. $1 \cdot 45 = 45$
39. about 3 hours; Method 1: $\frac{1}{3} \cdot 24 = 8$ and $\frac{1}{5} \cdot 24 \approx 5$;

R37 — Left column

$8 − 5 = 3$ 41. 1,200 43. Sample answer: about
400,000 people; .08 · 5,000,000 = 400,000 45. 3.6
ounces 47. Sample answer: Find 1% of $800, then
multiply by $\frac{3}{8}$. 49. Sometimes; sample answer: one
estimate for 37% of 60 is $\frac{2}{5} \times 60 = 24$. This is greater
than the actual answer because $\frac{2}{5}$ is greater than 37%.
Another estimate is $\frac{1}{3} \times 60 = 20$. This is less than the
actual answer because $\frac{1}{3}$ is less than 37%. 51. B
53. D 55. 64.8 57. 157.1 59. Sample answer: $1 + 0 = 1$
61. Sample answer: $1 - \frac{1}{2} = \frac{1}{2}$ 63. 50 65. 357.1
67. 0.7 69. 0.75

Pages 363–365   Lesson 7-4
1. $p = 88$ 3. 300; 264 3. 75 = n 150; 50%
5. 3 = 0.12 · w; 25 7. 39 loaves 9. $p = 0.39 \cdot 65$; 25.4
11. $p = 0.53 \cdot 470$; 249.1 13. 26 = $n \cdot 96$; 27.1%
15. 30 = $n \cdot 64$; 46.9% 17. 84 = 0.75 · w; 112
19. 64 = 0.8 · w; 80 21. 4,400 games 23. 1 25. $p =$
0.004 · 82.1; 0.3 27. 230 = $n \cdot 200$; 115% 29. about
42% 31. about 27% 33. Sample answer: 30 is 125%
of what number?; 24 35. Sample answer: It may be
easier if the percent and the base are known because
after writing the percent as a decimal or fraction, the
only step is to multiply. When using the percent
proportion, you must first find the cross products
and then divide. 37. H 39. $1.95 41. 170.73%
43. 37 yr

Pages 366–367   Lesson 7-5
1. Sample answer: Look for a rule or pattern in the
data or number facts, estimation, guess and check,
make an organized list, or work backward. 3. Sample
answer; $10 · 12 = $120 5. 500; 60% · 830 ≈ 500
7. 2 quarters, 1 dime, 4 nickels, and 3 pennies 9. $30
11. $3.50 13. 15 · 18 + 18 · 120 = 630 ft³. Then convert
630 ft³ to square yards; 630 ÷ (3 · 3) = 70 yd²

Pages 372–374   Lesson 7-6
1. 20% decrease 3. 19% increase 5. C 7. 40% increase
9. 71% decrease 11. 25% decrease 13. 5% decrease
15. 13% increase 17. 38% decrease 19. 2% increase
21. 75% decrease 23. 150% increase 25. 400%
29. about $31 billion 31. 23% 33. 2005 to 2006; 50%
35. The $60 sound system since 10 is a greater part of
60 than of 90. 37. No; after a 10% increase, the
quantity is greater than the original quantity.
Decreasing a larger number by the same percent
results in a greater change. 39. D 41. Sample
answer: 0.5 · 800 or 400 students 43. $n = 0.21 · 62$;
13.0 45. 0.065 47. 0.0825

Pages 377–378   Lesson 7-7
1. $3.10 3. $1,338.75 5. $98.90 7. $1,605
9. $4.90 11. $7.99 13. $96.26 15. $7.50 17. $180.00
19. $35.79 21. $333.60 23. $25 25. $50, $25;
The percent of discount is 50%. All of the other pairs
have a discount of 25%. 27. C 29. C 31. 9%
decrease 33. about 72% 35. 18

R37 — Right column

Pages 381–382   Lesson 7-8
1. $38.40 3. $5.80 5. $1,417.50 7. $1,219.00
9. $21.38 11. $123.75 13. $45.31 15. $14.06
17. $1,353.13 19. $116.25 21. Yes, he would have
$5,208. 23. $825.60, $852.02, $879.28 25. C
27. $21.39 29. 37% decrease 31. $1\frac{1}{5}$ 33. $2\frac{2}{15}$

Pages 384–388   Chapter 7   Study Guide and Review
1. true 3. true 5. false; 10% 7. true 9. false;
original 11. 39 13. 135 15. 14 games 17. 0.3
19. $27.49 21. Sample answer: 40; $\frac{1}{3} \cdot 120 = 40$
23. Sample answer: 20; $\frac{1}{5} \cdot 100 = 20$ 25. Sample
answer: 360; $0.1 \cdot 400 = 40$; $9 \cdot 40 = 360$ 27. 32 =
$p \cdot 50$; 64% 29. $n = 42 \cdot 300$; 126 31. 108 = 0.12 · w;
900 33. 333 35. Sample answer: $700 × 0.4 = $280
37. 93% increase 39. 10% increase 41. $26.75
43. $8,440 45. 14% 47. $3.51 49. $1,500
51. $101.25 53. $311.85

Chapter 8 Statistics: Analyzing Data

Page 395   Chapter 8   Getting Ready
1. 95.89, 96.02, 96.2 3. 22, 22.012, 22.02 5. 74.7, 74.67,
74.65 7. 3.340, 3.304, 3.04 9. 2.32

Pages 398–401   Lesson 8-1
1.

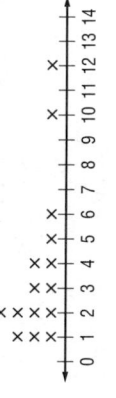

Cost of Video Games ($)

3. clusters: 6–12; gaps: 12–20; outlier: 20; range: 20 − 4,
or 16 5. 1 or 2 glasses per day 7. 5 glasses
9.

Snowfall (in.)

11.

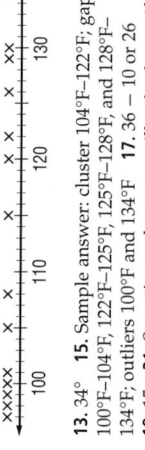

Basketball Scores (pts)

13. 34° 15. Sample answer: cluster 104°F–122°F; gaps
104°F–104°F, 122°F–125°F, 125°F–128°F, and 128°F–
134°F; outliers 100°F and 134°F 17. 36 − 10 or 26
19. 15 21. Sometimes; the range will only change if
the new data value lies above or below the greatest
and least points, respectively, of the original data set.
23. 10 25. about 72% 27. Sample answer: range
28; cluster 1–19; gap 19–29; outlier 29

For Homework Help, go to Hotmath.com

29.

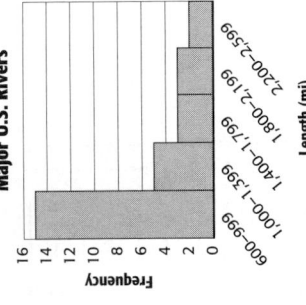

The House of Representatives, Southwestern States

4 8 12 16 20 24 28 32 36 40 44 48 52

Sample answer: The data are more clustered between 4 and 25 with a range of 35 and a gap from 25 to 39. Most frequently occurring is 7, 8, and 9. 39 is an outlier. **31.** Sample answer: The range of a data set excluding the outlier(s) is a lesser value than the range of the same data set including the outlier(s). This is because any outliers will lie below and above the least and greatest values, respectively, of the data set and the range will change to include these values.
33. Sample answer: A frequency table shows the number of times data occur by using tally marks. A line plot shows the number of times data occur by using ×s. A frequency table usually shows intervals of data and is useful when a summary is needed. A line plot shows individual data points and is useful when you need to see how all the data points are spread out. **35.** C **37.** $60 **39.** $4.46 **41.** 47 **43.** 12.6

Pages 405–408   Lesson 8-2

1. 52.3; 57; 59 **3.** 26.5, 25.5, 23, and 25 **5.** Sample answer: Either the mean, median, or mode could be used to represent the data. The mean is slightly less than most of the data items, and therefore is a less accurate description of the data. **7.** 87; 90; 80 and 93 **9.** $12; $9; $6 **11.** 46, 45, 44 **13.** Sample answer: The mean, 15.6, is higher than most of the data. The median, 1, or mode, 1, best represents the data. **15.** $3.50, $3.50, $3.50 **17.** Always; Sample answer: Any value that is added which is greater than the maximum value, 23, will increase the average, or mean, of the values. **19.** Sometimes; Sample answer: The mean of the data set is currently 14.5. If a value that is greater than 14.5 is added, the mean will increase. If a value that is less than 14.5 is added, the mean will decrease. If a value that is exactly 14.5 is added, the mean will remain unchanged. **21.** Sample answer: A length of 960 inches is much greater than the other pieces of data. So, if this piece of data is added, the mean will increase. **23.** 10 points; Sample answer: The sum of the points for the first thirteen games is 158. In order for the average number of points to be 12, the total number of points for fourteen games would need to be 12 × 14 or 168. So, 168 − 158 or 10 points need to be scored during the last game. **25.** Sample answer: 4, 5, 2, 2, 3, 3, 1, 0, 1, 2, 4, 68, 5; the mean, 7.7, is not the best representation since it is greater than all the data items except one. **27.** Sometimes; if there is an odd number of items, the median is the middle number. If there is an even number of items, the median is the mean of the two middle numbers. **29.** Mean; a mode must be a member of the data set, and it is impossible to have 2.59 family members. **31.** H

33.

High Temperatures for July in Kentucky

94 96 98 100 102 104 106

35. $10.43 **37.** Commutative (×) **39.** ones **41.** tenths

Pages 412–414   Lesson 8-3

1. Height of Trees(ft) **3.** 5 **5.** mean

Stem	Leaf
0	8 8
1	0 2 5 5 6 8
2	0 5

2|0 = 20 ft

7. Low Temperatures (°F)

Stem	Leaf
1	3 3 5
2	0 4 8
3	0 1 2 2 5 6 8 8 8

1|3 = 13°F

9. School Play Attendance

Stem	Leaf
22	5 7 9
23	0
24	3 6
25	
26	7 9 9
27	8 8 8

26|7 = 267 people

11. 4; 1 **13.** $45 **15.** mean **17.** 26 **19.** Sample answer: Yes; Thirty-six of the 56 signers were 30–49 years. Since 36 out of 56 is greater than half, you can say that the majority of the signers were 30–49 years old.

21. Average Length (ft) of Crocodiles

Stem	Leaf
6	3
7	
8	1
9	8 8
10	
11	4
12	
13	6
14	
15	
16	0 3 3 3
17	
18	
19	5

13|6 = 13.6 ft

23. Diana; three out of the six or 50% of the pieces of ribbon are 20–30 inches in length.

Sample answer: A reasonable length for an average crocodile is about 16 feet.

---

7. histogram

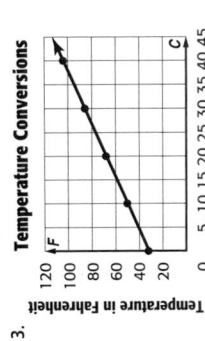

Major U.S. Rivers

Frequency: 0 2 4 6 8 10 12 14 16

Length (mi): 600-999, 1,000-1,399, 1,400-1,799, 1,800-2,199, 2,200-2,599

25. Fiber in Cereal (g)

0 1 2 3 4 5

Stem	Leaf
0	0 1 1 1 1 1 1
2	3 3 3 4 5 5

0|1 = 1 gram

Both representations show the frequency of data occurring. The line plot gives a good picture of the spread of the data. The stem-and-leaf plot shows individual grams of fiber as in the line plot, as well as intervals. See students' favorites and reasons. **27.** C **29.** 48.7; 50; 55

31. Test Scores

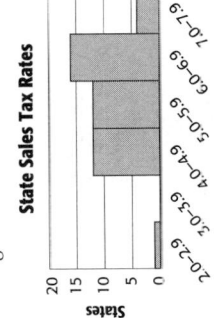

77 78 79 80 81 82 83 84 85 86 87 88 89 90 91 92 93 94

33. $\frac{3}{8}$ **35.** Sample answer: 20; 20–120

Pages 418–421   Lesson 8-4

1. histogram

State Sales Tax Rates

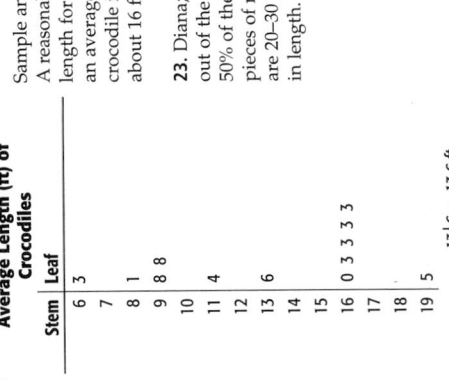

States: 5 10 15 20

Percent: 2.0-2.9, 3.0-3.9, 4.0-4.9, 5.0-5.9, 6.0-6.9, 7.0-7.9

3. health **5.** bar graph

Most Threatened Reptiles

Number of Species: 5 10 15 20 25 30 35 40

Country: Australia, China, Indonesia, U.S., India

9. 13 students **11.** The 60–69 interval is three times larger than the 70–79 interval. **13.** 43 **15.** Sample answer: The number of zoos with 0.0–0.9 million visitors is about 4 times the number of zoos with 3.0–3.9 million visitors. **17.** a **19.** b **21.** about 15.8% **23.** Sample answer: It is easier to compare two sets of data. **25.** tennis **27.** Yes, 20% of girls prefer basketball and 35% of boys prefer basketball. **29.** Sample answer: Each interval represents a portion of the data set. The number of items in each interval is indicated by the frequency, typically shown along the vertical scale. By adding the frequencies for each interval, you can determine the number of values in the data set. **31.** C

33. Number of Wins

Stem	Leaf
1	5 7 9
2	3 5 6
3	0 1 2 6
4	0 1 3 4 5 6 7 7
5	0 0 0 1 2 3 3 5 6

5|3 = 53 wins

35. Mental math; the numbers are easy to compute mentally. Sample answer: $\frac{1}{5}$ of $50 is $10 and $50 − $10 = $40. So, he will need an additional $40.

Pages 424–425   Lesson 8-5

1. Sample answer: Graphs provide a visual representation of a situation involving comparisons. A graphical model can sometimes show conclusively what is often difficult to interpret from looking at lists alone.

3.

Temperature Conversions

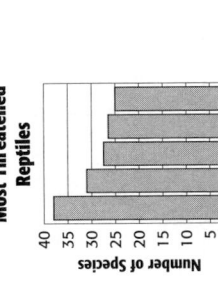

Temperature in Fahrenheit: 20 40 60 80 100 120

Temperature in Celsius: 5 10 15 20 25 30 35 40 45

Lesson 8-6 (continued)

5. Taylor   **7.** Wednesday   **9.** 27, 29   **11.** 2

Pages 428–431   Lesson 8-6

1. Sample answer: The graph shows a positive relationship. That is, as the years pass, the population increases.   **3.** about 155–160 people   **5.** about 400   **7.** about 95 min   **9.** Sample answer: As sleep decreases, the math test score decreases.

11.   Free Throws Made out of Attempts

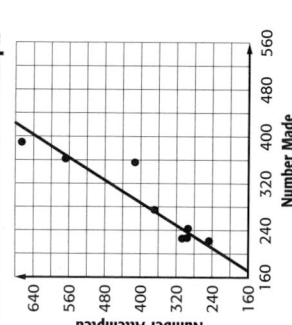

13. There is a positive relationship. That is, as the number of attempts increases, the number of free throws made increases.   **15.** about $55,000   **17.** Sample answer: Both lines have a positive trend. The population of Phoenix, Arizona, is now more than San Diego, California. However, Jim Galvin had 365 wins and Cy Young had 511 wins.   **19.** mode; the other three are ways to display data.   **21.** Graphs often show trends over time. If you continue the pattern, you can use it to make a prediction.   **23.** J

25.   Favorite Color

27. 83°; 83°

Pages 435–437   Lesson 8-7

1. 19,800   **3.** about 59   **5.** 1,419 people   **7.** 62,280 teens   **9.** b.   **11.** a.   **13.** about 38 people   **15.** about 1,040   **19.** D   **21.** B   **23.** It takes Dale a little bit longer to run each successive mile of the 5-mile run.
25. −24   **27.** 54   **29.** $\frac{3}{10}$ or 0.3   **31.** $\frac{9}{2}$ or 4.5

Pages 440–443   Lesson 8-8

1. The conclusion is invalid. This is a biased sample, since people in other states might have more umbrellas than those in Arizona. The sample is a convenience sample since all the people are from the same state.   **3.** This is an unbiased random survey, so the sample is valid; about 102 students.   **5.** The conclusion is invalid. This is a biased, convenience sample.

7. The conclusion is valid. This is an unbiased random sample.   **9.** The conclusion is invalid. This is a biased, convenience sample.   **11.** This is an unbiased random sample, so the results are valid; about 132 boxes.   **13.** This sample is a voluntary response sample. Therefore, no valid conclusion can be made.   **15.** about 443   **17.** Sample answer: This is an unbiased random sample. The time a student spends on the Internet during this week may not be typical of other weeks.   **19.** Sample answer: This is a convenience sample. The softball team may not represent the entire student population.   **21.** Not necessarily; Sample answer: Because you may be surveying different people in each sample, you may get different results.   **23.** Sample answer: If the entire population is too large to survey, it will be less time-consuming and easier to use a sample.   **25.** Yes; Sample answer: Every 10th person at a basketball game is asked whether they prefer basketball or baseball. This survey is a convenience sample because people attending a basketball game probably prefer basketball.   **27.** C   **29.** about 292 students   **31.** $58.44   **33.** $\frac{5}{8}$ **35.** true

Pages 447–449   Lesson 8-9

1. Graph B; From the length of the bars, it appears that Cy Young had about 3 times as many wins as Jim Galvin. However, Jim Galvin had 365 wins and Cy Young had 511 wins. So, the conclusion is not valid.   **3.** Sample answer: The mean is 8,638 and the median is 8,941. Since the median is greater than the mean, use the median to emphasize the average length.   **5.** The sample is a biased convenience sample. Mr. Kessler's first period class may not be representative of all his students. The display is biased because the data used to create the display came from a biased sample.   **7.** The median or the mode because they are much closer in value to most of the pieces of data.   **9.** The sample is a biased convenience sample. The first 100 batteries produced may not be representative of all the batteries produced. The display is biased because the data used to create the display came from a biased sample.

11.   Monthly Cost to Rent an Apartment

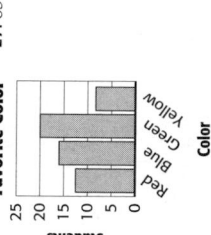

13. Sample answer: Outliers may distort measures of central tendency; data shown in graphs may be exaggerated or minimized by manipulating scales and intervals.   **15.** G   **17.** about 391 teens

Pages 450–454   Chapter 8   Study Guide and Review

1. true   **3.** true   **5.** false; outlier   **7.** true
9.   Temperatures

Sample answer: no significant clusters, gaps, or outliers.

7 8 9 10 11 12 13 14

11.   Number of Calories

Sample answer: cluster 42–44; no gaps or outliers.

40 41 42 43 44 45 46 47

13. 84.3°; 86°; none

15.   Hours Worked

Stem	Leaf
2	1 3 6 9
3	1 2 7 8
4	6
5	4

3|2 = 32 hours

17.   Birthdates

Stem	Leaf
0	3 5 7 9
1	0 1 2 4 6 8
2	1 4

1|2 = 12

19. 10.75 million   **21.** *Crazy Horse*   **23.** Sample answer: The graph shows a positive relationship. That is, as the number of people in a family increases, the number of telephone calls per week increases.   **25.** about 208   **27.** 162 teens   **29.** The conclusion is valid. This is an unbiased random sample.   **31.** The graph does not include the hot summer months or the cold winter months, which could have higher electricity bills.

Chapter 9 Probability

Page 459   Chapter 9   Getting Ready

1. 105   **3.** 52   **5.** 160   **7.** 210   **9.** 360   **11.** 5,040   **13.** $315   **15.** $\frac{1}{6}$ **17.** $\frac{1}{3}$ **19.** 5   **21.** 4

Pages 462–464   Lesson 9-1

1. $\frac{1}{8}$ **3.** $\frac{1}{8}$ **5.** $\frac{3}{5}$ **7.** $\frac{23}{30}$ **9.** 1   **11.** $\frac{1}{20}$ **13.** $\frac{3}{10}$ **15.** $\frac{19}{20}$ **17.** $\frac{5}{8}$ **19.** $\frac{7}{20}$ **21.** 1   **23.** $\frac{3}{4}$ **25.** 60%   **27.** $\frac{14}{33}$ **29.** Sample answer: The complementary event is the chance of no rain. Its probability is 63%   **31a.** 1; Sample answer: Since 2032 is a leap year, there will be 29 days in February, making this event certain to happen;   **31b.** 0; Sample answer: Since 2058 is not a

leap year, there will only be 28 days in February, making this event impossible to happen.   **33.** 0.33; 0.33, 0.44 are probabilities that are not complementary because 0.33 + 0.44 ≠ 1. The other sets of probability are complementary.   **35.** C   **37.** There are no labels on the vertical scale.   **39.** $\frac{1}{3}$ **41.** $\frac{1}{2}$ **43.** $\frac{9}{16}$

Pages 467–470   Lesson 9-2

1. Sample answer:

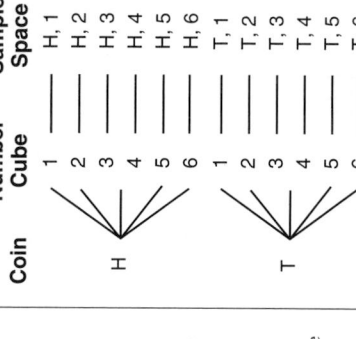

	\multicolumn{6}{c}{Outcomes}					
	1	**2**	**3**	**4**	**5**	**6**
1	1,1	1,2	1,3	1,4	1,5	1,6
2	2,1	2,2	2,3	2,4	2,5	2,6
3	3,1	3,2	3,3	3,4	3,5	3,6
4	4,1	4,2	4,3	4,4	4,5	4,6
5	5,1	5,2	5,3	5,4	5,5	5,6
6	6,1	6,2	6,3	6,4	6,5	6,6

3. C   **5.** Sample answer:

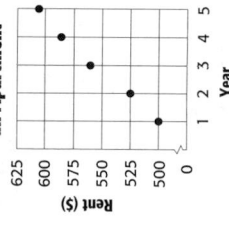

Shape | Number | Sample Space

heads — 1 → heads, 1; 2 → heads, 2; 3 → heads, 3; 4 → heads, 4; 5 → heads, 5
tails — 1 → tails, 1; 2 → tails, 2; 3 → tails, 3; 4 → tails, 4; 5 → tails, 5

7. Sample answer:

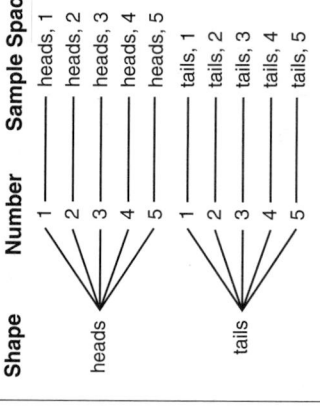

Coin | Number Cube | Sample Space

H — 1 → H, 1; 2 → H, 2; 3 → H, 3; 4 → H, 4; 5 → H, 5; 6 → H, 6
T — 1 → T, 1; 2 → T, 2; 3 → T, 3; 4 → T, 4; 5 → T, 5; 6 → T, 6

For Homework Help, go to Hotmath.com

9. Sample answer:

Color	Speeds	Sample Space
purple	10	purple, 10-speed
purple	18	purple, 18-speed
purple	21	purple, 21-speed
purple	24	purple, 24-speed
green	10	green, 10-speed
green	18	green, 18-speed
green	21	green, 21-speed
green	24	green, 24-speed
black	10	black, 10-speed
black	18	black, 18-speed
black	21	black, 21-speed
black	24	black, 24-speed
silver	10	silver, 10-speed
silver	18	silver, 18-speed
silver	21	silver, 21-speed
silver	24	silver, 24-speed

11. Sample answer:

Outcomes		
Short Sleeve	Gray	Small
Short Sleeve	Gray	Medium
Short Sleeve	Gray	Large
Short Sleeve	White	Small
Short Sleeve	White	Medium
Short Sleeve	White	Large
Long Sleeve	Gray	Small
Long Sleeve	Gray	Medium
Long Sleeve	Gray	Large
Long Sleeve	White	Small
Long Sleeve	White	Medium
Long Sleeve	White	Large

13. Sample answer:

Quarter	Dime	Nickel	Sample Space
H	H	H	H, H, H
H	H	T	H, H, T
H	T	H	H, T, H
H	T	T	H, T, T
T	H	H	T, H, H
T	H	T	T, H, T
T	T	H	T, T, H
T	T	T	T, T, T

There are 8 equally likely outcomes with 4 favoring Elba. So, the probability that Elba wins is $\frac{1}{2}$. **15.** $\frac{1}{8}$
17. $\frac{3}{8}$ **19.** $\frac{1}{8}$ **21.** 16 **25.** Sample answer: Mei can draw a model of the situation using a tree diagram to show the sample space. Then she can determine the probability. The probability of guessing correctly is $\frac{1}{4}$.

Right/Wrong	Right/Wrong	Sample Space
R	R	R, R
R	W	R, W
W	R	W, R
W	W	W, W

27. Sample game: Each player tosses a coin 10 times. If it comes up heads, player 1 receives 1 point. If it comes up tails, player 2 receives 1 point. The player with the most points at the end of the 20 tosses wins. **29.** $\frac{2}{5}$
31. $\frac{13}{20}$ **33.** $\frac{3}{10}$ **35.** The cost is increasing over time. In about a year's time, the cost has more than tripled. **37.** $3,876 **39.** 15.6 **41.** 154 **43.** 460

Pages 472–474   Lesson 9-3
1. 8 **3.** 24 **5.** 12 **7.** 84 **9.** 24 **11.** 6 possible routes; $\frac{1}{6}$ **13.** 7,776 **15.** No; the number of selections is $32 \cdot 11$ or 352, which is less than 365. **17.** 2; 4; 8; 2^n; Sample answer: I used a pattern to determine the number of outcomes for n coins. One coin: 2^1 outcomes, two coins: $2 \cdot 2$ or 2^2 outcomes, three coins: $2 \cdot 2 \cdot 2$ or 2^3 outcomes, n coins: 2^n outcomes. **19.** Sample answer: When there are multiple events, the Fundamental Counting Principle is a much faster method of obtaining the total number of outcomes than drawing a tree diagram. The Fundamental Counting Principle also saves paper space and can often be done mentally. When you need to see what the specific outcomes are, make a tree diagram since the Fundamental Counting Principle only gives the number of outcomes. **21.** 6 **23.** $\frac{1}{2}$ **25.** $\frac{1}{5}$, 0.22, 27%, 20.1 **27.** 6 **29.** 120

Pages 476–478   Lesson 9-4
1. 5,040 **3.** $\frac{1}{20}$ **5.** 24 **7.** 720 **9.** $\frac{1}{90}$ **11.** $\frac{1}{12}$ **13.** Sample answer: Calculator; An exact answer is required. $24 \times 23 \times 22 \times 21 = 255{,}024$ **15.** $\frac{1}{4}$ **17.** Sample answer: The number of ways you can order 3 books on a shelf is $3 \cdot 2 \cdot 1$ or 6. **19.** H

21.

Meat	Cheese	Outcomes
turkey	cheddar	turkey, cheddar
turkey	Swiss	turkey, Swiss
ham	cheddar	ham, cheddar
ham	Swiss	ham, Swiss
salami	cheddar	salami, cheddar
salami	Swiss	salami, Swiss

23. $1\frac{13}{15}$ **25.** $4\frac{11}{48}$ **27.** 56 **29.** 3

35.

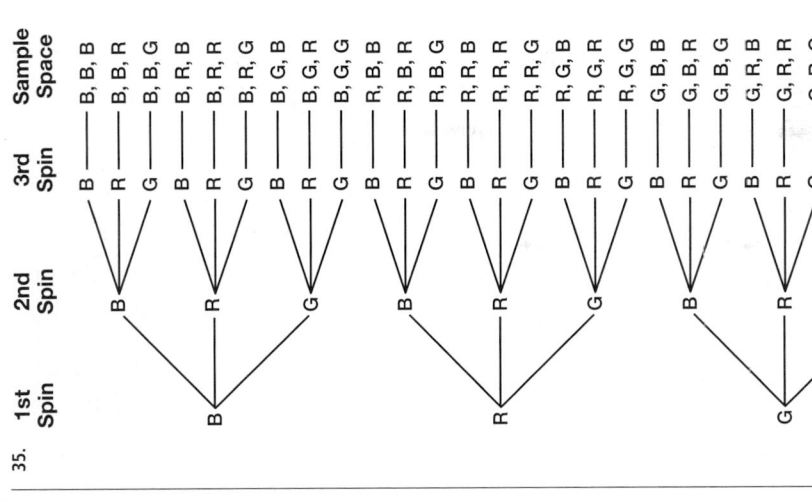

1st Spin	2nd Spin	3rd Spin	Sample Space
B	B	B	B, B, B
B	B	R	B, B, R
B	B	G	B, B, G
B	R	B	B, R, B
B	R	R	B, R, R
B	R	G	B, R, G
B	G	B	B, G, B
B	G	R	B, G, R
B	G	G	B, G, G
R	B	B	R, B, B
R	B	R	R, B, R
R	B	G	R, B, G
R	R	B	R, R, B
R	R	R	R, R, R
R	R	G	R, R, G
R	G	B	R, G, B
R	G	R	R, G, R
R	G	G	R, G, G
G	B	B	G, B, B
G	B	R	G, B, R
G	B	G	G, B, G
G	R	B	G, R, B
G	R	R	G, R, R
G	R	G	G, R, G
G	G	B	G, G, B
G	G	R	G, G, R
G	G	G	G, G, G

37. These events are dependent, not independent. Selecting one book and not returning it to the shelf limits your choices for the next pick to 2 books, not 3, as on the first pick. **39.** G **41.** 6 **43.** −48 **45.** 80

Pages 498–502   Chapter 9   Study Guide and Review
1. true **3.** false; probability **5.** false; independent events **7.** false; disjoint **9.** $\frac{1}{6}$ **11.** $\frac{13}{18}$ **13.** 8%

Pages 482–483   Lesson 9-5
1. 21 ways **3.** 6 **5.** 210 **7.** 924 **9.** $\frac{1}{20}$ **11.** 10; $\frac{1}{10}$ **13.** permutation; 90 **15.** 15 **17.** The number of ways you can choose three CDs from a collection of ten CDs is 120 ways. **19.** H **21.** 72 **23.** Sample answer: $\frac{1}{2} - 0 = \frac{1}{2}$ **25.** $\frac{1}{5}$

Pages 484–485   Lesson 9-6
1. Sample answer: Results would vary slightly. **3.** No; Sample answer: the experiment produces about 1–2 correct answers, so using a spinner with 4 sections is not a good way to answer a 5-question multiple-choice quiz. **5.** 30 **7.** 65 is a reasonable answer because 40% of 160 is 64. **9.** No, the 6th row should have the numbers 1, 5, 10, 10, 5, 1. **11.** No; Sample answer: the experiment produces about 2–3 correct answers, so using a number cube is not a good way to answer a 5-question true-false quiz. **13.** $195

Pages 488–490   Lesson 9-7
1. $\frac{14}{25}$ **3.** The experimental probability, $\frac{14}{25}$ or 56%, is close to its theoretical probability of $\frac{1}{2}$ or 50%. **5.** 22 people **7.** $\frac{9}{10}$; the experimental probability, $\frac{9}{10}$ or 90%, is close to its theoretical probability of $\frac{5}{6}$, or about 83% **9.** $\frac{3}{35}$ **11.** 134 **13.** $\frac{6}{25}$, $\frac{13}{50}$ **15.** $\frac{13}{25}$ **17.** No; The experimental probability that a mother will receive jewelry is $\frac{17}{100}$ Out of 750 mothers that receive gifts, only about 128 can expect to receive jewelry not 250. **19.** Yes; Sample answer: If there are 40 unsharpened pencils in the box, then there are twice as many unsharpened pencils as there are sharpened pencils. If there are five sharpened pencils in the sample that was taken out, then there should be ten unsharpened pencils which would give a total of 15 pencils in the sample, which was the size of the sample. It is important to note that this was only one sample. To be sure that the sample represents the population, other samples should be taken and compared to the first sample. **21.** B **23.** 6 **25.** 60% **27.** 55% **29.** 78%

Pages 495–497   Lesson 9-8
1. $\frac{1}{30}$ **3.** $\frac{1}{10}$ **5.** $\frac{2}{9}$ **7.** $\frac{1}{90}$ **9.** $\frac{2}{7}$ **11.** $\frac{1}{2}$ **13.** $\frac{1}{6}$ **15.** $\frac{3}{25}$ **17.** 0 **19.** $\frac{3}{16}$ **21.** $\frac{15}{92}$ **23.** $\frac{5}{7}$ **25.** $\frac{4}{7}$ **27.** $\frac{3}{20}$ **29.** $\frac{1}{10}$ **31.** $\frac{1}{1{,}024}$ **33.** 21%

For Homework Help, go to **Hotmath.com**

15.

Outcomes	
Pepperoni	Water
Pepperoni	Milk
Pepperoni	Juice
Mushroom	Water
Mushroom	Milk
Mushroom	Juice
Cheese	Water
Cheese	Milk
Cheese	Juice

17. 36 19. $\frac{1}{12}$ 21. 40,320 23. 105 25. 364 27. No; Sample answer: the experiment produces about 3 correct answers, so tossing a coin is not a good way to answer a 6-question true-false quiz. 29. 8 31. $\frac{5}{16}$ 33. $\frac{9}{32}$ 35. $\frac{23}{32}$ 37. $\frac{3}{64}$, $\frac{1}{20}$ 39. $\frac{1}{16}$, $\frac{7}{120}$ 41. $\frac{1}{3}$

Chapter 10 Geometry: Polygons

Page 509 Chapter 10 Getting Ready

1. 306 3. 0.15 5. 0.11 7. 44 9. 105 11. 14 13. 36

Pages 512-513 Lesson 10-1

1. ∠MNP, ∠PNM, ∠N, ∠1; obtuse 3. ∠1 and ∠3; Sample answer: Since ∠1 and ∠3 are opposite angles formed by the intersection of two lines, they are vertical angles. 5. ∠DEF, ∠FED, ∠E, ∠5; right 7. ∠MNP, ∠PNM, ∠N, ∠7; straight 9. ∠RTS, ∠STR, ∠T, ∠9; acute 11. neither 13. adjacent 15. vertical 17. ∠1 and ∠2; Sample answer: Since ∠1 and ∠2 share a common vertex, a common side, and do not overlap, they are adjacent angles. 19. True; Sample answer:

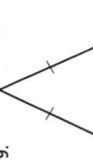

Pages 516-517 Lesson 10-2

1. supplementary 3. 135 5. supplementary 7. supplementary 9. neither 11. 65° 13. 137° 15. Sample answer: ∠CGK, ∠KGJ 17. adjacent; vertical 19. m∠1 = 180° − m∠2; m∠3 = 180° − m∠2; Sample answer: m∠1 and m∠3 both equal the same expression. 21. m∠E = 39°, m∠F = 51° 23. B 25. ∠P, ∠1, ∠RPQ, ∠QPR; acute 27. 223.2 29. 0.12

Pages 520-523 Lesson 10-3

1. **Blood Types in U.S.**

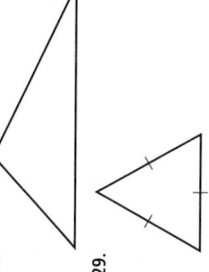

3. blue

5. **U.S. Steel Roller Coasters**
(sit down 86%, inverted 8%, other 6%)

7. **Endangered Species in U.S.**
(birds 45%, mammals 40%, amphibians 6%, reptiles 8%)

9. paper 11. 48 million tons 13. about 12 million 15. 15 17. bar graph

Birthplaces of Presidents
(States: Virginia, Ohio, Massachusetts, New York, Texas; Number of Presidents 0–8)

19. **Sizes of U.S Great Lakes**
(Superior 34%, Huron 24%, Michigan 24%, Ontario 8%, Erie 10%)

21. Lake Ontario is one third the size of Lake Michigan. 23. No; a 50% increase in 126 students is 189, and 189 is not equal to 366. So, it is not reasonable to say that 50% more students said they could make a difference. Since 300% of 126 is 378, it is reasonable to say that 300% more students said they could make a difference than those who said they cannot make a difference. 25. 12.5%; English is half of the circle. Since Science is half of English, Science is half of 50% or 25%. Math is half of Science, which is half of 25% or 12.5%. 27. Sample answer: No; the sum of the

there are 4 right angles. 41. Never; Sample answer: A trapezoid has only one pair of parallel sides. A parallelogram has 2 pairs of parallel sides. 43. Sometimes; Sample answer; A rhombus is only a square if all 4 angles are right angles. 45. Since a square has all the properties of a rectangle and a rhombus, the diagonals of a square must be congruent and perpendicular. Nothing can be concluded about the diagonals of a parallelogram unless more information is provided. If a quadrilateral is a parallelogram, it is not necessarily a rectangle or a rhombus. So, it would not necessarily have the properties of a rectangle or a rhombus. 47. J 49. Neva: hamster, Sophie: turtle, Seth: dog 51. right, scalene 53. 720 55. $3.45 57. 3 59. 7

Pages 527-529 Lesson 10-4

1. 44 3. 45 5. C 7. right, scalene
9.
(triangle)

11. 118 13. 27 15. 90 17. 53° 19. acute, equilateral 21. obtuse, isosceles 23. obtuse, isosceles 25. right
27.
(triangle)

29.
(triangle)

31. 79.5 33. 79.2 35. 21.3 37. 80° 39. 60 41. 77.5
43.
Sample answer: All of the angles are acute and there are no congruent sides. 45. Never; Sample answer: The sum of the three angles in a triangle is 180°. If a triangle has two obtuse angles, the sum of these two angles, not including the third angle, would already be greater than 180°. 47. B 49. about 101° 51. supplementary 53. about $9

Pages 530-531 Lesson 10-5

1. Sample answer: They used inductive reasoning because they made a rule after seeing four examples. 3. See students' work; none of the angles are congruent. 5. Julio: mango, Rashanda: banana, Perry: orange. 7. $3.75 9. 196 sq units 11. 3 packs 13. Sample answer: addition and division; Find the score that when added to the others, 5, is equal to 82. The answer is 79.

Pages 535-538 Lesson 10-6

1. rectangle 3. parallelogram 5. 120° 7. 64° 9. square 11. quadrilateral 13. trapezoid 15. 56° 17. 67° 19. 90° 21. 116° 23. Bricks A, B, and D are rectangles and brick C is a square. 25. 129.1° 27. 131.8° 29. trapezoids, squares, scalene triangles, equilateral triangles 31. right isosceles triangles, squares, trapezoids 33. No; a quadrilateral with three right angles will have both pairs of opposite sides parallel. So, it cannot be a trapezoid. 35. 45 37. 80 39. Property B states that there are 4 right angles; Sample answer: A rectangle has 4 right angles in addition to property A. So, property B must state that

Pages 543-545 Lesson 10-7

1. rectangle PQRS 3. 45 mm 5. triangle CAB 7. 25 mi 9. 7.2 in. 11. 6 ft 13. 12 m 15. 1,207 feet 17. 120 m 19. 1:16 21. B 23. C 25. trapezoid 27. 69° 29. 90 31. 120

Pages 549-551 Lesson 10-8

1. decagon; not regular 3. hexagon; regular 5. 128.6° 7. not a polygon; the figure is not simple 9. isosceles right triangle; not regular 11. hexagon; not regular 13. 144° 15. 90° 17. No; the figure is a decagon. Each angle of a decagon measures 144°, since 144° does not divide evenly into 360°, a decagon cannot make a tessellation. 19. hexagon and triangle 21. octagon and square 23. $36\frac{1}{4}$ yd 25. No; the stop sign is an octagon in shape. An octagon cannot make a tessellation. So, there will be some steel that is wasted after the nine signs are cut from the sheet.
27. trapezoid
29. square 31. pentagon hexagon

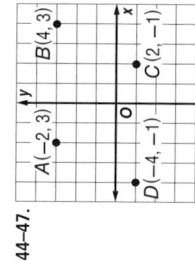

section of honeycomb
the Pentagon

33. Sample answer: A copy of the parallelogram can fit next to it since 45° + 135° = 180° and above or below it since 135° + 45° = 180°. 35. B 37. trapezoid
39. 1.5 m per s 41. $3\frac{1}{6}$ 43. $4\frac{37}{40}$
44–47.

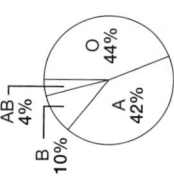

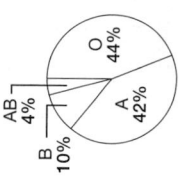

(coordinate graph with points A(−2, 3), B(4, 3), C(2, −1), D(−4, −1))

For Homework Help, go to Hotmath.com

Lesson 10-9

Pages 555–557

1.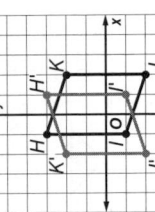

3. $D'(7, 0)$, $E'(4, -2)$, $F'(8, 4)$, $G'(12, -3)$

5.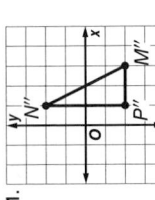

7. $P'(6, 5)$, $Q'(11, 0)$, $R'(3, 11)$

9. $P'(-3, 0)$, $Q'(2, -2)$, $R'(-6, 6)$

11. 3 units right and 1 unit up; $(3, 1)$
13.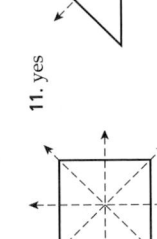

15. Sample answer: There are two main images, the small fish and the large fish. The fish are translated to different parts of the picture. These translations allow for the tessellation of the fish.

17. $F'\left(8\frac{1}{2}, 2\frac{1}{2}\right)$, $G'\left(4\frac{1}{2}, \frac{1}{2}\right)$, $H'\left(2\frac{1}{2}, 1\frac{1}{2}\right)$

19. 5 units left and 3 units down; $(-5, -3)$ **21.** 5 units right and 4 units up; $(5, 4)$ **23.** Transformation A is not a translation; the others are translations. **25.** B **27.** octagon **29.** $2 \times 4 \times 3$ or 24 dinners **31.** The range would be 62 instead of 55. **33.** The range would be 8 instead of 6. **35.** Sample answer: 0.567 **37.** Sample answer: 1.026 **39.** no **41.** yes

Pages 560–562 **Lesson 10-10**
1. no **3.** yes **5.** $A'(5, -8)$, $B'(1, -2)$, and $C'(6, -4)$

7. $Q'(-2, -5)$, $R'(-4, -5)$, and $S'(-2, 3)$

9. yes

11. yes

13. yes

15. $T'(-6, 1)$, $U'(-2, 3)$, and $V'(5, 4)$

17. $A'(2, -4)$, $B'(-2, -4)$, $C'(2, -8)$, $D'(-2, -8)$ **19.** $R'(5, 3)$, $S'(4, -2)$, $T'(2, 3)$

21. $H'(1, 3)$, $I'(1, -1)$, $J'(-2, -2)$, and $K'(-2, 2)$

23. There is a line of symmetry vertically down the center of the picture. **25.** 1 **27.** figures A and C **29.** Sample answer: A reflection over the y-axis followed by a reflection over the x-axis.

31.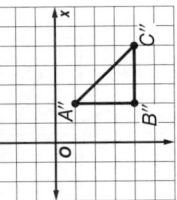

33. x-axis **35.** y-axis **37.** $J'(7, -4)$, $K''(-7, -1)$, and $L''(-2, 2)$ **39.** C
41. $F'(1, 6)$, $G'(3, 4)$, $H'(2, 1)$

43. Sample answer: $\frac{1}{2} + 8 = 8\frac{1}{2}$ **45.** Sample answer: $12 \div 6 = 2$

Pages 563–566 **Chapter 10** **Study Guide and Review**
1. false; supplementary angles **3.** false; acute angle **5.** false; $(-2, 1)$ **7.** $\angle 1$ and $\angle 4$. Sample answer: Since $\angle 1$ and $\angle 4$ are opposite angles formed by the intersection of two lines, they are vertical **9.** neither
11.

Favorite Shades of Blue

Other 18%
Navy 35%
Sky/Light Blue 30%
Aquamarine 17%

13. 45 **15.** right, isosceles **17.** parallelogram
19. 10 cm **21.** 8m **23.** nonagon; regular

Chapter 11 Measurement: Two- and Three-Dimensional Figures

Page 571   Chapter 11   Getting Ready

1. 136   3. 1,248   5. 77   7. $41.67   9. 121   11. 36
13. 12.6   15. 31.4   17. 254.5

Pages 574–576   Lesson 11-1

1. 135 cm²   3. 17.5 in²   5. 32 in²   7. 60 cm²
9. 0.2 cm²   11. 49.5 yd²   13. 190.625 m²
15. 525 mm²   17. 216 in² or 1.5 ft²   19. 972 in² or
0.8 yd²   21. 42,000 mi²   23. 15 in.   25. $11\frac{2}{3}$ ft²
27. False; if the base and height are each doubled, then the area is $2b \cdot 2h = 4bh$, or 4 times greater.
29. D   31. $A(2, 5)$, $B'(1, 2)$, $C'(4, 1)$

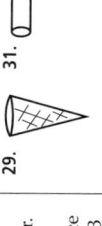

33. Sample answer: The sum of the measures of an octagon is 1,080°. Each angle measure is $1,080° \div 8$ or 135°. Since 135 does not go into 360 evenly, an octagon does not tessellate the plane.   35. 84   37. 19.5

Pages 580–582   Lesson 11-2

1. 6 in²   3. 90.4 ft²   5. 147 in²   7. 4.5 cm²
9. 183.7 in²   11. about 95,000 mi²   13. 125 ft
15. Sample answer: 10 cm²   17. Sample answer: 7 ft²

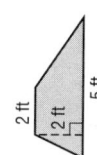

4 in.

5 in.

2 ft

2 ft

5 ft

19. 6,500 ft²   21. Sample answer: the ratio of the area is the square of the ratio of the bases.   23. The area of a triangle is half the area of a parallelogram with the same base and height, because two of these triangles make up the parallelogram.   25. 11,000 ft²
27. $J'(-1, 4)$, $K'(1, -1)$, $L(3, 2)$

25. $P'(-2, 1)$, $Q'(-8, 0)$, and $R'(-7, 9)$

27. $P'(1, -2)$, $Q'(-5, -3)$, and $R'(-4, 6)$

29. $R'(-1, -3)$, $S'(2, -6)$, and $T'(6, -1)$

31. $E'(4, -2)$, $F'(-2, -2)$, $G'(-2, 5)$, $H'(4, -5)$

---

29. 25%   31. 156.3   33. 91.1   35. 72.4

Pages 586–588   Lesson 11-3

1. 31.4 ft   3. 44 m   5. 67.2 cm   7. 50.2 ft   9. 22.6 cm
11. 66 ft   13. 33 in.   15. 33.9 km   17. $38\frac{1}{2}$ mi
19. $28\frac{2}{7}$ in.   21. 94.2 ft   23. 11.0 in.   29. 8.0 ft
31. 4.8 yd   33. Sample answer: Using the circumference formula, you find that the unicycle travels $3.14 \cdot 10 \cdot 2$ or 62.8 inches on one revolution. So, in 5 revolutions, it will travel $62.8 \cdot 5$ or 314 inches. To change into feet, divide 314 by 12. So, the unicycle will travel $26\frac{1}{6}$ feet in 5 revolutions.   37. Elsa; Logan incorrectly applied the formula that uses the diameter.
39. Both will be doubled. If the value of x is doubled, the diameter will be $2x$ instead of x. The circumference will increase from $2\pi x$ to $2\pi(2x)$ or $4\pi x$.   41. C   43. B
45. 3.7 ft²   47. $\frac{15}{27}$ or $\frac{5}{9}$ 49. 153.9   51. 63.6

Pages 591–593   Lesson 11-4

1. 78.5 m²   3. 201.1 m²   5. B   7. 28.3 in²
9. 227.0 cm²   11. 32.2 mm²   13. 124.7 cm²   15. 44.2 ft²
17. 338.2 yd²   19. 2,827.4 ft²   21. Sample answer:
$3 \cdot 6^2 = 108$ ft²   23. 32, 60   25. about 50.3 cm²
27. 29.0 m²   29. 52,276.1 km²   0.1 = 1,582.9 yd²
31. 62.8 m²   33. 103.5 cm²   35. Sample answer: If the radius of a circular garden is 6 feet, how much room is there for gardening? about 113.1 ft²   37. J   39. 50.2 yd
41. 120 in²   43. 100.1 m²   45. 113.04   47. 150.5

Pages 594–595   Lesson 11-5

1. Sample answer: Finding the areas of the separate geometric figures and then adding is easier than trying to find the area of the irregular figure as a whole.
3. Sample answer: Find the area of the wall below to determine how much paint to buy. To solve, find the area of the triangle and the area of the rectangle, then add. The answer is 77 ft².

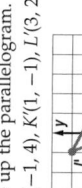

2 ft

6 ft

11 ft

5. Sample answer: Asia, 17,251,712.4 mi²; Africa, 11,616,153.02; N. America, 9,488,441.82 mi²; S. America, 6,900,684.96 m²; Antarctica, 5,118,008.012 mi²; Europe, 3,852,882.436 mi²; Australia/Oceania, 3,047,802,524 mi²   7. B   9. 175.84 ft²

Pages 597–599   Lesson 11-6

1. 112 m²   3. 145 m²   5. 195 ft²   7. 58.6 in²

9. 257.1 mm²   11. 66.2 yd²   13. approximately
847.2 ft²   15. 196.1 in²   17. $x^2 + \frac{1}{2}(6x)$ or $x^2 + 3x$
19. $467.4 \div 350 \approx 1.34$; Since only whole gallons of paint can be purchased, you will need 2 gallons of paint. At $20 each, the cost will be $2 \cdot 20 or $40.
21. Sample answer: Add the areas of a small rectangle and a trapezoid. Area of a rectangle: $3 \times 1 = 3$; Area of trapezoid: $(\frac{1}{2} \times 6.5 (4 + 5)) = 29.25$; $3 + 29.25 = 32.25$. So, an approximate area is $32.25 = 2,400$ or 77,400 mi².
23. B   25. Sample answer: about 30% of $500 or $150
27. 452.2 in²

29.

31.

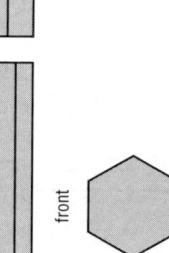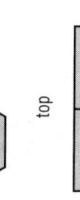

Pages 605–606   Lesson 11-7

1. square; square pyramid   3. circle; cylinder
5. triangle; triangular pyramid   7. rectangle;
rectangular pyramid   9. cone   11. trapezoid;
trapezoidal prism   13. octagon; octagonal prism
15. triangular prism and rectangular prism
17. rectangular prism   19. Sample answer: A cone has only one base that is a circle. A pyramid also has only one base, but its base is a polygon. They both have only one vertex. A cone does not have any lateral faces and a pyramid has at least three lateral faces.
21. F   23. 102.0 m²   25. 53°   27. square   29. circle

Pages 610–612   Lesson 11-8

1.

front   side   side   top

3.

side   front

top

5.

top   front

Right section (R51)

Pages 646–647   Lesson 12-3

1. Sample answer: making a model helps you see what is happening in the problem to help solve it.
3. 8 cars and 4 motorcycles 5. 47 in. 7. $5\frac{1}{3}$ min
9. Sample answer: The boxes could be arranged on the shelf 4 boxes wide and 5 boxes deep. 11. $125\frac{7}{16}$ ft²
13. 6 DVDs

Pages 651–653   Lesson 12-4

1. 108 ft² 3. Yes; the surface area of the box is 252 in². The surface area of the paper is 288 in². Since 252 in² < 288 in², she has enough paper.
5. 314 cm² 7. 833.1 mm² 9. 125.4 in² or $124\frac{3}{8}$ in²
11. 234 in² 13. 243.8 ft² 15. 64.5 in² 17. $s = 6x^2$
19. Sample answer: Not all sides of the rectangular prism will be painted. The top will not be painted. The number of square feet to be painted is (18)(12) + 2(18)(6) + 2(12)(6). 21. Surface area measures the area of the faces, and area is measured in square units.
23. G 25. 12.4 ft 27. 804.2 ft² 29. 145.3 yd²

Pages 657–659   Lesson 12-5

1. 88.0 mm² 3. about 471.2 m² 5. 1,215.8 m²
7. 272.0 mm² 9. 1,120.0 in² or $1,119\frac{44}{45}$ in²
11. 61.3 cm² 13. Sample answer: $2 \cdot 3 \cdot 4^2 + 2 \cdot 3 \cdot 4 \cdot 4$ or 192 m² 15. 205.0 in² 17. No; the surface area of the side of the cylinder will double, but the area of the bases will not. 19. A cylinder with radius 6 cm and height 3 cm has a greater surface area than a cylinder with height 6 cm and radius 3 cm; Sample answer: The first cylinder has a surface area of 339.3 cm² while the second cylinder has a surface area of 169.6 cm².
21. G 23. 112 cm² 25. 12.8 in. 27. 7.2 cm

Pages 660–662   Chapter 12   Study Guide and Review

1. false; right triangle 3. true 5. true 7. false; positive and negative 9. false; cylinder 11. 2
13. 7 15. 4 17. 7.8 19. 21.1 21. 11 ft 23. 26.7 in.
25. 29.8 ft 27. 875 in² 29. 202 yd² 31. 43 ft²
33. 2,261.9 in²

For Homework Help, go to Hotmath.com

35.
37.

39. 639.6 in³ 41. 1,330 ft³ 43. 3,728.7 mm³
45. 942 in.³

Chapter 12 Geometry and Measurement

Page 635   Chapter 12   Getting Ready

1. 16 3. 169 5. 89 7. 225 9. 130 yr 11. 226
13. 42.1 15. 527.8

Pages 637–639   Lesson 12-1

1. 6 3. 9 5. 2.6 7. 7.1 9. 10 ft 11. 4 13. 8
15. 11 17. 20 19. 2.8 21. 9.4 23. 23.9 25. 52.9
27. 6 29. 50 31. 81 33. 0.7 35. 1.7 37. 3.8
39. 3.17 cm 43. Sample answer: 17, 18, 19 45. 2
47. 5 49. It cannot be written as a fraction. 51. G
53. 28.3 in³ 55. acute 57. obtuse 59. 74 61. 16

Pages 643–645   Lesson 12-2

1. 26 mm 3. 18.5 cm 5. 4.0 ft 7. 16.1 m 9. 14.1 m
11. 5.4 ft 13. 2.8 yd 15. 25 in. 17. 5.6 mi 19. 72.1 in.
21. Sample answer: The plank will not fit horizontally or vertically. However, the diagonal of the doorway measures about 18 feet. So, the plank will fit through the doorway if you tilt it diagonally. 23. about 10.4 in. 27. G 29. 1,413 in³ 31. 0.08 33. 2.65

Left section (R50)

7. top side front
9. top side front
11.
13.
15. top side front
17.
19. Sample answer:
21. top side front
23. top side front

25. Sample answer:

29. B 31. sphere 33. 96 ft² 35. 112.8 in² 37. $77.39
39. 22 41. 68

Pages 616–618   Lesson 11-9

1. 220 in³ 3. 63 yd³ 5. 37.5 ft³ < 63 ft³; second cabinet 7. 90 ft³ 9. 236.3 cm³ 11. 108 m³
13. 20.4 mm³ 15. 40 ft³ > 36 ft³, so too much was bought 17. $166\frac{1}{4}$ yd³ 19. 2,157,165 ft³ 21. 306.52 = 19.4t; 15.8 m 23. Sample answer: $5 \times 4 \times 2$ or 40 ft³
25. 6 ft 27. No; the area of Prism A is 80 in², and the area of Prism B is 640 in², which is eight times greater. 29. D
31.

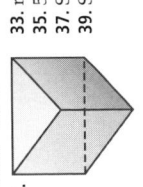

33. rectangle; rectangular prism 35. 50 mph
37. Sample answer: $5 \cdot 3^2$ or 45 39. Sample answer: $3 \cdot 2^2 \cdot 2$ or 24

Pages 620–623   Lesson 11-10

1. 141.4 in³ 3. 617.7 ft³ 5. about 603.2 cm³
7. 4,071.5 ft³ 9. 2,770.9 yd³ 11. 35.6 m³ 13. 103.4 m³
15. 288.6 in³ 17. about 226.2 in³ 19. 124,642.7 m³
21. d. 23. a. 25. 2,375 cm³ 27. 8 in. 29. The volume is 8 times greater than the previous cylinder.
31. Sample answer:

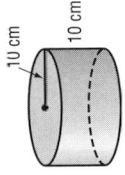

33. 1 to 4 35. D 37. 152.9 m³
39. Sample answer:

41. $\frac{1}{4}$ 43. $\frac{5}{12}$

Pages 626–630   Chapter 11   Study Guide and Review

1. rectangular prism 3. trapezoid 5. cylinder
7. circle 9. 2,520 in² 11. 36 ft² 13. 527.3 yd²
15. 75.4 in. 17. $26\frac{2}{5}$ ft 19. 29.8 ft 21. 1,520.5 cm²
23. 800 cakes 25. $105 27. 67.8 yd² 29. triangle; triangular prism 31. cylinder 33. rectangular pyramid

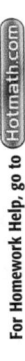

Index

length units, 298
weight units, 298

Cylinders, 604, 619
surface area, 656–659
volume, 619, 620

Data analysis
analyze, 397
bar graphs, 415, 416
center, 402, 403
clusters, 397
gap, 397
line graphs, 426
line plots, 396–401
mean, 402
median, 403
mode, 403
outliers, 397
range, 397
scatter plots, 427–428
stem-and-leaf plots, 410, 411

Data displays, *See also* Data analysis
biased, 446

Data-Driven Decision Making, 48, 75, 100, 123, 147, 173, 201, 225, 247, 275, 317, 337, 368, 389, 423, 455, 479, 503, 539, 567, 602, 631, 648, 663

Data file, 16–19

Decagon, 546

Decimals, 196, 197
adding, 673
bar notation, 197
comparing, 670
converting, 196–200, 206–210
dividing, 740
estimating, 736
expanded notation, 669
multiplying, 738
ordering, 670
place value, 735
repeating, 197
rounding, 736
subtracting, 673
terminating, 197
writing as percents, 207

Deductive reasoning, 530

Degrees, 510

Dependent events, 493

Diagnose Readiness. *See* Concepts and Skills Bank

Diagnostic Assessment, 23, 79, 127, 179, 229, 281, 341, 395, 459, 509, 571, 635

Diameter, 584

Differentiated Homework Options, 28, 32, 36, 40, 46, 51, 55, 60, 65, 82, 86, 91, 98, 105, 110, 117, 131, 139, 145, 154, 159, 166, 183, 188, 194, 199, 204, 209, 213, 218, 233, 239, 245, 255, 261, 268, 284, 295, 301, 307, 313, 324, 331, 346, 353, 358, 364, 372, 377, 381, 399, 406, 412, 418, 429, 436, 441, 447, 463, 468, 473, 477, 482, 489, 495, 512, 516, 521, 527, 535, 543, 549, 555, 560, 574, 581, 586, 591, 598, 605, 610, 616, 621, 638, 644, 652, 658

Differentiated Instruction. *See also* Learning Styles, 22F, 22, 28, 36, 50, 71, 78F, 78, 80, 87, 98, 109, 110, 116, 117, 120, 122, 126F, 126, 139, 155, 158, 170, 178F, 178, 191, 205, 219, 222, 228F, 228, 246, 250, 252, 266, 269, 272, 274, 280F, 280, 282a, 285, 287a, 308, 319, 330, 334, 340F, 340, 347, 366, 373, 385, 394F, 394, 451, 458F, 458, 464, 481, 490, 491, 499, 508F, 508, 522, 531, 541, 545, 564, 570F, 570, 582, 590, 603, 615, 620, 622, 627, 634F, 634, 639, 647, 659, 661

Dimensional analysis, 748

Direct proportional relationships. *See* Proportional Reasoning, Proportional Relationships

Discount, 375–376

Discrete Mathematics. *See* Combinations, Counting, Permutations, Probability, Sequences, Statistics

Disjoint events, 494

Distributive Property, 53

Dividend, 114

Divisibility patterns, 734

Division
dividend, 114
divisor, 114
fractions, 265
integers, 114
mixed numbers, 266
phrases indicating, 128
Property of Equality, 142
quotient, 114
solving equations, 259
Domain, 63

Edges, 603

English Language Learners (ELL) *See also* English Learner Guide under separate cover. 22C, 25a, 25b, 30a, 30b, 34a, 34b, 38a, 38b, 42a, 42b, 44a, 44b, 49a, 49b, 53a, 53b, 57a, 57b, 63a, 63b, 80a, 80b, 84a, 84b, 88a, 88b, 95a, 95b, 103a, 103b, 107a, 107b, 112a, 112b, 114a, 114b, 126C, 128a, 128b, 136a, 136b, 142a, 142b, 148a, 148b, 151a, 151b, 156a, 156b, 163a, 163b, 178C, 181a, 181b, 186a, 186b, 190a, 190b, 192a, 192b, 196a, 196b, 202a, 202b, 206a, 206b, 211a, 211b, 215a, 215b, 228C, 230a, 230b, 236a, 236b, 242a, 242b, 248a, 248b, 252a, 252b, 258a, 258b, 265a, 265b, 280C, 282a, 282b, 287a, 287b, 293a, 293b, 298a, 298b, 304a, 304b, 310a, 310b, 318a, 318b, 320a, 320b, 328a, 329b, 340C, 344a, 344b, 350a, 350b, 355a, 355b, 361a, 361b, 366a, 366b, 369a, 369b, 375a, 375b, 379a, 379b, 394C, 396a, 396b, 402a, 402b, 410a, 410b, 415a, 415b, 424a, 424b, 426a, 426b, 434a, 434b, 438a, 438b, 444a, 444b, 460b, 465a, 465b, 471a, 471b, 475a, 475b, 480a, 480b, 484a, 484b, 486a, 492a, 492b, 508C, 510a, 510b, 514a, 514b, 518a, 518b, 524a, 524b, 530a, 530b, 533a, 533b, 540a, 540b, 546a, 546b, 553a, 553b, 558a, 558b, 570C, 572a, 572b, 578a, 578b, 584a, 584b, 589a, 589b, 594a, 594b, 596a, 596b, 603a, 603b, 608a, 608b, 613a, 613b, 619a, 619b, 634C, 636a, 636b, 640a, 640b, 646a, 646b, 649a, 649b, 656a, 656b

Equality
Addition Property, 138
Division Property, 142
Multiplication Property, 259
Subtraction Property, 136
Equals sign (=), 49
Equations, 49, 129
addition, 136
checking solutions of, 138, 143
division, 259
linear, 164
models of, 134–135, 142, 151
multiplication, 143
solution of, 49
solving, 49, 50, 136–139, 142, 143, 259
two-step, 151, 152
solving using concrete models,

Index

Magnifications. *See* Dilations

Magnitude. *See* Relative Error

Manipulatives
addition table, 486
Algebra tiles, 134–135, 142, 151
calculator, *See* Graphing
   Calculator Lab
cardboard box, 600
centimeter cubes, 57, 211, 607,
   613, 649
chenille stems, 162
circular objects, 583
colored cubes, 491
computer, See Spreadsheet Lab
counters, 93–94, 101–102, 107,
   114, 134–135
cups, 402
dot paper, 540, 654–655
drinking glass, 426
geoboards, 250
geomirror, 558
grid paper, 192, 202, 320,
   342–343, 532, 572, 577, 578,
   613, 619, 640, 656
gymnasium, 320
index card, 552
isometric dot paper, 608–612
marbles, 426
number cubes, 486
paper bag, 491
paper plates, 265, 589
paper strips, 369
pattern blocks, 553
pennies, 402
protractor, 518, 532, 540
ruler, 236, 532, 540, 583
scissors, 162
soup can, 619, 656
straightedge, 524
tape, 552
tiles, 34, 636
toothpicks, 62
water, 426

Mass
changing units of, 305
gram, 304
kilogram, 304
milligram, 305

Materials, 22, 62, 68, 78, 93, 101,
126, 134, 162, 168, 228, 250, 280, 316,
327, 340, 342, 383, 394, 409, 422, 432,
458, 491, 508, 532, 552, 570, 577, 583,
600, 607, 624, 634, 654

Math Lab
exploring factors, 180
inverse proportionality, 316

multiplying fractions, 250
percent of a number, 342

Math Online, *See* Internet
Connections

Mathematical Background. *See*
Focus on Mathematical Content

Mean, 117, 402, 409

Measurement. *See also* Customary
system and Metric system
angles, 510, 678
area
   circles, 589
   composite figures, 596–599
   parallelograms, 572
   rectangles, 157
   trapezoids, 577, 578
   triangles, 577, 578
circumference, 583–587
converting between systems,
   748
effect of changing dimensions,
   157, 576, 622, 654–655
indirect, 542
perimeter
irregular figures, 157
rectangles, 156
Pythagorean Theorem, 640–645
surface area
   cylinders, 649–653
   rectangular prisms, 651–652
volume
   cylinders, 619–620
   rectangular prisms, 613–614

Measurement Lab, 162
circumference of circles, 583
graphing relationships, 162
nets and surface area, 600–601
representing relationships, 162
surface area, changes in, 654–655
triangles and trapezoids, 577
volume, changes in, 654–655

Measures of central tendency,
402–409
mean, 402, 404, 409
median, 403, 404, 409
mode, 403, 404
summary, 404

Median, 403, 404, 409

Mental Math
as a method of computation,
   10–11
adding unit fractions, 240
evaluating expressions using
   properties, 54
finding unit rates, 287
fraction-decimal equivalencies,
   197

solving equations, 49
solving proportions, 311
techniques for problem solving,
   10–11
writing fractions or mixed
   numbers as decimals, 196

Meter, 304

Metric system, 304–309
capacity units, 304
conversions
   between systems, 747
   capacity units, 304
   length units, 304
   mass units, 304
   unit conversion table, 304
   length units, 304
   mass units, 304
   unit abbreviations, 304

Mid-Chapter Quiz, 48, 100, 147,
201, 247, 317, 368, 423, 479, 539,
602, 648

Millimeter, 304

Mini Lab
adding fractions on a ruler, 236
angle relationships, 514
area of a circle, 589
area of a parallelogram, 572
area of a triangle, 578
converting length units, 304
finding a pattern, 44
finding the mean, 402
folding triangles, 524
making a scale drawing, 320
making predictions, 426
modeling division by a fraction,
   265
modeling division of integers,
   114
modeling multiples, 211
modeling multiplicative
   inverses, 258
modeling percent of change, 369
modeling primes, 181
modeling subtraction of
   integers, 128
patterns and sequences, 57
percents, 329
perimeter and area, 34
permutations, 475
probability game, 465, 486
Pythagorean Theorem, 640
rates, 287
similar figures, 540
solving equations using models,
   142
square roots, 636
squares, 34
tessellations, 553
volume of cylinders, 619

Index **R67**

Index